Stanley Gibbons

Great Britain
CONCISE
Stamp Catalogue

2016 edition

STANLEY GIBBONS LTD
London and Ringwood

By Appointment to
Her Majesty The Queen
Philatelists
Stanley Gibbons Ltd
London

Published by *Stanley Gibbons Publications*
Editorial, Sales Offices and Distribution Centre:
7 Parkside, Christchurch Road, Ringwood,
Hants BH24 3SH

First Edition — May 1986	17th Edition — April 2002
Second Edition — May 1987	18th Edition — April 2003
Third Edition — May 1988	19th Edition — April 2004
Fourth Edition — May 1989	20th Edition — May 2005
Fifth Edition — May 1990	21st Edition — April 2006
Sixth Edition — May 1991	22nd Edition — April 2007
Seventh Edition — May 1992	23rd Edition — April 2008
Eighth Edition — April 1993	24th Edition — April 2009
Ninth Edition — April 1994	24th Edition — reprinted June 2009
Tenth Edition — April 1995	25th Edition — May 2010
11th Edition — April 1996	26th Edition — April 2011
12th Edition — April 1997	27th Edition — April 2012
13th Edition — April 1998	28th Edition — April 2013
14th Edition — April 1999	29th Edition — April 2014
15th Edition — May 2000	30th Edition — May 2015
16th Edition — April 2001	31st Edition — May 2016

© Stanley Gibbons Ltd. 2016

ISBN 10: 0-85259-972-2
ISBN 13: 978-0-85259-972-3

Item No. R2887-16

Printed by
GraphyCemS, Spain

Contents

Why do up to 6xMORE Collectors Bid in a UPA Auction than our competitors...??

Perhaps the reason why is that —I firmly believe Collectors Want Stamps **NOT Charges**... so at **UPA** you'll find:

1 NO Pernicious Buyer's Premiums

2 NO Extra Charges for anything

3 NEW Loyalty Post-Free UPA Bonus to Regular Collector Clients

4 And, YES, ALL Lots Guaranteed

5 PLUS Your 1st £55 Winnings FREE

6 and MASSIVE CHOICE - up to 26,510 Different Lots

NEW POST-FREE UPA Loyalty Bonus

Preface

For nearly a century, following the publication of the very first Stanley Gibbons 'Descriptive Price List and Catalogue of British Colonial and Foreign Postage Stamps' in November 1865, collectors of Great Britain stamps had to rely on the main SG Catalogue ('Part1' from the late 19th century) for their regular annual update of discoveries, new issues and, of course, current market prices.

Many very worthy handbooks had been published on a wide variety of topics, but most were limited to one or two editions and soon became superceded by new research. What was needed was a regularly revised handbook/catalogue which would keep up to date with new research and discoveries and the market for British Stamps at a specialist level – and so in 1963, the Stanley Gibbons *Great Britain Specialised Catalogue* appeared, with Volume 1, Queen Victoria, being published in October of that year and having to be reprinted twice within two months. Volume 2, 'The Four Kings' arrived in 1967, also requiring a reprint within a couple of months.

Later that same year a new Great Britain catalogue, *Collect British Stamps*, made its debut designed to meet the needs of the collector seeking a more straightforward listing, and, like the Specialised Catalogue it proved to be an instant success.

It may seem surprising now that it was a further 19 years before the Great Britain *Concise* appeared on the scene, neatly filling the gap between *Collect British Stamps* and the Specialised. During the intervening years, the semi-specialist had had 'Part 1' to rely on, which in the days when many collected the whole Commonwealth, made sense, but when, particularly in the 1980s, many Commonwealth countries (or their agents!) stepped up their output of new issues to new heights, collectors deserted them in favour of the 'home country' and a semi-specialised GB catalogue was needed – and the *Concise* was born! Based on the listings in 'Part 1', it incorporated a number of other features, not present in the main catalogue, most notably inverted watermarks, booklets, first day covers, presentation packs and gutter pairs.

Now, as we celebrate the 30th anniversary of that first *Concise* Catalogue, we can see that it has come quite a long way since 1986. Some of this relates to technology, such as the introduction of colour illustrations, some is purely a reflection of the introduction of new postal or philatelic products, like Post & Go Stamps and Smilers sheets, while others have been adopted to meet the needs of collectors looking for more regular updates than is possible in the more occasional Specialised catalogues. So the *Concise* has, over the years, seen more plate flaws, 'Specimen' stamps, Telegraphs and much else culled from the Specialised, while the needs of collectors of Post & Go stamps and Security Machins (with their popular date and source codes) have been met by tables, specially devised for this catalogue by specialist dealer John M. Deering.

As editors, the eternal question concerns the position of the dividing line between the various catalogues; which features should appear only in the specialised and which should also be included here? Each year there are suggestions that this feature or that should be added, but they are counterbalanced by the views of other collectors who feel that the lists are rather too complex already.

After careful consideration, the two head types on the England 'Emblem' regionals have been added this year, having been felt to be 'Specialised only' at the time of discovery. Much of the detail on the Post & Go and Security Machin sections, however, remains confined to the separate tables, rather than being given full listing.

A long overdue piece of 'tidying up' has been undertaken with the distinction between stamps printed from photogravure cylinders ('Photo') and those printed from electronically engraved cylinders ('Gravure') being recognised following Glenn Morgan's masterful series of articles on the subject in GSM, February to April 2016. Where they exist the two are not separately listed, but the descritive notes have been revised to reflect the true production methods involved.

PRICES

Once again prices have been carefully reviewed throughout, but while they are widespread, affecting most sections from line-engraved to Security Machins, and varied in degree – from slight adjustments to dramatic percentage increases, there is no one area which stands out, although it will surprise no one to know that definitive have gone up a lot more than commemoratives again!

As well as John Deering, we would also like to thank Rowan Baker and Gary Burgess for their help in reviewing the prices of more modern issues.

ACKNOWLEDGEMENTS

As always, we would like to thank individual collectors, specialist societies, auction houses and members of the philatelic trade for their assistance in keeping this catalogue up to date. A list of some of those who have contributed to this edition is given on page viii; we apologise to anyone we have missed.

We would also like to express our appreciation to all our colleagues who have contributed to this latest edition. In the catalogue editorial department, Clare de la Feuillade, Lesley Brine, Lorraine Holcombe, Sue Price, Babs Hawkins, Gary Keeping and Les Fuller have all played their part, while in the Studio, Martin Field, Maite Da Vila, Bethany Redwood-Pain and Hayley Tear have been responsible for design and text corrections. We would also like to thank members of the Great Britain Specialist Department for their help throughout the year.

HUGH JEFFERIES
VINCE CORDELL

April 2016

Features of this Catalogue

The Concise Catalogue, now in its 31st year of publication, has established itself as an essential guide for the "one-country" collector of Great Britain. As the popularity of Great Britain stamps continues to grow — the Concise Catalogue supplies the information you need to enhance your collection.

✦ All issues from the Penny Black of 1840 to 1 April 2015 including Regional, Postage Due, Official and Postal Fiscal stamps.

✦ All different stamp designs are illustrated.

✦ Every basic stamp listed, including those with different watermarks or perforations and those showing graphite lines or phosphor bands.

✦ Unmounted mint and mounted mint prices quoted for 1887 "Jubilee" series and all King Edward VII and King George V issues.

✦ Missing colours, missing embossing, watermark errors, imperforate errors and phosphor omitted varieties from those stamps normally issued with phosphor bands.

✦ Booklet panes listed up to 1952, including inverted watermark varieties.

✦ Gutter Pairs and "Traffic light" Gutter Pairs listed in mint sets.

✦ First Day Covers for Special Issues from 1924 and for King Edward VIII and King George VI definitives. For the present reign the coverage also extends to Prestige Booklet panes and Regionals. All British Post Office special First Day of Issue postmarks are illustrated and priced on cover.

✦ Post Office Picture Cards (PHQ cards) are priced as sets, both mint and used with First Day of Issue postmarks.

✦ Presentation, Collector and Gift Packs, including the scarce versions with foreign inscriptions.

✦ Quick-reference diagrams for listed Machin decimal booklet panes.

✦ Design Index for Commemorative and Special Stamps after the Philatelic Information Section.

✦ Machin and commemorative underprints given separate catalogue numbers.

✦ Post Office Yearbooks.

✦ Royal Mail Postage Labels priced in mint or used sets and on British Post Office First Day Covers.

✦ Royal Mail Post & Go stamps; with notes on machine types, errors, date codes and special inscriptions.

✦ Notes on Postage Due bisects based on research by Mr. P. Frost.

✦ Wartime issues for the Channel Islands.

✦ Separate section for Post Office Stamp Booklets with dated editions of King George VI and Queen Elizabeth listed separately.

✦ Post Office Label Sheets, popularly known as 'Generic Smilers'.

✦ Specimen overprints up to 1952.

✦ Helpful introductory section providing definitions and guidance for the collector and including all watermark illustrations shown together to assist identification.

✦ Addresses for specialist philatelic societies covering Great Britain stamps.

✦ Post Office Telegraph Stamps

✦ Apart from the newly listed booklet panes, the following have been added to this edition: 279Wi, 281Wi, 678a, 906b, 1403a, 1404a, 1629a,1649a, 2045Ea, 3367ab,3368ab, **MS**3601a, O3c, O3ca, O9da, O15a, EN1ba, EN6b, EN7b, EN11b, EN17a

We would like to thank all those who have assisted in the compilation of this catalogue. Special thanks for amendments to this edition are due to Rowan Baker, Gary Burgess, John and Tina Carlson, Robert Cooke, Keith Emerson, Caryll Gomes, Allan Grant, Mike Kimberley, Andrew Lajer, Tony Lester, Peter McCulloch, Chris Neve, Robert Oliver, John Peart, Kevin Samuels, David Smythe, Frank Spencer, Len Stanway, Julian Tremayne, Barry Trowbridge, John Vincent, Brian Wenden and Richard West.

Great Britain Philatelic Societies

The Great Britain Philatelic Society.
Hon. Membership Secretary: Peter Tanner, "High Standings", 13 Huberts Close, Gerrards Cross, Bucks SL9 7EN.

The Modern British Philatelic Circle. Hon. Membership Secretary: A. J. Wilkins, 3 Buttermere Close, Brierley Hill, West Midlands, DY5 3SD.

The Great Britain Collectors' Club.
Secretary: Mr S. McGill, 10309 Brookhollow Circle, Highlands Ranch, CO 80129, USA

Stanley Gibbons Holdings Plc

**Stanley Gibbons Limited,
Stanley Gibbons Auctions**
399 Strand, London WC2R 0LX
Tel: +44 (0)207 836 8444
Fax: +44 (0)207 836 7342
E-mail: help@stanleygibbons.com
Website: www.stanleygibbons.com
for all departments, Auction and
Specialist Stamp Departments.
Open Monday–Friday 9.30 a.m. to 5
p.m.
Shop. Open Monday–Friday 9 a.m.
to 5.30 p.m. and Saturday 9.30 a.m.
to 5.30 p.m.

**Stanley Gibbons Publications
Gibbons Stamp Monthly and
Philatelic Exporter**
7 Parkside, Christchurch Road,
Ringwood, Hampshire BH24 3SH.
Tel: +44 (0)1425 472363
Fax: +44 (0)1425 470247
E-mail: help@stanleygibbons.com
Publications Mail Order.
FREEPHONE 0800 611622
Monday–Friday 8.30 a.m. to 5 p.m.

**Stanley Gibbons (Guernsey)
Limited**
18–20 Le Bordage, St Peter Port,
Guernsey GY1 1DE.
Tel: +44 (0)1481 708270
Fax: +44 (0)1481 708279
E-mail: investment@stanleygibbons.
com

Stanley Gibbons (Jersey) Limited
18 Hill Street, St Helier, Jersey,
Channel Islands JE2 4UA.
Tel: +44 (0)1534 766711
Fax: +44 (0)1534 766177
E-mail: investment@stanleygibbons.
com

Stanley Gibbons (Asia) Limited
Room 618, 6/F
100 Queen's Road,
Central,
Hong Kong
Tel: +852 3180 93708
E-mail: elee@stanleygibbons.com

Fraser's
(a division of Stanley Gibbons Ltd)
Bloomsbury House, 24 Maddox
Street, Mayfair, London W1S 1PP
Autographs, photographs, letters and
documents
Tel: +44 (0) 20 7836 9325
Fax: +44 (0) 20 7495 9499
E-mail: sales@frasersautographs.com
Website: www.frasersautographs.com
Monday–Friday 9 a.m. to 5.30 p.m.
and Saturday 10 a.m. to 4 p.m.

**Stanley Gibbons Publications
Overseas Representation**
Stanley Gibbons Publications
are represented overseas by the
following

**Australia Renniks Publications
Pty Ltd**
Unit 3 37-39 Green Street,
Banksmeadow, NSW 2019,
Australia
Tel: +612 9695 7055
Website: www.renniks.com

Canada Unitrade Associates
99 Floral Parkway, Toronto,
Ontario M6L 2C4, Canada
Tel: +1 416 242 5900
Website: www.unitradeassoc.com

Germany Schaubek Verlag Leipzig
Am Glaeschen 23, D-04420
Markranstaedt, Germany
Tel: +49 34 205 67823
Website: www.schaubek.de

Italy Ernesto Marini S.R.L.
V. Struppa, 300, Genova, 16165,
Italy
Tel: +3901 0247-3530
Website: www.ernestomarini.it

Japan Japan Philatelic
PO Box 2, Suginami-Minami,
Tokyo 168-8081,
Japan
Tel: +81 3330 41641
Website: www.yushu.co.jp

Netherlands also covers Belgium
Denmark, Finland & France
Uitgeverij Davo BV
PO Box 411, Ak Deventer, 7400
Netherlands
Tel: +315 7050 2700
Website: www.davo.nl

New Zealand House of Stamps
PO Box 12, Paraparaumu,
New Zealand
Tel: +61 6364 8270
Website: www.houseofstamps.co.nz

New Zealand Philatelic Distributors
PO Box 863
15 Mount Edgecumbe Street
New Plymouth 4615, New Zealand
Tel: +6 46 758 65 68
Website: www.stampcollecta.com

Norway Skanfil A/S
Spanav. 52 / Boks 2030
N-5504 Haugesund, Norway
Tel: +47-52703940
E-mail: magne@skanfil.no

Singapore C S Philatelic Agency
Peninsula Shopping Centre #04-29
3 Coleman Street, 179804, Singapore
Tel: +65 6337-1859
Website: www.cs.com.sg

South Africa Mr. Thematic
737 Redwood Street,
Randparkridge Ext 14
Gauteng, South Africa
Tel: +1606 553107
E-mail: ianfrith146@gmail.com,
chrisb@asapcc.co.za

Sweden Chr Winther Sorensen AB
Box 43, S-310 20 Knaered, Sweden
Tel: +46 43050743
Website: www.collectia.se

USA Regency Superior Ltd
229 North Euclid Avenue
Saint Louis, Missouri 63108, USA
PO Box 8277, St Louis,
MO 63156-8277, USA
Toll Free Tel: (800) 782-0066
Tel: (314) 361-5699
Website: www.RegencySuperior.com
Email: info@regencysuperior.com

Prices

The prices quoted in this catalogue are the estimated selling prices of Stanley Gibbons Ltd at the time of publication. They are, *unless it is specifically stated otherwise,* for examples in fine condition for the issue concerned. Superb examples are worth more; those of a lower quality considerably less.

All prices are subject to change without prior notice and Stanley Gibbons Ltd may from time to time offer stamps below catalogue price. Individual low value stamps sold at 399, Strand are liable to an additional handling charge. Purchasers of new issues are asked to note that the prices charged for them contain an element for the service rendered and so may exceed the prices shown when the stamps are subsequently catalogued.

No guarantee is given to supply all stamps priced, since it is not possible to keep every catalogued item in stock.

Quotation of prices
The prices in the left-hand column are for unused stamps and those in the right-hand column are for used.

A dagger (†) denotes that the item listed does not exist in that condition and a blank, or dash, that it exists, or may exist, but no market price is known.

Prices are expressed in pounds and pence sterling. One pound comprises 100 pence (£1 = 100p).

The method of notation is as follows: pence in numerals (e.g. 5 denotes five pence); pounds and pence up to £100, in numerals (e.g. 4·25 denotes four pounds and twenty-five pence); prices above £100 expressed in whole pounds with the "£" sign shown.

Unused and Used stamps
The prices for unused stamps of Queen Victoria issued before 1887 are for lightly hinged examples. Unused stamps of the 1887 "Jubilee" issue and from the reigns of King Edward VII and King George V are priced in both unmounted and mounted condition. Unused prices for King Edward VIII to Queen Elizabeth II issues are for unmounted mint (though when not available, mounted mint stamps are often supplied at a lower price). Prices for used stamps are for fine postally used examples, usually cancelled by a clear operational circular datestamp.

Prices quoted for bisects on cover or on large piece are for those dated during the period officially authorised.

Minimum price
The minimum price quoted is 10 pence. For individual stamps, prices between 10 pence and 95 pence are provided as a guide for catalogue users. The lowest price *charged* for individual stamps or sets purchased from Stanley Gibbons Ltd is £1.

Set prices
Set prices are generally for one of each value, excluding shades and varieties, but including major colour changes.

Where there are alternative shades, etc., the cheapest is usually included. The number of stamps in the set is always stated for clarity.

The mint and used prices for sets containing *se-tenant* pieces are based on the prices quoted for such combinations, and not on those for individual stamps.

Gutter Pairs
These, and traffic light gutter pairs, are priced as complete sets.

Used on Cover prices
To assist collectors, cover prices are quoted in a third column for postage and Official stamps issued in the reign of Queen Victoria and in boxed notes for the 1887 "Jubilee" issue and for King Edward VII stamps.

The cover should be of non-philatelic origin, bearing the correct postal rate for the period and distance involved and cancelled with the markings normal to the offices concerned. Purely philatelic items have a cover value only slightly greater than the catalogue value for the corresponding used stamps. This applies generally to those high-value stamps used philatelically rather than in the normal course of commerce.

Oversized covers, difficult to accommodate on an album page, should be reckoned as worth little more than the corresponding value of the used stamps. The condition of a cover affects its value. Except for "wreck covers", serious damage or soiling reduce the value where the postal markings and stamps are ordinary ones. Conversely, visual appeal adds to the value and this can include freshness of appearance, important addresses, old-fashioned but legible handwriting, historic town-names, etc. The prices quoted are a base on which further value would be added to take account of the cover's postal historical importance in demonstrating such things as unusual, scarce or emergency cancels, interesting routes, significant postal markings, combination usage, the development of postal rates, and so on.

However, it should also be noted that multiples of some stamps are frequently more commonly found on cover than single usages and in such cases the cover might be worth less than the price quoted.

First Day Cover prices
Prices are quoted for commemorative first day covers from 1924 British Empire Exhibition pair onwards. These prices are for special covers (from 1937) franked with complete sets and cancelled by ordinary operational postmarks to the end of 1962 or the various standard "First Day of Issue" markings from 1963.

Prices are provided for King Edward VIII and King George VI definitives on plain covers with operational postmarks of the first day of issue. For some values special covers also exist and these are worth more than the prices quoted.

The Philatelic Bureau and other special "First Day of

Issue" postmarks provided by the Post Office since 1963 are listed under each issue. Prices quoted are for these postmarks used on illustrated covers (from 1964 those produced by the Post Office), franked with complete sets.

The British Post Office did not introduce special First Day of Issue postmarks for definitive issues until the first instalment of the Machin £sd series, issued 5 June 1967, although "First Day" treatment had been provided for some Regional stamps from 8 June 1964 onwards. Prices for the First Day Covers from 1952 to 1966, showing definitive stamps are for the stamps indicated, used on illustrated envelopes and postmarked with operational cancellations.

From 1967 onwards the prices quoted are for stamps as indicated, used on illustrated envelopes and postmarked with special First Day of Issue handstamps. Other definitives issued during this period were not accepted for "First Day" treatment by the British Post Office.

Guarantee

All stamps are guaranteed genuine originals in the following terms:

If not as described, and returned by the purchaser, we undertake to refund the price paid to us in the original transaction. If any stamp is certified as genuine by the Expert Committee of the Royal Philatelic Society, London, or by B.P.A. Expertising Ltd, the purchaser shall not be entitled to make any claim against us for any error, omission or mistake in such certificate.

Consumers' statutory rights are not affected by the above guarantee.

The recognised Expert Committees in this country are those of the Royal Philatelic Society, 41 Devonshire Place, London W1G 6JY, and B.P.A. Expertising Ltd, P.O. Box 1141, Guildford, Surrey GU5 0WR. They do not undertake valuations under any circumstances and fees are payable for their services.

Contacting the Catalogue Editor

The Editor is always interested in hearing from people who have new information which will improve or correct the Catalogue. As a general rule he must see and examine the actual stamps before they can be considered for listing; photographs or photocopies are insufficent evidence.

Submissions should be made in writing to the Catalogue Editor, Stanley Gibbons Publications. The cost of return postage for items submitted is appreciated, and this should include the registration fee if required.

Where information is solicited purely for the benefit of the enquirer, the editor cannot undertake to reply if the answer is already contained in these published notes or if return postage is omitted. Written or email communications are greatly preferred to enquiries by telephone and the editor regrets that he or his staff cannot see personal callers without a prior appointment being made. Correspondence may be subject to delay during the production period of each new edition.

Please note that the following classes of material are outside the scope of this Catalogue:

(a) Non-postal revenue or fiscal stamps.
(b) Postage stamps used fiscally.
(c) Local carriage labels and private local issues.
(d) Punctured postage stamps (perfins).
(e) Bogus or phantom stamps.
(f) Railway or airline letter fee stamps, bus or road transport company labels.
(g) Postal stationery cut-outs.
(h) All types of non-postal labels and souvenirs.
(i) Documentary labels for the postal service, e.g. registration, recorded delivery, airmail etiquettes, etc.
(j) Privately applied embellishments to official issues and privately commissioned items generally.
(k) Stamps for training postal staff.

> We regret we do not give opinions as to the genuineness of stamps, nor do we identify stamps or number them by our Catalogue.

General Abbreviations

Alph	Alphabet
Anniv	Anniversary
Brt	Bright (colour)
C.	Overprinted in carmine
Des	Designer; designed
Dp	Deep (colour)
Eng	Engraver; engraved
Horiz	Horizontal; horizontally
Imp, Imperf	Imperforate
Inscr	Inscribed
L	Left
Litho	Lithographed
Lt	Light (colour)
mm	Millimetres
MS	Miniature sheet
Opt(d)	Overprint(ed)
P, Perf	Perforated
Photo	Photogravure
Pl	Plate
Pr	Pair
Ptd	Printed
Ptg	Printing
PVA	Polyvinyl alcohol (gum)
R	Right
R.	Row
Recess	Recess-printed
T	Type
Typo	Typographed (Letterpress)
Un	Unused
Us	Used
Vert	Vertical; vertically
W or wmk	Watermark
Wmk s	Watermark sideways

(†) = Does not exist.

(—) (or blank price column) = Exists, or may exist, but no market price is known.

/ between colours means "on" and the colour following is that of the paper on which the stamp is printed.

Printers

B.W.	Bradbury Wilkinson & Co, Ltd.
Cartor	Cartor S.A., La Loupe, France
D.L.R.	De La Rue & Co, Ltd, London, and (from 1961) Bogota, Colombia. De La Rue Security Print (formerly Harrison & Sons Ltd) from 8 September 1997.
Enschedé	Joh. Enschedé en Zonen, Haarlem, Netherlands.
Harrison	Harrison & Sons, Ltd, High Wycombe.
ISP	International Security Printers (Walsall and/or Cartor
J.W.	John Waddington Security Print, Ltd, Leeds.
P.B.	Perkins Bacon Ltd, London.
Questa	Questa Colour Security Printers, Ltd.
Waterlow	Waterlow & Sons, Ltd, London.
Walsall	Walsall Security Printers, Ltd.

Philatelic information

Catalogue Numbers

The catalogue number appears in the extreme left column. The boldface Type numbers in the next column are merely cross-reference to illustrations. Catalogue numbers in the *Gibbons Stamp Monthly* Supplements are provisional only and may need to be altered when the lists are consolidated.

Our Catalogue numbers are universally recognised in specifying stamps and as a hallmark of status.

Inverted and other watermark varieties incorporate "Wi", etc., within the number. Other items which appear in this Catalogue but not *Part 1 (British Commonwealth) Catalogue*, incorporate "Ea", etc.

Catalogue Illustrations

Stamps and first day postmarks are illustrated at three-quarters linear size. Stamps not illustrated are the same size and format as the value shown, unless otherwise indicated. Overprints, surcharges and watermarks are normally actual size. Illustrations of varieties are often enlarged to show the detail. Illustrations of miniature sheets are half linear size and their dimensions, in millimetres, are stated with the width given first.

Designers

Designers' names are quoted where known, though space precludes naming every individual concerned in the production of a set. In particular, photographers supplying material are usually named only when they also make an active contribution in the design stage; posed photographs of reigning monarchs are, however, an exception to this rule.

Printing Errors

Errors in printing are of major interest to this Catalogue. Authenticated items meriting consideration would include: background, centre or frame inverted or omitted; centre or subject transposed; error of colour; error or omission of value; double prints and impressions; printed both sides; and so on. Designs *tête-bêche*, whether intentionally or by accident, are listable. Colours only partially omitted are not listed. However, stamps with embossing, phosphor or both omitted and stamps printed on the gummed side are included.

Printing technology has radically improved over the years, during which time gravure and lithography have become predominant. Varieties nowadays are more in the nature of flaws which are almost always outside the scope of this book.

In no catalogue, however, do we list such items as: dry prints, kiss prints, doctor-blade flaws, colour shifts or registration flaws (unless they lead to the complete omission of a colour from an individual stamp), lithographic ring flaws, and so on. Neither do we recognise fortuitous happenings like paper creases or confetti flaws.

Paper Types

All stamps listed are deemed to be on "ordinary" paper of the wove type and white in colour; only departures from this are normally mentioned.

A coloured paper is one that is coloured right through (front and back of the stamp). In the Catalogue the colour of the paper is given in *italics*, thus:

purple/*yellow* = purple design on yellow paper.

Papers have been made specially white in recent years by, for example, a very heavy coating of chalk. We do not classify shades of whiteness of paper as distinct varieties. The availability of many postage stamps for revenue purposes made necessary some safeguard against the illegitimate re-use of stamps with removable cancellations. This was at first secured by using fugitive inks and later by printing on chalky (chalk-surfaced) paper, both of which made it difficult to remove any form of obliteration without also damaging the stamp design. Stamps which exist on both ordinary and chalk-surfaced papers are separately listed.

The "traditional" method of indentifying chalk-surfaced papers has been that, when touched with a silver wire, a black mark is left on the paper, and the listings in this catalogue are based on that test. However, the test itself is now largely discredited, for, although the mark can be removed by a soft rubber, some damage to the stamp will result from its use.

The difference between chalk-surfaced and pre-war ordinary papers is fairly clear: chalk-surfaced papers being smoother to the touch and showing a characteristic sheen when light is reflected off their surface. Under good magnification tiny bubbles or pock marks can be seen on the surface of the stamp and at the tips of the perforations the surfacing appears "broken". Traces of paper fibres are evident on the surface of ordinary paper and the ink shows a degree of absorption into it.

Initial chalk-surfaced paper printings by De La Rue had a thinner coating than subsequently became the norm. The characteristics described above are less pronounced in these printings.

Perforation Measurement

The gauge of a perforation is the number of holes in a length of 2 cm.

The Gibbons *Instanta* gauge is the standard for measuring perforations. The stamp is viewed against a dark background with the transparent gauge put on top of it. Though the gauge measures to decimal accuracy, perforations read from it are generally quoted in the Catalogue to the nearest half. For example:

Just over perf 12¾ to just under 13¼ .... = perf 13
Perf 13¼ exactly, rounded up .... = perf 13½
Just over perf 13¼ to just under 13¾ .... = perf 13½
Perf 13¾ exactly, rounded up .... = perf 14

However, where classification depends on it, actual quarter-perforations are quoted. Perforations are usually abbreviated (and spoken) as follows, though sometimes they may be spelt out for clarity.

P 14: perforated alike on all sides (read: "perf 14").

P 14 x 15: the first figure refers to top and bottom, the

second to left and right sides (read: "perf 14 by 15"). This is a compound perforation.

Such headings as "P 13 x 14 (vert) and P 14 x 13 (horiz)" indicate which perforations apply to which stamp format—vertical or horizontal.

From 1992 onwards most definitive and greetings stamps from both sheets and booklets occur with a large elliptical (oval) hole inserted in each line of vertical perforations as a security measure. The £10 definitive, No. 1658, is unique in having two such holes in the horizontal perforations.

Stamps which have the elliptical perforations hole towards the top in error are normally outside the scope of this catalogue, but in 2013 a booklet was issued in which the entire print run contained Machin stamps in this format. These are listed as U3012b and U3017.

Elliptical Perforations

Perforation Errors
Authenticated errors, where a stamp normally perforated is accidentally issued imperforate, are listed provided no traces of perforations (blind holes or indentations) remain. They must be provided as pairs, both stamps wholly imperforate, and are only priced in that form.

Numerous part-perforated stamps have arisen from the introduction of the Jumelle Press. This has a rotary perforator with rows of pins on one drum engaging with holes on another. Engagement is only gradual when the perforating unit is started up or stopped, giving rise to perforations "fading out", a variety mentioned above as not listed.

Stamps from the Jumelle printings sometimes occur imperforate between stamp and sheet margin. Such errors are not listed in this catalogue, but are covered by the volumes of the *Great Britain Specialised Catalogue*.

Pairs described as "imperforate between" have the line of perforations between the two stamps omitted.

Imperf between (vertical pair)

Imperf horizontally (vertical pair)

Imperf between (horiz pair): a horizontal pair of stamps with perfs all around the edges but none between the stamps.

Imperf between (vert pair): a vertical pair of stamps with perfs all around the edges but none between the stamps. Where several of the rows have escaped perforation the resulting varieties are listable. Thus:

Imperf vert (horiz pair): a horizontal pair of stamps perforated at top and bottom; all three vertical directions are imperf—the two outer edges and between the stamps.

Imperf horiz (vert pair): a vertical pair perforated at left and right edges; all three horizontal directions are imperf—the top, bottom and between the stamps.

Varieties of double, misplaced or partial perforation caused by error or machine malfunction are not listable, neither are freaks, such as perforations placed diagonally from paper folds, nor missing holes caused by broken pins.

Phosphor Issues
Machines which sort mail electronically have been introduced progressively and the British Post Office issued the first stamps specially marked for electronic sorting in 1957. This first issue had easily visible graphite lines printed on the back beneath the gum (see Nos. 561/6). They were issued in the Southampton area where the experiment was carried out.

The graphite lines were replaced by phosphor bands, activated by ultraviolet light. The bands are printed on the front of the stamps and show as a matt surface against the usual smooth or shiny appearance of the untreated surface of the paper. The bands show clearly in the top or bottom horizontal margins of the sheet.

The first phosphor issues appeared in 1959 (see Nos. 599/609) and these stamps also had graphite lines on the back. Further details will be found in the listings above No. 599 and 619. From 1962 onwards most commemoratives were issued in versions with or without bands. From 1967 all commemorative stamps had phosphor bands, but from 1972 they were replaced by "all-over" phosphor covering the entire area of the stamp.

After a considerable period of development a special paper was produced in which the phosphor had been incorporated into the coating. From 15 August 1979 to April 1996 phosphorised paper was accepted for use generally, replacing phosphor bands on most issues for all values except the second class letter rate. Phosphorised paper can only be identified by ultraviolet light. The Stanley Gibbons Ultraviolet Lamp is firmly recommended for use in identifying the phosphor stamps listed in this Catalogue. *Warning*. Never stare at the lighted lamp but follow the manufacturer's instructions. Phosphor bands were reintroduced for all issues from April 1996.

During the years 1967 to 1972, when all issues, except the high values, should have shown phosphor bands, a number of stamps appeared with them omitted in error. These varieties are listed in this Catalogue. Stamps with "all-over" phosphor omitted can only be detected by the use of an ultraviolet lamp and these varieties are listed in the Stanley Gibbons *Great Britain Specialised Catalogue*. Note that prices are for unmounted mint examples only. Varieties such as double or misplaced bands are not listed in this Catalogue.

Gum Description
All stamps listed are assumed to have gum of some kind and original gum (o.g.) means that which was present on the stamp as issued to the public. Deleterious climates

Multi-value Coil Strip

and the presence of certain chemicals can cause gum to crack and, with early stamps, even make the paper deteriorate. Unscrupulous fakers are adept in removing it and regumming the stamp to meet the unreasoning demand often made for "full o.g." in cases where such a thing is virtually impossible.

The gum normally used on stamps has been gum arabic until the late 1960's when synthetic adhesives were introduced. Harrison and Sons Ltd for instance used *polyvinyl alcohol*, known to philatelists as PVA (see note above SG723).

From 1993 many stamps have been issued with self-adhesive gum. Unused prices are for such stamps with backing paper attached, as issued. Initially such stamps were issued with a water-soluble layer of gum allowing used examples to be "soaked off", but with the 2008 Christmas issue, most self-adhesive stamps are issued without the water-soluble layer of gum, preventing their removal from paper without damage. It is recommended that used stamps from this later period be collected "on piece".

Colour Identification

The 200 colours most used for stamp identification are given in the Stanley Gibbons Stamp Colour Key. The Catalogue has used the Colour Key as a standard for describing new issues for some years. The names are also introduced as lists are rewritten, though exceptions are made for those early issues where traditional names have become universally established.

In compound colour names the second is the predominant one, thus:
orange-red = a red tending towards orange.
red-orange = an orange containing more red than usual.

When comparing actual stamps with colour samples in the Colour Key, view in a good north daylight (or its best substitute: fluorescent "colour-matching" light). Sunshine is not recommended. Choose a solid portion of the stamp design; if available, marginal markings such as solid bars of colour or colour check dots are helpful. Shading lines in the design can be misleading as they appear lighter than solid colour. Furthermore, the listings refer to colours as issued: they may deteriorate into something different through the passage of time.

Shades are particularly significant when they can be linked to specific printings. In general, shades need to be quite marked to fall within the scope of this Catalogue.

Modern colour printing by lithography is prone to marked differences of shade, even within a single run, and variations can occur within the same sheet. Such shades are not listed.

Errors of Colour

Major colour errors in stamps or overprints which qualify for listing are: wrong colours; albinos (colourless impressions), where these have Expert Committee certificates; colours completely omitted, but only on unused stamps (if found on used stamps the information is usually footnoted) and with good credentials, missing colours being frequently faked.

Colours only partially omitted are not recognised. Colour shifts, however spectacular, are not listed.

Booklet Stamps

Single stamps from booklets are listed if they are distinguishable in some way (such as watermark or phosphor bands) from similar sheet stamps.

Booklet panes are listed where they contain stamps of different denominations *se-tenant*, where stamp-size printed labels are included, or where such panes are otherwise identifiable. Booklet panes are placed in the listing under the lowest denomination present.

Booklet panes containing single values issued up to 1952 are also listed in this catalogue. Users should note that prices are for panes with the binding margin intact and full perforations on the other three sides.

Booklet Pane with Printed Labels

Se-tenant Pane of Four

In the listing of complete booklets the numbers and prefix letters are the same as used in the Stanley Gibbons *Great Britain Specialised Catalogue*.

Coil Stamps

Stamps only issued in coil form are given full listing. If stamps are issued in both sheets and coils, the coil stamps are listed separately only where there is some feature (e.g. watermark sideways or gum change) by which single stamps can be distinguished. Coil strips containing different values *se-tenant* are also listed.

Coil join pairs are generally too random and easily faked to permit listing; similarly ignored are coil stamps which have accidentally suffered an extra row of perforations from the claw mechanism in a malfunctioning vending machine.

Gutter pair

Gutter Pairs

In 1988 the recess-printed Castle high value definitives were issued in sheets containing four panes separated by a gutter margin. All modern Great Britain commemoratives and special stamps are produced in sheets containing two panes separated by a blank horizontal or vertical margin known as a gutter. This feature first made its appearance on some supplies of the 1972 Royal Silver Wedding 3p and marked the introduction of Harrison & Sons' new "Jumelle" stamp-printing press. There are advantages for both the printer and the Post Office in such a layout which has been used for most commemorative issues since 1974.

Traffic Light Gutter Pair

The term "gutter pair" is used for a pair of stamps separated by part of the blank gutter margin as illustrated above. Most printers include some form of colour check device on the sheet margins, in addition to the cylinder or plate numbers. Harrison & Sons use round "dabs", or spots of colour, resembling traffic lights. For the period from the 1972 Royal Silver Wedding until the end of 1979 these colour dabs appeared in the gutter margin. There was always one example to every double-pane sheet of stamps. They can also be found in the high value Machin issue printed in photogravure. Gutter pairs showing these "traffic lights" are worth considerably more than the normal version.

From the 2004 Entente Cordiale set, Walsall reintroduced traffic lights in the gutters of certain sets. Where these extend over more than one section of gutter margin on any value, they are priced in blocks rather than pairs.

Miniature Sheets

A miniature sheet contains a single stamp or set with wide inscribed or decorated margins. The stamps often also exist in normal sheet format. This Catalogue lists, with **MS** prefix, complete miniature sheets which have been issued by the Post Office and which are valid for postal purposes.

Stamps from miniature sheets, not also available in normal sheet format, are not individually listed or priced in this catalogue.

Where such stamps have also appeared in a booklet, and the booklet pane differs in layout or design to the miniature sheet (e.g. "Britain Alone" (2nd issue), Nos. 3082/5) these stamps are listed separately, but if the booklet pane is the same as the miniature sheet (e.g. "Astronomy" , Nos. **MS**2315/a) they are only listed as complete miniature sheets or booklet panes.

Miniature Sheet containing a set of stamps

Se-tenant Combinations

Se-tenant means "joined together". Some sets include stamps of different design arranged *se-tenant* as blocks or strips and, in mint condition, these are usually collected unsevered as issued. The set prices quoted in this catalogue refer to the unsevered combination plus singles of any other values in the set.

Presentation and Souvenir Packs

Special Packs comprising slip-in cards with printed commemorative inscriptions and notes on the back and with protective covering, were introduced in 1964 for the Shakespeare issue. Definitive issues first appeared in Presentation Packs in 1960. Notes will be found in the listings to describe souvenir packs issued on special occasions.

Issues of 1968–1969 (British Paintings to the Prince of Wales Investiture) were also issued in packs with text in German for sale through the Post Office's German Agency and these are also included.

Collectors packs, first called gift packs, containing commemoratives issued in the preceding 12 months, first appeared in 1967. These are listed and priced.

It should be noted that prices given for presentation packs are for items as originally sold, including any additional inserts, such as questionnaire forms and publicity material.

13 August 1975 Public Railways Presentation Pack

Yearbooks

Special Post Office Yearbooks were first available in 1984. They contain all of the commemorative issues for one year in a hardbound book, illustrated in colour complete with slip case. These are listed and priced.

Commemorative First Day Covers

Until 1963 the Post Office did not provide any special first day of issue postmark facilities for collectors. Several philatelic organisations and stamp dealers did produce pictorial covers for the various commemorative issues and collectors serviced these to receive ordinary operational postmarks. Occasionally a special handstamp was produced which coincided with a new stamp issue, or relevant slogan postmarks, like the 1953 "Long Live the Queen" type, were in general use at the time.

On 21 March 1963 the Post Office installed special posting boxes at 11 main post offices so that collectors could obtain "uniformly high standard" impressions, from normal operational postmarks, for their first day covers. From 7 May 1963 special "First Day of Issue" slogans (Type A) were applied to mail posted in these special boxes, whose number had, by then, risen to 30. The Philatelic Bureau accepted orders by post for such covers from the issue of 16 May 1963 onwards.

The slogan type was replaced on 23 April 1964 by "First Day of Issue" handstamps (Type B). These were, initially, of considerable size, but were later replaced by smaller versions (Type C) which remained in use at nearly 200 principal offices until the Christmas issue of 2 November 1998. From 1970 the Bureau postmarks as Type C were inscribed "British Philatelic Bureau".

Since 1972 the Post Office has provided for virtually all issues an additional "alternative" pictorial "First Day of Issue" cancellation, at a location connected with the issue. Being available from the Bureau, these cancellations are illustrated and listed in this catalogue.

From 12 January 1999 (Millennium Inventors' Tale issue) the "alternative" pictorial postmark has been applied to all covers posted in special first day boxes throughout the country, replacing the local, non-pictorial, cancels. A bilingual version is used when the "alternative" office is in Wales. For collectors who prefer plain postmarks a non-pictorial version of the "alternative" postmark is available from Royal Mail Special Handstamp Centres.

"First Day of Issue" postmarks of standard or pictorial type have occasionally been provided on a "one-off" basis for places linked to particular stamp issues, eg Weymouth for the 1975 Sailing set. Such postmarks, which are not available from the Bureau, are footnoted only.

Royal Mail established Special Handstamp Centres in 1990 where all sponsored special handstamps and many

"First Day of Issue" postmarks are now applied.

Pictorial local "First Day of Issue" postmarks were in use between 1988 and 1998 applied to covers posted in first day boxes and sent to main offices or Special Handstamp Centres. These included Birmingham (1993–98), Durham (1988–98), City of London (1989–98), London (1993–98), Newcastle upon Tyne (1992–94), and St Albans (1995–98). Different designs were used at the Glasgow Handstamp Centre for various places, 1993–98. As these postmarks were not available from the Bureau they are not included in this catalogue.

Type A. First day of Issue Slogan

Type B. Large Handstamp   **Type C.** Small Handstamp

Type D. Maltese Cross   **Type E**

Type F. £ Sign   **Type G.** Three Lions

Type H. Four Castles   **Type I.** Windsor Keep

Type J. Millennium   **Type K.** Arms of Post Office
(2000 issues are inscr
"Beyond 2000")

Illustrations shown at 75 percent.

First day cover prices for modern issues are based on those with a Philatelic Bureau (later, "Tallents House") postmark.

Post Office Label Sheets

This catalogue lists complete "Generic Smilers" sheets in a section following the booklet listings. "Personalised" and "Corporate" sheets are not listed, neither are identifiable single stamps from label sheets.

No Value Indicated Stamps

From 22 August 1989 various definitive and special stamps appeared inscribed "2nd", "1st" or "E" instead of a face value. These were sold at the current minimum rates for these services which were as follows:

Inland Postage Rate	2nd Class	1st Class
5 September 1988	14p.	19p.
2 October 1989	15p.	20p.
17 September 1990	17p.	22p.
16 September 1991	18p.	24p.
1 November 1993	19p.	25p.
8 July 1996	20p.	26p.
26 April 1999	19p.	26p.
17 April 2000	19p.	27p.
8 May 2003	20p.	28p.
1 April 2004	21p.	28p.
7 April 2005	21p.	30p.
3 April 2006	23p.	32p.
2 April 2007	24p.	34p.
7 April 2008	27p.	36p.
6 April 2009	30p.	39p.
6 April 2010	32p.	41p.
4 April 2011	36p.	46p.
30 April 2012	50p.	60p.
31 March 2014	53p.	62p.
30 March 2015	54p.	63p.
29 March 2016	55p	64p

European Airmail Rate

26 April 1999	30p.
25 October 1999	34p.
27 April 2000	36p.
2 July 2001	37p.
27 March 2003	38p.
1 April 2004	40p.

From June 2004, European Airmail rate stamps reverted to showing a face value.

From 21 August 2006 "Large" letters were charged at a higher rate following the introduction of "Pricing in Proportion". Rates as follows:

Inland Postage Rate	2nd Class Large	1st Class Large
21 August 2006	37p.	44p.
2 April 2007	40p.	48p.
7 April 2008	42p.	52p.
6 April 2009	47p.	61p.
6 April 2010	51p.	66p.
4 April 2011	58p.	75p.
30 April 2012	69p.	90p.
31 March 2014	73p.	93p.
30 March 2015	74p	95p
29 March 2016	75p	96p

PHQ Card cancelled on First Day of Issue

PHQ Cards

From 1973 the Post Office produced sets of picture cards to accompany commemorative issues which can be sent through the post as postcards. Each card shows an enlarged colour reproduction of one stamp, initially of a single value from one set and subsequently of all values.

The Post Office gives each card a "PHQ" serial number, hence the term. The cards are usually on sale shortly before the date of issue of the stamps, but there is no officially designated "first day". Cards are priced in fine mint condition for complete sets as issued. Used prices are for cards franked with the stamp affixed, on the obverse, as illustrated; the stamp being cancelled with an official postmark for first day of issue or reverse.

Watermark Types

Stamps are on unwatermarked paper except where the heading to the set states otherwise.

AS DESCRIBED (Read through front of stamp)		AS SEEN DURING WATERMARK DETECTION (Stamp face down and back examined))
GvR	Normal	Ʀvᗺ
ꓤʌᗺ	Inverted	ᗺʌꓤ
ꓤvᗺ	Reversed	GvR
ᗺʌꓤ	Inverted and reversed	ꓤʌᗺ
GvR (sideways)	Sideways	ꓤvᗺ (sideways)
GvR (sideways)	Sideways inverted	Ʀvᗺ (sideways)
Ʀvᗺ (sideways)	Sideways reversed	GvR (sideways)
ᗺʌꓤ (sideways)	Sideways inverted and reversed	GvR (sideways)

Watermarks are detected for Catalogue description by one of four methods: (1) holding stamps to the light; (2) laying stamps face down on a dark background; (3) by use of the Morley-Bright Detector, which works by revealing the thinning of the paper at the watermark; or (4) by the more complex electric watermark detectors such as the Stanley Gibbons Detectamark Spectrum.

The diagram below shows how watermark position is described in the Catalogue. Watermarks are usually impressed so that they read normally when looked through from the printed side. However, since philatelists customarily detect watermarks by looking at the back of the stamp, the watermark diagram also makes clear what is actually seen. Note that "G v R" is only an example and illustrations of the different watermarks employed are shown in the listings. The illustrations are actual size and shown in normal positions (from the front of the stamps).

Watermark Errors and Varieties

Watermark errors are recognised as of major importance. They comprise stamps showing the wrong watermark devices or stamps printed on paper with the wrong watermark. Stamps printed on paper showing broken or deformed bits on the dandy roll, are not listable.

Underprints

From 1982 various values appeared with underprints, printed on the reverse, in blue, over the gum. These were usually from special stamp booklets, sold at a discount by the Post Office, but in 1985 surplus stocks of such underprinted paper were used for other purposes.

In this Catalogue stamps showing underprints are priced mint only. Used examples can be obtained, but care has to be taken in floating the stamps since the devices were printed on top of the gum and will be removed as the gum dissolves.

2 Small Crown   **4** Large Crown   **9** (Extends over three stamps)   **13** V R

15 Small Garter   **16** Medium Garter   **17** Large Garter   **20** Emblems   **33** Spray of Rose   **39** Maltese Cross

40 Large Anchor   **47** Small Anchor   **48** Orb   **49** Imperial Crown   **100** Simple Cypher   **103** Multiple Cypher

110 Single Cypher   **111** Block Cypher   **117** PUC £1   **125** E 8 R   **127**

133   **153** Tudor Crown   **165** St. Edward's Crown   **179** Multiple Crowns   **F5** Double-lined Anchor   **F6** Single-lined Anchor

General Types of watermark as seen through the front of the stamp

Underprint Types

1 Star with central dot   **2** Double-lined Star   **3** Double-lined "D"

4 Multiple double lined stars

5 Multiple double-lined "D"
(Types **4/5** are shown ¾ actual size)

Note: Types 4/5 are arranged in a random pattern so that the stamps from the same sheet or booklet pane will show the underprint in a slightly different position to the above. Stamps, when inspected, should be placed the correct way up, face down, when comparing with the illustrations.

Specimen Stamps

From 1847 stamps have been overprinted "SPECIMEN" for a variety of purposes, including the provision of samples to postmasters, as a security overprint on printers' or official reference copies and, from 1859, on examples of current British stamps sent to the International Bureau of the Univeral Postal Union for distribution to member nations.

Numerous styles were employed for these "Specimen" overprints, which are now listed in this catalogue up to the end of the reign of King George VI. The different types are illustrated here. Note that for ease of reference type numbers are the same as those given in the *Stanley Gibbons Great Britain Specialised Catalogue* and "missing" type numbers may have been used on stamps outside

the scope of this catalogue or may refer to "Cancelled" overprints, which are, likewise, not listed here.

SPECIMEN	SPECIMEN
1	2
SPECIMEN	SPECIMEN
4	5
SPECIMEN	SPECIMEN
6	7
SPECIMEN	SPECIMEN
8	9
SPECIMEN	SPECIMEN
10	11
SPECIMEN	SPECIMEN
12	13
SPECIMEN	SPECIMEN
15	16

SPECIMEN
17

	SPECIMEN
	22
SPECIMEN	SPECIMEN
23	26
SPECIMEN	SPECIMEN
29	30
SPECIMEN	SPECIMEN
31	32

"Specimen" stamps are listed with details of the types of "Specimen" overprints found. The different types are not listed here and where more than one type was used the price given is for the cheapest version. Imperforate overprints are also not listed, unless the stamp was normally issued in that form.

More detailed listings will be found in Volumes 1 and 2 of the *Great Britain Specialised Catalogue*.

Commemorative Design Index

This index gives an easy reference to the inscriptions and designs of the Special Stamps 1953 to April 2016. Where a complete set shares an inscription or type of design, then only the catalogue number of the first stamp is given in addition to separate entries for stamps depicting popular thematic subjects. Paintings, inventions, etc., are indexed under the name of the artist or inventor, where this is shown on the stamp.

In 1840, the Penny Black made history by becoming the world's first postage stamp - and it's rare and historic stamps (and coins) like this that could play a part in your financial future.

Due to supply-demand dynamics, the market for tangible, heritage assets continues to grow, as global collectors and astute investors seek these finite assets.

It's an alternative that offers strong portfolio diversification and the potential for capital growth over time.

Of course, past performance is not necessarily a guide for future - but uncorrelated with more traditional asset classes, rare stamps and coins could offer you a buffer against market volatility.

It's a market where experience and expertise make all the difference. And one name stands tall above all others: **Stanley Gibbons**, with our 158 years of 'stock-picking' experience.

With no management, storage or insurance fees to erode your capital – we only charge a commission on exit on any portfolio growth – investing in rare stamps (or coins) could prove a strong alternative investment for you.

So to potentially both anchor and grow your portfolio, why not invest in history?

It could be a smart move for your future - find out more with our free investment guide.

Could history help secure your financial future?

— Est.1856 —
STANLEY GIBBONS
Investment

Stanley Gibbons Shop

The home of stamp collecting since 1856
399 Strand London

Visit 399 Strand:

- Get advice from our experienced and knowledgeable staff

- See first hand our superb range of top quality stamps, albums and accessories

- Get insider tips on how to enhance and expand your collection

- Ask for guidance on techniques for care and storage of your stamps and covers

- View our specialist material

- All Stanley Gibbons stamps come with a lifetime guarantee of authenticity from our stamp specialists.

Everything for the stamp collector.

399 Strand opening hours
- Mon-Fri 9am-5.30pm
- Sat 9:30am-5.30pm • Sun Closed

Stanley Gibbons Limited
399 Strand, London, WC2R 0LX
+44 (0)20 7557 4436
www.stanleygibbons.com

Est 1856
STANLEY
GIBBONS

Stanley Gibbons

Great Britain Department

Stanley Gibbons, a name synonymous with quality.

Ever since the birth of our hobby Stanley Gibbons has been at the forefront of GB philately and we invite collectors access to one of the finest GB stocks in the world by registering for our renowned free monthly brochure. Whatever your budget or collecting interests you will find a range of the highest quality material for the discerning collector.

Simply **Mark Facey** on **020 7557 4424** email **mfacey@stanleygibbons.com**,
Michael Barrell on **020 7557 4448** email **mbarrell@stanleygibbons.com**
or **Victoria Lajer** on **020 7557 4464** email **vlajer@stanleygibbons.com**

Est 1856

STANLEY GIBBONS

Proud
PTS
members

Stanley Gibbons
399 Strand, London, WC2R 0LX
+44 (0)20 7836 8444
www.stanleygibbons.com

UNITED KINGDOM OF GREAT BRITAIN AND IRELAND

Queen Victoria
20 June 1837–22 January 1901

PARLIAMENTARY ENVELOPES. When the Uniform Penny Postage was introduced on 10 January 1840 the free franking privileges of Members of Parliament were abolished. During the same month, special envelopes were introduced for mail posted from the Houses of Parliament and these remained in use until the introduction of stamps and the Mulready stationery in May 1840. Envelopes are priced in used condition only.

Inscribed	*Houses of Parliament* in black (16 Jan 1840)		
PE2	1d. envelope	*from*	£18000
PE3	2d. envelope	*from*	£45000
PE4	4d. envelope	*from*	

Inscribed	*House of Lords* in vermilion (Jan 1840)		
PE5	1d. envelope	*from*	£25000
PE8	2d. envelope		

Inscribed	*House of Commons* in black (Jan 1840)		
PE9	1d. envelope	*from*	£6000

MULREADY ENVELOPES AND LETTER SHEETS, so called from the name of the designer, William Mulready, were issued concurrently with the first British adhesive stamps.

1d. black	Envelopes:	£350 unused;	£550 used.
	Letter Sheets:	£325 unused;	£525 used.
2d. blue	Envelopes:	£450 unused;	£2500 used.
	Letter Sheets:	£425 unused;	£2400 used.

LINE-ENGRAVED ISSUES
GENERAL NOTES

Brief notes on some aspects of the line-engraved stamps follow, but for further information and a full specialist treatment of these issues collectors are recommended to consult Volume 1 of the Stanley Gibbons *Great Britain Specialised Catalogue*.

Alphabet I

Alphabet II

Alphabet III

Alphabet IV

Typical Corner Letters of the four Alphabets

Alphabets. Four different styles were used for the corner letters on stamps prior to the issue with letters in all four corners, these being known to collectors as:

> *Alphabet I.* Used for all plates made from 1840 to the end of 1851. Letters small.
> *Alphabet II.* Plates from 1852 to mid-1855. Letters larger, heavier and broader.
> *Alphabet III.* Plates from mid-1855 to end of period. Letters tall and more slender.
> *Alphabet IV.* 1861. 1d. Die II, Plates 50 and 51 only. Letters were hand-engraved instead of being punched on the plate. They are therefore inconsistent in shape and size but generally larger and outstanding.

While the general descriptions and the illustrations of typical letters given above may be of some assistance, only long experience and published aids can enable every stamp to be allocated to its particular Alphabet without hesitation, as certain letters in each are similar to those in one of the others.

Blued Paper. The blueing of the paper of the earlier issues is believed to be due to the presence of prussiate of potash in the printing ink, or in the paper, which, under certain conditions, tended to colour the paper when the sheets were damped for printing. An alternative term is bleuté paper.

Corner Letters. The corner letters on the early British stamps were intended as a safeguard against forgery, each stamp in the sheet having a different combination of letters. Taking the first 1d. stamp, printed in 20 horizontal rows of 12, as an example, the lettering is as follows:

> Row 1.   A A, A B, A C, etc. to A L.
> Row 2.   B A, B B, B C, etc. to B L.
> and so on to
> Row 20   T A, T B, T C, etc. to T L.

On the stamps with four corner letters, those in the upper corners are in the reverse positions to those in the lower corners.

Thus in a sheet of 240 (12×20) the sequence is:

	AA	BA	CA		LA
Row 1.				etc. to	
	AA	AB	AC		AL
	AB	BB	CB		LB
Row 2.				etc. to	
	BA	BB	BC		BL
	and so on to				
	AT	BT	CT		LT
Row 20.				etc. to	
	TA	TB	TC		TL

Placing letters in all four corners was not only an added precaution against forgery but was meant to deter unmarked parts of used stamps being pieced together and passed off as an unused whole.

Dies. The first die of the 1d. was used for making the original die of the 2d., both the No Lines and White Lines issues. In 1855 the 1d. Die I was amended by retouching the head and deepening the lines on a transferred impression of the original. This later version, known to collectors as Die II, was used for making the dies for the 1d. and 2d. with letters in all four corners and also for the 1½d.

The two dies are illustrated above No. 17 in the catalogue.

Double letter

Guide line in corner

King George VI

We are always looking to buy KGVI collections,
especially good collections of cylinder blocks.
Drop us a line for a free, no-obligation valuation.

Est. 1975

MARK BLOXHAM
S T A M P S   L T D

Proud

PTS

Member

W: www.philatelic.co.uk   T: +44 (0)1661 871953   E: mark@philatelic.co.uk

Guide line through value

Double Corner Letters. These are due to the workman placing his letter-punch in the wrong position at the first attempt, when lettering the plate, and then correcting the mistake; or to a slight shifting of the punch when struck. If a wrong letter was struck in the first instance, traces of a wrong letter may appear in a corner in addition to the correct one. A typical example is illustrated.

Guide Lines and Dots. When laying down the impressions of the design on the early plates, fine vertical and horizontal guide lines were marked on the plates to assist the operative. These were usually removed from the gutter margins, but could not be removed from the stamp impression without damage to the plate, so that in such cases they appear on the printed stamps, sometimes in the corners, sometimes through "POSTAGE" or the value. Typical examples are illustrated.

Guide dots or cuts were similarly made to indicate the spacing of the guide lines. These too sometimes appear on the stamps.

Ivory Head

"Ivory Head". The so-called "ivory head" variety is one in which the Queen's Head shows white on the back of the stamp. It arises from the comparative absence of ink in the head portion of the design, with consequent absence of blueing. (See "Blued Paper", on page 1).

Line-engraving. In this context "line-engraved" is synonymous with recess-printing, in which the engraver cuts recesses in a plate and printing (the coloured areas) is from these recesses. "Line-engraved" is the traditional philatelic description for these stamps; other equivalent terms found are "engraving in *taille-douce*" (French) or "in *intaglio*" (Italian).

Plates. Until the introduction of the stamps with letters in all four corners, the number of the plate was not indicated in the design of the stamp, but was printed on the sheet margin. By long study of identifiable blocks and the minor variation in the design, coupled with the position of the corner letters, philatelists are now able to allot many of these stamps to their respective plates. Specialist collectors often endeavour to obtain examples of a given stamp printed from its different plates and our catalogue accordingly reflects this depth of detail.

Maltese Cross   Type of Town postmark

Type of Penny Post cancellation

Example of 1844 type postmark

Postmarks. The so-called "Maltese Cross" design was the first employed for obliterating British postage stamps and was in use from 1840 to 1844. Being hand-cut, the obliterating stamps varied greatly in detail and some distinctive types can be allotted to particular towns or offices. Local types, such as those used at Manchester, Norwich, Leeds, etc., are keenly sought. A red ink was first employed, but was superseded by black, after some earlier experiments, in February 1841. Maltese Cross obliterations in other colours are rare.

Obliterations of this type, numbered 1 to 12 in the centre, were used at the London Chief Office in 1843 and 1844.

Some straight-line cancellations were in use in 1840 at the Penny Post receiving offices, normally applied on the envelope, the adhesives then being obliterated at the Head Office. They are nevertheless known, with or without Maltese Cross, on the early postage stamps.

In 1842 some offices in S.W. England used dated postmarks in place of the Maltese Cross, usually on the back of the letter since they were not originally intended as obliterators. These town postmarks have likewise been found on adhesives.

In 1844 the Maltese Cross design was superseded by numbered obliterators of varied type, one of which is illustrated. They are naturally comparatively scarce on the first 1d. and 2d. stamps.

Like the Maltese Cross they are found in various colours, some of which are rare.

Re-entry

"Union Jack" re-entry

Re-entries. Re-entries on the plate show as a doubling of part of the design of the stamp generally at top or bottom. Many re-entries are very slight while others are most marked. A typical one is illustrated.

The *"Union Jack"* re-entry, so-called owing to the effect of the re-entry on the appearance of the corner stars (see illustration) occurs on stamp L K of Plate 75 of the 1d. red, Die I.

T A (T L)   M A (M L)

Varieties of Large Crown Watermark

I   II

Two states of Large Crown Watermark

Watermarks. Two watermark varieties, as illustrated, consisting of crowns of entirely different shape, are found in sheets of the Large Crown paper and fall on stamps lettered M A and T A (or M L and T L when the paper is printed on the wrong side). Both varieties are found on the 1d. rose-red of 1857, while the M A (M L) variety comes also on some plates of the 1d. of 1864 (Nos. 43, 44) up to about Plate 96. On the 2d. the T A (T L) variety is known on plates 8 and 9, and the M A (M L) on later prints of plate 9. These varieties may exist inverted, or inverted reversed on stamps lettered A A and A L and H A and H L, and some are known.

In 1861 a minor alteration was made in the Large Crown watermark by the removal of the two vertical strokes, representing fleurs-de-lis, which projected upwards from the uppermost of the three horizontal curves at the base of the Crown. Hence two states are distinguishable, as illustrated.

CONDITION–IMPERFORATE LINE-ENGRAVED ISSUES

The prices quoted for the 1840 and 1841 imperforate Line engraved issues are for "fine" examples. As condition is most important in assessing the value of a stamp, the following definitions will assist collectors in the evaluation of individual examples.

Four main factors are relevant when considering quality.

(a) Impression. This should be clean and the surface free of any rubbing or unnatural blurring which would detract from the appearance.
(b) Margins. This is perhaps the most difficult factor to evaluate. Stamps described as "fine", the standard adopted in this catalogue for pricing purposes, should have margins of the recognised width, defined as approximately one half of the distance between two adjoining unsevered stamps. Stamps described as "very fine" or "superb" should have margins which are proportionately larger than those of a "fine" stamp. Examples with close margins should not, generally, be classified as "fine".

Stanley Gibbons
Great Britain Department

Stanley Gibbons, a name synonymous with quality.

Ever since the birth of our hobby Stanley Gibbons has been at the forefront of GB philately and we invite collectors access to one of the finest GB stocks in the world by registering for our renowned free monthly brochure. Whatever your budget or collecting interests you will find a range of the highest quality material for the discerning collector.

(c) Cancellation. On a "fine" stamp this should be reasonably clear and not noticeably smudged. A stamp described as "superb" should have a neat cancellation, preferably centrally placed or to the right.

(d) Appearance. Stamps, at the prices quoted, should always be without any tears, creases, bends or thins and should not be toned on either the front or back. Stamps with such defects are worth only a proportion of the catalogue price.

Good

Fine

Very Fine

Superb

The actual size illustrations of 1840 1d. blacks show the various grades of quality. When comparing these illustrations it should be assumed that they are all from the same plate and that they are free of any hidden defects.

PRINTERS. Nos. 1/53a were recess-printed by Perkins, Bacon & Petch, known from 1852 as Perkins, Bacon & Co.

STAMPS ON COVER. Prices are quoted, for those Victorian and Edwardian issues usually found used on cover. In general these prices refer to single examples of the cheapest versions of each basic stamp, with other shades, plates or varieties, together with unusual frankings and postmarks, being worth more. However multiples of some stamps may be more common than single usages and in this case the covers might be worth considerably less than the price quoted.

---

1   **1a**   **2** Small Crown

(Eng Charles and Frederick Heath)

1840 (6 May). Letters in lower corners. *Wmk* Small Crown, W **2**. *Imperf.*

			Un	Used	Used on cover
1	**1**	1d. intense black	£17500	£525	
2		1d. black	£12500	£375	£750
		Wi. Watermark inverted	£50000	£2500	
3		1d. grey-black (worn plate)	£16500	£500	
4	**1a**	2d. deep full blue	£45000	£1150	
5		2d. blue	£38000	£900	£2500
		Wi. Watermark inverted	£90000	£6250	
6		2d. pale blue	£48000	£1000	

The 1d. stamp in black was printed from Plates 1 to 11. Plate 1 exists in two states (known to collectors as 1a and 1b), the latter being the result of extensive repairs.

Repairs were also made to plates 2, 5, 6, 8, 9, 10 and 11, and certain impressions exist in two or more states.

The so-called "Royal reprint" of the 1d. black was made in 1864, from Plate 66, Die II, on paper with Large Crown watermark, inverted. A printing was also made in carmine, on paper with the same watermark, upright.

For 1d. black with "VR" in upper corners see No. V1 under Official Stamps.

The 2d. stamps were printed from Plates 1 and 2.

Plates of 1d. black

	Un	Used	Used on cover
1*a*	£18500	£375	£1000
1*b*	£12500	£375	£750
2	£12500	£375	£750
3	£20000	£500	£900
4	£12500	£375	£775
5	£12500	£375	£775
6	£13500	£375	£775

		Un	Used	
7		£13500	£400	£825
8		£16500	£525	£1000
9		£21000	£625	£1200
10		£26500	£950	£3500
11		£23000	£4600	£16000

Varieties of 1d. black

			Un	Used
a.	On *bleuté* paper (Plates 1 to 8)	*from*		£775
b.	Double letter in corner	*from*	£13000	£400
bb.	Re-entry	*from*	£13500	£450
bc.	"PB" re-entry (Plate 5, 3rd state)		—	£10500
c.	Guide line in corner		£13000	£400
cc.	Large letters in each corner (E J, I L, J C and P A) (Plate 1b)		£13500	£550
d.	Guide line through value		£13000	£450
g.	Obliterated by Maltese Cross			
	In red		—	£400
	In black		—	£375
	In blue		—	£12000
	In magenta		—	£3000
	In yellow		—	—
	In violet			£12000
h.	Obliterated by Maltese Cross with number in centre	*from*	—	£20000
i.	Obliterated "Penny Post" in black (without Maltese Cross)	*from*	—	£5500
j.	Obliterated by town postmark (without Maltese Cross)			
	In black	*from*	—	£17500
	In yellow	*from*	—	£60000
	In red	*from*	—	£18500
k	Obliterated by 1844 type postmark in black	*from*	—	£1800

OFFICIAL STAMP

In 1840 the 1d. black (Type **1**), with "V R" in the upper corners, was prepared for official use, but was never issued for postal purposes. Obliterated specimens are those which were used for experimental trials of obliterating inks, or those that passed through the post by oversight.

V **1**

1840. Prepared for use but not issued; *V R* in upper corners. *Imperf.*

			Un	Used
V1	V **1**	1d. black	£32000	£35000

Plates of 2d. blue

Plate			Un	Used	Used on cover
1		*Shades from*	£38000	£900	£2500
2		*Shades from*	£48000	£1000	£3000

Varieties of 2d. blue

			Un	Used
a.	Double letter in corner		—	£975
aa.	Re-entry		—	£1100
b.	Guide line in corner		—	£925
c.	Guide line through value		—	£925
e.	Obliterated by Maltese Cross			
	In red		—	£1000
	In black		—	£900
	In blue		—	£15000
	In magenta		—	£12000
f.	Obliterated by Maltese Cross with number in centre	*from*	—	£18000
g.	Obliterated "Penny Post" in black (without Maltese Cross)	*from*	—	£16000
h.	Obliterated by town postmark (without Maltese Cross) in black	*from*	—	£10000
i.	Obliterated by 1844 type postmark			
	In black	*from*	—	£2500
	In blue	*from*	—	£18000

1841 (10 Feb). Printed from 'black' plates. *Wmk* W **2**. Paper more or less blued. *Imperf.*

			Un	Used	Used on cover
7	**1**	1d. red-brown (*shades*)	£2700	£130	£240
		a. "PB" re-entry (Plate 5, 3rd state)	—	£2600	
		Wi. Watermark inverted (Plates 1b, 8 and 10) *from*	—	£3250	

The first printings of the 1d. in red-brown were made from Plates 1b, 2, 5 and 8 to 11 used for the 1d. black.

1d. red-brown from "black" plates

Plate	Un	Used	Used on cover
1b	£23000	£375	£650
2	£25000	£325	£550
5	£12000	£200	£400
8	£13000	£190	£350
9	£6500	£190	£325
10	£2800	£190	£325
11	£11500	£130	£350

1841 (late Feb). Plate 12 onwards. *Wmk* W **2**. Paper more or less blued. *Imperf.*

			Un	Used	Used on cover
8	1	1d. red-brown	£600	32·00	40·00
		s. Opt. "SPECIMEN" (1)	£3500		
		Wi. Watermark inverted	£5000	£400	
8a		1d. red-brown on very blue paper	£700	32·00	
9		1d. pale red-brown (worn plates)	£675	40·00	
10		1d. deep red-brown	£900	45·00	
11		1d. lake-red	£5250	£850	
12		1d. orange-brown	£2000	£275	

Error. No letter "A" in right lower corner (Stamp B (A), Plate 77)

12a	1	1d. red-brown	—	£26000

The error "No letter A in right corner" was due to the omission to insert this letter on stamp B A of Plate 77. The error was discovered some months after the plate was registered and was then corrected.

There are innumerable variations in the colour shade of the 1d. "red" and those given in the above list represent colour groups each covering a wide range.

Varieties of 1d. red-brown, etc.

		Un	Used
b.	Major re-entry from	—	90·00
c.	Double letter in corner from	—	38·00
d.	Double Star (Plate 75) "Union Jack" re-entry	£34000	£3000
e.	Guide line in corner	—	32·00
f.	Guide line through value	—	35·00
g.	Thick outer frame to stamp	—	35·00
h.	Ivory head	£600	35·00
i.	Treasury roulette	£85000	£7200
j.	Left corner letter "S" inverted (Plates 78, 105, 107) ....from	—	£160
k.	P converted to R (Plates 30/1, 33, 83, 86) .... from	—	80·00
l.	Obliterated by Maltese Cross		
	In red	—	£4800
	In black	—	60·00
	In blue	—	£675
m.	Obliterated by Maltese Cross with number in centre		
	No. 1	—	£180
	No. 2	—	£180
	No. 3	—	£225
	No. 4	—	£600
	No. 5	—	£180
	No. 6	—	£160
	No. 7	—	£160
	No. 8	—	£160
	No. 9	—	£180
	No. 10	—	£320
	No. 11	—	£350
	No. 12	—	£350
n.	Obliterated "Penny Post" in black (without Maltese Cross)	—	£1100
o.	Obliterated by town postmark (without Maltese Cross)		
	In black ....from	—	£825
	In blue ....from	—	£2700
	In green ....from	—	£5500
	In yellow...from	—	—
	In red ....from	—	£15000
p.	Obliterated by 1844 type postmark		
	In blue ....from	—	£250
	In red ....from	—	£9750
	In green ....from	—	£3250
	In violet ....from	—	£4000
	In black...from	—	32·00
	In olive-yellow/brown ....from	—	£2000

Stamps with thick outer frame to the design are from plates on which the frame-lines have been straightened or recut, particularly Plates 76 and 90.

For "Union Jack" re-entry see General Notes to Line-engraved Issues.

In "P converted to R" the corner letter "R" is formed from the "P", the distinctive long tail having been hand-cut.

KEY TO LINE-ENGRAVED ISSUES

S.G Nos.	Description	Date	Wmk	Perf	Die	Alphabet
	THE IMPERFORATE ISSUES					
1/3	1d. black	6.5.40	SC	Imp	I	I
4/6	2d. no lines	8.5.40	SC	Imp	I	I
	PAPER MORE OR LESS BLUED					
7	1d. red-brown	Feb 1841	SC	Imp	I	I
8/12	1d. red-brown	Feb 1841	SC	Imp	I	I
8/12	1d. red-brown	6.2.52	SC	Imp	I	II
13/15	2d. white lines	13.3.41	SC	Imp	I	I
	THE PERFORATED ISSUES					
	ONE PENNY VALUE					
16a	1d. red-brown	1848	SC	Roul	I	I
16b	1d. red-brown	1850	SC	16	I	I
16c	1d. red-brown	1853	SC	16	I	II
17/18	1d. red-brown	Feb 1854	SC	16	I	II
22	1d. red-brown	Jan 1855	SC	14	I	II
24/5	1d. red-brown	28.2.55	SC	14	II	II
21	1d. red-brown	1.3.55	SC	16	II	II
26	1d. red-brown	15.5.55	LC	16	II	II
29/33	1d. red-brown	Aug 1855	LC	14	II	III
	NEW COLOURS ON WHITE PAPER					
37/41	1d. rose-red	Nov 1856	LC	14	II	III
36	1d. rose-red	26.12.57	LC	16	II	III
42	1d. rose-red	1861	LC	14	II	IV
	TWO PENCE VALUE					
19, 20	2d. blue	1.3.54	SC	16	I	I
23	2d. blue	22.2.55	SC	14	I	I
23a	2d. blue	5.7.55	SC	16	I	II
20a	2d. blue	18.8.55	SC	16	I	II
27	2d. blue	20.7.55	LC	14	I	II
34	2d. blue	20.7.55	LC	14	I	II
35	2d. blue	2.7.57	LC	14	I	III
36a	2d. blue	1.2.58	LC	16	I	III
	LETTERS IN ALL FOUR CORNERS					
48/9	½d. rose-red	1.10.70	W9	14	—	
43/4	1d. rose-red	1.4.64	LC	14	II	
53a	1½d. rosy mauve	1860	LC	14	II	
51/3	1½d. rose-red	1.10.70	LC	14	II	
45	2d. blue	July 1858	LC	14	II	
46/7	2d. thinner lines	7.7.69	LC	14	II	

Watermarks: SC = Small Crown, T **2**. LC = Large Crown, T **4**.
Dies: See notes above No. 17 in the catalogue.
Alphabets: See General Notes to this section.

3 White lines added

1841 (13 Mar)–**51**. White lines added. *Wmk* W **2**. Paper more or less blued. *Imperf.*

			Un	Used	Used on cover
13	3	2d. pale blue	£9500	£110	
14		2d. blue	£6250	90·00	£350
		s. Opt. "SPECIMEN" (1)	£9000		
		Wi. Watermark inverted	£24000	£875	
15		2d. deep full blue	£8500	£110	
15aa		2d. violet-blue (1851)	£28000	£1800	

The 2d. stamp with white lines was printed from Plates 3 and 4.

No. 15aa came from Plate 4 and the quoted price is for examples on thicker, lavender tinted paper.

Plates of 2d. blue

Plate		Un	Used
3 shades	from	£6250	£100
4 shades	from	£6250	90·00

Varieties of 2d. blue

		Un	Used
a.	Guide line in corner	—	£110
b.	Guide line through value	£6750	£110
bb.	Double letter in corner	—	£120
be.	Re-entry	£8250	£200
c.	Ivory head	£6250	£100
e.	Obliterated by Maltese Cross		
	In red	—	—
	In black	—	£275
	In blue	—	£5000
f.	Obliterated by Maltese Cross with number in centre		
	No. 1	—	£700
	No. 2	—	£700

			Un	Used
	No. 3		—	£700
	No. 4		—	£700
	No. 5		—	£850
	No. 6		—	£700
	No. 7		—	£1200
	No. 8		—	£1000
	No. 9		—	£1200
	No. 10		—	£1500
	No. 11		—	£850
	No. 12		—	£550

g. Obliterated by town postmark (without Maltese Cross)

			Un	Used
	In black	from	—	£3500
	In blue	from	—	£4500

h. Obliterated by 1844 type postmark

			Un	Used
	In black	from	—	90·00
	In blue	from	—	£1000
	In red	from	—	£28000
	In green	from	—	£9000

1841 (Apr). Trial printing (unissued) on Dickinson silk-thread paper. No wmk. *Imperf.*

			Un	Used
16	1	1d. red-brown (Plate 11)		£7750

Eight sheets were printed on this paper, six being gummed, two ungummed, but we have only seen examples without gum.

1848. *Wmk W **2**.* Rouletted approx 11½ by Henry Archer.

			Un	Used
16a	1	1d. red-brown (Plates 70, 71)		£25000

1850. *Wmk W **2**. P* 16 by Henry Archer.

			Un	Used	Used on cover
16b	1	1d. red-brown (Alph 1) (from Plates 90–101, 105, 107, 108, 116) from	£3500	£625	£2000
		bWi.Watermark inverted	—	£3750	

1853. *Wmk W **2**.* Government Trial Perforation.

			Un	Used
16c	1	1d. red-brown (p 16) (Alph II) (on cover)		

SEPARATION TRIALS. Although the various trials of machines for rouletting and perforating were unofficial, Archer had the consent of the authorities in making his experiments, and sheets so experimented upon were afterwards used by the Post Office.

As Archer ended his experiments in 1850 and plates with corner letters of Alphabet II did not come into issue until 1852, perforated stamps with corner letters of Alphabet I may safely be assumed to be Archer productions, if genuine.

The Government trial perforation is believed to have been done on Archer's machines after they had been purchased in 1853. As Alphabet II was by that time in use, the trials can be distinguished from the perforated stamps listed below by being dated prior to 24 February 1854, the date when the perforated stamps were officially issued.

Die I, Alphabet I, stamps from plates 74 and 113 perforated 14 have been recorded for many years, but it is now generally recognised that the type of comb machine used, producing one extension hole in the side margins, cannot be contemporary with other trials of this period.

Die I   Die II   **4** Large Crown

Die I: The features of the portrait are lightly shaded and consequently lack emphasis.

Die II: (Die I retouched): The lines of the features have been deepened and appear stronger. The eye is deeply shaded and made more lifelike. The nostril and lips are more clearly defined, the latter appearing much thicker. A strong downward stroke of colour marks the corner of the mouth. There is a deep indentation of colour between lower lip and chin. The band running from the back of the ear to the chignon has a bolder horizontal line below it than in Die I.

1854–57. Paper more or less blued.

*(a) Wmk Small Crown, W **2**. P* 16.

			Un	Used	Used on cover
17	1	1d. red-brown (Die I) (24.2.54)	£375	35·00	60·00
		a. Imperf three sides (horiz pair)	†	£7500	
		Wi. Watermark inverted	—	£200	
18		1d. yellow-brown (Die I)	£450	50·00	
19	3	2d. blue (Plate 4) (12.3.54)	£4700	£100	£200
		a. Imperf three sides (horiz pair)	†	—	
		s. Opt. "SPECIMEN" (2)	£2000		

			Un	Used	Used on cover
		Wi. Watermark inverted		£325	
20		2d. pale blue (Plate 4)	£5500	£110	
20a		2d. blue (Plate 5) (18.8.55)	£10000	£350	£550
		aWi. Watermark inverted	—	£900	
21	1	1d. red-brown (Die II) (22.2.55)	£550	65·00	£110
		a. Imperf (Plates 2, 14)			
		Wi. Watermark inverted	£1750	£260	

*(b) Wmk Small Crown, W **2**. P* 14.

			Un	Used	Used on cover
22	1	1d. red-brown (Die I) (1.55)	£900	90·00	£160
			—	£300	
23	3	2d. blue (Plate 4) (22.2.55)	£13000	£225	£375
		s. Opt. "SPECIMEN" (2)	£1700		
		Wi. Watermark inverted	£18500	£650	
23a		2d. blue (Plate 5) (4.7.55)	£14000	£350	£525
		b. Imperf (Plate 5)			
		aWi. Watermark inverted	—	£750	
24	1	1d. red-brown (Die II) (27.2.55)	£675	70·00	£110
		Wi. Watermark inverted	£2400	£350	
24a		1d. deep red-brown (very blue paper) (Die II)	£825	£110	
25		1d. orange-brown (Die II)	£1900	£170	

*(c) Wmk Large Crown, W **4**. P* 16.

			Un	Used	Used on cover
26	1	1d. red-brown (Die II) (15.5.55)	£2400	£130	£240
		a. Imperf (Plate 7)	—	£450	
27	3	2d. blue (Plate 5) (20.7.55)	£18500	£450	£575
		a. Imperf	—	£12000	
		Wi. Watermark inverted	—	£1000	

*(d) Wmk Large Crown, W **4**. P* 14.

			Un	Used	Used on cover
29	1	1d. red-brown (Die II) (6.55)	£240	22·00	40·00
		a. Imperf (shades) (Plates 22, 24, 25, 32, 43)	£4000	£3500	
		s. Opt. "SPECIMEN" (2)	£700		
		Wi. Watermark inverted	£1000	£150	
30		1d. brick-red (Die II)	£375	45·00	
31		1d. plum (Die II) (2.56)	£3800	£900	
32		1d. brown-rose (Die II)	£375	55·00	
33		1d. orange-brown (Die II) (3.57)	£725	60·00	
34	3	2d. blue (Plate 5) (20.7.55)	£2850	70·00	£200
		Wi. Watermark inverted	—	£325	
35		2d. blue (Plate 6) (2.7.57)	£3400	70·00	£200
		a. Imperf	—	£12000	
		b. Imperf horiz (vert pair)	†		
		Wi. Watermark inverted	—	£325	

17/35a **For well-centred, lightly used +125%*

1856–58. *Wmk Large Crown, W **4**.* Paper no longer blued.

(a) P 16.

			Un	Used	Used on cover
36	1	1d. rose-red (Die II) (26.12.57)	£2750	70·00	£160
		Wi. Watermark inverted	—	£475	
36a	3	2d. blue (Plate 6) (1.2.58)	£14500	£375	£550
		aWi. Watermark inverted	—	£1000	

(b) Die II. P 14.

			Un	Used	Used on cover
37	1	1d. red-brown (11.56)	£2400	£375	£1100
38		1d. pale red (9.4.57)	£100	35·00	
		a. Imperf	£4800	£3600	
		s. Opt. "SPECIMEN" (6, 7, 10)	£200		
39		1d. pale rose (3.57)	£110	35·00	
40		1d. rose-red (9.57)	50·00	12·00	23·00
		a. Imperf	£5000	£3800	
		b. Imperf vert (horiz pair)	†		
		Wi. Watermark inverted	£180	85·00	
41		1d. deep rose-red (7.57)	£160	20·00	

1861. Letters engraved on plate instead of punched (Alphabet IV).

			Un	Used	Used on cover
42	1	1d. rose-red (Die II) (Plates 50 & 51)	£250	40·00	70·00
		a. Imperf	—	£5750	
		Wi. Watermark inverted	£750	£200	

36/42a **For well-centred, lightly used +125%*

The original die (Die I) was used to provide roller dies for the laying down of all the line-engraved stamps from 1840 to 1855. In that year a new master die was laid down (by means of a Die I roller die) and the impression was retouched by hand engraving by William Humphrys. This retouched die, always known to philatelists as Die II, was from that time used for engraving all new roller dies.

One Penny. The numbering of the 1d. plates recommenced at 1 on the introduction of Die II. Plates 1 to 21 were Alphabet II from which a scarce plum shade exists. Corner letters of Alphabet III appear on Plate 22 and onwards. As an experiment, the corner letters were engraved by hand on Plates 50 and 51 in 1856, instead of being punched (Alphabet IV), but punching was again resorted to from Plate 52 onwards. Plates 50 and 51 were not put into use until 1861.

Two Pence. Unlike the 1d. the old sequence of plate numbers continued. Plates 3 and 4 of the 2d. had corner letters of Alphabet I, Plate 5 Alphabet II and Plate 6 Alphabet III. In Plate 6 the white lines are thinner than before.

In both values, varieties may be found as described in the preceding issues—ivory heads, inverted watermarks, re-entries, and double letters in corners.

The change of perforation from 16 to 14 was decided upon late in 1854 since the closer holes of the former gauge tended to cause the sheets of stamps to break up when handled, but for a time both gauges were in concurrent use. Owing to faulty alignment of

the impressions on the plates and to shrinkage of the paper when dampened, badly perforated stamps are plentiful in the line-engraved issues.

5

6

Showing position of the plate number on the 1d. and 2d. values.
(Plate 170 shown)

1864–79. *Letters in all four corners.* Wmk Large Crown, W **4**. Die II. *P* **14**.

			Un	Used*	Used on cover
43	5	1d. rose-red (1.4.64)	25·00	2·75	8·00
		s. Opt. "SPECIMEN" (1, 6, 8, 9)			
		.... from	£225		
44		1d. lake-red	25·00	2·75	
		a. Imperf ....from	£8500	£4500	
		Wi. Watermark inverted.........from	£100	30·00	

*43/4a **For well-centred, lightly used** +125%

The following plate numbers are known imperf (No. 44a); 72, 79, 80, 81, 82, 83, 84, 85, 86, 87, 88, 90, 91, 92, 93, 96, 97, 98, 100, 101, 102, 103, 104, 105, 107, 108, 109, 112, 113, 114, 116, 117, 120, 121, 122, 136, 137, 142, 146, 148, 158, 162, 164, 166, 171, 174, 191 and 202.

The numbering of this series of 1d. red plates follows after that of the previous 1d. stamp, last printed from Plate 68.

Plates 69, 70, 75, 126 and 128 were prepared for this issue but rejected owing to defects, and stamps from these plates do not exist, so that specimens which appear to be from these plates (like many of those which optimistic collectors believe to be from Plate 77) bear other plate numbers. Owing to faulty engraving or printing it is not always easy to identify the plate number. Plate 77 was also rejected but some stamps printed from it were used. One specimen is in the Tapling Collection and six or seven others are known. Plates 226 to 228 were made but not used.

Specimens from most of the plates are known with watermark. The variety of watermark described in the General Notes to this section occurs on stamp M A (or M L) on plates up to about 96 (Prices from £120 used).

Re-entries in this issue are few, the best being on stamps M K and T K of Plate 71 and on S L and T L, Plate 83.

Plate	Un	Used	Plate	Un	Used
71	50·00	4·00	111	65·00	3·00
72	55·00	5·00	112	85·00	3·00
73	55·00	4·00	113	65·00	15·00
74	55·00	2·75	114	£300	15·00
76	50·00	2·75	115	£120	3·00
77	—	£600000	116	95·00	11·00
78	£120	2·75	117	60·00	2·75
79	45·00	2·75	118	65·00	2·75
80	60·00	2·75	119	60·00	2·75
81	60·00	3·00	120	25·00	2·75
82	£120	5·00	121	55·00	11·00
83	£145	9·00	122	25·00	2·75
84	75·00	3·00	123	55·00	2·75
85	55·00	4·00	124	40·00	2·75
86	65·00	5·00	125	55·00	2·75
87	45·00	2·75	127	70·00	3·00
88	£175	9·50	129	55·00	10·00
89	55·00	2·75	130	70·00	3·00
90	55·00	2·75	131	80·00	20·00
91	70·00	7·00	132	£175	27·00
92	50·00	2·75	133	£150	11·00
93	65·00	2·75	134	25·00	2·75
94	60·00	6·00	135	£120	30·00
95	55·00	2·75	136	£120	24·00
96	60·00	2·75	137	40·00	3·00
97	55·00	4·50	138	30·00	2·75
98	65·00	7·00	139	75·00	20·00
99	70·00	6·00	140	30·00	2·75
100	75·00	3·00	141	£150	11·00
101	75·00	11·00	142	90·00	30·00
102	60·00	2·75	143	75·00	17·00
103	65·00	4·50	144	£120	25·00
104	95·00	6·00	145	45·00	3·00
105	£120	9·00	146	55·00	7·00
106	70·00	2·75	147	65·00	4·00
107	75·00	9·00	148	55·00	4·00
108	£100	3·00	149	55·00	7·00
109	£110	4·50	150	25·00	2·75
110	75·00	11·00	151	75·00	11·00

Plate	Un	Used	Plate	Un	Used
152	75·00	7·50	189	90·00	8·50
153	£130	11·00	190	65·00	7·00
154	65·00	2·75	191	45·00	9·00
155	65·00	3·00	192	65·00	2·75
156	60·00	2·75	193	45·00	2·75
157	65·00	2·75	194	65·00	10·00
158	45·00	2·75	195	65·00	10·00
159	45·00	2·75	196	65·00	6·50
160	45·00	2·75	197	70·00	11·00
161	75·00	9·00	198	55·00	7·00
162	65·00	9·00	199	70·00	7·00
163	65·00	4·00	200	75·00	2·75
164	65·00	4·00	201	45·00	6·00
165	60·00	2·75	202	75·00	10·00
166	60·00	7·00	203	45·00	20·00
167	60·00	2·75	204	70·00	3·00
168	65·00	10·00	205	70·00	4·00
169	75·00	9·00	206	70·00	11·00
170	50·00	2·75	207	75·00	11·00
171	25·00	2·75	208	70·00	18·00
172	45·00	2·75	209	60·00	10·00
173	90·00	11·00	210	85·00	15·00
174	45·00	2·75	211	90·00	25·00
175	75·00	4·50	212	75·00	13·00
176	75·00	3·00	213	75·00	13·00
177	55·00	2·75	214	85·00	23·00
178	75·00	4·50	215	85·00	23·00
179	65·00	3·00	216	90·00	23·00
180	75·00	6·50	217	90·00	9·00
181	60·00	2·75	218	85·00	10·00
182	£120	6·50	219	£120	85·00
183	70·00	4·00	220	55·00	9·00
184	45·00	3·00	221	90·00	20·00
185	65·00	4·00	222	£100	50·00
186	85·00	3·00	223	£120	75·00
187	65·00	2·75	224	£150	65·00
188	90·00	12·00	225	£3200	£800

1858-76 *Wmk* Large Crown. Die II. *P.* **14**

			Un	Used*	Used on cover
45	6	2d. blue (thick lines) (7.58)	£350	14·00	50·00
		a. Imperf (Plate 9)		£13000	
		s. Opt. "SPECIMEN" (1, 7)	£650		
		Wi. Watermark inverted	£1700	£240	
		Plate			
		7	£2000	65·00	
		8	£1850	42·00	
		9	£350	15·00	
		12	£3000	£140	
46		2d. blue (thin lines) (1.7.69)	£375	27·00	75·00
		s. Opt. "SPECIMEN" (pl. 14, 15)			
		(6, 8, 9, 10)	£250		
		Wi. Watermark inverted	£2250	£300	
47		2d. deep blue (thin lines)	£375	27·00	
		a. Imperf (Plate 13)	£12000		
		Plate			
		13	£375	30·00	
		14	£500	38·00	
		15	£525	38·00	

*45/7 **For well-centred, lightly used** +125%

Plates 10 and 11 of the 2d. were prepared but rejected. Plates 13 to 15 were laid down from a new roller impression on which the white lines were thinner.

There are some marked re-entries and repairs, particularly on Plates 7, 8, 9 and 12.

Stamps with inverted watermark may be found and also the T A (T L) and M A (M L) watermark varieties (see General Notes to this section).

Though the paper is normally white, some printings showed blueing and stamps showing the "ivory head" may therefore be found.

7

Showing the plate number (9)

half penny

9

1870 (1 Oct)-**79**. *Wmk W* **9,** extending over three stamps. *P* 14.

			Un	Used*	Used on cover
48	7	½d. rose-red	£110	28·00	70·00
49		½d. rose	£110	28·00	
		a. Imperf (Plates 1, 4, 5, 6, 8, 14) ......from	£4500	£3200	
		s. Opt. "SPECIMEN" (various plates) (2, 8, 9, 10)	£225		
		Wi. Watermark inverted	£450	£150	
		Wj. Watermark reversed	£450	£150	
		Wk. Watermark inverted & reversed	£300	£100	
		Plate			
		1	£325	95·00	
		3	£240	50·00	
		4	£150	45·00	
		5	£110	28·00	
		6	£120	28·00	
		8	£600	£120	
		9	£6000	£850	
		10	£130	28·00	
		11	£120	28·00	
		12	£120	28·00	
		13	£120	28·00	
		14	£120	28·00	
		15	£175	45·00	
		19	£300	60·00	
		20	£350	80·00	

*48/9a **For well-centred, lightly used** +200%

The ½d. was printed in sheets of 480 (24×20) so that the check letters run from

```
A A   X T
       to
A A   T X
```

Plates 2, 7, 16, 17 and 18 were not completed while Plates 21 and 22, though made, were not used.

Owing to the method of perforating, the outer side of stamps in either the A or X row (ie the left or right side of the sheet) is imperf.

Stamps may be found with watermark inverted or reversed, or without watermark, the latter due to misplacement of the paper when printing.

8   Position of plate number

1870 (1 Oct)-**74**. *Wmk W* **4**. *P* 14.

			Un	Used*	Used on cover
51	8	1½d. rose-red	£500	75·00	£275
		s. Opt. "SPECIMEN" (pl. 1) (2, 6)	£550		
		sa. Opt. "SPECIMEN" (pl. 3) (8, 9, 10)	£300		
52		1½d. lake-red	£600	75·00	
		a. Imperf (Plates 1 & 3) ......from	£10000	†	
		Wi. Watermark inverted	£3000	£500	
		Plate			
		(1)	£725	£100	
		3	£500	75·00	
		Error of lettering. OP–PC for CP–PC (Plate 1)			
53	8	1½d. rose-red	£30000	£2000	£7500

Prepared for use in 1860, but not issued; blued paper.

			Un	Used*	Used on cover
53a	8	1½d. rosy mauve (Plate 1)	£8500	—	
		b. Error of lettering, OP–PC for CP–PC	—	†	
		s. Opt. "SPECIMEN" (2, 6)	£2250		

*51/3 **For well-centred, lightly used** +125%

Owing to a proposed change in the postal rates, 1½d. stamps were first printed in 1860, in rosy mauve, No. 53a, but the change was not approved and the greater part of the stock was destroyed, although three or four postally used examples have been recorded.

In 1870 a 1½d. stamp was required and was issued in rose-red. Plate 1 did not have the plate number in the design of the stamps, but on stamps from Plate 3 the number will be found in the frame as shown above. Plate 2 was defective and was not used.

The error of lettering OP–PC on Plate 1 was apparently not noticed by the printer, and therefore not corrected.

EMBOSSED ISSUES

Volume 1 of the Stanley Gibbons Great Britain Specialised Catalogue gives further detailed information on the embossed issues.

PRICES. The prices quoted are for cut-square stamps with average to fine embossing. Stamps with exceptionally clear embossing are worth more.

10   **11**   **12**

13   Position of die number

(Primary die engraved at the Royal Mint by William Wyon. Stamps printed at Somerset House)

1847–54. *Imperf* (For paper and wmk see footnote).

			Un	Used	Used on cover
54	10	1s. pale green (11.9.47)	£24000	£1000	£1900
		s. Opt. "SPECIMEN" (red opt)	£3000		
		sa. Opt. "SPECIMEN" (black opt) (1, 2)	£2800		
55		1s. green	£24000	£1000	
56		1s. deep green	£28500	£1200	
		Die 1 (1847)	£24000	£1000	
		Die 2 (1854)	£26500	£1100	
57	11	10d. brown (6.11.48)	£11500	£1500	£3200
		s. Opt. "SPECIMEN" (1, 2)	£3000		
		Die 1 (1848)	£12000	£1500	
		Die 2 (1850)	£11500	£1500	
		Die 3 (1853)	£11500	£1500	
		Die 4 (1854)	£13000	£1750	
58	12	6d. mauve (watermark reversed) (1.3.54)	£19500	£1000	
		s. Opt. "SPECIMEN" (1, 2)	£3900		
59		6d. dull lilac	£19500	£1000	£1900
60		6d. purple (watermark upright)	£19500	£1000	
		Wi. Watermark inverted	£19500	£1000	
		Wk. Watermark inverted and reversed	£19500	£1000	
61		6d. violet	£32000	£4000	

The 1s. and 10d. are on "Dickinson" paper with "silk" threads. The 6d. is on paper watermarked V R in single-lined letters, *W* 13, which may be found in four ways—upright, inverted, upright reversed, and inverted reversed. In this listing the reversed watermark is taken to be 'normal'. **Collectors are reminded that Types 10/12 were also used to print postal stationery. 6d. stamps without watermark and 10d. and 1s. stamps without "silk" threads come from this source and should not be confused with the adhesives, Nos. 54/61.**

The die numbers are indicated on the base of the bust. Only Die 1 (1 *W W*) of the 6d. was used for the adhesive stamps. The 10d. is from Die 1 (W.W.1 on stamps), and Dies 2 to 4 (2W.W., 3W.W. and 4W.W.) but the number and letters on stamps from Die 1 are seldom clear and many specimens are known without any trace of them. Because of this the stamp we previously listed as "No die number" has been deleted. That they are from Die 1 is proved by the existence of blocks showing stamps with and without the die number. The 1s. is from Dies 1 and 2 (W.W.1, W.W.2).

The normal arrangement of the "silk" threads in the paper was in pairs running down each vertical row of the sheets, the space between the threads of each pair being approximately 5 mm and between pairs of threads 20 mm. Varieties due to misplacement of the paper in printing show a single thread on the first stamp from the sheet margin and two threads 20 mm apart on the other stamps of the row. Faulty manufacture is the cause of stamps with a single thread in the middle.

Through bad spacing of the impressions, which were handstruck, all values may be found with two impressions more or less overlapping. Owing to the small margin allowed for variation of spacing, specimens with good margins on all sides are not common.

Double impressions are known of all values.

Later printings of the 6d. had the gum tinted green to enable the printer to distinguish the gummed side of the paper.

SURFACE-PRINTED ISSUES

GENERAL NOTES

Volume 1 of the Stanley Gibbons *Great Britain Specialised Catalogue* gives further detailed information on the surface-printed issues.

"Abnormals". The majority of the great rarities in the surface printed group of issues are the so-called "abnormals", whose existence is due to the practice of printing six sheets from every plate as soon as made, one of which was kept for record purposes at Somerset House, while the others were perforated and usually issued. If such plates were not used for general production or if, before they came into full use, a change of watermark or colour took place, the six sheets originally printed would differ from the main issue in plate, colour or watermark, and, if issued would be extremely rare.

The abnormal stamps of this class listed in this Catalogue and distinguished, where not priced, by an asterisk (*) are:

No.	
78	3d. Plate 3 (with white dots)
152	4d. vermilion, Plate 16
153	4d. sage-green, Plate 17
109	6d. mauve, Plate 10
124/a	6d. pale chestnut & 6d. chestnut, Plate 12
145	6d. pale buff, Plate 13
88	9d. Plate 3 (hair lines)
98	9d. Plate 5 (see footnote to No. 98)
113	10d. Plate 2
91	1s. Plate 3 ("Plate 2")
148/50	1s. green, Plate 14
120	2s. blue, Plate 3

Those which may have been issued, but of which no specimens are known, are 2½d. wmk Anchor, Plates 4 and 5; 3d. wmk Emblems, Plate 5; 3d. wmk Spray, Plate 21, 6d. grey, wmk Spray, Plate 18; 8d. orange, Plate 2; 1s. wmk Emblems, Plate 5; 5s. wmk Maltese Cross, Plate 4.

The 10d. Plate 1, wmk Emblems (No. 99), is sometimes reckoned among the abnormals, but was an error, due to the use of the wrong paper.

Corner Letters. With the exception of the 4d., 6d. and 1s. of 1855–57, the ½d., 1½d., 2d. and 5d. of 1880, the 1d. lilac of 1881 and the £5 (which had letters in lower corners only, and in the reverse order to the normal), all the surface-printed stamps issued prior to 1887 had letters in all four corners, as in the later line-engraved stamps. The arrangement was the same, the letters running in sequence right across and down the sheets, whether these were divided into panes or not. The corner letters existing naturally depend on the number of stamps in the sheet and their arrangement.

Imprimaturs and Imperforate Stamps. The Post Office retained in their records (now in the National Postal Museum) one imperforate sheet from each plate, known as the Imprimatur (or officially approved) sheet. Some stamps were removed from time to time for presentation purposes and have come on to the market, but these imperforates are not listed as they were not issued. Full details can be found in Volume 1 of the *Great Britain Specialised Catalogue.*

However, other imperforate stamps are known to have been issued and these are listed where it has been possible to prove that they do not come from the Imprimatur sheets. It is therefore advisable to purchase these only when accompanied by an Expert Committee certificate of genuineness.

Plate Numbers. All stamps from No. 75 to No. 163 bear in their designs either the plate number or, in one or two earlier instances, some other indication by which one plate can be distinguished from another. With the aid of these and of the corner letters it is thus possible to "reconstruct" a sheet of stamps from any plate of any issue or denomination.

Surface-printing. In this context the traditional designation "surface-printing" is synonymous with typo(graphy)—a philatelic term—or letterpress—the printers' term—as meaning printing from (the surface of) raised type. It is also called relief printing, as the image is in relief (in French, en épargne), unwanted parts of the design having been cut away. Duplicate impressions can be electrotyped or stereotyped from an original die, the resulting clichés being locked together to form the printing plate.

Wing Margins. As the vertical gutters (spaces) between the panes, into which sheets of stamps of most values were divided until the introduction of the Imperial Crown watermark, were perforated through the centre with a single row of holes, instead of each vertical row of stamps on the inner side of the panes having its own line of perforation as is now usual, a proportion of the stamps in each sheet have what is called a "wing margin" about 5 mm wide on one or other side.

The stamps with "wing margins" are the watermark Emblems and Spray of Rose series (3d., 6d., 9d., 10d., 1s. and 2s.) with letters D, E, H or I in S.E. corner, and the watermark Garter series (4d. and 8d.) with letters F or G in S.E. corner. Knowledge of this lettering will enable collectors to guard against stamps with wing margin cut down and re-perforated, but note that wing margin stamps of Nos. 62 to 73 are also to be found re-perforated.

PRINTERS. The issues of Queen Victoria, Nos. 62/214, were typo by Thomas De La Rue & Co.

PERFORATIONS. All the surface-printed issues of Queen Victoria are perf 14, with the exception of Nos. 126/9.

KEY TO SURFACE-PRINTED ISSUES 1855-83

S.G. Nos.	Description	Watermark	Date of Issue
	NO CORNER LETTERS		
62	4d. carmine	Small Garter	31.7.55
63/5	4d. carmine	Medium Garter	25.2.56
66/a	4d. carmine	Large Garter	Jan 1857
69/70	6d. lilac	Emblems	21.10.56
71/3	1s. green	Emblems	1.11.56
	SMALL WHITE CORNER LETTERS		
75/7	3d. rose	Emblems	1.5.62
78	3d. carmine (dots)	Emblems	Aug 1862
79/82	4d. red	Large Garter	15.1.62
83/5	6d. lilac	Emblems	1.12.62

S.G. Nos.	Description	Watermark	Date of Issue
86/8	9d. bistre	Emblems	15.1.62
89/91	1s. green	Emblems	1.12.62
	LARGE WHITE CORNER LETTERS		
92	3d. rose	Emblems	1.3.65
102/3	3d. rose	Spray	July 1867
93/4	4d. vermilion	Large Garter	4.7.65
96/7	6d. lilac	Emblems	7.3.65
104/7	6d. lilac	Spray	21.6.67
108/9	6d. lilac	Spray	8.3.69
122/4	6d. chestnut	Spray	12.4.72
125	6d. grey	Spray	24.4.73
98	9d. straw	Emblems	30.10.65
110/11	9d. straw	Spray	3.10.67
99	10d. brown	Emblems	11.11.67
112/14	10d. brown	Spray	1.7.67
101	1s. green	Emblems	19.1.65
115/17	1s. green	Spray	13.7.67
118/20b	2s. blue	Spray	1.7.67
121	2s. brown	Spray	27.2.80
126/7	5s. rose	Cross	1.7.67
128	10s. grey	Cross	26.9.78
129	£1 brown-lilac	Cross	26.9.78
130, 134	5s. rose	Anchor	25.11.82
131, 135	10s. grey-green	Anchor	Feb 1883
132, 136	£1 brown-lilac	Anchor	Dec 1882
133, 137	£5 orange	Anchor	21.3.82
	LARGE COLOURED CORNER LETTERS		
138/9	2½d. rosy mauve	Anchor	1.7.75
141	2½d. rosy mauve	Orb	1.5.76
142	2½d. blue	Orb	5-2.80
157	2½d. blue	Crown	23.3.81
143/4	3d. rose	Spray	5.7.73
158	3d. rose	Crown	Jan 1881
159	3d. on 3d. lilac	Crown	1.1.83
152	4d. vermilion	Large Garter	1.3.76
153	4d. sage-green	Large Garter	12.3.77
154	4d. brown	Large Garter	15.8.80
160	4d. brown	Crown	9.12.80
145	6d. buff	Spray	15.3.73
146/7	6d. grey	Spray	20.3.74
161	6d. grey	Crown	1.1.81
162	6d. on 6d. lilac	Crown	1.1.83
156a	8d. purple-brown	Large Garter	July 1876
156	8d. orange	Large Garter	11.9.76
148/50	1s. green	Spray	1.9.73
151	1s. brown	Spray	14.10.80
163	1s. brown	Crown	24.5.81

Watermarks:		
	Anchor	W **40, 47**
	Cross	W **39**
	Crown	W **49**
	Emblems	W **20**
	Large Garter	W **17**
	Medium Garter	W **16**
	Orb	W **48**
	Small Garter	W **15**
	Spray	W **33**

14

15 Small Garter

16 Medium Garter

17 Large Garter

1855–57. No corner letters.

*(a) Wmk Small Garter, W **15**. Highly glazed, deeply blued paper*
(31 July 1855)

			Un	Used*	Used on cover
62	**14**	4d. carmine (*shades*)	£8500	£450	£780
		a. Paper slightly blued	£9000	£450	
		b. White paper	£20000	£1100	

			Un	Used*	cover
		s. Opt. "SPECIMEN" (2, 3)	£1200		
		Wi. Watermark inverted	£11000	£1200	

(b) Wmk Medium Garter, W **16**.

(i) Thick, blued highly glazed paper 25 February 1856.

63	14	4d. carmine (*shades*)	£14000	£575	£1100
		a. White paper	£12000		
		s. Opt. "SPECIMEN" (2)	£1100		
		Wi. Watermark inverted	—	£1250	

(ii) Ordinary thin white paper – September 1856.

64	14	4d. pale carmine .	£13000	£475	£1000
		a. Stamp printed double	†	—	
		s. Opt. "SPECIMEN" (2)	£1100		
		Wi. Watermark inverted	£17000	£1200	

(iii) Ordinary white paper, specially prepared ink – 1 November 1856.

65	14	4d. rose or deep rose	£13000	£500	£1000
		s. Opt. "SPECIMEN" (4)	£1850		
		Wi Watermark inverted	†		

(c) Wmk Large Garter, W **17**. *Ordinary white paper – January 1857.*

66	14	4d. rose-carmine	£2100	£150	£225
		a. Rose	£1750	£150	
		aWi. Watermark inverted	£4800	£400	
		aWj. Watermark inverted and reversed			
		b. Thick glazed paper	£6500	£375	
		bWi. Watermark inverted			
		s. Opt. "SPECIMEN" (2, 7)	£450		

*62/6b **For well-centred, lightly used** +125%

18   **19**

20 Emblems wmk (normal)   **20a** Watermark error, three roses and shamrock   **20b** Watermark error, three roses and thistle

(d) Wmk Emblems, W **20**.

			Un	Used*	Used on cover
69	18	6d. deep lilac (21.10.56)	£1800	£175	
		s. Opt. "SPECIMEN" (2, 4, 7, 8)	£600		
70		6d. pale lilac	£1350	£125	£240
		a. Azure paper	£9000	£950	
		b. Thick paper	£4000	£425	
		c. Error. Watermark *W* **20a**			
		Wi. Watermark inverted	£3000	£400	
		Wj. Watermark reversed		£475	
		Wk. Watermark inverted and reversed			
71	19	1s. deep green (1.11.56)	£5750	£550	
		s. Opt. "SPECIMEN" (2, 4, 7)	£975		
72		1s. green	£3250	£350	£425
73		1s. pale green	£3250	£350	
		a. Azure paper	—	£2000	
		b. Thick paper	—	£400	
		c. Imperf	†	—	
		Wi. Watermark inverted	—	£675	
		Wj. Watermark reversed	—	£1400	
		Wk. Watermark inverted and reversed			

*69/73b **For well-centred, lightly used** +125%

21   **22**

23   **24**   **25** Plate 2

A. White dots added   B. Hair lines

1862–64. A small uncoloured letter in each corner, the 4d. wmk Large Garter, *W* **17**, the others Emblems, *W* **20**.

			Un	Used*	Used on cover
75	21	3d. deep carmine-rose (Plate 2) (1.5.62)	£4800	£575	
		s. Opt. "SPECIMEN" (2, 5, 6, 8)	£500		
76		3d. bright carmine-rose	£2700	£350	£600
		a. Error. Watermark *W* **20b** (stamp TF)		£9000	
		Wi .Watermark inverted	—	£1200	
77		3d. pale carmine-rose	£2700	£350	
		b. Thick paper	£4000	£475	
		Wj. Watermark reversed			
78		3d. rose (with white dots, Type A, Plate 3) (8.62)	£45000	£17000	
		a. Imperf (Plate 3)	£6750		
		s. Opt. "SPECIMEN" (2)	£2000		
79	22	4d. brt red (Plate 3) (15.1.62)	£2200	£170	
		s. Opt. "SPECIMEN" (2, 5, 6, 8)	£425		
80		4d. pale red	£2000	£140	£300
		Wi. Watermark inverted		£375	
81		4d. brt red (Hair lines, Type B, Plate 4) (16.10.63)	£2300	£185	
		s. Opt. "SPECIMEN" (2)	£500		
82		4d. pale red (Hair lines, Type B, Plate 4)	£2100	£150	£300
		a. Imperf (Plate 4)	£3700		
		Wi. Watermark inverted	£6700	£375	
83	23	6d. dp lilac (Plate 3) (1.12.62)	£2800	£150	
84		6d. lilac	£2250	£130	£225
		a. Azure paper	—	£1400	
		b. Thick paper	—	£375	
		c. Error. Shamrock missing from wmk (stamp TF)			
		d. Error. Watermark *W* **20b** (stamp TF)	—	£8000	
		e. Hyphen omitted (KA)*		£7750	
		s. Opt. "SPECIMEN" (2, 5, 8)	£600		
		Wi. Watermark inverted	£8250	£450	
		Wj. Watermark reversed		£550	
		Wk. Watermark inverted and reversed .	£12000		
85		6d. lilac (Hair lines, Plate 4) (20.4.64)	£3000	£225	£350
		a. Imperf (watermark inverted)	£4250		
		Eb. Imperf and watermark upright	£4750		
		c. Thick paper	£4000	£275	
		d. Error. Watermark *W* **20b** (stamp TF)			
		s. Opt. "SPECIMEN" (2)	£600		
		Wi. Watermark inverted	£8250	£475	
		Wj. Watermark reversed			
		Wk. Watermark inverted and reversed			
86	24	9d. bistre (Plate 2) (15.1.62)	£5800	£575	£1200
		s. Opt. "SPECIMEN" (2, 6)	£750		
		Wi. Watermark inverted	£10000	£700	
		Wj. Watermark reversed	—	£850	
		Wk. Watermark inverted and reversed			
87		9d. straw	£4000	£475	£1000
		a. On azure paper			
		b. Thick paper	£6000	£550	
		c. Error. Watermark *W* **20b** (stamp TF)	†	—	
		Wi. Watermark inverted	£6800	—	
88		9d. bistre (Hair lines, Plate 3) (5.62)	£32000	£13500	
89	25	1s. dp green (Plate No. 1 = Plate 2) (1.12.62)	£4800	£500	
90		1s. green (Plate No. 1 = Plate 2)	£3200	£300	£450
		a. "K" in lower left corner in white circle (stamp KD)	£20000	£2700	
		awi. Watermark inverted	—	£4250	
		ab. "K" normal (stamp KD)		£2200	
		b. On azure paper			

Stanley Gibbons
Great Britain Department

Stanley Gibbons, a name synonymous with quality.

Ever since the birth of our hobby Stanley Gibbons has been at the forefront of GB philately and we invite collectors access to one of the finest GB stocks in the world by registering for our renowned free monthly brochure. Whatever your budget or collecting interests you will find a range of the highest quality material for the discerning collector.

Fine Stamps and Postal History

Visit our website to view hundreds of fine GB items:

www.andrewglajer.co.uk

Andrew G Lajer Ltd
sales@andrewglajer.co.uk / T: 01189 344151
The Old Post Office, Davis Way, Hurst, Berkshire, RG10 0TR

c. Error. Watermark *W* **20b**
(stamp TF) ....
d. Thick paper .... — £375
da. Thick paper, "K" in circle as No.
90a .... — £3750
s. Opt. "SPECIMEN" (2, 5, 8) £550
Wi. Watermark inverted .... — £450
Wj. Watermark reversed ....
Wk. Watermark inverted and
reversed .... — £475

91 1s. deep green (Plate No. 2 =
Plate 3) £35000
a. Imperf £7250
as. Opt. "SPECIMEN" (2) £4200
aWi. Watermark inverted £7250

***75/91* For well-centred, lightly used +125%**

The 3d. as Type **21**, but with network background in the spandrels, was never issued. Opt. "SPECIMEN" *price* £800.

The plates of this issue may be distinguished as follows:

3d. Plate 2 No white dots.
    Plate 3 White dots as illustration A.
4d. Plate 3 No hair lines. Roman I next to lower corner letters.
    Plate 4 Hair lines in corners. (Illustration B.). Roman II.
6d. Plate 3 No hair lines.
    Plate 4 Hair lines in corners.
9d. Plate 2 No hair lines.
    Plate 3 Hair lines in corners. Beware of faked lines.
1s. Plate 2 Numbered 1 on stamps
    Plate 3 Numbered 2 on stamps & with hair lines.

*One used example on piece has been recorded, cancelled by a Glasgow Duplex postmark dated 06.1.1863.

The 9d. on azure paper (No. 87a) is very rare, only one confirmed example being known.

The variety "K" in circle, No. 90a, is believed to be due to a damaged letter having been cut out and replaced. It is probable that the punch was driven in too deeply, causing the flange to penetrate the surface, producing an indentation showing as an uncoloured circle.

The watermark variety "three roses and a shamrock" illustrated in *W* **20a** was evidently due to the substitution of an extra rose for the thistle in a faulty watermark bit. It is found on stamp TA of Plate 4 of the 3d., Plates 1 (No. 70c), 3, 5 and 6 of the 6d., Plate 4 of the 9d. and Plate 4 of the 1s.

Similar problems occurred on stamp TF of the 6d. and 9d. Here the shamrock emblem became detached and a used example of the 6d. (No. 84) is known showing it omitted. It was replaced by a third rose (*W* **20b**) and this variety exists on the 6d. (Nos. 84/5 and 97) and 9d. (Nos. 87 and 98).

26   27

28 (with hyphen)   **28a** (without hyphen)

29   30   31

1865–67. Large uncoloured corner letters. *Wmk* Large Garter (4d.); others Emblems.

			Un	Used*	Used on cover
92	**26**	3d. rose (Plate 4) (1.3.65)	£2500	£250	£500
		a. Error. Watermark *W* **20a**	£6500	£1250	
		b. Thick paper	£3500	£325	
		s. Opt. "SPECIMEN" (2)	£4500		
		Wi. Watermark inverted	—	£600	
		Wj. Watermark reversed			
		Wk. Watermark inverted and reversed			
93	**27**	4d. dull vermilion (4.7.65)	£650	90·00	
		s. Opt. "SPECIMEN" (pl. 14) (8)	£500		
94		4d. vermilion	£575	75·00	£140
		a. Imperf (Plates 11, 12)	£8500		
		Wi. Watermark inverted	£575	75·00	

			Un	Used*	Used on cover
		Plate			
		7 (1865)	£650	£130	
		8 (1866)	£600	90·00	
		9 (1867)	£600	90·00	
		10 (1868)	£825	£150	
		11 (1869)	£625	90·00	
		12 (1870)	£575	75·00	
		13 (1872)	£650	75·00	
		14 (1873)	£775	£110	
96	**28**	6d. dp lilac (with hyphen)(7.3.65)	£1900	£190	
		s. Opt. "SPECIMEN" (pl. 5) (2)	£4750		
97		6d. lilac (with hyphen)	£1200	£140	£225
		a. Thick paper	£1600	£175	
		b. Stamp doubly printed (Plate 6)	—	£15000	
		c. Error. Watermark *W* **20a** (Pl 5) .... *from*	—	£2400	
		d. Error. Watermark *W* **20b** (Plate 5)			
		e. Imperf (Plate 5)	—	£250	
		Wi. Watermark inverted			
		Wj. Watermark reversed			
		Wk. Watermark inverted and reversed.	†	—	
		Plate			
		5 (1865)	£1150	£140	
		6 (1867)	£3800	£250	
98	**29**	9d. straw (Plate 4) (25.10.65)	£4800	£600	£1400
		a. Thick paper	£5800	£850	
		b. Error. Watermark *W* **20a**	—	£2500	
		c. Error. Watermark *W* **20b** (stamp TF)	£13000		
		s. Opt. "SPECIMEN" (2)	£925		
		Wi. Watermark inverted	—	£1650	
99	**30**	10d. red-brown (Plate 1) (11.11.67)	*	£55000	
101	**31**	1s. green (Plate 4) (19.1.65)	£2850	£275	£450
		a. Error. Watermark *W* **20a**	—	£1700	
		ab. Error. Watermark *W* **20b**			
		b. Thick paper	£3500	£380	
		c. Imperf between (vert pair)	—	£16000	
		s. Opt. "SPECIMEN" (2)	£625		
		Wi. Watermark inverted	—	£650	
		Wj. Imperf watermark inverted			
		Wk. Watermark inverted and reversed	—	£650	

***92/101c* For well-centred, lightly used +100%**

From mid-1866 to about the end of 1871 4d. stamps of this issue appeared generally with watermark inverted.

Unused examples of No. 98 from Plate 5 exist, but this was never put to press and all evidence points to such stamps originating from a portion of the Imprimatur sheet which was perforated by De La Rue in 1887 for insertion in albums to be presented to members of the Stamp Committee (*Price* £20000 *un*).

The 10d. stamps, No. 99, were printed in error on paper watermarked "Emblems" instead of on "Spray of Rose".

No. 95 is vacant.

32

33 Spray of Rose

34

1867–80 *Wmk* Spray of Rose. *W* **33**.

			Un	Used*	Used on cover
102	**26**	3d. deep rose (12.7.67)	£800	£100	
103		3d. rose	£525	60·00	£110
		a. Imperf (Plates 5, 6) ....*from*	£11000		
		s. Opt. "SPECIMEN" (pl. 5) (8)	£275		
		sa. Opt. "SPECIMEN" (pl. 6) (2, 8)....	£300		
		sb. Opt. "SPECIMEN" (pl. 7) (2, 6)...	£300		
		sc. Opt. "SPECIMEN" (pl. 8) (8)	£300		
		sd. Opt. "SPECIMEN" (pl. 10) (2, 8, 9)	£270		
		Wi. Watermark inverted	£2250	£300	
		Plate			
		4 (1867)	£1850	£300	
		5 (1868)	£525	70·00	
		6 (1870)	£550	70·00	
		7 (1871)	£650	70·00	
		8 (1872)	£625	60·00	
		9 (1872)	£625	70·00	
		10 (1873)	£875	£150	
104	**28**	6d. lilac (with hyphen) (Plate 6) (21.6.67)	£1850	£135	£225
		a. Imperf		£6000	
		Wi. Watermark inverted	—	£350	
105		6d. dp lilac (with hyphen) (Plate 6)....	£1850	£135	

			Un	Used*	Used on cover
106		6d. purple (with hyphen) (Plate 6)	£1850	£175	
107		6d. brt violet (with hyphen) (Plate 6) (22.7.68)	£1750	£175	
108	28a	6d. dull violet (without hyphen) (Plate 8) (8.3.69)	£1250	£175	
		s. Opt. "SPECIMEN" (pl. 8) (1, 8)	£350		
		Wi. Watermark inverted	—	£275	
109		6d. mauve (without hyphen)	£700	90·00	£140
		a. Imperf (Plate Nos. 8 & 9)	£12000	£5000	
		s. Opt. "SPECIMEN" (pl. 9) (6, 8)	£350		
		Wi. Watermark inverted	—	£250	
		Plate			
		8 (1869, mauve)	£800	£140	
		9 (1870, mauve)	£700	90·00	
		10 (1869, mauve)	*	£37500	
110	29	9d. straw (Plate No. 4) (3.10.67)	£2500	£325	£525
		s. Opt. "SPECIMEN" (2, 8, 9, 10, 11)	£425		
		Wi. Watermark inverted	—	£650	
111		9d. pale straw (Plate No. 4)	£2400	£300	
		a. Imperf (Plate 4)	£22000		
112	30	10d. red-brown (1.7.67)	£3600	£400	£850
		s. Opt. "SPECIMEN" (2, 5, 6, 8, 9, 10, 11)	£500		
		Wi. Watermark inverted	—	£1000	
113		10d. pale red-brown	£3600	£400	
114		10d. deep red-brown	£5000	£600	
		a. Imperf (Plate 1)	£17000		
		Plate			
		1 (1867)	£3600	£400	
		2 (1867)	£55000	£17000	
115	31	1s. deep green (13.7.67)	£1300	70·00	
117		1s. green	£800	45·00	90·00
		a. Imperf between (horiz pair) (Pl 7)			
		b. Imperf (Plate 4)	£10000	£6500	
		s. Opt. "SPECIMEN" (pl. 4) (1, 8, 9)	£400		
		sa. Opt. "SPECIMEN" (pl. 5) (2, 6, 8, 9)	£425		
		sb. Opt. "SPECIMEN" (pl. 6) (8, 9)	£425		
		sc. Opt. "SPECIMEN" (pl. 7) (9)	£400		
		Wi. Watermark inverted	£2400	£180	
		Plate			
		4 (1867)	£975	65·00	
		5 (1871)	£800	45·00	
		6 (1871)	£1200	45·00	
		7 (1873)	£1400	90·00	
118	32	2s. dull blue (1.7.67)	£4200	£225	£825
		s. Opt. "SPECIMEN" (2, 5, 8, 9, 10, 11)	£600		
		Wi. Watermark inverted	—	£875	
119		2s. deep blue	£5000	£240	
		a. Imperf (Plate 1)	£23000		
120		2s. pale blue	£5000	£275	
		aa. Imperf (Plate 1)	£22000		
120a		2s. cobalt	£25000	£3000	
120b		2s. milky blue	£24000	£2000	
		Plate			
		1 (1867)	£4200	£225	
		3 (1868)	*	£16500	
121		2s. brown (Plate No. 1) (27.2.80)	£30000	£4250	
		a. Imperf	£30000		
		b. No watermark	†	—	
		s. Opt. "SPECIMEN" (9)	£3800		
		Wi. Watermark inverted	—	£6000	

*102/21 **For well-centred, lightly used +75%**

Examples of the 1s. from Plates 5 and 6 without watermark are postal forgeries used at the Stock Exchange Post Office in the early 1870s. (*Prices from £850*)

1872–73. Uncoloured letters in corners. *Wmk* Spray, *W* **33**.

			Un	Used*	Used on cover
122	34	6d. deep chestnut (Plate 11) (12.4.72)	£1300	£125	
		s. Opt. "SPECIMEN" (2, 6, 8)	£325		
122a		6d. chestnut (Plate 11) (22.5.72)	£800	65·00	£150
		Wi. Watermark inverted	—	£325	
122b		6d. pale chestnut (Plate 11) (1872)	£700	65·00	
123		6d. pale buff (19.10.72)	£1100	£125	£250
		Wi. Watermark inverted	—	£375	
		Plate			
		11 (1872, pale buff)	£1100	£125	
		12 (1872, pale buff)	£3400	£350	
124		6d. chestnut (Plate 12) (1872)	*	£3800	
124a		6d. pale chestnut (Plate 12) (1872)	*	£3500	
125		6d. grey (Plate No. 12) (24.4.73)	£1900	£300	£375
		a. Imperf	£12000		
		s. Opt. "SPECIMEN" (6, 8, 9)	£375		
		Wi. Watermark inverted	£6250	£750	

*122/5 **For well-centred, lightly used +50%**

35

36

37

38

39 Maltese Cross

40 Large Anchor

1867–83. Uncoloured letters in corners.

(a) Wmk Maltese Cross, W **39**. P 15½×15.

			Un	Used*
126	35	5s. rose (1.7.67)	£11000	£675
		s. Opt. "SPECIMEN" (2, 6)	£1100	
127		5s. pale rose	£11000	£675
		a. Imperf (Plate 1)	£18000	
		s. Opt. "SPECIMEN" (pl. 2) (8, 9)	£1750	
		Plate		
		1 (1867)	£11000	£675
		2 (1874)	£18000	£1500
128	36	10s. greenish grey (Plate 1) (26.9.78)	£60000	£3200
		s. Opt. "SPECIMEN" (8, 9)	£4250	
129	37	£1 brown-lilac (Plate 1) (26.9.78)	£90000	£4500
		s. Opt. "SPECIMEN" (9)	£6250	

(b) Wmk Large Anchor, W **40**. P 14.

(i) Blued paper

			Un	Used*
130	35	5s. rose (Plate 4) (25.11.82)	£42000	£4800
		s. Opt. "SPECIMEN" (9)	£5250	
		Wi. Watermark inverted	—	£18000
131	36	10s. grey-green (Plate 1) (2.83)	£135000	£5200
		s. Opt. "SPECIMEN" (9)	£10,000	
132	37	£1 brown-lilac (Plate 1) (12.82)	£175000	£10000
		s. Opt. "SPECIMEN" (9)	£12500	
133	38	£5 orange (Plate 1) (21.3.82)	£70000	£15000
		s. Opt. "SPECIMEN" (9, 11)	£3500	

(ii) White paper.

			Un	Used*
134	35	5s. rose (Plate 4)	£35000	£4200
135	36	10s. greenish grey (Plate 1)	£160000	£4500
136	37	£1 brown-lilac (Plate 1)	£200000	£9000
		s. Opt. "SPECIMEN" (6, 9)	£11500	
137	38	£5 orange (Plate 1)	£14500	£4750
		s. Opt. "SPECIMEN" (9, 11, 16)	£4500	

*126/37 **For well-centred, lightly used +75%**

PUBLIC AUCTIONS
ALWAYS INCLUDE
EXTENSIVE GREAT BRITAIN

Our Public Sales include interesting and unusual material, with individual collections offered intact, specialised ranges, better singles or sets and Postal History.

5 Mosley Street, Newcastle upon Tyne, NE1 1YE
Tel: 0191 232 7268 Fax: 0191 261 4130
Email: info@corbitts.com Website: www.corbitts.com

Members of: Philatelic Traders Society • American Stamp Dealers Association • American Philatelic Society

**COMPLIMENTARY CATALOGUE
AVAILABLE ON REQUEST**

41

42

43

44

45

46

47 Small Anchor

48 Orb

1873–80. Large coloured letters in the corners.

(a) Wmk Small Anchor, W **47**.

			Un	Used*	Used on cover
138	41	2½d. rosy mauve (*blued paper*) (1.7.75)	£875	£190	
		a. Imperf	£250		
		s. Opt. "SPECIMEN" (pl. 1) (8) ..	£3000	£350	
		Wi. Watermark inverted	£3000	£350	
		Plate			
		1 (*blued paper*) (1875)	£875	£190	
		2 (*blued paper*) (1875)	£8000	£1650	
		3 (*blued paper*) (1875)	—	£5750	
139		2½d. rosy mauve (*white paper*)	£650	£120	£180
		Wi. Watermark inverted	£2750	£250	
		Plate			
		1 (*white paper*) (1875)	£650	£120	
		2 (*white paper*) (1875)	£650	£120	
		3 (*white paper*) (1875)	£1000	£175	
		Error of Lettering L H—F L *for* L H—H L (*Plate* 2).			
140	41	2½d. rosy mauve	£34000	£2750	

(b) Wmk Orb, W **48**.

			Un	Used*	Used on cover
141	41	2½d. rosy mauve (1.5.76)	£525	80·00	£125
		s. Opt. "SPECIMEN" (pl. 3) (10)	£4200		
		sa. Opt. "SPECIMEN" (pl. 5) (9) ..	£220		
		sb. Opt. "SPECIMEN" (pl. 6) (8, 9)	£220		
		sc. Opt. "SPECIMEN" (pl. 7) (9) ..	£220		
		sd. Opt. "SPECIMEN" (pl. 10) (9)	£220		
		se. Opt. "SPECIMEN" (pl. 16) (9)	£220		
		Wi. Watermark inverted	£1900	£200	
		Plate			
		3 (1876)	£1350	£150	
		4 (1876)	£525	85·00	
		5 (1876)	£525	85·00	
		6 (1876)	£525	85·00	
		7 (1877)	£525	85·00	
		8 (1877)	£525	85·00	
		9 (1877)	£525	85·00	
		10 (1878)	£550	85·00	
		11 (1878)	£525	85·00	
		12 (1878)	£525	85·00	
		13 (1878)	£525	85·00	
		14 (1879)	£525	85·00	
		15 (1879)	£525	85·00	
		16 (1879)	£525	85·00	
		17 (1880)	£1700	£300	
142	41	2½d. blue (5.2.80)	£575	55·00	90·00
		s. Opt. "SPECIMEN" (pl. 17) (9)	£160		
		Wi. Watermark inverted	£2100	£275	
		Plate			
		17 (1880)	£575	75·00	
		18 (1880)	£575	55·00	
		19 (1880)	£575	55·00	
		20 (1880)	£575	55·00	

(c) Wmk Spray, W **33**.

			Un	Used*	Used on cover
143	42	3d. rose (5.7.73)	£450	80·00	£120
		s. Opt. "SPECIMEN" (pl. 14) (2)	£280		

			Un	Used*	Used on cover
		sa. Opt. "SPECIMEN" (pl. 17) (8, 9)	£250		
		sb. Opt. "SPECIMEN" (pl. 18) (8, 9, 10)	£250		
		sc. Opt. "SPECIMEN" (pl. 19) (9, 10)	£250		
		Wi. Watermark inverted	£1650	£350	
144		3d. pale rose	£450	80·00	
		Plate			
		11 (1873)	£450	80·00	
		12 (1873)	£525	80·00	
		14 (1874)	£525	80·00	
		15 (1874)	£450	80·00	
		16 (1875)	£450	80·00	
		17 (1875)	£525	80·00	
		18 (1875)	£525	80·00	
		19 (1876)	£450	80·00	
		20 (1879)	£850	£140	
145	43	6d. pale buff (Plate 13) (15.3.73)	*	£25000	
146		6d. deep grey (20.3.74)	£600	£120	£150
		s. Opt. "SPECIMEN" (pl. 14) (8, 10)	£300		
		sa. Opt. "SPECIMEN" (pl. 15) (8, 9)	£300		
		sb. Opt. "SPECIMEN" (pl. 16) (9)	£300		
147		6d. grey	£500	90·00	
		Wi. Watermark inverted	£1800	£350	
		13 (1874)	£500	90·00	
		14 (1875)	£500	90·00	
		15 (1876)	£500	90·00	
		16 (1878)	£500	90·00	
		17 (1880)	£950	£180	
148	44	1s. deep green (1.9.73)	£1100	£225	
150		1s. green	£650	£160	£240
		s. Opt. "SPECIMEN" (pl. 11) (8)	£350		
		sa. Opt. "SPECIMEN" (pl. 12) (8, 9, 10)	£350		
		sb. Opt. "SPECIMEN" (pl. 13) (9)	£350		
		Wi. Watermark inverted	£2400	£375	
		Plate			
		8 (1873)	£825	£175	
		9 (1874)	£825	£175	
		10 (1874)	£775	£200	
		11 (1875)	£775	£175	
		12 (1875)	£650	£160	
		13 (1876)	£650	£160	
		14 (—)*	*	£40000	
151		1s. orange-brown (Plate 13) (14.10.80)	£4750	£700	£1800
		s. Opt. "SPECIMEN" (9)	£550		
		Wi. Watermark inverted	£11000	£1800	

(d) Wmk Large Garter, W **17**.

			Un	Used*	Used on cover
152	45	4d. vermilion (1.3.76)	£3200	£525	£1100
		s. Opt. "SPECIMEN" (pl. 15) (9)	£400		
		Wi. Watermark inverted	—	£1000	
		Plate			
		15 (1876)	£3200	£525	
		16 (1877)	*	£35000	
153		4d. sage-green (12.3.77)	£1400	£300	£600
		s. Opt. "SPECIMEN" (pl. 15) (9)	£350		
		sa. Opt. "SPECIMEN" (pl. 16) (9)	£350		
		Wi. Watermark inverted	£3000	£625	
		Plate			
		15 (1877)	£1600	£325	
		16 (1877)	£1400	£300	
		17 (1877)	*	£20000	
154		4d. grey-brown (Plate 17) (15.8.80)	£2800	£550	£1700
		a. Imperf	£22000		
		s. Opt. "SPECIMEN" (9)	£350		
		Wi. Watermark inverted	—	£1200	
156	46	8d. orange (Plate 1) (11.9.76)	£1850	£350	£625
		s. Opt. "SPECIMEN" (8, 9)	£350		
		Wi. Watermark inverted	—	£900	

*138/56 **For well-centred, lightly used +100%**

1876 (July). *Prepared for use but not issued.*

			Un	Used*	
156a	46	8d. purple-brown (Plate 1)	£9750		
		s. Opt. "SPECIMEN" (8, 9)	£6000		

KEY TO SURFACE-PRINTED ISSUES

1880–1900

S.G. Nos.	Description	Date of Issue
164/5	½d. green	14.10.80
187	½d. slate-blue	1.4.84
197/e	½d. vermilion	1.1.87
213	½d. blue-green	17.4.1900
166	1d. Venetian red	1.1.80

GREAT BRITAIN
POSTAL HISTORY
and STAMPS
to 1930

Postal History from 1300 and Fine Stamps from Queen Victoria to King George V

YOUR WANTS LIST IS WELCOME!

BUYING Collections and single items of Postal History and Fine Stamps

170/1	1d. lilac, Die I	12.7.81
172/4	1d. lilac, Die II	12.12.81
167	1½d. Venetian red	14.10.80
188	1½d. lilac	1.4.84
198	1½d. purple and green	1.1.87
168/a	2d. rose	8.12.80
189	2d. lilac	1.4.84
199/200	2d. green and red	1.1.87
190	2½d. lilac	1.4.84
201	2½d. purple on blue paper	1.1.87
191	3d. lilac	1.4.84
202/4	3d. purple on yellow paper	1.1.87
192	4d. dull green	1.4.84
205/a	4d. green and brown	1.1.87
206	4½d. green and carmine	15.9.92
169	5d. indigo	15.3.81
193	5d. dull green	1.4.84
207	5d. purple and blue, Die I	1.1.87
207a	5d. purple and blue, Die II	1888
194	6d. dull green	1.4.84
208/a	6d. purple on rose-red paper	1.1.87
195	9d. dull green	1.8.83
209	9d. purple and blue	1.1.87
210/b	10d. purple and carmine	24.2.90
196	1s. dull green	1.4.84
211	1s. green	1.1.87
214	1s. green and carmine	11.7.1900
175	2s.6d. lilac on blued paper	2.7.83
178/9	2s.6d. lilac	1884
176	5s. rose on blued paper	1.4.84
180/1	5s. rose	1884
177/a	10s. ultramarine on blued paper	1.4.84
182/3a	10s. ultramarine	1884
185	£1 brown-lilac, wmk Crowns	1.4.84
186	£1 brown-lilac, wmk Orbs	6.1.88
212	£1 green	28.1.91

Note that the £5 value used with the above series is listed as Nos. 133 and 137.

49 Imperial Crown   **(50)**

1880–83. *Wmk* Imperial Crown, W **49**.

			Un	Used*	Used on cover
157	**41**	2½d. blue (23.3.81)	£450	35·00	55·00
		s. Opt. "SPECIMEN" (pl. 23) (9)....	£175		
		Wi. Watermark inverted	—	£550	
		Plate			
		21 (1881)	£500	45·00	
		22 (1881)	£450	45·00	
		23 (1881)	£450	35·00	
158	**42**	3d. rose (3.81)	£500	£100	£175
		s. Opt. "SPECIMEN" (pl. 21) (9)....	£250		
		Wi. Watermark inverted	—	£580	
		Plate			
		20 (1881)	£900	£150	
		21 (1881)	£500	£100	
159	**50**	3d. on 3d lilac (C.) (Plate 21)			
		(1.1.83)	£650	£160	£450
		s. Opt. "SPECIMEN" (9)	£300		
		Wi. Watermark inverted	—		
160	**45**	4d. grey-brown (8.12.80)	£450	75·00	£190
		s. Opt. "SPECIMEN" (pl. 17) (9)....	£250		
		sa. Opt. "SPECIMEN" (pl. 18) (9)....	£275		
		Wi. Watermark inverted	—	£650	
		Plate			
		17 (1880)	£475	80·00	
		18 (1882)	£450	75·00	
161	**43**	6d. grey (1.1.81)	£400	80·00	£120
		s. Opt. "SPECIMEN" (pl. 18) (9)....	£275		
		Wi. Watermark inverted	—	£650	
		Plate			
		17 (1881)	£425	80·00	
		18 (1882)	£400	80·00	
162	**50**	6d. on 6d. lilac (C.) (Plate 18)			
		(1.1.83)	£675	£150	£425
		a. Slanting dots (various) ..*from*	£1800	£450	
		b. Opt double	—	£12500	
		s. Opt. "SPECIMEN" (9)	£300		
		Wi. Watermark inverted	£3500	£850	
163	**44**	1s. orange-brown (24.5.81)	£750	£170	£550

		s. Opt. "SPECIMEN" (pl. 13) (9)....	£350	
		sa. Opt. "SPECIMEN" (pl. 14) (9)....	£350	
		Wi. Watermark inverted	£3000	£875
		Plate		
		13 (1881)	£875	£170
		14 (1881)	£750	£170

*157/63 **For well-centred, lightly used +75%**

The 1s. plate 14 (line perf 14) exists in purple but was not issued in this shade (*Price* £15000 *unused*). Examples were included in a few of the Souvenir Albums prepared for members of the "Stamp Committee of 1884".

52   **53**

54   **55**   **56**

1880–81. *Wmk* Imperial Crown, W **49**.

164	**52**	½d. deep green (14.10.80)	55·00	22·00	30·00
		a. Imperf	£5000		
		b. No watermark	£10000		
		s. Opt. "SPECIMEN" (9)	60·00		
		Wi. Watermark inverted	£2400	£575	
165		½d. pale green	55·00	22·00	
166	**53**	1d. Venetian red (1.1.80)	35·00	15·00	30·00
		a. Imperf	£5800		
		b. Error. Wmk 48	†	£27000	
		s. Opt. "SPECIMEN" (9)	£100		
		Wi. Watermark inverted	—	£350	
167	**54**	1½d. Venetian red (14.10.80)	£250	60·00	£160
		s. Opt. "SPECIMEN" (9)	80·00		
		Wi. Watermark inverted	†		
168	**55**	2d. pale rose (8.12.80)	£340	£120	£300
		s. Opt. "SPECIMEN" (9)	£110		
		Wi. Watermark inverted	£3000	£780	
168a		2d. deep rose	£360	£120	
169	**56**	5d. indigo (15.3.81)	£725	£175	£325
		a. Imperf	£6750	£4500	
		s. Opt. "SPECIMEN" (9, 12, 13).	£160		
		Wi. Watermark inverted	—	£4800	

*164/9 **For well-centred, lightly used +75%**

Two used examples of the 1d. value have been reported on the Orb (fiscal) watermark.

57   Die I   Die II

1881. *Wmk* Imperial Crown, W **49**.

		(a) 14 dots in each corner, Die I (12 July)			
170	**57**	1d. lilac	£225	40·00	55·00
		s. Opt. "SPECIMEN" (9)	70·00		
		Wi. Watermark inverted	—	£600	
171		1d. pale lilac	£225	40·00	
		(b) 16 dots in each corner, Die II (13 December).			
172	**57**	1d. lilac	2·75	2·20	4·00
		s. Opt. "SPECIMEN" (9, 12)	60·00		
		Wi. Watermark inverted	60·00	35·00	
172a		1d. bluish lilac	£475	£150	
173		1d. deep purple	2·75	2·20	
		a. Printed both sides	£900	†	
		b. Frame broken at bottom	£975	£350	
		c. Printed on gummed side	£900	†	
		d. Imperf three sides (pair)	£8250	†	
		e. Printed both sides but impression on back inverted	£1000	†	
		f. No watermark	£8000	†	
		g. Blued paper	—		
174		1d. mauve	2·75	1·70	
		a. Imperf (pair)	£7500		

Stanley Gibbons.
The stamp of quality.

When it comes to buying rare and valuable stamps, ensure you're in safe hands. If you're purchasing valuable items for your collection there are many things for you to consider. Condition, rarity, provenance.... and most importantly, the knowledge and integrity of the dealer.

Our name has been synonymous with stamp collecting since 1856. Our expert knowledge and eye for detail means you can trust us to offer you exceptional items at a fair price, coupled with a Lifetime Guarantee of Authenticity for complete peace of mind.

Our reputation for what The Times newspaper called 'honest dealing' is one of the reasons why we have proudly held the Royal Warrant for Philately for more than 100 years.

Whatever you collect, explore our stunning range of specialist material in our new online store.

*170/4 **For well-centred, lightly used +50%***

1d. stamps with the words "PEARS SOAP" printed on the back in orange, blue or mauve *price from £550, unused.*

The variety "frame broken at bottom" (No. 173b) shows a white space just inside the bottom frame-line from between the "N" and "E" of "ONE" to below the first "N" of "PENNY", breaking the pearls and cutting into the lower part of the oval below "PEN".

58   **59**

60

1883–84. *Coloured letters* in the corners. *Wmk* Large Anchor, *W* **40**.

(a) Blued paper.

			Un	Used*
175	**58**	2s.6d. lilac (2.7.83)	£6750	£1500
		s. Opt. "SPECIMEN" (9)	£625	
176	**59**	5s. rose (1.4.84)	£18000	£4000
		s. Opt. "SPECIMEN" (9, 11)	£1600	
177	**60**	10s. ultramarine (1.4.84)	£40000	£8250
		s. Opt. "SPECIMEN" (9)	£2850	
177*a*		10s. cobalt (5.84)	£62000	£13500
		s. Opt. "SPECIMEN" (9)	£5500	

(b) White paper.

178	**58**	2s.6d. lilac	£600	£160
		s. Opt. "SPECIMEN" (9, 11, 12, 13)	£425	
179		2s.6d. deep lilac	£825	£225
		a. On blued paper	£9000	£3600
		Wi. Watermark inverted	—	£11500
180	**59**	5s. rose	£1100	£250
		Wi. Watermark inverted	†	£12500
181		5s. crimson	£975	£250
		s. Opt. "SPECIMEN" (9, 11, 12, 13)	£450	
182	**60**	10s. cobalt	£42000	£8250
		s. Opt. "SPECIMEN" (9)	£3400	
183		10s. ultramarine	£2250	£525
		s. Opt. "SPECIMEN" (9, 11, 13)	£550	
183*a*		10s. pale ultramarine	£2500	£550

*175/83a **For well-centred, lightly used +50%***

For No. 180 perf 12 see second note below No. 196.

61

Broken frames, Plate 2

1884 (1 Apr). *Wmk* Three Imperial Crowns, *W* **49**.

185	**61**	£1 brown-lilac	£32000	£3000
		a. Frame broken	£60000	£5000
		s. Opt. "SPECIMEN" (9, 11, 12)	£2800	
		Wi. Watermark inverted	—	£38000

1888 (Feb). Watermark Three Orbs, *W* **48**.

186	**61**	£1 brown-lilac	£72000	£4500
		a. Frame broken	£150000	£9000
		s. Opt. "SPECIMEN" (11)	£6800	

*185/6a **For well-centred, lightly used +50%***

The broken-frame varieties, Nos. 185a and 186a, are on Plate 2 stamps JC and TA, as illustrated. See also No. 212a.

62   **63**   **64**

65   **66**

1883 (1 Aug.). (9d.) or 1884 (1 Apr) (others). *Wmk* Imperial Crown, *W* **49** (sideways on horiz designs).

187	**52**	½d. slate-blue	35·00	10·00	20·00
		a. Imperf	£3750		
		s. Opt. "SPECIMEN" (9)	50·00		
		Wi. Watermark inverted	£3000	£350	
188	**62**	1½d. lilac	£125	45·00	£120
		a. Imperf	£3750		
		s. Opt. "SPECIMEN" (9)	85·00		
		Wi. Watermark inverted	£3000	£280	
189	**63**	2d. lilac	£230	80·00	£150
		a. Imperf	£4800		
		s. Opt. "SPECIMEN" (9)	85·00		
		Wi. Watermark sideways inverted	£600		
190	**64**	2½d. lilac	95·00	20·00	30·00
		a. Imperf	£4800		
		s. Opt. "SPECIMEN" (9)	85·00		
		Wi. Watermark sideways inverted	£600		
191	**65**	3d. lilac	£280	£100	£180
		a. Imperf	£4800		
		s. Opt. "SPECIMEN" (9)	85·00		
		Wi. Watermark inverted	†	£1200	
192	**66**	4d. dull green	£580	£210	£350
		a. Imperf	£4800		
		s. Opt. "SPECIMEN" (9)	£190		
193	**62**	5d. dull green	£580	£210	£350
		a. Imperf	£5500		
		s. Opt. "SPECIMEN" (9)	£190		
194	**63**	6d. dull green	£625	£240	£380
		a. Imperf	£5750		
		s. Opt. "SPECIMEN" (9)	£220		
		Wi. Watermark sideways inverted	£1400		
195	**64**	9d. dull green (1.8.83)	£1250	£480	£4750
		s. Opt. "SPECIMEN" (9)	£425		
		Wi. Watermark sideways inverted	£2000	£775	
196	**65**	1s. dull green	£1600	£325	£625
		a. Imperf	£8750		
		s. Opt. "SPECIMEN" (9)	£375		
		Wi. Watermark-inverted			

*187/96 **For well-centred, lightly used +100%***

The above prices are for stamps in the true dull green colour. Stamps which have been soaked, causing the colour to run, are virtually worthless.

Stamps of the above set and No. 180 are also found perf 12; these are official perforations, but were never issued. A second variety of the 5d. is known with a line instead of a stop under the "d" in the value; this was never issued and is therefore only known unused (*Price* £38,000).

71   **72**   **73**

74 **75** **76**

77 **78** **79**

80 **81** **82**

Die I   Die II

Die I: Square dots to right of "d".
Die II: Thin vertical lines to right of "d".

1887 (1 Jan)–**92**. *Jubilee* issue. New types. The bicoloured stamps have the value tablets, or the frames including the value tablets, in the second colour. *Wmk* Imperial Crown, *W* **49** (Three Crowns on £1).

			Unmtd Mint	Mtd Mint	Used*
197	71	½d. vermilion	2·50	1·75	1·20
		a. Printed on gummed side .	£4500	£3500	
		b. Printed both sides			
		c. Doubly printed	—	£32000	
		d. Imperf (showing bottom margins)	6500	£5000	
		s. Opt. "SPECIMEN" (9, 10, 12)		35·00	
		Wi. Watermark inverted	90·00	60·00	60·00
197e		½d. orange-vermilion	2·50	1·75	1·20
198	72	1½d. dull purple & pale green ..	25·00	18·00	8·00
		a. Purple part of design double	—	—	£9000
		s. Opt. "SPECIMEN" (6, 9, 12)..		55·00	
		Wi. Watermark inverted	£1600	£1200	£500
199	73	2d. green & scarlet	£550	£425	£260
200		2d. grey-green & carmine	50·00	35·00	15·00
		s. Opt. "SPECIMEN" (9, 10, 12)		60·00	
		Wi. Watermark inverted	£1600	£1200	£525
201	74	2½d. purple/*blue*	45·00	25·00	5·00
		a. Printed on gummed side .	£18000	£15000	
		b. Imperf three sides	—	£9500	
		c. Imperf	—	£12000	
		Ed. Missing "d" in value	†	†	£9500
		s. Opt. "SPECIMEN" (6, 9, 12, 13)		75·00	
		Wi. Watermark inverted	£4500	£3500	£1400
202	75	3d. purple/*yellow*	45·00	25·00	5·00
		a. Imperf (wmk inverted)	—	£11000	
		s. Opt. "SPECIMEN" (6, 9, 12)..		60·00	
		Wi. Watermark inverted	—	—	£725
203		3d. deep purple/*yellow*	60·00	30·00	5·00
204		3d. purple/*orange* (1890)	£1300	£800	
205	76	4d. green & purple-brown	60·00	40·00	18·00
		aa. Imperf	—	£12000	
		s. Opt. "SPECIMEN" (6, 9, 10, 12)		60·00	
		Wi. Watermark inverted	£1600	£1200	£650
205a		4d. green & dp brown	60·00	40·00	18·00
206	77	4½d. green & carmine (15.9.92)	17·00	11·00	45·00
		s. Opt. "SPECIMEN" (9, 13)	£500	£400	
		Wi. Watermark inverted			
206a		4½d. green & dp brt carmine....	£1000	£750	£650
207	78	5d. dull purple & blue (Die I)	£1100	£800	£120
		s. Opt. "SPECIMEN" (9, 12)	£160	£110	
207a		5d. dull purple and blue (Die II) (1888)	60·00	42·00	15·00

		s. Opt. "SPECIMEN" (9, 12)	90.00	65·00	
		Wi. Watermark inverted		£17000	£1250
208	79	6d. purple/*rose-red*	60·00	40·00	15·00
		s. Opt. "SPECIMEN" (9, 10, 12)		65·00	
		Wi. Watermark inverted	£10000	£7500	£2000
208a		6d. deep purple/*rose-red*	60·00	40·00	15·00
209	80	9d. dull purple & blue	£110	75·00	48·00
		s. Opt. "SPECIMEN" (6, 9, 12)..	£100	70·00	
		Wi. Watermark inverted	£11000	£8000	£2800
210	81	10d. dull purple and carmine (shades) (24.2.90)	90·00	60·00	45·00
		aa. Imperf	—	£17500	
		s. Opt. "SPECIMEN" (9, 13, 15)	£150	£110	
		Wi. Watermark inverted	£13000	£9500	£3000
210a		10d. dull purple and deep dull carmine		£800	£625	£250
210b		10d. dull purple & scarlet	£170	95·00	65·00
211	82	1s. dull green	£375	£275	80·00
		s. Opt. "SPECIMEN" (9, 10, 12)	£100	75·00	
		Wi. Watermark inverted	£2200	£1700	£975
212	61	£1 green (28.1.91)	£7500	£4000	£800
		a. Frame broken	£16500	£8500	£2000
		s. Opt. "SPECIMEN" (9, 11, 13, 15, 16)		£1100	
		Wi. Watermark inverted	—	£110000	£13000

*197/212a For well-centred, lightly used +50%
The broken-frame varieties, No. 212a, are on Plate 2 stamps JC or TA, as illustrated above No. 185.
½d. stamps with "PEARS SOAP" printed on the back in orange, blue or mauve, *price from £525 each*.
No used price is quoted for No. 204 as it is not possible to authenticate the paper colour on stamps in used condition.

1900. *Colours changed.* Wmk Imperial Crown, *W* **49**.

213	71	½d. blue-green (17.4)	2·50	2·00	2·25
		a. Printed on gummed side .	—	—	†
		b. Imperf	£9500	£7500	
		s. Opt. "SPECIMEN" (11, 15)...		£650	
		Wi. Watermark inverted	90·00	60·00	60·00
214	82	1s. green & carmine (11.7)	£100	65·00	£140
		s. Opt. "SPECIMEN" (15)		£950	
		Wi. Watermark inverted	£2600	£1900	£1100
Set of 14			£950	£650	£380

*213/14 For well-centred, lightly used +50%
The ½d. No. 213, in bright blue, is a colour changeling caused by a constituent of the ink used for some months in 1900.

USED ON COVER PRICES					
No. 197	£7	No. 205	£42	No. 209	£275
No. 198	£25	No. 206	£100	No. 210	£300
No. 200	£28	No. 207	£275	No. 211	£190
No. 201	£8	No. 207a	£50	No. 213	£6·50
No. 202	£38	No. 208	£95	No. 214	£1000

DEPARTMENTAL OFFICIALS

The following Official stamps were exclusively for the use of certain government departments. Until 1882 official mail used ordinary postage stamps purchased at post offices, the cash being refunded once a quarter. Later the government departments obtained Official stamps by requisition.

Official stamps were on sale to the public for a short time at Somerset House but they were not sold from post offices. The system of only supplying the Government departments with stamps was open to abuse so that all official stamps were withdrawn on 13 May 1904.

OVERPRINTS, PERFORATIONS, WATERMARKS. All official stamps were overprinted by Thomas De La Rue & Co. and are perf 14. Except for the 5s., and 10s. on Anchor, they are on Crown watermarked paper unless otherwise stated.

INLAND REVENUE

These stamps were used by revenue officials in the provinces, mail to and from Head Office passing without a stamp. The London Office used these stamps only for foreign mail.

I.R.   **I. R.**

OFFICIAL   **OFFICIAL**
(O **1**)   (O **2**)

Optd with Types O **1** (½d. to 1s.) or O **2** (others).

1882–1901. *Stamps of Queen Victoria.*

(a) Issues of 1880–81

		Un	*Used	Used on cover
O1	½d. dp green (1.11.82)	£135	60·00	£120
	s. Opt. "SPECIMEN" (9)	£325		
O2	½d. pale green	90·00	40·00	
O3	1d. lilac (Die II) (1.10.82)	8·00	6·00	30·00

	a. Optd in blue-black	£300	£125
	b. "OFFICIAL" omitted	—	£12500
	c. Imperf	£4500	
	ca. Imperf, optd in blue-black	£4500	
	s. Opt. "SPECIMEN" (9, 15)	£180	
	Wi. Watermark inverted	—	£2200
O4	6d. grey (Plate 18) (3.11.82)	£575	£140
	s. Opt. "SPECIMEN" (9, 15)	£325	

No. O3 with the lines of the overprint transposed is an essay.

(b) Issues of 1884–88

O5	½d. slate-blue (8.5.85)	85·00	35·00	£135
	s. Opt. "SPECIMEN" (9)	£325		
O6	2½d. lilac (12.3.85)	£525	£180	£1400
	s. Opt. "SPECIMEN" (9)	£325		
O7	1s. dull green (12.3.85)	£6000	£1900	
	s. Opt. "SPECIMEN" (9)	£1250		
O8	5s. rose (*blued paper*) (wmk Anchor) (12.3.85)	£17500	£6500	
	a. Raised stop after "R"	£18500	£7250	
	s. Opt. "SPECIMEN" (9, 11)	£2750		
O9	5s. rose (wmk Anchor) (3.90)	£12000	£2500	
	a. Raised stop after "R"	£14000	£3200	
	b. Optd in blue-black	£14000	£3200	
	s. Opt. "SPECIMEN" (9, 11, 13, 16) ..	£1750		
O9c	10s. cobalt (*blued paper*) (wmk Anchor) (12.3.85)	£38000	£9500	
	ca. Raised stop after "R"			
	cb. cobalt (white paper) (wmk Anchor)	£22000	£7750	
	cs. Opt. "SPECIMEN" (11)	£4500		
O9d	10s. ultramarine (*blued paper*) (wmk Anchor) (12.3.85)	£25000	£7500	
	da Raised stop after "R"	£27000	£8500	
	ds. Opt. "SPECIMEN" (10)	£3750		
O10	10s. ultramarine (wmk Anchor) (3.90)	£11500	£3750	
	a. Raised stop after "R"	£12500	£4500	
	b. Optd in blue-black	£12500	£4500	
	s. Opt. "SPECIMEN" (9, 10, 11, 16) ..	£2750		
O11	£1 brown-lilac (wmk Crowns) (12.3.85)	£75000	£30000	
	a. Frame broken	£100000	—	
	b. Optd in blue-black	£160000		
	s. Opt. "SPECIMEN" (11)	£5500		
O12	£1 brown-lilac (wmk Orbs) (3.90) ..	£100000	£40000	
	a. Frame broken	£150000		
	s. Opt. "SPECIMEN" (9)	£9500		

Nos. O3, O13, O15 and O16 may be found showing worn impressions of the overprints with thicker letters.

(c) Issues of 1887–92

O13	½d. vermilion (15.5.88)	15·00	7·00	£110
	a. Without "I.R."	£7000		
	b. Imperf	£7000		
	c. Opt double (imperf)	£8000		
	s. Opt. "SPECIMEN" (9, 15)	£120		
O14	2½d. purple/*blue* (2.92)	£175	30·00	£450
	s. Opt. "SPECIMEN" (9, 13, 15)	£120		
O15	1s. dull green (1887)	£1000	£375	£3750
	a. Optd in blue-black	£2250		
	s. Opt. "SPECIMEN" (9, 15)	£260		
O16	£1 green (6.92)	£12500	£2500	
	a. No stop after "R"	—	£4000	
	b. Frame broken	£20000	£5250	
	s. Opt. "SPECIMEN" (9, 10, 15)	£2250		

(d) Issues of 1887 and 1900.

O17	½d. blue-green (4.01)	20·00	15·00	£350
	s. Opt. "SPECIMEN" (15)	£160		
O18	6d. purple/rose-red (1.7.01)	£500	£150	
	s. Opt. "SPECIMEN" (15, 16)	£250		
O19	1s. green and carmine (12.01)	£4250	£1800	
	s. Opt. "SPECIMEN" (15)	£1100		

*O1/19 **For well-centred, lightly used +35%**

OFFICE OF WORKS

These were issued to Head and Branch (local) offices in London and to Branch (local) offices at Birmingham, Bristol, Edinburgh, Glasgow, Leeds, Liverpool, Manchester and Southampton. The overprints on stamps of value 2d. and upwards were created later in 1902, the 2d. for registration fees and the rest for overseas mail.

O.W.

OFFICIAL

(O **3**)

Optd with Type O **3**

1896 (24 Mar)–02. Stamps of Queen Victoria.

				Used on
		Un	*Used	Cover
O31	½d. vermilion	£350	£150	£800
	s. Opt. "SPECIMEN" (9, 15)	£325		
O32	½d. blue-green (2.02)	£475	£225	
	s. Opt. "SPECIMEN" (15)	£450		
O33	1d. lilac (Die II)	£500	£150	£1000
	s. Opt. "SPECIMEN" (9, 15, 16)	£325		
O34	5d. dull purple & blue (II) (29.4.02)	£4000	£1400	
	s. Opt. "SPECIMEN" (16)	£1250		
O35	10d. dull purple & carmine (28.5.02)	£7250	£2250	
	s. Opt. "SPECIMEN" (16)	£2600		

ARMY

Letters to and from the War Office in London passed without postage. The overprinted stamps were distributed to District and Station Paymasters nationwide, including Cox and Co., the Army Agents, who were paymasters to the Household Division.

ARMY   ARMY

OFFICIAL   OFFICIAL

(O **4**)   (O **5**)

1896 (1 Sept)–01. Stamps of Queen Victoria optd with Type O 4 (½d., 1d.) or O 5 (2½d., 6d.).

				Used on
		Un	*Used	cover
O41	½d. vermilion	8·00	3·00	65·00
	a. "OFFICIAl" (R.13/7)	£300	£130	
	b. Lines of opt transposed	£4700		
	s. Opt. "SPECIMEN" (9)	£225		
	Wi. Watermark inverted	£800	£375	
O42	½d. blue-green (6.00)	10·00	15·00	
	s. Opt. "SPECIMEN" (15)	£325		
	Wi. Watermark inverted	£1000	£650	
O43	1d. lilac (Die II)	8·00	7·00	£110
	a. "OFFICIAl" (R.13/7)	£240	£150	
	s. Opt. "SPECIMEN" (9)	£225		
O44	2½d. purple/*blue*	50·00	35·00	£775
	s. Opt. "SPECIMEN" (9)	£225		
O45	6d. purple/rose-red (20.9.01)	£110	60·00	£1700
	s. Opt. "SPECIMEN" (15)	£425		

Nos. O41a and O43a occur in sheets overprinted by Forme 1.

GOVERNMENT PARCELS

These stamps were issued to all departments, including Head Office, for use on parcels weighing over 3 lb. Below this weight government parcels were sent by letter post to avoid the 55% of the postage paid from accruing to the railway companies, as laid down by parcel-post regulations. Most government parcels stamps suffered heavy postmarks in use.

GOVT
PARCELS

(O **7**)

Optd as Type O **7**

1883 (1 Aug)–86. Stamps of Queen Victoria.

O61	1½d. lilac (1.5.86)	£400	£100
	a. No dot under "T"	£775	£175
	b. Dot to left of "T"	£775	£175
	s. Opt. "SPECIMEN" (9)	£220	
O62	6d. dull green (1.5.86)	£3500	£1400
	s. Opt. "SPECIMEN" (9)	£300	
O63	9d. dull green	£2750	£1200
	s. Opt. "SPECIMEN" (9)	£300	
O64	1s. orange-brown (watermark Crown, Pl 13)	£1750	£300
	a. No dot under "T"	£2750	£500
	b. Dot to left of "T"	£2750	£500
	s. Opt. "SPECIMEN" (9)	£325	
O64c	1s. orange-brown (Pl 14)	£3500	£600
	ca. No dot under "T"	£4500	£850
	cb. Dot to left of "T"		

1887–90. Stamps of Queen Victoria.

O65	1½d. dull purple & pale green (29.10.87)	£160	28·00
	a. No dot under "T"	£260	75·00
	b. Dot to right of "T"	£260	75·00
	c. Dot to left of "T"	£260	75·00
	s. Opt. "SPECIMEN" (9, 10, 13, 15)	£300	
O66	6d. purple/rose-red (19.12.87)	£275	75·00

	a. No dot under "T"	£375	£120	
	b. Dot to right of "T"	£375	£120	
	c. Dot to left of "T"	£375	£120	
	s. "SPECIMEN" (9, 13, 15)	£250		
O67	9d. dull purple & blue (21.8.88)	£425	£120	
	s. Optd. "SPECIMEN" (9, 10, 13, 15)	£300		
	Wi. Watermark inverted			
O68	1s. dull green (25.3.90)	£700	£275	
	a. No dot under "T"	£1000	£500	
	b. Dot to right of "T"	£1000	£500	
	c. Dot to left of "T"	£1000	£500	
	d. Optd in blue-black			
	s. Opt. "SPECIMEN" (9, 13, 15)	£300		

1891–1900. Stamps of Queen Victoria.

O69	1d. lilac (Die II) (18.6.97)	£100	30·00
	a. No dot under "T"	£160	75·00
	b. Dot to left of "T"	£160	75·00
	c. Opt inverted	£7500	£3500
	d. Ditto. Dot to left of "T"	£8500	£4500
	s. Opt. "SPECIMEN" (15)	£450	
	Wi. Watermark inverted	—	£500
O70	2d. grey-green & carmine (24.10.91)	£250	50·00
	a. No dot under "T"	£400	£125
	b. Dot to left of "T"	£400	£125
	s. "SPECIMEN" (9, 11, 13, 15)	£300	
O71	4½d. green & carmine (29.9.92)	£400	£275
	b. Dot to right of "T"	£400	£275
	s. Opt. "SPECIMEN" (9, 13, 15)	£300	
	Wi. Watermark inverted	—	£9000
O72	1s. green & carmine (11.00)	£650	£275
	a. Opt inverted	†	£17500
	s. Opt. "SPECIMEN" (9)	£400	

*O61/72 **For well-centred lightly used +100%**

The "no dot under T" variety occured on R.12/3 and 20/2. The "dot to left of T" comes four times in the sheet on R.2/7, 6/7, 7/9 and 12/9. The best example of the "dot to right of T" is on R.20/1. All three varieties were corrected around 1897.

BOARD OF EDUCATION

BOARD
OF
EDUCATION

(O **8**)
Optd with Type O **8**

1902 (19 Feb). Stamps of Queen Victoria.

O81	5d. dull purple & blue (II)	£5750	£1500
	s. Opt. "SPECIMEN" (15)	£1400	
O82	1s. green & carmine	£12000	£6000
	s. Opt. "SPECIMEN" (15)	£3000	

POST OFFICE TELEGRAPH STAMPS

The telegraph system in the United Kingdom was originally operated by private companies, some of which issued their own stamps.

The Post Office took over the service in 1870, producing telegraph forms with impressed 1s. stationery dies and blank forms to which postage stamps were applied.

To assist in the separate accounting of revenues from the postal and telegraph services, special Post Office Telegraph stamps were issued from 1 February 1876 and from 1 May of that year the use of postage stamps to pre-pay telegraph services was prohibited.

Telegraph stamps were in use for little over five years, when it was decided to withdraw them and postage stamps were, once again, used for telegraph services.

PLATE NUMBERS Like the postage stamps of the period, all telegraph stamps showed their plate number within the design. These are listed under their respective values.

WATERMARKS To differentiate them from postage stamps, all telegraph stamps were in horizontal format and the watermarks appear sideways. Apart from the Shamrock watermark, WW**12**, all were as used for postage stamps of the period. For the purposes of this listing, watermark sideways refers to the top of the watermark device pointing to the right of the stamp *as viewed from the gummed side of the stamp*; watermark sideways inverted refers to the top of the device pointing to the left.

T **1**

T **2**

T **3**

T **4**

T **5**

T **6**

T **7**

T **8**

T **9**

T **10**

T **11**

T **12**

1876 (1 February). Wmks as listed. *P* 15×15½ (5s. *T* **11**, 10s., £5), P 14 (others).

T1	T **1**	½d. orange (WT**12**) (Plate 5) (1.4.80)	28·00	35·00
		a. Imperf. (vert. pair)	£2000	
		s. Optd "SPECIMEN" (9)	65·00	
T2	T **2**	1d. red-brown (WT**12**)	28·00	22·00
		Wi. Watermark inverted	£300	£175
		s. Optd "SPECIMEN" (9, 10)	65·00	
		Plate 1	28·00	28·00
		2	35·00	28·00
		3	35·00	28·00
T3	T **3**	3d. carmine (W**33** sideways)	£100	50·00
		Wi. Watermark sideways inverted	£300	£280
		s. Optd "SPECIMEN" (9, 10)	80·00	
		Plate 1	£100	75·00
		2	£100	60·00
		3	£125	90·00
T4		3d. carmine (W**49** sideways inverted) (6.6.81)	£150	£120
		Plate 3	£150	£120
		4 (watermark sideways)	£475	£250
		5. (watermark sideways)	£475	£250
T5	T **4**	4d. sage-green (W**17** sideways inverted) (Plate 1) (1.3.77)	£150	£125
		a. Imperf (vert. pair)	—	—
		wi. Watermark sideways	—	—
		s. Optd "SPECIMEN" (9,11)	75·00	
T6	T **5**	6d. grey (W**33** sideways) (1.3.77)	£125	75·00
		s. Optd "SPECIMEN" (9,11)	75·00	
		Plate 1	£125	75·00
		2	£300	£160

T7		6d. grey (W**49** sideways inverted) (1.81)	£240	£150
		a. Imperf (vert. pair)		
T8	T **6**	1s. deep green (W**33** sideways)	£120	50·00
		Wi. Watermark sideways inverted	£500	
		Plate s. Optd "SPECIMEN" (9,10)	£110	
		1	£180	65·00
		2	£140	65·00
		3	£140	55·00
		4	£200	55·00
		5	£120	50·00
		6	£120	50·00
		7	£350	55·00
		8	£180	55·00
		9	£180	55·00
		10	£220	70·00
T9		1s. brown-orange (W**33** sideways) (10.80)	£225	£150
		s. Optd "SPECIMEN" (9)	£120	
		Plate 10	£225	£150
		12	£250	£190
T10		1s. brown-orange (W**49** sideways) (2.81?)	£250	£190
		a. Imperf (vert. pair)		
		Wi. Watermark sideways inverted	£250	£190
		s. Optd "SPECIMEN" (12)	£300	
		Plate 11	£250	£190
		12	£550	£300
T11	T **7**	3s. slate-blue (W**33** sideways) (Plate 1) (1.3.77)	£175	75·00
		Wi. Watermark sideways inverted	—	£500
		s. Optd "SPECIMEN" (8, 9, 11)	£120	
T12		3s. slate-blue (W**49** sideways inverted) (Plate 1) (8.81)	£6500	£3800
T13	T **8**	5s. rose (W**39**) (P15×15½)	£1100	£200
		s. Optd "SPECIMEN" (8, 9, 10)	£250	
		Plate 1	£1100	£200
		2	£2250	£375
T14		5s. rose (W**39**) (P. 14) (Plate 2) (1880)	£7000	£600
T15		5s. rose (W**40**) (P. 14) (Plate 3) (5.81)	£7000	£1100
		s. Optd "SPECIMEN" (9, 12)	£1000	
T16	T **9**	10s. grey-green (W**39**) (Plate 1) (13.77)	£1750	£450
		s. Optd "SPECIMEN" (8, 9, 11)	£400	
T17	T **10**	£1 brown-lilac (WT**12** sideways ×3) (Plate 1) (1.3.77)	£8250	£950
		s. Optd "SPECIMEN" (8, 9, 11)	£900	
T18	T **11**	£5 orange (WT**12** sideways inverted ×3), (Plate 1) (1.3.77)	£30000	£3200
		s. Optd "SPECIMEN" (8, 9, 11)	£2800	

*T1/18 **For well-centred lightly used + 75%**

Stanley Gibbons
Great Britain Department

Stanley Gibbons, a name synonymous with quality.

Ever since the birth of our hobby Stanley Gibbons has been at the forefront of GB philately and we invite collectors access to one of the finest GB stocks in the world by registering for our renowned free monthly brochure. Whatever your budget or collecting interests you will find a range of the highest quality material for the discerning collector.

Simply contact Mark Facey on **020 7557 4424** email **mfacey@stanleygibbons.com**
or Michael Barrell on **020 7557 4448** email **mbarrell@stanleygibbons.com** to register

Est 1856
STANLEY GIBBONS

Stanley Gibbons
399 Strand, London, WC2R 0LX
+44 (0)20 7836 8444
www.stanleygibbons.com

King Edward VII

22 January 1901 – 6 May 1910

PRINTINGS. Distinguishing De La Rue printings from the provisional printings of the same values made by Harrison & Sons Ltd. or at Somerset House may prove difficult in some cases. For very full guidance Volume 2 of the Stanley Gibbons *Great Britain Specialised Catalogue* should prove helpful.

Note that stamps perforated 15×14 must be Harrison; the 2½d., 3d. and 4d. in this perforation are useful reference material, their shades and appearance in most cases matching the Harrison perf 14 printings.

Except for the 6d. value, all stamps on chalk-surfaced paper were printed by De La Rue.

Of the stamps on ordinary paper, the De La Rue impressions are usually clearer and of a higher finish than those of the other printers. The shades are markedly different except in some printings of the 4d., 6d. and 7d. and in the 5s., 10s. and £1.

Used stamps in good, clean, unrubbed condition and with dated postmarks can form the basis of a useful reference collection, the dates often assisting in the assignment to the printers.

PRICES. For Nos. 215/456a prices are quoted for unmounted mint, mounted mint and used stamps.

USED STAMPS. For well-centred, lightly used examples of King Edward VII stamps, add the following percentages to the used prices quoted below:

De La Rue printings (Nos. 215/66)—3d. values + 35%, 4d. orange + 100%, 6d. + 75%, 7d. and 1s. + 25%, all other values + 50%.
Harrison printings (Nos. 267/86)—all values and perforations + 75%. *Somerset House printings* (Nos. 287/320)—1s. values + 25%, all other values + 50%.

83   84   85

86   87   88

89   90   91

92   93

94   95   96

97

(Des E. Fuchs)

1902 (1 Jan)–**10**. Printed by De La Rue & Co. *Wmk* Imperial Crown *W* **49** (½d. to 1s. Three Crowns on £1); Large Anchor, *W* **40** (2s.6d. to 10s.). Ordinary paper. *P* 14.

			Unmtd mint	Mtd mint	Used
215	83	½d. dull blue-green (1.1.02)	2·75	2·00	1·50
		s. Opt. "SPECIMEN" (15)		£350	
		Wi. Watermark inverted	£3750	£2750	£2000
216		½d. blue-green	2·75	2·00	1·50
217		½d. pale yellowish green (26.11.04)	2·75	2·00	1·50
218		½d. yellowish green	2·75	2·00	1·50
		a. Booklet pane. No. 218×5 plus St. Andrew's Cross label	£975	£700	
		aw. Ditto. Wmk inverted	£975	£700	
		b. Booklet pane. No. 218×6 (6.06)	£375	£275	
		bw. Ditto. Wmk inverted	£375	£275	
		c. Doubly printed (bottom row on one pane) (Control H9)	£37500	£27500	
		s. Opt. "SPECIMEN" (17, 22)		£275	
		Wi. Watermark inverted	22·00	12·00	9·00
219		1d. scarlet (1.1.02)	2·75	2·00	1·50
		a. Booklet pane. No. 219×6 (16.3.04)	£325	£250	
		aw. Ditto. Wmk inverted	£325	£250	
		s. Opt. "SPECIMEN" (15, 16, 17, 22)		£250	
220		1d. brt scarlet	2·75	2·00	1·50
		a. Imperf (pair)	†	£35000	
		Wi. Watermark inverted	8·00	4·00	3·00
221	84	1½d. dull purple and green (21.3.02)	80·00	48·00	24·00
		s. Opt. "SPECIMEN" (15)		£275	
222		1½d. slate-purple & green	95·00	50·00	24·00
		Wi. Watermark inverted	—	—	£900
223		1½d. pale dull purple and green (chalk-surfaced paper) (7.05)	75·00	45·00	24·00
		s. Opt. "SPECIMEN" (17)		£700	
224		1½d. slate-purple & bluish green (chalk-surfaced paper)	75·00	45·00	22·00
225	85	2d. yellowish green and carmine-red (25.3.02)	£125	70·00	25·00
		s. Opt. "SPECIMEN" (16)		£550	
		Wi. Watermark inverted	£28000		
226		2d. grey-green and carmine-red (1904)	£125	70·00	35·00
227		2d. pale grey-green and carmine-red (chalk-surfaced paper) (4.06)	80·00	45·00	32·00
		s. Opt. "SPECIMEN" (17)		£700	
		Wi. Watermark inverted		£20000	

BB STAMPS LTD

Est. 1988

Retail Pricelist of

GREAT BRITAIN
Postage Stamps 1840 - Date

Spring 2016
List 28

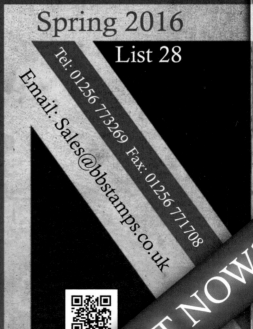

228		2d. pale grey-green and scarlet (*chalk-surfaced paper*) (1909)	80·00	45·00	32·00
229		2d. dull blue-green and carmine (*chalk-surfaced paper*) (1907)	£180	90·00	50·00
230	**86**	2½d. ultramarine (1.1.02)	34·00	20·00	12·00
		s. Opt. "SPECIMEN" (15, 17)		£125	
231		2½d. pale ultramarine	34·00	20·00	12·00
		Wi. Watermark inverted	—	—	£4200
232	**87**	3d. dull purple/orange-yellow (20.3.02)	95·00	50·00	18·00
		s. Opt. "SPECIMEN" (15)		£350	
		Wi. Watermark inverted			
		a. Chalk-surfaced paper (3.06)	£425	£225	90·00
232b		3d. dp purple/orange-yellow	85·00	45·00	18·00
232c		3d. pale reddish purple/orange-yellow (*chalk-surfaced paper*) (3.06)	£425	£225	85·00
		cs. Opt. "SPECIMEN" (17)		£700	
233		3d. dull reddish purple/yellow (*lemon back*) (*chalk-surfaced paper*)	£425	£225	85·00
233b		3d. pale purple/lemon (*chalk-surfaced paper*)	85·00	45·00	20·00
234		3d. purple/lemon (*chalk-surfaced paper*)	85·00	45·00	20·00
235	**88**	4d. green and grey-brown (27.3.02)	£125	70·00	35·00
		s. Opt. "SPECIMEN" (16)		£450	
		Wi. Watermark inverted			
236		4d. green & chocolate-brown	£125	70·00	35·00
		a. Chalk-surfaced paper (1.06)	75·00	40·00	20·00
		Wi. watermark inverted			£9500
238		4d. deep green and chocolate-brown (*chalk-surfaced paper*) (1.06)	75·00	40·00	20·00
239		4d. brown-orange (1.11.09)	£350	£180	£140
		s. Opt. "SPECIMEN" (17)		£700	
240		4d. pale orange (12.09)	45·00	20·00	18·00
241		4d. orange-red (12.09)	45·00	20·00	18·00
242	**89**	5d. dull purple and ultramarine (14.5.02)	£135	65·00	22·00
		aas. Opt. "SPECIMEN" (16)		£350	
		a. Chalk-surfaced paper (5.06)	£115	55·00	22·00
244		5d. slate-purple and ultramarine (*chalk-surfaced paper*) (5.06)	£100	50·00	22·00
		as. Opt. "SPECIMEN" (17)		£700	
		Wi. Watermark inverted	£8000	£5500	
245	**83**	6d. pale dull purple (1.1.02)	80·00	45·00	22·00
		aas. Opt. "SPECIMEN" (15)		£400	
		a. Chalk-surfaced paper (1.06)	85·00	45·00	22·00
246		6d. slate-purple	85·00	45·00	22·00
248		6d. dull purple (*chalk-surfaced paper*) (1.06)	85·00	45·00	22·00
		s. Opt. "SPECIMEN" (17)		£700	
		Wi. Watermark inverted	—	—	£3500
249	**90**	7d. grey-black (4.5.10)	24·00	15·00	22·00
		s. Opt. "SPECIMEN" (17)		£700	
249a		7d. dp grey-black	£170	£115	£100
250	**91**	9d. dull purple and ultramarine (7.4.02)	£250	£140	75·00
		aas. Opt. "SPECIMEN" (16)		£450	
		a. Chalk-surfaced paper (6.05)	£250	£140	75·00
		aWi. Watermark inverted	—	—	£3500
251		9d. slate-purple & ultramarine	£250	£140	75·00
		a. Chalk-surfaced paper (6.05)	£225	£120	75·00
		as. Opt. "SPECIMEN" (17)		£725	
254	**92**	10d. dull purple and carmine (3.7.02)	£275	£150	75·00
		aas. Opt. "SPECIMEN" (16)		£500	
		a. No cross on crown	£775	£425	£300
		b. Chalk-surfaced paper (9.06)	£275	£140	75·00
255		10d. slate-purple and carmine (*chalk-surfaced paper*) (9.06)	£275	£140	75·00
		a. No cross on crown	£725	£450	£275
		as. Opt. "SPECIMEN" (17)		£700	
256		10d. dull purple and scarlet (*chalk-surfaced paper*) (9.10)	£260	£140	75·00
		a. No cross on crown	£725	£425	£250
257	**93**	1s. dull green and carmine (24.3.02)	£220	£100	40·00
		aas. Opt. "SPECIMEN" (16)		£400	
		a. Chalk-surfaced paper (9.05)	£220	£100	40·00
		as. Opt. "SPECIMEN" (17)		£725	
259		1s. dull green & scarlet (*chalk-surfaced paper*) (9.10)	£230	£100	55·00
260	**94**	2s.6d. lilac (5.4.02)	£525	£280	£150
		s. Opt. "SPECIMEN" (15, 16)		£400	
		Wi. Watermark inverted	£7500	£5000	£3500
261		2s.6d. pale dull purple (*chalk-surfaced paper*) (7.10.05)	£675	£350	£180

		s. Opt. "SPECIMEN" (17)		£3250	
		Wi. Watermark inverted	£11000	£7500	£4250
262		2s.6d. dull purple (*chalk-surfaced paper*)	£600	£350	£180
263	**95**	5s. brt carmine (5.4.02)	£850	£450	£220
		s. Opt. "SPECIMEN" (16, 17)		£400	
		Wi. Watermark inverted	—	£65000	£5750
264		5s. dp brt carmine	£900	£450	£220
265	**96**	10s. ultramarine (5.4.02)	£2000	£1000	£500
		s. Opt. "SPECIMEN" (16, 17)		£500	
		Wi. Watermark inverted	—	—	£40000
266	**97**	£1 dull blue-green (16.6.02)	£3500	£2000	£825
		s. Opt. "SPECIMEN" (16, 17)		£1400	
		Wi. Watermark inverted	—	£110000	£24000

USED ON COVER PRICES					
No. 215	£2.50	No. 217	£2.50	No. 219	£2.50
No. 222	£50	No. 225	£50	No. 230	£25
No. 232	£35	No. 236a	£45	No. 240	£40
No. 242	£50	No. 245	£60	No. 249	£200
No. 250	£250	No. 254	£225	No. 257	£175
No. 260	£1250	No. 263	£1750		

97a

1910 (May). Prepared for use, by De La Rue but not issued. *Wmk* Imperial Crown, *W* **49**. *P* 14.

266a	**97a**	2d. Tyrian plum	—	£115000	
		s. Opt. "SPECIMEN" (17)		£62000	

One example of this stamp is known used, but it was never issued to the public.

1911. Printed by Harrison & Sons. Ordinary paper. *Wmk* Imperial Crown *W* **49**.

(a) P 14.

267	**83**	½d. dull yellow-green (3.5.11)	3·75	2·75	1·50
		s. Opt. "SPECIMEN" (22)		£325	
		Wi. Watermark inverted	90·00	60·00	60·00
268		½d. dull green	4·25	3·00	1·50
269		½d. deep dull green	17·00	11·00	6·00
270		½d. pale bluish green	80·00	40·00	40·00
		a. Booklet pane. Five stamps plus St. Andrew's Cross label	£1250	£800	
		aw. Ditto. Wmk inverted	£1250	£800	
		b. Booklet pane. No. 272×6	£425	£325	
		bw. Ditto. Wmk inverted	£425	£325	
		c. Watermark sideways	†	†	£35000
		d. Imperf (pair)	—	£40000	†
271		½d. brt green (fine impression) (6.11)	£425	£275	£170
272		1d. rose-red (3.5.11)	15·00	8·00	12·00
		a. No wmk (brick-red)	75·00	50·00	—
		b. Booklet pane. No. 272×6	£325	£250	
		bw. Ditto. Wmk inverted	£325	£250	
		s. Opt. "SPECIMEN" (22)		£325	
		Wi. Watermark inverted	80·00	50·00	50·00
273		1d. deep rose-red	15·00	8·00	12·00
274		1d. rose-carmine	85·00	55·00	30·00
275		1d. aniline pink (5.11)	£1250	£750	£375
275a		1d. aniline rose	£300	£180	£140
276	**86**	2½d. brt blue (10.7.11)	£175	65·00	38·00
		Wi. Watermark inverted	£2100	£1250	
277	**87**	3d. purple/lemon (12.9.11)	£225	£125	£225
		s. Opt. "SPECIMEN" (22)		£300	
277a		3d. grey/lemon	£7000	£4500	
278	**88**	4d. brt orange (12.7.11)	£225	£120	55·00
		s. Opt. "SPECIMEN" (22)		£240	
Set of 5			£575	£290	£290

(b) P 15×14.

279	**83**	½d. dull green (30.10.11)	65·00	40·00	45·00
		Wi. Watermark inverted	†	†	£3500
279a		½d. deep dull green	80·00	40·00	45·00
280		1d. rose-red (4.10.11)	80·00	45·00	25·00
281		1d. rose-carmine	35·00	15·00	15·00
		Wi. Watermark inverted	†	†	
282		1d. pale rose-carmine	40·00	22·00	15·00
283	**86**	2½d. brt blue (14.10.11)	50·00	22·00	15·00
		s. Opt. "SPECIMEN" (22)			
284		2½d. dull blue	50·00	22·00	15·00
		Wi. Watermark inverted	—	—	£3000
285	**87**	3d. purple/lemon (22.9.11)	70·00	45·00	15·00
285a		3d. grey/lemon	£4250	£3250	
286	**88**	4d. brt orange (11.11.11)	60·00	30·00	15·00

Set of 5 .... £250 £130 90·00

USED ON COVER PRICES					
No. 267	£4	No. 272	£18	No. 276	£55
No. 277	£550	No. 278	£175	No. 279	£100
No. 281	£30	No. 283	£35	No. 285	£40
No. 286	£65				

1911–13. Printed at Somerset House. Ordinary paper. *Wmk as 1902–10. P 14.*

287	84	1½d. reddish purple and bright green (13.7.11)	90·00	45·00	38·00
288		1½d. dull purple and green........	60·00	30·00	30·00
289		1½d. slate-purple and green (9.12)..	65·00	30·00	30·00
290	85	2d. dp dull green and red (8.8.11)...............................	60·00	28·00	22·00
		s. Opt. "SPECIMEN" (22)...........		£325	
291		2d. dp dull green & carmine ..	60·00	28·00	22·00
292		2d. grey-green and bright carmine (carmine shows clearly on back) (11.3.12)..	55·00	28·00	28·00
293	89	5d. dull reddish purple and bright blue (7.8.11)	60·00	30·00	22·00
		s. Opt. "SPECIMEN" (2)		—	
294		5d. deep dull reddish purple and bright blue	55·00	30·00	22·00
295	83	6d. royal purple (31.7.11).......	£110	50·00	90·00
296		6d. bright magenta (*chalk-surfaced paper*) (31.10.11).	£17500	£12500	
		s. Opt. "SPECIMEN" (2)		£5750	
297		6d. dull purple.............................	60·00	30·00	22·00
		s. Opt. "SPECIMEN" (2)		£400	
298		6d. reddish purple (11.11)	60·00	30·00	28·00
		a. No cross on crown (various shades)..................	£1800	£1200	
299		6d. very deep reddish purple (11.11).....................................	£120	55·00	45·00
300		6d. dark purple (3.12)................	60·00	30·00	22·00
301		6d. dull purple "Dickinson" coated paper* (3.13).............	£425	£250	£190
303		6d. deep plum (*chalk-surfaced paper*) (7.13)........	60·00	30·00	75·00
		a. No cross on crown	£1950	£1250	
305	90	7d. slate-grey (1.8.12)	30·00	15·00	22·00
		s. Opt. "SPECIMEN" (26)..........		£350	
306	91	9d. reddish purple and light blue (24.7.11)	£200	95·00	75·00
		s. Opt. "SPECIMEN" (22)		£450	
306a		9d. dp dull reddish purple and dp brt blue (9.11).......	£200	95·00	75·00
307		9d. dull reddish purple and blue (10.11)	£125	60·00	60·00
307a		9d. dp plum & blue (7.13)	£125	60·00	60·00
308		9d. slate-purple and cobalt-blue (3.12)..........................	£325	£160	£110
309	92	10d. dull purple and scarlet (9.10.11)	£200	95·00	75·00
		s. Opt. "SPECIMEN" (22)..........		£375	
310		10d. dull reddish purple and aniline pink...........................	£500	£275	£225
311		10d. dull reddish purple and carmine (5.12).....................	£150	80·00	60·00
		a. No cross on crown	£2800	£1800	
312	93	1s. dark green and scarlet (13.7.11)	£240	£120	60·00
		s. Opt. "SPECIMEN" (22, 23, 26)..		£350	
313		1s. deep green and scarlet (9.10.11)	£180	80·00	40·00
		Wi. Wmk inverted......................	£240	£150	†
314		1s. green & carmine (15.4.12)	£140	60·00	35·00
315	94	2s.6d. dull greyish purple (15.9.11)	£1750	£950	£450
		s. Opt. "SPECIMEN" (22)..........		£425	
316		2s.6d. dull reddish purple	£600	£300	£180
		Wi. Watermark inverted...........	†	†	—
317		2s.6d. dark purple.......................	£650	£325	£190
318	95	5s. carmine (29.2.12)............	£875	£425	£200
		s. Opt. "SPECIMEN" (26)...........		—	
319	96	10s. blue (14.1.12)..................	£2100	£1100	£600
320	97	£1 deep green (3.9.11)............	£3000	£2000	£750
		s. Opt. "SPECIMEN" (22)..........		£2200	

*No. 301 was on an experimental coated paper which does not respond to the silver test.

USED ON COVER PRICES					
No. 288	£60	No. 305	£200	No. 316	£1700
No. 290	£55	No. 307	£190	No. 318	£1750
No. 293	£65	No. 311	£225		
No. 297	£90	No. 314	£200		

DEPARTMENTAL OFFICIALS

INLAND REVENUE

These stamps were used by revenue officials in the provinces, mail to and from Head Office passing without a stamp. The London Office used these stamps only for foreign mail.

1902–04. Stamps of King Edward VII optd with type O **1** or O **2**. Ordinary paper.

		Un	Used	Used on cover
O20	½d. blue-green (4.2.02).............	32·00	4·50	£150
	s. Opt. "SPECIMEN" (15).............	£425		
O21	1d. scarlet (4.2.02)..................	22·00	3·00	95·00
	s. Opt. "SPECIMEN" (15).............	£425		
O22	2½d. ultramarine (19.2.02).........	£1000	£275	
	s. Opt. "SPECIMEN" (15, 16)......	£580		
O23	6d. pale dull purple (14.3.04)..........	£500000	£200000	
	s. Opt. "SPECIMEN" (16).............	£45000		
O24	1s. dull green & carmine (29.4.02)..	£3750	£900	
	s. Opt. "SPECIMEN" (16).............	£1200		
O25	5s. brt carmine (29.4.02).........	£45000	£11000	
	a. Raised stop after "R"............	£50000	£13000	
	s. Opt. "SPECIMEN" (16).............	£8500		
O26	10s. ultramarine (29.4.02).........	£100000	£48000	
	a. Raised stop after "R"............	£125000	£48000	
	s. Opt. "SPECIMEN" (16).............	£24000		
O27	£1 blue-green (29.4.02)............	£62500	£25000	
	s. Opt. "SPECIMEN" (16).............	£16000		

OFFICE OF WORKS

These were issued to Head and Branch (local) offices in London and to Branch (local) offices at Birmingham, Bristol, Edinburgh, Glasgow, Leeds, Liverpool, Manchester and Southampton. The overprints on stamps of value 2d. and upwards were created later in 1902, the 2d. for registration fees and the rest for overseas mail.

1902 (11 Feb)–03. Stamps of King Edward VII optd with type O **3**. Ordinary paper.

		Un	Used	Used on cover
O36	½d. blue-green (2.02)................	£575	£180	£2000
	s. Opt. "SPECIMEN" (15).............	£425		
O37	1d. scarlet.................................	£575	£180	£425
	s. Opt. "SPECIMEN" (15).............	£425		
O38	2d. yellowish green & carmine-red (27.4.02)	£2000	£450	£3250
	s. Opt. "SPECIMEN" (16).............	£850		
O39	2½d. ultramarine (29.4.02).........	£3500	£675	£4250
	s. Opt. "SPECIMEN" (16).............	£900		
O40	10d. dull purple & carmine (28.5.03)	£47500	£7000	
	s. Opt. "SPECIMEN" (16)..................	£8000		

*O31/40 **For well-centred, lightly used +25%**

ARMY

ARMY

OFFICIAL

(O **6**)

1902–03. Stamps of King Edward VII optd with Type O **4** (Nos. O48/**50**) or Type O **6** (O 52). Ordinary paper.

		Un	Used	Used on cover
O48	½d. blue-green (11.2.02)..................	5·50	2·25	£100
	s. Opt. "SPECIMEN" (15).............	£350		
O49	1d. scarlet (11.2.02)..................	5·50	2·25	£100
	a. "ARMY" omitted.......................	†	—	
	s. Opt. "SPECIMEN" (15).............	£350		
O50	6d. pale dull purple (23.8.02)..........	£175	80·00	
	s. Opt. "SPECIMEN" (16).............	£425		
O52	6d. pale dull purple (12.03)..........	£3000	£1600	

GOVERNMENT PARCELS

1902. Stamps of King Edward VII optd with type O **7**. Ordinary paper.

		Un	Used	Used on cover
O74	1d. scarlet (30.10.02)............		75·00	22·00
	s. Opt. "SPECIMEN" (16).............		£350	
O75	2d. yellowish green & carmine-red (29.4.02).........................		£225	60·00
	s. Opt. "SPECIMEN" (16).............		£350	
O76	6d. pale dull purple (19.2.02)........		£275	60·00
	a. Opt double, one albino.........		£35000	
	s. Opt. "SPECIMEN" (16).............		£350	
O77	9d. dull purple & ultramarine (28.8.02)........		£650	£175
	s. Opt. "SPECIMEN" (16).............		£500	

O78	1s. dull green & carmine (17.12.02)	£1350	£300
	s. Opt. "SPECIMEN" (16)	£550	

BOARD OF EDUCATION

1902 (19 Feb)–**04**. Stamps of King Edward VII optd with type O **8**. Ordinary paper.

		Un	*Used	Used on cover
O83	½d. blue-green	£180	40·00	£550
	s. Opt. "SPECIMEN" (15)	£375		
O84	1d. scarlet	£180	40·00	£550
	s. Opt. "SPECIMEN" (15)	£375		
O85	2½d. ultramarine	£4850	£450	
	s. Opt. "SPECIMEN" (15)	£1100		
O86	5d. dull purple & ultramarine (6.2.04)	£35000	£10000	
	s. Opt. "SPECIMEN" (16)	£7000		
O87	1s. dull green & carmine (23.12.02)	£200000		
	s. Opt. "SPECIMEN" (16)	£38000		

ROYAL HOUSEHOLD

R.H.

OFFICIAL

(O **9**)

1902. Stamps of King Edward VII optd with Type O **9**. Ordinary paper.

		Un	*Used	Used on cover
O91	½d. blue-green (29.4.02)	£375	£200	£1100
	s. Opt. "SPECIMEN" (16)	£750		
O92	1d. scarlet (19.2.02)	£325	£175	£1000
	s. Opt. "SPECIMEN" (15)	£750		

ADMIRALTY

ADMIRALTY   ADMIRALTY

OFFICIAL   OFFICIAL
(O **10**)   (O **11**)
(with different "M")

1903 (1 Apr). Stamps of King Edward VII optd with Type O **10**. Ordinary paper.

		Un	*Used	Used on cover
O101	½d. blue-green	30·00	15·00	
	s. Opt. "SPECIMEN" (16)	£400		
O102	1d. scarlet	20·00	8·00	£300
	s. Opt. "SPECIMEN" (16)	£400		
O103	1½d. dull purple & green	£325	£150	
	s. Opt. "SPECIMEN" (16)	£500		
O104	2d. yellowish green & carmine-red	£350	£160	
	s. Opt. "SPECIMEN" (16)	£500		
O105	2½d. ultramarine	£475	£150	
	s. Opt. "SPECIMEN" (16)	£500		
O106	3d. dull purple/orange-yellow	£425	£160	
	s. Opt. "SPECIMEN" (16)	£500		

1903–04. Stamps of King Edward VII optd with Type O **11**. Ordinary paper.

		Un	*Used	Used on cover
O107	½d. blue-green (9.03)	60·00	25·00	£500
	s. Opt. "SPECIMEN" (16)	£400		
O108	1d. scarlet (12.03)	60·00	25·00	£160
	s. Opt. "SPECIMEN" (16)	£400		
O109	1½d. dull purple & green (2.04)	£1200	£650	
O110	2d. yellowish green & carmine-red (3.04)	£2700	£900	
	s. Opt. "SPECIMEN" (16)	£750		
O111	2½d. ultramarine (3.04)	£2900	£950	
	s. Opt. "SPECIMEN" (16)	£950		
O112	3d. dull purple/orange-yellow (12.03)	£2600	£400	
	s. Opt. "SPECIMEN" (16)	£750		

Stamps of various issues perforated with a Crown and initials ("H.M.O.W.", "O.W.", "B.T." or "S.O.") or with initials only ("H.M.S.O." or "D.S.I.R.") have also been used for official purposes, but these are outside the scope of this catalogue.

Stanley Gibbons

Great Britain Department

Stanley Gibbons, a name synonymous with quality.

Ever since the birth of our hobby Stanley Gibbons has been at the forefront of GB philately and we invite collectors access to one of the finest GB stocks in the world by registering for our renowned free monthly brochure. Whatever your budget or collecting interests you will find a range of the highest quality material for the discerning collector.

Est 1856

STANLEY GIBBONS

Proud
PTS
members

Stanley Gibbons
399 Strand, London, WC2R 0LX
+44 (0)20 7836 8444
www.stanleygibbons.com

SELLING YOUR STAMPS?

Warwick and Warwick have an expanding requirement for world collections, single country collections, single items, covers, proof material and specialised collections, with G.B. material being particularly in demand. Our customer base is increasing dramatically and we need an ever-larger supply of quality material to keep pace with demand. The market has never been stronger and if you are considering the sale of your collection, now is the time to act.

FREE VALUATIONS
We will provide a free, professional and without obligation valuation of your collection. Either we will make you a fair, binding private treaty offer, or we will recommend inclusion of your property in our next specialist public auction.

FREE TRANSPORTATION
We can arrange insured transportation of your collection to our Warwick offices completely free of charge. If you decline our offer, we ask you to cover the return carriage costs only.

FREE VISITS
Visits by our valuers are possible anywhere in the country or abroad, usually within 48 hours, in order to value larger collections. Please telephone for details.

ADVISORY DAYS
We are staging a series of advisory days across the country. Please visit our website or telephone for further details.

EXCELLENT PRICES
Because of the strength of our customer base we are in a position to offer prices that we feel sure will exceed your expectations.

ACT NOW
Telephone or email Ian Hunter today with details of your property.

Warwick & Warwick Ltd.
Auctioneers and Valuers
Chalon House, Scar Bank, Millers Road,
Warwick CV34 5DB
Tel: 01926 499031 Fax: 01926 491906
E-mail: ian.hunter@warwickandwarwick.com
www.warwickandwarwick.com

Warwick & Warwick

King George V

6 May 1910 – 20 January 1936

Further detailed information on the issues of King George V will be found in Volume 2 of the Stanley Gibbons *Great Britain Specialised Catalogue.*

PRINTERS. Types 98 to 102 were typographed by Harrison & Sons Ltd, with the exception of certain preliminary printings made at Somerset House and distinguishable by the controls "A.11", "B.11" or "B.12" (the Harrison printings do not have a full stop after the letter). The booklet stamps, Nos. 334/7, and 344/5 were printed by Harrison only.

WATERMARK VARIETIES. Many British stamps to 1967 exist without watermark owing to misplacement of the paper, and with either inverted, reversed, or inverted and reversed watermarks. A proportion of the low-value stamps issued in booklets have the watermark inverted in the normal course of printing.

Low values with *watermark sideways* are normally from stamp rolls used on machines with sideways delivery or, from June 1940, certain booklets.

STAMPS WITHOUT WATERMARK. Stamps found without watermark, due to misplacement of the sheet in relation to the dandy roll, are not listed here but will be found in the *Great Britain Specialised Catalogue.*

The 1½d. and 5d. 1912–22, and ½d., 2d. and 2½d., 1924–26, listed here, are from whole sheets completely without watermark.

| **98** | **99** | **100** Simple Cypher |

For type difference with T **101/2** see notes below the latter.

| Die A | Die B |

Dies of Halfpenny

Die A. The three upper scales on the body of the right hand dolphin form a triangle; the centre jewel of the cross inside the crown is suggested by a comma.

Die B. The three upper scales are incomplete; the centre jewel is suggested by a crescent.

| Die A | Die B |

Dies of One Penny

Die A. The second line of shading on the ribbon to the right of the crown extends right across the wreath; the line nearest to the crown on the right hand ribbon shows as a short line at the bottom of the ribbon. Die B. The second line of shading is broken in the middle; the first line is little more than a dot.

(Des Bertram Mackennal and G. W. Eve. Head from photograph by W. and D. Downey. Die eng J. A. C. Harrison)

1911–12. *Wmk* Imperial Crown, *W* **49**. *P* 15×14.

321	**98**	½d. pale green (Die A) (22.6.11)	10·00	5·00	4·00
322		½d. green (Die A) (22.6.11)	8·00	4·00	4·00
		a. Error. Perf 14 (8.11)	—	£20000	£1000
		s. Opt. "SPECIMEN" (22)		£800	
		Wi. Watermark inverted	£20000	—	£2000
323		½d. bluish green (Die A)	£400	£300	£180
324		½d. yellow-green (Die B)	18·00	12·00	1·50
		a. booklet pane No. 324×6 (8.11)	£350	£250	
		aw. Ditto, Wmk inverted	£275	£200	
		s. Opt. "SPECIMEN" (22)		£350	
325		½d. bright green (Die B)	13·00	8·00	1·50
		a. Watermark sideways	—		£5500
		Wi. Watermark inverted	35·00	20·00	7·50
326		½d. bluish green (Die B)	£260	£160	£100
327	**99**	1d. carmine-red (Die A) (22.6.11)	10·00	4·50	2·50
		c. Watermark sideways	†	†	£17000
		s. Opt. "SPECIMEN" (22)		£550	
		Wi. Watermark inverted	£2200	£1500	£1250
328		1d. pale carmine (Die A) (22.6.11)	25·00	14·00	3·00
		a. No cross on crown	£1250	£850	£500
329		1d. carmine (Die B)	15·00	10·00	3·00
		a. Booklet pane, No. 329×6 (8.11)	£350	£250	
		aw. Ditto, Wmk inverted	£275	£200	
		s. Opt. "SPECIMEN" (22)		£550	
		Wi. Watermark inverted	35·00	20·00	7·50
330		1d. pale carmine (Die B)	15·00	10·00	4·00
		a. No cross on crown	£1100	£800	£500
331		1d. rose-pink (Die B)	£225	£125	45·00
332		1d. scarlet (Die B) (6.12)	75·00	45·00	18·00
		a. Booklet pane, No. 332×6 (8.11)	£550	£400	
		aw. Ditto, Wmk inverted	£550	£400	
		s. Opt. "SPECIMEN" (22)		£750	
		Wi. Watermark inverted	75·00	45·00	18·00
333		1d. aniline scarlet (Die B)	£375	£240	£110
		a. Booklet pane, No. 333×6 (8.11)	£2000	£1500	
		aw. Ditto, Wmk inverted	£2000	£1500	
		Wi. Watermark inverted	£375	£240	£110

For note on the aniline scarlet No. 333 see below No. 343.

1912 (28 Sept). Booklet stamps. *Wmk* Royal Cypher (*Simple*), *W* **100**. P 15×14.

334	**98**	½d. pale green (Die B)	90·00	45·00	40·00
335		½d. green (Die B)	90·00	45·00	40·00
		a. Booklet pane, No. 334 ×6 (9.12)	£500	£375	
		aw. Ditto, Wmk inverted	£500	£375	
		s. Opt. "SPECIMEN" (22, 26)		£300	
		Wi. Watermark inverted	90·00	45·00	40·00
		Wj. Watermark reversed	£1750	£1100	£800
		Wk. Watermark inverted and reversed	£1600	£1100	£800
336	**99**	1d. scarlet (Die B)	40·00	30·00	30·00
		a. Booklet pane, No. 336×6 (9.12)	£400	£275	
		aw. Ditto, Wmk inverted	£400	£275	
		s. Opt. "SPECIMEN" (22, 26)		£325	
		Wi. Watermark inverted	40·00	30·00	30·00
		Wj. Watermark reversed	£1750	£1100	£800
		Wk. Watermark inverted and reversed	—	—	£850
337		1d. bright scarlet (Die B)	40·00	30·00	30·00

Stanley Gibbons
Auctions

Welcome consignments for future Auctions,
be it single items or complete collections.

If you are looking to sell your collection then come to
Stanley Gibbons Auctions where:

Outstanding realisations and percentage of lots sold
Mailing list and client list second to none
Stanley Gibbons Auctions is perfect for sellers and buyers alike.

101   **102**   **103** Multiple Cypher

107   **108**

No. 357ab

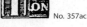

No. 357ac

No. 357a

Type differences

½d. In T **98** the ornament above "P" of "HALFPENNY" has two thin lines of colour and the beard is undefined. In T **101** the ornament has one thick line and the beard is well defined.

1d. In T **99** the body of the lion is unshaded and in T **102** it is shaded.

1912 (1 Jan). *Wmk* Imperial Crown, *W* **49**. *P* 15×14.

338	101	½d. deep green	28·00	15·00	8·00
339		½d. green	15·00	8·00	4·00
		s. Opt. "SPECIMEN" (26)		£325	
340		½d. yellow-green	15·00	8·00	4·00
		a. No cross on crown	£190	£100	55·00
		Wi. Watermark inverted	£1500	£1100	£650
341	102	1d. bright scarlet	10·00	5·00	2·00
		a. No cross on crown	£150	£110	55·00
		b. Printed double, one albino	£275	£180	
		Wi. Watermark inverted	£650	£425	£400
342		1d. scarlet	10·00	5·00	2·00
343		1d. aniline scarlet*	£275	£175	£100
		a. No cross on crown	£2000	£1400	

*Our prices for the aniline scarlet 1d. stamps, Nos. 333 and 343, are for the specimens in which the colour is suffused on the surface of the stamp and shows through clearly on the back. Specimens without these characteristics but which show "aniline" reactions under the quartz lamp are relatively common.

1912 (Aug). *Wmk* Royal Cypher (*Simple*), *W* **100**. *P* 15×14.

344	101	½d. green	14·00	7·00	3·00
		a. No cross on crown	£300	£200	£125
		s. Opt. "SPECIMEN" (26)		£550	
		Wi. Watermark inverted	£550	£350	£225
		Wj. Watermark reversed	£550	£350	£225
		Wk. Watermark inverted and reversed	15·00	8·00	4·50
345	102	1d. scarlet	15·00	8·00	4·50
		a. No cross on crown	£175	£100	50·00
		Wi. Watermark inverted	28·00	18·00	25·00
		Wj. Watermark reversed	£200	£125	£125
		Wk. Watermark inverted and reversed	20·00	12·00	20·00

1912 (Sept). *Wmk* Royal Cypher (*Multiple*), *W* **103**. *P* 15×14.

346	101	½d. green (Oct)	20·00	12·00	8·00
		a. No cross on crown	£280	£175	£125
		b. Imperf	£250	£175	
		c. Watermark sideways	†	†	£4000
		d. Printed on gummed side	—	—	†
		Wi. Watermark inverted	20·00	12·00	20·00
		Wj. Watermark reversed	22·00	15·00	20·00
		Wk. Watermark inverted and reversed	£150	£100	£100
347		½d. yellow-green	20·00	15·00	8·00
348		½d. pale green	25·00	15·00	8·00
349	102	1d. bright scarlet	25·00	18·00	10·00
350		1d. scarlet	25·00	18·00	10·00
		a. No cross on crown	£225	£150	60·00
		b. Imperf	£225	£150	
		c. Watermark sideways	£325	£190	£220
		d. Watermark sideways. No cross on crown	£1200	£750	
		Wi. Watermark inverted	40·00	22·00	28·00
		Wj. Watermark reversed	40·00	22·00	28·00
		Wk. Watermark inverted and reversed	£1600	£1000	£650

104   **105**   **106**

Die I

Die II

Two Dies of the 2d.

Die I.—Inner frame-line at top and sides close to solid of background. Four complete lines of shading between top of head and oval frame-line. These four lines do not extend to the oval itself. White line round "TWO-PENCE" thin.

Die II.—Inner frame-line further from solid of background. Three lines between top of head and extending to the oval. White line round "TWOPENCE" thicker.

(Des Bertram Mackennal (heads) and G. W. Eve (frames). Coinage head (½, 1½, 2, 3 and 4d.); large medal head (1d., 2½d.); intermediate medal head (5d. to 1s.); small medal head used for fiscal stamps. Dies eng J. A. C. Harrison) (Typo by Harrison & Sons Ltd., except the 6d. printed by the Stamping Department of the Board of Inland Revenue, Somerset House. The latter also made printings of the following which can only be distinguished by the controls: ½d. B.13; 1½d. A.12; 2d. C.13; 2½d. A.12; 3d. A12, B.13, C.13; 4d. B.13; 5d. B.13; 7d. C.13; 8d. C.13; 9d. agate B.13; 10d. C.13; 1s. C.13)

1912–24. *Wmk* Royal Cypher (*Simple*), *W* **100**. Chalk-surfaced paper (6d.). *P* 15×14.

351	105	½d. green (16.1.13)	3·00	1·00	1·00
		a. Partial double print (half of bottom row) (Control G15)	—	£25000	
		b. Gummed both sides	£27500	—	—
		c. Booklet pane, No. 351×6 (4.13)	£140	£120	
		cw. Ditto, Wmk inverted	£140	£100	
		s. Opt. "SPECIMEN" (23, 26)		£150	
		Wi. Watermark inverted	4·00	3·00	1·50
		Wj. Watermark reversed	80·00	55·00	55·00
		Wk. Watermark inverted and reversed	6·00	4·00	3·50
352		½d. bright green	3·00	1·00	1·00
353		½d. deep green	10·00	5·00	2·00
354		½d. yellow-green	10·00	6·00	3·00
355		½d. very yellow (Cyprus) green (1914)	£13000	£9000	†
356		½d. blue-green	60·00	40·00	25·00
357	104	1d. bright scarlet (8.10.12)	3·00	1·00	1·00
		a. "Q" for "O" (R. 1/4) (Control E14)	£240	£175	£175
		ab. "Q" for "O" (R. 4/11) (Control T22)	£450	£350	£190
		ac. Reversed "Q" for "O" (R. 15/9) (Control T22)	£400	£300	£240
		ad. Inverted "Q" for "O" (R. 20/3)	£500	£375	£240
		b. *Tête-bêche* (pair)	—	£80000	†

Embassy Philatelists
POSTAL AUCTIONS

Est. 30 Years

(Pl.225)

(SG 177a)

(SG 173g)

(MAGENTA)

(SG 346c)

('CHROME')

('CAMBRIDGE')

		c. Booklet pane, No. 357 ×6 (4.13)	£175	£120	
		cw. Ditto, Wmk inverted	£175	£120	
		s. Opt. "SPECIMEN" (23, 26)		£200	
		Wi. Watermark inverted	4·00	2·00	1·00
		Wj. Watermark reversed	£145	95·00	95·00
		Wk. Watermark inverted and reversed	6·00	3·00	3·00
358		1d. vermilion	9·00	5·00	2·50
359		1d. pale rose-red	30·00	20·00	5·00
360		1d. carmine-red	20·00	11·00	5·00
361		1d. scarlet-vermilion	£180	£125	50·00
		a. Printed on back	£450	£300	†
362	**105**	1½d. red-brown (15.10.12)	10·00	6·00	1·50
		a. "PENCF" (R. 15/12)	£400	£300	£250
		b. Booklet pane. Four stamps plus two printed labels (2.24)	£800	£600	
		bw. Ditto, Wmk inverted	£775	£600	
		c. Booklet pane, No. 362 ×6 (10.18)	£200	£150	
		cw. Ditto. Wmk inverted	£200	£150	
		s. Opt. "SPECIMEN" (23, 26)		£125	
		Wi. Watermark inverted	9·00	5·00	2·00
		Wj. Watermark reversed	70·00	50·00	50·00
		Wk. Watermark inverted and reversed	15·00	8·00	8·00
363		1½d. chocolate-brown	20·00	11·00	2·00
		a. No watermark	£350	£240	£240
364		1½d. chestnut	5·00	3·00	1·00
		a. "PENCF" (R. 15/12)	£175	£125	£110
365		1½d. yellow-brown	30·00	20·00	16·00
366	**106**	2d. orange-yellow (Die I) (20.8.12)	14·00	8·00	3·00
367		2d. reddish orange (Die I) (11.13)	10·00	6·00	3·00
368		2d. orange (Die I)	8·00	4·00	3·00
		a. Booklet pane. No. 368 ×6 (7.20)	£425	£350	
		aw. Ditto, Wmk inverted	£275	£275	
		s. Opt. "SPECIMEN" (26)		£250	
		Wi. Watermark inverted	22·00	12·00	12·00
		Wj. Watermark reversed	25·00	15·00	12·00
		Wk. Watermark inverted and reversed	18·00	10·00	10·00
369		2d. brt orange (Die I)	8·00	5·00	3·00
370		2d. orange (Die II) (9.21)	8·00	5·00	3·50
		a. Booklet pane. No. 370 ×6 (8.21)	£500	£350	
		aw. Ditto, Wmk inverted	£500	£350	
		s. Opt. "SPECIMEN" (15, 23)		£800	
		Wi. Watermark inverted	60·00	40·00	40·00
		Wk. Watermark inverted and reversed	£200	£140	£130
371	**104**	2½d. cobalt-blue (18.10.12)	22·00	12·00	4·00
371a		2½d. bright blue (1914)	22·00	12·00	4·00
372		2½d. blue	22·00	12·00	4·00
		s. Opt. "SPECIMEN" (15, 23, 26)		£120	
		Wi. Watermark inverted	£120	85·00	75·00
		Wj. Watermark reversed	95·00	65·00	65·00
		Wk. Watermark inverted and reversed	45·00	28·00	28·00
373		2½d. indigo-blue* (1920)	£5000	£3500	£2500
373a		2½d. dull Prussian blue* (12.20)	£1850	£1500	£850
374	**106**	3d. dull reddish violet (9.10.12)	22·00	12·00	3·00
375		3d. violet	15·00	8·00	3·00
		s. Opt. "SPECIMEN" (15, 23, 26)		£250	
		Wi. Watermark inverted	£160	95·00	£110
		Wj. Watermark reversed	£800	£450	£450
		Wk. Watermark inverted and reversed	40·00	30·00	30·00
376		3d. bluish violet (11.13)	15·00	9·00	3·00
377		3d. pale violet	17·00	10·00	3·00
378		4d. dp grey-green (15.1.13)	75·00	45·00	25·00
379		4d. grey-green	25·00	15·00	2·00
		s. Opt. "SPECIMEN" (15, 23, 26)		£125	
		Wi. Watermark inverted	50·00	30·00	30·00
		Wj. Watermark reversed	£500	£300	£300
		Wk. Watermark inverted and reversed	£110	80·00	80·00
380		4d. pale grey-green	40·00	25·00	5·00
381	**107**	5d. brown (30.6.13)	25·00	15·00	5·00
		s. Opt. "SPECIMEN" (15, 23, 26)		£250	
		Wi. Watermark inverted	£1800	£1200	£1100
		Wj. Watermark reversed	†	†	—
		Wk. Watermark inverted and reversed	£500	£400	£400
382		5d. yellow-brown	25·00	15·00	5·00

		a. No watermark	£2000	£1200	
383		5d. bistre-brown	£250	£185	75·00
384		6d. dull purple (1.8.13)	45·00	25·00	10·00
		s. Opt. "SPECIMEN" (15, 23, 26)		£200	
385		6d. reddish purple (8.13)	30·00	15·00	7·00
		a. Perf 14 (9.20)	£150	90·00	£110
		Wi. Watermark inverted	85·00	50·00	50·00
		Wj. Watermark reversed	£5500	£4500	
		Wk. Watermark inverted and reversed	£150	£100	£100
386		6d. deep reddish purple	85·00	50·00	5·00
387		7d. olive (1.8.13)	35·00	20·00	10·00
		s. Opt. "SPECIMEN" (26)		£200	
		Wi. Watermark inverted	85·00	50·00	55·00
		Wj. Watermark reversed	†	†	†
		Wk. Watermark inverted and reversed	£6000	£5000	
388		7d. bronze-green (1915)	£120	70·00	25·00
389		7d. sage-green (1917)	£120	70·00	18·00
390		8d. black/yellow (1.8.13)	55·00	32·00	11·00
		s. Opt. "SPECIMEN" (26)		£250	
		Wi. Watermark inverted	£220	£150	£150
		Wj. Watermark reversed	£350	£240	£240
		Wk. Watermark inverted and reversed	£7000	£5500	
391		8d. black/yellow-buff (granite) (5.17)	60·00	40·00	15·00
392	**108**	9d. agate (30.6.13)	30·00	15·00	6·00
		a. Printed double, one albino			
		s. Opt. "SPECIMEN" (26)		£425	
		Wi. Watermark inverted	£240	£175	£175
		Wk. Watermark inverted and reversed	£240	£175	£175
393		9d. deep agate	45·00	25·00	6·00
393a		9d. olive-green (9.22)	£225	£110	30·00
		as. Opt. "SPECIMEN" (15, 23)		£750	
		aWi. Watermark inverted	£1200	£900	£750
		aWk. Watermark inverted and reversed	£1500	£1100	£950
393b		9d. pale olive-green	£250	£120	40·00
394		10d. turquoise-blue (1.8.13)	40·00	22·00	20·00
		s. Opt. "SPECIMEN" (15, 23, 26)		£425	
		Wi. Watermark inverted	£4200	£3000v	£2000
		Wk. Watermark inverted and reversed	£475	£325	£275
394a		10d. deep turquoise-blue	£150	90·00	30·00
395		1s. bistre (1.8.13)	40·00	20·00	4·00
		s. Opt. "SPECIMEN" (15, 23, 26, 31)		£375	
		Wi. Watermark inverted	£350	£250	£200
		Wk. Watermark inverted and reversed	£120	70·00	70·00
396		1s. bistre-brown	55·00	35·00	12·00
		Set of 15	£475	£250	95·00

Imperf stamps of this issue exist but may be war-time colour trials.

†The impression of No. 361a is set sideways and is very pale. Nos. 362a and 364a occur on Plates 12 and 29 and are known from Controls L18, M18, M19, O19 and Q21. The flaws were corrected by 1921.

* No. 373 comes from Control O20 and also exists on toned paper.

No. 373a comes from Control R21 and also exists on toned paper, but both are unlike the rare Prussian blue shade of the 1935 2½d. Jubilee issue.

Examples of the 2d., T **106** which were in the hands of philatelists, are known bisected in Guernsey from 27 December 1940 to February 1941.

See also Nos. 418/29.

1913 (Aug). *Wmk* Royal Cypher (*Multiple*), *W* **103**. *P* 15×14.

397	**105**	½d. bright green	£250	£150	£180
		a. Watermark sideways	†	†	£18000
		Wi. Watermark inverted	£1200	£900	
398	**104**	1d. dull scarlet	£350	£225	£225
		Wi. Watermark inverted	£1600	£1100	

Both these stamps were originally issued in rolls only. Subsequently sheets were found, so that horizontal pairs and blocks are known but are of considerable rarity.

109

Stanley Gibbons

Great Britain Department

Stanley Gibbons, a name synonymous with quality.

Ever since the birth of our hobby Stanley Gibbons has been at the forefront of GB philately and we invite collectors access to one of the finest GB stocks in the world by registering for our renowned free monthly brochure. Whatever your budget or collecting interests you will find a range of the highest quality material for the discerning collector.

A

110 Single Cypher

Major Re-entries on 2s.6d.

No. 400a

Nos. 406/7a

No. 415b

No. 417a

(Des Bertram Mackennal. Dies eng J. A. C. Harrison. Recess)

*High values, so-called "Sea Horses" design: T **109**. Background around portrait consists of horizontal lines, Type A. Wmk Single Cypher, W **110**.*
P 11×12.

1913 (30 June). Printed by Waterlow Bros & Layton.

399	**109**	2s.6d. deep sepia-brown	£850	£400	£200
		s. Opt. "SPECIMEN" (23, 26)		£650	
400		2s.6d. sepia-brown	£600	£300	£150
		a. Re-entry (Plate 3, R. 2/1)	£2800	£1800	£800
401		5s. rose-carmine	£1300	£625	£325
		s. Opt. "SPECIMEN" (26)		£950	
402		10s. indigo-blue (1 Aug)	£2000	£1200	£475
		s. Opt. "SPECIMEN" (23, 26, 29)		£1200	
403		£1 green (1 Aug)	£4800	£3500	£1400
		s. Opt. "SPECIMEN" (23, 26)		£3250	
404		£1 dull blue-green (1 Aug)	£4800	£3500	£1600

*399/404 **For well-centred, lightly used+35%***

1915 (Sept–Dec). Printed by De la Rue & Co.

405	**109**	2s.6d. deep yellow-brown (Oct)	£680	£375	£250
		Wi. Watermark inverted	£2400	£1500	
406		2s.6d. yellow-brown (inc. worn plates)	£550	£325	£225
		a. Re-entry (Plate 3, R. 2/1)	£3000	£2000	£950
		s. Opt. "SPECIMEN" (23)		£1400	
		Wi. Watermark inverted	£1800	£1250	£875
		Wj. Watermark reversed	£1800	£1250	£1000
		Wk. Watermark inverted and reversed	£4750	£4000	
407		2s.6d. grey brown (inc. worn plates)	£700	£400	£300
		a. Re-entry (Plate 3, R. 2/1)	£3000	£2000	£950
		Wi. Watermark inverted	£1800	£1250	£1000
		Wj. Watermark reversed	£1800	£1250	£1000
408		2s.6d. sepia (seal-brown)	£550	£325	£250
		Wi. Watermark inverted	£1800	£1250	£1000
		Wj. Watermark reversed	£1800	£1250	£1000
409		5s. bright carmine	£1100	£650	£400
		s. Opt. "SPECIMEN" (23)		£1250	
		Wi. Watermark inverted	£6750	£4750	
		Wj. Watermark reversed	£6250	£4500	
		Wk. Watermark inverted and reversed	—	£18000	†
410		5s. pale carmine (worn plate)	£1400	£800	£500
411		10s. deep blue (Dec)	£5500	£3750	£1000
		s. Opt. "SPECIMEN" (26)		£2800	
412		10s. blue	£4000	£3250	£875
		Wi. Watermark inverted and reversed	—	—	†
413		10s. pale blue	£4250	£3500	£875

*405/13 **For well-centred, lightly used +45%***

No. 406/7 were produced from the original Waterlow plates as were all De La Rue 5s. and 10s. printings. Examples of No. 406/7, 410 and 411 occur showing degrees of plate wear. 412wi. one damaged mint example is recorded.

1918 (Dec)–**19**. Printed by Bradbury, Wilkinson & Co, Ltd.

413a	**109**	2s.6d. olive-brown	£350	£190	£100
		as. Opt. "SPECIMEN" (15, 23, 26, 31, 32)		£1000	
414		2s.6d. chocolate-brown	£325	£160	75·00
415		2s.6d. reddish brown	£325	£160	75·00
415a		2s.6d. pale brown	£340	£175	85·00
		b. Major re-entry (Plate 3/5L, R. 1/2)	£1600	£1000	£500
416		5s. rose-red (1.19)	£475	£325	£135
		s. Opt. "SPECIMEN" (15, 23, 26, 31, 32)		£1200	
417		10s. dull grey-blue (1.19)	£850	£475	£175
		a. Re-entry (Plate 1/3L, R. 1/1)	£2250	£1800	£1000
		s. Opt. "SPECIMEN" (15, 23, 26, 31, 32)		£1400	

Set of 4 (inc. no. 403)	£5800	£4000	£1500

*413a/17 **For well-centred, lightly used +35%***

DISTINGUISHING PRINTINGS. Note that the £1 value was only printed by Waterlow.

Waterlow and De La Rue stamps measure exactly 22.1 mm vertically. In the De La Rue printings the gum is usually patchy and yellowish, and the colour of the stamp, particularly in the 5s., tends to show through the back. The holes of the perforation are smaller than those of the other two printers, but there is a thick perforation tooth at the top of each vertical side.

In the Bradbury Wilkinson printings the height of the stamp is 22.6 – 23.1 mm due to the use of curved plates. On most of the 22.6 mm high stamps a minute coloured guide dot appears in the margin just above the middle of the upper frame-line.

For (1934) re-engraved Waterlow printings see Nos. 450/2.

Note: All illustrations of re-entries on Nos. 399–417 are copyright GB Philatelic Publications Ltd and Bryan Kearsley and are reproduced with their permission.

UNITED KINGDOM OF GREAT BRITAIN AND NORTHERN IRELAND

111 Block Cypher   **111a**

The watermark Type **111a**, as compared with Type **111**, differs as follows: Closer spacing of horizontal rows (12½ mm instead of 14½ mm). Letters shorter and rounder. Watermark thicker. The dandy roll to produce watermark Type **111a** was provided by Somerset House in connection with experiments in paper composition undertaken during 1924–25. These resulted in a change from rag only paper to that made from a mixture including esparto and sulphite.

(Typo by Waterlow & Sons, Ltd (all values except 6d.) and later, 1934–35, by Harrison & Sons, Ltd (all values). Until 1934 the 6d. was printed at Somerset House where a printing of the 1½d. was also made in 1926 (identifiable only by control E.26). Printings by Harrisons in 1934–35 can be identified, when in mint condition, by the fact that the gum shows a streaky appearance vertically, the Waterlow gum being uniformly applied, but Harrisons also used up the balance of the Waterlow "smooth gum" paper)

1924 (Feb)–**26**. *Wmk* Block Cypher, *W* **111**. *P* 15×14.

418	**105**	½d. green	2·00	1·00	1·00
		a. Watermark sideways (5.24)	18·00	9·00	3·25
		aWi. Watermark sideways inverted	£600	£450	
		b. Doubly printed	£16000	£12000	†
		c. No watermark	£6000	—	—
		d. Booklet pane. No. 418×6 (2.24)	£120	85·00	
		dw. Ditto, Wmk inverted	£120	85·00	
		s. Opt. "SPECIMEN" (15, 23, 30, 32)		90·00	
		Wi. Watermark inverted	7·00	3·50	1·00
419	**104**	1d. scarlet	2·00	1·00	1·00
		a. Watermark sideways	40·00	20·00	15·00
		b. Experimental paper, W **111a** (10.24)	40·00	22·00	
		c. Partial double print, one inverted	—	—	
		d. Inverted "Q" for "O" (R. 20/3)	£850	£500	
		e. Booklet pane. No. 419×6 (2.24)	£120	85·00	
		ew. Ditto, Wmk inverted	£120	85·00	
		s. Opt. "SPECIMEN" (15, 23, 30, 32)		90·00	
		Wi. Watermark inverted	7·00	4·00	1·50
420	**105**	1½d. red-brown	2·00	1·00	1·00
		a. Tête-bêche (pair)	£750	£500	£800
		b. Watermark sideways (8.24)	20·00	10·00	3·50
		bWi. Watermark sideways inverted	—	£900	
		c. Printed on the gummed side	£1200	£750	
		d. Booklet pane. Four stamps plus two printed labels (3.24)	£300	£225	
		dw. Ditto, Wmk inverted	£300	£225	
		e. Booklet pane. No 420×6 (2.24)	70·00	50·00	
		ew. Ditto, Wmk inverted	70·00	50·00	
		f. Ditto. Watermark sideways	£14000	£10000	
		g. Experimental paper, W **111a** (10.24)	£160	£120	£120
		h. Double impression	—	—	†
		s. Opt. "SPECIMEN" (15, 23, 30, 32)		90·00	
		Wi. Watermark inverted	3·50	2·00	1·00
421	**106**	2d. orange (Die II) (7.24)	4·00	2·50	2·50
		a. No watermark	£2250	£1800	
		b. Watermark sideways (7.26)	£210	£100	£100

		c. Partial double print	—	£35000	†
		s. Opt. "SPECIMEN" (23, 32)		£100	
		Wi. Watermark inverted	90·00	55·00	55·00
422	**104**	2½d. blue (10.10.24)	10·00	5·00	3·00
		a. No watermark	£3800	£2800	
		b. Watermark sideways	†	†	£18000
		s. Opt. "SPECIMEN" (23, 32)		£550	
		Wi. Watermark inverted	£140	90·00	90·00
423	**106**	3d. violet (10.10.24)	20·00	10·00	2·50
		s. Opt. "SPECIMEN" (23, 32)		£750	
		Wi. Watermark inverted	£135	90·00	70·00
424		4d. grey-green (10.10.24)	28·00	12·00	2·50
		a. Printed on the gummed side	£6000	£4000	†
		s. Opt. "SPECIMEN" (23, 32)		£650	
		Wi. Watermark inverted	£240	£150	£150
425	**107**	5d. brown (17.10.24)	40·00	20·00	3·00
		s. Opt. "SPECIMEN" (23, 26, 32)		£140	
		Wi. Watermark inverted	£210	£150	£150
426		6d. reddish purple (*chalk-surfaced paper*) (9.24)	20·00	12·00	2·50
		Wi. Watermark inverted	90·00	60·00	60·00
		Wk. Watermark inverted and reversed	£700	£450	£400
426a		6d. purple (6.26)	8·00	4·00	1·50
		as. Opt. "SPECIMEN" (23, 26, 32)		£425	
		aWi. Watermark inverted	£140	90·00	90·00
427	**108**	9d. olive-green (11.11.24)	40·00	12·00	3·50
		s. Opt. "SPECIMEN" (23, 26, 32)		£140	
		Wi. Watermark inverted	£175	£120	£120
428		10d. turquoise-blue (28.11.24)	85·00	40·00	40·00
		s. Opt. "SPECIMEN" (23, 32)		£750	
		Wi. Watermark inverted	£3750	£2750	£2000
429		1s. bistre-brown (10.24)	50·00	22·00	3·00
		s. Opt. "SPECIMEN" (23, 32)		£550	
		Wi. Watermark inverted	£600	£375	£375
Set of 12			£250	£110	60·00

There are numerous shades in this issue.

The 6d. on chalk-surfaced and ordinary papers was printed by both Somerset House and Harrisons. The Harrison printings have streaky gum, differ slightly in shade, and that on chalk-surfaced paper is printed in a highly fugitive ink. The prices quoted are for the commonest (Harrison) printing in each case.

112

Scratch across the Lion's nose (left pane, R.1/4)   Tail to "N" of "EXHIBITION" (Left pane, R.1/5)

(Des H. Nelson. Eng J. A. C. Harrison. Recess Waterlow)

1924–25. *British Empire Exhibition*. W **111**. *P* 14.

(a) Dated "1924" (23.4.24).

430	**112**	1d. scarlet	12·00	10·00	11·00
		a. Scratch across the Lion's nose	£225	£150	75·00
		b. Tail to "N" of EXHIBITION	£225	£150	75·00
		s. Opt. "SPECIMEN" (15, 23, 30)		£1100	
431		1½d. brown	20·00	15·00	15·00
		s. Opt. "SPECIMEN" (15, 23, 30)		£1100	
Set of 2			30·00	25·00	26·00
First Day Cover					£450

(b) Dated "1925" (9.5.25).

432	**112**	1d. scarlet	25·00	15·00	30·00
		s. Opt. "SPECIMEN" (30)		£1000	
433		1½d. brown	60·00	40·00	70·00
		s. Opt. "SPECIMEN" (30)		£1000	
Set of 2			80·00	55·00	£100
First Day Cover					£1700

113   **114**   **115**

118   **119**   **120**

116 St. George and the Dragon

117

Des J. Farleigh (T **113** and **115**), E. Linzell (T **114**) and H. Nelson (T **116**). Eng C. G. Lewis (T **113**), T. E. Storey (T **115**), both at the Royal Mint; J. A. C. Harrison, of Waterlow (T **114** & **116**). Typo by Waterlow from plates made at the Royal Mint, except T **116**, recess by Bradbury, Wilkinson from die and plate of their own manufacture

1929 (10 May). *Ninth U.P.U. Congress, London.*

(a) W **111**. *P* 15×14.

434	**113**	½d. green	3·00	2·25	2·25
		a. Watermark sideways	80·00	55·00	50·00
		b. Booklet pane. No. 434×6 (5.29)	£250	£200	
		bw. Ditto. Wmk inverted	£300	£225	
		Wi. Watermark inverted	35·00	15·00	12·00
435	**114**	1d. scarlet	3·00	2·25	2·25
		a. Watermark sideways	£140	95·00	90·00
		b. Booklet pane. No. 435×6 (5.29)	£250	£200	
		bw. Ditto. Wmk inverted	£300	£225	
		Wi. Watermark inverted	35·00	15·00	12·00
436		1½d. purple-brown	3·00	2·25	1·75
		a. Watermark sideways	90·00	60·00	55·00
		b. Booklet pane. Four stamps plus two printed labels	£500	£375	
		bw Ditto. Wmk inverted	£500	£375	
		c. Booklet pane. No. 436×6 (5.29)	85·00	60·00	
		cw. Ditto. Wmk inverted	£110	80·00	
		Wi. Watermark inverted	15·00	5·00	6·00
437	**115**	2½d. blue	28·00	10·00	10·00
		s. Opt. "SPECIMEN" (32)		£3000	
		Wi. Watermark inverted	£3750	£2750	£1100

(b) W **117**. *P* 12.

438	**116**	£1 black	£1100	£750	£550
		s. Opt. "SPECIMEN" (32, red opt)		£3000	
Set of 4 (to 2½d.)			35·00	15·00	14·50
First Day Cover (4 vals.)					£675
First Day Cover (5 vals.)					£14000

PRINTERS. All subsequent issues to No. 1919 were printed in photogravure by Harrison & Sons Ltd *except where otherwise stated.*

121   **122**

1934–36. W **111**. *P* 15×14.

439	**118**	½d. green (17.11.34)	1·00	50	50
		a. Watermark sideways	17·00	10·00	5·00
		aWi. Watermark sideways inverted	£600	£450	£150
		b. Imperf three sides	£7750	£5250	
		c. Booklet pane. No. 439×6 (1.35)	£120	85·00	
		cw. Ditto. Wmk inverted	£130	95·00	
		s. Opt. "SPECIMEN" (23, 32)		£500	
		Wi. Watermark inverted	22·00	11·00	1·50
440	**119**	1d. scarlet (24.9.34)	1·00	50	50
		a. Imperf (pair)	£7000	£5000	
		b. Printed on gummed side	£1000	£750	
		c. Watermark sideways (30.4.35)	40·00	20·00	12·00
		cWi. Watermark sideways inverted	£190	£125	—
		d. Double impression	†	†	£24000
		e. Imperf between (pair)	£12500	£8500	
		f. Imperf (three sides) (pair)	£9500	£7000	
		g. Booklet pane. No. 440×6 (1.35)	£120	85·00	
		gw. Ditto. Wmk inverted	£130	95·00	
		s. Opt. "SPECIMEN" (23, 32)		£600	
		Wi. Watermark inverted	20·00	9·00	3·00
441	**118**	1½d. red-brown (20.8.34)	1·00	50	50
		a. Imperf (pair)	£1700	£1250	
		b. Imperf (three sides) (lower stamp in vert pair)	£6750	£4800	
		c. Imperf between (horiz pair)			
		d. Watermark sideways	15·00	10·00	5·00
		dWi. Watermark sideways inverted			
		e. Booklet pane. Four stamps plus two printed labels (1.35)	£275	£200	
		ew. Ditto. Wmk inverted	£275	£200	
		f. Booklet pane. No. 441×6 (1.35)	42·00	30·00	
		fw. Ditto. Wmk inverted	55·00	40·00	
		s. Opt. "SPECIMEN" (23, 32)		£650	
		Wi. Watermark inverted	8·00	4·00	1·00
442	**120**	2d. orange (19.1.35)	1·50	75	75
		a. Imperf (pair)	£7250	£5750	
		b. Watermark sideways (30.4.35)	£225	£125	90·00
		s. Opt. "SPECIMEN" (30, 32)		—	
443	**119**	2½d. bright blue (18.3.35)	2·50	1·50	1·25
		s. Opt. "SPECIMEN" (23)		£700	
444	**120**	3d. reddish violet (18.3.35)	3·00	1·50	1·25
		s. Opt. "SPECIMEN" (23, 30)		£650	
		Wi. Watermark inverted	—	—	£9000
445		4d. dp grey-green (2.12.35)	4·00	2·00	1·25
		s. Opt. "SPECIMEN" (23, 30)		£700	
		Wi. Watermark inverted	†	†	£9000
446	**121**	5d. yellow-brown (17.2.36)	13·00	6·50	2·75
		s. Opt. "SPECIMEN" (23)		£650	
447	**122**	9d. dp olive-green (2.12.35)	20·00	12·00	2·25
		s. Opt. "SPECIMEN" (23)		£650	
448		10d. turquoise-blue (24.2.36)	30·00	15·00	10·00
		s. Opt. "SPECIMEN" (23, 32)		£700	
449		1s. bistre-brown (24.2.36)	40·00	15·00	1·25
		a. Double impression	—	—	†
		s. Opt. "SPECIMEN" (23, 32)		£125	
Set of 11			95·00	50·00	20·00

Owing to the need for wider space for the perforations the size of the designs of the ½d. and 2d. were once, and the 1d. and 1½d. twice reduced from that of the first printings.

The format description, size in millimetres and S.G. catalogue number are given but further details will be found in the *Great Britain Specialised Catalogue*, Volume 2.

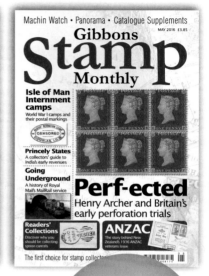

Description	Size	S.G. Nos.	Date of Issue
½d. intermediate format	18.4×22.2	—	19.11.34
½d. small format	17.9×21.7	439	14.2.35
1d. large format	18.7×22.5	—	24.9.34
1d. intermediate format	18.4×22.2	—	1934
1d. small format	17.9×21.7	440	8.2.35
1½d. large format	18.7×22.5	—	20.8.34
1½d. intermediate format	18.4×22.2	—	1934
1½d. small format	17.9×21.7	441	7.2.35
2d. intermediate format	18.4×22.2	—	21.1.35
2d. small format	18.15×21.7	442	1935

There are also numerous minor variations, due to the photographic element in the process.

Examples of 2d., T **120**, which were in the hands of philatelists are known bisected in Guernsey from 27 December 1940 to February 1941.

B	**123**

(Eng. J.A.C. Harrison. Recess Waterlow)

1934 (16 Oct). T **109** (re-engraved). Background around portrait consists of horizontal and diagonal lines, Type B. W **110**. P 11×12.

450	**109**	2s.6d. chocolate-brown	£150	80·00	40·00
		s. Opt. "SPECIMEN" (23, 30)		£3250	
451		5s. bright rose-red	£400	£175	85·00
		s. Opt. "SPECIMEN" (23, 30)		£3250	
452		10s. indigo	£500	£350	80·00
		s. Opt. "SPECIMEN" (23, 30)		£3250	
Set of 3			£1000	£575	£190

There are numerous other minor differences in the design of this issue.

(Des B. Freedman)

1935 (7 May). Silver Jubilee. W **111**. P 15×14.

453	**123**	½d. green	1·00	1·00	1·00
		a. Booklet pane. No. 453×4			
		(5.35)	70·00	50·00	
		aw. Ditto. Wmk inverted	80·00	60·00	
		s. Opt. "SPECIMEN" (23)		£1400	
		Wi. Watermark inverted	15·00	8·00	3·00
454		1d. scarlet	2·00	1·50	2·00
		a. Booklet pane. No. 454×4			
		(5.35)	60·00	45·00	
		aw. Ditto. Wmk inverted	75·00	55·00	
		s. Opt. "SPECIMEN" (23)		£1400	
		Wi. Watermark inverted	15·00	8·00	4·00
455		1½d. red-brown	1·25	1·00	1·00
		a. Booklet pane. No. 455×4			
		(5.35)	25·00	18·00	
		aw. Ditto. Wmk inverted	30·00	22·00	
		s. Opt. "SPECIMEN" (23)		£1400	
		Wi. Watermark inverted	5·00	3·00	1·50
456		2½d. blue	8·00	5·00	6·50
		s. Opt. "SPECIMEN" (23)		£1750	
456a		2½d. Prussian blue	£18500	£13500	£15000
Set of 4			11·00	7·50	9·50
First Day Cover					£650

The 1d., 1½d. and 2½d. values differ from T **123** in the emblem in the panel at right.

Four sheets of No. 456a, printed in the wrong shade, were issued in error by the Post Office Stores Department on 25 June 1935. It is known that three of the sheets were sold from the sub-office at 134 Fore Street, Upper Edmonton, London, between that date and 4 July.

King Edward VIII

20 January – 10 December 1936

Further detailed information on the stamps of King Edward VIII will be found in Volume 2 of the Stanley Gibbons *Great Britain Specialised Catalogue*.

> **PRICES.** From S.G. 457 prices quoted in the first column are for stamps in unmounted mint condition.

124	**125**

(Des H. Brown, adapted Harrison using a photo by Hugh Cecil)

1936. W **125**. P 15×14.

457	**124**	½d. green (1.9.36)	30	30
		a. Double impression		
		b. Booklet pane. No. 457×6 (10.36)	30·00	
		bw. Ditto. Wmk inverted	45·00	
		s. Opt. "SPECIMEN" (30, 32)	£750	
		Wi. Watermark inverted	10·00	5·00
458		1d. scarlet (14.9.36)	60	50
		a. Booklet pane. No. 458×6 (10.36)	25·00	
		aw. Ditto. Wmk inverted	40·00	
		s. Opt. "SPECIMEN" (30, 32)	£750	
		Wi. Watermark inverted	9·00	5·00
459		1½d. red-brown (1.9.36)	30	30
		a. Booklet pane. Four stamps plus two printed labels (10.36)	85·00	
		aw. Ditto. Wmk inverted	85·00	
		b. Booklet pane. No. 459×6 (10.36)	15·00	
		bw. Ditto. Wmk inverted	15·00	
		c. Booklet pane. No. 459×2	30·00	
		cw. Ditto. Wmk inverted	30·00	
		d Imperf (pair)	£40000	
		s. Opt. "SPECIMEN" (30, 32)	£750	
		Wi. Watermark inverted	1·00	1·00
460		2½d. bright blue (1.9.36)	30	85
		s. Opt. "SPECIMEN" (30)	£800	
Set of 4			1·25	1·75

	First Day Covers	
1.9.36	½d., 1½d., 2½d. (457, 459/60)	£175
14.9.36	1d. (458)	£200

King George VI
11 December 1936 – 6 February 1952

Further detailed information on the stamps of King George VI will be found in Volume 2 of the Stanley Gibbons *Great Britain Specialised Catalogue*.

126 King George VI and Queen Elizabeth   **127**

Colon flaw (Cyl. 7 No dot, R. 10/1, later corrected)

(Des E. Dulac)

1937 (13 May). *Coronation.* W **127**. P 15×14.
461	**126**	1½d. maroon	30	30
		a. Colon flaw	70·00	
		s. Opt. "SPECIMEN" (32)	£750	
First Day Cover				35·00

128   **129**   **130**

King George VI and National Emblems

(Des T **128/9**, E. Dulac (head) and E. Gill (frames). T **130**, E. Dulac (whole stamp))

1937–47. W **127**. P 15×14.
462	**128**	½d. green (10.5.37)	30	25
		a. Watermark sideways (1.38)	75	60
		ab. Booklet pane of 4 (6.40)	£110	
		b. Booklet pane. No 462×6 (8.37)	50·00	
		bw. Ditto. Wmk inverted	80·00	
		c. Booklet pane. No 462×2 (8.37)	£120	
		cw. Ditto. Wmk inverted	£120	
		s. Opt "SPECIMEN" (32)		
		Wi. Watermark inverted	10·00	60
463		1d. scarlet (10.5.37)	30	25
		a. Watermark sideways (2.38)	20·00	9·00
		ab. Booklet pane of 4 (6.40)	£175	
		b. Booklet pane. No 463×6 (2.38)	65·00	
		bw. Ditto. Wmk inverted	£275	
		c. Booklet pane. No 463×2 (2.38)	£125	
		cw. Ditto. Wmk inverted	£125	
		s. Opt "SPECIMEN" (32)		
		Wi. Watermark inverted	40·00	3·00
464		1½d. red-brown (30.7.37)	30	25
		a. Watermark sideways (2.38)	1·25	1·25
		b. Booklet pane. Four stamps plus two printed labels (8.37)	£140	
		bw. Ditto. Wmk inverted	£140	
		c. Booklet pane. No 464×6 (8.37)	60·00	
		cw. Ditto. Wmk inverted	£100	

		d. Booklet pane. No 464×2 (1.38)	35·00	
		dw. Ditto. Wmk inverted	50·00	
		e. Imperf three sides (pair)	£6500	
		s. Opt "SPECIMEN" (26)		
		Wi. Watermark inverted	15·00	1·25
465		2d. orange (31.1.38)	1·20	50
		a. Watermark sideways (2.38)	75·00	40·00
		b. Bisected (on cover)	†	50·00
		c. Booklet pane. No 465×6 (6.40)	£175	
		cw. Ditto. Wmk inverted	£425	
		s. Opt. "SPECIMEN" (26)	£325	
		Wi. Watermark inverted	60·00	22·00
466		2½d. ultramarine (10.5.37)	40	25
		a. Watermark sideways (6.40)	75·00	35·00
		b. *Tête-bêche* (horiz pair)	£22000	
		c. Booklet pane. No 466×6 (6.40)	£150	
		cw. Ditto. Wmk inverted	£375	
		Wi. Watermark inverted	55·00	22·00
467		3d. violet (31.1.38)	5·00	1·00
		s. Opt. "SPECIMEN" (26, 30)	£300	
468	**129**	4d. grey-green (21.11.38)	60	75
		a. Imperf (pair)	£9000	
		b. Imperf three sides (horiz pair)	£9500	
		s. Opt. "SPECIMEN" (23)	£200	
469		5d. brown (21.11.38)	3·50	85
		a. Imperf (pair)	£8500	
		b. Imperf three sides (horiz pair)	£9000	
		s. Opt. "SPECIMEN" (23)	£250	
470		6d. purple (30.1.39)	1·50	60
		s. Opt. "SPECIMEN" (23)	£250	
471	**130**	7d. emerald-green (27.2.39)	5·00	60
		a. Imperf three sides (horiz pair)	£9000	
		s. Opt. "SPECIMEN" (23)	£250	
472		8d. bright carmine (27.2.39)	7·50	80
		s. Opt. "SPECIMEN" (23)	£250	
473		9d. deep olive-green (1.5.39)	6·50	80
		s. Opt. "SPECIMEN" (23)	£250	
474		10d. turquoise-blue (1.5.39)	7·00	80
		aa. Imperf (pair)		
		aas. Opt. "SPECIMEN" (23)	£250	
474a		11d. plum (29.12.47)	3·00	2·75
		as. Opt. "SPECIMEN" (30)	£275	
475		1s. bistre-brown (1.5.39)	9·00	75
		s. Opt. "SPECIMEN" (23, 33)	£160	
Set of 15			45·00	10·00

For later printings of the lower values in apparently lighter shades and different colours, see Nos. 485/90 and 503/8.

No. 465b was authorised for use in Guernsey from 27 December 1940 until February 1941.

Nos. 468b and 469b are perforated at foot only and each occurs in the same sheet as Nos. 468a and 469a.

No. 471a is also perforated at foot only, but occurs on the top row of a sheet.

First Day Covers
10.5.37	½d., 1d., 2½d. (462/3, 466)	45·00
30.7.37	1½d. (464)	45·00
31.1.38	2d., 3d. (465, 467)	£100
21.11.38	4d., 5d. (468/9)	65·00
30.1.39	6d. (470)	60·00
27.2.39	7d., 8d. (471/2)	85·00
1.5.39	9d., 10d., 1s. (473/4, 475)	£500
29.12.47	11d. (474a)	55·00

131   **132**

133

Mark in shield (R. 1/7)

Gashed diadem (R. 2/7)

Gashed crown (R. 5/5)

Broken stem (R. 1/4)

Blot on scroll (R. 2/5)

Scratch on scroll (R. 4/6)

(Des E. Dulac (T **131**) and Hon. G. R. Bellew (T **132**). Eng J. A. C. Harrison. Recess Waterlow)

1939–48. W **133**. P 14.

476	**131**	2s.6d. brown (4.9.39)	95·00	8·00
		aa. Mark in shield	£190	80·00
		ab. Gashed diadem	£190	80·00
		ac. Gashed crown	£190	80·00
		as. Opt. "SPECIMEN" (23)	£300	
476b		2s.6d. yellow-green (9.3.42)	15·00	1·50
		bs. Opt. "SPECIMEN" (23)	£300	
477		5s. red (21.8.39)	20·00	2·00
		s. Opt. "SPECIMEN" (23)	£300	
478	**132**	10s. dark blue (30.10.39)	£260	22·00
		aa. Broken stem	£275	75·00
		ab. Blot on scroll	£275	75·00
		ac. Scratch on scroll	£350	£100
		as. Opt. "SPECIMEN" (23)	£500	
478b		10s. ultramarine (30.11.42)	45·00	5·00
		bs. Opt. "SPECIMEN" (30)	£425	
478c		£1 brown (1.10.48)	25·00	26·00
		cs. Opt. "SPECIMEN" (30)	—	
Set of 6			£425	60·00

First Day Covers

21.8.39	5s. (477)	£850
4.9.39	2s.6d. brown (476)	£1800
30.10.39	10s. dark blue (478)	£3250
9.3.42	2s.6d. yellow-green (476b)	£1750
30.11.42	10s. ultramarine (478b)	£3750
1.10.48	£1 (478c)	£325

The 10s. dark blue was pre-released in Northern Ireland on 3 October 1939.

134 Queen Victoria and King George VI

(Des H. L. Palmer)

1940 (6 May). *Centenary of First Adhesive Postage Stamps.* W **127**. P 14½×14.

479	**134**	½d. green	30	75
		s. Opt. "SPECIMEN" (23, 30)	—	
480		1d. scarlet	1·00	75
		s. Opt. "SPECIMEN" (23, 30)	—	
481		1½d. red-brown	50	1·50
		s. Opt. "SPECIMEN" (23, 30)	—	
482		2d. orange	1·00	75
		a. Bisected (on cover)	†	40·00
		s. Opt. "SPECIMEN" (23, 30)	—	
483		2½d. ultramarine	2·25	50
		s. Opt. "SPECIMEN" (23, 30)	—	
484		3d. violet	3·00	3·50
		s. Opt. "SPECIMEN" (23, 30)	—	
Set of 6			8·75	5·25
First Day Cover				55·00

No. 482a was authorised for use on Guernsey from 27 December 1940 until February 1941.

1941–42. Head as Nos. 462/7, but with lighter background to provide a more economic use of the printing ink. W **127**. P 15×14.

485	**128**	½d. pale green (1.9.41)	30	30
		a. Tête-bêche (horiz pair)	£18000	
		b. Imperf (pair)	£8500	
		c. Booklet pane. No 485×6 (3.42)	30·00	
		cw. Ditto. Wmk inverted	45·00	
		d. Booklet pane. No 485×4 (1948)	—	
		e. Booklet pane. No 485×2 (12.47)	15·00	
		s. Opt. "SPECIMEN" (23)	—	
		Wi. Watermark inverted	4·00	50
486		1d. pale scarlet (11.8.41)	30	30
		a. Watermark sideways (10.42)	5·00	4·50
		b. Imperf (pair)	£8000	
		c. Imperf three sides (horiz pair)	£8500	
		d. Booklet pane. No 486×4 (1948)	—	
		e. Booklet pane. No 486×2 (12.47)	40·00	
		s. Opt. "SPECIMEN" (23)	—	
487		1½d. pale red-brown (28.9.42)	60	80
		a. Booklet pane. No 487×4 (1948)	—	
		b. Booklet pane. No 487×2 (12.47)	15·00	
		s. Opt. "SPECIMEN" (23)	—	
488		2d. pale orange (6.10.41)	50	50
		a. Watermark sideways (6.42)	28·00	19·00
		b. Tête-bêche (horiz pair)	£18000	
		c. Imperf (pair)	£7500	
		d. Imperf pane*	£20000	
		e. Booklet pane. No 488×6 (3.42)	30·00	
		ew. Ditto. Wmk inverted	30·00	
		s. Opt. "SPECIMEN" (23)	—	
		Wi. Watermark inverted	4·00	1·00
489		2½d. light ultramarine (21.7.41)	30	30
		a. Watermark sideways (8.42)	15·00	12·00
		b. Tête-bêche (horiz pair)	£18000	
		c. Imperf (pair)	£4800	
		d. Imperf pane*	£15000	
		e. Imperf three sides (horiz pair)	£7500	
		f. Booklet pane. No 489×6 (3.42)	20·00	
		fw. Ditto. Wmk inverted	20·00	
		s. Opt. "SPECIMEN" (23)	—	
		Wi. Watermark inverted	1·50	1·00
490		3d. pale violet (3.11.41)	2·50	1·00
		s. Opt. "SPECIMEN" (32)	—	
Set of 6			3·50	2·75

First Day Covers

21.7.41	2½d. (489)	45·00
11.8.41	1d. (486)	22·00
1.9.41	½d. (485)	22·00
6.10.41	2d. (488)	60·00
3.11.41	3d. (490)	£110
28.9.42	1½d. (487)	55·00

135

136

Extra porthole aft (Cyl. 11 No dot, R. 16/1)

Extra porthole fore (Cyl. 8 Dot, R. 5/6)

Seven berries (Cyl. 4 No dot, R. 12/5)

(Des H. L. Palmer (T **135**) and R. Stone (T **136**))

1946 (11 June). *Peace. W* **127**. *P* 15×14.

491	**135**	2½d. ultramarine		20	20
		a. Extra porthole aft		95·00	
		b. Extra porthole fore		£120	
		s. Opt. "SPECIMEN" (30)		—	
492	**136**	3d. violet		20	50
		a. Seven berries		50·00	
		s. Opt. "SPECIMEN" (30)		—	
Set of 2				40	50
First Day Cover					65·00

137

138 King George VI and Queen Elizabeth

(Des G. Knipe and Joan Hassall from photographs by Dorothy Wilding)

1948 (26 Apr). *Royal Silver Wedding. W* **127**. *P* 15×14 (2½d.) or 14×15 (£1).

493	**137**	2½d. ultramarine		35	20
		s. Opt. "SPECIMEN" (30)		—	
494	**138**	£1 blue		40·00	40·00
		s. Opt. "SPECIMEN" (30)		—	
Set of 2				40·00	40·00
First Day Cover					£425

1948 (10 May). Stamps of 1d. and 2½d. showing seaweed-gathering were on sale at eight Head Post Offices in Great Britain, but were primarily for use in the Channel Islands and are listed there (see Nos. C1/2, after Royal Mail Post & Go Stamps).

139 Globe and Laurel Wreath

140 "Speed"

141 Olympic Symbol

142 Winged Victory

White blob on Lands End (Cyl. 3 No dot R. 7/3)

Spot below "9" (Cyl. 3 No dot R. 8/4)

Crown flaw (Cyl. 1 No dot, R. 20/2, later retouched)

(Des P. Metcalfe (T **139**), A. Games (T **140**), S. D. Scott (T **141**) and E. Dulac (T **142**))

1948 (29 July). *Olympic Games. W* **127**. *P* 15×14.

495	**139**	2½d. ultramarine		50	10
		s. Opt. "SPECIMEN" (30)		£450	

496	**140**	3d. violet		50	50
		a. Crown flaw		75·00	
		s. Opt. "SPECIMEN" (30)		£450	
497	**141**	6d. bright purple		3·25	75
		s. Opt. "SPECIMEN" (30)		£450	
498	**142**	1s. brown		4·50	2·00
		a. White blob on Lands End		95·00	
		b. Spot below "9"		95·00	
		s. Opt. "SPECIMEN" (30)		£450	
Set of 4				8·00	3·00
First Day Cover					45·00

143 Two Hemispheres

144 UPU Monument, Berne

145 Goddess Concordia, Globe and Points of Compass

146 Posthorn and Globe

Lake in Asia (Cyl. 3 Dot, R. 14/1)

Lake in India (Cyl. 2 No dot, R. 8/2)

Retouched background to "1/-" (R. 8/5)

(Des Mary Adshead (T **143**), P. Metcalfe (T **144**), H. Fleury (T **145**) and Hon. G. R. Bellew (T **146**))

1949 (10 Oct). *75th Anniv of Universal Postal Union. W* **127**. *P* 15×14.

499	**143**	2½d. ultramarine		25	10
		a. Lake in Asia		£140	
		b. Lake in India		£100	
		s. Opt. "SPECIMEN" (31)		—	
500	**144**	3d. violet		25	50
		s. Opt. "SPECIMEN" (31)		—	
501	**145**	6d. bright purple		50	75
		s. Opt. "SPECIMEN" (31)		—	
502	**146**	1s. brown		1·00	1·25
		a. Retouched background to "1/-"		75·00	
		s. Opt. "SPECIMEN" (31)		—	
Set of 4				1·50	2·50
First Day Cover					80·00

1950–52. 4d. as No. 468 and others as Nos. 485/9, but colours changed. *W* **127**. *P* 15×14.

503	**128**	½d. pale orange (3.5.51)		30	30
		a. Imperf (pair)		£7000	
		b. *Tête-bêche* (horiz pair)		£20000	
		c. Imperf pane*		£18000	
		d. Booklet pane. No 503×6 (5.51)		10·00	
		dw. Ditto. Wmk inverted		10·00	
		e. Booklet pane. No 503×4 (5.51)		15·00	
		ew. Ditto. Wmk inverted		15·00	
		f. Booklet pane. No 503×2 (5.51)		15·00	
		Wi. Watermark inverted		50	50
504		1d. light ultramarine (3.5.51)		30	30
		a. Watermark sideways (5.51)		1·10	1·25
		b. Imperf (pair)		£4800	
		c. Imperf three sides (horiz pair)		£6500	
		d. Booklet pane. Three stamps plus three printed labels (3.52)		18·00	

	dw. Ditto. Wmk inverted	18·00		
	e. Ditto. Partial *tête-bêche* pane	£8500		
	f. Booklet pane. No 504×6 (1.53)	40·00		
	fw. Ditto. Wmk inverted	45·00		
	g. Booklet pane. No 504×4 (5.51)	20·00		
	gw. Ditto. Wmk inverted	35·00		
	h. Booklet pane. No 504×2 (5.51)	15·00		
	Wi. Watermark inverted	4·50	2·50	
505	1½d. pale green (3.5.51)	65	60	
	a. Watermark sideways (9.51)	3·25	5·00	
	b. Booklet pane. No 505×6 (3.52)	30·00		
	bw. Ditto. Wmk inverted	40·00		
	c. Booklet pane. No 505×4 (5.51)	15·00		
	cw. Ditto. Wmk inverted	20·00		
	d. Booklet pane. No 505×2 (5.51)	15·00		
	Wi. Watermark inverted	6·00	1·00	
506	2d. pale red-brown (3.5.51)	75	40	
	a. Watermark sideways (5.51)	1·75	2·00	
	b. *Tête-bêche* (horiz pair)	£18000		
	c. Imperf three sides (horiz pair)	£8000		
	d. Booklet pane. No 506×6 (5.51)	40·00		
	dw. Ditto. Wmk inverted	25·00		
	Wi. Watermark inverted	6·00	6·50	
507	2½d. pale scarlet (3.5.51)	60	40	
	a. Watermark sideways (5.51)	1·75	1·75	
	b. *Tête-bêche* (horiz pair)			
	c. Booklet pane. No 507×6 (5.51)	8·00		
	cw. Ditto. Wmk inverted	10·00		
	Wi. Watermark inverted	2·00	1·25	
508 **129**	4d. light ultramarine (2.10.50)	2·00	1·75	
	a. Double impression	†	£7000	
Set of 6		4·00	3·25	

* BOOKLET ERRORS. Those listed as "imperf panes" show one row of perforations either at the top or at the bottom of the pane of 6.
No. 504c is perforated at foot only and occurs in the same sheet as No. 504b.
No. 506c is also perforated at foot only.

First Day Covers

2.10.50	4d. (508)		£120
3.5.51	½d., 1d., 1½d., 2d., 2½d. (503/7)		55·00

147 H.M.S. *Victory*

148 White Cliffs of Dover

149 St. George and the Dragon

150 Royal Coat of Arms

(Des Mary Adshead (T **147/8**), P. Metcalfe (T **149/50**).
Recess Waterlow)

1951 (3 May). W **133**. *P* 11×12.

509	**147**	2s.6d. yellow-green	7·50	1·00
		s. Opt. "SPECIMEN" (30)	£1000	
510	**148**	5s. red	35·00	1·00
		s. Opt. "SPECIMEN" (30)	£1000	
511	**149**	10s. ultramarine	15·00	7·50
		s. Opt. "SPECIMEN" (30)	£1000	
512	**150**	£1 brown	45·00	18·00
		s. Opt. "SPECIMEN" (30)	£1000	
Set of 4			£100	25·00
First Day Cover				£950

151 "Commerce and Prosperity"

152 Festival Symbol

(Des E. Dulac (T **151**), A. Games (T **152**))

1951 (3 May). Festival of Britain. W **127**. *P* 15×14.

513	**151**	2½d. scarlet	20	15
514	**152**	4d. ultramarine	30	35
Set of 2			40	40
First Day Cover				38·00

Stanley Gibbons
Great Britain Department

BY APPOINTMENT TO
HER MAJESTY THE QUEEN
PHILATELISTS
STANLEY GIBBONS LTD
LONDON

Stanley Gibbons, a name synonymous with quality.

Ever since the birth of our hobby Stanley Gibbons has been at the forefront of GB philately and we invite collectors access to one of the finest GB stocks in the world by registering for our renowned free monthly brochure. Whatever your budget or collecting interests you will find a range of the highest quality material for the discerning collector.

Simply contact Mark Facey on **020 7557 4424** email **mfacey@stanleygibbons.com**
or Michael Barrell on **020 7557 4448** email **mbarrell@stanleygibbons.com** to register

Est 1856

STANLEY GIBBONS

Proud PTS members

Stanley Gibbons
399 Strand, London, WC2R 0LX
+44 (0)20 7836 8444
www.stanleygibbons.com

Queen Elizabeth II

6 February 1952

Further detailed information on the stamps of Queen Elizabeth II will be found in Volumes 3, 4 and 5 of the Stanley Gibbons *Great Britain Specialised Catalogue*.

153 Tudor Crown	154

155	156	157

158	159	160

Queen Elizabeth II and National Emblems

1½d. Extra white dot below "d" at left (Cyl. 13 dot, R.17/10

I	II

Two types of the 2½d.

Type I:— In the frontal cross of the diadem, the top line is only half the width of the cross.

Type II:— The top line extends to the full width of the cross and there are signs of strengthening in other parts of the diadem.

(Des Enid Marx (T **154**), M. Farrar-Bell (T **155/6**), G. Knipe (T **157**), Mary Adshead (T **158**), E. Dulac (T **159/60**). Portrait by Dorothy Wilding)

1952–54. *W* **153**. *P* 15×14.

515	**154**	½d. orange-red (31.8.53)	25	15
		Wi. Watermark inverted (3.54)	2·00	2·00
516		1d. ultramarine (31.8.53)	30	20
		a. Booklet pane. Three stamps plus three printed labels	40·00	
		Wi. Watermark inverted (3.54)	6·00	3·00
517		1½d. green (5.12.52)	25	20
		a. Watermark sideways (15.10.54)	1·20	1·20
		b. Imperf pane*		
		c. Extra dot	28·00	
		Wi. Watermark inverted (5.53)	1·30	1·30
518		2d. red-brown (31.8.53)	30	20

		a. Watermark sideways (8.10.54)	2·00	2·00
		Wi. Watermark inverted (3.54)	30·00	22·00
519	**155**	2½d. carmine-red (Type I) (5.12.52)	30	15
		a. Watermark sideways (15.11.54)	12·00	12·00
		b. Type II (booklets) (5.53)	1·30	1·30
		bWi. Watermark inverted (5.53)	1·00	1·00
520		3d. deep lilac (18.1.54)	1·50	90
521	**156**	4d. ultramarine (2.11.53)	3·25	1·30
522	**157**	5d. brown (6.7.53)	1·00	3·50
523		6d. reddish purple (18.1.54)	4·00	1·00
		a. Imperf three sides (pair)	£3750	
524		7d. bright green (18.1.54)	9·50	5·50
525	**158**	8d. magenta (6.7.53)	1·25	85
526		9d. bronze-green (8.2.54)	23·00	4·75
527		10d. Prussian blue (8.2.54)	18·00	4·75
528		11d. brown-purple (8.2.54)	35·00	15·00
529	**159**	1s. bistre-brown (6.7.53)	80	50
530	**160**	1s.3d. green (2.11.53)	4·50	3·25
531		1s.6d. grey-blue (2.11.53)	14·00	3·75
Set of 17			£100	40·00

See also Nos. 540/56, 561/6, 570/94 and 599/618a.

* BOOKLET ERRORS. This pane of 6 stamps is completely imperf (see No. 540a, etc).

Stamps with *sideways watermark* come from left-side delivery coils and stamps with *inverted watermark* are from booklets.

For stamps as Types **154/5** and **157/60** with face values in decimal currency see Nos. 2031/3, 2258/9, **MS**2326, **MS**2367 and 2378/9.

First Day Covers

5.12.52	1½d., 2½d. (517, 519)	28·00
6.7.53	5d., 8d., 1s. (522, 525, 529)	60·00
31.8.53	½d., 1d., 2d. (515/16, 518)	60·00
2.11.53	4d., 1s.3d., 1s.6d. (521, 530/1)	£200
18.1.54	3d., 6d., 7d. (520, 523/4)	£125
8.2.54	9d., 10d., 11d. (526/8)	£250

161	162

163	164

(Des E. Fuller (2½d.), M. Goaman (4d.), E. Dulac (1s.3d.), M. Farrar-Bell (1s.6d.). Portrait (except 1s.3d.) by Dorothy Wilding)

1953 (3 June). *Coronation*. W **153**. *P* 15×14.

532	**161**	2½d. carmine-red	20	25
533	**162**	4d. ultramarine	1·10	1·90
534	**163**	1s.3d. deep yellow-green	5·00	3·00
535	**164**	1s.6d. deep grey-blue	10·00	4·75
Set of 4			16·00	9·00
First Day Cover				80·00

For a £1 value as Type **163** see Nos. **MS**2147 and 2380.

165 St. Edward's Crown

166 Carrickfergus Castle

167 Caernarvon Castle

168 Edinburgh Castle

169 Windsor Castle

(Des L. Lamb. Portrait by Dorothy Wilding. Recess Waterlow (until 31.12.57) and De La Rue (subsequently))

1955–58. W **165**. P 11×12.

536	**166**	2s.6d. black-brown (23.9.55)	15·00	2·00
		a. De La Rue printing (17.7.58)	30·00	2·50
		Wi. Watermark inverted	†	£3000
537	**167**	5s. rose-carmine (23.9.55)	40·00	4·00
		a. De La Rue printing (30.4.58)	65·00	10·00
538	**168**	10s. ultramarine (1.9.55)	90·00	14·00
		a. De La Rue printing. Dull ultramarine (25.4.58)	£225	22·00
539	**169**	£1 black (1.9.55)	£140	35·00
		a. De La Rue printing (28.4.58)	£350	65·00
Set of 4 (Nos. 536/9)			£250	50·00
Set of 4 (Nos. 536a/9a)			£600	90·00
First Day Cover (538/9)				£850
First Day Cover (536/7)				£650

See also Nos. 595/8a & 759/62.

On 1 January 1958, the contract for printing the high values, T **166** to **169**, was transferred to De La Rue & Co, Ltd. The work of the two printers is very similar, but the following notes will be helpful to those attempting to identify Waterlow and De La Rue stamps of the W **165** issue.

The De La Rue sheets are printed in pairs and have a -│ or │-shaped guide-mark at the centre of one side-margin, opposite the middle row of perforations, indicating left and right-hand sheets respectively.

The Waterlow sheets have a small circle (sometimes crossed) instead of a "│-" and this is present in both side-margins opposite the 6th row of stamps, though one is sometimes trimmed off. Short dashes are also present in the perforation gutter between the marginal stamps marking the middle of the four sides and a cross is at the centre of the sheet. The four corners of the sheet have two lines forming a right-angle as trimming marks, but some are usually trimmed off. All these gutter marks and sheet trimming marks are absent in the De La Rue printings. De La Rue used the Waterlow die and no alterations were made to it, so that no difference exists in the design or its size, but the making of new plates at first resulted in slight but measurable variations in the width of the gutters between stamps, particularly the horizontal, as follows:

	Waterlow	De La Rue
Horiz gutters, mm	3.8 to 4.0	3.4 to 3.8

Later D.L.R. plates were however less distinguishable in this respect.

For a short time in 1959 the D.L.R. 2s.6d. appeared with one dot in the bottom margin below the first stamp. It is possible to sort singles with reasonable certainty by general characteristics. The individual lines of the D.L.R. impression are cleaner and devoid of the whiskers of colour of Waterlow's, and the whole impression lighter and softer.

Owing to the closer setting of the horizontal rows the strokes of the perforating comb are closer; this results in the topmost tooth on each side of De La Rue stamps being narrower than the corresponding teeth in Waterlow's which were more than normally broad.

Shades also help. The 2s.6d. D.L.R. is a warmer, more chocolate shade than the blackish brown of Waterlow; the 5s. a lighter red with less carmine than Waterlow's; the 10s. more blue and less ultramarine; the £1 less intense black.

The paper of D.L.R. printings is uniformly white, identical with that of Waterlow printings from February 1957 onwards, but earlier Waterlow printings are on paper which is creamy by comparison.

In this and later issues of T **166/9** the dates of issue given for changes of watermark or paper are those on which supplies were first sent by the Supplies Department to Postmasters.

A used example of No. 538a has been reported with watermark inverted.

1½d. Two white dots extending upwards from shamrock at left appearing as rabbit's ears. Occurs in booklets in position 2 or 5 in pane of 6

2½d. "Swan's head" flaw. Top of "2" is extended and curled. Occurs in booklets in positions 1 and 4 in pane of 6

1955–58. W **165**. P 15×14.

540	**154**	½d. orange-red (booklets 8.55, sheets 12.12.55)	20	15
		a. Part perf pane*	£5250	
		Wi. Watermark inverted (9.55)	45	40
541		1d. ultramarine (19.9.55)	30	15
		a. Booklet pane. Three stamps plus three printed labels	18·00	
		b. Tête-bêche (horiz pair)	—	
		Wi. Watermark inverted (9.55)	65	60
542		1½d. green (booklet 8.55, sheets 11.10.55)	25	30
		a. Watermark sideways (7.3.56)	35	70
		b. Tête-bêche (horiz pair)	—	
		c. Extra dot	28·00	
		d. "Rabbit's ears"	42·00	
		Wi. Watermark inverted (8.55)	75	70
543		2d. red-brown (6.9.55)	25	35
		aa. Imperf between (vert pair)	£4750	
		a. Watermark sideways (31.7.56)	55	70
		ab. Imperf between (horiz pair)	£4750	
		Wi. Watermark inverted (9.55)	11·00	9·00
543b		2d. light red-brown (17.10.56)	30	20
		ba. Tête-bêche (horiz pair)	—	
		bb. Imperf pane*	£6000	
		bc. Part perf pane*	£6000	
		bWi. Watermark inverted (1.57)	9·00	7·00
		d. Watermark sideways (5.3.57)	8·00	7·00
544	**155**	2½d. carmine-red (Type I) (28.9.55)	30	25
		a. Watermark sideways (Type I) (23.3.56)	1·50	1·80
		b. Type II (booklets 9.55, sheets 1957)	45	45
		ba. Tête-bêche (horiz pair)	—	
		bb. Imperf pane*	—	
		bc. Part perf pane*	£5250	
		bd. "Swan's head" flaw	95·00	
		bWi. Watermark inverted (9.55)	55	70
545		3d. deep lilac (17.7.56)	40	25
		aa. Tête-bêche (horiz pair)	£3000	
		a. Imperf three sides (pair)	£2750	
		b. Watermark sideways (22.11.57)	18·00	17·00
		Wi. Watermark inverted (1.10.57)	1·25	1·25
546	**156**	4d. ultramarine (14.11.55)	1·30	45
547	**157**	5d. brown (21.9.55)	6·00	6·00
548		6d. reddish purple (20.12.55)	4·50	1·20
		aa. Imperf three sides (pair)	£5250	
		a. Deep claret (8.5.58)	4·50	1·40
		ab. Imperf three sides (pair)	£5250	
549		7d. bright green (23.4.56)	50·00	10·00
550	**158**	8d. magenta (21.12.55)	7·00	1·30
551		9d. bronze-green (15.12.55)	20·00	2·75
552		10d. Prussian blue (22.9.55)	20·00	2·75
553		11d. brown-purple (28.10.55)	1·00	1·10
554	**159**	1s. bistre-brown (3.11.55)	22·00	65
555		1s.3d. green (27.3.56)	30·00	1·60
556	**160**	1s.6d. grey-blue (27.3.56)	23·00	1·60
Set of 18			£160	27·00

The dates given for Nos. 540/556 are those on which they were first issued by the Supplies Dept to postmasters.

In December 1956 a completely imperforate sheet of No. 543b was noticed by clerks in a Kent post office, one of whom purchased it against P.O. regulations. In view of this irregularity we do not consider it properly issued.

Types of 2½d. In this issue, in 1957, Type II formerly only found in stamps from booklets, began to replace Type I on sheet stamps.

*BOOKLET ERRORS. Those listed as "imperf panes" show one row of perforations either at top or bottom of the booklet pane; those as "part perf panes" have one row of 3 stamps imperf on three sides.

For Nos. 542 and 553 in Presentation Pack, see after No. 586.

170 Scout Badge and "Rolling Hitch"

171 "Scouts coming to Britain"

178 Welsh Dragon

172 Globe within a Compass

(Des Mary Adshead (2½d.), P. Keely (4d.), W. H. Brown (1s.3d.))

1957 (1 Aug). *World Scout Jubilee Jamboree.* W **165**. P 15×14.

557	**170**	2½d. carmine-red	50	50
558	**171**	4d. ultramarine	75	1·50
559	**172**	1s.3d. green	5·50	4·50
Set of 3			6·00	5·75
First Day Cover				28·00

3d. Short scale (Cyl. 2 Dot, R.1/1)   **3d.** Shoulder flaw (Cyl. 2 Dot, R. 12/2)

(Des R. Stone (3d.), W. H. Brown (6d.), P. Keely (1s.3d.))

1958 (18 July). *Sixth British Empire and Commonwealth Games,* Cardiff. W **165**. P 15×14.

567	**176**	3d. deep lilac	20	20
		a. Short scale	40·00	
		b. Shoulder flaw	40·00	
568	**177**	6d. reddish purple	60	45
569	**178**	1s.3d. green	2·25	2·50
Set of 3			2·50	2·75
First Day Cover				85·00

173

½d. to 1½d., 2½d., 3d. 2d.
Graphite line arrangements
(Stamps viewed from back)

(Adapted F. Langfield)

1957 (12 Sept). *46th Inter-Parliamentary Union Conference.* W **165**. P 15×14.

560	**173**	4d. ultramarine	2·00	1·50
First Day Cover				£150

GRAPHITE-LINED ISSUES. These were used in connection with automatic sorting machinery, first introduced experimentally at Southampton. The graphite lines are printed in black on the back, beneath the gum; two lines per stamp, except for the 2d. In November 1959 phosphor bands were introduced (see notes after No. 598).

1d. Extra stop before "1d." at right. Occurs in sideways delivery coils (Roll No. 2). This was retouched on No. 571.

1d. Stop below "d" at left missing. Occurs on sideways delivery coils (Roll No. 3). The dot was added for No. 571.

1957 (19 Nov). Graphite-lined issue. Two graphite lines on the back, except 2d. value, which has one line. W **165**. P 15×14.

561	**154**	½d. orange-red	50	40
562		1d. ultramarine	70	60
		a. Extra stop	40·00	
		b. Stop omitted	40·00	
563		1½d. green	2·00	1·75
		a. Both lines at left	£1600	£600
564		2d. light red-brown	2·40	2·40
		a. Line at left	£700	£250
565	**155**	2½d. carmine-red (Type II)	8·50	7·00
566		3d. deep lilac	1·40	1·20
Set of 6			14·00	12·00
First Day Cover				90·00

No. 564a results from a misplacement of the line and horizontal pairs exist showing one stamp without line. No. 563a results from a similar misplacement. See also Nos. 587/94.

176 Welsh Dragon

177 Flag and Games Emblem

179 Multiple Crowns

½d. "d" at right joined to shamrock by white line. Occurs on vertical delivery coils (Roll No. 11).

1958–65. W **179**. P 15×14.

570	**154**	½d. orange-red (25.11.58)	10	10
		a. Watermark sideways (26.5.61)	75	75
		c. Part perf pane*	£4500	
		d. "d" joined to shamrock	30·00	
		Wi. Watermark inverted (11.58)	1·50	1·50
		k. Chalk-surfaced paper (15.7.63)	2·50	2·75
		kWi. Watermark inverted	2·75	3·00
		l. Booklet pane. No. 570a×4	7·50	
		m. Booklet pane. No. 570k×3 *se-tenant* with 574k	9·00	
		n. Booklet pane. No. 570a×2 *se-tenant* with 574l×2 (1.7.64)	2·25	
571		1d. ultramarine (booklets 11.58, sheets 24.3.59)	10	10
		aa. Imperf (vert pair from coil)		
		a. Watermark sideways (26.5.61)	1·50	1·50
		b. Part perf pane*	£5000	
		c. Imperf pane	£6500	
		d. *Tête-bêche* (horiz pair)		
		Wi. Watermark inverted (11.58)	50	50
		l. Booklet pane. No. 571a×4	12·00	
		m. Booklet pane. No. 571a×2 *se-tenant* with 575a×2 (1d. values at left) (16.8.65)	12·00	
		ma. Ditto. 1d. values at right	13·00	
572		1½d. green (booklets 12.58, sheets 30.8.60)	10	15
		a. Imperf three sides (horiz strip of 3)	£8500	
		b. Watermark sideways (26.5.61)	9·00	9·00
		c. *Tête-bêche* (horiz pair)		
		Wi. Watermark inverted (12.58)	1·50	1·25
		l. Booklet pane. No. 572b×4	40·00	
573		2d. light red-brown (4.12.58)	10	10
		a. Watermark sideways (3.4.59)	1·00	1·00
		Wi. Watermark inverted (10.4.61)	£140	70·00
574	**155**	2½d. carmine-red (Type II) (booklets 11.58, sheets 15.9.59)	10	20
		a. Imperf strip of 3		
		b. *Tête-bêche* (horiz pair)	—	
		c. Imperf pane*	—	
		ca. Part perf pane	£3750	

	d. "Swan's head" flaw	£100		
	Wi. Watermark inverted (Type II)			
	(11.58)	4·50	3·00	
	e. Watermark sideways (Type I)			
	(10.11.60)	40	60	
	ea. Imperf strip of 6			
	f. Type I (wmk upright) (4.10.61)	70	70	
	k. Chalk-surfaced paper (Type II)			
	(15.7.63)	50	80	
	kWi. Do. Watermark inverted (15.7.63) ..	75	1·30	
	l. Watermark sideways (Type II)			
	(1.7.64)	70	1·30	
575	3d. deep lilac (booklets 11.58, sheets			
	8.12.58)	20	15	
	a. Watermark sideways (24.10.58)	50	55	
	b. Imperf pane*	£4250		
	c. Part perf pane*	£4000		
	d. Phantom "R" (Cyl 41 no dot)	£375		
	Eda. Do. First retouch	30·00		
	Edb. Do. Second retouch	30·00		
	e. Phantom "R" (Cyl 37 no dot)	55·00		
	Eea. Do. Retouch	20·00		
	Wi. Watermark inverted (11.58)	50	55	
	l. Booklet pane. No. 575a×4			
	(26.5.61)	3·25		
576 **156**	4d. ultramarine (29.10.58)	45	35	
	a. Deep ultramarine†† (28.4.65)	15	15	
	ab. Watermark sideways (31.5.65)	70	55	
	ac. Imperf pane*	£5500		
	ad. Part perf pane*	£4500		
	ae. Double impression	£3000		
	al. Booklet pane. No. 576ab×4			
	(16.8.65)	3·25		
	aWi. Watermark inverted (21.6.65)	60	75	
577	4½d. chestnut (9.2.59)	10	25	
	Ea. Phantom frame	£100		
578 **157**	5d. brown (10.11.58)	30	40	
579	6d. deep claret (23.12.58)	30	25	
	a. Imperf three sides (pair)	£4000		
	b. Imperf (pair)	£4500		
580	7d. brt green (26.11.58)	50	45	
581 **158**	8d. magenta (4.2.60)	60	40	
582	9d. bronze-green (24.3.59)	60	40	
583	10d. Prussian blue (18.11.58)	1·00	50	
584 **159**	1s. bistre-brown (30.10.58)	75	30	
585	1s.3d. green (17.6.59)	75	30	
586 **160**	1s.6d. grey-blue (16.12.58)	5·00	40	
	Set of 17 (one of each value)	9·00	4·25	
	First Day Cover (577)		£250	
	Presentation Pack**	£275		

* **BOOKLET ERROR.** See note after No. 556.

** This was issued in 1960 and comprises Nos. 542, 553, 570/1 and 573/86. It exists in two forms: (a) inscribed "10s6d" for sale in the U.K.; and (b) inscribed "$1.80" for sale in the U.S.A.

†† This "shade" was brought about by making more deeply etched cylinders, resulting in apparent depth of colour in parts of the design. There is no difference in the colour of the ink.

Sideways watermark. The 2d., 2½d., 3d. and 4d. come from coils and the ½d., 1d., 1½d., 2½d., 3d. and 4d. come from booklets. In coil stamps the sideways watermark shows the top of the watermark to the left *as seen from the front of the stamp*. In the *booklet* stamps it comes equally to the left or right.

Nos. 570k and 574k only come from 2s. "Holiday Resort" experimental undated booklets issued in 1963, in which one page contained 1 × 2½d. *se-tenant* with 3×½d. (See No. 570m).

No. 574l comes from coils, and the "Holiday Resort" experimental booklets dated "1964" comprising four panes each containing two of these 2½d. stamps *se-tenant* vertically with two ½d. No. 570a. (See No. 570n).

2½d. imperf. No. 574a comes from a booklet with watermark upright. No. 574da is from a coil with sideways watermark.

No. 574ca is partially perforated at top. Only one example has been recorded, from which the top right stamp has been removed.

No. 574e comes from sheets bearing cylinder number 42 and is also known on vertical delivery coils.

In 1964 No. 575 was printed from cylinder number 70 no dot and dot on an experimental paper which is distinguishable by an additional watermark letter "T" lying on its side, which occurs about four times in the sheet, usually in the side margins, 48,000 sheets were issued.

No. 575 is known imperforate and *tête-bêche*. These came from booklet sheets which were not issued (*price £25 per pair*).

Phantom "R" varieties

179a Nos. 575d and 615a (Cyl 41 no dot)   **179b** No. 575Eda

179c No. 575e (Cyl 37 no dot)

179d Phantom Frame variety Nos. 577Ea and 616Eba

3d. An incomplete marginal rule revealed an "R" on cyls 37 and 41 no dot below R. 20/12. It is more noticeable on cyl 41 because of the wider marginal rule. The "R" on cyl 41 was twice retouched, the first being as illustrated here (No. 575Eda) and traces of the "R" can still be seen in the second retouch.

No. 575d is best collected in a block of 4 or 6 with full margins in order to be sure that it is not 615a with phosphor lines removed.

The retouch on cyl 37 is not easily identified: there is no trace of the "R" but the general appearance of that part of the marginal rule is uneven.

4½d. An incomplete marginal rule revealed a right-angled shaped frame-line on cyl 8 no dot below R. 20/12. It occurs on ordinary and phosphor.

DOLLIS HILL TRIAL STAMPS. From 1957 to 1972 trials were carried out at the Post Office Research Station, Dollis Hill, London, to determine the most efficient method of applying phosphor to stamps in connection with automatic letter sorting. Stamps were frequently applied to "live" mail to test sorting machinery.

The 2d. light red-brown and 3d. deep lilac stamps from these trials exist on unwatermarked paper, *prices from £300 (2d.), £350 (3d.), mint or used*.

WHITER PAPER. On 18 May 1962 the Post Office announced that a whiter paper was being used for the current issue (including Nos. 595/8). This is beyond the scope of this catalogue, but the whiter papers are listed in Vol. 3 of the Stanley Gibbons *Great Britain Specialised Catalogue*.

1958 (24 Nov)–**61**. Graphite-lined issue. Two graphite lines on the back, except 2d. value, which has one line. *W* **179**. *P* 15×14.

587	**154**	½d. orange-red (15.6.59)	9·00	9·00
		Wi. Watermark inverted (4.8.59)	3·25	4·00
588		1d. ultramarine (18.12.58)	2·00	1·50
		a. Misplaced graphite lines (7.61)*	80	1·20
		b. Three graphite lines	65·00	60·00
		Wi. Watermark inverted (4.8.59)	1·50	2·00
589		1½d. green (4.8.59)	90·00	80·00
		Wi. Watermark inverted (4.8.59)	75·00	60·00
590		2d. light red-brown (24.11.58)	10·00	3·50
		a. One line at left	£975	
591	**155**	2½d. carmine-red (Type II) (9.6.59)	12·00	10·00
		Wi. Watermark inverted (21.8.59)	65·00	50·00
592		3d. deep lilac (24.11.58)	90	65
		a. Misplaced graphite lines (5.61)*	£550	£425
		b. One graphite line	£750	£325
		c. Three graphite lines	£150	£120
		Wi. Watermark inverted (4.8.59)	1·00	1·25
593	**156**	4d. ultramarine (29.4.59)	5·50	5·00
		a. Misplaced graphite lines (1961)*	£2400	

594		4½d. chestnut (3.6.59)	6·50	5·00
Set of 8 (cheapest)			£110	70·00

Nos. 587/9 were only issued in booklets or coils (587/8).

* No. 588a (in coils), and Nos. 592a/c and 593a (all in sheets) result from the use of a residual stock of graphite-lined paper. As the use of graphite lines had ceased, the register of the lines in relation to the stamps was of no importance and numerous misplacements occurred - two lines close together, one line only, etc. No. 588a refers to two lines at left or right; No. 592a refers to stamps with two lines only at left and both clear of the perforations No. 592b refers to stamps with a single line and Nos. 588b, 592c and 593a to stamps with two lines at left (with left line down perforations) and traces of a third line down the opposite perforations.

No. 592 Wi was included in 4s.6d. booklets, L15 and L16, dated

April and June 1959. These represent production dates not issue dates.

(Recess D.L.R. (until 31.12.62), then B.W.)

1959–**68**. W **179**. P 11×12.

595	**166**	2s.6d. black-brown (22.7.59)	10·00	75
		Wi. Watermark inverted	—	£3250
		a. B.W. printing (1.7.63)	35	40
		aWi. Watermark inverted	£3250	£280
		k. Chalk-surfaced paper (30.5.68)	50	1·50
596	**167**	5s. scarlet-vermilion (15.6.59)	45·00	2·00
		Wi. Watermark inverted	£9000	£600
		a. B.W. ptg. Red (shades) (3.9.63)	1·20	50
		ab. Printed on the gummed side	£1600	
		aWi. Watermark inverted	£400	£300
597	**168**	10s. blue (21.7.59)	55·00	5·00
		a. B.W. ptg. Bright ultramarine (16.10.63)	4·50	4·50
		aWi. Watermark inverted	—	£3250
598	**169**	£1 black (23.6.59)	£120	12·00
		Wi. Watermark inverted	—	£2500
		a. B.W. printing (14.11.63)	13·00	8·00
		aWi. Watermark inverted	£15000	£3750
		k. Chalk-surfaced paper	£5250	
Set of 4 (Nos. 595/8)			£195	17·00
Set of 4 (Nos. 595a/8a)			15·00	11·00
Presentation Pack (1960)*			£1400	

The B.W. printings have a marginal Plate Number. They are generally more deeply engraved than the D.L.R. showing more of the Diadem detail and heavier lines on Her Majesty's face. The vertical perf is 11.9 to 12 against D.L.R. 11.8.

* This exists in three forms: (a) inscribed "$6.50" for sale in the U.S.A.; (b) without price for sale in the U.K.; (c) inscribed "£1 18s" for sale in the U.K.
See also Nos. 759/62.

PHOSPHOR BAND ISSUES. These are printed on the front and are wider than graphite lines. They are not easy to see but show as broad vertical bands at certain angles to the light.

Values representing the rate for printed papers (and when this was abolished in 1968 for second issue class mail) have one band and others two, three or four bands as stated, according to the size and format.

In the small size stamps the bands are on each side with the single band at left (except where otherwise stated). In the large size commemorative stamps the single band may be at left, centre or right, varying in different designs. The bands are vertical on both horizontal and vertical designs except where otherwise stated.

The phosphor was originally applied typographically but later usually by photogravure and sometimes using flexography, a typographical process using rubber cylinders.

Three different types of phosphor have been used, distinguishable by the colour emitted under an ultra-violet lamp, the first being green, then blue and now violet. Different sized bands are also known. All these are fully listed in Vol. 3 of the Stanley Gibbons Great Britain Specialised Catalogue.

Varieties. Misplaced and missing phosphor bands are known but such varieties are beyond the scope of this Catalogue.

1959 (18 Nov). Phosphor-Graphite issue. Two phosphor bands on front and two graphite lines on back, except 2d. value, which has one band on front and one line on back. (a) W **165**. P 15×14.

599	**154**	½d. orange-red	4·25	4·25
600		1d. ultramarine	11·00	11·00
601		1½d. green	4·50	4·50

(b) W **179**.

605	**154**	2d. light red-brown (1 band)	6·00	4·25
		a. Error. W **165**	£200	£175
606	**155**	2½d. carmine-red (Type II)	22·00	18·00
607		3d. deep lilac	12·00	8·00
608	**156**	4d. ultramarine	20·00	16·00
609		4½d. chestnut	30·00	20·00
Set of 8			£100	80·00
Presentation Pack			£300	

Examples of the 2½d., No. 606, exist showing watermark W **165** in error. It is believed that phosphor-graphite stamps of this value with this watermark were not used by the public for postal purposes.

The Presentation Pack was issued in 1960 and comprises two each of Nos. 599/609. It exists in two forms: (a) inscribed "3s 8d" for sale in the U.K. and (b) inscribed "50c" for sale in the U.S.A.

1960 (22 June)–**67**. Phosphor issue. Two phosphor bands on front, except where otherwise stated. W **179**. P 15×14.

610	**154**	½d. orange-red	10	15
		a. Watermark sideways (14.7.61)	15·00	15·00
		b. "d" joined to shamrock	25·00	
		Wi. Watermark inverted (14.8.60)	1·50	1·50
		l. Booklet pane. No. 610a×4	45·00	
611		1d. ultramarine	10	10
		a. Watermark sideways (14.7.61)	1·10	1·10
		Wi. Watermark inverted (14.8.60)	65	65
		l. Booklet pane. No. 611a×4	10·00	
		m. Booklet pane. No. 611a×2 se-tenant with 615d×2† (16.8.65)	18·00	
		ma. Booklet pane. No. 611a×2 se-tenant with 615dEa×2 (16.8.65)	18·00	
		n. Booklet pane. No. 611a×2 se-tenant with 615b×2†† (11.67)	10·00	
612		1½d. green	15	15
		a. Watermark sideways (14.7.61)	18·00	18·00
		Wi. Watermark inverted (14.8.60)	25·00	22·00
		l. Booklet pane. No. 612a×4	45·00	
613		2d. light red-brown (1 band)	22·00	22·00
613a		2d. light red-brown (2 bands) (4.10.61)	10	15
		aa. Imperf three sides*** (pair)	—	
		ab. Watermark sideways (6.4.67)	1·00	1·00
614	**155**	2½d. carmine-red (Type II) (2 bands)*	40	30
		Wi. Watermark inverted (14.8.60)	£170	£140
614a		2½d. carmine-red (Type II) (1 band) (4.10.61)	60	75
		aWi. Watermark inverted (3.62)	50·00	42·00
614b		2½d. carmine-red (Type I) (1 band) (4.10.61)	45·00	40·00
615		3d. deep lilac (2 bands)	60	55
		aa. Phantom "R" (Cyl 41 no dot)	55·00	
		Wi. Watermark inverted (14.7.61)	50	90
		a. Imperf three sides (horiz pair)	£2000	
		b. Watermark sideways (14.8.61)	1·80	1·80
		l. Booklet pane. No. 615b×4	25·00	
615c		3d. deep lilac (1 band at right) (29.4.65)	60	55
		cEa. Band at left	60	70
		cWi. Watermark inverted (band at right) (2.67)	8·00	7·00
		cWia. Watermark inverted (band at left) (2.67)	80·00	80·00
		d. Watermark sideways (band at right) (16.8.65)	5·50	5·00
		dEa. Watermark sideways (band at left)	5·50	5·00
		e. One centre band (8.12.66)	40	45
		eWi. Watermark inverted (8.67)	4·00	4·00
		ea. Wmk sideways (19.6.67)	1·00	1·00
616	**156**	4d. ultramarine	3·50	3·50
		a. Deep ultramarine (28.4.65)	25	25
		aa. Part perf pane	£5500	
		ab. Wmk sideways	1·10	1·10
		aWi. Watermark inverted (21.6.65)	75	75
		al. Booklet pane. No. 616ab×4	2·50	
616b		4½d. chestnut (13.9.61)	55	30
		Eba. Phantom frame	£100	
616c	**157**	5d. brown (9.6.67)	55	35
617		6d. purple	55	30
617a		7d. bright green (15.2.67)	70	50
617b	**158**	8d. magenta (28.6.67)	70	55
617c		9d. bronze-green (29.12.66)	70	65
617d		10d. Prussian blue (30.12.66)	1·00	1·00
617e	**159**	1s. bistre-brown (28.6.67)	1·00	35
618		1s.3d. green	1·90	2·50
618a	**160**	1s.6d. grey-blue (12.12.66)	2·00	2·00
Set of 17 (one of each value)			10·50	8·00

The automatic facing equipment was brought into use on 6 July 1960 but the phosphor stamps may have been released a few days earlier.

The stamps with watermark sideways are from booklets except Nos. 613ab and 615ea which are from coils. No. 616ab comes from both booklets and coils.

No. 615a. See footnote after No. 586.

* No. 614 with two bands on the creamy paper was originally from cylinder 50 dot and no dot. When the change in postal rates took place in 1965 it was reissued from cylinder 57 dot and no dot on the whiter paper. Some of these latter were also released in error in districts of S.E. London in September 1964. The shade of the reissue is slightly more carmine.

*** This comes from the bottom row of a sheet which is imperf at bottom and both sides.

† Booklet pane No. 611m shows the 1d. stamps at left and No. 611ma the 1d. stamps at right.

†† Booklet pane No. 611n comes from 2s. booklets of January and March 1968. The two bands on the 3d. stamp were intentional because of the technical difficulties in producing one band and two band stamps se-tenant.

The Phosphor-Graphite stamps had the phosphor applied by typography but the Phosphor issue can be divided into those with the phosphor applied typographically and others where it was applied by photogravure. Moreover the photogravure form can be further divided into those which phosphoresce green and others which phosphoresce blue under ultra-violet light. From 1965 violet phosphorescence was introduced in place of the blue. All these are fully listed in Vol. 3 of the Stanley Gibbons *Great Britain Specialised Catalogue*.

Unlike previous one-banded phosphor stamps, No. 615c has a broad band extending over two stamps so that alternate stamps have the band at left or right (same prices either way). No. 615cWi comes from the 10s phosphor booklet of February 1967 and No. 615eWi comes from the 10s. phosphor booklets of August 1967 and February 1968.

Nos. 615a (Phantom "R") and 615Eba (Phantom frame), see illustrations following No. 586.

180 Postboy of 1660   **181** Posthorn of 1660

Broken mane (Cyl. 1 No dot, R. 17/2)

(Des R. Stone (3d.), Faith Jaques (1s.3d.))

1960 (7 July). *Tercentenary of Establishment of General Letter Office.* W 179 (sideways on 1s.3d.). *P* 15×14 (3d.) or 14×15 (1s.3d.).

619	**180**	3d. deep lilac	50	50
		a. Broken mane	70·00	
620	**181**	1s.3d. green	3·75	4·25
Set of 2			4·00	4·50
First Day Cover				65·00

182 Conference Emblem

(Des R. Stone (emblem, P. Rahikainen))

1960 (19 Sept). *First Anniversary of European Postal and Telecommunications Conference.* Chalk-surfaced paper. W **179**. *P* 15×14.

621	**182**	6d. bronze-green and purple	2·00	50
622		1s.6d. brown and blue	9·50	5·00
Set of 2			11·00	5·25
First Day Cover				65·00

SCREENS. Up to this point all photogravure stamps were printed in a 200 screen (200 dots per linear inch), but all later commemorative stamps are a finer 250 screen. Exceptionally No. 622 has a 200 screen for the portrait and a 250 screen for the background.

184 "Growth of Savings"

183 Thrift Plant   **185** Thrift Plant

(Des P. Gauld (2½d.), M. Goaman (others))

1961 (28 Aug). *Centenary of Post Office Savings Bank.* Chalk-surfaced paper. W **179** (sideways on 2½d.) *P* 14×15 (2½d.) or 15×14 (others).

A. "Timson" Machine

623A	**183**	2½d. black and red	25	25
		a. Black omitted	£27000	
624A	**184**	3d. orange-brown and violet	20	20
		a. Orange-brown omitted	£600	
		Eb. Perf through side sheet margin	35·00	38·00
625A	**185**	1s.6d. red and blue	2·50	2·25
Set of 3			2·75	2·50
First Day Cover				75·00

B. "Thrissell" Machine

623B	**183**	2½d. black and red	2·25	2·25
624B	**184**	3d. orange-brown and violet	40	40
		a. Orange-brown omitted	£1750	

2½d. TIMSON. Cyls 1E-1F. Deeply shaded portrait (brownish black).

2½d. THRISSELL. Cyls 1D-1B or 1D (dot)-1B (dot). Lighter portrait (grey-black).

3d. TIMSON. Cyls 3D-3E. Clear, well-defined portrait with deep shadows and bright highlights.

3d. THRISSELL. Cyls 3C-3B or 3C (dot)-3B (dot). Dull portrait, lacking in contrast.

Sheet marginal examples *without* single extension perf hole on the short side of the stamp are always "Timson", as are those with large punch-hole *not* coincident with printed three-sided box guide mark.

The 3d. "Timson" perforated completely through the right hand side margin comes from a relatively small part of the printing perforated on a sheet-fed machine.

Normally the "Timsons" were perforated in the reel, with three large punch-holes in both long margins and the perforations completely through both short margins. Only one punch-hole coincides with the guide-mark.

The "Thrissells" have one large punch-hole in one long margin, coinciding with guide-mark and one short margin imperf (except sometimes for encroachments).

186 C.E.P.T. Emblem   **187** Doves and Emblem

188 Doves and Emblem

(Des M. Goaman (doves T. Kurpershoek))

1961 (18 Sept). *European Postal and Telecommunications (C.E.P.T.) Conference, Torquay.* Chalk-surfaced paper. W **179**. *P* 15×14.

626	**186**	2d. orange, pink and brown	15	10
		a. Orange omitted	£18500	
		b. Pink omitted		
627	**187**	4d. buff, mauve and ultramarine	15	15
628	**188**	10d. turquoise, pale green and Prussian blue	15	50
		a. Pale green omitted	£27500	
		b. Turquoise omitted	£8000	
Set of 3			40	60
First Day Cover				6·00

189 Hammer Beam Roof, Westminster Hall

190 Palace of Westminster

(Des Faith Jaques)

1961 (25 Sept). *Seventh Commonwealth Parliamentary Conference.* Chalk-surfaced paper. W **179** (sideways on 1s.3d.) P 15×14 (6d.) or 14×15 (1s.3d.).

629	**189**	6d. purple and gold	25	25
		a. Gold omitted	£2750	
630	**190**	1s.3d. green and blue	2·50	2·75
		a. Blue (Queen's head) omitted	£45000	
		b. Green omitted		
Set of 2			2·75	3·00
First Day Cover				30·00

191 "Units of Productivity"

192 "National Productivity"

193 "Unified Productivity"

3d. Lake in Scotland (Cyls. 2A-2B Dot, R. 1/3)

3d. Kent omitted (Cyls. 2C-2B No. Dot, R. 18/2)

3d. Lake in Yorkshire (Cyls. 2C-2B Dot, R/19/1)

(Des D. Gentleman)

1962 (14 Nov). *National Productivity Year.* Chalk-surfaced paper. W **179** (inverted on 2½d. and 3d.). P 15×14.

631	**191**	2½d. myrtle-green and carmine-red (shades)	20	20
		Ea. Blackish olive and carmine-red	25	15
		p. One phosphor band. *Blackish olive and carmine-red*	60	50
632	**192**	3d. light blue and violet (shades)	50	25
		a. Light blue (Queen's head) omitted	£6500	
		b. Lake in Scotland	65·00	
		c. Kent omitted	70·00	
		d. Lake in Yorkshire	35·00	
		p. Three phosphor bands	1·50	80
633	**193**	1s.3d. carmine, light blue and deep green	1·50	1·70
		a. Light blue (Queen's head) omitted	£17500	
		p. Three phosphor bands	35·00	22·00
Set of 3 (Ordinary)			2·00	1·90
Set of 3 (Phosphor)			35·00	22·00
First Day Cover (Ordinary)				55·00
First Day Cover (Phosphor)				£150

194 Campaign Emblem and Family

195 Children of Three Races

(Des M. Goaman)

1963 (21 Mar). *Freedom from Hunger.* Chalk-surfaced paper. W **179** (inverted). P 15×14.

634	**194**	2½d. crimson and pink	25	10
		p. One phosphor band	3·00	1·20
635	**195**	1s.3d. bistre-brown and yellow	1·90	1·90
		p. Three phosphor bands	30·00	23·00
Set of 2 (Ordinary)			2·00	2·00
Set of 2 (Phosphor)			30·00	23·00
First Day Cover (Ordinary)				35·00
First Day Cover (Phosphor)				50·00

196 "Paris Conference"

(Des R. Stone)

1963 (7 May). *Paris Postal Conference Centenary.* Chalk-surfaced paper. W **179** (inverted). P 15×14.

636	**196**	6d. green and mauve	50	50
		a. Green omitted	£6500	
		p. Three phosphor bands	6·50	7·00
First Day Cover (Ordinary)				16·00
First Day Cover (Phosphor)				38·00

197 Posy of Flowers

198 Woodland Life

"Caterpillar" flaw (Cyl. 3B Dot, R. 3/2)

(Des S. Scott (3d.), M. Goaman (4½d.))

1963 (16 May). *National Nature Week.* Chalk-surfaced paper. W **179**. P 15×14.

637	**197**	3d. yellow, green, brown and black	15	15
		a. "Caterpillar" flaw	75·00	
		p. Three phosphor bands	60	60
		pa. "Caterpillar" flaw	75·00	
638	**198**	4½d. black, blue, yellow, magenta and brown-red	35	35
		p. Three phosphor bands	3·25	3·25
Set of 2 (Ordinary)			50	50
Set of 2 (Phosphor)			3·50	3·50
First Day Cover (Ordinary)				22·00
First Day Cover (Phosphor)				40·00

Special First Day of Issue Postmark

	Ordinary	Phosphor
London E.C. (Type A)	24·00	30·00

This postmark was used on First Day Covers serviced by the Philatelic Bureau.

199 Rescue at Sea

200 19th-century Lifeboat

201 Lifeboatmen

(Des D. Gentleman)

1963 (31 May). *Ninth International Lifeboat Conference,* Edinburgh. Chalk-surfaced paper. *W* **179**. *P* 15×14.

639	**199**	2½d. blue, black and red	25	25
		p. One phosphor band	50	60
640	**200**	4d. red, yellow, brown, black and blue	50	50
		p. Three phosphor bands	50	60
641	**201**	1s.6d. sepia, yellow and grey-blue	3·00	3·25
		p. Three phosphor bands	48·00	28·00
Set of 3 (Ordinary)			3·25	3·50
Set of 3 (Phosphor)			48·00	28·00
First Day Cover (Ordinary)				35·00
First Day Cover (Phosphor)				55·00

Special First Day of Issue Postmark

Ordinary Phosphor
London.. 65·00   80·00
This postmark was used on First Day Covers serviced by the Philatelic Bureau.

202 Red Cross

203

204

(Des H. Bartram)

1963 (15 Aug). *Red Cross Centenary Congress.* Chalk-surfaced paper. *W* **179**. *P* 15×14.

642	**202**	3d. red and deep lilac	25	25
		a. Red omitted	£18750	
		p. Three phosphor bands	1·10	1·00
		pa. Red omitted	£50000	
643	**203**	1s.3d. red, blue and grey	3·00	3·00
		p. Three phosphor bands	35·00	30·00
644	**204**	1s.6d. red, blue and bistre	3·00	3·00
		p. Three phosphor bands	35·00	27·00
Set of 3 (Ordinary)			5·00	5·75
Set of 3 (Phosphor)			65·00	55·00
First Day Cover (Ordinary)				40·00
First Day Cover (Phosphor)				90·00

Special First Day of Issue Postmark

1863 RED CROSS CENTENARY A CENTURY OF SERVICE 1963

Ordinary Phosphor
London E.C.. 75·00   £100
This postmark was used on First Day Covers serviced by the Philatelic Bureau.

205 Commonwealth Cable

(Des P. Gauld)

1963 (3 Dec). *Opening of COMPAC* (Trans-Pacific Telephone Cable). Chalk-surfaced paper. *W* **179**. *P* 15×14.

645	**205**	1s.6d. blue and black	2·75	2·50
		a. Black omitted	£8750	
		p. Three phosphor bands	16·00	16·00
First Day Cover (Ordinary)				28·00
First Day Cover (Phosphor)				40·00

Special First Day of Issue Postmark

Ordinary Phosphor
Philatelic Bureau, London E.C.1 (Type A).................. 45·00   50·00

PRESENTATION PACKS. Special Packs comprising slip-in cards with printed commemorative inscriptions and descriptive notes on the back and with protective covering, were introduced in 1964 with the Shakespeare issue. These are listed and priced. Issues of 1968-69 (British Paintings to the Prince of Wales Investiture) were also issued in packs with text in German for sale through the Post Office's German Agency and these are also quoted. Subsequently, however, the packs sold in Germany were identical with the normal English version with the addition of a separate printed insert card with German text. These, as also English packs with Japanese and Dutch printed cards for sale in Japan and the Netherlands respectively, are listed in Vols. 3 and 5 of the Stanley Gibbons *Great Britain Specialised Catalogue*.

206 Puck and Bottom (*A Midsummer Night's Dream*)

207 Feste (*Twelfth Night*)

208 Balcony Scene (*Romeo and Juliet*)

209 Eve of Agincourt (*Henry V*)

210 Hamlet contemplating Yorick's Skull *Hamlet* and Queen Elizabeth II

(Des D. Gentleman. Photo Harrison & Sons (3d., 6d., 1s.3d., 1s.6d.). Des C. and R. Ironside. Recess B.W. (2s.6d.))

1964 (23 Apr). *Shakespeare Festival.* Chalk-surfaced paper. *W* **179**. *P* 11×12 (2s.6d.) or 15×14 (others).

646	**206**	3d. yellow-bistre, black and deep violet-blue (*shades*)	15	15
		p. Three phosphor bands	25	30
647	**207**	6d. yellow, orange, black and yellow-olive (*shades*)	30	30
		p. Three phosphor bands	75	1·00

648	**208**	1s.3d. cerise, blue-green, black and sepia (shades)	75	1·00
		Wi. Watermark inverted	£950	
		p. Three phosphor bands	4·00	6·50
		pWi. Watermark inverted	£400	
649	**209**	1s.6d. violet, turquoise, black and blue (shades)	1·00	85
		Wi. Watermark inverted	£1300	
		p. Three phosphor bands	8·00	8·00
650	**210**	2s.6d. deep slate-purple (shades)	2·75	2·75
		Wi. Watermark inverted	£1000	
	Set of 5 (Ordinary)		4·50	4·50
	Set of 4 (Phosphor)		12·00	14·00
	First Day Cover (Ordinary)			12·00
	First Day Cover (Phosphor)			17·00
	Presentation Pack (Ordinary)		30·00	

The 3d. is known with yellow-bistre missing in the top two-thirds of the figures of Puck and Bottom. This occurred in the top row only of a sheet.

Special First Day of Issue Postmark

FIRST DAY OF ISSUE
23 APR 1964
STRATFORD-UPON-AVON, WKS.

	Ordinary	Phosphor
Stratford-upon-Avon, Warwicks	15·00	22·00

This postmark was used on First Day Covers serviced by the Philatelic Bureau, as well as on covers posted at Stratford P.O.

211 Flats near Richmond Park *Urban Development*

212 Shipbuilding Yards, Belfast *Industrial Activity*

213 Beddgelert Forest Park, Snowdonia *Forestry*

214 Nuclear Reactor, Dounreay *Technological Development*

Short line under 2½d. (Cyl. 3D, various positions)

(Des D. Bailey)

1964 (1 July). *20th International Geographical Congress*, London. Chalk-surfaced paper. *W* 179. *P* 15×14.

651	**211**	2½d. black, olive-yellow, olive-grey and turquoise-blue	10	10
		a. Short line under 2½d.	14·00	
		p. One phosphor band	40	50
652	**212**	4d. orange-brown, red-brown, rose, black and violet	30	30
		a. Violet (face value) omitted	£300	
		c. Violet and red-brown (dock walls) omitted	£550	
		d. Red brown (dock walls) omitted		
		Wi. Watermark inverted	£850	
		p. Three phosphor bands	1·20	1·20
653	**213**	8d. yellow-brown, emerald, green and black	75	85
		a. Green (lawn) omitted	£24000	
		Wi. Watermark inverted	£2200	
		p. Three phosphor bands	2·50	3·50
654	**214**	1s.6d. yellow-brown, pale pink, black and brown	3·50	3·50
		Wi. Watermark inverted	55·00	
		p. Three phosphor bands	28·00	22·00
	Set of 4 (Ordinary)		4·50	4·50

	Set of 4 (Phosphor)		30·00	25·00
	First Day Cover (Ordinary)			22·00
	First Day Cover (Phosphor)			40·00
	Presentation Pack (Ordinary)		£160	

A used example of the 4d. is known with the red-brown omitted.

Special First Day of Issue Postmark

	Ordinary	Phosphor
G.P.O. Philatelic Bureau, London E.C.1 (Type B)	25·00	35·00

215 Spring Gentian

216 Dog Rose

217 Honeysuckle

218 Fringed Water Lily

Broken petal (Cyl. 3A Dot, R. 1/2)

Line through "INTER" (Cyl. 2A No dot, R. 1/1)

(Des M. and Sylvia Goaman)

1964 (5 Aug). *Tenth International Botanical Congress*, Edinburgh. Chalk-surfaced paper. *W* 179. *P* 15×14.

655	**215**	3d. violet, blue and sage-green	25	25
		a. Blue omitted	£24000	
		b. Sage-green omitted	£28000	
		c. Broken petal	65·00	
		p. Three phosphor bands	40	40
		pc. Broken petal	65·00	
656	**216**	6d. apple-green, rose, scarlet and green	50	50
		p. Three phosphor bands	2·50	2·75
657	**217**	9d. lemon, green, lake and rose-red	1·70	2·25
		a. Green (leaves) omitted	£26000	
		b. Line through "INTER"	65·00	
		Wi. Watermark inverted	75·00	
		p. Three phosphor bands	4·50	4·50
		pb. Line through "INTER"	65·00	
658	**218**	1s.3d. yellow, emerald, reddish violet and grey-green	2·50	2·50
		a. Yellow (flowers) omitted	£50000	
		Wi. Watermark inverted	£2500	
		p. Three phosphor bands	25·00	20·00
	Set of 4 (Ordinary)		4·50	4·50
	Set of 4 (Phosphor)		30·00	25·00
	First Day Cover (Ordinary)			30·00
	First Day Cover (Phosphor)			40·00
	Presentation Pack (Ordinary)		£160	

Unissued Goaman designs of the 3d and 9d values on perforated and gummed paper are known.

Special First Day of Issue Postmark

	Ordinary	Phosphor
G.P.O. Philatelic Bureau, London E.C.1 (Type B)	28·00	45·00

219 Forth Road Bridge

220 Forth Road and Railway Bridges

(Des A. Restall)

1964 (4 Sept). *Opening of Forth Road Bridge*. Chalk-surfaced paper. *W* 179. *P* 15×14.

659	**219**	3d. black, blue and reddish violet	10	10
		p. Three phosphor bands	1·00	1·50
660	**220**	6d. blackish lilac, light blue and carmine-red	40	40
		a. Light blue omitted	£7500	
		Wi. Watermark inverted	5·00	

p. Three phosphor bands	4·50	4·75
pWi. Watermark inverted	£875	
Set of 2 (Ordinary)	50	50
Set of 2 (Phosphor)	5·00	5·75
First Day Cover (Ordinary)		7·00
First Day Cover (Phosphor)		18·00
Presentation Pack (Ordinary)	£450	

Special First Day of Issue Postmarks

	Ordinary	Phosphor
G.P.O. Philatelic Bureau, London E.C.1 (Type B)	20·00	28·00
North Queensferry, Fife	40·00	£130
South Queensferry, West Lothian	32·00	95·00

The Queensferry postmarks were applied to First Day Covers sent to a temporary Philatelic Bureau at Edinburgh.

221 Sir Winston Churchill

(Des D. Gentleman and Rosalind Dease, from photograph by Karsh)

1965 (8 July). *Churchill Commemoration*. Chalk-surfaced paper. *W* **179**. *P* 15×14.

I. "REMBRANDT" Machine

661	**221**	4d. black and olive-brown	15	10
		Wi. Watermark inverted	3·00	
		p. Three phosphor bands	25	25

II. "TIMSON" Machine

661a	**221**	4d. black and olive-brown	35	35

III. "L. & M. 4" Machine

662	–	1s.3d. black and grey	45	40
		Wi. Watermark inverted	£140	
		p. Three phosphor bands	2·50	3·00
Set of 2 (Ordinary)			60	50
Set of 2 (Phosphor)			2·75	3·25
First Day Cover (Ordinary)				7·00
First Day Cover (Phosphor)				9·00
Presentation Pack (Ordinary)			70·00	

The 1s.3d. shows a closer view of Churchill's head.

Two examples of the 4d. value exist with the Queen's head omitted, one due to something adhering to the cylinder and the other due to a paper fold. The stamp also exists with Churchill's head omitted, also due to a paper fold.

4d. REMBRANDT, Cyls 1A-1B dot and no dot. Lack of shading detail on Churchill's portrait. Queen's portrait appears dull and coarse. This is a rotary machine which is sheet-fed.

4d. TIMSON. Cyls 5A-6B no dot. More detail on Churchill's portrait – furrow on forehead, his left eyebrow fully drawn and more shading on cheek. Queen's portrait lighter and sharper. This is a reel-fed two-colour 12-in. wide rotary machine and the differences in impressions are due to the greater pressure applied by this machine.

1s.3d. Cyls 1A-1B no dot. The "Linotype and Machinery No. 4" machine is an ordinary sheet-fed rotary press machine. Besides being used for printing the 1s.3d. stamps it was also employed for overprinting the phosphor bands on both values.

Special First Day of Issue Postmark

	Ordinary	Phosphor
G.P.O. Philatelic Bureau, London E.C.1 (Type B)	8·00	12·00

A First Day of Issue handstamp was provided at Bladon, Oxford, for this issue.

222 Simon de Montfort's Seal

223 Parliament Buildings (after engraving by Hollar, 1647)

(Des S. Black (6d.), R. Guyatt (2s.6d.))

1965 (19 July). *700th Anniversary of Simon de Montfort's Parliament*. Chalk-surfaced paper. *W* **179**. *P* 15×14.

663	**222**	6d. olive-green	20	20
		p. Three phosphor bands	60	1·00
664	**223**	2s.6d. black, grey and pale drab	80	1·50
		Wi. Watermark inverted	60·00	
Set of 2 (Ordinary)			1·00	1·50
First Day Cover (Ordinary)				15·00
First Day Cover (Phosphor)				26·00
Presentation Pack (Ordinary)			85·00	

Special First Day of Issue Postmark

	Ordinary
G.P.O. Philatelic Bureau, London E.C.1 (Type B)	15·00

A First Day of Issue handstamp was provided at Evesham, Worcs, for this issue.

224 Bandsmen and Banner   **225** Three Salvationists

(Des M. Farrar-Bell (3d.), G. Trenaman (1s.6d.))

1965 (9 Aug). *Salvation Army Centenary*. Chalk-surfaced paper. *W* **179**. *P* 15×14.

665	**224**	3d. indigo, grey-blue, cerise, yellow and brown	25	25
		p. One phosphor band	25	40
666	**225**	1s.6d. red, blue, yellow and brown	1·00	1·50
		p. Three phosphor bands	2·50	2·75
Set of 2 (Ordinary)			1·10	1·60
Set of 2 (Phosphor)			2·50	3·00
First Day Cover (Ordinary)				23·00
First Day Cover (Phosphor)				32·00

The Philatelic Bureau did not provide First Day Cover services for Nos. 665/70.

226 Lister's Carbolic Spray   **227** Lister and Chemical Symbols

(Des P. Gauld (4d.), F. Ariss (1s.))

1965 (1 Sept). *Centenary of Joseph Lister's Discovery of Antiseptic Surgery*. Chalk-surfaced paper. *W* **179**. *P* 15×14.

667	**226**	4d. indigo, brown-red and grey-black.	25	15
		a. Brown-red (tube) omitted	£650	
		b. Indigo omitted	£7000	
		p. Three phosphor bands	25	25
		pa. Brown-red (tube) omitted	£7500	
668	**227**	1s. black, purple and new blue	1·00	1·10
		Wi. Watermark inverted	£675	
		p. Three phosphor bands	2·00	2·50
		pWi. Watermark inverted	£550	
Set of 2 (Ordinary)			1·00	1·20
Set of 2 (Phosphor)			2·00	2·50
First Day Cover (Ordinary)				12·00
First Day Cover (Phosphor)				15·00

228 Trinidad Carnival Dancers   **229** Canadian Folk-dancers

(Des D. Gentleman and Rosalind Dease)

1965 (1 Sept). *Commonwealth Arts Festival*. Chalk-surfaced paper. *W* **179**. *P* 15×14.

669	**228**	6d. black and orange	20	20

700th Anniversary of Parliament

		p. Three phosphor bands.......................	30	50
670	229	1s.6d. black and light reddish violet	80	1·10
		p. Three phosphor bands.......................	2·50	3·50
Set of 2 (Ordinary)..			1·00	1·20
Set of 2 (Phosphor)...			2·50	3·50
First Day Cover (Ordinary).....................................				17·00
First Day Cover (Phosphor)				22·00

230 Flight of Supermarine Spitfires

231 Pilot in Hawker Hurricane Mk I

232 Wing-tips of Supermarine Spitfire and Messerschmitt Bf 109

233 Supermarine Spitfires attacking Heinkel He-111H Bomber

234 Supermarine Spitfire attacking Junkers Ju 87B "Stuka" Dive-bomber

235 Hawker Hurricanes Mk I over Wreck of Dornier Do-17Z Bomber

236 Anti-aircraft Artillery in Action

237 Air-battle over St. Paul's Cathedral

(Des D. Gentleman and Rosalind Dease (4d.×6 and 1s.3d.), A. Restall (9d.))

1965 (13 Sept). *25th Anniv of Battle of Britain.* Chalk-surfaced paper. *W* **179**. *P* 15×14.

671	230	4d. yellow-olive and black......................	25	25
		a. Block of 6. Nos. 671/6......................	8·00	8·00
		p. Three phosphor bands.......................	50	50
		pa. Block of 6. Nos. 671p/6p..................	10·00	12·00
672	231	4d. yellow-olive, olive-grey and black.	25	25
		p. Three phosphor bands.......................	50	50
673	232	4d. red, new blue, yellow-olive, olive-grey and black	25	25
		p. Three phosphor bands.......................	50	50
674	233	4d. olive-grey, yellow-olive and black.	25	25
		p. Three phosphor bands.......................	50	50
675	234	4d. olive-grey, yellow-olive and black.	25	25
		p. Three phosphor bands.......................	50	50
676	235	4d. olive-grey, yellow-olive, new blue and black..	25	25
		a. New blue omitted..............................	†	£6500
		p. Three phosphor bands.......................	50	50
677	236	9d. bluish violet, orange and slate purple...	1·70	1·70
		Wi. Watermark inverted	£100	
		p. Three phosphor bands.......................	1·70	2·50
678	237	1s.3d. lt grey, dp grey, black, lt blue and bright blue...	1·70	1·70
		a. Face value omitted*..........................	£1500	
		Wi. Watermark inverted	£190	
		p. Three phosphor bands.......................	1·70	2·50
		pWi. Watermark inverted	5·00	
Set of 8 (Ordinary)..			10·00	10·00
Set of 8 (Phosphor)...			12·00	14·00
First Day Cover (Ordinary).....................................				25·00
First Day Cover (Phosphor)				30·00
Presentation Pack (Ordinary)................................			70·00	

Nos. 671/6 were issued together *se-tenant* in blocks of 6 (3×2) within the sheet. No. 676a is only known commercially used on cover from Truro.

*No. 678a is caused by a 12 mm downward shift of black which resulted in the value being omitted from the top row of one sheet.

Special First Day of Issue Postmark

	Ordinary	Phosphor
G.P.O. Philatelic Bureau, London E.C.1 (Type C).............	25·00	28·00

238 Tower and Georgian Buildings

239 Tower and "Nash" Terrace, Regent's Park

(Des C. Abbott)

1965 (8 Oct). *Opening of Post Office Tower.* Chalk-surfaced paper. *W* **179** (sideways on 3d.). *P* 14×15 (3d.) or 15×14 (1s.3d.).

679	238	3d. olive-yellow, new blue and bronze-green....................................	15	15
		a. Olive-yellow (Tower) omitted..........	£6750	£2400
		p. One phosphor band at right	15	15
		pEa. Band at left...................................	15	15
		pEb. Horiz pair. Nos. 679p/pEa..............	30	50
680	239	1s.3d. bronze-green, yellow-green and blue...	45	45
		Wi. Watermark inverted	£175	
		p. Three phosphor bands.......................	50	50
		pWi. Watermark inverted	£200	
Set of 2 (Ordinary)..			60	60
Set of 2 (Phosphor)...			65	65
First Day Cover (Ordinary).....................................				6·50
First Day Cover (Phosphor)				7·00
Presentation Pack (Ordinary)................................			10·00	
Presentation Pack (Phosphor).............................			10·00	

The one phosphor band on No. 679p was produced by printing broad phosphor bands across alternate vertical perforations. Individual stamps show the band at right or left.

Special First Day of Issue Postmark

	Ordinary	Phosphor
G.P.O. Philatelic Bureau, London E.C.1 (Type C).............	10·00	12·00

The Philatelic Bureau did not provide First Day Cover services for Nos. 681/4

240 U.N. Emblem

241 I.C.Y. Emblem

Broken circle (Cyl. 1A Dot, R. 11/4)

Lake in Russia (Cyl. 1A Dot, R. 19/3)

(Des J. Matthews)

1965 (25 Oct). *20th Anniv of U.N.O. and International Co-operation Year.* Chalk-surfaced paper. *W* **179**. *P* 15×14.

681	240	3d. black, yellow-orange and light blue...	25	20
		a. Broken circle	65·00	
		b. Lake in Russia.................................	65·00	
		p. One phosphor band	25	30
		pa. Broken circle	65·00	
		pb. Lake in Russia.................................	65·00	
682	241	1s.6d. black, brt purple and light blue.....	1·00	80

	Wi. Watermark inverted		£2200
	p. Three phosphor bands	2·75	3·00
Set of 2 (Ordinary)		1·10	90
Set of 2 (Phosphor)		2·75	3·00
First Day Cover (Ordinary)			12·00
First Day Cover (Phosphor)			14·00

242 Telecommunications Network

243 Radio Waves and Switchboard

1s.6d. Red pin with arm
(Cyl. 1D, R. 1/4)

(Des A. Restall)

1965 (15 Nov). *International Telecommunications Union Centenary.* Chalk-surfaced paper. *W* **179**. *P* 15×14.

683	**242**	9d. red, ultramarine, deep slate, violet, black and pink	50	40
		Wi. Watermark inverted	30·00	
		p. Three phosphor bands	1·00	75
		pWi. Watermark inverted	£110	
684	**243**	1s.6d. red, greenish blue, indigo, black and light pink	1·50	1·20
		a. Light pink omitted	£4500	£2500
		b. Red pin with arm	—	
		Wi. Watermark inverted		£300
		p. Three phosphor bands	4·25	5·25
		pb. Red pin with arm	35·00	
Set of 2 (Ordinary)			1·80	1·50
Set of 2 (Phosphor)			4·75	5·50
First Day Cover (Ordinary)				17·00
First Day Cover (Phosphor)				20·00

Originally scheduled for issue on 17 May 1965, supplies from the Philatelic Bureau were sent in error to reach a dealer on that date and another dealer received his supply on 27 May.

244 Robert Burns (after Skirving chalk drawing)

245 Robert Burns (after Nasmyth portrait)

(Des G. Huntly)

1966 (25 Jan). *Burns Commemoration.* Chalk-surfaced paper. *W* **179**. *P* 15×14.

685	**244**	4d. black, dp violet-blue and new blue	20	15
		p. Three phosphor bands	50	50
686	**245**	1s.3d. black, slate-blue and yellow-orange	65	70
		p. Three phosphor bands	2·25	2·25
Set of 2 (Ordinary)			75	75
Set of 2 (Phosphor)			2·50	2·50
First Day Cover (Ordinary)				4·00
First Day Cover (Phosphor)				6·00
Presentation Pack (Ordinary)			60·00	

Special First Day of Issue Postmarks
(35 mm diameter)

	Ordinary	*Phosphor*
Alloway, Ayrshire	12·00	12·00
Ayr	12·00	12·00
Dumfries	18·00	18·00
Edinburgh	18·00	18·00
Glasgow	18·00	18·00
Kilmarnock, Ayrshire	18·00	18·00

A special Philatelic Bureau was set up in Edinburgh to deal with First Day Covers of this issue. The Bureau serviced covers to receive the above postmarks, and other versions were applied locally. The locally applied handstamps were 38-39 mm in diameter, the Bureau postmarks, applied by machine, 35 mm. The Ayr, Edinburgh, Glasgow and Kilmarnock postmarks are similar in design to that for Alloway. Similar handstamps were also provided at Greenock and Mauchline, but the Bureau did not provide a service for these.

246 Westminster Abbey

247 Fan Vaulting, Henry VII Chapel

(Des Sheila Robinson. Photo Harrison (3d.). Des and eng Bradbury, Wilkinson. Recess (2s.6d.))

1966 (28 Feb). *900th Anniversary of Westminster Abbey.* Chalk-surfaced paper (3d.). *W* **179**. *P* 15×14 (3d.) or 11×12 (2s.6d.).

687	**246**	3d. black, red-brown and new blue	20	20
		p. One phosphor band	20	25
688	**247**	2s.6d. black	80	80
Set of 2			90	90
First Day Cover (Ordinary)				6·00
First Day Cover (Phosphor)				14·00
Presentation Pack (Ordinary)			55·00	

Special First Day of Issue Postmark

	Ordinary
G.P.O. Philatelic Bureau, London E.C.1 (Type B)	10·00

The Bureau did not provide a First Day Cover service for the 3d. phosphor stamp

248 View near Hassocks, Sussex **249** Antrim, Northern Ireland

250 Harlech Castle, Wales **251** Cairngorm Mountains Scotland

4d. Green flaw on tree trunk (Cyl. 1B Dot, R. 3/4)

6d. "AN" for "AND" (Cyl. 1A No dot, R. 10/3)

1s.3d. Broken "D" (Cyl. 2B, R. 14/2)

(Des L. Rosoman. Queen's portrait, adapted by D. Gentleman from coinage)

1966 (2 May). *Landscapes.* Chalk-surfaced paper. *W* **179**. *P* 15×14.

689	**248**	4d. black, yellow-green and new blue	10	15
		a. Green flaw	35·00	
		p. Three phosphor bands	10	15

		pa. Green flaw	35·00		
690	**249**	6d. black, emerald and new blue..........	15	20	
		a. "AN" for "AND"	65·00		
		Wi. Watermark inverted	6·00		
		p. Three phosphor bands....................	15	20	
		pa. "AN" for "AND"	65·00		
		pWi. Watermark inverted	£170		
691	**250**	1s.3d. black, greenish yellow and			
		greenish blue............................	25	35	
		a. Broken "D"..................................	35·00		
		p. Three phosphor bands....................	25	35	
		pa. Broken "D"..................................	35·00		
692	**251**	1s.6d. black, orange and Prussian blue....	40	35	
		Wi. Watermark inverted	22·00		
		p. Three phosphor bands....................	40	40	
	Set of 4 (Ordinary)			80	95
	Set of 4 (Phosphor)			80	1·00
	First Day Cover (Ordinary).................................			7·00	
	First Day Cover (Phosphor)...............................			8·50	

Blocks of four of Nos. 689 and 690 are known with the Queen's head and face value omitted on one stamp and a partial omission on the second, due to a paper fold (*Price per block.* £10000)

Special First Day of Issue Postmark

	Ordinary	*Phosphor*
G.P.O. Philatelic Bureau, London E.C.1 (Type B)............	10·00	12·00

First Day of Issue handstamps were provided at Lewes, Sussex; Coleraine, Co. Londonderry; Harlech, Merioneth and Grantown-on-Spey, Morayshire, for this issue.

252 Players with Ball

253 Goalmouth Mêlée

254 Goalkeeper saving Goal

(Des D. Gentleman (4d.), W. Kempster (6d.), D. Caplan (1s.3d.). Queen's portrait adapted by D. Gentleman from coinage)

1966 (1 June). *World Cup Football Championship.* Chalk-surfaced paper. *W* **179** (sideways on 4d.). *P* 14×15 (4d.) or 15×14 (others).

693	**252**	4d. red, reddish purple, bright blue,			
		flesh and black................................	10	25	
		p. Two phosphor bands......................	10	25	
694	**253**	6d. black, sepia, red, apple-green and			
		blue...	15	25	
		a. Black omitted	£225		
		b. Apple-green omitted...........................	£7000		
		c. Red omitted	£12500		
		Wi. Watermark inverted	5·00		
		p. Three phosphor bands......................	15	25	
		pa. Black omitted	£3250		
695	**254**	1s.3d. black, blue, yellow, red and light			
		yellow-olive..............................	50	1·00	
		a. Blue omitted	£380		
		Wi. Watermark inverted	£150		
		p. Three phosphor bands......................	50	1·00	
		pWi. Watermark inverted	2·00		
	Set of 3 (Ordinary)...			70	1·25
	Set of 3 (Phosphor)..			70	1·25
	First Day Cover (Ordinary)			20·00	
	First Day Cover (Phosphor)			22·00	
	Presentation Pack (Ordinary)			20·00	

Special First Day of Issue Postmark

	Ordinary	*Phosphor*
G.P.O. Philatelic Bureau, London E.C.1 (Type C)............	20·00	25·00

A First Day of Issue handstamp was provided at Wembley, Middx, for this issue.

255 Black-headed Gull

256 Blue Tit

257 European Robin

258 Blackbird

(Des J. Norris Wood)

1966 (8 Aug). *British Birds.* Chalk-surfaced paper. *W* **179**. *P* 15×14.

696	**255**	4d. grey, black, red, emerald-green,			
		brt blue, greenish yellow and			
		bistre	20	20	
		Wi. Watermark inverted	4·00		
		a. Block of 4. Nos. 696/9....................	1·00	2·00	
		ab. Black (value), etc. omitted* (*block*			
		of four)	£20000		
		c. Black only omitted*	£5000		
		aWi. Watermark inverted (*block of four*)	18·00		
		p. Three phosphor bands......................	20	20	
		pWi. Watermark inverted	20·00		
		pa. Block of 4. Nos. 696p/9p................	1·00	2·00	
		paWi. Watermark inverted (*block of four*)	85·00		
697	**256**	4d. black, greenish yellow, grey,			
		emerald-green, brt blue and			
		bistre	20	20	
		b. Black "4d" only omitted....................	£2000		
		Wi. Watermark inverted	4·00		
		p. Three phosphor bands......................	20	20	
		pWi. Watermark inverted	20·00		
698	**257**	4d. red, greenish yellow, black,			
		grey, bistre, reddish brown and			
		emerald-green............................	20	20	
		a. Black only omitted	£2000		
		Wi. Watermark inverted	4·00		
		p. Three phosphor bands......................	20	20	
		pWi. Watermark inverted	20·00		
699	**258**	4d. black, reddish brown, greenish			
		yellow, grey and bistre**	20	20	
		b. Black "4d" only omitted....................	£2000		
		Wi. Watermark inverted	4·00		
		p. Three phosphor bands......................	20	20	
		pWi. Watermark inverted	20·00		
	Set of 4 (Ordinary)			1·00	2·00
	Set of 4 (Phosphor)			1·00	2·00
	First Day Cover (Ordinary).................................			8·00	
	First Day Cover (Phosphor)...............................			8·00	
	Presentation Pack (Ordinary)			13·00	

Nos. 696/9 were issued together *se-tenant* in blocks of four within the sheet.

Nos. 697b and 699b are the result of a partial impression of the black, rendering the "4d" only omitted.

* In No. 696ab the blue, bistre and reddish brown are also omitted but in No. 696ac only the black is omitted.

** In No. 699 the black was printed over the bistre. Other colours omitted, and the stamps affected:

d.	Greenish yellow (Nos. 696/9)	£1100
pd.	Greenish yellow (Nos. 696p/9p)	£2000
e.	Red (Nos. 696 and 698)	£1100
f.	Emerald-green (Nos. 696/8)	£200
pf.	Emerald-green (Nos. 696p/8p)	£200
g.	Bright blue (Nos. 696/7)	£700
pg.	Bright blue (Nos. 696p and 697p)	£6000
h.	Bistre (Nos. 696/9)	£200
ph.	Bistre (Nos. 696p/9p)	£2750
j.	Reddish brown (Nos. 698/9)	£125
pj.	Reddish brown (Nos. 698p and 699p)........................	£175

The prices quoted are for each stamp.

Special First Day of Issue Postmark

	Ordinary	*Phosphor*
G.P.O. Philatelic Bureau, London E.C.1 (Type C)............	22·00	22·00

259 Cup Winners

1966 (18 Aug). *England's World Cup Football Victory.* Chalk-surfaced paper. *W* **179** (sideways). *P* 14×15.

700	**259**	4d. red, reddish purple, bright blue, flesh and black		30	30
		First Day Cover			13·00

These stamps were only put on sale at post offices in England, the Channel Islands and the Isle of Man, and at the Philatelic Bureau in London and also, on 22 August, in Edinburgh on the occasion of the opening of the Edinburgh Festival as well as at Army post offices at home and abroad.

The Philatelic Bureau did not service First Day Covers for this stamp, but a First Day of Issue handstamp was provided inscribed "Harrow & Wembley" to replace the "Wembley, Middx", postmark of the initial issue.

260 Jodrell Bank Radio Telescope

261 British Motor-cars

262 "SRN 6" Hovercraft

263 Windscale Reactor

6d. Broken "D"
(Cyl .1C, R. 19/6)

(Des D. and A. Gillespie (4d., 6d.), A. Restall (others))

1966 (19 Sept). *British Technology.* Chalk-surfaced paper. *W* **179**. *P* 15×14.

701	**260**	4d. black and lemon		15	10
		p. Three phosphor bands		10	10
702	**261**	6d. red, dp blue and orange		25	20
		a. Red (Mini-cars) omitted		£22000	—
		b. Deep blue (Jaguar & inscr) omitted		£18500	
		c. Broken "D"		35·00	
		p. Three phosphor bands		15	25
		pc. Broken "D"		35·00	
703	**262**	1s.3d. black, orange-red, slate and light greenish blue		50	40
		p. Three phosphor bands		35	40
704	**263**	1s.6d. black, yellow-green, bronze-green, lilac and deep blue		50	60
		p. Three phosphor bands		50	60
		Set of 4 (Ordinary)		1·25	1·10
		Set of 4 (Phosphor)		1·00	1·10
		First Day Cover (Ordinary)			5·00
		First Day Cover (Phosphor)			5·00
		Presentation Pack (Ordinary)		20·00	

Special First Day of Issue Postmark

	Ordinary	*Phosphor*
G.P.O. Philatelic Bureau, Edinburgh 1 (Type C)	10·00	10·00

264   265

266   267

268   269

270 Norman Ship

271 Norman Horsemen attacking Harold's Troops

Club flaw (Cyl. 1A No dot, R. 7/2)

(All the above are scenes from the Bayeux Tapestry)

(Des D. Gentleman. Photo. Queen's head die-stamped (6d., 1s.3d.))

1966 (14 Oct). *900th Anniv of Battle of Hastings.* Chalk-surfaced paper. *W* **179** (sideways on 1s.3d.). *P* 15×14.

705	**264**	4d. black, olive-green, bistre, deep blue, orange, magenta, green, blue and grey		10	10
		a. Strip of 6. Nos. 705/10		1·90	2·25
		ab. Imperforate strip of six		£3800	
		aWi. Strip of 6. Watermark inverted		45·00	
		Wi. Watermark inverted		7·00	
		p. Three phosphor bands		10	10
		pa. Strip of 6. Nos. 705p/10p		1·90	2·25
		pWi. Watermark inverted		3·00	
		paWi. Strip of 6. Watermark inverted		20·00	
706	**265**	4d. black, olive-green, bistre, deep blue, orange, magenta, green, blue and grey		10	10
		Wi. Watermark inverted		7·00	
		p. Three phosphor bands		10	10
		pWi. Watermark inverted		2·00	
707	**266**	4d. black, olive-green, bistre, deep blue, orange, magenta, green, blue and grey		10	10
		Wi. Watermark inverted		7·00	
		p. Three phosphor bands		10	10

		pWi. Watermark inverted		3·00	
708	**267**	4d. black, olive-green, bistre, deep blue, magenta, green, blue and grey		10	10
		Wi. Watermark inverted		7·00	
		p. Three phosphor bands		10	10
		pWi. Watermark inverted		3·00	
709	**268**	4d. black, olive-green, bistre, deep blue, orange, magenta, green, blue and grey		10	10
		Wi. Watermark inverted		7·00	
		p. Three phosphor bands		10	10
		pWi. Watermark inverted		3·00	
710	**269**	4d. black, olive-green, bistre, deep blue, orange, magenta, green, blue and grey		10	10
		Wi. Watermark inverted		7·00	
		p. Three phosphor bands		10	10
		pWi. Watermark inverted		3·00	
711	**270**	6d. black, olive-green, violet, blue, green and gold		10	10
		Wi. Watermark inverted		42·00	
		p. Three phosphor bands		10	10
		pWi. Watermark inverted		55·00	
712	**271**	1s.3d. black, lilac, bronze-green, rosine, bistre-brown and gold		20	75
		a. Lilac omitted		£5250	
		b. Club flaw		28·00	
		Wi. Watermark sideways inverted (top of crown pointing to right)*		35·00	
		p. Four phosphor bands		20	75
		pa. Lilac omitted		£1500	
		pb. Club flaw		28·00	
		pWi. Watermark sideways inverted (top of crown pointing to right)*		35·00	
Set of 8 (Ordinary)				2·00	2·75
Set of 8 (Phosphor)				2·00	2·75
First Day Cover (Ordinary)				8·00	
First Day Cover (Phosphor)				9·00	
Presentation Pack (Ordinary)				10·00	

Nos. 705/10 show battle scenes and they were issued together *se-tenant* in horizontal strips of six within the sheet.

* The normal sideways watermark shows the tops of the Crowns pointing to the left, as seen from the *back of the stamp*. Other colours omitted in the 4d. values and the stamps affected:

b.	Olive-green (Nos. 705/10)	65·00
pb.	Olive-green (Nos. 705p/10p)	65·00
c.	Bistre (Nos. 705/10)	65·00
pc.	Bistre (Nos. 705p/10p)	65·00
d.	Deep blue (Nos. 705/10)	75·00
pd.	Deep blue (Nos. 705p/10p)	75·00
e.	Orange (Nos. 705/7 and 709/10)	65·00
pe.	Orange (Nos. 705p/7p and 709p/10p)	65·00
f.	Magenta (Nos. 705/10)	65·00
pf.	Magenta (Nos. 705p/10p)	65·00
g.	Green (Nos. 705/10)	65·00
pg.	Green (Nos. 705p/10p)	65·00
h.	Blue (Nos. 705/10)	65·00
ph.	Blue (Nos. 705p/10p)	65·00
j.	Grey (Nos. 705/10) .	65·00
pj.	Grey (Nos. 705p/10p)	65·00
pk.	Magenta and green (Nos. 705p/10p)	75·00

The prices quoted are for each stamp.

Nos. 705 and 709, with grey and blue omitted, have been seen commercially used, posted from Middleton-in-Teesdale.

The 6d. phosphor is known in a yellowish gold as well as the reddish gold as used in the 1s.3d.

Three examples of No. 712 in a right-hand top corner block of 10 (2×5) are known with the Queen's head omitted as a result of a double paper fold prior to die-stamping. The perforation is normal. Of the other seven stamps, four have the Queen's head misplaced and three are normal.

MISSING GOLD HEADS. The 6d. and 1s.3d. were also issued with the die-stamped gold head omitted but as these can also be removed by chemical means we are not prepared to list them unless a way is found of distinguishing the genuine stamps from the fakes which will satisfy the Expert Committees.

The same remarks apply to Nos. 713/14.

Special First Day of Issue Postmark

	Ordinary	*Phosphor*
G.P.O. Philatelic Bureau, Edinburgh 1 (Type C)	10·00	12·00

A First Day of Issue handstamp was provided at Battle, Sussex, for this issue.

272 King of the Orient   **273** Snowman

Missing "T" (Cyl. 1E No dot, R. 6/2)

(Des Tasveer Shemza (3d.), J. Berry (1s.6d.) (winners of children's design competition). Photo, Queen's head die-stamped)

1966 (1 Dec). *Christmas, Children's Paintings.* Chalk-surfaced paper. W 179 (sideways on 3d.). P 14×15.

713	**272**	3d. black, blue, green, yellow and gold		10	25
		a. Queen's head double*		£7000	†
		ab. Queen's head double, one albino..		£650	
		b. Green omitted			£4250
		c. Missing "T"		25·00	
		p. One phosphor band at right		10	25
		pEa. Band at left		10	25
		pEb. Horiz pair. Nos. 713p/pEa		20	60
		pc. Missing "T"		45·00	
714	**273**	1s.6d. blue, red, pink, black and gold		30	50
		a. Pink (hat) omitted		£4500	
		Wi. Watermark inverted		30·00	
		p. Two phosphor bands		30	50
		pWi. Watermark inverted		90·00	
Set of 2 (Ordinary)				35	70
Set of 2 (Phosphor)				35	70
First Day Cover (Ordinary)				2·50	
First Day Cover (Phosphor)				2·00	
Presentation Pack (Ordinary)				12·00	

No. 713a refers to stamps showing two impressions, one directly below the other, both with embossing. Examples showing two partial strikes on opposite sides of the stamp, caused by a colour shift are common.

The single phosphor band on No. 713p was produced by printing broad phosphor bands across alternate perforations. Individual* show the band at right or left.

Special First Day of Issue Postmarks

	Ordinary	*Phosphor*
G.P.O. Philatelic Bureau, Edinburgh 1 (Type C)	7·00	7·00
Bethlehem, Llandeilo, Carms (Type C)	8·00	8·00

274 Sea Freight   **275** Air Freight

Broken strut (Cyl. 2J No dot, R. 13/6)

(Des C. Abbott)

1967 (20 Feb). *European Free Trade Association (EFTA).* Chalk-surfaced paper. *W* **179**. *P* 15×14.

715	**274**	9d. deep blue, red, lilac, green, brown, new blue, yellow and black	25	20
		a. Black (Queen's head, etc.), brown, new blue and yellow omitted	£1300	
		b. Lilac omitted	£135	
		c. Green omitted	£135	
		d. Brown (rail trucks) omitted	95·00	
		e. New blue omitted	£135	
		f. Yellow omitted	£135	
		p. Three phosphor bands	25	20
		pb. Lilac omitted	£225	
		pc. Green omitted	£135	
		pd. Brown omitted	95·00	
		pe. New blue omitted	£135	
		pf. Yellow omitted	£180	
		pWi. Watermark inverted	95·00	
716	**275**	1s.6d. violet, red, deep blue, brown, green, blue-grey, new blue, yellow and black	50	45
		a. Red omitted		
		b. Deep blue omitted	£550	
		c. Brown omitted	£135	
		d. Blue-grey omitted	£135	
		e. New blue omitted	£135	
		f. Yellow omitted	£135	
		g. Green omitted	£3750	
		h. Broken strut	40·00	
		Wi. Watermark inverted	30·00	
		p. Three phosphor bands	25	40
		pa. Red omitted		
		pb. Deep blue omitted	£550	
		pc. Brown omitted	95·00	
		pd. Blue-grey omitted	£135	
		pf. New blue omitted	£135	
		ph. Broken strut	40·00	
		pWi. Watermark inverted	30·00	
Set of 2 (Ordinary)			60	60
Set of 2 (Phosphor)			60	55
First Day Cover (Ordinary)				3·00
First Day Cover (Phosphor)				3·00
Presentation Pack (Ordinary)			20·00	

Special First Day of Issue Postmark

	Ordinary	Phosphor
G.P.O. Philatelic Bureau, Edinburgh 1 (Type C)	6·00	6·00

276 Hawthorn and Bramble

277 Larger Bindweed and Viper's Bugloss

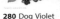

278 Ox-eye Daisy, Coltsfoot and Buttercup

279 Bluebell, Red Campion and Wood Anemone

(Des Rev. W. Keble Martin (T **276/9**), Mary Grierson (others))

1967 (24 Apr). *British Wild Flowers.* Chalk-surfaced paper. *W* **179**. *P* 15×14.

717	**276**	4d. grey, lemon, myrtle-green, red, agate and slate-purple	20	20
		a. Block of 4. Nos. 717/20	80	2·25
		aWi. Block of 4. Watermark inverted	9·00	
		b. Grey double*		
		c. Red omitted	£5000	
		f. Slate-purple omitted	£5500	

		Wi. Watermark inverted	2·00	
		p. Three phosphor bands	10	15
		pa. Block of 4. Nos. 717p/20p	80	2·00
		paWi. Block of 4. Watermark inverted	9·00	
		pd. Agate omitted	£4500	
		pf. Slate-purple omitted	£550	
		pWi. Watermark inverted	2·00	
718	**277**	4d. grey, lemon, myrtle-green, red, agate and violet	20	20
		b. Grey double*		
		Wi. Watermark inverted	2·00	
		p. Three phosphor bands	10	15
		pd. Agate omitted	£4500	
		pe. Violet omitted		
		pWi. Watermark inverted	2·00	
719	**278**	4d. grey, lemon, myrtle-green, red and agate	20	20
		b. Grey double*		
		Wi. Watermark inverted	2·00	
		p. Three phosphor bands	10	15
		pd. Agate omitted	£4500	
		pWi. Watermark inverted	2·00	
720	**279**	4d. grey, lemon, myrtle-green, reddish purple, agate and violet	20	20
		b. Grey double*		
		c. Reddish purple omitted	£2250	
		d. Value omitted†	£12000	
		Wi. Watermark inverted	2·00	
		p. Three phosphor bands	10	15
		pd. Agate omitted	£4500	
		pe. Violet omitted		
		pWi. Watermark inverted	2·00	
721	**280**	9d. lavender-grey, green, reddish violet and orange-yellow	20	25
		Wi. Watermark inverted	1·30	
		p. Three phosphor bands	15	25
722	**281**	1s.9d. lavender-grey, green, greenish yellow and orange	25	35
		p. Three phosphor bands	20	30
Set of 6 (Ordinary)			1·00	2·25
Set of 6 (Phosphor)			1·00	2·00
First Day Cover (Ordinary)				5·00
First Day Cover (Phosphor)				5·00
Presentation Pack (Ordinary)			14·00	
Presentation Pack (Phosphor)			14·00	

Nos. 717/20 were issued together *se-tenant* in blocks of four within the sheet.

* The double impression of the grey printing affects the Queen's head, value and inscription.

† No. 720d was caused by something obscuring the face value on R14/6 during the printing of one sheet.

Special First Day of Issue Postmark

	Ordinary	Phosphor
G.P.O. Philatelic Bureau, Edinburgh 1 (Type C)	8·00	10·00

PHOSPHOR BANDS. Issues from No. 723 are normally with phosphor bands only, except for the high values but most stamps have appeared with the phosphor bands omitted in error. Such varieties are listed under "Ey" numbers and are priced unused only. See also further notes after 1971–96 Decimal Machin issue.

PHOSPHORISED PAPER. Following the adoption of phosphor bands the Post Office started a series of experiments involving the addition of the phosphor to the paper coating before the stamps were printed. No. 743c was the first of these experiments to be issued for normal postal use. See also notes after 1971–96 Decimal Machin issue.

PVA GUM. Polyvinyl alcohol was introduced by Harrisons in place of gum arabic in 1968. As it is almost invisible a small amount of pale yellowish colouring was introduced to make it possible to check that the stamps had been gummed. Although this can be distinguished from gum arabic in unused stamps there is, of course, no means of detecting it in used examples. Where the two forms of gum exist on the same stamps, the PVA type are listed under "Ev" numbers, except in the case of the 1d. and 4d. (vermilion), both once centre band, which later appeared with gum arabic and these have "Eg" numbers. "Ev" and "Eg" numbers are priced unused only. All stamps printed from No. 763 onwards were issued with PVA gum only *except where otherwise stated.*

It should be further noted that gum arabic is shiny in appearance, and that, normally, PVA gum has a matt appearance. However, depending upon the qualities of the paper ingredients and the resultant absorption of the gum, occasionally, PVA gum has a shiny appearance. In such cases, especially in stamps from booklets, it is sometimes impossible to be absolutely sure which gum has been used except by testing the stamps chemically which destroys them. Therefore, whilst all gum arabic is shiny it does not follow that all shiny gum is gum arabic.

282	282a

I	II

Two types of the 2d.

I. Value spaced away from left side of stamp (cylinders 1 no dot and dot).

II. Value close to left side from new multipositive used for cylinders 5 no dot and dot onwards. The portrait appears in the centre, thus conforming to the other values.

Three types of the Machin head, known as Head A, B or C, are distinguished by specialists. These are illustrated in Vol. 3 of the *Great Britain Specialised Catalogue*.

(Des after plaster cast by Arnold Machin)

1967 (5 June)–**70**. Chalk-surfaced paper. Two phosphor bands except where otherwise stated. PVA gum except Nos. 725m, 728, 729, 731, 731Ea, 740, 742/Ea, 743/a and 744/Ea. No wmk. *P* 15×14.

723	282	½d. orange-brown (5.2.68)	30	75
		Ey. Phosphor omitted	30·00	
724		1d. light olive (*shades*) (2 bands) (5.2.68)	20	10
		a. Imperf (coil strip)†	£3500	
		b. Part perf pane*		
		c. Imperf pane*	£5750	
		d. Uncoated paper (1970)**	£150	
		Ey. Phosphor omitted	4·00	
		l. Booklet pane. No. 724×2 se-tenant with 730×2 (6.4.68)	3·00	
		lEy. Booklet pane. Phosphor omitted.	90·00	
		m. Booklet pane. No. 724×4 se-tenant with 734×2 (6.1.69)	3·50	
		mEy. Booklet pane. Phosphor omitted.	£225	
		n. Booklet pane. No. 724×6, 734×3, 734Eb×3 & 735×3 se-tenant (1.12.69)	8·50	
		na. Booklet pane. Uncoated paper**.	£925	
		nEy. Booklet pane. Phosphor omitted.	£225	
725		1d. yellowish olive (1 centre band) (16.9.68)	45	55
		Eg. Gum arabic (27.8.69)	80	
		l. Booklet pane. No. 725×4 se-tenant with 732×2	4·00	
		lEy. Booklet pane. Phosphor omitted.	35·00	
		m. Coil strip. No. 728×2 se-tenant with 729, 725Eg & 733Eg (27.8.69)	1·90	
726		2d. lake-brown (Type I) (2 bands) (5.2.68)	20	15
		Ey. Phosphor omitted	40·00	
727		2d. lake-brown (Type II) (2 bands) (1969)	30	40
		Ey. Phosphor omitted	2·00	
728		2d. lake-brown (Type II) (1 centre band) (27.8.69)	1·00	1·50
729		3d. violet (*shades*) (1 centre band) (8.8.67)	30	10
		a. Imperf (vert pair)	£950	
		Ey. Phosphor omitted	4·00	
		Ev. PVA gum (*shades*) (12.3.68)	30	
		Evy. Phosphor omitted	4·00	
730		3d. violet (2 bands) (6.4.68)	30	45
		a. Uncoated paper**		
731		4d. deep sepia (*shades*) (2 bands)	30	30
		Ey. Phosphor omitted	4·00	
		Ea. Deep olive-brown	1·50	45
		Eay. Phosphor omitted	6·00	
		b. Part perf pane*	£4000	
		Ev. PVA gum (*shades*) (22.1.68)	1·50	
		Evy. Phosphor omitted	4·00	
732		4d. deep olive-brown (*shades*) (1 centre band) (16.9.68)	30	30
		a. Part perf pane*	£4250	
		l. Booklet pane. Two stamps plus two printed labels	1·00	
		lEy. Booklet pane. Phosphor omitted.	45·00	
733		4d. bright vermilion (1 centre band) (6.1.69)	20	10
		a. *Tête-bêche* (horiz pair)	£5000	
		b. Uncoated paper**	20·00	
		Ey. Phosphor omitted	4·00	
		l. Booklet pane. Two stamps plus two printed labels (3.3.69)	1·00	

		lEy. Booklet pane. Phosphor omitted.	75·00	
		Eg. Gum arabic (27.8.69)	1·00	
		Egy. Phosphor omitted	£1650	
734		4d. bright vermilion (1 band at left) (6.1.69)	1·90	2·50
		a. Uncoated paper**	£425	
		Eb. One band at right (1.12.69)	2·00	2·75
		Eba. Ditto. Uncoated paper**	£425	
735		5d. royal blue (*shades*) (1.7.68)	20	20
		a. Imperf pane*	£3500	
		b. Part perf pane*	£2500	
		c. Imperf (pair)††	£275	
		d. Uncoated paper**	40·00	
		Ey. Phosphor omitted	6·50	
		Ee. Deep blue	1·50	35
		Eey. Phosphor omitted	6·00	
736		6d. brt reddish purple (shades) (5.2.68)	50	40
		Ey. Phosphor omitted	35·00	
		Ea. Bright magenta	15·00	15·00
		Eb. Claret	2·00	2·00
		Eby. Phosphor omitted	45·00	
737	282a	7d. bright emerald (1.7.68)	1·00	1·00
		Ey. Phosphor omitted	£100	
738		8d. bright vermilion (1.7.68)	1·25	1·75
		Ey. Phosphor omitted	£450	
739		8d. light turquoise-blue (6.1.69)	1·00	1·50
		Ey. Phosphor omitted	80·00	
740		9d. myrtle-green (8.8.67)	1·00	1·50
		Ey. Phosphor omitted	60·00	
		Ev. PVA gum (29.11.68)	2·00	
		Evy. Phosphor omitted	85·00	
741	282	10d. drab (1.7.68)	1·00	1·25
		a. Uncoated paper**	60·00	
		Ey. Phosphor omitted	70·00	
742		1s. light bluish violet (*shades*)	45	45
		Ey. Phosphor omitted	85·00	
		Ea. Pale bluish violet	2·25	1·00
		Ev. Ditto. PVA gum (26.4.68)	1·50	
		Evy. Phosphor omitted	12·00	
743		1s.6d. greenish blue and deep blue (*shades*) (8.8.67)	50	50
		a. Greenish blue omitted	£160	
		Ey. Phosphor omitted	15·00	
		Ev. PVA gum (28.8.68)	75	
		Eva. Greenish blue omitted	£100	
		Evy. Phosphor omitted	22·00	
		Evb. Prussian blue and indigo	2·50	2·50
		Evby. Phosphor omitted	18·00	
		c. Phosphorised paper (*Prussian blue and indigo*) (10.12.69)	1·10	1·20
		ca. Prussian blue omitted	£450	
744		1s.9d. dull orange and black (*shades*)	1·00	1·00
		Ey. Phosphor omitted	65·00	
		Ea. Bright orange and black	2·50	1·50
		Ev. PVA gum (*bright orange and black*) (16.11.70)	3·00	
Set of 16 (one of each value and colour)			7·00	8·00
Presentation Pack (one of each value) (1968)			15·00	
Presentation Pack (German) (1969)			£150	

* BOOKLET ERRORS. See note after No. 556.

** Uncoated paper. This does not respond to the chalky test, and may be further distinguished from the normal chalk-surfaced paper by the fibres which clearly show on the surface, resulting in the printing impression being rougher, and by the screening dots which are not so evident. The 1d., 4d. and 5d. come from the £1 "Stamps for Cooks" Booklet (1969); the 3d. and 10d. from sheets (1969). The 20p. and 50p. high values (Nos. 830/1) exist with similar errors.

† No. 724a occurs in a vertical strip of four, top stamp perforated on three sides, bottom stamp imperf three sides and the two middle stamps completely imperf.

†† No. 735c comes from the original state of cylinder 15 which is identifiable by the screening dots which extend through the gutters of the stamps and into the margins of the sheet. This must not be confused with imperforate stamps from cylinder 10, a large quantity of which was stolen from the printers early in 1970.

The 1d. with centre band and PVA gum (725) only came in the September 1968 10s. booklet (No. XP6). The 1d., 2d. and 4d. with centre band and gum arabic (725Eg, 728 and 733Eg respectively) only came in the coil strip (725m). The 3d. (No. 730) appeared in booklets on 6.4.68, from coils during Dec 68 and from sheets in Jan 1969. The 4d. with one side band at left (734) came from 10s. (band at left) and £1 (band at left or right) booklet *se-tenant* panes, and the 4d. with one side band at right (734Eb) came from the £1 booklet *se-tenant* panes only.

The 4d. (731) in shades of washed-out grey are colour changelings which we understand are caused by the concentrated solvents used in modern dry cleaning methods.

For decimal issue, see Nos. X841, etc.

First Day Covers

5.6 67	4d., 1s., 1s.9d. (731, 742, 744)		3·50
8.8.67	3d., 9d., 1s.6d. (729, 740, 743)		3·50
5.2.68	½d., 1d., 2d., 6d. (723/4, 726, 736)		3·75
1.7.68	5d., 7d., 8d., 10d. (735, 737/8, 741)		4·50

283 "Master Lambton" (Sir Thomas Lawrence)

284 "Mares and Foals in a Landscape" (George Stubbs)

285 "Children Coming Out of School" (L. S. Lowry)

(Des S. Rose)

1967 (10 July). *British Paintings* (1st series). Chalk-surfaced paper. Two phosphor bands. No wmk. P 14×15 (4d.) or 15×14 (others).

748	**283**	4d. rose-red, lemon, brown, black, new blue and gold	10	10
		a. Gold (value and Queen's head) omitted	£350	
		b. New blue omitted	£21000	
		Ey. Phosphor omitted	7·00	
749	**284**	9d. Venetian red, ochre, grey-black, new blue, greenish yellow and black	15	15
		a. Black (Queen's head and value) omitted	£1200	
		ab. Black (Queen's head only) omitted	£2500	
		Ey. Phosphor omitted	£500	
750	**285**	1s.6d. greenish yellow, grey, rose, new blue, grey-black and gold	35	35
		a. Gold (Queen's head) omitted	£350	
		b. New blue omitted	£350	
		c. Grey (clouds and shading) omitted	£175	
		Ey. Phosphor omitted	£300	
Set of 3			50	50
First Day Cover				2·50
Presentation Pack			35·00	

Special First Day of Issue Postmark

G.P.O. Philatelic Bureau, Edinburgh 1 (Type C) .... 5·00
A First Day of Issue handstamp was provided at Bishop Auckland, Co. Durham, for this issue.

286 *Gypsy Moth IV*

(Des M. and Sylvia Goaman)

1967 (24 July). *Sir Francis Chichester's World Voyage*. Chalk-surfaced paper. Three phosphor bands. No wmk. P 15×14.

751	**286**	1s.9d. black, brown-red, light emerald and blue	20	20
First Day Cover				1·00

Special First Day of Issue Postmarks

G.P.O. Philatelic Bureau, Edinburgh 1 .... 7·00
Greenwich, London SE10 .... 7·00
Plymouth, Devon .... 7·00
The Philatelic Bureau and Greenwich postmarks are similar in design to that for Plymouth. A First Day of Issue handstamp was provided at Chichester, Sussex for this issue.

287 Radar Screen   **288** *Penicillium notatum*

289 Vickers VC-10 Jet Engines   **290** Television Equipment

Broken scale (Cyl. 1c, R. 10/2)

(Des C. Abbott (4d., 1s.), Negus-Sharland team (others))

1967 (19 Sept). *British Discovery and Invention*. Chalk-surfaced paper. Three phosphor bands (4d.) or two phosphor bands (others). W 179 (sideways on 1s.9d.). P 14×15 (1s.9d.) or 15×14 (others).

752	**287**	4d. greenish yellow, black and vermilion	10	10
		a. Broken scale	45·00	
		Ey. Phosphor omitted	5·00	
753	**288**	1s. blue-green, lt greenish blue, slate-purple and bluish violet	20	20
		Wi. Watermark inverted	20·00	
		Ey. Phosphor omitted	10·00	
754	**289**	1s.6d. black, grey, royal blue, ochre and turquoise-blue	25	25
		Wi. Watermark inverted	£240	
		Ey. Phosphor omitted	£525	
755	**290**	1s.9d. black, grey-blue, pale olive-grey, violet and orange	30	30
		a. Pale olive-grey omitted		£4500
		b. Orange (Queen's head) omitted	£30000	
		Ey. Phosphor omitted	£525	
Set of 4			75	75
First Day Cover				2·00
Presentation Pack			6·00	

Special First of Issue Postmark

G.P.O. Philatelic Bureau, Edinburgh (Type C) .... 4·00

WATERMARK. All issues from this date are on unwatermarked paper *unless otherwise stated*

291 "The Adoration of the Shepherds" (School of Seville)

292 "Madonna and Child" (Murillo)

293 "The Adoration of the Shepherds" (Louis le Nain)

(Des S. Rose)

1967 *Christmas, Paintings*. Chalk-surfaced paper. One phosphor band (3d.) or two phosphor bands (others). P 15×14 (1s.6d.) or 14×15 (others).

756	**291**	3d. olive-yellow, rose, blue, black and gold (27.11)	10	15
		a. Gold (value and Queen's head) omitted	£110	

		ab. Gold (Queen's head only) omitted	£2750	
		b. Printed on the gummed side	£625	
		c. Rose omitted	£3700	
		Ey. Phosphor omitted	1·00	
757	292	4d. bright purple, greenish yellow, new blue, grey-black and gold (18.10)	10	15
		a. Gold (value and Queen's head) omitted	80·00	
		ab. Gold (Queen's head only) omitted	£4500	
		b. Gold ("4D" only) omitted	£3000	
		c. Greenish yellow (Child, robe and Madonna's face) omitted	£7500	
		d. Greenish yellow and gold omitted	£15000	
		Ey. Phosphor omitted	£125	
758	293	1s.6d. bright purple, bistre, lemon, black, orange-red, ultramarine and gold (27.11)	15	15
		a. Gold (value and Queen's head) omitted	£18000	
		ab. Gold (face value only) omitted	£3000	
		b. Ultramarine omitted	£850	
		c. Lemon omitted	£20000	
		Ey. Phosphor omitted	12·00	

Set of 3 .... 30 30
First Day Covers (2) .... 1·50

Distinct shades exist of the 3d. and 4d. values but are not listable as there are intermediate shades. For the 4d., stamps from one machine show a darker background and give the appearance of the yellow colour being omitted, but this is not so and these should not be confused with the true missing yellow No. 757c.

No. 757b comes from stamps in the first vertical row of a sheet.

The 3d. and 4d. values are known imperforate. They are of proof status.

Special First Day of Issue Postmarks

G.P.O. Philatelic Bureau, Edinburgh 1 (4d.) (18 Oct.) (Type C)	50
G.P.O. Philatelic Bureau, Edinburgh 1 (3d., 1s.6d.) (27 Nov.) (Type C)	1·00
Bethlehem, Llandeilo, Carms (4d.) (18 Oct.) (Type C)	2·00
Bethlehem, Llandeilo, Carms (3d., 1s.6d.) (27 Nov.) (Type C)	3·00

Gift Pack 1967
1967 (27 Nov.). Comprises Nos. 715p/22p and 748/58.
GP758c Gift Pack .... 3·00

(Recess Bradbury, Wilkinson)

1967–68. No wmk. White paper. *P* 11×12.

759	166	2s.6d. black-brown (1.7.68)	30	45
760	167	5s. red (10.4.68)	70	75
761	168	10s. bright ultramarine (10.4.68)	7·75	4·75
762	169	£1 black (4.12.67)	7·50	4·50
Set of 4			15·00	8·00

PVA GUM. All the following issues from this date have PVA gum except where footnotes state otherwise.

294 Tarr Steps, Exmoor

295 Aberfeldy Bridge

296 Menai Bridge

297 M4 Viaduct

(Des A. Restall (9d.), L. Rosoman (1s.6d.), J. Matthews (others))

1968 (29 Apr). *British Bridges*. Chalk-surfaced paper. Two phosphor bands. *P* 15×14.

763	294	4d. black, bluish violet, turquoise-blue and gold	10	10
		a. Printed on gummed side	35·00	
		Ey. Phosphor omitted		
764	295	9d. red-brown, myrtle-green, ultramarine, olive-brown, black and gold	15	15
		a. Gold (Queen's head) omitted	£280	
		b. Ultramarine omitted	†	£7000
		Ey. Phosphor omitted	15·00	
765	296	1s.6d. olive-brown, red-orange, brt green, turquoise-green and gold	25	25
		a. Gold (Queen's head) omitted	£425	
		b. Red-orange (rooftops) omitted	£450	
		Ey. Phosphor omitted	50·00	
766	297	1s.9d. olive-brown, greenish yellow, dull green, dp ultramarine and gold	30	30

	a. Gold (Queen's head) omitted	£425
	Ey. Phosphor omitted	10·00
	Eya. Gold (Queen's head) & Phosphor omitted	
Set of 4		70 70
First Day Cover		1·50
Presentation Pack		5·00

No. 764b is only known on First Day Covers posted from Canterbury, Kent, or the Philatelic Bureau, Edinburgh.

Used examples of the 1s.6d. and 1s.9d. are known with both the gold and the phosphor omitted.

Special First Day of Issue Postmarks

297a

G.P.O. Philatelic Bureau, Edinburgh 1	5·00
Bridge, Canterbury, Kent	6·00
Aberfeldy, Perthshire (Type A) (9d. value only)	10·00
Menai Bridge, Anglesey (Type A) (1s.6d. value only)	10·00

The Bridge, Canterbury, postmark is similar in design to that for the Philatelic Bureau.

298 "TUC" and Trades Unionists

299 Mrs. Emmeline Pankhurst (statue)

300 Sopwith Camel and English Electric Lightning Fighters

301 Captain Cook's *Endeavour* and Signature

(Des D. Gentleman (4d.), C. Abbott (others))

1968 (29 May). *Anniversaries* (1st series). Events described on stamps. Chalk surfaced paper. Two phosphor bands. *P* 15×14.

767	298	4d. emerald, olive, blue and black	10	10
		Ey. Phosphor omitted	12·00	
768	299	9d. reddish violet, bluish grey and black	15	15
		Ey. Phosphor omitted	7·00	
769	300	1s. olive-brown, blue, red, slate-blue and black	15	15
		Ey. Phosphor omitted	10·00	
770	301	1s.9d. yellow-ochre and blackish brown	35	35
		Ey. Phosphor omitted	£190	
Set of 4			65	65
First Day Cover				5·00
Presentation Pack			5·00	

Special First Day of Issue Postmarks

301a

301c

301b

301d

G.P.O. Philatelic Bureau, Edinburgh 1 (Type C)		7·00
Manchester (4d. value only)		1·00
Aldeburgh, Suffolk (9d. value only)		2·00
Hendon, London NW4 (1s. value only)		3·00
Whitby, Yorkshire (1s.9d. value only)		4·00

The Philatelic Bureau postmark was used on sets of four, but the other postmarks were only available on single stamps.

302 "Queen Elizabeth I" (unknown artist)

303 "Pinkie" (Sir Thomas Lawrence)

304 "Ruins of St. Mary Le Port" (John Piper)

305 "The Hay Wain" (John Constable)

(Des S. Rose)

1968 (12 Aug). *British Paintings* (2nd series). Queen's head embossed. Chalk-surfaced paper. Two phosphor bands. P 15×14 (1s.9d.) or 14×15 (others).

771	**302**	4d. black, vermilion, greenish yellow, grey and gold	10	10
		a. Gold (value and Queen's head) omitted	£350	
		b. Vermilion omitted*	£700	
		Ec. Embossing omitted	90·00	
		Ey. Phosphor omitted	1·50	
		Eya. Gold (value and Queen's head) and phosphor omitted	£4000	
772	**303**	1s. mauve, new blue, greenish yellow, black, magenta and gold	10	20
		a. Gold (value and Queen's head) omitted	£7500	
		Eb. Gold (value and Queen's head), embossing and phosphor omitted	£750	
		Ec. Embossing omitted		
		Ey. Phosphor omitted	7·00	
773	**304**	1s.6d. slate, orange, black, mauve, greenish yellow, ultramarine and gold	20	25
		a. Gold (value and Queen's head) omitted	£350	
		Eb. Embossing omitted	£300	
		Ey. Phosphor omitted	10·00	
774	**305**	1s.9d. greenish yellow, black, new blue, red and gold	25	40

	a. Gold (value and Queen's head) and embossing omitted	£1000
	b. Red omitted	£14000
	Ec. Embossing omitted	£140
	Ey. Phosphor omitted	20·00
Set of 4		60 · 85
First Day Cover		2·00
Presentation Pack (P. O. Pack No. 1)		6·00
Presentation Pack (German) (P. O. Pack No. 1)		19·00

No. 774a is only known with the phosphor also omitted.
* The effect of this is to leave the face and hands white and there is more yellow and olive in the costume.

The 4d. also exists with the value only omitted resulting from a colour shift.

Special First Day of Issue Postmark
G.P.O. Philatelic Bureau, Edinburgh 1 (Type C)		5·00

Gift Pack 1968
1968 (16 Sept). Comprises Nos. 763/74.
GP774c	Gift Pack	6·00
GP774d	Gift Pack (German)	80·00

Collectors Pack 1968
1968 (16 Sept). Comprises Nos. 752/8 and 763/74.
CP774e	Collectors Pack	7·00

306 Boy and Girl with Rocking Horse

307 Girl with Doll's House

308 Boy with Train Set

(Des Rosalind Dease. Head printed in gold and then embossed)

1968 (25 Nov). *Christmas*, Children's Toys. Chalk-surfaced paper. One centre phosphor band (4d.) or two phosphor bands (others). P 15×14 (4d.) or 14×15 (others).

775	**306**	4d. black, orange, vermilion, ultramarine, bistre and gold	10	15
		a. Gold omitted	£6000	
		b. Vermilion omitted*	£650	
		c. Ultramarine omitted	£550	
		d. Bistre omitted		
		e. Orange omitted	†	—
		Ef. Embossing omitted	6·00	
		Ey. Phosphor omitted	5·00	
776	**307**	9d. yellow-olive, black, brown, yellow, magenta, orange, turquoise-green and gold	15	25
		a. Yellow omitted	£175	
		b. Turquoise-green (dress) omitted	£22000	
		Ec. Embossing omitted	6·00	
		Ey. Phosphor omitted	10·00	
		Eya. Embossing and phosphor omitted	10·00	
777	**308**	1s.6d. ultramarine, yellow-orange, bright purple, blue-green, black and gold	15	50
		Ea. Embossing omitted		
		Ey. Phosphor omitted	15·00	
Set of 3			35	80
First Day Cover				1·00
Presentation Pack (P. O. Pack No. 4)			5·00	
Presentation Pack (German)			19·00	

* The effect of the missing vermilion is shown on the rocking horse, saddle and faces which appear orange instead of red.

A single used example of the 4d. exists with the bistre omitted.

No. 775c is only known with phosphor also omitted.

Two machines were used for printing the 4d. value:

Stamps from cylinders 1A-1B-2C-1D-1E in combination with 1F, 2F or 3F (gold) were printed entirely on the Rembrandt sheet-fed machine. They invariably have the Queen's head level with the top of the boy's head and the sheets are perforated through the left side margin.

Stamps from cylinders 2A-2B-3C-2D-2E in combination with 1F, 2F, 3F or 4F (gold) were printed on the reel-fed Thrissell machine in five colours (its maximum colour capacity) and subsequently sheet-fed on the Rembrandt machine for the Queen's head and the embossing. The position of the Queen's head is generally lower than on the stamps printed at one operation but it varies in different parts of the sheet and is not, therefore, a sure indication for identifying single stamps. Another small difference is that the boy's grey pullover is noticeably "moth-eaten" in the Thrissell printings and is normal on the Rembrandt. The Thrissell printings are perforated through the top margin.

Special First Day of Issue Postmarks

G.P.O. Philatelic Bureau, Edinburgh 1 (Type C)	3·00
Bethlehem, Llandeilo, Carms (Type C)	7·00

309 R.M.S. *Queen Elizabeth 2*

310 Elizabethan Galleon

311 East Indiaman

312 *Cutty Sark*

313 S.S. *Great Britain*

314 R.M.S. *Mauretania I*

(Des D. Gentleman)

1969 (15 Jan). *British Ships*. Chalk-surfaced paper. Two vertical phosphor bands at right (1s.), one horizontal phosphor band (5d.) or two phosphor bands (9d.). P 15×14.

778	309	5d. black, grey, red and turquoise	10	15
		a. Black (Queen's head, value, hull and inscr) omitted	£3500	
		b. Grey (decks, etc.) omitted	£280	
		c. Red (inscription) omitted	£300	
		Ey. Phosphor omitted	5·00	
		Eya. Red and phosphor omitted	£250	
779	310	9d. red, blue, ochre, brown, black and grey	10	25
		a. Strip of 3. Nos. 779/81	1·30	1·50
		ab. Red and blue omitted	£3800	
		ac. Blue omitted	£3800	
		Ey. Phosphor omitted	12·00	
		Eya. Strip of 3. Nos. 779/81. Phosphor omitted	40·00	
780	311	9d. ochre, brown, black and grey	10	25
		Ey. Phosphor omitted	12·00	
781	312	9d. ochre, brown, black and grey	10	25
		Ey. Phosphor omitted	12·00	
782	313	1s. brown, black, grey, green and greenish yellow	40	35
		a. Pair. Nos. 782/3	1·30	1·50
		ab. Greenish yellow omitted	£4800	
		Ey. Phosphor omitted	28·00	

	Eya. Pair. Nos. 782/3. Phosphor omitted	65·00	
783 314	1s. red, black, brown, carmine and grey	40	35
	a. Carmine (hull overlay) omitted	£40000	
	b. Red (funnels) omitted	£30000	
	c. Carmine and red omitted	£30000	
	Ey. Phosphor omitted	30·00	
Set of 6		2·40	2·75
First Day Cover			6·00
Presentation Pack (P. O. Pack No. 5)		6·00	
Presentation Pack (German) (P. O. Pack No. 5)		60·00	

The 9d. and 1s. values were arranged in horizontal strips of three and pairs respectively throughout the sheet. No. 779ab is known only with the phosphor also omitted.

Special First Day of Issue Postmark

G.P.O. Philatelic Bureau, Edinburgh 1 (Type C)	8·00

315 Concorde in Flight

316 Plan and Elevation Views

317 Concorde's Nose and Tail

(Des M. and Sylvia Goaman (4d.), D. Gentleman (9d., 1s.6d.))

1969 (3 Mar). *First Flight of Concorde*. Chalk-surfaced paper. Two phosphor bands. P 15×14.

784	315	4d. yellow-orange, violet, greenish blue, blue-green and pale green	25	25
		a. Violet (value etc.) omitted	£850	
		b. Yellow-orange omitted	£850	
		Ey. Phosphor omitted	1·00	
		Eya. Yellow-orange and phosphor omitted	£850	
785	316	9d. ultramarine, emerald, red and grey-blue	55	75
		a. Face value and inscr omitted	£40000	
		Ey. Phosphor omitted	£100	
786	317	1s.6d. deep blue, silver-grey and light blue	75	1·00
		a. Silver-grey omitted	£850	
		Ey. Phosphor omitted	9·00	
Set of 3			1·00	1·50
First Day Cover				3·00
Presentation Pack (P. O. Pack No. 6)			12·00	
Presentation Pack (German)			95·00	

No. 785a is caused by a colour shift of the grey-blue. On the only known example the top of the Queen's head appears across the perforations at foot. No. 786a affects the Queen's head which appears in the light blue colour.

Special First Day of Issue Postmarks

G.P.O Philatelic Bureau, Edinburgh (Type C)	4·00
Filton, Bristol (Type C)	12·00

318 Queen Elizabeth II
(See also Type **357**)

(Des after plaster cast by Arnold Machin. Recess Bradbury, Wilkinson)

1969 (5 Mar). P 12.

787	318	2s.6d. brown	35	30
788		5s. crimson-lake	1·80	60
789		10s. deep ultramarine	6·00	7·00
790		£1 bluish black	3·25	1·50
Set of 4			10·00	8·50
First Day Cover				9·50

Presentation Pack (P. O. Pack No. 7)	16·00
Presentation Pack (German)	80·00

Special First Day of Issue Postmarks

G.P.O. Philatelic Bureau (Type C)	12·00
Windsor, Berks (Type C)	18·00

For decimal issue, see Nos. 829/31b and notes after No. 831b in Machin Decimal Definitives section.

319 Page from *Daily Mail*, and Vickers FB-27 Vimy Aircraft

320 Europa and CEPT Emblems

321 ILO Emblem

322 Flags of NATO Countries

323 Vickers FB-27 Vimy Aircraft and Globe showing Flight

(Des P. Sharland (5d., 1s., 1s.6d.), M. and Sylvia Goaman (9d., 1s.9d.))

1969 (2 Apr). *Anniversaries* (2nd series). Events described on stamps. Chalk-surfaced paper. Two phosphor bands. P 15×14.

791	**319**	5d. black, pale sage-green, chestnut and new blue	10	15
		Ey. Phosphor omitted		
792	**320**	9d. pale turquoise, dp blue, lt emerald-green and black	15	25
		aEy. Phosphor omitted		
		a. Uncoated paper*	£1800	
		Ey. Phosphor omitted	18·00	
793	**321**	1s. brt purple, dp blue and lilac	15	25
		Eya. Phosphor omitted	10·00	
794	**322**	1s.6d. red, royal blue, yellow-green, black, lemon and new blue	15	30
		e. Black omitted	£125	
		f. Yellow-green (from flags) omitted	90·00	
		g. Lemon (from flags) omitted	†	£4500
		Ey. Phosphor omitted	9·00	
		Eya. Yellow-green and phosphor omitted	95·00	
795	**323**	1s.9d. yellow-olive, greenish yellow and pale turquoise-green	40	40
		a. Uncoated paper*	£275	
		Ey. Phosphor omitted	6·00	
Set of 5			85	1·20
First Day Cover				4·00
Presentation Pack (P. O. Pack No. 9)			5·00	
Presentation Pack (German)			95·00	

*Uncoated paper. The second note after No. 744 also applies here. No. 794g is only known used on First Day Cover from Liverpool. A trial of the 9d value in green and red is known.

Special First Day of Issue Postmarks

G.P.O. Philatelic Bureau, Edinburgh (Type C)	4·00

324 Durham Cathedral   **325** York Minster

326 St. Giles, Edinburgh

327 Canterbury Cathedral

328 St. Paul's Cathedral   **329** Liverpool Metropolitan Cathedral

(Des P. Gauld)

1969 (28 May). *British Architecture* (1st series). Cathedrals. Chalk-surfaced paper. Two phosphor bands. P 15×14.

796	**324**	5d. grey-black, orange, pale bluish violet and black	10	10
		a. Block of 4. Nos. 796/9	1·10	1·25
		ab. Block of 4. Uncoated paper†	£1000	
		b. Pale bluish violet omitted	£24000	
797	**325**	5d. grey-black, pale bluish violet, new blue and black	10	10
		b. Pale bluish violet omitted	£24000	
798	**326**	5d. grey-black, purple, green and black	10	10
		c. Green omitted*	£100	
799	**327**	5d. grey-black, green, new blue and black	10	10
800	**328**	9d. grey-black, ochre, pale drab, violet and black	25	30
		a. Black (value) omitted	£300	
		Ey. Phosphor omitted	45·00	
		Eya. Black and phosphor omitted	£350	
801	**329**	1s.6d. grey-black, pale turquoise, pale reddish violet, pale yellow-olive and black	25	35
		a. Black (value) omitted	£5000	
		b. Black (value) double	£5000	
		Ey. Phosphor omitted	20·00	
Set of 6			1·40	1·70
First Day Cover				4·00
Presentation Pack (P. O. Pack No. 10)			6·00	
Presentation Pack (German)			48·00	

*The missing green on the roof top is known on R. 2/5, R. 8/5 and R. 10/5 but all are from different sheets and it only occurred in part of the printing, being "probably caused by a batter on the impression cylinder". Examples are also known with the green partly omitted.

†Uncoated paper. The second note after No. 744 also applies here.

Nos. 796/9 were issued together *se-tenant* in blocks of four throughout the sheet.

Special First Day of Issue Postmark

G.P.O. Philatelic Bureau, Edinburgh (Type C)	4·00

330 The King's Gate, Caernarvon Castle

331 The Eagle Tower, Caernarvon Castle

332 Queen Eleanor's Gate, Caernarvon Castle

333 Celtic Cross, Margam Abbey

334 H.R.H. The Prince
of Wales (after photograph
by G. Argent)

(Des D. Gentleman)

1969 (1 July). *Investiture of H.R.H. The Prince of Wales.* Chalk-surfaced paper. Two phosphor bands. P 14×15.

802	**330**	5d. dp olive-grey, lt olive-grey, dp grey, light grey, red, pale turquoise-green, black and silver ..	10	15
		a. Strip of 3. Nos. 802/4	50	1·00
		b. Black (value and inscr) omitted......	£750	
		c. Red omitted*	£1700	
		d. Deep grey omitted**.............................	£575	
		e. Pale turquoise-green omitted	£1600	
		f. Light grey omitted	£14000	
		Ey. Phosphor omitted	5·00	
		Eya. Strip of 3. Nos. 802/4. Phosphor omitted	15·00	
803	**331**	5d. dp olive-grey, lt olive-grey, dp grey, light grey, red, pale turquoise-green, black and silver ..	10	15
		b. Black (value and inscr) omitted......	£750	
		c. Red omitted*	£1700	
		d. Deep grey omitted**.............................	£575	
		e. Pale turquoise-green omitted	£1600	
		f. Light grey (marks on walls, window frames, etc) omitted	£14000	£8000
		Ey. Phosphor omitted	5·00	
804	**332**	5d. dp olive-grey, lt olive-grey, dp grey, lt grey, red, pale turquoise-green, black and silver	10	15
		b. Black (value and inscr) omitted......	£750	
		c. Red omitted*	£1700	
		d. Deep grey omitted**.............................	£575	
		e. Pale turquoise-green omitted	£1600	
		f. Light grey omitted	£14000	
		Ey. Phosphor omitted	5·00	
805	**333**	9d. dp grey, lt grey, black and gold	15	30
		Ey. Phosphor omitted	25·00	
806	**334**	1s. blackish yellow-olive and gold	15	30
		Ey. Phosphor omitted	18·00	
Set of 5.......			75	1·40
First Day Cover ...				1·70
Presentation Pack† (P. O. Pack No. 11)			3·00	
Presentation Pack (German)...			48·00	

Nos. 802/4 were issued together *se-tenant* in strips of three throughout the sheet.

* The 5d. value is also known with the red misplaced downwards and where this occurs the red printing does not take very well on the silver background and in some cases is so faint it could be mistaken for a missing red. However, the red can be seen under a magnifying glass and caution should therefore be exercised when purchasing copies of Nos. 802/4c.

** The deep grey affects the dark portions of the windows and doors.

† In addition to the generally issued Presentation Pack a further pack in different colours and with all texts printed in both English and Welsh was made available exclusively through Education Authorities for free distribution to all schoolchildren in Wales and Monmouthshire *(Price £40).*

No. 803f is only known commercially used on cover.

Special First Day of Issue Postmarks

G.P.O. Philatelic Bureau, Edinburgh 1 (Type C)	3·00
Day of Investiture, Caernarvon..	5·00

335 Mahatma Gandhi   "Tooth" flaw (Cyl. 2A, R. 20/3)

(Des B. Mullick)

1969 (13 Aug). *Gandhi Centenary Year.* Chalk-surfaced paper. Two phosphor bands. P 15×14.

807	**335**	1s.6d. black, green, red-orange and grey	40	30
		a. "Tooth" flaw...	35·00	
		b. Printed on the gummed side	£1750	

Ey. Phosphor omitted	4·00	
First Day Cover		1·00

Special First Day of Issue Postmark

G.P.O. Philatelic Bureau, Edinburgh (Type C)	1·50

Collectors Pack 1969
1969 (15 Sept). Comprises Nos. 775/86 and 791/807.

CP807b	Collectors Pack	25·00

336 National Giro "G" Symbol   **337** Telecommunications–
International Subscriber
Dialling

338 Telecommunications–   **339** Postal Mechanisation–
Pulse Code Modulation   Automatic Sorting

(Des D. Gentleman. Litho De La Rue)

1969 (1 Oct). *Post Office Technology Commemoration.* Chalk-surfaced paper. Two phosphor bands. P 13½×14.

808	**336**	5d. new blue, greenish blue, lavender and black..	10	10
		Ey. Phosphor omitted	5·00	
809	**337**	9d. emerald, violet-blue and black	20	25
810	**338**	1s. emerald, lavender and black	20	25
		Ey. Phosphor omitted	£325	
811	**339**	1s.6d. bright purple, light blue, grey-blue and black................................	50	50
Set of 4.......			90	1·00
First Day Cover ...				2·00
Presentation Pack (P. O. Pack No. 13)............................			5·00	

Special First Day of Issue Postmark

G.P.O.Philatelic Bureau, Edinburgh (Type C)..................................	2·00

340 Herald Angel   **341** The Three Shepherds

342 The Three Kings

(Des F. Wegner. Queen's head (and stars 4d., 5d. and scrollwork 1s.6d.) printed in gold and then embossed)

1969 (26 Nov). *Christmas,* Traditional Religious Themes. Chalk-surfaced paper. Two phosphor bands (5d., 1s.6d.) or one centre band (4d.). P 15×14.

812	**340**	4d. vermilion, new blue, orange, brt purple, light green, bluish violet, blackish brown and gold	10	10
		a. Gold (Queen's head etc.) omitted..	£13000	
		Eb. Centre band 3½ mm	30	20
813	**341**	5d. magenta, light blue, royal blue, olive-brown, green, greenish yellow, red and gold	15	15
		a. Lt blue (sheep, etc.) omitted............	£110	
		b. Red omitted*...	£2700	
		c. Gold (Queen's head) omitted	£1200	
		d. Green omitted.......................................	£450	
		e. Olive-brown, red and gold omitted	£17000	
		Ef. Embossing omitted................................	25·00	
		Ey. Phosphor omitted	5·00	
814	**342**	1s.6d. greenish yellow, brt purple, bluish violet, dp slate, orange, green, new blue and gold	20	20
		a. Gold (Queen's head etc.) omitted..	£180	
		b. Deep slate (value) omitted................	£550	

c. Greenish yellow omitted	£550	
e. New blue omitted	£140	
Ef. Embossing omitted	12·00	
Ey. Phosphor omitted	6·00	
Eya. Embossing and phosphor omitted	12·00	
Set of 3	40	40
First Day Cover		1·00
Presentation Pack (P. O. Pack No. 14)	5·00	

* The effect of the missing red is shown on the hat, leggings and purse which appear as dull orange.

No. 812 has one centre band 8 mm. wide but this was of no practical use in the automatic facing machines and after about three-quarters of the stamps had been printed the remainder were printed with a 3½mm. band (No. 812Eb).

No. 813e was caused by a paper fold and also shows the phosphor omitted.

Used copies of the 5d. have been seen with the olive-brown or greenish yellow (tunic at left) omitted.

Special First Day of Issue Postmarks

P.O. Philatelic Bureau, Edinburgh (Type C)	2·00
Bethlehem, Llandeilo, Carms (Type C)	3·00

343 Fife Harling   **344** Cotswold Limestone

345 Welsh Stucco   **346** Ulster Thatch

5d. Lemon omitted from left chimney (Cyl. 1H, R. 12/2)

(Des D. Gentleman (5d., 9d.), Sheila Robinson (1s., 1s.6d.))

1970 (11 Feb). *British Rural Architecture.* Chalk-surfaced paper. Two phosphor bands. *P* 15×14.

815	**343**	5d. grey, grey-black, black, lemon, greenish blue, orange-brown, ultramarine and green	10	10
		a. Lemon omitted	£175	
		b. Grey (Queen's head and cottage shading) omitted		
		c. Greenish blue (door) omitted	†	£4800
		d. Grey black (inscription & face value) omitted	£20000	
		e. Grey black (face value only) omitted	£17000	
		f. Green omitted (cobblestones)		
		g. Lemon omitted from left chimney	35·00	
		Ey. Phosphor omitted	2·00	
816	**344**	9d. orange-brown, olive-yellow, bright green, black, grey-black and grey	20	25
		Ey. Phosphor omitted	10·00	
817	**345**	1s. deep blue, reddish lilac, drab and new blue	25	25
		a. New blue omitted	£150	
		Ey. Phosphor omitted	15·00	
818	**346**	1s.6d. greenish yellow, black, turquoise-blue and lilac	30	40
		a. Turquoise-blue omitted	£21000	
		Ey. Phosphor omitted	5·00	
Set of 4			75	90
First Day Cover				1·50
Presentation Pack (P. O. Pack No. 15)			6·00	

Used examples of the 5d. exist, one of which is on piece, with the greenish blue colour omitted.

Special First Day of Issue Postmark

British Philatelic Bureau, Edinburgh (Type C)	2·00

347 Signing the Declaration of Arbroath   **348** Florence Nightingale attending Patients

349 Signing of International Co-operative Alliance   **350** Pilgrims and *Mayflower*

351 Sir William Herschel, Francis Baily, Sir John Herschel and Telescope

(Des F. Wegner (5d., 9d. and 1s.6d.), Marjorie Saynor (1s., 1s.9d.). Queen's head printed in gold and then embossed)

1970 (1 Apr). *Anniversaries* (3rd series). Events described on stamps. Chalk-surfaced paper. Two phosphor bands. *P* 15×14.

819	**347**	5d. black, yellow-olive, blue, emerald, greenish yellow, rose-red, gold and orange-red	10	10
		a. Gold (Queen's head) omitted	£4250	
		b. Emerald omitted	£550	
		Ey. Phosphor omitted	£380	
820	**348**	9d. ochre, deep blue, carmine, black, blue-green, yellow-olive, gold and blue	15	15
		a. Ochre omitted	£550	
		Eb. Embossing omitted	15·00	
		Ey. Phosphor omitted	5·00	
821	**349**	1s. green, greenish yellow, brown, black, cerise, gold and lt blue	20	25
		a. Gold (Queen's head) omitted	90·00	
		Eb. Green and embossing omitted	£170	
		c. Green omitted	£170	
		d. Brown omitted	£320	
		Ee. Embossing omitted	12·00	
		Ey. Phosphor omitted	5·00	
		Eya. Brown and phosphor omitted	£320	
		Eyb. Embossing and phosphor omitted	22·00	
822	**350**	1s.6d. greenish yellow, carmine, deep yellow-olive, emerald, black, blue, gold and sage-green	20	30
		a. Gold (Queen's head) omitted	£320	
		b. Emerald omitted	£170	
		Ec. Embossing omitted	6·00	
		Ey. Phosphor omitted	5·00	
823	**351**	1s.9d. black, slate, lemon, gold and bright purple	25	30
		a. Lemon (trousers and document) omitted	£10000	£6000
		Eb. Embossing omitted	75·00	
		Ey. Phosphor omitted	5·00	
Set of 5			80	1·00
First Day Cover				2·00
Presentation Pack (P. O. Pack No. 16)			5·00	

No. 823a is known mint, or used on First Day Cover postmarked London WC.

Special First Day of Issue Postmark

British Philatelic Bureau, Edinburgh (Type C)	2·50

First Day of Issue handstamps were provided at Arbroath, Angus; Billericay, Essex; Boston, Lincs and Rochdale, Lancs for this issue.

352 "Mr. Pickwick and Sam Weller" (*Pickwick Papers*)

353 "Mr. and Mrs. Micawber" (*David Copperfield*)

354 "David Copperfield and Betsy Trotwood" (*David Copperfield*)

355 "Oliver asking for more" (*Oliver Twist*)

356 "Grasmere" (from engraving by J. Farrington, R.A.)

(Des Rosalind Dease. Queen's head printed in gold and then embossed)

1970 (3 June). *Literary Anniversaries* (1st series). Death Centenary of Charles Dickens (novelist) (5d.×4) and Birth Bicentenary of William Wordsworth (poet) (1s.6d.). Chalk-surfaced paper. Two phosphor bands. P 14×15.

824	**352**	5d. black, orange, silver, gold and magenta	10	25
		a. Block of 4. Nos. 824/7	75	1·50
		ab. Imperf (block of four)	£2500	
		ac. Silver (inscr) omitted (block of four)	—	
825	**353**	5d. black, magenta, silver, gold and orange	10	25
826	**354**	5d. black, light greenish blue, silver, gold and yellow-bistre	10	25
		b. Yellow-bistre (value) omitted	£10000	
827	**355**	5d. black, yellow-bistre, silver, gold and light greenish blue	10	25
		b. Yellow-bistre (background) omitted	£25000	
		c. Lt greenish blue (value) omitted*	£825	
		d. Lt greenish blue and silver (inscr at foot) omitted	£35000	
828	**356**	1s.6d. yellow-olive, black, silver, gold and bright blue	25	50
		a. Gold (Queen's head) omitted	£10000	
		b. Silver ("Grasmere") omitted	£250	
		c. Bright blue (face value) omitted	£22500	
		d. Bright blue and silver omitted	£27500	
		Ee. Embossing omitted	6·00	
		Ey. Phosphor omitted	5·00	
		Eya. Embossing and phosphor omitted	22·00	
Set of 5			90	1·80
First Day Cover				3·00
Presentation Pack (P. O. Pack No. 17)			6·00	

Nos. 824/7 were issued together *se-tenant* in blocks of four throughout the sheet.

* No. 827c (unlike No. 826b) comes from a sheet on which the colour was only partially omitted so that, although No. 827 was completely without the light greenish blue colour, it was still partially present on No. 826.

Essays exist of Nos. 824/7 showing the Queen's head in silver and with different inscriptions. (*Price* £13000 *per block of 4*).

Special First Day of Issue Postmarks

British Philatelic Bureau, Edinburgh (Type C)	3·00
Cockermouth, Cumberland (Type C) (No. 828 only)	4·00
Rochester, Kent (Type C) (Nos. 824/7)	4·00

A First Day of Issue handstamp was provided at Broadstairs, Kent, for this issue.

For Nos. 829/31*b* see Decimal Machin Definitives section.

358 Runners

359 Swimmers

360 Cyclists

(Des A. Restall. Litho D.L.R.)

1970 (15 July). *Ninth British Commonwealth Games*. Chalk-surfaced paper. Two phosphor bands. P 13½×14.

832	**358**	5d. pink, emerald, greenish yellow and deep yellow-green	25	25
		a. Greenish yellow omitted	£20000	
		Ey. Phosphor omitted	£200	
833	**359**	1s.6d. light greenish blue, lilac, bistre-brown and Prussian blue	50	50
		Ey. Phosphor omitted	60·00	
834	**360**	1s.9d. yellow-orange, lilac, salmon and deep red-brown	50	50
Set of 3			1·10	1·10
First Day Cover				1·40
Presentation Pack (P. O. Pack No. 19)			5·00	

Special First Day of Issue Postmark

British Philatelic Bureau, Edinburgh (Type C)	4·00

Collectors Pack 1970

1970 Sept 14 Comprises Nos. 808/28 and 832/4.

CP834*a* Collectors Pack	35·00

361 1d. Black (1840)

362 1s. Green (1847)

363 4d. Carmine (1855)

(Des D. Gentleman)

1970 (18 Sept). *Philympia 70* Stamp Exhibition. Chalk-surfaced paper. Two phosphor bands. P 14×14½.

835	**361**	5d. grey-black, brownish bistre, black and dull purple	25	10
		a. Dull purple (Queen's head) omitted	—	
		Ey. Phosphor omitted	5·00	
836	**362**	9d. light drab, bluish green, stone, black and dull purple	25	30
		Ey. Phosphor omitted	12·00	
837	**363**	1s.6d. carmine, light drab, black and dull purple	25	45
		Ey. Phosphor omitted	4·00	
Set of 3			70	75
First Day Cover				1·50
Presentation Pack (P. O. Pack No. 21)			5·00	

Special First Day of Issue Postmark

British Post Office Philatelic Bureau, Edinburgh (Type D)	2·00

364 Shepherds and Apparition of the Angel

365 Mary, Joseph and Christ in the Manger

366 The Wise Men bearing gifts

(Des Sally Stiff after De Lisle Psalter. Queen's head printed in gold and then embossed)

1970 (25 Nov). *Christmas, Robert De Lisle Psalter.* Chalk-surfaced paper. One centre phosphor band (4d.) or two phosphor bands (others). P 14×15.

838	**364**	4d. brown-red, turquoise-green, pale chestnut, brown, grey-black, gold and vermilion	15	10
		Ea. Embossing omitted	50·00	
		Ey. Phosphor omitted	60·00	
839	**365**	5d. emerald, gold, blue, brown-red, ochre, grey-black and violet	15	15
		a. Gold (Queen's head) omitted	†	£3500
		b. Emerald omitted	£140	
		c. Imperf (pair)	£500	
		d. Ochre omitted	£8000	†
		Ed. Embossing omitted	15·00	
		Ey. Phosphor omitted	5·00	
840	**366**	1s.6d. gold, grey-black, pale turquoise-green, salmon, ultramarine, ochre and yellow-green	25	30
		a. Salmon omitted	£220	
		b. Ochre omitted	£140	
		Ec. Embossing omitted	35·00	
		Ey. Phosphor omitted	5·00	
		Eya. Embossing and phosphor omitted		
Set of 3			50	50
First Day Cover				1·00
Presentation Pack (P. O. Pack No. 22)			5·00	

Special First Day of Issue Postmarks

First Day of Issue 25 Nov 70
Gloria in Excelsis
Bethlehem
Llandeilo
Carms

British Post Office Philatelic Bureau, Edinburgh (Type D)	1·50
Bethlehem, Llandeilo, Carms	2·00

Nos. 841/880 are no longer used. For 1971-96 definitives in decimal currency with conventional perforations on all sides, see Nos. X841/1058 in the Decimal Machin Definitives section.

(New Currency. 100 new pence = £1)

368 "A Mountain Road" (T. P. Flanagan)

369 "Deer's Meadow" (Tom Carr)

370 "Slieve na brock" (Colin Middleton)

(Colin Middleton)

1971 (16 June). *Ulster 1971 Paintings.* Chalk-surfaced paper. Two phosphor bands. P 15×14.

881	**368**	3p. yellow-buff, pale yellow, Venetian red, black, blue and drab	25	25
		Ey. Phosphor omitted	6·00	
		a. Venetian red omitted		—
882	**369**	7½p. olive-brown, brownish grey, pale olive-grey, deep blue, cobalt and grey-blue	50	50
		a. Pale olive-grey omitted*	£380	
		Ey. Phosphor omitted	25·00	
883	**370**	9p. greenish yellow, orange, grey, lavender-grey, bistre, black, pale ochre-brown and ochre-brown	50	50
		a. Orange (flowers) omitted	£4500	
		Ey. Phosphor omitted	25·00	
Set of 3			1·00	1·00
First Day Cover				1·75
Presentation Pack (P.O. Pack No. 26a)			7·50	

* This only affects the boulder in the foreground, which appears whitish and it only applied to some stamps in the sheet.

Special First Day of Issue Postmarks

FIRST DAY OF ISSUE
16 JUNE 1971
BELFAST

British Post Office Philatelic Bureau, Edinburgh (Type D, see Introduction)	2·50
Belfast	8·00

First Day of Issue handstamps, in the same design as that for Belfast, were provided at Armagh, Ballymena, Coleraine, Cookstown, Enniskillen, Londonderry, Newry, Omagh and Portadown for this issue.

371 John Keats (150th Death Anniv)

372 Thomas Gray (Death Bicentenary)

373 Sir Walter Scott (Birth Bicentenary)

(Des Rosalind Dease. Queen's head printed in gold and then embossed)

1971 (28 July). *Literary Anniversaries* (2nd series). Chalk-surfaced paper. Two phosphor bands. P 15×14.

884	**371**	3p. black, gold and greyish blue	25	10
		a. Gold (Queen's head) omitted	£275	
		Ey. Phosphor omitted	5·00	
885	**372**	5p. black, gold and yellow-olive	45	50
		a. Gold (Queen's head) omitted	£1450	
		Ey. Phosphor omitted	35·00	
886	**373**	7½p. black, gold and yellow-brown	45	45
		Eb. Embossing omitted	40·00	
		Ey. Phosphor omitted	25·00	
Set of 3			1·00	1·00
First Day Cover				2·00
Presentation Pack (P.O. Pack No. 32)			7·50	

Special First Day of Issue Postmarks

FIRST DAY OF ISSUE 28 JULY 1971
LONDON EC

British Post Office Philatelic Bureau, Edinburgh (Type D, see Introduction)	3·00
London EC	8·00

374 Servicemen and Nurse of 1921

375 Roman Centurion

376 Rugby Football, 1871

(Des F. Wegner)

1971 (25 Aug). *Anniversaries* (4th series). Events described on stamps. Chalk-surfaced paper. Two phosphor bands. *P* 15×14.

887	**374**	3p. red-orange, grey, dp blue, olive-green, olive-brown, black, rosine and violet-blue	25	25
		a. Deep blue omitted*	£1200	
		b. Red-orange (nurse's cloak) omitted	£850	
		c. Olive-brown (faces, etc.) omitted	£700	
		d. Black omitted		
		e. Grey omitted		£5500
		f. Olive-green omitted		£5500
		Ey. Phosphor omitted	3·00	
888	**375**	7½p. grey, yellow-brown, vermilion, mauve, grey-black, black, silver, gold and ochre	50	50
		a. Grey omitted	£300	
		b. Ochre omitted		
		Ey. Phosphor omitted	18·00	
889	**376**	9p. new blue, myrtle-green, grey-black, lemon, olive-brown, magenta and yellow-olive	50	50
		a. Olive-brown omitted	£325	
		b. New blue omitted	£12500	
		c. Myrtle-green omitted		£3250
		d. Lemon (jerseys) omitted		£4500
		Ey. Phosphor omitted	£450	
Set of 3			1·10	1·10
First Day Cover				2·50
Presentation Pack (P.O. Pack No. 32A)			7·50	

* The effect of the missing deep blue is shown on the sailor's uniform, which appears as grey.

Special First Day of Issue Postmarks

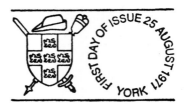

British Post Office Philatelic Bureau, Edinburgh (Type D, see Introduction)	3·00
Maidstone	16·00
Twickenham	16·00
York	16·00

377 Physical Sciences Building, University College of Wales, Aberystwyth

378 Faraday Building, Southampton University

379 Engineering Department, Leicester University

380 Hexagon Restaurant, Essex University

(Des N. Jenkins)

1971 (22 Sept). *British Architecture* (2nd series). Modern University Buildings. Chalk-surfaced paper. Two phosphor bands. *P* 15×14.

890	**377**	3p. olive-brown, ochre, lemon, black and yellow-olive	10	10
		a. Lemon omitted	†	£8000
		b. Black (windows) omitted	£16000	
		Ey. Phosphor omitted	9·00	
891	**378**	5p. rose, black, chestnut and lilac	25	20
		Ey. Phosphor omitted	75·00	
892	**379**	7½p. ochre, black and purple-brown	45	55
		Ey. Phosphor omitted	15·00	
893	**380**	9p. pale lilac, black, sepia-brown and dp blue	75	80
		a. Pale lilac omitted	£6750	
		Ey. Phosphor omitted	20·00	
Set of 4			1·40	1·50
First Day Cover				2·00
Presentation Pack (P.O. Pack No. 33)			10·00	

Mint examples of the 5p. exist with a larger "P" following the face value.

No. 890a is only known used on commercial cover from Wantage.

No. 890b is only a partial omission with traces of black on the wall at the far right.

Special First Day of Issue Postmarks

British Post Office Philatelic Bureau, Edinburgh (Type D, see
Introduction).. 2·50
Aberystwyth... 12·00
Colchester.. 12·00
Leicester.. 12·00
Southampton.. 12·00

Collectors Pack 1971
1971 (29 Sept). Comprises Nos. 835/40 and 881/93.
CP893*a* Collectors Pack .... 50·00

381 "Dream of the Wise Men"   **382** "Adoration of the Magi"

383 "Ride of the Magi"

(Des Clarke-Clements-Hughes design team, from stained-glass
windows, Canterbury Cathedral. Queen's head printed in gold and
then embossed)
1971 (13 Oct). *Christmas, Stained-glass Windows.* Ordinary paper. One
centre phosphor band (2½p.) or two phosphor bands (others).
P 15×14.

894	**381**	2½p. new blue, black, lemon, emerald, reddish violet, carmine-red, carmine-rose and gold	10	10
		a. Imperf (pair)	£725	
		Eb. Embossing omitted		
895	**382**	3p. black, reddish violet, lemon, new blue, carmine-rose, emerald, ultramarine and gold	10	10
		a. Gold (Queen's head) omitted	£2700	
		b. Carmine-rose omitted	£6250	
		c. Lemon (window panels) omitted	£350	
		d. New blue omitted	†	£7000
		e. Reddish violet (tunics etc) omitted	£8000	
		f. Carmine-rose and lemon omitted		£8000
		g. Reddish violet and embossing omitted		£5500
		Eh. Embossing omitted	15·00	
		Ey. Phosphor omitted	5·00	
		Eya. Embossing and phosphor omitted	£100	
896	**383**	7½p. black, lilac, lemon, emerald, new blue, rose, green and gold	55	75
		a. Gold (Queen's head) omitted	£300	
		b. Lilac omitted	£1450	
		c. Emerald omitted	£750	
		d. Lemon omitted		£4500
		Ef. Embossing omitted	50·00	
		Ef. Embossing double	50·00	
		Ey. Phosphor omitted	12·00	
		Eya. Embossing and phosphor omitted	32·00	

Set of 3 70   85
First Day Cover .... 2·00
Presentation Pack (P.O. Pack No. 35) .... 6·00

Special First Day of Issue Postmarks

British Post Office Philatelic Bureau, Edinburgh (Type D, see
Introduction).. 2·50
Bethlehem, Llandeilo, Carms.. 10·00
Canterbury... 10·00

WHITE CHALK-SURFACED PAPER. From No. 897 all issues, with the
exception of Nos. 904/8, were printed on fluorescent white paper,
giving a stronger chalk reaction than the original cream paper.

384 Sir James Clark Ross   **385** Sir Martin Frobisher

386 Henry Hudson   **387** Capt. Scott

(Des Marjorie Saynor. Queen's head printed in gold and then
embossed)
1972 (16 Feb). *British Polar Explorers.* Two phosphor bands. *P* 14×15.

897	**384**	3p. yellow-brown, indigo, slate-black, flesh, lemon, rose, brt blue & gold	10	10
		a. Gold (Queen's head) omitted	£220	
		b. Slate-black (hair, etc.) omitted	£9000	
		c. Lemon omitted	£14000	
		Ed. Embossing omitted	45·00	
		Ee. Gold (Queen's head) and embossing omitted	£300	
		Ey. Phosphor omitted	5·00	
		Eya. Embossing and phosphor omitted	35·00	
898	**385**	5p. salmon, flesh, purple-brown, ochre, black and gold	15	15
		a. Gold (Queen's head) omitted	£300	
		Eb. Embossing omitted	25·00	
		Ey. Phosphor omitted	12·00	
		Eya. Gold and phosphor omitted	£325	
		Eyb. Embossing and phosphor omitted		
899	**386**	7½p. reddish violet, blue, deep slate, yellow-brown, buff, black and gold	45	50
		a. Gold (Queen's head) omitted	£550	
		Ey. Phosphor omitted	20·00	
900	**387**	9p. dull blue, ultramarine, black, greenish yellow, pale pink, rose-red and gold	70	85
		Ey. Phosphor omitted	£325	

Set of 4 .... 1·20   1·50
First Day Cover .... 2·50
Presentation Pack (P.O. Pack No. 39) .... 7·00
An example of the 3p. is known used on piece with the flesh
colour omitted.

Special First Day of Issue Postmarks

Philatelic Bureau, Edinburgh	5·00
London WC	12·00

388 Statuette of Tutankhamun **389** 19th-century Coastguard

390 Ralph Vaughan Williams and Score

(Des Rosalind Dease (3p.), F. Wegner (7½p.), C. Abbott (9p.). Queen's head printed in gold and then embossed (7½p., 9p.))

1972 (26 Apr). *Anniversaries* (5th series). Events described on stamps. Two phosphor bands. *P* 15×14.

901	388	3p. black, grey, gold, dull bistre-brown, blackish brown, pale stone and light brown...............	25	25
		a. Face value omitted	£17500	
902	389	7½p. pale yellow, new blue, slate-blue, violet-blue, slate and gold	50	50
		Ea. Embossing omitted..............................	£225	
		Ey. Phosphor omitted.................................	£275	
903	390	9p. bistre-brown, black, sage-green, dp slate, yellow-ochre, brown and gold	50	50
		a. Gold (Queen's head) omitted............	£4250	
		b. Brown (facial features) omitted........	£5750	
		c. Deep slate omitted............................	£25000	
		Ed. Embossing omitted.............................		
		Ey. Phosphor omitted...............................	35·00	
Set of 3			1·10	1·10
First Day Cover				2·25
Presentation Pack (P.O. Pack No. 40)..			7·00	

Special First Day of Issue Postmarks

Philatelic Bureau, Edinburgh	3·00
London EC	7·00

391 St. Andrew's, Greensted-juxta-Ongar, Essex   **392** All Saints, Earls Barton, Northants

393 St. Andrew's, Letheringsett, Norfolk   **394** St. Andrew's, Helpringham, Lincs

395 St. Mary the Virgin, Huish Episcopi, Somerset

(Des R. Maddox. Queen's head printed in gold and then embossed)

1972 (21 June). *British Architecture* (3rd series). Village Churches. Ordinary paper. Two phosphor bands. *P* 14×15.

904	391	3p. violet-blue, black, lt yellow-olive, emerald-green, orange-vermilion and gold.....................	10	10
		a. Gold (Queen's head) omitted............	£250	
		b. Orange-vermilion omitted....................		£5500
		Ec. Embossing omitted.............................	35·00	
		Ey. Phosphor omitted.................................	8·00	
		Eya. Gold (Queen's head) and phosphor omitted..............................	£350	
		Eyb. Embossing and phosphor omitted	22·00	
905	392	4p. deep yellow-olive, black, emerald, violet-blue, orange-vermilion and gold.....................	10	20
		a. Gold (Queen's head) omitted............	£7500	
		b. Violet-blue omitted	£300	
		Ec. Embossing omitted.............................	12·00	
		Eya. Phosphor omitted.................................	20·00	
906	393	5p. deep emerald, black, royal blue, light yellow-olive, orange-vermilion and gold.....................	15	20
		a. Gold (Queen's head) omitted............	£300	
		b. Red omitted..	†	£3500
		Eb. Embossing omitted.............................	50·00	
		Ey. Phosphor omitted.................................	25·00	
907	394	7½p. orange-red, black, dp yellow-olive, royal blue, lt emerald and gold.......	50	75
		Ey. Phosphor omitted.................................	20·00	
		Eya. Embossing and phosphor omitted	50·00	
908	395	9p. new blue, black, emerald-green, dp yellow-olive, orange-vermilion and gold.....................	50	80
		Ea. Embossing omitted.............................	22·00	
		Ey. Phosphor omitted.................................	25·00	
Set of 5			1·20	1·90
First Day Cover				2·75
Presentation Pack (P.O. Pack No. 41)..			10·00	

Nos. 905a and 906a only exist with the phosphor omitted.

Special First Day of Issue Postmarks

Philatelic Bureau, Edinburgh .... 3·50
Canterbury .... 8·00

Special First Day of Issue Postmarks

Philatelic Bureau, Edinburgh .... 3·50
London W1 .... 10·00

"Belgica 72" Souvenir Pack

1972 (24 June). Comprises Nos. 894/6 and 904/8.
CP908*b* Souvenir Pack .... 10·00
  This pack was specially produced for sale at the "Belgica '72" Stamp Exhibition, held in Brussels between 24 June and 9 July. It contains information on British stamps with a religious theme with text in English, French and Flemish, and was put on sale at Philatelic Bureaux in Britain on 26 June.

396 Microphones, 1924–69

397 Horn Loudspeaker

398 T.V. Camera, 1972

399 Oscillator and Spark Transmitter, 1897

(Des D. Gentleman)

1972 (13 Sept). *Broadcasting Anniversaries.* 75th Anniv of Marconi and Kemp's Radio Experiments (9p.), and 50th Anniv of Daily Broadcasting by the B.B.C. (others). Two phosphor bands. *P* 15×14.

909	**396**	3p. pale brown, black, grey, greenish yellow and brownish slate	10	10
		a. Greenish yellow (terminals) omitted	£6000	
910	**397**	5p. brownish slate, lake-brown, salmon, lt brown, black and red-brown	10	20
		Ey. Phosphor omitted	6·00	
		Eya. Phosphor on back but omitted on front	45·00	
911	**398**	7½p. lt grey, slate, brownish slate, magenta and black	45	50
		a. Brownish slate (Queen's head) omitted	†	£4500
		Eya. Phosphor on back but omitted on front	45·00	
		Ey. Phosphor omitted	12·00	
912	**399**	9p. lemon, brown, brownish slate, deep brownish slate, bluish slate and black	50	50
		a. Brownish slate (Queen's head) omitted	£7500	
		Ey. Phosphor omitted	13·00	
Set of 4			1·00	1·10
First Day Cover				2·75
Presentation Pack (P.O. Pack No. 43)			4·25	

  In addition to the generally issued Presentation Pack a further pack exists inscribed "1922–1972". This pack of stamps commemorating the 50th Anniversary of the B.B.C. was specially produced as a memento of the occasion for the B.B.C. staff. It was sent with the good wishes of the Chairman and Board of Governors, the Director-General and Board of Management. The pack contains Nos. 909/11 only (*Price* £35).
  No. 911a is only found in First Day Covers posted from the Philatelic Bureau in Edinburgh.

400 Angel holding Trumpet   **401** Angel playing Lute

402 Angel playing Harp

(Des Sally Stiff. Photo and embossing)

1972 (18 Oct). *Christmas, Angels.* One centre phosphor band (2½p.) or two phosphor bands (others). *P* 14×15.

913	**400**	2½p. cerise, pale reddish brown, yellow-orange, orange-vermilion, lilac, gold, red-brown and deep grey	10	10
		a. Gold omitted	£1750	
		Eb. Embossing omitted	15·00	
		c. Deep grey omitted	£3250	
		Ey. Phosphor omitted	15·00	
914	**401**	3p. ultramarine, lavender, lt turquoise-blue, brt green, gold, red-brown and bluish violet	10	10
		a. Red-brown omitted	£1500	
		b. Bright green omitted	£300	
		c. Bluish violet omitted	£300	
		d. Lavender omitted	£2000	
		e. Gold omitted	£300	
		Ef. Embossing omitted	10·00	
		Ey. Phosphor omitted	8·00	
		Eya. Embossing and phosphor omitted	15·00	
915	**402**	7½p. dp brown, pale lilac, lt cinnamon, ochre, gold, red-brown and blackish violet	50	45
		a. Ochre omitted	£300	
		b. Blackish violet (shadow) omitted		
		Ec. Embossing omitted	20·00	
		Ey. Phosphor omitted	12·00	
		Eya. Embossing and phosphor omitted	30·00	
Set of 3			60	60
First Day Cover				1·50
Presentation Pack (P.O. Pack No. 44)			4·00	

  The gold printing on the 3p. is from two cylinders: 1E and 1F. Examples have been seen with the gold of the 1F cylinder omitted, but these are difficult to detect on single stamps.

Special First Day of Issue Postmarks

Philatelic Bureau, Edinburgh... 2·00
Bethlehem, Llandeilo, Carms... 6·50

403 Queen Elizabeth and Duke of Edinburgh

404 "Europe"

(Des J. Matthews from photo by N. Parkinson)

1972 (20 Nov). *Royal Silver Wedding.* 'All-over' phosphor (3p.) or without phosphor (20p.). P 14×15.

I. "Rembrandt" Machine

916	**403**	3p. brownish black, dp blue & silver.....	40	40
		a. Silver omitted..................................	£775	
917		20p. brownish black, reddish purple and silver..	1·20	1·20

II. "Jumelle" Machine

918	**403**	3p. brownish black, dp blue & silver.....	40	10
Set of 2			1·50	1·50
Gutter Pair (No. 918)			1·00	
Traffic Light Gutter Pair			20·00	
First Day Cover				2·00
Presentation Pack (P.O. Pack No. 45)			4·00	
Presentation Pack (Japanese)			9·50	
Souvenir Book			4·00	

The souvenir book is a twelve-page booklet containing photographs of the Royal Wedding and other historic events of the royal family and accompanying information. The 3p. "JUMELLE" has a lighter shade of the brownish black than the 3p. "REMBRANDT". It also has the brown cylinders less deeply etched, which can be distinguished in the Duke's face which is slightly lighter, and in the Queen's hair where the highlights are sharper.

3p. "REMBRANDT". Cyls. 3A-1B-11C no dot. Sheets of 100 (10×10).

3p. "JUMELLE". Cyls. 1A-1B-3C dot and no dot. Sheets of 100 (two panes 5×10, separated by gutter margin).

Special First Day of Issue Postmarks

Philatelic Bureau, Edinburgh... 2·00
Windsor, Berks.. 6·00

Collectors Pack 1972

1972 (20 Nov). Comprises Nos. 897/917.

CP918*a* Collectors Pack .... 35·00

(Des P. Murdoch)

1973 (3 Jan). *Britain's Entry into European Communities.* Two phosphor bands. P 14×15.

919	**404**	3p. dull orange, bright rose-red, ultramarine, lt lilac and black	25	25
920		5p. new blue, brt rose-red, ultramarine, cobalt-blue and black	25	50
		a. Pair. Nos. 920/1........................	1·00	1·25
921		5p. lt emerald-green, brt rose-red, ultramarine, cobalt-blue & black.....	25	50
Set of 3			1·10	1·40
First Day Cover				2·00

Presentation Pack (P.O. Pack No. 48) .... 3·00
Nos. 920/1 were printed horizontally *se-tenant* throughout the sheet.

Special First Day of Issue Postmark

Philatelic Bureau, Edinburgh.. 2·50

405 Oak Tree

(Des D. Gentleman)

1973 (28 Feb). *Tree Planting Year.* British Trees (1st issue). Two phosphor bands. P 15×14.

922	**405**	9p. brownish black, apple-green, deep olive, sepia, blackish green and brownish grey...........................	35	40
		a. Brownish black (value and inscr) omitted..................................	£875	
		b. Brownish grey (Queen's head) omitted..................................	£825	
		Ey. Phosphor omitted......................	90·00	
First Day Cover				1·70
Presentation Pack (P.O. Pack No. 49)			2·75	

See also No. 949.

Special First Day of Issue Postmark

Philatelic Bureau, Edinburgh.. 2·00

CHALK-SURFACED PAPER. The following issues are printed on chalk-surfaced paper but where "all-over" phosphor has been applied there is no chalk reaction except in the sheet margins outside the phosphor area.

406 David Livingstone

407 H. M. Stanley

408 Sir Francis Drake   **409** Walter Raleigh

410 Charles Sturt

(Des Marjorie Saynor. Queen's head printed in gold and then embossed)

1973 (18 Apr). *British Explorers.* 'All-over' phosphor. P 14×15.

923	**406**	3p.	orange-yellow, light orange-brown, grey-black, light turquoise-blue, turquoise-blue and gold	40	25
		a.	Pair. Nos. 923/4	80	1·00
		b.	Gold (Queen's head) omitted	£150	
		c.	Turquoise-blue (background and inscr) omitted	£2500	
		d.	Light orange-brown omitted	£1500	
		Ee.	Embossing omitted	35·00	
924	**407**	3p.	orange-yellow, light orange-brown, grey-black, light turquoise-blue, turquoise-blue and gold	40	25
		b.	Gold (Queen's head) omitted	£150	
		c.	Turquoise-blue (background and inscr) omitted	£2500	
		d.	Light orange-brown omitted	£1500	
		Ee.	Embossing omitted	35·00	
925	**408**	5p.	light flesh, chrome-yellow, orange-yellow, sepia, brownish grey, grey-black, violet-blue and gold	40	50
		a.	Gold (Queen's head) omitted	£275	
		b.	Grey-black omitted	£4700	
		c.	Sepia omitted	£6000	
		Ed.	Embossing omitted	9·00	
926	**409**	7½p.	light flesh, reddish brown, sepia, ultramarine, grey-black, bright lilac and gold	40	50
		a.	Gold (Queen's head) omitted	£11500	
		b.	Ultramarine (eyes) omitted	—	£5000
927	**410**	9p.	flesh, pale stone, grey-blue, grey-black, brown-grey, Venetian red, brown-red and gold	40	75
		a.	Gold (Queen's head) omitted	£250	
		b.	Brown-grey printing double from	£850	
		c.	Grey-black omitted	£5250	
		d.	Brown-red (rivers on map) omitted	£1600	
		Ee.	Embossing omitted	40·00	
		Set of 5		1·70	1·70
		First Day Cover			2·50
		Presentation Pack (P.O. Pack No. 50)		4·50	

Nos. 923/4 were issued horizontally *se-tenant* throughout the sheet.

Caution is needed when buying missing gold heads in this issue as they can be removed by using a hard eraser, etc., but this invariably affects the "all-over" phosphor. Genuine examples have the phosphor intact. Used examples off cover cannot be distinguished as much of the phosphor is lost in the course of floating.

In the 5p. value the missing grey-black affects the doublet, which appears as brownish grey, and the lace ruff, which is entirely missing. The missing sepia affects only Drake's hair, which appears much lighter.

The double printing of the brown-grey (cylinder 1F) on the 9p., is a most unusual type of error to occur in a multicoloured photogravure issue. Two sheets are known and it is believed that they stuck to the cylinder and went through a second time. This would result in the following two sheets missing the colour but at the time of going to press this error has not been reported. The second print is slightly askew and more prominent in the top half of the sheets. Examples from the upper part of the sheet showing a clear double impression of the facial features are worth a substantial premium over the price quoted.

Special First Day of Issue Postmark

Philatelic Bureau, Edinburgh .... 3·00

First Day of Issue handstamps were provided at Blantyre, Glasgow, and Denbigh for this issue.

411   **412**   **413**

(T **411**/13 show sketches of W.G. Grace by Harry Furniss)

(Des E. Ripley. Queen's head printed in gold and then embossed)

1973 (16 May). *County Cricket 1873–1973.* 'All-over' phosphor. P 14×15.

928	**411**	3p.	black, ochre and gold	25	25
		a.	Gold (Queen's head) omitted	£7000	
		Eb.	Embossing omitted	25·00	
929	**412**	7½p.	black, light sage-green and gold	75	75
		Eb.	Embossing omitted	35·00	
930	**413**	9p.	black, cobalt and gold	1·25	1·00
		Eb.	Embossing omitted	85·00	
		Set of 3		2·00	1·80
		First Day Cover			2·50
		Presentation Pack (P.O. Pack No. 51)		5·00	
		Souvenir Book		7·00	
		PHQ Cards (No. 928) (1)		70·00	£275

Nos. 928/30 with two phosphor bands are known.

The souvenir book is a 24-page illustrated booklet containing a history of County Cricket with text by John Arlott.

The P.H.Q. card did not become available until mid-July. The used price quoted is for an example used in July or August 1973.

Special First Day of Issue Postmarks

Philatelic Bureau, Edinburgh .... 3·00
Lords, London NW .... 8·00

414 "Self-portrait"   **415** "Self-portrait"
(Reynolds)   (Raeburn)

416 "Nelly O'Brien"
(Reynolds)

417 "Rev. R. Walker
(The Skater)" (Raeburn)

(Des S. Rose. Queen's head printed in gold and then embossed)

1973 (4 July). *British Paintings* (3rd series). 250th Birth Anniv of Sir Joshua Reynolds and 150th Death Anniv of Sir Henry Raeburn. 'All-over' phosphor. P 14×15.

931	414	3p. rose, new blue, jet-black, magenta, greenish yellow, black, ochre and gold	10	10
		a. Gold (Queen's head) omitted	£160	
		Ec. Gold (Queen's head) and embossing omitted	£180	
932	415	5p. cinnamon, greenish yellow, new blue, light magenta, black, yellow-olive and gold	30	30
		a. Gold (Queen's head) omitted	£180	
		b. Greenish yellow omitted	£1350	
		Ec. Embossing omitted	30·00	
933	416	7½p. greenish yellow, new blue, light magenta, black, cinnamon and gold	30	30
		a. Gold (Queen's head) omitted	£250	
		b. Cinnamon omitted	£24000	
		Ec. Embossing omitted	25·00	
934	417	9p. brownish rose, black, dull rose, pale yellow, brownish grey, pale blue and gold	60	60
		b. Brownish rose omitted	£190	
		Ec. Embossing omitted	£150	
Set of 4			1·20	1·20
First Day Cover				2·00
Presentation Pack (P.O. Pack No. 52)			3·25	

Special First Day of Issue Postmark

Philatelic Bureau, Edinburgh .... 2·50

418 Court Masque Costumes

419 St. Paul's Church, Covent Garden

420 Prince's Lodging, Newmarket

421 Court Masque Stage Scene

(Des Rosalind Dease. Litho and typo B.W.)

1973 (15 Aug). *400th Birth Anniv of Inigo Jones (architect and designer).* 'All-over' phosphor. P 15×14.

935	418	3p. deep mauve, black and gold	10	25
		a. Pair. Nos. 935/6	30	50
		ab. Face values omitted	£17500	
		Eac. Deep mauve ptg double (pair)	£7000	
		Ec. 9 mm. phosphor band*	15·00	

936	419	3p. deep brown, black and gold	10	25
937	420	5p. blue, black and gold	35	50
		a. Pair. Nos. 937/8	1·00	1·00
		Ec. 9 mm. phosphor band*	18·00	
938	421	5p. grey-olive, black and gold	35	50
Set of 4			1·20	1·40
First Day Cover				2·00
Presentation Pack (P.O. Pack No. 53)			3·50	
PHQ Card (No. 936) (2)			£200	£200

T 3p. and T 5p. value were printed horizontally *se-tenant* within the sheet.

No. 935ab is caused by the omission of virtually all the black printing from one horizontal row.

*On part of the printings for both values the "all-over" phosphor band missed the first vertical row and a 9 mm. phosphor band was applied to correct this.

Special First Day of Issue Postmark

Philatelic Bureau, Edinburgh .... 3·00

422 Palace of Westminster seen from Whitehall

423 Palace of Westminster seen from Millbank

(Des R. Downer. Recess and typo B.W.)

1973 (12 Sept). *19th Commonwealth Parliamentary Conference.* 'All-over' phosphor. P 15×14.

939	422	8p. black, brownish grey and stone	45	50
940	423	10p. gold and black	45	40
Set of 2			80	80
First Day Cover				1·50
Presentation Pack (P.O. Pack No. 54)			3·00	
Souvenir Book			7·00	
PHQ Card (No. 939) (3)			40·00	£150

The souvenir book is a twelve-page booklet containing a history of the Palace of Westminster.

Special First Day of Issue Postmark

Philatelic Bureau, Edinburgh .... 2·00

424 Princess Anne and Capt. Mark Phillips

(Des C. Clements and E. Hughes from photo by Lord Lichfield)

1973 (14 Nov). *Royal Wedding.* 'All-over' phosphor. P 15×14.

941	424	3½p. dull violet and silver	25	25
		a. Imperf (horiz pair)	£8750	
942		20p. deep brown and silver	1·00	75
		a. Silver omitted	£8250	
Set of 2			1·10	90
Set of 2 Gutter Pairs			2·75	
Set of 2 Traffic Light Gutter Pairs			£110	
First Day Cover				1·50
Presentation Pack (P.O. Pack No. 56)			2·75	
PHQ Card (No. 941) (4)			9·00	50·00

Special First Day of Issue Postmarks

Philatelic Bureau, Edinburgh	2·00
Westminster Abbey, London SW1	5·00
Windsor, Berks	5·00

425

426

427

428

429

430

(T **425**/**30** show scenes from the carol "Good King Wenceslas")

(Des D. Gentleman)

1973 (28 Nov). *Christmas, Good King Wenceslas.* One centre phosphor band (3p.) or 'All-over' phosphor (3½p.). *P* 15×14.

943	**425**	3p. grey-black, violet-blue, slate, brown, rose-red, rosy mauve, turquoise-green, salmon-pink and gold	20	25
		a. Strip of 5. Nos. 943/7	2·25	2·50
		ab. Rosy mauve omitted (strip of 5)	£17000	
		b. Imperf (horiz strip of 5)	£8000	
		c. Black (face value) omitted*	£12750	
		Eg. Gum arabic	25	
		Ega. Strip of 5. Nos. 943Eg/7Eg	3·00	
		Egb. Imperf (strip of 5. Nos. 943 Eg/7Eg)	£7750	
944	**426**	3p. grey-black, violet-blue, slate, brown, rose-red, rosy mauve, turquoise-green, salmon-pink and gold	20	25
		Eg. Gum arabic	25	
945	**427**	3p. grey-black, violet-blue, slate, brown, rose-red, rosy-mauve, turquoise-green, salmon-pink and gold	20	25
		Eg. Gum arabic	25	
946	**428**	3p. grey-black, violet-blue, slate, brown, rose-red, rosy mauve, turquoise-green, salmon-pink and gold	20	25

		Eg. Gum arabic	25	
947	**429**	3p. grey-black, violet-blue, slate, brown, rose-red, rosy mauve, turquoise-green, salmon-pink and gold	20	25
		Eg. Gum arabic	25	
948	**430**	3½p. salmon-pink, grey-black, red-brown, blue, turquoise-green, brt rose-red, rosy mauve, lavender-grey and gold	20	25
		a. Imperf (pair)	£600	
		b. Grey-black (value, inscr, etc.) omitted	£180	
		c. Salmon-pink omitted	£120	
		d. Blue (leg, robes) omitted	£300	
		e. Rosy mauve (robe at right) omitted	£160	
		f. Blue and rosy mauve omitted	£700	
		g. Brt rose-red (King's robe) omitted	£170	
		h. Red-brown (logs, basket, etc.) omitted		
		i. Turquoise-green (leg, robe, etc.) omitted	£6250	
		j. Gold (background) omitted	†	£2800
Set of 6			2·25	2·50
First Day Cover				3·00
Presentation Pack (P.O. Pack No. 57)			4·00	

The 3p. values depict the carol "Good King Wenceslas" and were printed horizontally *se-tenant* within the sheet.

Examples of No. 948j are only known used on covers from Gloucester. The 3½p. has also been seen with the lavender-grey omitted used on piece.

The 3p. and 3½p. are normally with PVA gum with added dextrin, but the 3½p. also exists with normal PVA gum.

* No. 943c is known in a corner marginal strip of five showing a progressive dry print of black leaving a total omission on the first stamp. Adjacent similar strips of five all show traces of black.

Special First Day of Issue Postmarks

Philatelic Bureau, Edinburgh	3·50
Bethlehem, Llandeilo, Carms.	6·00

Collectors Pack 1973

1973 (28 Nov). Comprises Nos. 919/48.

CP948*k* Collectors Pack		27·00

431 Horse Chestnut

(Des D. Gentleman)

1974 (27 Feb). *British Trees* (2nd issue). 'All-over' phosphor. *P* 15×14.

949	**431**	10p. light emerald, bright green, greenish yellow, brown-olive, black and brownish grey	40	35
Gutter Pair			1·75	
Traffic Light Gutter Pair			65·00	
First Day Cover				1·20
Presentation Pack (P.O. Pack No. 59)			2·50	
PHQ Card (5)			£150	£150

The pack number is stated to be 58 on the reverse but the correct number is 59.

Philatelic Bureau, Edinburgh.. 1·50

432 First Motor Fire-engine, 1904

433 Prize-winning Fire-engine, 1863

434 First Steam Fire-engine, 1830

435 Fire-engine, 1766

(Des D. Gentleman)

1974 (24 Apr). *Bicentenary of the Fire Prevention (Metropolis) Act.* 'All-over' phosphor. *P* 15×14.

950	**432**	3½p. grey-black, orange-yellow, greenish yellow, dull rose, ochre and grey..........................	25	10
		a. Imperf (pair)...............................	£1200	
951	**433**	5½p. greenish yellow, dp rosy magenta, orange-yellow, lt emerald, grey-black and grey..........................	25	30
952	**434**	8p. greenish yellow, lt blue-green, lt greenish blue, lt chestnut, grey-black and grey..........................	50	50
953	**435**	10p. grey-black, pale reddish brown, lt brown, orange-yellow and grey......	50	50
Set of 4			1·40	1·30
Set of 4 Gutter Pairs.................................			3·00	
Set of 4 Traffic Light Gutter Pairs...........			60·00	
First Day Cover				3·00
Presentation Pack (P.O. Pack No. 60)......			4·00	
PHQ Card (No. 950) (6)..............................			£140	£150

The 3½p. exists with ordinary PVA gum.

Philatelic Bureau, Edinburgh.. 3·50

436 P & O Packet, *Peninsular*, 1888

437 Farman H.F. III Biplane, 1911

438 Airmail-blue Van and Postbox, 1930

439 Imperial Airways Short S.21 Flying Boat *Maia*, 1937

5½p. "Bomb burst" damage to wheels at left (Cyl. 1C, R. 6/4)

(Des Rosalind Dease)

1974 (12 June). *Centenary of Universal Postal Union.* 'All-over' phosphor. *P* 15×14.

954	**436**	3½p. dp brownish grey, brt mauve, grey-black and gold..............................	25	10
955	**437**	5½p. pale orange, lt emerald, grey-black and gold..............................	25	30
		a. "Bomb burst"..............................	25·00	
956	**438**	8p. cobalt, brown, grey-black & gold....	25	35
957	**439**	10p. dp brownish grey, orange, grey-black and gold..............................	50	40
Set of 4			1·10	1·00
Set of 4 Gutter Pairs.................................			2·50	
Set of 4 Traffic Light Gutter Pairs...........			45·00	
First Day Cover				2·00
Presentation Pack (P.O. Pack No. 64)......			4·00	

Philatelic Bureau, Edinburgh.. 2·50

440 Robert the Bruce

441 Owain Glyndwr

442 Henry the Fifth

443 The Black Prince

(Des F. Wegner)

1974 (10 July). *Medieval Warriors.* 'All-over' phosphor. *P* 15×14.

958	**440**	4½p. greenish yellow, vermilion, slate-blue, red-brown, reddish brown, lilac-grey and gold..........................	25	10
959	**441**	5½p. lemon, vermilion, slate-blue, red-brown, reddish brown, olive-drab and gold..........................	25	35
960	**442**	8p. dp grey, vermilion, greenish yellow, new blue, red-brown, dp cinnamon and gold..........................	50	50
961	**443**	10p. vermilion, greenish yellow, new blue, red-brown, reddish brown, lt blue and gold..........................	50	50

Set of 4	1·40	1·30
Set of 4 Gutter Pairs	3·00	
Set of 4 Traffic Light Gutter Pairs	60·00	
First Day Cover		3·00
Presentation Pack (P.O. Pack No. 65)	4·00	
PHQ Cards (set of 4) (7)	28·00	65·00

Imperforate pairs of SG961 are known and thought to be of proof status (£700 per pair).

Special First Day of Issue Postmark

Philatelic Bureau, Edinburgh	3·50

444 Churchill in Royal Yacht Squadron Uniform

445 Prime Minister, 1940

446 Secretary for War and Air, 1919

447 War Correspondent, South Africa, 1899

(Des C. Clements and E. Hughes)

1974 (9 Oct). *Birth Centenary of Sir Winston Churchill.* 'All-over' phosphor. P 14×15.

962	**444**	4½p. Prussian blue, pale turquoise-green and silver	20	15
963	**445**	5½p. sepia, brownish grey and silver	35	35
964	**446**	8p. crimson, lt claret and silver	60	50
965	**447**	10p. lt brown, stone and silver	60	50
Set of 4			1·60	1·40
Set of 4 Gutter Pairs			4·00	
Set of 4 Traffic Light Gutter Pairs			35·00	
First Day Cover				2·00
Presentation Pack (P.O. Pack No. 66)			4·00	
Souvenir Book			3·00	
PHQ Card (No. 963) (8)			6·00	32·00

The souvenir book consists of an illustrated folder containing a biography of Sir Winston.

Nos. 962/5 come with PVA gum containing added dextrin, but the 8p. also exists with normal PVA.

Special First Day of Issue Postmarks

Philatelic Bureau, Edinburgh	3·50
Blenheim, Woodstock, Oxford	10·00
House of Commons, London SW	10·00

448 "Adoration of the Magi" (York Minster, circa 1355)

449 "The Nativity" (St. Helen's Church, Norwich, circa 1480)

450 "Virgin and Child" (Ottery St. Mary Church, circa 1350)

451 "Virgin and Child" (Worcester Cathedral, circa 1224)

(Des Peter Hatch Partnership)

1974 (27 Nov). *Christmas, Church Roof Bosses.* One phosphor band (3½p.) or 'All-over' phosphor (others). P 15×14.

966	**448**	3½p. gold, lt new blue, lt brown, grey-black and lt stone	10	10
		a. Light stone (background shading) omitted	£45000	
		Ey. Phosphor omitted	12·00	
967	**449**	4½p. gold, yellow-orange, rose-red, lt brown, grey-black & lt new blue	10	10
968	**450**	8p. blue, gold, lt brown, rose-red, dull green and grey-black	25	50
969	**451**	10p. gold, dull rose, grey-black, lt new blue, pale cinnamon and lt brown	50	50
Set of 4			85	1·10
Set of 4 Gutter Pairs			2·25	
Set of 4 Traffic Light Gutter Pairs			36·00	
First Day Cover				2·00
Presentation Pack (P.O. Pack No. 67)			3·00	

The phosphor band on the 3½p. was first applied down the centre of the stamp but during the printing this was deliberately placed to the right between the roof boss and the value; however, intermediate positions, due to shifts, are known.

Two used examples of the 3½p. have been reported with the light brown colour omitted.

Special First Day of Issue Postmarks

Philatelic Bureau, Edinburgh	2·50
Bethlehem, Llandeilo, Carms	5·00

Collectors Pack 1974
1974 (27 Nov). Comprises Nos. 949/69.

CP969a Collectors Pack	16·00

452 Invalid in Wheelchair

(Des P. Sharland)

1975 (22 Jan). *Health and Handicap Funds.* 'All-over' phosphor. *P* 15×14.

970	**452**	4½p. +1½p. azure and grey-blue	25	25
		Gutter Pair	60	
		Traffic Light Gutter Pair	2·25	
		First Day Cover		1·00

Special First Day of Issue Postmark

Philatelic Bureau, Edinburgh .... 1·50

453 "Peace-Burial at Sea"

454 "Snowstorm-Steamer off a Harbour's Mouth"

455 "The Arsenal, Venice"

456 "St. Laurent"

(Des S. Rose)

1975 (19 Feb). *Birth Bicentenary of J. M. W. Turner (painter).* 'All-over' phosphor. *P* 15×14.

971	**453**	4½p. grey-black, salmon, stone, blue and grey	25	25
972	**454**	5½p. cobalt, greenish yellow, lt yellow brown, grey-black and rose	25	25
973	**455**	8p. pale yellow-orange, greenish yellow, rose, cobalt and grey-black	25	50
974	**456**	10p. dp blue, lt yellow-ochre, lt brown, dp cobalt and grey-black	50	50
		Set of 4	1·10	1·10
		Set of 4 Gutter Pairs	2·25	
		Set of 4 Traffic Light Gutter Pairs	8·00	
		First Day Cover		1·50
		Presentation Pack (P.O. Pack No. 69)	3·00	
		PHQ Card (No. 972) (9)	30·00	34·00

Special First Day of Issue Postmarks

London WC .... 5·00
Philatelic Bureau, Edinburgh .... 2·00

457 Charlotte Square, Edinburgh

458 The Rows, Chester

459 Royal Observatory, Greenwich

460 St. George's Chapel, Windsor

461 National Theatre, London

(Des P. Gauld)

1975 (23 Apr). *European Architectural Heritage Year.* 'All-over' phosphor. *P* 15×14.

975	**457**	7p. greenish yellow, brt orange, grey-black, red-brown, new blue, lavender and gold	15	15
		a. Pair. Nos. 975/6	90	1·00
976	**458**	7p. grey-black, greenish yellow, new blue, brt orange, red-brown and gold	15	15
977	**459**	8p. magenta, dp slate, pale magenta, lt yellow-olive, grey-black and gold	40	30
978	**460**	10p. bistre-brown, greenish yellow, dp slate, emerald-green, grey-black and gold	40	30
979	**461**	12p. grey-black, new blue, pale magenta and gold	40	35
		Set of 5	1·90	1·70
		Set of 5 Gutter Pairs	4·00	
		Set of 5 Traffic Light Gutter Pairs	22·00	
		First Day Cover		2·50
		Presentation Pack (P.O. Pack No. 70)	3·00	
		PHQ Cards (Nos. 975/7) (10)	11·00	40·00

Nos. 975/6 were printed horizontally *se-tenant* within the sheet.

Special First Day of Issue Postmark

Philatelic Bureau, Edinburgh .... 3·00

462 Sailing Dinghies

463 Racing Keel Yachts

464 Cruising Yachts

465 Multihulls

(Des A. Restall. Recess and photo)

1975 (11 June). *Sailing.* 'All-over' phosphor. *P* 15×14.

980	**462**	7p. black, bluish violet, scarlet, orange-vermilion, orange and gold	25	20
981	**463**	8p. black, orange-vermilion, orange, lavender, brt mauve, brt blue, dp ultramarine and gold	35	40
		a. Black omitted	£135	
982	**464**	10p. black, orange, bluish emerald, lt olive-drab, chocolate and gold	35	45
983	**465**	12p. black, ultramarine, turquoise-blue, rose, grey, steel-blue and gold	50	50
Set of 4			1·30	1·40
Set of 4 Gutter Pairs			2·75	
Set of 4 Traffic Light Gutter Pairs			25·00	
First Day Cover				2·00
Presentation Pack (P.O. Pack No. 71)			2·50	
PHQ Card (No. 981) (11)			5·75	30·00

On No. 981a the recess-printed black colour is completely omitted.

Special First Day of Issue Postmark

Philatelic Bureau, Edinburgh	2·50

A First Day of Issue handstamp was provided at Weymouth for this issue.

1825 Stockton and Darlington Railway
466 Stephenson's *Locomotion*, 1825

1876 North British Railway Drummond
467 *Abbotsford*, 1876

1923 Great Western Railway Castle Class
468 *Caerphilly Castle*, 1923

1975 British Rail Inter-City Service HST
469 High Speed Train, 1975

(Des B. Craker)

1975 (13 Aug). *150th Anniv of Public Railways.* 'All-over' phosphor. *P* 15×14.

984	**466**	7p. red-brown, grey-black, greenish yellow, grey and silver	25	25
985	**467**	8p. brown, orange-yellow, vermilion, grey-black, grey and silver	50	50
986	**468**	10p. emerald-green, grey-black, yellow-orange, vermilion, grey and silver	50	50
987	**469**	12p. grey-black, pale lemon, vermilion, blue, grey and silver	40	50
Set of 4			1·50	1·50
Set of 4 Gutter Pairs			3·25	
Set of 4 Traffic Light Gutter Pairs			12·00	
First Day Cover				2·50
Presentation Pack (P.O. Pack No. 72)			4·00	
Souvenir Book			4·00	
PHQ Cards (set of 4) (12)			70·00	70·00

The souvenir book is an eight-page booklet containing a history of the railways.

Special First Day of Issue Postmarks

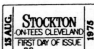

Philatelic Bureau, Edinburgh	3·00
Darlington, Co. Durham	12·00
Shildon, Co. Durham	15·00
Stockton-on-Tees, Cleveland	12·00

470 Palace of Westminster

(Des R. Downer)

1975 (3 Sept). *62nd Inter-Parliamentary Union Conference.* 'All-over' phosphor. *P* 15×14.

988	**470**	12p. lt new blue, black, brownish grey and gold	50	40
Gutter Pair			1·10	
Traffic Light Gutter Pair			3·00	
First Day Cover				80
Presentation Pack (P.O. Pack No. 74)			1·80	

Special First Day of Issue Postmark

Philatelic Bureau, Edinburgh	1·30

471 Emma and Mr. Woodhouse (*Emma*)

472 Catherine Morland (*Northanger Abbey*)

473 Mr. Darcy (*Pride and Prejudice*)

474 Mary and Henry Crawford (*Mansfield Park*)

(Des Barbara Brown)

1975 (22 Oct). *Birth Bicentenary of Jane Austen (novelist).* 'All-over' phosphor. *P* 14×15.

989	471	8½p. blue, slate, rose-red, lt yellow, dull green, grey-black and gold............	25	20
990	472	10p. slate, brt magenta, grey, lt yellow, grey-black and gold	45	45
991	473	11p. dull blue, pink, olive-sepia, slate, pale greenish yellow, grey-black and gold.....	45	45
992	474	13p. brt magenta, lt new blue, slate, buff, dull blue-green, grey-black & gold.............	50	50
		Set of 4	1·50	1·40
		Set of 4 Gutter Pairs	3·25	
		Set of 4 Traffic Light Gutter Pairs	7·00	
		First Day Cover		2·50
		Presentation Pack (P.O. Pack No. 75)	5·00	
		PHQ Cards (set of 4) (13)	24·00	42·00

Special First Day of Issue Postmarks

Philatelic Bureau, Edinburgh	3·00
Steventon, Basingstoke, Hants	6·00

475 Angels with Harp and Lute   **476** Angel with Mandolin

477 Angel with Horn   **478** Angel with Trumpet

(Des R. Downer)

1975 (26 Nov). *Christmas, Angels.* One phosphor band (6½p.), phosphor-inked background (8½p.), 'All-over' phosphor (others). *P* 15×14.

993	475	6½p. bluish violet, brt reddish violet, light lavender and gold	25	25
994	476	8½p. turquoise-green, brt emerald-green, slate, lt turquoise-green and gold	25	40
995	477	11p. vermilion, cerise, pink and gold	50	45
996	478	13p. drab, brown, brt orange, buff and gold	50	45
		Set of 4	1·40	1·40
		Set of 4 Gutter Pairs	3·00	
		Set of 4 Traffic Light Gutter Pairs	9·00	
		First Day Cover		1·80
		Presentation Pack (P.O. Pack No. 76)	3·00	

The 6½p. exists with both ordinary PVA gum and PVA containing added dextrin.

Special First Day of Issue Postmarks

Philatelic Bureau, Edinburgh	2·00
Bethlehem, Llandeilo, Dyfed	3·00

Collectors Pack 1975

1975 (26 Nov). Comprises Nos. 970/96.

CP996a Collectors Pack	9·00

479 Housewife   **480** Policeman

481 District Nurse   **482** Industrialist

(Des P. Sharland)

1976 (10 Mar). *Telephone Centenary.* 'All-over' phosphor. *P* 15×14.

997	479	8½p. greenish blue, deep rose, black and blue	25	20
		a. Deep rose (vase and picture frame) omitted	£6750	
998	480	10p. greenish blue, black and yellow-olive	40	40
999	481	11p. greenish blue, deep rose, black and bright mauve	50	50
1000	482	13p. olive-brown, deep rose, black and orange-red	60	60
		Set of 4	1·60	1·60
		Set of 4 Gutter Pairs	3·25	
		Set of 4 Traffic Light Gutter Pairs	9·00	
		First Day Cover		2·00
		Presentation Pack (P.O. Pack No. 78)	3·00	

Special First Day of Issue Postmark

Philatelic Bureau, Edinburgh	2·00

483 Hewing Coal (Thomas Hepburn)   **484** Machinery (Robert Owen)

485 Chimney Cleaning (Lord Shaftesbury)

486 Hands clutching Prison Bars (Elizabeth Fry)

(Des D. Gentleman)

1976 (28 Apr). *Social Reformers.* 'All-over' phosphor. *P* 15×14.

1001	**483**	8½p. lavender-grey, grey-black, black and slate-grey	25	20
1002	**484**	10p. lavender-grey, grey-black, grey and slate-violet	40	40
1003	**485**	11p. black, slate-grey and drab	50	50
1004	**486**	13p. slate-grey, black & dp dull green	60	60
Set of 4			1·60	1·60
Set of 4 Gutter Pairs			3·25	
Set of 4 Traffic Light Gutter Pairs			9·00	
First Day Cover				2·00
Presentation Pack (P.O. Pack No. 79)			2·75	
PHQ Card (No. 1001) (14)			6·00	20·00

Special First Day of Issue Postmark

Philatelic Bureau, Edinburgh .... 2·00

487 Benjamin Franklin (bust by Jean-Jacques Caffieri)

(Des P. Sharland)

1976 (2 June). *Bicentenary of American Revolution.* 'All-over' phosphor. *P* 14×15.

1005	**487**	11p. pale bistre, slate-violet, pale blue-green, black and gold	50	50
Gutter Pair			1·20	
Traffic Light Gutter Pair			2·50	
First Day Cover				1·50
Presentation Pack (P.O. Pack No. 80)			1·50	
PHQ Card (15)			5·00	20·00

Special First Day of Issue Postmark

Philatelic Bureau, Edinburgh .... 2·00

488 "Elizabeth of Glamis"

489 "Grandpa Dickson"

490 "Rosa Mundi"

491 "Sweet Briar"

(Des Kristin Rosenberg)

1976 (30 June). *Centenary of Royal National Rose Society.* 'All-over' phosphor. *P* 14×15.

1006	**488**	8½p. brt rose-red, greenish yellow, emerald, grey-black and gold	15	10
1007	**489**	10p. greenish yellow, brt green, reddish brown, grey-black and gold	40	40
1008	**490**	11p. brt magenta, greenish yellow, emerald, grey-blue, grey-black and gold	50	50
1009	**491**	13p. rose-pink, lake-brown, yellow-green, pale greenish yellow, grey-black and gold	65	65
		a. Value omitted*	£140000	
Set of 4			1·50	1·50
Set of 4 Gutter Pairs			3·25	
Set of 4 Traffic Light Gutter Pairs			10·00	
First Day Cover				2·00
Presentation Pack (P.O. Pack No. 81)			3·00	
PHQ Cards (set of 4) (16)			30·00	38·00

*During repairs to the cylinder the face value on R.1/9 was temporarily covered with copper. This covering was inadvertently left in place during printing, but the error was discovered before issue and most examples were removed from the sheets. Two mint and one used examples have so far been reported, but only one of the mint remains in private hands.

Special First Day of Issue Postmark

Philatelic Bureau, Edinburgh .... 2·00

492 Archdruid

493 Morris Dancing

494 Scots Piper   **495** Welsh Harpist

(Des Marjorie Saynor)

1976 (4 Aug). *British Cultural Traditions*. 'All-over' phosphor. P 14×15.

1010	492	8½p. yellow, sepia, bright rose, dull ultramarine, black and gold	25	20
1011	493	10p. dull ultramarine, brt rose-red, sepia, greenish yellow, black and gold	40	40
1012	494	11p. bluish green, yellow-brown, yellow-orange, black, brt rose-red and gold	45	45
1013	495	13p. dull violet-blue, yellow-orange, yellow, black, bluish green and gold	60	60

Set of 4 .... 1·50 1·50
Set of 4 Gutter Pairs .... 3·25
Set of 4 Traffic Light Gutter Pairs .... 12·00
First Day Cover .... 2·00
Presentation Pack (P.O. Pack No. 82) .... 2·50
PHQ Cards (set of 4) (17) .... 18·00 30·00

The 8½p. and 13p. commemorate the 800th anniversary of the Royal National Eisteddfod.

Special First Day of Issue Postmarks

Philatelic Bureau, Edinburgh .... 2·50
Cardigan, Dyfed .... 5·00

496 Woodcut from *The Canterbury Tales*   **497** Extract from *The Tretyse of Love*

498 Woodcut from *The Game and Play of Chesse*   **499** Early Printing Press

(Des R. Gay. Queen's head printed in gold and then embossed)

1976 (29 Sept). *500th Anniv of British Printing*. 'All-over' phosphor. P 14×15.

1014	496	8½p. black, lt new blue and gold	25	20
1015	497	10p. black, olive-green and gold	40	40
1016	498	11p. black, brownish grey and gold	45	45
1017	499	13p. chocolate, pale ochre and gold	60	60

Set of 4 .... 1·50 1·50
Set of 4 Gutter Pairs .... 3·25

Set of 4 Traffic Light Gutter Pairs .... 7·00
First Day Cover .... 2·00
Presentation Pack (P.O. Pack No. 83) .... 2·75
PHQ Cards (set of 4) (18) .... 10·00 28·00

Special First Day of Issue Postmarks

Philatelic Bureau, Edinburgh .... 2·00
London SW1 .... 3·00

500 Virgin and Child   **501** Angel with Crown

502 Angel appearing to Shepherds   **503** The Three Kings

(Des Enid Marx)

1976 (24 Nov). *Christmas, English Medieval Embroidery*. One phosphor band (6½p.) or 'All-over' phosphor (others). P 15×14.

1018	500	6½p. blue, bistre-yellow, brown and orange	25	25
		a. Imperf (pair)	£975	
1019	501	8½p. sage-green, yellow, brown-ochre, chestnut and olive-black	35	25
1020	502	11p. dp magenta, brown-orange, new blue, black and cinnamon	40	45
		a. Uncoated paper*	75·00	30·00
1021	503	13p. bright purple, new blue, cinnamon, bronze-green and olive-grey	45	50

Set of 4 .... 1·30 1·30
Set of 4 Gutter Pairs .... 2·75
Set of 4 Traffic Light Gutter Pairs .... 7·00
First Day Cover .... 1·80
Presentation Pack (P.O. Pack No. 87) .... 2·75
PHQ Cards (set of 4) (19) .... 4·50 26·00
*See footnote after No. 744.

Special First Day of Issue Postmarks

Philatelic Bureau, Edinburgh .... 2·50
Bethlehem, Llandeilo, Dyfed .... 3·50

Collectors Pack 1976
1976 (24 Nov). Comprises Nos. 997/1021.
CP1021a Collectors Pack .... 14·00

504 Lawn Tennis   **505** Table Tennis

506 Squash   **507** Badminton

(Des A. Restall)

1977 (12 Jan). *Racket Sports.* Phosphorised paper. *P* 15×14.

1022	**504**	8½p. emerald-green, black, grey and bluish green	25	20
		a. Imperf (horiz pair)	£3750	
1023	**505**	10p. myrtle-green, black, grey-black and deep blue-green	40	40
1024	**506**	11p. orange, pale yellow, black, slate-black and grey	45	40
		a. Imperf (horiz pair)	£12000	
1025	**507**	13p. brown, grey-black, grey and brt reddish violet	45	50
Set of 4			1·40	1·40
Set of 4 Gutter Pairs			3·00	
Set of 4 Traffic Light Gutter Pairs			7·50	
First Day Cover				2·00
Presentation Pack (P.O. Pack No. 89)			3·00	
PHQ Cards (set of 4) (20)			8·00	24·00

The only known example of No. 1024a is cut close at left.

Special First Day of Issue Postmark

Philatelic Bureau, Edinburgh .... 2·50

For Nos. 1026/8 see Decimal Machin Definitives section

509 Steroids—Conformational Analysis   **510** Vitamin C—Synthesis

511 Starch—Chromatography   **512** Salt—Crystallography

(Des J. Karo)

1977 (2 Mar). *Royal Institute of Chemistry Centenary.* 'All-over' phosphor. *P* 15×14.

1029	**509**	8½p. rosine, new blue, olive-yellow, brt mauve, yellow-brown, black and gold	25	20
		a. Imperf (horiz pair)	£6250	
1030	**510**	10p. brt orange, rosine, new blue, brt blue, black and gold	45	45

1031	**511**	11p. rosine, greenish yellow, new blue, deep violet, black and gold	45	45
1032	**512**	13p. new blue, brt green, black and gold	45	45
Set of 4			1·40	1·40
Set of 4 Gutter Pairs			3·00	
Set of 4 Traffic Light Gutter Pairs			7·00	
First Day Cover				1·80
Presentation Pack (P.O. Pack No. 92)			3·00	
PHQ Cards (set of 4) (21)			8·00	18·00

Special First Day of Issue Postmark

Philatelic Bureau, Edinburgh .... 2·75

513   **514**

515   **516**

T **513/16** differ in the decorations of "ER".

(Des R. Guyatt)

1977 (11 May–15 June). *Silver Jubilee.* 'All-over' phosphor. *P* 15×14.

1033	**513**	8½p. blackish green, black, silver, olive-grey and pale turquoise-green	25	25
		a. Imperf (pair)	£1200	
1034		9p. maroon, black, silver, olive-grey and lavender (15 June)	25	25
1035	**514**	10p. blackish blue, black, silver, olive-grey and ochre	25	25
		a. Imperf (horiz pair)	£4000	
1036	**515**	11p. brown-purple, black, silver, olive-grey and rose-pink	50	50
		a. Imperf (horiz pair)	£4000	
1037	**516**	13p. sepia, black, silver, olive-grey and bistre-yellow	50	50
		a. Imperf (pair)	£2750	
Set of 5			1·60	1·60
Set of 5 Gutter Pairs			3·50	
Set of 5 Traffic Light Gutter Pairs			6·00	
First Day Covers (2)				2·50
Presentation Pack (Nos. 1033, 1035/7) (P.O. Pack No. 94)			2·00	
Souvenir Book			3·00	
PHQ Cards (set of 5) (22)			14·00	20·00

The Souvenir book is a 16-page booklet containing a history of the Queen's reign.

Special First Day of Issue Postmarks

Philatelic Bureau, Edinburgh (1033, 1035/7) (11 May) .... 1·60
Philatelic Bureau, Edinburgh (1034) (15 June) .... 1·10
Windsor, Berks (1033, 1035/7) (11 May) .... 2·00
Windsor, Berks (1034) (15 June) .... 1·00

517 "Gathering of Nations"

(Des P. Murdoch. Recess and photo)

1977 (8 June). *Commonwealth Heads of Government Meeting, London.* 'All-over' phosphor. P 14×15.

1038	**517**	13p. black, blackish green, rose-carmine and silver	50	50
Gutter Pair			1·10	
Traffic Light Gutter Pair			1·50	
First Day Cover				1·30
Presentation Pack (P.O. Pack No. 95)			1·50	
PHQ Card (23)			5·00	6·00

Special First Day of Issue Postmarks

Philatelic Bureau, Edinburgh		1·50
London SW		2·00

518 Hedgehog

519 Brown Hare

520 Red Squirrel

521 Otter

522 Badger

(Des P. Oxenham)

1977 (5 Oct). *British Wildlife.* 'All-over' phosphor. P 14×15.

1039	**518**	9p. reddish brown, grey-black, pale lemon, brt turquoise-blue, brt magenta and gold	25	20

	a. Horiz strip of 5. Nos. 1039/43		1·50	1·80
	b. Imperf (vert pair)		£3000	
	c. Imperf (horiz pair. Nos. 1039/40)		£4750	
1040	**519**	9p. reddish brown, grey-black, pale lemon, brt turquoise-blue, brt magenta and gold	25	20
1041	**520**	9p. reddish brown, grey-black, pale lemon, brt turquoise-blue, brt magenta and gold	25	20
1042	**521**	9p. reddish brown, grey-black, pale lemon, brt turquoise-blue, brt magenta and gold	25	20
1043	**522**	9p. grey-black, reddish brown, pale lemon, brt turquoise-blue, brt magenta and gold	25	20
Set of 5			1·50	1·80
Gutter Strip of 10			3·25	
Traffic Light Gutter Strip of 10			5·00	
First Day Cover				3·00
Presentation Pack (P.O. Pack No. 96)			2·50	
PHQ Cards (set of 5) (25)			3·00	7·00

Nos. 1039/43 were printed horizontally *se-tenant* within the sheet.

Special First Day of Issue Postmark

Philatelic Bureau, Edinburgh		3·50

523 "Three French Hens, Two Turtle Doves and a Partridge in a Pear Tree"

524 "Six Geese-a-laying, Five Gold Rings, Four Colly Birds"

525 "Eight Maids-a-milking, Seven Swans-a-swimming"

526 "Ten Pipers piping, Nine Drummers drumming"

527 "Twelve Lords a-leaping, Eleven Ladies dancing"

528 "A Partridge in a Pear Tree"

(Des D. Gentleman)

1977 (23 Nov). *Christmas, The Twelve Days of Christmas.* One centre phosphor band (7p.) or 'All-over' phosphor (9p.). P 15×14.

1044	**523**	7p. slate, grey, brt yellow-green, new blue, rose-red and gold	20	15
	a. Horiz strip of 5. Nos. 1044/8		1·50	1·50
	ab. Imperf (strip of 5. Nos. 1044/8)		£5250	
1045	**524**	7p. slate, brt yellow-green, new blue and gold	20	15
1046	**525**	7p. slate, grey, brt yellow-green, new blue, rose-red and gold	20	15
1047	**526**	7p. slate, grey, brt yellow-green, new blue, rose-red and gold	20	15
1048	**527**	7p. slate, grey, brt yellow-green, new blue, rose-red and gold	20	15
1049	**528**	9p. pale brown, pale orange, bright emerald, pale greenish yellow, slate-black and gold	35	30
	a. Imperf (pair)		£2600	

Set of 6	1·50	1·50
Set of 6 Gutter Pairs..................................	3·25	
Traffic Light Gutter Pairs...........................	5·50	
First Day Cover		2·25
Presentation Pack (P.O. Pack No. 97).........	2·25	
PHQ Cards (set of 6) (26)............................	3·00	6·00

Nos. 1044/8 were printed horizontally *se-tenant* within the sheet.

Special First Day of Issue Postmarks

 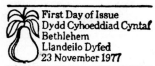

First Day of Issue
Dydd Cyhoeddiad Cyntaf
Bethlehem
Llandeilo Dyfed
23 November 1977

Philatelic Bureau, Edinburgh...2·50	
Bethlehem, Llandeilo, Dyfed ....3·00	

Collectors Pack 1977

1977 (23 Nov). Comprises Nos. 1022/5 and 1029/49.
CP1049b Collectors Pack.. 9·00

529 Oil–North Sea   **530** Coal–Modern Pithead
Production Platform

531 Natural Gas–Flame   **532** Electricity–Nuclear
Rising from Sea   Power Station and
Uranium Atom

(Des P. Murdoch)

1978 (25 Jan). *Energy Resources.* 'All-over' phosphor. P 14×15.

1050	**529**	9p. dp brown, orange-vermilion, grey-black, greenish yellow, rose-pink, new blue and silver..............................	25	25
1051	**530**	10½p. lt emerald-green, grey-black, red-brown, slate-grey, pale apple-green and silver..............................	25	25
1052	**531**	11p. greenish blue, brt violet, violet-blue, blackish brown, grey-black and silver..............................	50	50
1053	**532**	13p. orange-vermilion, grey-black, dp brown, greenish yellow, lt brown, lt blue and silver..............................	50	50
Set of 4			1·40	1·40
Set of 4 Gutter Pairs..................................			3·00	
Set of 4 Traffic Light Gutter Pairs............			4·50	
First Day Cover				1·80
Presentation Pack (P.O. Pack No. 99)			2·00	
PHQ Cards (set of 4) (27)............................			3·00	6·00

Special First Day of Issue Postmark

Philatelic Bureau, Edinburgh ....2·50

533 The Tower of London   **534** Holyroodhouse

535 Caernarvon Castle   **536** Hampton Court Palace

(Des R. Maddox (stamps), J. Matthews (miniature sheet))

1978 (1 Mar). *British Architecture* (4th series), Historic Buildings. 'All-over' phosphor. P 15×14.

1054	**533**	9p. black, olive-brown, new blue, brt green, lt yellow-olive and rose-red	25	20
1055	**534**	10½p. black, brown-olive, orange-yellow, brt green, lt yellow-olive and violet-blue..............................	25	40
1056	**535**	11p. black, brown-olive, violet-blue, brt green, lt yellow-olive and dull blue..............................	60	40
1057	**536**	13p. black, orange-yellow, lake-brown, brt green and light yellow- olive	60	40
Set of 4			1·50	1·50
Set of 4 Gutter Pairs..................................			3·25	
Set of 4 Traffic Light Gutter Pairs............			4·50	
First Day Cover				1·80
Presentation Pack (P.O. Pack No. 100).........			2·00	
PHQ Cards (set of 4) (28)............................			3·00	6·00
MS1058 121×89 mm. Nos. 1054/7 (sold at 53½p.)			1·50	1·75
	a. Imperforate		£18000	
	b. Lt yellow-olive (Queen's head) omitted		£25000	
	c. Rose-red (Union Jack on 9p.) omitted...........		£8500	
	d. Orange-yellow omitted		£12500	
	e. New blue (Union Jack on 9p.) omitted.........			
First Day Cover				2·25

The premium on No. **MS1058** was used to support the London 1980 International Stamp Exhibition. No. **MS1058d** is most noticeable on the 10½p. (spheres absent on towers) and around the roadway and arch on the 13p.

Special First Day of Issue Postmarks

Philatelic Bureau, Edinburgh (stamps)..2·00	
Philatelic Bureau, Edinburgh (miniature sheet)..........................2·50	
London EC (stamps)... 2·50	
London EC (miniature sheet) .... 3·00	

537 State Coach   **538** St. Edward's Crown

539 The Sovereign's Orb

540 Imperial State Crown

(Des J. Matthews)

1978 (31 May). *25th Anniv of Coronation.* 'All-over' phosphor. *P* 14×15.

1059	**537**	9p. gold and royal blue	35	25
1060	**538**	10½p. gold and brown-lake	45	45
1061	**539**	11p. gold and dp dull green	45	45
1062	**540**	13p. gold and reddish violet	50	50
Set of 4			1·60	1·50
Set of 4 Gutter Pairs			3·25	
Set of 4 Traffic Light Gutter Pairs			4·25	
First Day Cover				2·00
Presentation Pack (P.O. Pack No. 101)			2·00	
Souvenir Book			3·00	
PHQ Cards (set of 4) (29)			3·00	6·00

The souvenir book is a 16-page booklet illustrated with scenes from the Coronation.

Special First Day of Issue Postmarks

Philatelic Bureau, Edinburgh	2·00
London SW1	2·50

Shire Horse **9P**   10½P Shetland Pony

541 Shire Horse   **542** Shetland Pony

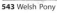

11P Merlyn Cymreig Welsh Pony   Thoroughbred 13P

543 Welsh Pony   **544** Thoroughbred

(Des P. Oxenham)

1978 (5 July). *Horses.* 'All-over' phosphor. *P* 15×14.

1063	**541**	9p. black, pale reddish brown, grey-black, greenish yellow, lt blue, vermilion and gold	20	10
		a. Imperf (vert pair)	—	
1064	**542**	10½p. pale chestnut, magenta, brownish grey, greenish yellow, greenish blue, grey-black and gold	35	40
1065	**543**	11p. reddish brown, black, lt green, greenish yellow, bistre, grey-black and gold	35	45
1066	**544**	13p. reddish brown, pale reddish brown, emerald, greenish yellow, grey-black and gold	45	50
Set of 4			1·20	1·30
Set of 4 Gutter Pairs			3·00	
Set of 4 Traffic Light Gutter Pairs			4·50	
First Day Cover				1·80
Presentation Pack (P.O. Pack No. 102)			1·80	
PHQ Cards (set of 4) (30)			2·25	5·75

Special First Day of Issue Postmarks

Philatelic Bureau, Edinburgh	2·00
Peterborough	2·50

545 "Penny-farthing" and 1884 Safety Bicycle

546 1920 Touring Bicycles

547 Modern Small-wheel Bicycles

548 1978 Road-racers

(Des F. Wegner)

1978 (2 Aug). *Centenaries of Cyclists' Touring Club and British Cycling Federation.* 'All-over' phosphor. *P* 15×14.

1067	**545**	9p. brown, dp dull blue, rose-pink, pale olive, grey-black and gold	25	20
		a. Imperf (pair)	£900	
1068	**546**	10½p. olive, pale yellow-orange, orange-vermilion, rose-red, lt brown, grey-black and gold	35	40
1069	**547**	11p. orange-vermilion, greenish blue, lt brown, pale greenish yellow, dp grey, grey-black and gold	40	40
1070	**548**	13p. new blue, orange-vermilion, lt brown, olive-grey, grey-black and gold	50	50
		a. Imperf (pair)	£2750	
Set of 4			1·30	1·40
Set of 4 Gutter Pairs			2·75	
Set of 4 Traffic Light Gutter Pairs			4·50	
First Day Cover				1·80
Presentation Pack (P.O. Pack No. 103)			1·80	
PHQ Cards (set of 4) (31)			2·25	5·00

Special First Day of Issue Postmarks

Philatelic Bureau, Edinburgh	2·00
Harrogate, North Yorkshire	2·50

549 Singing Carols round the Christmas Tree

550 The Waits

551 18th-century Carol Singers **552** "The Boar's Head Carol"

(Des Faith Jaques)

1978 (22 Nov). *Christmas, Carol singers.* One centre phosphor band (7p.) or 'All-over' phosphor (others). P 15×14.

1071	**549**	7p. brt green, greenish yellow, magenta, new blue, black and gold	25	25
		a. Imperf (pair)	£1000	
1072	**550**	9p. magenta, greenish yellow, new blue, sage-green, black and gold	25	25
		a. Imperf (pair)	£2600	
1073	**551**	11p. magenta, new blue, greenish yellow, yellow-brown, black and gold	50	50
		a. Imperf (horiz pair)	£2600	
1074	**552**	13p. salmon-pink, new blue, greenish yellow, magenta, black and gold	50	50
Set of 4			1·40	1·40
Set of 4 Gutter Pairs			3·00	
Set of 4 Traffic Light Gutter Pairs			4·25	
First Day Cover				1·80
Presentation Pack (P.O. Pack No. 104)			1·80	
PHQ Cards (set of 4) (32)			2·25	5·00

Special First Day of Issue Postmarks

Philatelic Bureau, Edinburgh	2·00
Bethlehem, Llandeilo, Dyfed	2·50

Collectors Pack 1978

1978 (22 Nov). Comprises Nos. 1050/7 and 1059/74.

CP1074a Collectors Pack	10·00

553 Old English Sheepdog **554** Welsh Springer Spaniel

555 West Highland Terrier **556** Irish Setter

(Des P. Barrett)

1979 (7 Feb). *Dogs.* 'All-over' phosphor. P 15×14.

1075	**553**	9p. grey-black, sepia, turquoise-green, pale greenish yellow, pale greenish blue and grey	25	20
1076	**554**	10½p. grey-black, lake-brown, apple-green, pale greenish yellow, pale greenish blue and grey	40	40
1077	**555**	11p. grey-black, claret, yellowish green, pale greenish yellow, cobalt and grey	40	40
		a. Imperf (horiz pair)	£6750	
1078	**556**	13p. grey-black, lake-brown, green, pale greenish yellow and dp turquoise-blue	40	50
Set of 4			1·30	1·30
Set of 4 Gutter Pairs			2·75	

Set of 4 Traffic Light Gutter Pairs	4·25	
First Day Cover		1·80
Presentation Pack (P.O. Pack No. 106)	1·80	
PHQ Cards (set of 4) (33)	2·50	5·00

Special First Day of Issue Postmarks

Philatelic Bureau, Edinburgh	2·00
London SW	2·50

557 Primrose **558** Daffodil

559 Bluebell **560** Snowdrop

(Des P. Newcombe)

1979 (21 Mar). *Spring Wild Flowers.* 'All-over' phosphor. P 14×15.

1079	**557**	9p. slate-black, dp brown, pale greenish yellow, dp olive, pale new blue and silver	25	20
		a. Imperf (vert pair)	£875	
1080	**558**	10½p. greenish yellow, grey-green, steel-blue, slate-black, new blue and silver	25	45
		a. Imperf (vert pair)	£4000	
1081	**559**	11p. slate-black, dp brown, ultramarine, lt greenish blue, pale greenish yellow and silver	50	45
		a. Imperf (horiz pair)	£3600	
1082	**560**	13p. slate-black, indigo, grey-green, sepia, ochre and silver	50	40
		a. Imperf (horiz pair)	£2750	
Set of 4			1·40	1·40
Set of 4 Gutter Pairs			3·00	
Set of 4 Traffic Light Gutter Pairs			4·25	
First Day Cover				1·80
Presentation Pack (P.O. Pack No. 107)			1·80	
PHQ Cards (set of 4) (34)			2·50	4·50

Special First Day of Issue Postmark

Philatelic Bureau, Edinburgh	2·00

561   562

563   564

(Des S. Cliff)

1979 (9 May). *First Direct Elections to European Assembly.* Phosphorised paper. *P* 15×14.

1083	**561**	9p. grey-black, vermilion, cinnamon, pale greenish yellow, pale turquoise-green and dull ultramarine	25	20
1084	**562**	10½p. grey-black, vermilion, cinnamon, pale greenish yellow, dull ultramarine, pale turquoise-green and chestnut	35	35
1085	**563**	11p. grey-black, vermilion, cinnamon, pale greenish yellow, dull ultramarine, pale turquoise-green and grey-green	40	40
1086	**564**	13p. grey-black, vermilion, cinnamon, pale greenish yellow, dull ultramarine, pale turquoise-green and brown	45	40
Set of 4			1·30	1·30
Set of 4 Gutter Pairs			2·75	
Set of 4 Traffic Light Gutter Pairs			4·25	
First Day Cover				1·80
Presentation Pack (P.O. Pack No. 108)			1·80	
PHQ Cards (set of 4) (35)			2·25	4·50

Nos. 1083/6 show Hands placing National Flags in Ballot Boxes.

Special First Day of Issue Postmarks

Philatelic Bureau, Edinburgh	2·00
London SW	2·50

565 "Saddling 'Mahmoud' for the Derby, 1936" (Sir Alfred Munnings)

566 "The Liverpool Great National Steeple Chase, 1839" (aquatint by F. C. Turner)

567 "The First Spring Meeting, Newmarket, 1793" (J. N. Sartorius)

568 "Racing at Dorsett Ferry, Windsor, 1684" (Francis Barlow)

(Des S. Rose)

1979 (6 June). *Horseracing Paintings.* Bicentenary of the Derby (9p.). 'All-over' phosphor. *P* 15×14.

1087	**565**	9p. lt blue, red-brown, rose-pink, pale greenish yellow, grey-black and gold	25	25
1088	**566**	10½p. bistre-yellow, slate-blue, salmon-pink, lt blue, grey-black and gold	25	25
1089	**567**	11p. rose, vermilion, pale greenish yellow, new blue, grey-black and gold	50	50
1090	**568**	13p. bistre-yellow, rose, turquoise, grey-black and gold	50	50
Set of 4			1·40	1·40
Set of 4 Gutter Pairs			3·00	
Set of 4 Traffic Light Gutter Pairs			4·25	
First Day Cover				1·80
Presentation Pack (P.O. Pack No. 109)			1·80	
PHQ Cards (set of 4) (36)			2·25	4·50

Special First Day of Issue Postmarks

Philatelic Bureau, Edinburgh	2·00
Epsom, Surrey	2·50

569 *The Tale of Peter Rabbit* (Beatrix Potter)

570 *The Wind in the Willows* (Kenneth Grahame)

571 *Winnie-the-Pooh* (A. A. Milne)

572 *Alice's Adventures in Wonderland* (Lewis Carroll)

(Des E. Hughes)

1979 (11 July). *International Year of the Child.* Children's Book Illustrations. 'All-over' phosphor. *P* 14×15.

1091	**569**	9p. dp bluish green, grey-black, bistre-brown, brt rose, greenish yellow and silver	30	25
1092	**570**	10½p. dull ultramarine, grey-black, olive-brown, brt rose, yellow-orange, pale greenish yellow and silver	35	35
1093	**571**	11p. drab, grey-black, greenish yellow, new blue, yellow-orange, agate and silver	40	40
1094	**572**	13p. pale greenish yellow, grey-black, brt rose, dp bluish green, olive-brown, new blue and silver	60	60
Set of 4			1·50	1·50
Set of 4 Gutter Pairs			3·50	
Set of 4 Traffic Light Gutter Pairs			4·25	
First Day Cover				2·00
Presentation Pack (P.O. Pack No. 110)			1·80	
PHQ Cards (set of 4) (37)			2·50	4·50

Nos. 1091/4 depict original illustrations from four books.

Special First Day of Issue Postmark

Philatelic Bureau, Edinburgh ....2·00
First Day of Issue handstamps were provided at Hartfield, East Sussex and Stourbridge, West Midlands for this issue.

573 Sir Rowland Hill   **574** Postman, *circa* 1839

575 London Postman, *circa* 1839   **576** Woman and Young Girl with Letters, 1840

(Des E. Stemp)

1979 (22 Aug–24 Oct). *Death Centenary of Sir Rowland Hill.* 'All-over' phosphor. P 14×15.

1095	**573**	10p. grey-black, brown-ochre, myrtle-green, pale greenish yellow, rosine, brt blue and gold.................	25	20
		a. Imperf (horiz pair)...........................	£8250	
1096	**574**	11½p. grey-black, brown-ochre, brt blue, rosine, bistre-brown, pale greenish yellow and gold.......................	25	35
1097	**575**	13p. grey-black, brown-ochre, brt blue, rosine, bistre-brown, pale greenish yellow and gold.......................	50	45
1098	**576**	15p. grey-black, brown-ochre, myrtle-green, bistre-brown, rosine, pale greenish yellow and gold..................	75	50

Set of 4 .... 1·60 1·40
Set of 4 Gutter Pairs .... 3·25
Set of 4 Traffic Light Gutter Pairs .... 4·25
First Day Cover .... 2·00
Presentation Pack (P.O. Pack No. 111)........ 2·50
PHQ Cards (set of 4) (38)............................ 2·25 4·25
MS1099 89×121 mm. Nos. 1095/8 (sold at 59½p.) (24 Oct)... 1·30 1·50
  a. Imperforate £9750
  b. Brown-ochre (15p. background, etc.) omitted £10000
  c. Gold (Queen's head) omitted................... £975
  d. Brown-ochre, myrtle-green and gold omitted £20000
  e. Brt blue (13p. background, etc.) omitted £18000
  f. Myrtle-green (10p. (background), 15p.) omitted £10000
  g. Pale greenish yellow omitted £875
  h. Rosine omitted £2750
  i. Bistre-brown omitted £2750
  j. Grey-black and pale greenish yellow omitted £90000
First Day Cover .... 2·00

The premium on No. **MS**1099 was used to support the London 1980 International Stamp Exhibition.
Examples of No. **MS**1099 showing face values on the stamps of 9p., 10½p., 11p. and 13p., with a sheet price of 53½p., were prepared, but not issued. (*Price* £40,000).

Special First Day of Issue Postmarks

Philatelic Bureau, Edinburgh (stamps (22 Aug).................................2·00
Philatelic Bureau, Edinburgh (miniature sheet) (24 Oct) ....2·00
London EC (stamps) (22 Aug)..2·00
London EC (miniature sheet) (24 Oct)...2·00
First Day of Issue handstamps were provided at Kidderminster, Worcs on 22 August (pictorial) and 24 October (Type C) and at Sanquhar, Dumfriesshire on 22 August and 24 October (both Type C).

577 Policeman on the Beat   **578** Policeman directing Traffic

579 Mounted Policewoman   **580** River Patrol Boat

(Des B. Sanders)

1979 (26 Sept). *150th Anniv of Metropolitan Police.* Phosphorised paper. P 15×14.

1100	**577**	10p. grey-black, red-brown, emerald, greenish yellow, brt blue and magenta	30	20
1101	**578**	11½p. grey-black, brt orange, purple-brown, ultramarine, greenish yellow and deep bluish green	35	35
1102	**579**	13p. grey-black, red-brown, magenta, olive-green, greenish yellow and deep dull blue	40	55
1103	**580**	15p. grey-black, magenta, brown, slate-blue, dp brown and greenish black	60	55

Set of 4 .... 1·50 1·50
Set of 4 Gutter Pairs .... 3·25
Set of 4 Traffic Light Gutter Pairs .... 4·25
First Day Cover .... 2·00
Presentation Pack (P.O. Pack No. 112)........ 1·80
PHQ Cards (set of 4) (39)............................ 2·25 4·25

Special First Day of Issue Postmarks

Philatelic Bureau, Edinburgh ....2·00
London SW ....2·00

581 The Three Kings

582 Angel appearing to the Shepherds

583 The Nativity

584 Mary and Joseph travelling to Bethlehem

585 The Annunciation

(Des F. Wegner)

1979 (21 Nov). *Christmas, Nativity Scenes.* One centre phosphor band (8p.) or phosphorised paper (others). *P* 15×14.

1104	**581**	8p. blue, grey-black, ochre, slate-violet and gold....................	25	20
		a. Imperf (pair)................................	£900	
1105	**582**	10p. brt rose-red, grey-black, chestnut, chrome-yellow, dp violet and gold.........	25	25
		a. Imperf between (vert pair)	£2250	
		b. Imperf (pair)................................	£1750	
1106	**583**	11½p. orange-vermilion, steel-blue, drab, grey-black, dp blue-green and gold............	25	35
1107	**584**	13p. brt blue, orange-vermilion, bistre, grey-black and gold....................	50	50
1108	**585**	15p. orange-vermilion, blue, bistre, grey-black, green and gold..............	50	50
Set of 5			1·60	1·60
Set of 5 Gutter Pairs			3·50	
Set of 5 Traffic Light Gutter Pairs			4·50	
First Day Cover				2·00
Presentation Pack (P.O. Pack No. 113)........			2·00	
PHQ Cards (set of 5) (40)...........			2·50	4·25

Special First Day of Issue Postmarks

Philatelic Bureau, Edinburgh ....2·00
Bethlehem, Llandeilo, Dyfed ....2·00

Collectors Pack 1979
1979 (21 Nov). Comprises Nos. 1075/98 and 1100/8.
CP1108*a* Collectors Pack............................ 12·00

586 Common Kingfisher

587 Dipper

588 Moorhen

589 Yellow Wagtails

(Des M. Warren)

1980 (16 Jan). *Centenary of Wild Bird Protection Act.* Phosphorised paper. *P* 14×15.

1109	**586**	10p. brt blue, brt yellow-green, vermilion, pale greenish yellow, grey-black and gold....................	20	10
1110	**587**	11½p. sepia, grey-black, dull ultramarine, vermilion, grey-green, pale greenish yellow and gold..................	40	35
1111	**588**	13p. emerald-green, grey-black, brt blue, vermilion, pale greenish yellow and gold....................	50	55
1112	**589**	15p. greenish yellow, brown, lt green, slate-blue, grey-black and gold	50	55
Set of 4			1·50	1·40
Set of 4 Gutter Pairs			3·50	
First Day Cover				2·00
Presentation Pack (P.O. Pack No. 115)........			2·25	
PHQ Cards (set of 4) (41)			2·25	4·50

Special First Day of Issue Postmarks

Philatelic Bureau, Edinburgh ....2·00
Sandy, Beds ....2·50

590 *Rocket* approaching Moorish Arch, Liverpool

591 First and Second Class Carriages passing through Olive Mount Cutting

592 Third Class Carriage and Sheep Truck crossing Chat Moss

593 Horsebox and Carriage Truck near Bridgewater Canal

594 Goods Truck and Mail-Coach at Manchester

Grey step and dot above (Cyl. 1A, R. 8/4)

(Des D. Gentleman)

1980 (12 Mar). *150th Anniv of Liverpool and Manchester Railway.* Phosphorised paper. *P* 15×14.

1113	**590**	12p. lemon, lt brown, rose-red, pale blue and grey-black	20	15
		a. Strip of 5. Nos. 1113/17	1·80	1·80
		ab. Imperf (horiz strip of 5. Nos. 1113/17)	£9000	
		ac. Lemon omitted (horiz strip of 5. Nos. 1113/17)	£50000	
1114	**591**	12p. rose-red, lt brown, lemon, pale blue and grey-black	20	15
1115	**592**	12p. pale blue, rose-red, lemon, lt brown and grey-black	20	15
1116	**593**	12p. lt brown, lemon, rose-red, pale blue and grey-black	20	15
		a. Grey step	25·00	
1117	**594**	12p. lt brown, rose-red, pale blue, lemon and grey-black	20	15
Set of 5			1·80	1·80
Gutter Block of 10			3·75	
First Day Cover				2·25
Presentation Pack (P.O. Pack No. 116)			2·25	
PHQ Cards (set of 5) (42)			3·25	4·50

Nos. 1113/7 were printed together, *se-tenant*, in horizontal strips of 5 throughout the sheet.

Special First Day of Issue Postmarks

Philatelic Bureau, Edinburgh	2·00
Liverpool	2·25
Manchester	2·25

INTERNATIONAL STAMP EXHIBITION
595 Montage of London Buildings

During the printing of No. 1118 the die was re-cut resulting in the following two types:

Type I (original). Top and bottom lines of shading in portrait oval broken. Hatched shading below left arm of Tower Bridge and hull of ship below right arm. Other points: Hatched shading on flag on Westminster Abbey, bottom right of Post Office Tower and archway of entrance to Westminster Abbey.

Type II (re-engraved). Lines in oval unbroken. Solid shading on bridge and ship. Also solid shading on flag, Post Office Tower and archway.

(Des J. Matthews. Eng G. Holt. Recess)

1980 (9 Apr–7 May). *London 1980* International Stamp Exhibition. Phosphorised paper. *P* 14½×14.

1118	**595**	50p. agate (I)	1·50	1·50
		Ea. Type II	1·30	1·30
Gutter Pair			3·25	
First Day Cover				2·00
Presentation Pack (P.O. Pack No. 117)			1·80	
PHQ Card (43)			1·00	3·00
MS1119 90×123 mm. No. 1118Ea (sold at 75p.) (7 May)			1·50	1·80
		a. Error. Imperf	£6800	
First Day Cover				2·00

Examples of No. 1118 are known in various shades of green.

Such shades result from problems with the drying of the printed sheets on the press, but are not listed as similar colours can be easily faked.

Special First Day of Issue Postmarks

Philatelic Bureau, Edinburgh (stamp) (9 Apr.)..............................2·00
Philatelic Bureau, Edinburgh (miniature sheet) (7 May) ....2·50
London SW (stamp) (9 Apr.) .... 2·50
London SW (miniature sheet) (7 May) ....2·50

Special First Day of Issue Postmarks

Philatelic Bureau, Edinburgh ....2·50
Kingston-upon-Thames ....2·50

596 Buckingham Palace   **597** The Albert Memorial

601 Charlotte Brontë (*Jane Eyre*)   **602** George Eliot (*The Mill on the Floss*)

598 Royal Opera House   **599** Hampton Court

603 Emily Brontë (*Wuthering Heights*)   **604** Mrs Gaskell (*North and South*)

(Des Barbara Brown)

1980 (9 July). *Famous Authoresses.* Phosphorised paper. *P* 15×14.

1125	**601**	12p. red-brown, brt rose, brt blue, greenish yellow, grey and gold	35	20
		Ea. Missing "p" in value (R. 4/6)	25·00	
1126	**602**	13½p. red-brown, dull vermilion, pale blue, pale greenish yellow, grey and gold	40	45
		a. Pale blue omitted..............................	£4000	
1127	**603**	15p. red-brown, vermilion, blue, lemon, grey and gold	40	45
1128	**604**	17½p. dull vermilion, slate-blue, ultramarine, pale greenish yellow, grey and gold	50	50
		a. Imperf and slate-blue omitted (pair)..	£1000	
Set of 4			1·50	1·50
Set of 4 Gutter Pairs..................................			3·75	
First Day Cover				2·00
Presentation Pack (P.O. Pack No. 119).......			1·80	
PHQ Cards (set of 4) (44).............................			2·50	3·00

No. 1125/8 show authoresses and scenes from novels. Nos. 1125/6 also include the 'Europa' C.E.P.T. emblem.

600 Kensington Palace

(Des Sir Hugh Casson)

1980 (7 May). *London Landmarks.* Phosphorised paper. *P* 14×15.

1120	**596**	10½p. grey, pale blue, rosine, pale greenish yellow, yellowish green and silver..................................	25	10
1121	**597**	12p. grey-black, bistre, rosine, yellowish green, pale greenish yellow and silver.....................................	25	15
		a. Imperf (vert pair)........................	£5000	
1122	**598**	13½p. grey-black, pale salmon, pale olive-green, slate-blue and silver.............	40	50
		a. Imperf (pair)................................	£5000	
1123	**599**	15p. grey-black, pale salmon, slate-blue, dull yellowish green, olive-yellow and silver...	50	75
1124	**600**	17½p. grey, slate-blue, red-brown, sepia, yellowish green, pale greenish yellow and silver..............................	75	75
		a. Silver (Queen's head) omitted............	£1500	
Set of 5			2·00	2·00
Set of 5 Gutter Pairs.................................			4·25	
First Day Cover				2·50
Presentation Pack (P.O. Pack No. 118).......			2·00	
PHQ Cards (set of 5) (43)..........................			2·25	3·00

No. 1124a shows the Queen's head in pale greenish yellow, this colour being printed beneath the silver for technical reasons.

Special First Day of Issue Postmarks

Philatelic Bureau, Edinburgh .... 2·00
Haworth, Keighley, W. Yorks ....2·50

605 Queen Elizabeth
the Queen Mother

(Des J. Matthews from photograph by N. Parkinson)

1980 (4 Aug). *80th Birthday of Queen Elizabeth the Queen Mother.* Phosphorised paper. P 14×15.

1129	**605**	12p. brt rose, greenish yellow, new blue, grey and silver	30	50
		a. Imperf (horiz pair)	£3250	
Gutter Pair			1·00	
First Day Cover				1·50
PHQ Card (45)			1·00	2·00

Special First Day of Issue Postmarks

Philatelic Bureau, Edinburgh	2·00
Glamis Castle, Forfar	3·00

606 Sir Henry Wood

607 Sir Thomas Beecham

608 Sir Malcolm Sargent

609 Sir John Barbirolli

(Des P. Gauld)

1980 (10 Sept). *British Conductors.* Phosphorised paper. P 14×15.

1130	**606**	12p. slate, rose-red, greenish yellow, bistre and gold	30	10
1131	**607**	13½p. grey-black, vermilion, greenish yellow, pale carmine-rose and gold	45	40
1132	**608**	15p. grey-black, brt rose-red, greenish yellow, turquoise-green and gold	50	55
1133	**609**	17½p. black, brt rose-red, greenish yellow, dull violet-blue and gold	50	55
Set of 4			1·60	1·50
Set of 4 Gutter Pairs			3·75	
First Day Cover				2·00
Presentation Pack (P.O. Pack No. 120)			1·80	
PHQ Cards (set of 4) (46)			2·25	3·75

Special First Day of Issues

Postmarks Philatelic Bureau, Edinburgh	2·00
London SW	2·25

610 Running

611 Rugby

612 Boxing

613 Cricket

(Des R. Goldsmith. Litho Questa)

1980 (10 Oct). *Sport Centenaries.* Phosphorised paper. P 14×14½.

1134	**610**	12p. pale new blue, greenish yellow, magenta, lt brown, reddish purple and gold	25	20
		a. Gold (Queen's head) omitted	£50000	
1135	**611**	13½p. pale new blue, olive-yellow, brt purple, orange-vermilion, blackish lilac and gold	50	50
1136	**612**	15p. pale new blue, greenish yellow, brt purple, chalky blue & gold	50	45
		a. Gold (Queen's head) omitted	£34000	
1137	**613**	17½p. pale new blue, greenish yellow, magenta, dp olive, grey-brown and gold	50	50
Set of 4			1·60	1·50
Set of 4 Gutter Pairs			3·75	
First Day Cover				2·00
Presentation Pack (P.O. Pack No. 121)			1·80	
PHQ Cards (set of 4) (47)			2·25	3·75

Centenaries: 12p. Amateur Athletics Association; 13½p. Welsh Rugby Union; 15p. Amateur Boxing Association; 17½p. First England-Australia Test Match.

Nos. 1134a and 1136a were caused by paper folds.

Special First Day of Issue Postmarks

Philatelic Bureau, Edinburgh	2·00
Cardiff	2·25

614 Christmas Tree   **615** Candles

616 Apples and Mistletoe   **617** Crown, Chains and Bell

618 Holly

(Des J. Matthews)

1980 (19 Nov). *Christmas.* One centre phosphor band (10p.) or phosphorised paper. P 15×14.

1138	**614**	10p. black, turquoise-green, greenish yellow, vermilion and blue...............	20	10
		a. Imperf (horiz pair)..............................	£3400	
1139	**615**	12p. grey, magenta, rose-red, greenish grey and pale orange.....................	20	20
1140	**616**	13½p. grey-black, dull yellow-green, brown, greenish yellow and pale olive-bistre..	40	40
		a. Imperf (pair).....................................	£5000	
1141	**617**	15p. grey-black, bistre-yellow, brt orange, magenta and new blue......	55	50
1142	**618**	17½p. black, vermilion, dull yellowish green and greenish yellow	55	50
Set of 5			1·80	1·50
Set of 5 Gutter Pairs..			4·00	
First Day Cover				2·00
Presentation Pack (P.O. Pack No. 122)...................			2·00	
PHQ Cards (set of 5) (48)			2·25	4·00

Special First Day of Issue Postmarks

Philatelic Bureau, Edinburgh ....2·00
Bethlehem, Llandeilo, Dyfed .... 2·50

Collectors Pack 1980
1980 (19 Nov). Comprises Nos. 1109/18 and 1120/42.
CP1142*a* Collectors Pack.. 15·00

619 St. Valentine's Day   **620** Morris Dancers

621 Lammastide   **622** Medieval Mummers

T **619/20** also include the "Europa" C.E.P.T. emblem.

(Des F. Wegner)

1981 (6 Feb). *Folklore.* Phosphorised paper. P 15×14.

1143	**619**	14p. cerise, green, yellow-orange, salmon-pink, black and gold	25	25
1144	**620**	18p. dull ultramarine, lemon, lake-brown, brt green, black and gold ..	50	50
1145	**621**	22p. chrome-yellow, rosine, brown, new blue, black and gold..................	75	80
1146	**622**	25p. brt blue, red-brown, brt rose-red, greenish yellow, black and gold......	1·00	1·10
Set of 4			2·25	2·40
Set of 4 Gutter Pairs..			4·75	
First Day Cover				2·50
Presentation Pack (P.O. Pack No. 124)...................			2·50	
PHQ Cards (set of 4) (49)..			2·25	3·25

Nos. 1143/4 also include the 'Europa' C.E.P.T. emblem.

Special First Day of Issue Postmarks

Philatelic Bureau, Edinburgh .... 2·60
London WC .... 2·75

623 Blind Man with Guide Dog   **624** Hands spelling "Deaf" in Sign Language

625 Disabled Man in Wheelchair   **626** Disabled Artist with Foot painting

(Des J. Gibbs)

1981 (25 Mar). *International Year of the Disabled.* Phosphorised paper. P 15×14.

1147	**623**	14p. drab, greenish yellow, brt rose-red, dull purple and silver	50	25
		a. Imperf (pair)...................................	£900	
1148	**624**	18p. dp blue-green, brt orange, dull vermilion, grey-black and silver.......	50	50
1149	**625**	22p. brown-ochre, rosine, purple-brown, greenish blue, black and silver...	75	85
1150	**626**	25p. vermilion, lemon, pale salmon, olive-brown, new blue, black and silver...	1·00	1·00
Set of 4			2·50	2·40
Set of 4 Gutter Pairs..			5·25	
First Day Cover				3·00
Presentation Pack (P.O. Pack No. 125)...................			2·75	
PHQ Cards (set of 4) (50)..			2·25	6·00

All known examples of No. 1147a are creased.

Special First Day of Issue Postmarks

Philatelic Bureau, Edinburgh ....3·00
Windsor ....3·00

627 *Aglais urticae*   **628** *Maculinea arion*

629 *Inachis io*   **630** *Carterocephalus palaemon*

(Des G. Beningfield)

1981 (13 May). *Butterflies*. Phosphorised paper. *P* 14×15.

1151	**627**	14p. greenish yellow, yellow-green, brt rose, brt blue, emerald and gold....	25	20
		a. Imperf (pair).....................................	£11000	
1152	**628**	18p. black, greenish yellow, dull yellowish green, brt mauve, brt blue, brt green and gold	75	70
1153	**629**	22p. black, greenish yellow, bronze-green, rosine, ultramarine, lt green and gold	70	85
1154	**630**	25p. black, greenish yellow, bronze-green, brt rose-red, ultramarine, brt emerald and gold........................	75	85
Set of 4			2·25	2·40
Set of 4 Gutter Pairs...			4·75	
First Day Cover				3·00
Presentation Pack (P.O. Pack No. 126)........................			2·50	
PHQ Cards (set of 4) (51)			2·25	6·00

Special First Day of Issue Postmarks

Philatelic Bureau, Edinburgh ....3·00
London SW ....3·00

631 Glenfinnan, Scotland   **632** Derwentwater, England

633 Stackpole Head, Wales   **634** Giant's Causeway, Northern Ireland

635 St. Kilda, Scotland

(Des M. Fairclough)

1981 (24 June). *50th Anniv of National Trust for Scotland. British Landscapes*. Phosphorised paper. *P* 15×14.

1155	**631**	14p. lilac, dull blue, reddish brown, bistre-yellow, black and gold...........	15	25
1156	**632**	18p. bottle green, brt blue, brown, bistre-yellow, black and gold...........	45	50
1157	**633**	20p. dp turquoise-blue, dull blue, greenish yellow, reddish brown, black and gold	70	75
1158	**634**	22p. chrome-yellow, reddish brown, new blue, yellow-brown, black and gold	75	1·00
1159	**635**	25p. ultramarine, new blue, olive-green, olive-grey and gold..............................	90	1·00
Set of 5			2·60	3·00
Set of 5 Gutter Pairs...			5·50	
First Day Cover				3·50
Presentation Pack (P.O. Pack No. 127)........................			3·00	
PHQ Cards (set of 5) (52)...			2·50	5·00

Special First Day of Issue Postmarks

Philatelic Bureau, Edinburgh ....3·50
Glenfinnan ....3·50
Keswick ....3·50

636 Prince Charles and Lady Diana Spencer

(Des J. Matthews from photograph by Lord Snowdon)

1981 (22 July). *Royal Wedding*. Phosphorised paper. *P* 14×15.

1160	**636**	14p. grey-black, greenish yellow, brt rose-red, ultramarine, pale blue, blue and silver...	75	25

1161   25p. drab, greenish yellow, brt rose-red,
ultramarine, grey-brown, grey-
black and silver .... 1·50   1·50

Set of 2	2·00	1·50
Set of 2 Gutter Pairs.............................	4·25	
First Day Cover		2·75
Presentation Pack (P.O. Pack No. 127a)	3·00	
Souvenir Book	3·00	
PHQ Cards (set of 2) (53)........................	1·50	5·00

    The souvenir book is a 12-page illustrated booklet with a set of mint stamps in a sachet attached to the front cover.

Special First Day of Issue Postmarks

Philatelic Bureau, Edinburgh ....3·00	
Caernarfon, Gwynedd ....4·00	
London EC...3·50	

637 "Expeditions"

638 "Skills"

639 "Service"

640 "Recreation"

(Des P. Sharland. Litho J.W.)

1981 (12 Aug). *25th Anniversary of Duke of Edinburgh's Award Scheme.* Phosphorised paper. *P* 14.

1162	**637**	14p. greenish yellow, magenta, pale new blue, black, emerald and silver	25	20
1163	**638**	18p. greenish yellow, magenta, pale new blue, black, cobalt and gold ...	45	50
1164	**639**	22p. greenish yellow, magenta, pale new blue, black, red-orange and gold	80	80
1165	**640**	25p. brt orange, mauve, pale new blue, black, flesh and bronze	90	1·00
Set of 4			2·25	2·40
Set of 4 Gutter Pairs.............................			5·00	
First Day Cover				3·00
Presentation Pack (P.O. Pack No. 128).................			2·50	
PHQ Cards (set of 4) (54)........................			2·50	4·50

Special First Day of Issue Postmarks

Philatelic Bureau, Edinburgh ....2·60	
London W2 ....2·75	

641 Cockle-dredging from *Linsey II*

642 Hauling in Trawl Net

643 Lobster Potting

644 Hoisting Seine Net

(Des B. Sanders)

1981 (23 Sept). *Fishing Industry.* Phosphorised paper. *P* 15×14.

1166	**641**	14p. slate, greenish yellow, magenta, new blue, orange-brown, olive-grey and bronze-green......................	25	25
1167	**642**	18p. slate, greenish yellow, brt crimson, ultramarine, black and greenish slate.......................	50	50
1168	**643**	22p. grey, greenish yellow, brt rose, dull ultramarine, reddish lilac and black.......................	85	85
1169	**644**	25p. grey, greenish yellow, brt rose, cobalt and black...........................	85	85
Set of 4			2·25	2·25
Set of 4 Gutter Pairs.............................			5·00	
First Day Cover				2·40
Presentation Pack (P.O. Pack No. 129).................			2·50	
PHQ Cards (set of 4) (55)........................			2·25	4·50

    Nos. 1166/9 were issued on the occasion of the centenary of the Royal National Mission to Deep Sea Fishermen.

Special First Day of Issue Postmarks

Philatelic Bureau, Edinburgh ....2·50	
Hull ....2·75	

645 Father Christmas

646 Jesus Christ

647 Flying Angel

648 Joseph and Mary arriving at Bethlehem

649 Three Kings approaching Bethlehem

(Des Samantha Brown (11½p.), Tracy Jenkins (14p.), Lucinda Blackmore (18p.), Stephen Moore (22p.), Sophie Sharp (25p.))

1981 (18 Nov). *Christmas. Children's Pictures.* One phosphor band (11½p.) or phosphorised paper (others). P 15×14.

1170	**645**	11½p. ultramarine, black, red, olive-bistre, brt green and gold..............	25	20
1171	**646**	14p. bistre-yellow, brt magenta, blue, greenish blue, brt green, black and gold..............	35	20
1172	**647**	18p. pale blue-green, bistre-yellow, brt magenta, ultramarine, black and gold..............	50	60
1173	**648**	22p. dp turquoise-blue, lemon, magenta, black and gold..............	75	75
1174	**649**	25p. royal blue, lemon, brt magenta, black and gold..............	85	85
Set of 5			2·50	2·40
Set of 5 Gutter Pairs			5·25	
First Day Cover				3·00
Presentation Pack (P.O. Pack No. 130)			3·00	
PHQ Cards (set of 5) 56)			2·25	5·50

Special First Day of Issue Postmarks

Philatelic Bureau, Edinburgh ....3·00
Bethlehem, Llandeilo, Dyfed ....3·00

Collectors Pack 1981
1981 (18 Nov). Comprises Nos. 1143/74.
CP1174*a* Collectors Pack..19·00

650 Charles Darwin and Giant Tortoises

651 Darwin and Marine Iguanas

652 Darwin, Cactus Ground Finch and Large Ground Finch

653 Darwin and Prehistoric Skulls

(Des D. Gentleman)

1982 (10 Feb). *Death Centenary of Charles Darwin.* Phosphorised paper. P 15×14.

1175	**650**	15½p. dull purple, drab, bistre, black and grey-black..............	50	20
1176	**651**	19½p. violet-grey, bistre-yellow, slate-black, red-brown, grey-black and black..............	50	60
1177	**652**	26p. sage green, bistre-yellow, orange, chalky blue, grey-black, red-brown and black..............	75	85
1178	**653**	29p. grey-brown, yellow-brown, brown-ochre, black and grey-black..............	95	90
Set of 4			2·50	2·40
Set of 4 Gutter Pairs			5·25	
First Day Cover				3·00
Presentation Pack (P.O. Pack No. 132)			3·00	
PHQ Cards (set of 4) (57)			2·50	6·00

Special First Day of Issue Postmarks

Philatelic Bureau, Edinburgh ....3·00
Shrewsbury ....3·00

654 Boys' Brigade

655 Girls' Brigade

656 Boy Scout Movement

657 Girl Guide Movement

(Des B. Sanders)

1982 (24 Mar). *Youth Organizations.* Phosphorised paper. P 14×15.

1179	**654**	15½p. gold, greenish yellow, pale orange, mauve, dull blue and grey-black......	25	15
1180	**655**	19½p. gold, greenish yellow, pale orange, brt rose, dp ultramarine, olive-bistre and grey-black..............	50	50
1181	**656**	26p. gold, greenish yellow, olive-sepia, rosine, dp blue, dp dull green and grey-black..............	85	85
1182	**657**	29p. gold, yellow, dull orange, cerise, dull ultramarine, chestnut and grey-black..............	1·00	1·10
Set of 4			2·40	2·40
Set of 4 Gutter Pairs			5·25	
First Day Cover				3·00
Presentation Pack (P.O. Pack No. 133)			3·00	
PHQ Cards (set of 4) (58)			2·50	6·00

Nos. 1179/82 were issued on the occasion of the 75th anniversary of the Boy Scout Movement; the 125th birth anniversary of Lord Baden-Powell and the centenary of the Boys' Brigade (1983).

Special First Day of Issue Postmarks

Edinburgh Philatelic Bureau ....3·00
Glasgow .... 3·00
London SW .... 3·00

658 Ballerina   **659** Harlequin

660 Hamlet   **661** Opera Singer

(Des A. George)

1982 (28 Apr). *Europa. British Theatre.* Phosphorised paper. *P* 14×15.
1183	**658**	15½p. carmine-lake, greenish blue, greenish yellow, grey-black, bottle green and silver	25	15
1184	**659**	19½p. rosine, new blue, greenish yellow, black, ultramarine and silver	50	50
1185	**660**	26p. carmine-red, brt rose-red, greenish yellow, black, dull ultramarine, lake-brown and silver	85	1·00
1186	**661**	29p. rose-red, greenish yellow, brt blue, grey-black and silver	1·00	1·00

Set of 4 .... 2·40 2·40
Set of 4 Gutter Pairs .... 5·25
First Day Cover .... 3·00
Presentation Pack (P.O. Pack No. 134)................... 3·00
PHQ Cards (set of 4) (59)...................................... 2·50 6·00

Special First Day of Issue Postmarks

Philatelic Bureau, Edinburgh ....3·00
Stratford-upon-Avon ....3·00

662 Henry VIII and *Mary Rose*   **663** Admiral Blake and *Triumph*

664 Lord Nelson and H.M.S. *Victory*   **665** Lord Fisher and H.M.S. *Dreadnought*

666 Viscount Cunningham and H.M.S. *Warspite*

(Des Marjorie Saynor. Eng C. Slania. Recess and photo)

1982 (16 June). *Maritime Heritage.* Phosphorised paper. *P* 15×14.
1187	**662**	15½p. black, lemon, brt rose, pale orange, ultramarine and grey	35	25
		a. Imperf (pair)	£4250	
1188	**663**	19½p. black, greenish yellow, brt rose-red, pale orange, ultramarine and grey	50	50
1189	**664**	24p. black, orange-yellow, brt rose-red, lake-brown, dp ultramarine and grey	75	85
1190	**665**	26p. black, orange-yellow, brt rose, lemon, ultramarine and grey	75	85
		a. Imperf (pair)	£9000	
1191	**666**	29p. black, olive-yellow, brt rose, orange-yellow, ultramarine and grey	1·00	1·00

Set of 5 .... 3·00 3·25
Set of 5 Gutter Pairs .... 6·50
First Day Cover .... 4·00
Presentation Pack (P.O. Pack No. 136)................... 3·50
PHQ Cards (set of 5) (60)...................................... 2·50 6·00

Nos. 1187/91 were issued on the occasion of Maritime England Year, the Bicentenary of the Livery Grant by the City of London to the Worshipful Company of Shipwrights and the raising of the *Mary Rose* from Portsmouth Harbour.

Several used examples of the 15½p. have been seen with the black recess (ship and waves) omitted...£1750

Special First Day of Issue Postmarks

Philatelic Bureau, Edinburgh ....4·00
Portsmouth ....4·00

667 "Strawberry Thief" (William Morris)   **668** Untitled (Steiner and Co)

669 "Cherry Orchard" (Paul Nash)

670 "Chevron" (Andrew Foster)

(Des Peter Hatch Partnership)

1982 (23 July). *British Textiles.* Phosphorised paper. *P* 14×15.

1192	**667**	15½p. blue, olive-yellow, rosine, dp blue-green, bistre and Prussian blue	25	25
		a. Imperf (horiz pair)	£4500	
1193	**668**	19½p. olive-grey, greenish yellow, brt magenta, dull green, yellow-brown and black	75	75
		a. Imperf (vert pair)	£6500	
1194	**669**	26p. brt scarlet, dull mauve, dull ultramarine and brt carmine	75	1·00
1195	**670**	29p. bronze-green, orange-yellow, turquoise-green, stone, chestnut and sage-green	1·00	1·25
Set of 4			2·50	2·75
Set of 4 Gutter Pairs			5·50	
First Day Cover				3·25
Presentation Pack (P.O. Pack No. 137)			3·00	
PHQ Cards (set of 4) (61)			2·50	6·00

Nos. 1192/5 were issued on the occasion of the 250th birth anniversary of Sir Richard Arkwright (inventor of spinning machine).

Special First Day of Issue Postmarks

Philatelic Bureau, Edinburgh	3·25
Rochdale	3·25

671 Development of Communications

672 Modern Technological Aids

(Des Delaney and Ireland)

1982 (8 Sept). *Information Technology.* Phosphorised paper. *P* 14×15.

1196	**671**	15½p. black, greenish yellow, brt rose-red, bistre-brown, new blue and lt ochre	50	25
		a. Imperf (pair)	£575	
1197	**672**	26p. black, greenish yellow, brt rose-red, olive-bistre, new blue and lt olive-grey	75	1·00
		a. Imperf (pair)	£4500	
Set of 2			1·10	1·10
Set of 2 Gutter Pairs			2·75	
First Day Cover				1·75
Presentation Pack (P.O. Pack No. 138)			2·00	
PHQ Cards (set of 2) (62)			2·00	5·25

Special First Day of Issue Postmarks

Philatelic Bureau, Edinburgh	2·00
London WC	2·50

673 Austin "Seven" and "Metro"

674 Ford "Model T" and "Escort"

675 Jaguar "SS 1" and "XJ6"

676 Rolls-Royce "Silver Ghost" and "Silver Spirit"

(Des S. Paine. Litho Questa)

1982 (13 Oct). *British Motor Cars.* Phosphorised paper. *P* 14½×14.

1198	**673**	15½p. slate, orange-vermilion, brt orange, drab, yellow-green, olive-yellow, bluish grey and black	50	25
1199	**674**	19½p. slate, brt orange, olive-grey, rose-red, dull vermilion, grey and black	75	75
		Ea. Rose-red, grey and black ptgs double	£1750	
		Eb. Black printed double	£5500	
1200	**675**	26p. slate, red-brown, brt orange, turquoise-green, myrtle-green, dull blue-green, grey and olive	75	75
1201	**676**	29p. slate, brt orange, carmine-red, reddish purple, grey and black	1·00	1·00
		Ea. Black ptg quadruple	£1600	
		Eb. Brt orange, carmine-red, grey and black ptgs double	£2400	
		Ec. Black ptg quadruple grey ptg triple and purple and carmine ptgs double	£2400	
Set of 4			2·75	2·75
Set of 4 Gutter Pairs			5·50	
First Day Cover				3·00
Presentation Pack (P.O. Pack No. 139)			3·25	
PHQ Cards (set of 4) (63)			2·50	6·00

The price for Nos. 1199Eb is for a complete doubling of both cars, examples showing doubling of only one car or parts of two cars are worth less.

Special First Day of Issue Postmarks

Philatelic Bureau, Edinburgh ....3·00
Birmingham ....3·75
Crewe ....3·75

677 "While Shepherds Watched"   **678** "The Holly and the Ivy"

679 "I Saw Three Ships"   **680** "We Three Kings"

681 "Good King Wenceslas"

(Des Barbara Brown)

1982 (17 Nov). *Christmas. Carols.* One phosphor band (12½p.) or phosphorised paper (others). *P* 15×14.

1202	**677**	12½p. black, greenish yellow, brt scarlet, steel blue, red-brown and gold.......	30	30
1203	**678**	15½p. black, bistre-yellow, brt rose-red, brt blue, brt green and gold	50	30
		a. Imperf (pair)................................	£7000	
1204	**679**	19½p. black, bistre-yellow, brt rose-red, dull blue, dp brown and gold..........	65	75
		a. Imperf (pair)................................	£7500	
1205	**680**	26p. black, bistre-yellow, brt magenta, brt blue, chocolate, gold and orange-red...................................	75	90
1206	**681**	29p. black, bistre-yellow, magenta, brt blue, chestnut, gold and brt magenta	1·00	1·00
Set of 5			3·00	3·00
Set of 5 Gutter Pairs..			6·50	
First Day Cover				3·25
Presentation Pack (P.O. Pack No. 140).............			3·50	
PHQ Cards (set of 5) (64)			2·50	6·00

Special Day of Issue Postmarks

Philatelic Bureau, Edinburgh ....3·25
Bethlehem, Llandeilo, Dyfed ....3·25

Collectors Pack 1982
1982 (Nov 17). Comprises Nos. 1175/1206.
CP1206*a* Collectors Pack.................................... 22·00

682 Atlantic Salmon   **683** Northern Pike

684 Brown Trout   **685** Eurasian Perch

(Des A. Jardine)

1983 (26 Jan). *British River Fish.* Phosphorised paper. *P* 15×14.

1207	**682**	15½p. grey-black, bistre-yellow, brt purple, new blue and silver..............	30	35
		a. Imperf (pair)................................	£4600	
1208	**683**	19½p. black, bistre-yellow, olive-bistre, dp claret, silver and dp bluish green..	60	60
1209	**684**	26p. grey-black, bistre-yellow, chrome-yellow, magenta, silver and pale blue	75	85
		a. Imperf (pair)................................	£4600	
1210	**685**	29p. black, greenish yellow, brt carmine, new blue and silver............	1·00	1·10
Set of 4			2·50	2·50
Set of 4 Gutter Pairs..			5·50	
First Day Cover				3·00
Presentation Pack (P.O. Pack No. 142).............			3·00	
PHQ Cards (set of 4) (65)			3·00	7·00

All known examples of No. 1209a are creased.

Special First Day of Issue Postmarks

Philatelic Bureau, Edinburgh ....2·75
Peterborough ....3·00

686 Tropical Island   **687** Desert

688 Temperate Farmland   **689** Mountain Range

(Des D. Fraser)

1983 (9 Mar). *Commonwealth Day. Geographical Regions.* Phosphorised paper. P 14×15.

1211	**686**	15½p. greenish blue, greenish yellow, brt rose, lt brown, grey-black, dp claret and silver	40	30
1212	**687**	19½p. brt lilac, greenish yellow, magenta, dull blue, grey-black, dp dull blue and silver	75	75
1213	**688**	26p. lt blue, greenish yellow, brt magenta, new blue, grey-black, violet and silver	75	75
1214	**689**	29p. dull violet-blue, reddish violet, slate-lilac, new blue, myrtle green, black and silver	1·00	1·00
Set of 4			2·50	2·50
Set of 4 Gutter Pairs			5·50	
First Day Cover				3·00
Presentation Pack (P.O. Pack No. 143)			3·00	
PHQ Cards (set of 4) (66)			2·50	6·50

Special First Day of Issue Postmarks

Philatelic Bureau, Edinburgh ....3·00
London SW ....3·00

690 Humber Bridge   **691** Thames Flood Barrier

692 *Iolair* (oilfield emergency support vessel)

(Des M. Taylor)

1983 (25 May). *Europa. Engineering Achievements.* Phosphorised paper. P 15×14.

1215	**690**	16p. silver, orange-yellow, ultramarine, black and grey	50	40
1216	**691**	20½p. silver, greenish yellow, brt purple, blue, grey-black and grey	1·00	1·00
1217	**692**	28p. silver, lemon, brt rose-red, chestnut, dull ultramarine, black and grey	1·00	1·00
Set of 3			2·25	2·00
Set of 3 Gutter Pairs			5·00	
First Day Cover				2·50
Presentation Pack (P.O. Pack No. 144)			3·00	
PHQ Cards (set of 3) (67)			2·50	5·75

Special First Day of Issue Postmarks

Philatelic Bureau, Edinburgh ....2·50
Hull ....2·75

693 Musketeer and Pikeman

694 Fusilier and Ensign, The Royal Scots (1633) The Royal Welch Fusiliers (mid-18th-century)

695 Riflemen, 95th Rifles (The Royal Green Jackets) (1805)

696 Sergeant (khaki service) and Guardsman (full dress), The Irish Guards (1900)

697 Paratroopers, The Parachute Regiment (1983)

(Des E. Stemp)

1983 (6 July). *British Army Uniforms.* Phosphorised paper. P 14×15.

1218	**693**	16p. black, buff, dp brown, slate-black, rose-red, gold and new blue	50	30
1219	**694**	20½p. black, buff, greenish yellow, slate-black, brown-rose, gold and brt blue	50	60
1220	**695**	26p. black, buff, slate-purple, green, bistre and gold	75	90
		a. Imperf (pair)	£9000	
1221	**696**	28p. black, buff, lt brown, grey, dull rose, gold and new blue	75	90
		a. Imperf (pair)	£5500	
1222	**697**	31p. black, buff, olive-yellow, grey, dp magenta, gold and new blue	75	85
Set of 5			3·00	3·25
Set of 5 Gutter Pairs			6·50	
First Day Cover				3·75
Presentation Pack (P.O. Pack No. 145)			3·50	
PHQ Cards (set of 5) (68)			3·50	6·50

Nos. 1218/22 were issued on the occasion of the 350th anniversary of the Royal Scots, the senior line regiment of the British Army.

Special First Day of Issue Postmarks

Philatelic Bureau, Edinburgh ....3·75
Aldershot ....3·75

20TH CENTURY GARDEN
SISSINGHURST
698 20th-century Garden, Sissinghurst

19TH CENTURY GARDEN
BIDDULPH GRANGE
699 19th-century Garden, Biddulph Grange

18TH CENTURY GARDEN
BLENHEIM
700 18th-century Garden, Blenheim

17TH CENTURY GARDEN
PITMEDDEN
701 17th-century Garden, Pitmedden

(Des Liz Butler. Litho J.W.)

1983 (24 Aug). *British Gardens.* Phosphorised paper. *P* 14.

1223	**698**	16p. greenish yellow, brt purple, new blue, black, brt green and silver......	50	30
1224	**699**	20½p. greenish yellow, brt purple, new blue, black, brt green and silver......	50	55
1225	**700**	28p. greenish yellow, brt purple, new blue, black, brt green and silver......	75	1·00
1226	**701**	31p. greenish yellow, brt purple, new blue, black, brt green and silver......	1·00	1·00

Set of 4	2·50	2·50
Set of 4 Gutter Pairs	5·50	
First Day Cover		3·00
Presentation Pack (P.O. Pack No. 146)	3·00	
PHQ Cards (set of 4) (69)	3·00	6·25

Nos. 1223/6 were issued on the occasion of the death bicentenary of "Capability" Brown (landscape gardener).

Special First Day of Issue Postmarks

Philatelic Bureau, Edinburgh	3·00
Oxford	3·50

702 Merry-go-round

703 Big Wheel, Helter-skelter and Performing Animals

704 Side Shows

705 Early Produce Fair

(Des A. Restall)

1983 (5 Oct). *British Fairs.* Phosphorised paper. *P* 15×14.

1227	**702**	16p. grey-black, greenish yellow, orange-red, ochre and turquoise-blue	35	35
1228	**703**	20½p. grey-black, yellow-ochre, yellow-orange, brt magenta, violet and black	75	75
1229	**704**	28p. grey-black, bistre-yellow, orange-red, violet and yellow-brown	75	1·00
1230	**705**	31p. grey-black, greenish yellow, red, dp turquoise-green, slate-violet and brown	1·00	1·00

Set of 4	2·50	2·75
Set of 4 Gutter Pairs	5·50	
First Day Cover		3·25
Presentation Pack (P.O. Pack No. 147)	3·00	
PHQ Cards (set of 4) (70)	3·00	6·25

Nos. 1227/30 were issued to mark the 850th anniversary of St. Bartholomew's Fair, Smithfield, London.

Special First Day of Issue Postmarks

Philatelic Bureau, Edinburgh	3·25
Nottingham	3·25

706 "Christmas Post" (pillar-box)

707 "The Three Kings" (chimney-pots)

708 "World at Peace" (Dove and Blackbird)

709 "Light of Christmas" (street lamp)

710 "Christmas Dove" (hedge sculpture)

(Des T. Meeuwissen)

1983 (16 Nov). *Christmas.* One phosphor band (12½p.) or phosphorised paper (others). *P* 15×14.

1231	**706**	12½p. black, greenish yellow, brt rose-red, brt blue, gold and grey-black .	30	30
		a. Imperf (horiz pair)	£4750	
1232	**707**	16p. black, greenish yellow, brt rose, pale new blue, gold and brown-purple	50	35
		a. Imperf (pair)	£3500	
1233	**708**	20½p. black, greenish yellow, brt rose, new blue, gold and blue	75	1·00
1234	**709**	28p. black, lemon, brt carmine, bluish violet, gold, dp turquoise-green and purple	75	1·00
1235	**710**	31p. black, greenish yellow, brt rose, new blue, gold, green and brown-olive	1·25	1·25

Set of 5	3·25	3·50
Set of 5 Gutter Pairs	7·00	

First Day Cover		4·00
Presentation Pack (P.O. Pack No. 148)........................	3·50	
PHQ Cards (set of 5) (71)......................................	3·00	6·25

Special First Day of Issue Postmarks

Philatelic Bureau, Edinburgh	4·00
Bethlehem, Llandeilo, Dyfed	4·00

Collectors Pack 1983
1983 (Nov 16). Comprises Nos. 1207/35.
CP1235a Collectors Pack................................ 25·00

711 Arms of the College of Arms

712 Arms of King Richard III (founder)

713 Arms of the Earl Marshal of England

714 Arms of the City of London

(Des J. Matthews)

1984 (17 Jan). *500th Anniv of College of Arms.* Phosphorised paper. P 14½.

1236	**711**	16p. black, chrome-yellow, reddish brown, scarlet-vermilion, brt blue and grey-black..........................	50	30
1237	**712**	20½p. black, chrome-yellow, rosine, brt blue and grey-black.......................	50	65
1238	**713**	28p. black, chrome-yellow, rosine, brt blue, dull green and grey-black.......	1·00	1·10
1239	**714**	31p. black, chrome-yellow, rosine, brt blue and grey-black	1·25	1·25
		a. Imperf (horiz pair)..........................	£15000	
Set of 4			3·00	3·00
Set of 4 Gutter Pairs..			6·50	
First Day Cover				3·50
Presentation Pack (P.O. Pack No. 150)........................			3·25	
PHQ Cards (set of 4) (72)......................................			3·00	6·50

Special First Day of Issue Postmarks

Philatelic Bureau, Edinburgh	3·50
London EC	3·50

715 Highland Cow

716 Chillingham Wild Bull

717 Hereford Bull

718 Welsh Black Bull

719 Irish Moiled Cow

(Des B. Driscoll)

1984 (6 Mar). *British Cattle.* Phosphorised paper. P 15×14.

1240	**715**	16p. grey-black, bistre-yellow, rosine, yellow-orange, new blue and pale drab..	35	30
		a. Imperf (vert pair)..........................	£16000	
1241	**716**	20½p. grey-black, greenish yellow, magenta, bistre, dull blue-green, pale drab and lt green.........................	60	60
1242	**717**	26p. black, chrome-yellow, rosine, reddish brown, new blue and pale drab..	80	80
1243	**718**	28p. black, greenish yellow, brt carmine, orange-brown, dp dull blue and pale drab.........................	90	90
1244	**719**	31p. grey-black, bistre-yellow, rosine, red-brown, lt blue and pale drab ...	1·00	1·20
		a. Imperf (pair).................................	—	
Set of 5			3·50	3·50
Set of 5 Gutter Pairs..			7·25	
First Day Cover				4·00
Presentation Pack (P.O. Pack No. 151)........................			4·00	
PHQ Cards (set of 5) (73)......................................			3·00	6·50

Nos. 1240/4 were issued on the occasion of the centenary of the Highland Cattle Society and the bicentenary of the Royal Highland and Agricultural Society of Scotland.

Special First Day of Issue Postmarks

Philatelic Bureau, Edinburgh	4·00
Oban, Argyll	4·50

720 Garden Festival Hall, Liverpool

721 Milburngate Centre, Durham

722 Bush House, Bristol

723 Commercial Street Development, Perth

(Des R. Maddox and Trickett and Webb Ltd)

1984 (10 Apr). *Urban Renewal.* Phosphorised paper. P 15×14.

1245	**720**	16p. brt emerald, greenish yellow, cerise, steel-blue, black, silver and flesh..	30	35

1246	721	20½p. brt orange, greenish yellow, dp dull blue, yellowish green, azure, black and silver	50	60
		a. Imperf (horiz pair)	£12500	
1247	722	28p. rosine, greenish yellow, Prussian blue, pale blue-green, black and silver	1·25	1·25
1248	723	31p. blue, greenish yellow, cerise, grey-blue, bright green, black and silver	1·25	1·25
		a. Imperf (pair)	£9500	
Set of 4			3·00	3·00
Set of 4 Gutter Pairs			6·50	
First Day Cover				3·50
Presentation Pack (P.O. Pack No. 152)			3·50	
PHQ Cards (set of 4) (74)			3·00	6·25

Nos. 1245/8 were issued on the occasion of 150th anniversaries of the Royal Institute of British Architects and the Chartered Institute of Building, and to commemorate the first International Gardens Festival, Liverpool.

Special First Day of Issue Postmarks

Philatelic Bureau, Edinburgh .... 3·50
Liverpool .... 3·50

724 C.E.P.T. 25th Anniversary Logo **725** Abduction of Europa

(Des J. Larrivière (T **724**), F. Wegner (T **725**))

1984 (15 May). *25th Anniv of C.E.P.T. ("Europa")* (**T 724**) and *Second Elections to European Parliament* (**T 725**). Phosphorised paper. P 15×14.

1249	724	16p. greenish slate, dp blue and gold....	60	50
		a. Horiz pair. Nos. 1249/50	1·50	1·50
		ab. Imperf (horiz pair)	£7750	
1250	725	16p. greenish slate, dp blue, black and gold	60	50
1251	724	20½p. Venetian red, dp magenta and gold	70	40
		a. Horiz pair. Nos. 1251/2	2·50	2·50
		ab. Imperf (horiz pair)	£9250	
1252	725	20½p. Venetian red, dp magenta, black and gold	70	40
Set of 4			3·50	3·50
Set of 2 Gutter Blocks of 4			7·50	
First Day Cover				4·00
Presentation Pack (P.O. Pack No. 153)			4·00	
PHQ Cards (set of 4) (75)			3·00	6·25

Nos. 1249/50 and 1251/2 were each printed together, *se-tenant*, in horizontal pairs throughout the sheets.

Special First Day of Issue Postmarks

Philatelic Bureau, Edinburgh .... 4·00
London SW.. 4·50

726 Lancaster House

(Des P. Hogarth)

1984 (5 June). *London Economic Summit Conference.* Phosphorised paper. P 14×15.

1253	726	31p. silver, bistre-yellow, brown-ochre, black, rosine, brt blue and reddish lilac	1·25	1·25
Gutter Pair			2·75	
First Day Cover				2·25
PHQ Card (76)			1·00	3·50

Special First Day of Issue Postmarks

 (View of Earth from "Apollo 11" related)

Philatelic Bureau, Edinburgh ....2·50
London SW ....2·50

727 View of Earth from "Apollo 11" **728** Navigational Chart of English Channel

729 Greenwich Observatory **730** Sir George Airy's Transit Telescope

(Des H. Waller. Litho Questa)

1984 (26 June). *Centenary of the Greenwich Meridian.* Phosphorised paper. P 14×14½.

1254	727	16p. new blue, greenish yellow, magenta, black, scarlet and blue-black	50	35
		Ea. Black ptg double	†	£2200
1255	728	20½p. olive-sepia, lt brown, pale buff, black and scarlet	75	80
1256	729	28p. new blue, greenish yellow, scarlet, black and brt purple	1·00	1·00
1257	730	31p. dp blue, cobalt, scarlet & black	1·00	1·10
Set of 4			3·00	3·00
Set of 4 Gutter Pairs			6·50	
First Day Cover				3·50
Presentation Pack (P.O. Pack No. 154)			3·50	
PHQ Cards (set of 4) (77)			3·00	6·25

On Nos. 1254/7 the Meridian is represented by a scarlet line.

Special First Day of Issue Postmarks

Philatelic Bureau, Edinburgh..3·50
London SE10...3·50

731 Bath Mail Coach, 1784   **732** Attack on Exeter Mail, 1816

733 Norwich Mail in Thunderstorm, 1827   **734** Holyhead and Liverpool Mails leaving London, 1828

735 Edinburgh Mail Snowbound, 1831

(Des K. Bassford and S. Paine. Eng C. Slania. Recess and photo)

1984 (31 July). *Bicentenary of First Mail Coach Run, Bath and Bristol to London*. Phosphorised paper. *P* 15×14.

1258	**731**	16p. pale stone, black, grey-black and brt scarlet....................	40	35
		a. Horiz strip of 5. Nos. 1258/62..........	2·50	2·75
		ab. Imperf (horiz pair. Nos. 1261/2).......	£9000	
1259	**732**	16p. pale stone, black, grey-black and brt scarlet....................	40	35
1260	**733**	16p. pale stone, black, grey-black and brt scarlet....................	40	35
1261	**734**	16p. pale stone, black, grey-black and brt scarlet....................	40	35
1262	**735**	16p. pale stone, black, grey-black and brt scarlet....................	40	35
Set of 5			2·50	2·75
Gutter Block of 10..			6·00	
First Day Cover				3·25
Presentation Pack (P.O. Pack No. 155)......................			3·00	
Souvenir Book			7·50	
PHQ Cards (set of 5) (78).......................................			3·00	6·50

Nos. 1258/62 were printed together, *se-tenant*, in horizontal strips of five throughout the sheet.

No. 1258ab also includes No. 1260 perforated at left only.

The souvenir book is a 24-page illustrated booklet with a set of mint stamps in a sachet attached to the front cover.

Special First Day of Issue Postmarks

Philatelic Bureau, Edinburgh ....3·50
Bristol ....4·00

736 Nigerian Clinic   **737** Violinist and Acropolis, Athens

738 Building Project, Sri Lanka   **739** British Council Library, Middle East

(Des F. Newell and J. Sorrell)

1984 (25 Sept). *50th Anniversary of the British Council*. Phosphorised paper. *P* 15×14.

1263	**736**	17p. grey-green, greenish yellow, brt purple, dull blue, black, pale green and yellow-green	50	35
1264	**737**	22p. crimson, greenish yellow, brt rose-red, dull green, black, pale drab and slate-purple........................	85	1·00
1265	**738**	31p. sepia, olive-bistre, red, black, pale stone and olive-brown...................	85	1·00
1266	**739**	34p. steel blue, yellow, rose-red, new blue, black, azure and pale blue.....	1·00	1·00
Set of 4			3·00	3·00
Set of 4 Gutter Pairs...			6·50	
First Day Cover				3·50
Presentation Pack (P.O. Pack No. 156)......................			3·25	
PHQ Cards (set of 4) (79).......................................			3·00	6·25

Special First Day of Issue Postmarks

London SW ....3·50
Philatelic Bureau, Edinburgh ....3·50

740 The Holy Family   **741** Arrival in Bethlehem

742 Shepherd and Lamb   **743** Virgin and Child

744 Offering of Frankincense

(Des Yvonne Gilbert)

1984 (20 Nov). *Christmas.* One phosphor band (13p.) or phosphorised paper (others). P 15×14.

1267	**740**	13p. pale cream, grey-black, bistre-yellow, magenta, red-brown and lake-brown	30	30
		Eu. Underprint Type **4**	70	
1268	**741**	17p. pale cream, grey-black, yellow, magenta, dull blue and dp dull blue	50	50
		a. Imperf (pair)	£6000	
1269	**742**	22p. pale cream, grey-black, olive-yellow, brt magenta, brt blue and brownish grey	75	75
1270	**743**	31p. pale cream, grey-black, bistre-yellow, magenta, dull blue and lt brown	1·00	1·00
1271	**744**	34p. pale cream, olive-grey, bistre-yellow, magenta, turquoise-green and brown-olive	1·00	1·00
Set of 5			3·25	3·25
Set of 5 Gutter Pairs			7·00	
First Day Cover				3·75
Presentation Pack (P.O. Pack No. 157)			3·75	
PHQ Cards (set of 5) (80)			3·00	6·25

Examples of No. 1267Eu from the 1984 Christmas booklet (No. FX7) show a random pattern of blue double-lined stars printed on the reverse over the gum.

Special First Day of Issue Postmarks

Philatelic Bureau, Edinburgh		3·75
Bethlehem, Llandeilo, Dyfed		3·75

Collectors Pack 1984

1984 (Nov 20). Comprises Nos. 1236/71.

CP1271a Collectors Pack .... 38·00

Post Office Yearbook

1984. Comprises Nos. 1236/71 in 24-page hardbound book with slip case, illustrated in colour .... 85·00

745 "Flying Scotsman"   **746** "Golden Arrow"

747 "Cheltenham Flyer"   **748** "Royal Scot"

749 "Cornish Riviera"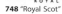

(Des T. Cuneo)

1985 (22 Jan). *Famous Trains.* Phosphorised paper. P 15×14.

1272	**745**	17p. black, lemon, magenta, dull blue, grey-black and gold	75	35
		a. Imperf (pair)	£5000	
1273	**746**	22p. black, greenish yellow, brt rose, dp dull blue, grey-black and gold	75	1·00

1274	**747**	29p. black, greenish yellow, magenta, blue, grey-black and gold	1·00	1·25
1275	**748**	31p. black, bistre-yellow, brt magenta, new blue, slate-black and gold	1·25	1·50
1276	**749**	34p. black, greenish yellow, brt rose, blue, slate-black and gold	2·50	2·50
Set of 5			5·75	6·00
Set of 5 Gutter Pairs			12·00	
First Day Cover				6·50
Presentation Pack (P.O. Pack No. 159)			6·00	
PHQ Cards (set of 5) (81)			6·00	15·00

Nos. 1272/6 were issued on the occasion of the 150th anniversary of the Great Western Railway Company.

Special First Day of Issue Postmarks

Philatelic Bureau, Edinburgh		6·50
Bristol		8·00

750 *Bombus terrestris* (bee)   **751** *Coccinella septempunctata* (ladybird)

752 *Decticus verrucivorus* (bush-cricket)   **753** *Lucanus cervus* (stag beetle)

754 *Anax imperator* (dragonfly)

(Des G. Beningfield)

1985 (12 Mar). *Insects.* Phosphorised paper. P 14×15.

1277	**750**	17p. black, greenish yellow, magenta, blue, azure, gold and slate-black	40	35
1278	**751**	22p. black, greenish yellow, brt rose-red, dull blue-green, slate-black and gold	60	60
1279	**752**	29p. black, greenish yellow, brt rose, greenish blue, grey-black, gold and bistre-yellow	85	90
1280	**753**	31p. black, greenish yellow, rose, pale new blue and gold	1·00	1·00
1281	**754**	34p. black, greenish yellow, magenta, greenish blue, grey-black & gold	1·00	90
		a. Imperf (vert pair)	£25000	
Set of 5			3·25	3·50

Set of 5 Gutter Pairs	7·00	
First Day Cover		4·00
Presentation Pack (P.O. Pack No. 160)	4·50	
PHQ Cards (set of 5) (82)	3·00	7·50

Nos. 1277/81 were issued on the occasion of the centenaries of the Royal Entomological Society of London's Royal Charter, and of the Selborne Society.

Special First Day of Issue Postmarks

Philatelic Bureau, Edinburgh	4·00
London SW	4·50

WATER·MUSIC
George Frideric Handel
755 "Water Music" (George Frederick Handel)

THE·PLANETS·SUITE
Gustav Holst
756 "The Planets Suite" (Gustav Holst)

THE·FIRST·CUCKOO
Frederick Delius
757 "The First Cuckoo" (Frederick Delius)

SEA·PICTURES
Edward Elgar
758 "Sea Pictures" (Edward Elgar)

(Des W. McLean)

1985 (14 May). *Europa. European Music Year. British Composers.* Phosphorised paper. *P* 14×14½.

1282	755	17p. black, brt yellow-green, deep magenta, new blue, grey & gold	55	40
		a. Imperf (vert pair)	£8500	
1283	756	22p. black, greenish yellow, brt magenta, new blue, grey-black and gold	75	90
		a. Imperf (pair)	£8500	
1284	757	31p. black, greenish yellow, magenta, greenish blue, grey-black & gold	1·50	1·25
1285	758	34p. black, olive-yellow, bistre, turquoise-blue, slate and gold	1·50	1·25
Set of 4			4·00	3·50
Set of 4 Gutter Pairs			8·50	
First Day Cover				4·00
Presentation Pack (P.O. Pack No. 161)			4·75	
PHQ Cards (set of 4) (83)			3·00	6·50

Nos. 1282/5 were issued on the occasion of the 300th birth anniversary of Handel.

Special First Day of Issue Postmarks

Philatelic Bureau, Edinburgh	4·50
Worcester	4·75

759 R.N.L.I. Lifeboat and Signal Flags

760 Beachy Head Lighthouse and Chart

761 "Marecs A" Communications Satellite and Dish Aerials

762 Buoys

(Des F. Newell and J. Sorrell. Litho J.W.)

1985 (18 June). *Safety at Sea.* Phosphorised paper. *P* 14.

1286	759	17p. black, azure, emerald, ultramarine, orange-yellow, vermilion, brt blue and chrome-yellow	40	40
1287	760	22p. black, azure, emerald, ultramarine, orange-yellow, vermilion, brt blue and chrome-yellow	60	75
1288	761	31p. black, azure, emerald, ultramarine, orange-yellow, vermilion and brt blue	1·00	1·00
1289	762	34p. black, azure, emerald, ultramarine, orange-yellow, vermilion and chrome-yellow	1·50	1·25
Set of 4			3·00	3·25
Set of 4 Gutter Pairs			7·00	
First Day Cover				3·75
Presentation Pack (P.O. Pack No. 162)			3·75	
PHQ Cards (set of 4) (84)			3·00	6·50

Nos. 1286/9 were issued on the occasion of the bicentenary of the unimmersible lifeboat and the 50th anniversary of radar.

Special First Day of Issue Postmarks

Philatelic Bureau, Edinburgh	3·75
Eastbourne	3·75

763 Datapost Motorcyclist, City of London

764 Rural Postbus

765 Parcel Delivery in Winter

766 Town Letter Delivery

(Des P. Högarth)

1985 (30 July). *350 Years of Royal Mail Public Postal Service.* Phosphorised paper. P 14×15.

1290	**763**	17p. black, greenish yellow, brt carmine, greenish blue, yellow-brown, grey-black and silver	50	40
		a. Imperf on 3 sides (vert pair)	£3750	
		Eu. Underprint Type **5**	1·00	
1291	**764**	22p. black, greenish yellow, cerise, steel-blue, lt green, grey-black and silver..	75	70
		a. Imperf (vert pair)	£24000	
1292	**765**	31p. black, greenish yellow, brt carmine, dull blue, drab, grey-black and silver	1·00	1·00
		a. Imperf	£4750	
1293	**766**	34p. black, greenish yellow, cerise, ultramarine, lt brown, grey-black and silver	1·50	1·50
		a. Imperf between (vert pair)	£2000	
		b. Imperf (vert pair)	—	
Set of 4			3·00	3·25
Set of 4 Gutter Pairs			6·50	
First Day Cover				3·75
Presentation Pack (P.O. Pack No. 163)			3·75	
PHQ Cards (set of 4) (85)			3·00	6·50

No. 1290a shows perforation indentations at right, but is imperforate at top, bottom and on the left-hand side.

Examples of No. 1290Eu from the 1985 £1·70 booklet (sold at £1·53) (No. FT4) show a blue double-lined D in a random pattern, on the reverse over the gum.

Special First Day of Issue Postmarks

Philatelic Bureau, Edinburgh .... 3·75
Bagshot, Surrey .... 3·75

767 King Arthur and Merlin

768 Lady of the Lake

769 Queen Guinevere and Sir Lancelot

770 Sir Galahad

(Des Yvonne Gilbert)

1985 (3 Sept). *Arthurian Legends.* Phosphorised paper. P 15×14.

1294	**767**	17p. grey-black, lemon, brown-lilac, ultramarine, grey-black & silver	50	40
		a. Imperf (pair)	£8750	
1295	**768**	22p. black, lemon, brown-lilac, pale blue, grey-black, silver and grey-black	75	75
1296	**769**	31p. black, lemon, magenta, turquoise-blue, grey-black, silver and grey-black	1·25	1·25
1297	**770**	34p. grey, lemon, magenta, new blue, grey-black, silver and grey-black	1·25	1·25
Set of 4			3·50	3·25
Set of 4 Gutter Pairs			7·50	
First Day Cover				3·75
Presentation Pack (P.O. Pack No. 164)			4·00	
PHQ Cards (set of 4) (86)			3·00	6·50

Nos. 1294/7 were issued on the occasion of the 500th anniversary of the printing of Sir Thomas Malory's *Morte d'Arthur.*

Trials are known with face value and inscription in a different type face.

Special First Day of Issue Postmarks

Philatelic Bureau, Edinburgh ....4·00
Tintagel, Cornwall ....4·00

771 Peter Sellers (from photo by Bill Brandt)

772 David Niven (from photo by Cornell Lucas)

773 Charlie Chaplin (from photo by Lord Snowdon)

774 Vivien Leigh (from photo by Angus McBean)

775 Alfred Hitchcock (from photo by Howard Coster)

(Des K. Bassford)

1985 (8 Oct). *British Film Year.* Phosphorised paper. P 14½.

1298	**771**	17p. grey-black, olive-grey, gold and silver	45	40
1299	**772**	22p. black, brown, gold and silver	60	75
1300	**773**	29p. black, lavender, gold and silver	1·00	1·25
1301	**774**	31p. black, pink, gold and silver	1·10	1·50
1302	**775**	34p. black, greenish blue, gold and silver	1·40	1·50
Set of 5			4·00	4·75
Set of 5 Gutter Pairs			9·00	
First Day Cover				5·50
Presentation Pack (P.O. Pack No. 165)			5·50	
Souvenir Book			11·50	
PHQ Cards (set of 5) (87)			3·00	10·00

The souvenir book is a 24-page illustrated booklet with a set of mint stamps in a sachet attached to the front cover.

Special First Day of Issue Postmarks

Philatelic Bureau, Edinburgh .... 5·50
London WC .... 5·50

776 Principal Boy

777 Genie

778 Dame

779 Good Fairy

780 *Pantomime* Cat

(Des A. George)

1985 (19 Nov). *Christmas. Pantomime Characters.* One phosphor band (12p.) or phosphorised paper (others). P 15×14.

1303	**776**	12p. new blue, greenish yellow, brt rose, gold, grey-black and silver......	50	30
		a. Imperf (pair).................................	£4750	
		Eu. Underprint Type **4**....................	1·00	
1304	**777**	17p. emerald, greenish yellow, brt rose, new blue, black, gold and silver	50	40
		a. Imperf (pair).................................	£8250	
1305	**778**	22p. brt carmine, greenish yellow, pale new blue, grey, gold and silver	75	1·10
1306	**779**	31p. brt orange, lemon, rose, slate-purple, silver and gold......................	1·25	1·40
1307	**780**	34p. brt reddish violet, brt blue, brt rose, black, grey-brown, gold & silver..	1·25	1·40
Set of 5			4·00	4·25
Set of 5 Gutter Pairs....................................			8·50	
First Day Cover				4·75
Presentation Pack (P.O. Pack No. 166)........................			4·25	
PHQ Cards (set of 5) (88)..............................			3·00	6·50
Christmas Folder (contains No. 1303×50)............................			35·00	

Examples of No. 1303Eu from the 1985 Christmas booklet (No. FX8) show a random pattern of blue double-lined stars printed on the reverse over the gum.

Special First Day of Issue Postmarks

Philatelic Bureau, Edinburgh	4·75
Bethlehem, Llandeilo, Dyfed	5·00

Collectors Pack 1985

1985 Nov 19 Comprises Nos. 1272/1307.

CP1307*a* Collectors Pack..	35·00

Post Office Yearbook

1985. Comprises Nos. 1272/1307 in 32-page hardbound book with slip case, illustrated in colour.. 75·00

17 PENCE · INDUSTRY YEAR 1986
781 Light Bulb and North Sea Oil Drilling Rig (Energy)

22 PENCE · INDUSTRY YEAR 1986
782 Thermometer and Pharmaceutical Laboratory (Health)

31 PENCE · INDUSTRY YEAR 1986
783 Garden Hoe Steelworks (Steel)

34 PENCE · INDUSTRY YEAR 1986
784 Loaf of Bread and Cornfield (Agriculture)

(Des K. Bassford. Litho Questa)

1986 (14 Jan). *Industry Year.* Phosphorised paper. P 14½×14.

1308	**781**	17p. gold, black, magenta, greenish yellow and new blue.................	75	40
1309	**782**	22p. gold, pale turquoise-green, black, magenta, greenish yellow & blue...	50	75
1310	**783**	31p. gold, black, magenta, greenish yellow and new blue.................	1·25	1·40
1311	**784**	34p. gold, black, magenta, greenish yellow and new blue.................	1·25	1·40
Set of 4			3·50	3·50
Set of 4 Gutter Pairs....................................			7·50	
First Day Cover				4·00
Presentation Pack (P.O. Pack No. 168)..........			3·75	
PHQ Cards (set of 4) (89)..............................			3·50	6·50

Special First Day of Issue Postmarks

Philatelic Bureau, Edinburgh	4·00
Birmingham	4·00

785 Dr. Edmond Halley as Comet

786 *Giotto* Spacecraft approaching Comet

787 "Maybe Twice in a Lifetime"

788 Comet orbiting Sun and Planets

(Des R. Steadman)

1986 (18 Feb). *Appearance of Halley's Comet.* Phosphorised paper. P 15×14.

1312	**785**	17p. black, bistre, rosine, blue, grey-black, gold and dp brown	50	40
		a. Imperf (pair).................................	£22000	
1313	**786**	22p. orange-vermilion, greenish yellow, brt purple, new blue, black and gold.......................................	75	75

1314	787	31p. black, greenish yellow, brt purple, dp turquoise-blue, grey-black and gold	1·25	1·25
		a. Imperf (pair)	£22000	
1315	788	34p. blue, greenish yellow, magenta, dp turquoise-blue, black & gold	1·25	1·40

Set of 4 .... 3·50 3·50
Set of 4 Gutter Pairs .... 7·50
First Day Cover .... 4·00
Presentation Pack (P.O. Pack No. 168*) ... 3·75
PHQ Cards (set of 4) (90) .... 3·50 6·50

*The presentation pack was incorrectly numbered '169'.

Special First Day of Issue Postmarks

Philaelic Bureau, Edinburgh .... 4·00
London SE10 .... 4·50

789 Queen Elizabeth in 1928, 1942 and 1952
790 Queen Elizabeth in 1958, 1973 and 1982

(Des J. Matthews)

1986 (21 Apr). *60th Birthday of Queen Elizabeth II. Phosphorised paper.* P 15×14.

1316	789	17p. grey-black, turquoise-green, brt green, green and dull blue	60	50
		a. Pair. Nos. 1316/17	1·50	1·50
1317	790	17p. grey-black, dull blue, greenish blue and indigo	60	50
1318	789	34p. grey-black, dp dull purple, yellow-orange and red	1·25	1·25
		a. Pair. Nos. 1318/19	3·00	4·00
1319	790	34p. grey-black, olive-brown, yellow-brown, olive-grey and red	1·25	1·25

Set of 4 .... 4·50 5·00
Set of 2 Gutter Blocks of 4 .... 9·50
First Day Cover .... 5·50
Presentation Pack (P.O. Pack No. 170) ... 5·50
Souvenir Book .... 8·50
PHQ Cards (set of 4) (91) .... 5·00 6·50

Nos. 1316/17 and 1318/19 were each printed together, *se-tenant*, in horizontal pairs throughout the sheet.

The souvenir book is a special booklet, fully illustrated and containing a mint set of stamps.

Special First Day of Issue Postmarks

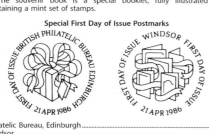

Philatelic Bureau, Edinburgh .... 5·50
Windsor .... 5·50

791 Barn Owl
792 Pine Marten

793 Wild Cat
794 Natterjack Toad

(Des K. Lilly)

1986 (20 May). *Europa. Nature Conservation–Endangered Species. Phosphorised paper.* P 14½×14.

1320	791	17p. gold, greenish yellow, rose, yellow-brown, olive-grey, new blue and black	40	45
1321	792	22p. gold, greenish yellow, reddish brown, olive-yellow, turquoise-blue, grey-black and black	80	1·00
1322	793	31p. gold, brt yellow-green, lt brown, ultramarine, olive-brown and black	1·50	1·25
1323	794	34p. gold, greenish yellow, brt rose-red, brt green, grey-black and black	1·65	1·40

Set of 4 .... 4·00 3·75
Set of 4 Gutter Pairs .... 8·50
First Day Cover .... 4·25
Presentation Pack (P.O. Pack No. 171) ... 4·50
PHQ Cards (set of 4) (92) .... 3·50 6·50

Special First Day of Issue Postmarks

Philatelic Bureau, Edinburgh .... 4·50
Lincoln .... 4·75

795 Peasants working in Fields
796 Freemen working at Town Trades

797 Knight and Retainers
798 Lord at Banquet

(Des Tayburn Design Consultancy)

1986 (17 Jun). *900th Anniversary of Domesday Book. Phosphorised paper.* P 15×14.

1324	795	17p. yellow-brown, vermilion, lemon, brt emerald, orange-brown, grey and brownish grey	40	45
1325	796	22p. yellow-ochre, red, greenish blue, chestnut, grey-black and brownish grey	85	85
1326	797	31p. yellow-brown, vermilion, green, Indian red, grey-black and brownish grey	1·25	1·40
1327	798	34p. yellow-ochre, bright scarlet, grey-brown, new blue, lake-brown, grey-black and grey	1·25	1·40

Set of 4 .... 3·50 3·75
Set of 4 Gutter Pairs .... 7·50
First Day Cover .... 4·25
Presentation Pack (P.O. Pack No. 172) ... 4·00
PHQ Cards (set of 4) (93) .... 3·50 6·50

Philatelic Bureau, Edinburgh...4·50
Gloucester... 4·50

799 Athletics

800 Rowing

801 Weightlifting

802 Rifle Shooting

803 Hockey

(Des N. Cudworth)

1986 (15 July). *Thirteenth Commonwealth Games, Edinburgh and World Hockey Cup for Men, London* (34p.). Phosphorised paper. P 15×14.

1328	**799**	17p. black, greenish yellow, orange-vermilion, ultramarine, chestnut and emerald	40	45
1329	**800**	22p. black, lemon, scarlet, new blue, royal blue, chestnut and dp ultramarine	55	75
		a. Imperf (pair)	—	
1330	**801**	29p. grey-black, greenish yellow, scarlet, new blue, brown-ochre, brown-rose and pale chestnut	75	1·00
1331	**802**	31p. black, greenish yellow, rose, blue, dull yellow-green, chestnut and yellow-green	1·50	1·75
1332	**803**	34p. black, lemon, scarlet, brt emerald, red-brown and vermilion	1·75	1·75
		a. Imperf (pair)	£7250	
Set of 5			4·00	4·50
Set of 5 Gutter Pairs			8·75	
First Day Cover				5·00
Presentation Pack (P.O. Pack No. 173)			4·50	
PHQ Cards (set of 5) (94)			3·50	7·50

No. 1332 also marked the centenary of the Hockey Association.

Philatelic Bureau, Edinburgh...5·00
Head Post Office, Edinburgh..5·00

804 Prince Andrew and Miss Sarah Ferguson (from photo by Gene Nocon)

805 Prince Andrew and Miss Sarah Ferguson (from photo by Gene Nocon)

(Des J. Matthews)

1986 (22 July). *Royal Wedding.* One phosphor band (12p.) or phosphorised paper (17p.). P 14×15.

1333	**804**	12p. lake, greenish yellow, cerise, ultramarine, black and silver	50	45
1334	**805**	17p. steel blue, greenish yellow, cerise, ultramarine, black & gold	1·00	1·25
		a. Imperf (pair)	£1600	
Set of 2			1·50	1·50
Set of 2 Gutter Pairs			3·25	
First Day Cover				2·00
Presentation Pack (P.O. Pack No. 174)			1·75	
PHQ Cards (set of 2) (95)			2·25	5·00

Philatelic Bureau, Edinburgh...2·50
London, SW1..2·75

806 Stylized Cross on Ballot Paper

(Des J. Gibbs. Litho Questa)

1986 (19 Aug). *32nd Commonwealth Parliamentary Association Conference.* Phosphorised paper. P 14×14½.

1335	**806**	34p. pale grey-lilac, black, vermilion, yellow and ultramarine	1·25	1·25
		a. Imperf between (vert pair)	£5000	
Gutter Pair			2·75	
First Day Cover				1·75
PHQ Card (96)			1·00	3·00

Philatelic Bureau, Edinburgh...2·00
London, SW1..2·00

807 Lord Dowding and Hawker Hurricane Mk I

808 Lord Tedder and Hawker Typhoon IB

809 Lord Trenchard and de Havilland D.H.9A

810 Sir Arthur Harris and Avro Type 683 Lancaster

811 Lord Portal and de Havilland DH.98 Mosquito

(Des B. Sanders)

1986 (16 Sept). *History of the Royal Air Force.* Phosphorised paper. P 14½.

1336	807	17p. pale blue, greenish yellow, brt rose, blue, black and grey-black	50	45
		a. Imperf (pair)	£5500	
1337	808	22p. pale turquoise-green, greenish yellow, magenta, new blue, black and grey-black	75	95
		a. Face value omitted*	£1300	
		b. Queen's head omitted*	£1300	
1338	809	29p. pale drab, olive-green, magenta, blue, grey-black and black	1·25	1·25
1339	810	31p. pale flesh, greenish yellow, magenta, ultramarine, black and grey-black	1·75	1·60
1340	811	34p. buff, greenish yellow, magenta, blue, grey-black and black	1·75	1·90
Set of 5			5·00	5·50
Set of 5 Gutter Pairs			12·00	
First Day Cover				6·00
Presentation Pack (P.O. Pack No. 175)			5·50	
PHQ Cards (set of 5) (97)			4·50	10·00

Nos. 1336/40 were issued to celebrate the 50th anniversary of the first R.A.F. Commands.

* Nos. 1337a/b come from three consecutive sheets on which the stamps in the first vertical row are without the face value and those in the second vertical row the Queen's head.

Special First Day of Issue Postmarks

Philatelic Bureau, Edinburgh	6·00
Farnborough	6·00

812 The Glastonbury Thorn

813 The Tanad Valley Plygain

814 The Hebrides Tribute

815 The Dewsbury Church Knell

816 The Hereford Boy Bishop

(Des Lynda Gray)

1986 (18 Nov–2 Dec). *Christmas. Folk Customs.* One phosphor band (12p., 13p.) or phosphorised paper (others). P 15×14.

1341	812	12p. gold, greenish yellow, vermilion, dp brown, emerald and dp blue (2.12)	50	50
		a. Imperf (pair)	£5500	
1342		13p. dp blue, greenish yellow, vermilion, dp brown, emerald and gold	30	40
		Eu. Underprint Type 4 (2.12)	1·00	
1343	813	18p. myrtle-green, yellow, vermilion, dp blue, black, reddish brown and gold	50	50
1344	814	22p. vermilion, olive-bistre, dull blue, dp brown, dp green and gold	1·00	1·00
1345	815	31p. dp brown, yellow, vermilion, violet, dp dull green, black and gold	1·25	1·00
1346	816	34p. violet, lemon, vermilion, dp dull blue, reddish brown and gold	1·25	1·10
Set of 6			4·25	4·00
Set of 6 Gutter Pairs			9·00	
First Day Covers (2)				4·50
Presentation Pack (Nos. 1342/6) (P.O. Pack No. 176)			5·00	
PHQ Cards (Nos. 1342/6) (set of 5) (98)			3·50	6·50
Christmas Folder (contains No. 1342Eu×36)			17·00	

No. 1341 represented a discount of 1p., available between 2 and 24 December 1986, on the current second class postage rate.

Special First Day of Issue Postmarks

Philatelic Bureau, Edinburgh (Nos. 1342/6) (18 Nov)	3·75
Bethlehem, Llandeilo, Dyfed (Nos. 1342/6) (18 Nov)	4·00
Philatelic Bureau, Edinburgh (No. 1341) (2 Dec)	1·00

Collectors Pack 1986
1986 Nov 18 Comprises Nos. 1308/40 and 1342/6.
CP1346a Collectors Pack	38·00

Post Office Yearbook
1986 Nov 18 Comprises Nos. 1308/46 in 32-page hardbound book with slip case, illustrated in colour | 70·00 |

817 North American Blanket Flower

818 Globe Thistle

819 Echeveria

820 Autumn Crocus

(Adapted J. Matthews)

1987 (20 Jan). *Flower Photographs by Alfred Lammer.* Phosphorised paper. *P* 14½×14.

1347	**817**	18p. silver, greenish yellow, rosine, dp green and black	40	40
1348	**818**	22p. silver, greenish yellow, new blue, greenish blue and black	70	85
1349	**819**	31p. silver, greenish yellow, scarlet, blue-green, dp green and black	1·10	1·25
		a. Imperf (pair)	£11000	
1350	**820**	34p. silver, greenish yellow, magenta, dull blue, dp green and black	1·10	1·25
Set of 4			3·25	3·50
Set of 4 Gutter Pairs			7·50	
First Day Cover				4·00
Presentation Pack (P.O. Pack No. 178)			4·00	
PHQ Cards (set of 4) (99)			3·00	7·00

Special First Day of Issue Postmarks

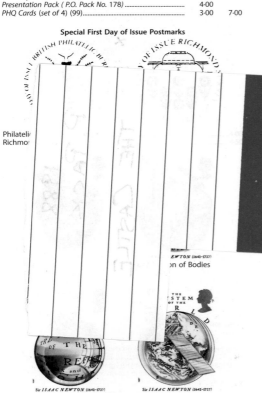

Philateli[c]
Richmo[nd]

823 Optick Treatise

824 *The System of the World*

(Des Sarah Godwin)

1987 (24 Mar). *300th Anniversary of "The Principia Mathematica" by Sir Isaac Newton.* Phosphorised paper. *P* 14×15.

1351	**821**	18p. black, greenish yellow, cerise, blue-green, grey-black and silver	50	40
		a. Imperf (pair)	£10000	
1352	**822**	22p. black, greenish yellow, brt orange, blue, brt emerald, silver and bluish violet	75	75
1353	**823**	31p. black, greenish yellow, scarlet, new blue, bronze-green, silver and slate-green	1·25	1·50
1354	**824**	34p. black, greenish yellow, red, brt blue, grey-black and silver	1·25	1·25
Set of 4			3·50	3·50
Set of 4 Gutter Pairs			8·00	
First Day Cover				4·00
Presentation Pack (P.O. Pack No. 179)			4·00	
PHQ Cards (set of 4) (100)			3·00	6·50

Special First Day of Issue Postmarks

Philatelic Bureau, Edinburgh .... 4·00
Woolsthorpe, Lincs .... 4·25

825 Willis Faber and Dumas Building, Ipswich

826 Pompidou Centre, Paris

827 Staatsgalerie, Stuttgart

828 European Investment Bank, Luxembourg

(Des B. Tattersfield)

1987 (12 May). *Europa. British Architects in Europe.* Phosphorised paper. *P* 15×14.

1355	**825**	18p. black, bistre-yellow, cerise, brt blue, dp grey and grey-black	50	40
1356	**826**	22p. black, greenish yellow, carmine, brt blue, dp grey and grey-black	75	75
1357	**827**	31p. grey-black, bistre-yellow, cerise, brt blue, brt green, black and dull violet	1·25	1·25
		a. Imperf (horiz pair)	£10000	
1358	**828**	34p. black, greenish yellow, cerise, brt blue, grey-black and dp grey	1·25	1·25
Set of 4			3·50	3·50
Set of 4 Gutter Pairs			8·00	
First Day Cover				4·00
Presentation Pack (P.O. Pack No. 180)			4·00	
PHQ Cards (set of 4) (101)			3·00	6·50

Special First Day of Issue Postmarks

Philatelic Bureau, Edinburgh .... 4·00
Ipswich .... 4·00

829 Brigade Members with Ashford Litter, 1887

830 Bandaging Blitz Victim, 1940

831 Volunteer with fainting Girl, 1965

832 Transport of Transplant Organ by Air Wing, 1987

(Des Debbie Cook. Litho Questa)

1987 (16 June). *Centenary of St. John Ambulance Brigade.* Phosphorised paper. P 14×14½.

1359	829	18p. new blue, greenish yellow, magenta, black, silver and pink	40	45
		Ea. Black ptg double	†	£1200
		Eb. Black ptg triple	†	£1700
1360	830	22p. new blue, greenish yellow, magenta, black, silver and cobalt	60	75
1361	831	31p. new blue, greenish yellow, magenta, black, silver and bistre-brown	1·25	1·25
1362	832	34p. new blue, greenish yellow, magenta, black, silver and greenish grey	1·25	1·25
Set of 4			3·25	3·50
Set of 4 Gutter Pairs			8·00	
First Day Cover				4·00
Presentation Pack (P.O. Pack No. 181)			4·00	
PHQ Cards (set of 4) (102)			3·00	6·50

Special First Day of Issue Postmarks

Philatelic Bureau, Edinburgh	4·00
London, EC1	4·00

833 Arms of the Lord Lyon King of Arms   **834** Scottish Heraldic Banner of Prince Charles

835 Arms of Royal Scottish Academy of Painting, Sculpture and Architecture

836 Arms of Royal Society of Edinburgh

(Des J. Matthews)

1987 (21 July). *300th Anniversary of Revival of Order of the Thistle.* Phosphorised paper. P 14½.

1363	833	18p. black, lemon, scarlet, blue, dp green, slate and brown	50	40
1364	834	22p. black, greenish yellow, carmine, new blue, dp green, grey and lake-brown	75	90
1365	835	31p. black, greenish yellow, scarlet, new blue, dull green, grey and grey-black	1·40	1·40
1366	836	34p. black, greenish yellow, scarlet, dp ultramarine, dull green, grey and yellow-brown	1·50	1·40
Set of 4			3·75	3·75
Set of 4 Gutter Pairs			8·00	
First Day Cover				4·25
Presentation Pack (P.O. Pack No. 182)			4·00	
PHQ Cards (set of 4) (103)			3·00	6·50

Special First Day of Issue Postmarks

Philatelic Bureau, Edinburgh	4·25
Rothesay, Isle of Bute	4·50

837 Crystal Palace, "Monarch of the Glen" (Landseer) and Grace Darling   **838** Great Eastern, Beeton's Book of Household Management and Prince Albert

839 Albert Memorial, Ballot Box and Disraeli   **840** Diamond Jubilee Emblem, Newspaper Placard for Relief of Mafeking and Morse Key

(Des M. Dempsey. Eng C. Slania. Recess and photo)

1987 (8 Sept). *150th Anniversary of Queen Victoria's Accession.* Phosphorised paper. P 15×14.

1367	837	18p. pale stone, dp blue, lemon, rose, greenish blue, brown-ochre and grey-black	50	45
1368	838	22p. pale stone, dp brown, lemon, rose, grey-black & brown-ochre	80	75
1369	839	31p. pale stone, dp lilac, lemon, cerise, brown-ochre, greenish blue and grey-black	1·25	1·50
1370	840	34p. pale stone, myrtle-green, yellow-ochre, reddish brown and brown-ochre	1·35	1·60
Set of 4			3·50	4·00
Set of 4 Gutter Pairs			7·50	
First Day Cover				4·50

Presentation Pack (P.O. Pack No. 183)	....	4·25	
PHQ Cards (set of 4) (104)	....	3·00	6·50

Special First Day of Issue Postmarks

Philatelic Bureau, Edinburgh .... 4·50
Newport, Isle of Wight ....4·50

847 Sleeping Child and Father Christmas in Sleigh

848 Child reading

849 Child playing Recorder and Snowman

841 Pot by Bernard Leach

842 Pot by Elizabeth Fritsch

843 Pot by Lucie Rie

844 Pot by Hans Coper

(Des T. Evans)

1987 (13 Oct). *Studio Pottery.* Phosphorised paper. *P* 14½×14.

1371	**841**	18p. gold, lemon, lt red-brown, chestnut, lt grey and black	50	40
1372	**842**	26p. blue over silver, yellow-orange, brt purple, lavender, bluish violet, grey-brown and black	70	75
1373	**843**	31p. rose-lilac over silver, greenish yellow, cerise, new blue, grey-lilac and black	1·25	1·25
1374	**844**	34p. copper, yellow-brown, reddish brown, grey-lilac and black	1·40	1·50
		a. Imperf (vert pair)	£8500	
Set of 4			3·50	3·50
Set of 4 Gutter Pairs			7·50	
First Day Cover				4·00
Presentation Pack (P.O. Pack No. 184)			4·00	
PHQ Cards (set of 4) (105)			3·00	6·50

Special First Day of Issue Postmarks

Philatelic Bureau, Edinburgh .... 4·00
St. Ives, Cornwall .... 4·00

845 Decorating the Christmas Tree

846 Waiting for Father Christmas

(Des M. Foreman)

1987 (17 Nov). *Christmas.* One phosphor band (13p.) or phosphorised paper (others). *P* 15×14.

1375	**845**	13p. gold, greenish yellow, rose, greenish blue and black	30	30
		Eu. Underprint Type **4**	95	
1376	**846**	18p. gold, greenish yellow, brt purple, greenish blue, brt blue and black	40	40
1377	**847**	26p. gold, greenish yellow, new blue, brt blue and black	80	1·00
1378	**848**	31p. gold, greenish yellow, scarlet, brt magenta, dull rose, greenish blue and black	1·10	1·25
1379	**849**	34p. gold, greenish yellow, dull rose, greenish blue, brt blue and black	1·25	1·50
Set of 5			3·50	4·00
Set of 5 Gutter Pairs			7·50	
First Day Cover				4·50
Presentation Pack (P.O. Pack No. 185)			4·00	
PHQ Cards (set of 5) (106)			3·00	6·50
Christmas Folder (contains No. 1375Eu×36)			17·00	

Examples of the 13p. value from special folders, containing 36 stamps and sold for £4·60, show a blue underprint of doublelined stars printed on the reverse over the gum.

Special First Day of Issue Postmarks

Philatelic Bureau, Edinburgh ....4·50
Bethlehem, Llandeilo, Dyfed .... 4·50

Collectors Pack 1987

1987 Nov 17 Comprises Nos. 1347/79.
CP1379a Collectors Pack .... 38·00

Post Office Yearbook

1987 Nov 17 Comprises Nos. 1347/79 in 32-page hardbound book with slip case, illustrated in colour... 35·00

850 Short-spined Sea scorpion ("Bull-rout") (Jonathan Couch)

851 Yellow Waterlily (Major Joshua Swatkin)

852 Whistling ("Bewick's") Swan (Edward Lear)

853 *Morchella esculenta* (James Sowerby)

(Des. E. Hughes)

1988 (19 Jan). *Bicentenary of Linnean Society. Archive Illustrations.* Phosphorised paper. P 15×14.

1380	**850**	18p. grey-black, stone, orange-yellow, brt purple, olive-bistre and gold.....	55	35
1381	**851**	26p. black, stone, bistre-yellow, dull orange, greenish blue, gold and pale bistre	85	1·00
1382	**852**	31p. black, stone, greenish yellow, rose-red, dp blue, gold and olive-bistre	1·10	1·25
		a. Imperf (horiz pair)................	£6700	
1383	**853**	34p. black, stone, yellow, pale bistre, olive-grey, gold and olive-bistre......	1·25	1·40
Set of 4			3·25	3·50
Set of 4 Gutter Pairs			8·00	
First Day Cover				4·00
Presentation Pack (P.O. Pack No. 187)			4·00	
PHQ Cards (set of 4) (107)			3·00	6·50

Special First Day of Issue Postmarks

Philatelic Bureau, Edinburgh ....4·00
London, W1 ....4·50

854 Revd William Morgan (Bible translator, 1588)

855 William Salesbury (New Testament translator, 1567)

856 Bishop Richard Davies (New Testament translator, 1567)

857 Bishop Richard Parry (editor of Revised Welsh Bible, 1620)

(Des K. Bowen)

1988 (1 Mar). *400th Anniv of Welsh Bible.* Phosphorised paper. P 14½×14.

1384	**854**	18p. grey-black, greenish yellow, cerise, blue, black and emerald	40	40
		a. Imperf (vert pair)................	£8000	
1385	**855**	26p. grey-black, yellow, brt rose-red, turquoise-blue, black and orange...	70	95
1386	**856**	31p. black, chrome-yellow, carmine, new blue, grey-black and blue	1·25	1·25
1387	**857**	34p. grey-black, greenish yellow, cerise, turquoise-green, black and brt violet...............	1·40	1·25
Set of 4			3·25	3·50
Set of 4 Gutter Pairs			8·00	
First Day Cover				4·00
Presentation Pack (P.O. Pack No. 188)			4·00	
PHQ Cards (set of 4) (108)			3·00	6·50

Special First Day of Issue Postmarks

Philatelic Bureau, Edinburgh ....4·00
Ty Mawr, Wybrnant, Gwynedd ....4·50

858 Gymnastics (Centenary of British Amateur Gymnastics Association)

859 Downhill Skiing (Ski Club of Great Britain)

860 Tennis (Centenary of Lawn Tennis Association)

861 Football (Centenary of Football League)

(Des J. Sutton)

1988 (22 Mar). *Sports Organizations.* Phosphorised paper. P 14½.

1388	**858**	18p. violet-blue, greenish yellow, rosine, brt rose, new blue and silver......................	40	40
		a. Imperf (pair).................		
1389	**859**	26p. violet-blue, greenish yellow, vermilion, carmine, yellow-orange and silver	70	80
1390	**860**	31p. violet-blue, greenish yellow, rose, blue, pale greenish blue, silver and brt orange	1·10	1·25
1391	**861**	34p. violet-blue, greenish yellow, vermilion, blue, brt emerald, silver and pink	1·25	1·25
Set of 4			3·25	3·25
Set of 4 Gutter Pairs			8·00	
First Day Cover				3·75
Presentation Pack (P.O. Pack No. 189)			4·00	
PHQ Cards (set of 4) (109)			2·50	6·00

Special First Day of Issue Postmarks

Philatelic Bureau, Edinburgh ....4·00
Wembley ....5·00

862 *Mallard* and Mailbags on Pick-up Arms

863 Loading Transatlantic Mail on Liner *Queen Elizabeth*

864 Glasgow Tram No. 1173 and Pillar Box

865 Imperial Airways Handley Page H.P.45 *Horatius* and Airmail Van

(Des M. Dempsey)

1988 (10 May). *Europa. Transport and Mail Services in 1930s.* Phosphorised paper. P 15×14.

1392	862	18p. brown, yellow, rose-red, dull blue, dp brown, reddish violet and black	50	35
1393	863	26p. brown, yellow, orange-vermilion, dull blue, violet-blue, brt emerald and black	1·00	1·00
1394	864	31p. brown, yellow-orange, carmine, dull purple, violet-blue, brt green and black	1·25	1·25
1395	865	34p. brown, orange-yellow, carmine-rose, bluish violet, brt blue, sepia and black	1·60	1·50
Set of 4			4·00	3·75
Set of 4 Gutter Pairs			9·00	
First Day Cover				4·25
Presentation Pack (P.O. Pack No. 190)			4·25	
PHQ Cards (set of 4) (110)			2·25	6·00

Trials exist with alternative face values; 19p, 27p, 32p and 35p.

Special First Day of Issue Postmarks

Philatelic Bureau, Edinburgh .... 4·25
Glasgow .... 4·50

866 Early Settler and Sailing Clipper

867 Queen Elizabeth II with British and Australian Parliament Buildings

868 W. G. Grace (cricketer) and Tennis Racquet

869 Shakespeare, John Lennon (entertainer) and Sydney Opera House

(Des G. Emery. Litho Questa)

1988 (21 June). *Bicentenary of Australian Settlement.* Phosphorised paper. P 14½.

1396	866	18p. deep ultramarine, orange-yellow, scarlet, black, bluish grey and emerald	40	50
		a. Horiz pair. Nos. 1396/7	1·25	1·50
1397	867	18p. deep ultramarine, orange-yellow, black, bluish grey and emerald	40	50
1398	868	34p. deep ultramarine, orange-yellow, scarlet, black, bluish grey and emerald	1·00	1·25
		a. Horiz pair. Nos. 1398/9	2·50	3·00
1399	869	34p. deep ultramarine, orange-yellow, black, bluish grey and emerald	1·00	1·25
Set of 4			3·50	4·00
Set of 2 Gutter Blocks of 4			8·25	
First Day Cover				4·50
Presentation Pack (P.O. Pack No. 191)			4·00	
Souvenir Book			15·00	
PHQ Cards (set of 4) (111)			2·25	6·00

Nos. 1396/7 and 1398/9 were each printed together, *se-tenant*, in horizontal pairs throughout the sheets, each pair showing a background design of the Australian flag.

The 40 page souvenir book contains the British and Australian sets which were issued on the same day in similar designs.

Special First Day of Issue Postmarks

Philatelic Bureau, Edinburgh ....4·50
Portsmouth ....4·50

870 Spanish Galeasse off The Lizard

871 English Fleet leaving Plymouth

872 Engagement off Isle of Wight

873 Attack of English Fire-ships, Calais

874 Armada in Storm, North Sea

(Des G. Evernden)

1988 (19 July). *400th Anniv of Spanish Armada.* Phosphorised paper. P 15×14.

1400	**870**	18p. slate-black, yellow-orange, brt carmine, brt blue, turquoise-blue, yellow-green and gold......	45	50
		a. Horiz strip of 5. Nos. 1400/4	3·00	3·00
1401	**871**	18p. slate-black, yellow-orange, brt carmine, brt blue, turquoise-blue, yellow-green and gold......	45	50
1402	**872**	18p. slate-black, yellow-orange, brt carmine, brt blue, turquoise-blue, yellow-green and gold......	45	50
1403	**873**	18p. slate-black, yellow-orange, brt carmine, brt blue, turquoise-blue, yellow-green and gold......	45	50
		a. "88" for "1988" in imprint (strip of 5)......	25·00	
1404	**874**	18p. slate-black, yellow-orange, brt carmine, brt blue, turquoise-blue, yellow-green and gold......	45	50
		a. "988" for "1988" in imprint (strip of 5)......	25·00	
Set of 5			3·00	3·00
Gutter Block of 10......			8·00	
First Day Cover				3·75
Presentation Pack (P.O. Pack No. 192)......			3·75	
PHQ Cards (set of 5) (112)......			2·75	7·00

Nos. 1400/4 were printed together, *se-tenant*, in horizontal strips of five throughout the sheet, forming a composite design.

On R. 3/10 the imprint reads "88", with traces of the "9" visible, on R. 4/4 it reads "988", both on the Dot pane. Both were quickly retouched to show "1988"

Special First Day of Issue Postmarks

Philatelic Bureau, Edinburgh ...... 4·00
Plymouth ...... 5·50

875 "The Owl and the Pussy-cat"

876 "Edward Lear as a Bird" (self-portrait)

877 "Cat" (from alphabet book)

878 "There was a Young Lady whose Bonnet..." (limerick)

(Des M. Swatridge and S. Dew)

1988 (6–27 Sept). *Death Centenary of Edward Lear (artist and author).* Phosphorised paper. P 15×14.

1405	**875**	19p. black, pale cream and carmine......	65	40
1406	**876**	27p. black, pale cream and yellow......	1·00	1·00
1407	**877**	32p. black, pale cream and emerald	1·25	1·40
1408	**878**	35p. black, pale cream and blue	1·40	1·40
Set of 4			4·00	3·75
Set of 4 Gutter Pairs......			9·00	
First Day Cover				4·25
Presentation Pack (P.O. Pack No. 193)......			4·25	
PHQ Cards (set of 4) (113)......			2·25	6·00
MS1409 122×90 mm. Nos. 1405/8 (sold at £1·35) (27 Sept)......			7·00	8·50
First Day Cover				8·50

The premium on No. **MS**1409 was used to support the "Stamp World London 90" International Stamp Exhibition.

Special First Day of Issue Postmarks

Philatelic Bureau, Edinburgh (stamps) (6 Sept) ......4·25
Philatelic Bureau, Edinburgh (miniature sheet) (27 Sept) ......9·00
London N7 (stamps) (6 Sept)......5·00
London N22 (miniature sheet) (27 Sept)......9·50

CARRICKFERGUS CASTLE
879 Carrickfergus Castle

CAERNARFON CASTLE
880 Caernarfon Castle

EDINBURGH CASTLE
881 Edinburgh Castle

WINDSOR CASTLE
882 Windsor Castle

(Des from photos by Prince Andrew, Duke of York. Eng C. Matthews. Recess Harrison)

1988 (18 Oct). Ordinary paper. P 15×14.

1410	**879**	£1 deep green......	4·25	60
1411	**880**	£1·50 maroon	4·50	1·25
1412	**881**	£2 indigo	8·00	1·50
1413	**882**	£5 deep brown	21·00	5·50
Set of 4			35·00	8·00
Set of 4 Gutter Pairs (vert or horiz)			80·00	
First Day Cover				35·00
Presentation Pack (P.O. Pack No. 18)			36·00	

For similar designs, but with silhouette of Queen's head see Nos. 1611/14 and 1993/6.

Special First Day of Issue Postmarks
(For illustrations see Introduction)

Philatelic Bureau Edinburgh (Type H) ......40·00
Windsor, Berkshire (Type 1)......45·00

883 Journey to Bethlehem

884 Shepherds and Star

885 Three Wise Men

886 Nativity

887 The Annunciation

(Des L. Trickett)

1988 (15 Nov). *Christmas. Christmas Cards.* One phosphor band (14p.) or phosphorised paper (others). *P* 15×14.

1414	**883**	14p. gold, orange-yellow, brt mauve, bluish violet, brt blue and grey-black	45	35
		a. Error. "13p" instead of "14p"	£12500	
		b. Imperf (pair)	£3600	
1415	**884**	19p. gold, yellow-orange, brt violet, ultramarine, rose-red, grey-black and brt blue	50	50
		a. Imperf (pair)	£2100	
1416	**885**	27p. gold, red, dp lavender, dp lilac, emerald, grey-black and brt blue	90	1·00
1417	**886**	32p. gold, orange-yellow, brt rose, dp mauve, violet, grey-black and brt blue	1·10	1·25
1418	**887**	35p. gold, green, reddish violet, brt blue, brt purple and grey-black	1·40	1·25
Set of 5			4·00	3·75
Set of 5 Gutter Pairs			9·50	
First Day Cover				4·25
Presentation Pack (P.O. Pack No. 194)			4·50	
PHQ Cards (set of 5) (114)			3·00	6·00

Examples of No. 1414a were found in some 1988 Post Office Yearbooks.

Special First Day of Issue Postmarks

Philatelic Bureau, Edinburgh	4·25
Bethlehem, Llandeilo, Dyfed	4·50

Collectors Pack 1988
1988 Nov 15 Comprises Nos. 1380/1408, 1414/18.
CP1418a Collectors Pack..................................... 35·00

Post Office Yearbook
1988 Nov 15 Comprises Nos. 1380/1404, **MS**1409, 1414/18 in 32-page hardbound book with slip case, illustrated in colour........................... 38·00

888 Atlantic Puffin   **889** Avocet

890 Oystercatcher

891 Northern Gannet

(Des D. Cordery)

1989 (17 Jan). *Centenary of Royal Society for the Protection of Birds.* Phosphorised paper. *P* 14×15.

1419	**888**	19p. grey, orange-yellow, orange-red, dull ultramarine, grey-black and silver	35	40
1420	**889**	27p. grey, bistre, rose, steel-blue, lavender, silver and grey-black	1·25	1·25
1421	**890**	32p. grey, bistre, scarlet, orange-red, lavender, silver and black	1·25	1·25
1422	**891**	35p. grey, lemon, rose-carmine, green, new blue, silver and black	1·25	1·25
Set of 4			3·50	3·50
Set of 4 Gutter Pairs			8·50	
First Day Cover				4·00
Presentation Pack (P.O. Pack No. 196)			4·00	
PHQ Cards (set of 4) (115)			3·00	7·00

Special First Day of Issue Postmarks

Philatelic Bureau, Edinburgh	4·00
Sandy, Bedfordshire	5·00

892 Rose

893 Cupid

894 Yachts

895 Fruit

896 Teddy Bear

(Des P. Sutton)

1989 (31 Jan). *Greetings Stamps.* Phosphorised paper. *P* 15×14.

1423	**892**	19p. black, greenish yellow, brt rose, red, new blue, lt green and gold	3·00	3·00
		a. Booklet pane. Nos. 1423/7×2 plus 12 half stamp-size labels	50·00	
		b. Horiz strip of 5. Nos. 1423/7	25·00	25·00
1424	**893**	19p. black, greenish yellow, brt rose, red, new blue, lt green and gold	3·00	3·00
1425	**894**	19p. black, greenish yellow, brt rose, red, new blue, lt green and gold	3·00	3·00

1426	**895**	19p. black, greenish yellow, brt rose, red, new blue, lt green and gold....	3·00	3·00
1427	**896**	19p. black, greenish yellow, brt rose, red, new blue, lt green and gold....	3·00	3·00
Set of 5			25·00	25·00
First Day Cover				20·00

Nos. 1423/7 were printed together, *se-tenant,* in horizontal strips of five, two such strips forming the booklet pane with twelve half stamp-size labels.

Nos. 1423/7 were only issued in £1·90 booklets No. KY1.

Special First Day of Issue Postmarks

Philatelic Bureau, Edinburgh	25·00
Lover, Salisbury, Wilts	25·00

897 Fruit and Vegetables   **898** Meat Products

899 Dairy Products   **900** Cereal Products

(Des Sedley Place Ltd)

1989 (7 Mar). *Food and Farming Year.* Phosphorised paper. *P* 14×14½.

1428	**897**	19p. brownish grey, greenish yellow, rose, new blue, black, pale grey and emerald	45	50
1429	**898**	27p. brownish grey, greenish yellow, brt carmine, new blue, black, pale grey and brt orange	90	85
1430	**899**	32p. brownish grey, greenish yellow, rose-red, new blue, black, pale grey and bistre-yellow	1·25	1·40
1431	**900**	35p. brownish grey, greenish yellow, brt carmine, new blue, black, pale grey and brown-red	1·40	1·50
Set of 4			3·50	3·50
Set of 4 Gutter Pairs			8·50	
First Day Cover				4·00
Presentation Pack (P.O. Pack No. 197)			4·00	
PHQ Cards (set of 4) (116)			2·25	6·50

Special First Day of Issue Postmarks

Philatelic Bureau, Edinburgh	4·00
Stoneleigh, Kenilworth, Warwicks	4·50

901 Mortar Board (150th Anniv of Public Education in England)   **902** Cross on Ballot Paper (3rd Direct Elections to European Parliament)

903 Posthorn (26th Postal, Telegraph and Telephone International Congress, Brighton)   **904** Globe (Inter-Parliamentary Union Centenary Conference, London)

(Des Lewis Moberly from firework set-pieces. Litho Questa)

1989 (11 Apr). *Anniversaries.* Phosphorised paper. *P* 14×14½.

1432	**901**	19p. new blue, greenish yellow, magenta and black	60	60
		a. Horiz pair. Nos. 1432/3	1·50	1·50
1433	**902**	19p. new blue, greenish yellow, magenta and black	60	60
1434	**903**	35p. new blue, greenish yellow, magenta and black	1·00	1·00
		a. Horiz pair. Nos. 1434/5	2·50	2·50
1435	**904**	35p. new blue, greenish yellow, magenta and black	1·00	1·00
Set of 4			3·50	3·50
Set of 2 Gutter Strips of 4			8·00	
First Day Cover				4·50
Presentation Pack (P.O. Pack No. 198)			4·00	
PHQ Cards (set of 4) (117)			2·25	6·50

Nos. 1432/3 and 1434/5 were each printed together, *se-tenant,* in horizontal pairs throughout the sheets. Stamps as No. 1435, but inscribed "ONE HUNDREDTH CONFERENCE" were prepared, but not issued.

Special First Day of Issue Postmarks

Philatelic Bureau, Edinburgh	5·00
London SW	6·00

905 Toy Train and Aeroplanes   **906** Building Bricks

907 Dice and Board Games

908 Toy Robot, Boat and Doll's House

(Des D. Fern)

1989 (16 May). *Europa. Games and Toys.* Phosphorised paper. *P* 14×15.

1436	**905**	19p. black, greenish yellow, vermilion, blue-green, blue, gold and pale ochre	65	50
1437	**906**	27p. black, greenish yellow, reddish orange, blue-green, blue and gold	95	1·00
1438	**907**	32p. black, greenish yellow, orange-red, blue-green, blue, gold and pale ochre	1·40	1·25
1439	**908**	35p. black, greenish yellow, reddish orange, blue-green, blue, gold and stone	1·50	1·25
Set of 4			4·00	3·75
Set of 4 Gutter Strips			9·00	
First Day Cover				4·25
Presentation Pack (P.O. Pack No. 199)			4·25	
PHQ Cards (set of 4) (118)			2·25	6·50

Special First Day of Issue Postmarks

Philatelic Bureau, Edinburgh	4·25
Leeds	5·00

909 Ironbridge, Shropshire

910 Tin Mine, St. Agnes Head, Cornwall

911 Cotton Mills, New Lanark, Strathclyde

912 Pontcysyllte Aqueduct, Clwyd

912a Horizontal versions of T **909**/12

(Des R. Maddox)

1989 (4–25 July). *Industrial Archaeology.* Phosphorised paper. *P* 14×15.

1440	**909**	19p. black, bistre-yellow, rose-red, apple-green, lt blue, grey-black and emerald	60	50
1441	**910**	27p. black, bistre-yellow, rose-red, apple-green, lt blue, grey-black and dull blue	1·00	1·10
1442	**911**	32p. black, yellow-orange, apple-green, yellow, dull blue, grey-black and dp reddish violet	1·10	1·25
1443	**912**	35p. black, yellow, brt rose, apple-green, dull blue, grey-black and vermilion	1·25	1·50
Set of 4			3·50	4·00
Set of 4 Gutter Pairs			8·50	
First Day Cover				4·50
Presentation Pack (P.O. Pack No. 200)			4·00	
PHQ Cards (set of 4) (119)			2·25	6·50
MS1444 **912a** 122×90 mm. As Nos. 1440/3, but horizontal. Each black, olive-yellow, brt rose-red, dull blue, apple-green, grey-black and vermilion (sold at £1.40) (25 July)			6·00	6·50
First Day Cover				7·00

The premium on No. **MS**1444 was used to support the "Stamp World London 90" International Stamp Exhibition.

Special First Day of Issue Postmarks

Philatelic Bureau, Edinburgh (stamps) (4 July)	4·50
Philatelic Bureau, Edinburgh (miniature sheet) (25 July)	7·00
Telford (stamps) (4 July)	5·00
New Lanark (miniature sheet) (25 July)	7·50

For Nos. 1445/52 see Decimal Machin Definitives section.

915 Snowflake (×10)

916 *Calliphora erythrocephala* (×5) (fly)

917 Blood Cells (×500)   **918** Microchip (×600)

(Des K. Bassford. Litho Questa)

1989 (5 Sept). *150th Anniv of Royal Microscopical Society.* Phosphorised paper. *P* 14½×14.

1453	**915**	19p. gold, lemon, pale blue, grey, black and grey-black	45	45
1454	**916**	27p. gold, lemon, drab, black and grey-black	95	1·00
1455	**917**	32p. gold, lemon, orange-vermilion, flesh, black and grey-black	1·10	1·25
1456	**918**	35p. gold, lemon, black, brt green and grey-black	1·25	1·25
Set of 4			3·50	3·75
Set of 4 Gutter Pairs			8·50	
First Day Cover				4·25
Presentation Pack (P.O. Pack No. 201)			4·00	
PHQ Cards (set of 4) (120)			2·25	6·50

Special First Day of Issue Postmarks

Philatelic Bureau, Edinburgh	4·25
Oxford	4·50

919 Royal Mail Coach   **920** Escort of Blues and Royals

921 Lord Mayor's Coach   **922** Passing St. Paul's

923 Blues and Royals Drum Horse

(Des P. Cox)

1989 (17 Oct). *Lord Mayor's Show, London.* Phosphorised paper. *P* 14×15.

1457	**919**	20p. gold, lemon, rose, orange, pale blue and black	45	50
		a. Horiz strip of 5. Nos. 1457/61	3·00	3·00
		ab. Imperf (horiz strip of 5. Nos. 1457/61)	£16000	
		ac. Imperf (horiz strip of 4. Nos. 1457/60)	£13000	
		ad. Imperf (horiz strip of 3. Nos. 1457/9)	£10000	
1458	**920**	20p. gold, lemon, rose, orange, pale blue and black	45	50
1459	**921**	20p. gold, lemon, rose, orange, pale blue and black	45	50
1460	**922**	20p. gold, lemon, rose, orange, pale blue and black	45	50
1461	**923**	20p. gold, lemon, rose, orange, pale blue and black	45	50
Set of 5			3·00	3·00
Gutter Strip of 10			8·00	
First Day Cover				3·50
Presentation Pack (P.O. Pack No. 202)			3·50	
PHQ Cards (set of 5) (121)			3·00	6·50

Nos. 1457/61 were printed together, *se-tenant,* in horizontal strips of five throughout the sheet. This issue commemorates the 800th anniversary of the installation of the first Lord Mayor of London.

Nos. 1457ab/ad come from a sheet partly imperf at left. Stamps of Types **919/23**, but each with face value of 19p., were prepared but not issued. One mint *se-tenant* strip has been recorded.

See also No. 2957.

Special First Day of Issue Postmarks

Philatelic Bureau, Edinburgh	4·00
London, EC4	4·50

924 14th-century Peasants from Stained-glass Window   **925** Arches and Roundels, West Front

926 Octagon Tower   **927** Arcade from West Transept

928 Triple Arch from West Front

(Des D. Gentleman)

1989 (14 Nov). *Christmas. 800th Anniv of Ely Cathedral.* One phosphor band (15p., 15p.+1p.) or phosphorised paper (others). *P* 15×14.

1462	**924**	15p. gold, silver and blue	40	40
1463	**925**	15p. +1p. gold, silver and blue	50	40
		a. Imperf (pair)	£4750	
1464	**926**	20p. +1p. gold, silver and rosine	65	80
		a. Imperf (pair)	£4750	
1465	**927**	34p. +1p. gold, silver and emerald	1·25	1·75
1466	**928**	37p. +1p. gold, silver and yellow-olive	1·40	1·90

Set of 5	3·75	4·75
Set of 5 Gutter Pairs	8·50	
First Day Cover		5·50
Presentation Pack (P.O. Pack No. 203)......	4·50	
PHQ Cards (set of 5) (122)	3·00	6·00

Trials are known showing different values and including an additional design.

Special First Day of Issue Postmarks

Philatelic Bureau, Edinburgh		5·50
Bethlehem, Llandeilo, Dyfed		5·50
Ely		5·50

Collectors Pack 1989

1989 Nov 14 Comprises Nos. 1419/22, 1428/43 and 1453/66.

CP1466a Collectors Pack..		38·00

Post Office Yearbook

1989 (14 Nov). Comprises Nos. 1419/22, 1428/44 and 1453/66 in hardbound book with slip case, illustrated in colour .... 42·00

929 Queen Victoria and Queen Elizabeth II

(Des J. Matthews (after Wyon and Machin)

1990 (10 Jan–12 June). *150th Anniversary of the Penny Black.*

(a) Photo Harrison. P 15×14.

1467	**929**	15p. bright blue (1 centre band)...............	80	80
		a. Imperf (pair)........................	£3000	
		l. Booklet pane. No. 1467×10 with horizontal edges of pane imperf (30.1.90)	10·00	
1468		15p. brt blue (1 side band at left) (30.1.90)...............................	3·75	3·75
		Ea. Band at right (20.3.90)	3·25	3·25
		l. Booklet pane. No. 1468×2 and 1470 plus label..............................	9·50	
1469		20p. brownish black and cream (phosphorised paper)...........................	1·00	1·00
		a. Imperf (pair)........................	£2400	
		l. Booklet pane. No. 1469×5 plus label with vertical edges of pane imperf (30.1.90)	8·00	
		m. Booklet pane. No. 1469×10 with horizontal edges of pane imperf (30.1.90)	11·00	
		n. Booklet pane. No. 1469×6 with margins all round (20.3.90)	5·00	
		r. Booklet pane. No. 1469×4 with three edges of pane imperf (17.4.90).....................................	8·00	
1470		20p. brownish black and cream (2 bands) (30.1.90)..........................	2·75	2·75
1471		29p. dp mauve (phosphorised paper)	1·75	1·75
1472		29p. dp mauve (2 bands) (20.3.90)..........	9·00	9·00
1473		34p. dp bluish grey (phosphorised paper)..	2·00	2·00
1474		37p. rosine (phosphorised paper)............	2·25	2·25

(b) Litho Walsall. P 14 (from booklets).

1475	**929**	15p. brt blue (1 centre band) (30.1.90) ..	1·50	1·75
		l. Booklet pane. No. 1475×4 with three edges of pane imperf..............	7·00	

		m. Booklet pane. No. 1475×10 with three edges of pane imperf (12.6.90)	12·00	
1476		20p. brownish black and cream (phosphorised paper) (30.1.90)........	1·75	1·90
		l. Booklet pane. No. 1476×5 plus label with vertical edges of pane imperf....................................	12·00	
		m. Booklet pane. No. 1476×4 with three edges of pane imperf.............	10·00	
		n. Booklet pane. No. 1476×10 with three edges of pane imperf (12.6.90)...................................	16·00	

(c) Litho Questa. P 15×14 (from booklets).

1477	**929**	15p. brt blue (1 centre band) (17.4.90) ..	2·50	2·75
1478		20p. brownish black (phosphorised paper) (17.4.90).............................	2·75	3·00
Set of 5 (Nos. 1467, 1469, 1471, 1473/4)...............................			7·00	7·00
First Day Cover (Nos. 1467, 1469, 1471, 1473/4)				7·00
Presentation Pack (Nos. 1467, 1469, 1471, 1473/4) (P.O. Pack No. 21)...			9·00	

Nos. 1475/6 do not exist perforated on all four sides, but come with either one or two adjacent sides imperforate.

Nos. 1468, 1468Ea, 1470, 1472 and 1475/8 were only issued in stamp booklets, Nos. JA1 to JD3. Nos. 1468Ea, 1470 and 1472 occur in the *se-tenant* pane from the 1990 London Life £5 booklet. This pane is listed as No. X906m.

For illustrations showing the difference between photogravure and lithography see beneath Type **367**.

For No. 1469 in miniature sheet see No. **MS**1501.

For No. 1476 with one elliptical hole on each vertical side see No. 2955.

For Type **929** redrawn with "1st" face value see Nos. 2133 and 2956.

Colour trials are known denominated 19p. in several colours.

Special First Day of Issue Postmark

Philatelic Bureau, Edinburgh (in red)		7·50
Windsor, Berks (Type G, see Introduction) (in red)		8·00

930 Kitten **931** Rabbit

932 Duckling **933** Puppy

(Des T. Evans. Litho Questa)

1990 (23 Jan). *150th Anniv of Royal Society for Prevention of Cruelty to Animals.* Phosphorised paper. P 14×14½.

1479	**930**	20p. new blue, greenish yellow, brt magenta, black and silver	75	50
		a. Silver (Queen's head and face value) omitted	£675	
1480	**931**	29p. new blue, greenish yellow, brt magenta, black and silver	1·25	1·25
		a. Imperf (horiz pair)............................	£8500	
1481	**932**	34p. new blue, greenish yellow, brt magenta, black and silver	1·25	1·50
		a. Silver (Queen's head and face value) omitted	£1250	
1482	**933**	37p. new blue, greenish yellow, brt magenta, black and silver	1·50	1·50
Set of 4			4·50	4·25

Set of 4 Gutter Pairs.. 9·50
First Day Cover .... 4·75
Presentation Pack (P.O. Pack No. 205)................... 4·75
PHQ Cards (set of 4) (123) .... 3·00 .... 7·50

Special First Day of Issue Postmarks

Philatelic Bureau, Edinburgh ....4·75
Horsham .... 5·00

934 Teddy Bear | **935** Dennis the Menace

936 Punch | **937** Cheshire Cat

938 The Man in the Moon | **939** The Laughing Policeman

940 Clown | **941** Mona Lisa

942 Queen of Hearts | **943** Stan Laurel (comedian)

(Des Michael Peters and Partners Ltd)

1990 (6 Feb). *Greetings Stamps. Smiles.* Two phosphor bands. *P* 15×14.
1483	**934**	20p. gold, greenish yellow, brt rose-red, new blue and grey-black....................	2·25	2·40
		a. Booklet pane. Nos. 1483/92 with margins all round....................	26·00	26·00
1484	**935**	20p. gold, greenish yellow, brt rose-red, new blue, dp blue and grey-black.	2·25	2·40
1485	**936**	20p. gold, greenish yellow, brt rose-red, new blue, dp blue and grey-black.	2·25	2·40
1486	**937**	20p. gold, greenish yellow, brt rose-red, new blue and grey-black....................	2·25	2·40
1487	**938**	20p. gold, greenish yellow, brt rose-red, new blue and grey-black....................	2·25	2·40
1488	**939**	20p. gold, greenish yellow, brt rose-red, new blue and grey-black....................	2·25	2·40
1489	**940**	20p. gold, greenish yellow, brt rose-red, new blue and grey-black....................	2·25	2·40
1490	**941**	20p. gold, greenish yellow, brt rose-red, new blue and grey-black....................	2·25	2·40
1491	**942**	20p. gold, greenish yellow, brt rose-red, new blue and grey-black....................	2·25	2·40
1492	**943**	20p. gold and grey-black....................	2·25	2·40
Set of 10...			30·00	26·00
First Day Cover				28·00

Nos. 1483/92 were only issued in £2 booklets No. KX1. The design of Nos. 1483, 1485/7, 1489 and 1492 extend onto the pane margin.
For Types **934/43** inscribed (1st), see Nos. 1550/59.

> **SET PRICES.** Please note that set prices for booklet greetings stamps are for complete panes. Sets of single stamps are worth considerably less.

Special First Day of Issue Postmarks

Philatelic Bureau, Edinburgh .... 28·00
Giggleswick, North Yorkshire .... 28·00

944 Alexandra Palace ("Stamp World London 90" Exhibition) | **945** Glasgow School of Art

946 British Philatelic Bureau, Edinburgh | **947** Templeton Carpet Factory, Glasgow

(Des P. Hogarth)

1990 (6–20 Mar). *Europa* (Nos. 1493 and 1495) and *Glasgow 1990 European City of Culture* (Nos. 1494 and 1496). Phosphorised paper. *P* 14×15.
1493	**944**	20p. silver, lemon, flesh, grey-brown, blue, grey-black and black................	50	40
		a. Booklet pane. No. 1493×4 with margins all round (20 Mar)...............	3·50	
1494	**945**	20p. silver, greenish yellow, dull orange, blue, grey-black and black...........	50	40
1495	**946**	29p. silver, stone, orange, olive-sepia, grey-blue, grey-black and black	1·25	1·75
1496	**947**	37p. silver, greenish-yellow, brt emerald, salmon, olive-sepia, brt blue and black....................................	1·50	1·75
Set of 4			3·50	4·00
Set of 4 Gutter Pairs..			8·00	
First Day Cover				4·25
Presentation Pack (P.O. Pack No. 206)...............			4·25	
PHQ Cards (set of 4) (124)...................................			3·00	6·00

Booklet pane No. 1493a comes from the £5 "London Life" booklet No. DX11.

Special First Day of Issue Postmarks

Philatelic Bureau, Edinburgh .... 4·25
Glasgow .... 5·00

948 Export Achievement Award

949 Technological Achievement Award

(Des S. Broom. Litho Questa)

1990 (10 Apr). *25th Anniv of Queen's Awards for Export and Technology.* P 14×14½.

1497	**948**	20p. new blue, greenish yellow, magenta, black and silver	50	60
		a. Horiz pair. Nos. 1497/8	1·40	1·60
1498	**949**	20p. new blue, greenish yellow, magenta, black and silver	50	60
1499	**948**	37p. new blue, greenish yellow, magenta, black and silver	1·25	1·25
		a. Horiz pair. Nos. 1499/500	3·00	3·00
1500	**949**	37p. new blue, greenish yellow, magenta, black and silver	1·25	1·25
Set of 4			4·00	4·25
Set of 2 Gutter Strips of 4			8·50	
First Day Cover				4·75
Presentation Pack (P.O. Pack No. 207)			4·50	
PHQ Cards (set of 4) (125)			3·00	6·00

Nos. 1497/8 and 1499/1500 were each printed together, *se-tenant*, in horizontal pairs throughout the sheets.

Special First Day of Issue Postmarks

Philatelic Bureau, Edinburgh .... 4·75
London, SW .... 5·00

949a

(Des Sedley Place Design Ltd. Eng C. Matthews. Recess and photo Harrison)

1990 (3 May). *Stamp World London '90 International Stamp Exhibition.* Sheet 122×89 mm containing No. 1469. Phosphorised paper. P 15×14.

MS1501	**949a**	20p. brownish black and cream (sold at £1)	5·50	5·50
		a. Error. Imperf	£16000	
		b. Black (recess-printing) omitted	£75000	
		c. Black (recess-printing) inverted	—	
First Day Cover				5·75
Souvenir Book (Nos. 1467, 1469, 1471, 1473/4 and MS1501)			20·00	

The premium on No. MS1501 was used to support the "Stamp World London '90" International Stamp Exhibition. In No. MS1501 only the example of the 20p. is perforated.

No. MS1501b shows an albino impression on the reverse. The 1d. black and Seahorse background are omitted due to one sheet becoming attached to the underside of another prior to recess printing. No. MS1501c shows the recess part of the design inverted in relation to the photogravure of Type **929**.

For the single 20p stamp, see No. 1469. For the same stamp redrawn with "1st" face value or with one elliptical hole on each vertical side see Nos. 2133 and 2955/6.

Special First Day of Issue Postmarks

Philatelic Bureau, Edinburgh (in red) .... 6·00
City of London (in red) .... 6·00

A First Day of Issue handstamp as Type B was provided at Alexandra Palace, London N22 for this issue.

KEW GARDENS 1840-1990
950 Cycad and Sir Joseph Banks Building

KEW GARDENS 1840-1990
951 Stone Pine and Princess of Wales Conservatory

KEW GARDENS 1840-1990
952 Willow Tree and Palm House

KEW GARDENS 1840-1990
953 Cedar Tree and Pagoda

(Des P. Leith)

1990 (5 June). *150th Anniv of Kew Gardens.* Phosphorised paper. P 14×15.

1502	**950**	20p. black, brt emerald, pale turquoise-green, lt brown and lavender	55	40
1503	**951**	29p. black, brt emerald, turquoise-green, reddish-orange and grey-black	75	1·00
1504	**952**	34p. Venetian red, brt green, cobalt, dull purple, turquoise-green and yellow-green	1·25	1·60
1505	**953**	37p. pale violet-blue, brt emerald, red-brown, steel-blue and brown-rose .	1·50	1·50
Set of 4			3·50	4·00
Set of 4 Gutter Pairs			8·00	
First Day Cover				4·50
Presentation Pack (P.O. Pack No. 208)			4·00	
PHQ Cards (set of 4) (126)			3·00	6·00

Special First Day of Issue Postmarks

Philatelic Bureau, Edinburgh	4·50
Kew, Richmond	5·00

954 Thomas Hardy and
Clyffe Clump, Dorset

(Des J. Gibbs)

1990 (10 July). *150th Birth Anniv of Thomas Hardy (author).* Phosphorised paper. *P* 14×15.

1506	**954**	20p. vermilion, greenish yellow, pale lake-brown, dp brown, lt red-brown and black	80	75
		a. Imperf (pair)	£10000	
Gutter Pair			1·75	
First Day Cover				1·50
Presentation Pack (P.O. Pack No. 209)			1·50	
PHQ Card (127)			1·00	2·25

Special First Day of Issue Postmarks

Philatelic Bureau, Edinburgh	2·00
Dorchester	2·50

955 Queen Elizabeth
the Queen Mother

956 Queen Elizabeth

957 Elizabeth, Duchess
of York

958 Lady Elizabeth
Bowes-Lyon

(Des J. Gorham from photographs by N. Parkinson (20p.), Dorothy Wilding (29p.), B. Park (34p.), Rita Martin (37p.))

1990 (2 Aug). *90th Birthday of Queen Elizabeth the Queen Mother.* Phosphorised paper. *P* 14×15.

1507	**955**	20p. silver, greenish yellow, magenta, turquoise-blue and grey-black	95	60
1508	**956**	29p. silver, indigo and grey-blue	1·40	1·50
1509	**957**	34p. silver, lemon, red, new blue and grey-black	2·00	2·50
1510	**958**	37p. silver, sepia and stone	2·25	2·50
Set of 4			6·00	6·50
Set of 4 Gutter Pairs			15·00	
First Day Cover				7·00
Presentation Pack (P.O. Pack No. 210)			7·00	
PHQ Cards (set of 4) (128)			5·50	8·00

For these designs with Queen's head and frame in black see Nos. 2280/3.

Special First Day of Issue Postmarks

Philatelic Bureau, Edinburgh	7·00
Westminster, SW1	7·00

For Nos. 1511/16 see Decimal Machin Definitives section.

959 Victoria Cross   **960** George Cross

961 Distinguished Service
Cross and Distinguished Service
Medal

962 Military Cross and Military
Medal

963 Distinguished Flying Cross
and Distinguished Flying Medal

(Des J. Gibbs and J. Harwood)

1990 (11 Sept). *Gallantry Awards.* Phosphorised paper. *P* 14×15 (vert) or 15×14 (horiz).

1517	**959**	20p. grey-black, pale stone, stone, bistre-brown and brt carmine	80	75
1518	**960**	20p. grey-black, pale stone, flesh, grey and ultramarine	80	75
1519	**961**	20p. grey-black, pale stone, flesh, pale blue and ultramarine	80	75
		a. Imperf (pair)	£3750	
1520	**962**	20p. grey-black, pale stone, ochre, pale blue, ultramarine, scarlet and violet	80	75
1521	**963**	20p. grey-black, pale stone, yellow-brown, bluish grey and purple	80	75

Set of 5	3·75	3·50
Set of 5 Gutter Pairs	8·50	
First Day Cover		4·00
Presentation Pack (P.O. Pack No. 211)............	4·00	
PHQ Cards (set of 5) (129)	3·00	8·00

For Type **959** with "all-over" phosphor and perf 14×14½ see No. 2666.

Special First Day of Issue Postmarks

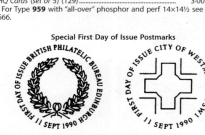

Philatelic Bureau, Edinburgh .... 4·00
Westminster, SW1 .... 4·75

964 Armagh Observatory, Jodrell Bank Radio Telescope and La Palma Telescope

965 Newton's Moon and Tides Diagram and Early Telescopes

966 Greenwich Old Observatory and Early Astronomical Equipment

967 Stonehenge, Gyroscope and Navigation by Stars

(Des J. Fisher. Litho Questa)

1990 (16 Oct). *Astronomy*. Phosphorised paper. *P* 14×14½.

1522	**964**	22p. cream, grey, dull blue-green, slate-blue, blue-green, orange-red, gold & black	65	50
		a. Gold (Queen's head) omitted............	£900	
1523	**965**	26p. black, yellow, dull purple, pale cream, brown-rose, new blue, greenish yellow, vermilion and gold	1·00	1·10
1524	**966**	31p. black, cream, pale cream, yellow-orange, salmon, lemon, vermilion and gold	1·25	1·40
1525	**967**	37p. black, pale buff, olive-bistre, pale cream, pale flesh, flesh, grey, rose-red and gold	1·50	1·40
Set of 4			3·75	4·00
Set of 4 Gutter Pairs			8·50	
First Day Cover				4·50
Presentation Pack (P.O. Pack No. 212)............			4·50	
PHQ Cards (set of 4) (130)			3·00	7·00

Nos. 1522/5 marked the centenary of the British Astronomical Association and the bicentenary of the Armagh Observatory.

Special First Day of Issue Postmarks

Philatelic Bureau, Edinburgh .... 4·50
Armagh .... 5·25

968 Building a Snowman

969 Fetching the Christmas Tree

970 Carol Singing

971 Tobogganing

972 Ice-skating

(Des J. Gorham and A. Davidson)

1990 (13 Nov). *Christmas*. One phosphor band (17p.) or phosphorised paper (others). *P* 15×14.

1526	**968**	17p. gold, greenish yellow, rose, new blue and grey-black	50	40
		a. Imperf (pair)	£4000	
		b. Booklet pane of 20	10·00	
1527	**969**	22p. gold, greenish yellow, magenta, new blue and black	70	50
		a. Imperf (horiz pair)...................	£4000	
1528	**970**	26p. gold, olive-yellow, pale magenta, agate, new blue, dull violet-blue and black	70	1·10
1529	**971**	31p. gold, greenish yellow, brt rose-red, dull mauve, new blue, turquoise-blue and grey-black	1·25	1·50
1530	**972**	37p. gold, greenish yellow, rose, new blue and slate-green	1·25	1·50
Set of 5			4·00	4·50
Set of 5 Gutter Pairs			10·00	
First Day Cover				5·00
Presentation Pack (P.O. Pack No. 213)............			4·50	
PHQ Cards (set of 5) (131)			3·00	7·00

Booklet pane No. 1526b has the horizontal edges of the pane imperforate.

Special First Day of Issue Postmarks

Philatelic Bureau, Edinburgh ....5·00
Bethlehem, Llandeilo, Dyfed ....5·00

Collectors Pack 1990

1990 (13 Nov). Comprises Nos. 1479/82, 1493/1510 and 1517/30.
CP1530a Collectors Pack.. 30·00

Post Office Yearbook

1990 (13 Nov). Comprises Nos. 1479/82, 1493/1500, 1502/10, 1517/30 in hardbound book with slip case, illustrated in colour YB1530a Yearbook .... 45·00

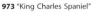

KING CHARLES SPANIEL
GEORGE STUBBS

A POINTER
GEORGE STUBBS

973 "King Charles Spaniel"   **974** "A Pointer"

TWO HOUNDS IN A LANDSCAPE
GEORGE STUBBS

A ROUGH DOG
GEORGE STUBBS

975 "Two Hounds in a   **976** "A Rough Dog"
Landscape"

FINO AND TINY
GEORGE STUBBS

977 "Fino and Tiny"

(Des Carroll, Dempsey and Thirkell Ltd)

1991 (8 Jan). *Dogs. Paintings by George Stubbs.* Phosphorised paper.
P 14×14½.

1531	**973**	22p. gold, greenish yellow, magenta, new blue, black and drab	50	50
		a. Imperf (pair)	£3500	
1532	**974**	26p. gold, greenish yellow, magenta, new blue, black and drab	75	1·25
1533	**975**	31p. gold, greenish yellow, magenta, new blue, black and drab	1·00	1·25
		a. Imperf (pair)	£5000	
1534	**976**	33p. gold, greenish yellow, magenta, new blue, black and drab	1·25	1·25
1535	**977**	37p. gold, greenish yellow, magenta, new blue, black and drab	1·25	1·25
Set of 5			4·50	5·00
Set of 5 Gutter Pairs			11·00	
First Day Cover				5·50
Presentation Pack (P.O. Pack No. 215)			5·00	
PHQ Cards (set of 5) (132)			3·50	8·00

Special First Day of Issue Postmarks

Philatelic Bureau, Edinburgh ....5·50
Birmingham ....5·50

978 Thrush's Nest   **979** Shooting Star and Rainbow

980 Magpies and Charm   **981** Black Cat
Bracelet

982 Common Kingfisher with   **983** Mallard and Frog
Key

984 Four-leaf Clover in Boot and   **985** Pot of Gold at End of
Match Box   Rainbow

986 Heart-shaped Butterflies   **987** Wishing Well and Sixpence

(Des T. Meeuwissen)

1991 (5 Feb). *Greetings Stamps. Good Luck.* Two phosphor bands.
P 15×14.

1536	**978**	(1st) silver, greenish yellow, magenta, new blue, olive-brown and black	1·25	1·00
		a. Booklet pane. Nos. 1536/45 plus 12 half stamp-size labels with margins on 3 sides	15·00	17·00
1537	**979**	(1st) silver, greenish yellow, magenta, new blue, olive-brown and black	1·25	1·00
1538	**980**	(1st) silver, greenish yellow, magenta, new blue, olive-brown and black	1·25	1·00
1539	**981**	(1st) silver, greenish yellow, magenta, new blue, olive-brown and black	1·25	1·00
1540	**982**	(1st) silver, greenish yellow, magenta, new blue, olive-brown and black	1·25	1·00
1541	**983**	(1st) silver, greenish yellow, magenta, new blue, olive-brown and black	1·25	1·00
1542	**984**	(1st) silver, greenish yellow, magenta, new blue, olive-brown and black	1·25	1·00
1543	**985**	(1st) silver, greenish yellow, magenta, new blue, olive-brown and black	1·25	1·00
1544	**986**	(1st) silver, greenish yellow, magenta, new blue, olive-brown and black	1·25	1·00
1545	**987**	(1st) silver, greenish yellow, magenta, new blue, olive-brown and black	1·25	1·00
Set of 10			15·00	17·00
First Day Cover				19·00

Nos. 1536/45 were only issued in £2·20 booklets, No. KX2 (*sold at £2·40 from 16 September 1991*)

The backgrounds of the stamps form a composite design.

Special First Day of Issue Postmarks

Philatelic Bureau, Edinburgh ....19·00
Greetwell, Lincs ....19·00

988 Michael Faraday (inventor of electric motor) (Birth Bicentenary)

989 Charles Babbage (computer science pioneer) (Birth Bicentenary)

990 Radar Sweep of East Anglia (50th Anniv of Operational Radar Network)

991 Gloster Whittle E28/39 over East Anglia (50th Anniv of First Flight of Sir Frank Whittle's Jet Engine)

(Des P. Till (Nos. 1546/7), J. Harwood (Nos. 1548/9))

1991 (5 Mar). *Scientific Achievements.* Phosphorised paper. *P* 14×15.

1546	**988**	22p. silver, olive-brown, greenish yellow, magenta, slate-blue, grey and black	60	60
		a. Imperf (pair)	£850	
1547	**989**	22p. silver, chrome-yellow, red, grey-black, brownish grey and sepia	60	60
1548	**990**	31p. silver, dp turquoise-green, violet-blue, steel-blue and dp dull blue	1·20	1·50
1549	**991**	37p. silver, olive-bistre, rose-red, turquoise-blue, new blue and grey-black	1·40	1·75
Set of 4			3·50	4·00
Set of 4 Gutter Pairs			8·50	
First Day Cover				4·50
Presentation Pack (P.O. Pack No. 216)			4·25	
PHQ Cards (set of 4) (133)			3·50	7·00

Special First Day of Issue Postmarks

Philatelic Bureau, Edinburgh ....4·50
South Kensington, London, SW7 ....4·75

992 Teddy Bear

(Des Michael Peters and Partners Ltd)

1991 (26 Mar). *Greeting Stamps. Smiles.* As Nos. 1483/92, but inscribed '1st' as T **992**. Two phosphor bands. *P* 15×14.

1550	**992**	(1st) gold, greenish yellow, brt rose-red, new blue and grey-black	1·25	1·00
		a. Booklet pane. Nos. 1550/9 plus 12 half stamp-size labels with margins on 3 sides	12·00	13·00
1551	**935**	(1st) gold, greenish yellow, brt rose-red, new blue, dp blue and grey-black	1·25	1·00

1552	**936**	(1st) gold, greenish yellow, brt rose-red, new blue, dp blue and grey-black	1·25	1·00
1553	**937**	(1st) gold, greenish yellow, bright rose-red, new blue and grey-black	1·25	1·00
1554	**938**	(1st) gold, greenish yellow, brt rose-red, new blue and grey-black	1·25	1·00
1555	**939**	(1st) gold, greenish yellow, brt rose-red, new blue and grey-black	1·25	1·00
1556	**940**	(1st) gold, greenish yellow, brt rose-red, new blue and grey-black	1·25	1·00
1557	**941**	(1st) gold, greenish yellow, brt rose-red, new blue and grey-black	1·25	1·00
1558	**942**	(1st) gold, greenish yellow, brt rose-red, new blue and grey-black	1·25	1·00
1559	**943**	(1st) gold and grey-black	1·25	1·00
Set of 10			12·00	13·00
First Day Cover				14·00

Nos. 1550/9 were originally issued in £2·20 booklets, No. KX3 (*sold at £2·40 from 16 September 1991 and at £2·50 from 1 November 1993*) The designs of Nos. 1550, 1552/4, 1556 and 1559 extend onto the pane margin.

The stamps were re-issued in sheets of 10, printed in photogravure by Questa, each with *se-tenant* label on 22 May 2000 in connection with "customised" stamps available at "Stamp Show 2000". The labels show either a pattern of ribbons at £2·95 (LS1), or a personal photograph for £5·95.

A similar sheet, but printed in lithography by Questa instead of in photogravure, appeared on 3 July 2001 (LS5). Stamps from this sheet were perforated 14½×14 instead of the previous 15×14. Sheets showing greetings on the labels were available from the Bureau or Postshops at £2·95 each or with personal photographs at £12·95 for two. Similar sheets each containing ten examples of Nos. 1550/1 and 1555/7 were only available with personal photograph. From 29 October 2001 sheets with personal photographs could also be purchased, on an experimental basis, from photo-booths situated at six post offices.

On 1 October 2002 three further sheets appeared printed in lithography by Questa. One contained Nos. 1550/1 each×10 with greetings labels and cost £5·95 (LS9). Both designs were also available in sheets of 20 with personal photographs at £14·95 a sheet.

> **SET PRICES.** Please note that set prices for booklet greetings stamps are for complete panes. Sets of single stamps are worth considerably less.

Special First Day of Issue Postmarks

Philatelic Bureau, Edinburgh ....14·00
Laugherton, Lincs ....14·00

993 Man Looking at Space

994 Man Looking at Space

995 Space Looking at Man

996 Space Looking at Man

(Des J. M. Folon)

1991 (23 Apr). *Europa. Europe in space.* Phosphorised paper. P 14½×14.

1560	**993**	22p. silver-mauve, greenish yellow, scarlet, violet-blue, brt blue, brt green and black	60	60
		a. Horiz pair. Nos 1560/1	1·50	1·50
1561	**994**	22p. silver-mauve, greenish yellow, scarlet, violet-blue, brt blue and black	60	60
1562	**995**	37p. silver-mauve, bistre-yellow, dull vermilion, blue and black	1·25	1·25
		a. Horiz pair. Nos 1562/3	3·50	3·00
1563	**996**	37p. silver-mauve, bistre-yellow, dull vermilion, blue and black	1·25	1·25
Set of 4			4·50	4·50
Set of 2 Gutter Pairs of 4			9·50	
First Day Cover				5·00
Presentation Pack (P.O. Pack No. 217)			5·00	
PHQ Cards (set of 4) (134)			3·00	7·00

Nos. 1560/1 and 1562/3 were each printed together, *se-tenant*, in horizontal pairs throughout the sheets, each pair forming a composite design.

Special First Day of Issue Postmarks

Philatelic Bureau, Edinburgh	5·00
Cambridge	5·50

997 Fencing

998 Hurdling

999 Diving

1000 Rugby

(Des Huntley Muir Partners)

1991 (11 June). *World Student Games, Sheffield* (Nos. 1564/6) and *World Cup Rugby Championship, London* (No. 1567). Phosphorised paper. P 14½×14.

1564	**997**	22p. black, greenish yellow, vermilion, brt orange, ultramarine and grey	60	50
1565	**998**	26p. pale blue, greenish yellow, red, brt blue and black	1·00	1·00
1566	**999**	31p. brt blue, bistre-yellow, rose, vermilion, new blue and black	1·25	1·25
1567	**1000**	37p. yellow-orange, greenish yellow, rose, brt blue, emerald and black	1·50	1·50
Set of 4			3·50	3·75
Set of 4 Gutter Pairs			8·00	
First Day Cover				4·25
Presentation Pack (P.O. Pack No. 218)			4·50	
PHQ Cards (set of 4) (135)			3·00	7·00

Special First Day of Issue Postmarks

Philatelic Bureau, Edinburgh	4·25
Sheffield	4·75

Rosa Silver Jubilee
1001 "Silver Jubilee"

Rosa Mme Alfred Carrière
1002 "Mme Alfred Carrière"

Rosa moyesii
1003 *Rosa moyesii*

Rosa Harvest Fayre
1004 "Harvest Fayre"

Rosa Mutabilis
1005 "Mutabilis"

(Des Yvonne Skargon. Litho Questa)

1991 (16 July). *Ninth World Congress of Roses, Belfast.* Phosphorised paper. P 14½×14.

1568	**1001**	22p. new blue, greenish yellow, magenta, black and silver	50	50
		a. Silver (Queen's head) omitted	£3800	
		Eb. Black printing double	£7000	£4500
1569	**1002**	26p. new blue, greenish yellow, magenta, black and silver	75	1·25
1570	**1003**	31p. new blue, greenish yellow, magenta, black and silver	1·00	1·25
1571	**1004**	33p. new blue, greenish yellow, magenta, black and silver	1·25	1·50
1572	**1005**	37p. new blue, greenish yellow, magenta, black and silver	1·50	1·50
Set of 5			4·50	5·50
Set of 5 Gutter Pairs			10·00	
First Day Cover				6·00
Presentation Pack (P.O. Pack No. 219)			5·00	
PHQ Cards (set of 5) (136)			3·00	9·00

Special First Day of Issue Postmarks

Philatelic Bureau, Edinburgh	6·00
Belfast	7·00

1006 Iguanodon   **1007** Stegosaurus

1008 Tyrannosaurus   **1009** Protoceratops

1010 Triceratops

(Des B. Kneale)

1991 (20 Aug). *150th Anniversary of Dinosaurs' Identification by Owen.*
Phosphorised paper. *P* 14½×14.

1573	**1006**	22p. grey, pale blue, magenta, brt blue, dull violet and grey-black	60	50
		a. Imperf (pair)	£4600	
1574	**1007**	26p. grey, greenish yellow, pale emerald, brt blue-green, pale brt blue, grey-black and black	1·10	1·25
1575	**1008**	31p. grey, lt blue, magenta, brt blue, pale blue, brown and grey-black	1·25	1·25
1576	**1009**	33p. grey, dull rose, pale brt blue, brt rose-red, yellow-orange, grey-black and black	1·50	1·50
1577	**1010**	37p. grey, greenish yellow, turquoise-blue, dull violet, yellow-brown and black	1·60	1·50
Set of 5			5·75	5·50
Set of 5 Gutter Pairs			12·00	
First Day Cover				6·00
Presentation Pack (P.O. Pack No. 220)			6·00	
PHQ Cards (set of 5) (137)			3·00	9·00

Special First Day of Issue Postmarks

Philatelic Bureau, Edinburgh ....6·00
Plymouth ....7·00

1011 Map of 1816   **1012** Map of 1906

1013 Map of 1959   **1014** Map of 1991

(Des H. Brown. Recess and litho Harrison (24p.), litho Harrison (28p.),
Questa (33p., 39p.))

1991 (17 Sept). *Bicentenary of Ordnance Survey. Maps of Hamstreet, Kent.*
Phosphorised paper. *P* 14½×14.

1578	**1011**	24p. black, magenta and cream	60	50
		Ea. Black (litho) printing treble and magenta printing double	£2000	
		Eb. Black (litho) and magenta printing double	£3200	
		Ec. Black (litho) printing double	£3200	
1579	**1012**	28p. black, brt yellow-green, new blue, reddish orange, magenta, olive-sepia and cream	1·00	95
1580	**1013**	33p. dull blue-green, orange-brown, magenta, olive-grey, greenish yellow, vermilion, greenish grey, pale blue, blue, dull orange, apple green and black	1·25	1·40
1581	**1014**	39p. black, magenta, greenish yellow and new blue	1·50	1·40
Set of 4			3·50	3·75
Set of 4 Gutter Pairs			8·50	
First Day Cover				4·25
Presentation Pack (P.O. Pack No. 221)			4·50	
PHQ Cards (set of 4) (138)			3·00	7·00

Mint examples of Type **1012** exist with a face value of 26p. (*Price £6500*).

Special First Day of Issue Postmarks

Philatelic Bureau, Edinburgh .... 4·50
Southampton ....5·50

1015 Adoration of the Magi   **1016** Mary and Jesus in Stable

1017 Holy Family and Angel   **1018** The Annunciation

1019 The Flight into Egypt

(Des D. Driver)

1991 (12 Nov). *Christmas. Illuminated Letters from 'Acts of Mary and Jesus' Manuscript in Bodleian Library, Oxford.* One phosphor band (18p.) or phosphorised paper (others). *P* 15×14.

1582 **1015** 18p. steel-blue, greenish yellow, rose-
red, orange-red, black and gold...... 75 35
    a. Imperf (pair)................................ £11000
    b. Booklet pane of 20..................... 8·25
1583 **1016** 24p. brt rose-red, greenish yellow,
vermilion, slate-blue, yellow-green,
grey-black and gold......................... 90 45
1584 **1017** 28p. reddish brown, bistre-yellow,
orange-vermilion, orange-red,
deep dull blue, grey-black and
gold.. 95 1·25
1585 **1018** 33p. green, greenish yellow, red,
orange-red, blue, grey and gold..... 1·10 1·50
    a. Imperf (pair)................................ £13000
1586 **1019** 39p. orange-red, greenish yellow,
orange-vermilion, dp dull blue,
olive-sepia, black and gold.............. 1·25 1·75
Set of 5 .... 4·50 4·75
Set of 5 Gutter Pairs....................................... 11·00
First Day Cover .... 5·50
Presentation Pack (P.O. Pack No. 222)......... 5·00
PHQ Cards (set of 5) (139) .... 3·00 7·50
Booklet pane No. 1582b has margins at left, top and bottom.

Collectors Pack 1991
1991 (12 Nov). Comprises Nos. 1531/5, 1546/9 and 1560/86.
CP1586a Collectors Pack.................................. 32·00

Post Office Yearbook
1991 (13 Nov). Comprises Nos. 1531/5, 1546/9 and
1560/86 in hardbound book with slip case,
illustrated in colour .... 45·00

1020 Fallow Deer in Scottish
Forest

1021 Hare on North Yorkshire
Moors

1022 Fox in the Fens

1023 Redwing and Home
Counties Village

1024 Welsh Mountain Sheep in
Snowdonia

(Des J. Gorham and K. Bowen)

1992 (14 Jan–25 Feb). *The Four Seasons. Wintertime.* One phosphor
band (18p.) or phosphorised paper (others). P 15×14.
1587 **1020** 18p. silver, greenish yellow, grey, dull
rose, new blue and black.................. 55 40
1588 **1021** 24p. silver, lemon, rose, blue and grey-
black.. 75 50
    a. Imperf (pair)................................ £850
1589 **1022** 28p. silver, greenish yellow, bright rose,
steel-blue and grey-black................. 1·00 1·25
1590 **1023** 33p. silver, greenish yellow, brt orange,
brt purple, greenish blue and grey 1·25 1·50

1591 **1024** 39p. silver, yellow, yellow-orange, grey,
vermilion, new blue and black........ 1·40 1·75
    a. Booklet pane. No. 1591×4 with
margins all round (25 Feb)............... 4·75
Set of 5 .... 4·50 5·00
Set of 5 Gutter Pairs....................................... 11·00
First Day Cover .... 5·50
Presentation Pack (P.O. Pack No. 224)......... 5·00
PHQ Cards (set of 5) (140) .... 3·00 8·00
Booklet pane No. 1591a comes from the £6 "Cymru-Wales" booklet
No. DX13.

1025 Flower Spray

1026 Double Locket

1027 Key

1028 Model Car and Cigarette
Cards

1029 Compass and Map

1030 Pocket Watch

1031 1854 1d. Red Stamp
and Pen

1032 Pearl Necklace and Pen

1033 Marbles

1034 Bucket, Spade and Starfish

(Des Trickett and Webb Ltd)

1992 (28 Jan). *Greetings Stamps. Memories.* Two phosphor bands.
P 15×14.

1592	**1025**	(1st) gold, greenish yellow, magenta, ochre, lt blue and grey-black...........	1·25	1·00
		a. Booklet pane. Nos. 1592/1601 plus 12 half stamp-size labels with margins on 3 sides	13·00	13·00
1593	**1026**	(1st) gold, greenish yellow, magenta, ochre, lt blue and grey-black...........	1·25	1·00
1594	**1027**	(1st) gold, greenish yellow, magenta, ochre, lt blue and grey-black...........	1·25	1·00
1595	**1028**	(1st) gold, greenish yellow, magenta, ochre, lt blue and grey-black...........	1·25	1·00
1596	**1029**	(1st) gold, greenish yellow, magenta, ochre, lt blue and grey-black...........	1·25	1·00
1597	**1030**	(1st) gold, greenish yellow, magenta, ochre, lt blue and grey-black...........	1·25	1·00
1598	**1031**	(1st) gold, greenish yellow, magenta, ochre, lt blue and grey-black...........	1·25	1·00
1599	**1032**	(1st) gold, greenish yellow, magenta, ochre, lt blue and grey-black...........	1·25	1·00
1600	**1033**	(1st) gold, greenish yellow, magenta, ochre, lt blue and grey-black...........	1·25	1·00
1601	**1034**	(1st) gold, greenish yellow, magenta, ochre, lt blue and grey-black...........	1·25	1·00
Set of 10			13·00	13·00
First Day Cover				15·00
Presentation Pack (P.O. Pack No. G1)........			17·00	

Nos. 1592/1601 were only issued in £2·40 booklets, No. KX4 (*sold at £2·50 from 1 November 1993 and at £2·60 from 8 July 1996*)
The backgrounds of the stamps form a composite design.

Special First Day of Issue Postmarks

Philatelic Bureau, Edinburgh...	15·00
Whimsey, Gloucestershire	15·00

1035 Queen Elizabeth in Coronation Robes and Parliamentary Emblem

1036 Queen Elizabeth in Garter Robes and Archiepiscopal Arms

1037 Queen Elizabeth with Baby Prince Andrew and Royal Arms

1038 Queen Elizabeth at Trooping the Colour and Service Emblems

1039 Queen Elizabeth and Commonwealth Emblem

(Des Why Not Associates. Litho Questa)

1992 (6 Feb). *40th Anniv of Accession.* Two phosphor bands. P 14½×14.

1602	**1035**	24p. new blue, greenish yellow, magenta, black, silver and gold	90	90
		a. Horiz strip of 5. Nos. 1602/6	6·00	6·50
1603	**1036**	24p. new blue, greenish yellow, magenta, black, silver and gold	90	90
1604	**1037**	24p. new blue, greenish yellow, magenta, black and silver	90	90
1605	**1038**	24p. new blue, greenish yellow, magenta, black, silver and gold	90	90
1606	**1039**	24p. new blue, greenish yellow, magenta, black, silver and gold	90	90
Set of 5			6·00	6·50
Gutter Block of 10...			15·00	
First Day Cover...				7·00
Presentation Pack (P.O. Pack No. 225)............			7·00	
PHQ Cards (set of 5) (141)			3·00	7·50

Nos. 1602/6 were printed together, *se-tenant*, in horizontal strips of five throughout the sheet.

Special First Day of Issue Postmarks

Philatelic Bureau, Edinburgh ....7·00
Buckingham Palace, London SW1 ....7·50

1040 Tennyson in 1888 and "The Beguiling of Merlin" (Sir Edward Burne-Jones)

1041 Tennyson in 1856 and "April Love" (Arthur Hughes)

1042 Tennyson in 1864 and "I am Sick of the Shadows" (John Waterhouse)

1043 Tennyson as a Young Man and "Mariana" (Dante Gabriel Rossetti)

(Des Irene von Treskow)

1992 (10 Mar). *Death Centenary of Alfred, Lord Tennyson (poet).* Phosphorised paper. P 14½×14.

1607	**1040**	24p. gold, greenish yellow, magenta, new blue and black	60	50
1608	**1041**	28p. gold, greenish yellow, magenta, new blue and black	85	85
1609	**1042**	33p. gold, greenish yellow, magenta, new blue, bistre and black	1·40	1·60
1610	**1043**	39p. gold, greenish yellow, magenta, new blue, bistre and black	1·50	1·60
Set of 4			4·00	4·00
Set of 4 Gutter Pairs...................................			9·00	
First Day Cover..				4·50
Presentation Pack (P.O. Pack No. 226).........			4·50	
PHQ Cards (Set of 4) (142)			3·00	7·00

Special First Day of Issue Postmarks

Philatelic Bureau, Edinburgh ....4·50
Isle of Wight ....4·50

1044 Caernarfon Castle

Elliptical hole in vertical perforations

CASTLE

Harrison Plates (Nos. 1611/14)

CASTLE

Enschedé Plates (Nos. 1993/6)

(Des from photos by Prince Andrew, Duke of York. Eng C. Matthews. Recess Harrison)

1992 (24 Mar)–**95**. Designs as Nos. 1410/13, but showing Queen's head in silhouette as *T* **1044**. *P* 15×14 (with one elliptical hole in each vertical side).

1611	**879**	£1 bottle green and gold†	5·50	1·00
1612	**1044**	£1·50 maroon and gold†	6·00	1·20
1613	**881**	£2 indigo and gold†	8·00	1·20
1613*a*	**879**	£3 reddish violet and gold† (22.8.95)	19·00	3·00
1614	**882**	£5 deep brown and gold†	18·00	3·00
		a. Gold† (Queen's head) omitted	£575	

Set of 5 .... 50·00   8·00
Set of 5 Gutter Pairs (vert or horiz) £100
First Day Cover (Nos. 1611/13, 1614) .... 35·00
First Day Cover (No. 1613a) .... 10·00
Presentation Pack (P.O. Pack No. 27) (Nos. 1611/13, 1614) .... 38·00
Presentation Pack (P.O. Pack No. 33) (No. 1613a) .... 30·00
PHQ Cards†† (Nos. 1611/13, 1614) (D2–5) .... 15·00   35·00
PHQ Cards (No. 1613a) (D8) .... 10·00   25·00

†The Queen's head on these stamps is printed in optically variable ink which changes colour from gold to green when viewed from different angles.

In 1994 the £1, £1·50, £2 and £5 were issued with the Queen's head re-etched, showing a pattern of diagonal lines, as opposed to the horizontal and diagonal lines of the original versions.

††The PHQ Cards for this issue did not appear until 16 February 1993. The Bureau FDI cancellation is 3 March 1993 (the date of issue of the £10).

The £1·50 (5 March 1996), £2 (2 May 1996), £3 (February 1997) and £5 (17 September 1996) subsequently appeared on PVA (white gum) instead of the tinted PVAD previously used.

See also Nos. 1410/3 and 1993/6.

Special First Day of Issue Postmarks

(for illustrations see Introduction)

Philatelic Bureau, Edinburgh (Type H) (£1, £1·50, £2, £5) ....35·00
Windsor, Berkshire (Type I) (£1, £1·50, £2, £5) ....35·00
Philatelic Bureau, Edinburgh (Type H) (£3) ....12·00
Carrickfergus, Antrim (as Type I) (£3) ....15·00

1045 British Olympic Association Logo (Olympic Games, Barcelona)

1046 British Paralympic Association Symbol (Paralympics '92, Barcelona)

1047 *Santa Maria* (500th Anniv of Discovery of America by Columbus)

1048 *Kaisei* (Japanese cadet brigantine) (Grand Regatta Columbus, 1992)

1049 British Pavilion, "EXPO '92", Seville

(Des K. Bassford (Nos. 1615/16, 1619), K. Bassford and S. Paine. Eng C. Matthews (Nos. 1617/18). Litho Questa (Nos. 1615/16, 1619) or recess and litho Harrison (Nos. 1617/18))

1992 (7 Apr). *Europa. International Events.* Phosphorised paper. *P* 14×14½.

1615	**1045**	24p. new blue, lemon, magenta & black	50	50
		a. Horiz. pair. Nos. 1615/16	2·25	1·75
1616	**1046**	24p. new blue, lemon, magenta & black	50	50
1617	**1047**	24p. black, grey, carmine, cream & gold	1·00	75
		a. Cream omitted		
1618	**1048**	39p. black, grey, carmine, cream & gold	1·40	1·50
1619	**1049**	39p. new blue, lemon, magenta & black	1·40	1·50

Set of 5 .... 4·50   4·50
Set of 3 Gutter Pairs and a Gutter Strip of 4 .... 11·00
First Day Cover .... 5·00
Presentation Pack (P.O. Pack No. 227) .... 5·25
PHQ Cards (set of 5) (143) .... 3·00   7·00

Nos. 1615/16 were printed together, *se-tenant*, in horizontal pairs throughout the sheet.

Special First Day of Issue Postmarks

Philatelic Bureau, Edinburgh ....5·00
Liverpool ....5·50

1050 Pikeman

1051 Drummer

1052 Musketeer   **1053** Standard Bearer

(Des J. Sancha)

1992 (16 June). *350th Anniv of the Civil War.* Phosphorised paper. P 14½×14.

1620	**1050**	24p. black, stone, bistre, scarlet, indigo, grey-green and yellow-ochre	60	50
		a. Imperf (pair)	£700	
1621	**1051**	28p. black, yellow-ochre, ochre, rose-pink, blue, dull yellow-green and slate-lilac	85	85
1622	**1052**	33p. black, ochre, pale orange, lemon, reddish orange, new blue and olive-green	1·40	1·50
1623	**1053**	39p. black, yellow-ochre, yellow, greenish yellow, vermilion, indigo and orange-brown	1·50	1·75
Set of 4			4·00	4·25
Set of 4 Gutter Pairs			9·50	
First Day Cover				4·75
Presentation Pack (P.O. Pack No. 228)			4·50	
PHQ Cards (set of 4) (144)			3·00	7·00

Special First Day of Issue Postmarks

Philatelic Bureau, Edinburgh ....4·75
Banbury, Oxfordshire ....4·75

1054 *The Yeomen of the Guard*   **1055** *The Gondoliers*

1056 *The Mikado*   **1057** *The Pirates of Penzance*

1058 *Iolanthe*

(Des Lynda Gray)

1992 (21 July). *150th Birth Anniv of Sir Arthur Sullivan (composer). Gilbert and Sullivan Operas.* One phosphor band (18p.) or phosphorised paper (others). P 14½×14.

1624	**1054**	18p. bluish violet, bistre-yellow, scarlet, stone, blue and grey-black	50	40
1625	**1055**	24p. purple-brown, lemon, scarlet, stone, blue, olive-bistre and black	80	60
		a. Imperf (pair)	£825	
1626	**1056**	28p. rose-red, lemon, stone, new blue, bluish violet, brt emerald and black	95	1·00
1627	**1057**	33p. blue-green, orange-yellow, scarlet, olive-bistre, blue, brown-purple and black	1·50	1·60
1628	**1058**	39p. dp blue, lemon, scarlet, stone, lavender, olive-bistre and lake-brown	1·60	1·60
Set of 5			4·50	4·75
Set of 5 Gutter Pairs			10·00	
First Day Cover				5·25
Presentation Pack (P.O. Pack No. 229)			5·00	
PHQ Cards (set of 5) (145)			3·00	6·25

Special First Day of Issue Postmarks

Philatelic Bureau, Edinburgh ....5·25
Birmingham ....5·25

1059 "Acid Rain Kills"   **1060** "Ozone Layer"

1061 "Greenhouse Effect"   **1062** "Bird of Hope"

Large full stop after "4" (Dot cyl. R. 10/6)

(Des Christopher Hall (24p.), Lewis Fowler (28p.), Sarah Warren (33p.), Alice Newton-Mold (39p.). Adapted Trickett and Webb Ltd)

1992 (15 Sept). *Protection of the Environment. Children's Paintings.* Phosphorised paper. P 14×14½.

1629	**1059**	24p. emerald, greenish yellow, pale olive-yellow, brt carmine and black	70	60
		a. Large full stop after "4"	20·00	
1630	**1060**	28p. vermilion, lemon, brt blue, new blue, brt green, ultramarine and black	1·10	1·25
1631	**1061**	33p. greenish blue, greenish yellow, brt rose-red, brt green, emerald, blue and black	1·25	1·50
1632	**1062**	39p. emerald, greenish yellow, brt magenta, brt orange, brt blue and black	1·40	1·50
Set of 4			4·00	4·25
Set of 4 Gutter Pairs			9·00	
First Day Cover				4·75

Presentation Pack (P.O. Pack No. 230).. 4·50
PHQ Cards (set of 4) (146) .... 3·00   6·25

Special First Day of Issue Postmarks

Philatelic Bureau, Edinburgh (in green)..4·75
Torridon (in green) ....5·00

1063 European Star

(Des D. Hockney)

1992 (13 Oct). *Single European Market. Phosphorised paper. P* 15×14.
1633   **1063** 24p. gold, greenish yellow, brt
                 magenta, dull ultramarine and
                 black.. 1·00   1·00
Gutter Pair .... 2·25
First Day Cover...   1·50
Presentation Pack (P.O. Pack No. 231)................................ 1·50
PHQ Card (147) .... 1·50   4·00

Special First Day of Issue Postmarks

Philatelic Bureau, Edinburgh ....1·75
Westminster ....2·50

1064 "Angel Gabriel", St.   **1065** "Madonna and Child", St.
James's, Pangbourne   Mary's, Bibury

1066 "King with Gold", Our Lady   **1067** "Shepherds", All Saints,
and St. Peter, Leatherhead   Porthcawl

1068 "Kings with Frankincense
and Myrrh", Our Lady and
St. Peter, Leatherhead

(Des Carroll, Dempsey and Thirkell Ltd from windows by Karl Parsons
(18, 24, 33p.) and Paul Woodroffe (28p. 39p.))

1992 (10 Nov). *Christmas. Stained Glass Windows.* One centre band
(18p.) or phosphorised paper (others). *P* 15×14.
1634   **1064** 18p. black, greenish yellow, mauve,
                 ultramarine, brt emerald and gold   50   30
                 a. Booklet pane of 20..................... 7·50
                 b. Imperf (pair)............................... £200
1635   **1065** 24p. black, greenish yellow, brt
                 purple, ultramarine, new blue, brt
                 greenish yellow and gold.................. 75   60
1636   **1066** 28p. black, lemon, rosine, ultramarine,
                 reddish lilac, red-orange and gold. 1·00   1·10
1637   **1067** 33p. brt ultramarine, greenish yellow,
                 rosine, brown, yellow-orange,
                 black and gold .... 1·25   1·50
1638   **1068** 39p. black, lemon, rosine, brt blue, dp
                 violet, yellow-orange and gold....... 1·25   1·50
Set of 5 .... 4·25   4·50
Set of 5 Gutter Pairs.. 9·50
First Day Cover ....   5·00
Presentation Pack (P.O. Pack No. 232)....................... 5·00
PHQ Cards (set of 5) (148)....................................... 3·00   7·50
       Booklet pane No. 1634a comes from a special £3 Christmas booklet
and has margins at left, top and bottom.

Special First Day of Issue Postmarks

Philatelic Bureau, Edinburgh ....5·00
Bethlehem, Llandeilo, Dyfed ....5·00
Pangbourne ....5·50

Collectors Pack 1992
1992 (10 Nov). Comprises Nos. 1587/91, 1602/10 and 1615/38.
CP1638a Collectors Pack... 32·00

Post Office Yearbook
1992 (11 Nov). Comprises Nos. 1587/91, 1602/10
and 1615/38 in hardbound book with slip case,
illustrated in colour .... 50·00

1069 Mute Swan Cob   **1070** Cygnet and
and St. Catherine's   Decoy
Chapel, Abbotsbury

1071 Swans and Cygnet   **1072** Eggs in Nest and
                             Tithe Barn, Abbotsbury

1073 Young Swan and
the Fleet

(Des D. Gentleman)

1993 (19 Jan). *600th Anniv of Abbotsbury Swannery.* One phosphor band
(18p.) or phosphorised paper (others). *P* 14×15.

1639	**1069**	18p. gold, greenish yellow, bistre, green, vermilion and black	1·25	70
1640	**1070**	24p. gold, cream, brt green, grey-brown, dull blue and grey-black	1·10	70
1641	**1071**	28p. gold, greenish grey, yellow-brown, myrtle-green, brown, vermilion and black	1·40	2·25
1642	**1072**	33p. gold, ochre, apple-green, olive-brown, brt orange and grey-black	1·75	2·50
1643	**1073**	39p. gold, cream, brt green, cobalt, lt brown and black	1·90	2·50
Set of 5			6·50	8·00
Set of 5 Gutter Pairs			15·00	
First Day Cover				8·50
Presentation Pack (P.O. Pack No. 234)			7·00	
PHQ Cards (set of 5) (149)			4·25	8·50

Special First Day of Issue Postmarks

Philatelic Bureau, Edinburgh ....8·50
Abbotsbury, Dorset ....8·50

1074 Long John Silver and
Parrot (*Treasure Island*)

1075 Tweedledum and
Tweedledee (*Alice Through
the Looking-Glass*)

1076 William (*William* books)

1077 Mole and Toad (*The Wind
in the Willows*)

1078 Teacher and Wilfrid ("*The
Bash Street Kids*")

1079 Peter Rabbit and Mrs.
Rabbit (*The Tale of Peter Rabbit*)

1080 Snowman (*The Snowman*)
and Father Christmas (*Father
Christmas*)

1081 The Big Friendly Giant
and Sophie (*The BFG*)

1082 Bill Badger and Rupert Bear

1083 Aladdin and the Genie

(Des Newell and Sorell)

1993 (2 Feb–10 Aug). *Greetings Stamps. Gift Giving.* Two phosphor
bands. *P* 15×14 (with one elliptical hole in each horizontal side).

1644	**1074**	(1st) gold, greenish yellow, magenta, pale brown, light blue and black	1·25	1·00
		a. Booklet pane. Nos. 1644/53	14·00	12·00
1645	**1075**	(1st) gold, cream and black	1·25	1·00
1646	**1076**	(1st) gold, greenish yellow, magenta, cream and new blue and black	1·25	1·00
1647	**1077**	(1st) gold, greenish yellow, magenta, cream and new blue and black	1·25	1·00
1648	**1078**	(1st) gold, greenish yellow, magenta, cream and new blue and black	1·25	1·00
1649	**1079**	(1st) gold, greenish yellow, magenta, cream and new blue and black	1·25	1·00
		a. gold, greenish yellow, magenta, cream, bright lilac and black (10 Aug)	1·40	1·40
		b. Booklet pane. No. 1649a×4 with margins all round (10 Aug)	5·00	
1650	**1080**	(1st) gold, greenish yellow, magenta, cream and new blue and black	1·25	1·00
1651	**1081**	(1st) gold, greenish yellow, magenta, cream and new blue and black	1·25	1·00
1652	**1082**	(1st) gold, greenish yellow, magenta, cream and new blue and black	1·25	1·00
1653	**1083**	(1st) gold, greenish yellow, magenta, cream and new blue and black	1·25	1·00
Set of 10			14·00	12·00
First Day Cover				13·00
Presentation Pack (P.O. Pack No. G2)			16·00	
PHQ Cards (set of 10) (GS1)			16·00	30·00

Nos. 1644/53 were issued in £2·40 booklets, No. KX5 (*sold at £2·50
from 1 November 1993*), together with a pane of 20 half stamp-sized
labels. The stamps and labels were affixed to the booklet cover by a
common gutter margin

No. 1649a and booklet pane 1649b come from the £6 (£5·64)
"Beatrix Potter" booklet No. DX15.

> **SET PRICES.** Please note that set prices for booklet greetings
> stamps are for complete panes. Sets of single stamps are worth
> considerably less.

Special First Day of Issue Postmarks

Philatelic Bureau, Edinburgh (No. 1644a) (2 Feb) ....13·00
Greetland (No. 1644a) (2 Feb) ....13·00
Philatelic Bureau, Edinburgh (No. 1649a) (10 Aug)........................6·00
Keswick (No. 1649a) (10 Aug)...6·00

1084 Decorated Enamel Dial

1085 Escapement, Remontoire and Fusée

1086 Balance, Spring and Temperature Compensator

1087 Back of Movement

(Des H. Brown and D. Penny. Litho Questa)

1993 (16 Feb). *300th Birth Anniv of John Harrison (inventor of the marine chronometer).* Details of 'H4' Clock. Phosphorised paper. P 14½×14.

1654	**1084**	24p. new blue, greenish yellow, magenta, black, grey-black and pale cream..........	60	60
1655	**1085**	28p. new blue, greenish yellow, magenta, black, grey-black and pale cream..........	1·00	1·25
1656	**1086**	33p. new blue, greenish yellow, magenta, black, grey-black and pale cream..........	1·40	1·25
1657	**1087**	39p. new blue, greenish yellow, magenta, black, grey-black and pale cream..........	1·50	1·50
Set of 4			4·00	4·00
Set of 4 Gutter Pairs			9·00	
First Day Cover				4·50
Presentation Pack (P.O. Pack No. 235)....			4·50	
PHQ Cards (set of 4) (150)			4·25	7·00

Special First Day of Issue Postmarks

Philatelic Bureau, Edinburgh ....4·50
Greenwich...4·75

1088 Britannia

(Des B. Craddock, adapted Roundel Design Group. Litho (silver die-stamped, Braille symbol for "TEN" embossed) Questa)

1993 (2 Mar). *Granite paper.* P 14×14½ (with two elliptical holes in each horizontal side).

1658	**1088**	£10 greenish grey, rosine, yellow, new blue, reddish violet, vermilion, violet, brt green and silver..........	40·00	12·00
		a. Silver omitted..................................	£6500	
		b. Braille symbol for "TEN" omitted	£4000	
First Day Cover				25·00
Presentation Pack (P.O. Pack No. 28)			45·00	
PHQ Card (D1)			8·00	60·00

The paper used for No. 1658 contains fluorescent coloured fibres which, together with the ink used on the shield, react under U.V. light.

Special First Day of Issue Postmarks

Philatelic Bureau, Edinburgh ....26·00
Windsor...28·00

1089 Dendrobium hellwigianum

1090 Paphiopedilum Maudiae "Magnificum"

1091 Cymbidium lowianum

1092 Vanda Rothschildiana

1093 Dendrobium vexillarius var albiviride

(Des Pandora Sellars)

1993 (16 Mar). *14th World Orchid Conference, Glasgow.* One phosphor band (18p.) or phosphorised paper (others). P 15×14.

1659	**1089**	18p. green, greenish yellow, magenta, pale blue, apple-green and slate	45	40
		a. Imperf (pair)...................................	£8500	
1660	**1090**	24p. green, greenish yellow, brt green and grey-black..........	75	60
1661	**1091**	28p. green, greenish yellow, red, brt turquoise-blue and drab..........	1·00	1·25
1662	**1092**	33p. green, greenish yellow, pale magenta, brt violet, brt green and grey..........	1·25	1·50
		a. Copyright logo and "1993" omitted (R. 10/6, dot pane)..........	15·00	15·00
1663	**1093**	39p. green, greenish yellow, red, pale olive-yellow, brt green, violet and grey-black..........	1·60	1·50
Set of 5			4·50	4·75
Set of 5 Gutter Pairs			10·00	
First Day Cover				5·25
Presentation Pack (P.O. Pack No. 236)....			5·00	
PHQ Cards (set of 5) (151)			4·50	7·00

Philatelic Bureau, Edinburgh	5·25
Glasgow	5·50

For Nos. 1664/72 and Y1667/1803 see Decimal Machin Definitives section.

1094 "Family Group" (bronze sculpture) (Henry Moore)

1095 "Kew Gardens" (lithograph) (Edward Bawden)

1096 "St. Francis and the Birds" (Stanley Spencer)

1097 "Still Life: Odyssey I" (Ben Nicholson)

(Des. A. Dastor)

1993 (11 May). *Europa. Contemporary Art.* Phosphorised paper. P 14×14½.

1767	**1094**	24p. brownish grey, lemon, magenta, turquoise-blue and grey-black	60	60
1768	**1095**	28p. brownish grey, buff, lt green, yellow-brown, brt orange, new blue and grey-black	90	1·00
1769	**1096**	33p. brownish grey, cream, greenish yellow, magenta, new blue and grey-black	1·25	1·40
1770	**1097**	39p. brownish grey, cream, yellow-ochre, rose-lilac, red, lt blue and grey-black	1·75	1·75
Set of 4			4·00	4·25
Set of 4 Gutter Pairs			9·00	
First Day Cover				4·75
Presentation Pack (P.O. Pack No. 237)			4·50	
PHQ Cards (set of 4) (152)			4·00	7·00

British Philatelic Bureau, Edinburgh	4·75
London SW	5·00

1098 Emperor Claudius (from gold coin)

1099 Emperor Hadrian (bronze head)

1100 Goddess Roma (from gemstone)

1101 Christ (Hinton St. Mary mosaic)

(Des J. Gibbs)

1993 (15 June). *Roman Britain.* Phosphorised paper with two phosphor bands. P 14×14½.

1771	**1098**	24p. black, pale orange, lt brown and silver	60	50
1772	**1099**	28p. black, greenish yellow, brt rose-red, silver, brt blue and grey-black	90	1·00
1773	**1100**	33p. black, greenish yellow, brt rose-red, silver and grey	1·30	1·50
1774	**1101**	39p. black, greenish yellow, rosine, silver, pale violet and grey	1·50	1·60
Set of 4			4·00	4·25
Set of 4 Gutter Pairs			9·00	
First Day Cover				4·75
Presentation Pack (P.O. Pack No. 238)			4·50	
PHQ Cards (set of 4) (153)			4·25	7·00

British Philatelic Bureau, Edinburgh	4·75
Caerllion	4·75

1102 *Midland Maid* and other Narrow Boats, Grand Junction Canal

1103 *Yorkshire Lass* and other Humber Keels, Stainforth and Keadby Canal

1104 *Valley Princess* and other Horse-drawn Barges, Brecknock and Abergavenny Canal

1105 Steam Barges, including *Pride of Scotland*, and Fishing Boats, Crinan Canal

(Des T. Lewery. Litho Questa)

1993 (20 July). *Inland Waterways.* Two phosphor bands. P 14½×14.

1775	**1102**	24p. new blue, greenish yellow, brt magenta, black, blue, vermilion, brownish grey and sage-green	50	50
1776	**1103**	28p. new blue, greenish yellow, brt magenta, black, blue, bluish grey, vermilion and sage-green	1·00	1·00
1777	**1104**	33p. new blue, greenish yellow, brt magenta, black, blue, vermilion, greenish grey and sage-green	1·25	1·25
1778	**1105**	39p. new blue, greenish yellow, brt magenta, black, blue, vermilion, sage-green and dull mauve	1·50	1·40
Set of 4			3·75	3·75
Set of 4 Gutter Pairs			8·50	
First Day Cover				4·25
Presentation Pack (P.O. Pack No. 239)			4·50	
PHQ Cards (set of 4) (154)			4·25	7·00

Nos. 1775/8 commemorate the bicentenary of the Acts of Parliament authorising the canals depicted.

Special First Day of Issue Postmarks

British Philatelic Bureau, Edinburgh .... 4·25
Gloucester .... 4·50

1106 Horse Chestnut   **1107** Blackberry

1108 Hazel   **1109** Rowan

1110 Pear

SHERLOCK HOLMES & DR.WATSON
"THE REIGATE SQUIRE"
1111 *The Reigate Squire*

SHERLOCK HOLMES & SIR HENRY
"THE HOUND OF THE BASKERVILLES"
1112 *The Hound of the Baskervilles*

SHERLOCK HOLMES & LESTRADE
"THE SIX NAPOLEONS"
1113 *The Six Napoleons*

SHERLOCK HOLMES & MYCROFT
" THE GREEK INTERPRETER"
1114 *The Greek Interpreter*

SHERLOCK HOLMES & MORIARTY
"THE FINAL PROBLEM"
1115 *The Final Problem*

(Des Charlotte Knox)

1993 (14 Sept). *The Four Seasons. Autumn. Fruits and Leaves.* One phosphor band (18p.) or phosphorised paper (others). P 15×14.

1779	**1106**	18p. black, greenish yellow, cerise, brt green, gold and chestnut..................	50	30
1780	**1107**	24p. black, lemon, cerise, myrtle-green, gold, brt green and brown..............	75	50
1781	**1108**	28p. grey, lemon, emerald, lake-brown and gold	1·10	1·25
1782	**1109**	33p. grey-black, greenish yellow, rosine, lt green, gold and brown	1·40	1·50
1783	**1110**	39p. myrtle-green, greenish yellow, rosine, olive-sepia, gold, apple-green and dp myrtle-green...............	1·50	1·50
Set of 5			4·75	4·50
Set of 5 Gutter Pairs...			10·50	
First Day Cover				5·00
Presentation Pack (P.O. Pack No. 240).............			5·00	
PHQ Cards (set of 5) (155)...............................			4·50	7·00

(Des A. Davidson. Litho Questa)

1993 (12 Oct). *Sherlock Holmes. Centenary of the Publication of 'The Final Problem'* Phosphorised paper. P 14×14½.

1784	**1111**	24p. new blue, greenish yellow, magenta, black and gold..................	50	60
		a. Horiz strip of 5. Nos. 1784/8	5·00	5·25
1785	**1112**	24p. new blue, greenish yellow, magenta, black and gold..................	50	60
1786	**1113**	24p. new blue, greenish yellow, magenta, black and gold..................	50	60
1787	**1114**	24p. new blue, greenish yellow, magenta, black and gold..................	50	60
1788	**1115**	24p. new blue, greenish yellow, magenta, black and gold..................	50	60
Set of 5			5·00	5·25
Gutter strip of 10..			11·00	
First Day Cover				5·75
Presentation Pack (P.O. Pack No. 241).............			5·50	
PHQ Cards (set of 5) (156)...............................			4·50	10·00

Nos. 1784/8 were printed together, *se-tenant*, in horizontal strips of five throughout the sheet.

Special First Day of Issue Postmarks

British Philatelic Bureau, Edinburgh...5·00
Taunton ....5·25

Special First Day of Issue Postmarks

British Philatelic Bureau, Edinburgh ....6·00
London NW1 ....7·50

A First Day of Issue handstamp was provided at Autumn Stampex, London SW1, for this issue.

For No. 1789 see Decimal Machin Definitives section.

1117 Bob Cratchit and Tiny Tim

1118 Mr. and Mrs. Fezziwig

1119 Scrooge

1120 The Prize Turkey

1121 Mr. Scrooge's Nephew

(Des Q. Blake)

1993 (9 Nov). *Christmas. 150th Anniv of Publication of 'A Christmas Carol' by Charles Dickens.* One phosphor band (19p.) or phosphorised paper (others). P 15×14.

1790	1117	19p. new blue, yellow, magenta, salmon, brt emerald and grey-black	60	40
		a. Imperf (pair)	£10000	
1791	1118	25p. yellow-orange, brown-lilac, steel-blue, lake-brown, lt green, grey-black and black	90	60
1792	1119	30p. cerise, bistre-yellow, dull blue, brown-rose, pale green, grey-black and black	1·25	1·50
1793	1120	35p. dp turquoise-green, lemon, vermilion, dull ultramarine, Indian red, bluish grey and black	1·40	1·60
1794	1121	41p. reddish purple, lemon, purple, lt blue, salmon, brt green and black	1·40	1·60
Set of 5			4·50	5·25
Set of 5 Gutter Pairs			10·00	
First Day Cover				5·75
Presentation Pack (P.O. Pack No. 242)			5·00	
PHQ Cards (set of 5) (157)			4·50	8·00

Special First Day of Issue Postmarks

British Philatelic Bureau, Edinburgh ....5·75
Bethlehem, Llandeilo ....5·75

A First Day of Issue handstamp (pictorial) was provided at the City of London for this issue.

Collectors Pack 1993
1993 (9 Nov). Comprises Nos. 1639/43, 1654/7, 1659/63, 1767/88 and 1790/4.
CP1794*a* Collectors Pack.. 45·00

Post Office Yearbook
1993 (9 Nov). Comprises Nos. 1639/43, 1654/7, 1659/63, 1767/88 *and* 1790/4 in hardbound book with slip case, illustrated in colour .... 85·00

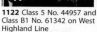
1122 Class 5 No. 44957 and Class B1 No. 61342 on West Highland Line

1123 Class A1 No. 60149 *Amadis* at Kings Cross

1124 Class 4 No. 43000 on Turntable at Blyth North

1125 Class 4 No. 42455 near Wigan Central

1126 Class "Castle" No. 7002 *Devizes Castle* on Bridge crossing Worcester and Birmingham Canal

(Des B. Delaney)

1994 (18 Jan). *The Age of Steam. Railway Photographs by Colin Gifford.* One phosphor band (19p.) or phosphorised paper with two bands (others). P 14½.

1795	1122	19p. dp blue-green, grey-black & black	55	45
1796	1123	25p. slate-lilac, grey-black and black	90	95
1797	1124	30p. lake-brown, grey-black & black	1·40	1·50
1798	1125	35p. dp claret, grey-black and black	1·75	1·80
1799	1126	41p. indigo, grey-black and black	1·80	1·90
Set of 5			6·00	6·00
Set of 5 Gutter Pairs			13·00	
First Day Cover				6·50
Presentation Pack (P.O. Pack No. 244)			6·50	
PHQ Cards (set of 5) (158)			5·75	17·00

Nos. 1796/9 are on phosphorised paper and also show two phosphor bands.

Special First Day of Issue Postmarks

Philatelic Bureau, Edinburgh ....7·00
York...7·00

A First Day of Issue handstamp (pictorial) was provided at Bridge of Orchy for this issue.

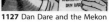
1127 Dan Dare and the Mekon

1128 The Three Bears

1129 Rupert Bear

1130 Alice (Alice in Wonderland)

1131 Noggin and the Ice Dragon

1132 Peter Rabbit posting Letter

1133 Red Riding Hood and the Wolf

1134 Orlando Marmalade Cat

1135 Biggles

1136 Paddington Bear on Station

(Des Newell and Sorrell)

1994 (1 Feb). *Greetings Stamps. 'Messages'* Two phosphor bands. P 15×14 (with one elliptical hole in each vertical side).

1800	**1127**	(1st) gold, greenish yellow, brt purple, bistre-yellow, new blue and black..	1·25	1·00
		a. Booklet pane. Nos. 1800/9..............	15·00	15·00
1801	**1128**	(1st) gold, greenish yellow, brt purple, bistre-yellow, new blue and black..	1·25	1·00
1802	**1129**	(1st) gold, greenish yellow, brt purple, bistre-yellow, new blue and black..	1·25	1·00
1803	**1130**	(1st) gold, bistre-yellow and black..........	1·25	1·00
1804	**1131**	(1st) gold, greenish yellow, brt purple, bistre-yellow, new blue and black..	1·25	1·00
1805	**1132**	(1st) gold, greenish yellow, brt purple, bistre-yellow, new blue and black..	1·25	1·00
1806	**1133**	(1st) gold, greenish yellow, brt purple, bistre-yellow, new blue and black..	1·25	1·00
1807	**1134**	(1st) gold, greenish yellow, brt purple, bistre-yellow, new blue and black..	1·25	1·00
1808	**1135**	(1st) gold, greenish yellow, brt purple, bistre-yellow, new blue and black..	1·25	1·00
1809	**1136**	(1st) gold, greenish yellow, brt purple, bistre-yellow, new blue and black..	1·25	1·00
Set of 10........			15·00	15·00
First Day Cover				16·00
Presentation Pack (P.O. Pack No. G3)............			18·00	
PHQ Cards (set of 10) (GS2)...................			16·00	30·00

Nos. 1800/9 were issued in £2·50 stamp booklets, No. KX6 (*sold at £2·60 from 8 July 1996*), together with a pane of 20 half stampsized labels

The stamps and labels were attached to the booklet cover by a common gutter margin.

Special First Day of Issue Postmarks

British Philatelic Bureau, Edinburgh.......................................16·00
Penn, Wolverhampton...16·00

1137 Castell Y Waun (Chirk Castle), Clwyd, Wales

1138 Ben Arkle, Sutherland, Scotland

1139 Mourne Mountains, County Down, Northern Ireland

1140 Dersingham, Norfolk, England

1141 Dolwyddelan, Gwynedd, Wales

1994 (1 Mar – 26 July). *25th Anniv of Investiture of the Prince of Wales. Paintings by Prince Charles.* One phosphor band (19p.) or phosphorised paper (others). P 15×14.

1810	**1137**	19p. grey-black, greenish yellow, magenta, new blue, black & silver .	55	40
1811	**1138**	25p. grey-black, orange-yellow, brt magenta, new blue, silver & black.	1·00	60
1812	**1139**	30p. grey-black, greenish yellow, magenta, new blue, silver & black .	1·10	1·50
		a. Booklet pane. No. 1812×4 with margins all round (26 July)..............	5·00	
1813	**1140**	35p. grey-black, greenish yellow, magenta, new blue, silver & black .	1·40	1·75
1814	**1141**	41p. grey-black, lemon, magenta, new blue, silver & black..............	1·50	1·75
Set of 5			5·00	5·50
Set of 5 Gutter Pairs.................			11·00	
First Day Cover				6·00
Presentation Pack (P.O. Pack No. 245)...........			5·50	
PHQ Cards (set of 5) (159)			5·75	11·50

Booklet pane No. 1812a comes from the £6·04 "Northern Ireland" booklet No. DX16.

Special First Day of Issue Postmarks

British Philatelic Bureau, Edinburgh..6·00
Caernarfon..6·00

1142 Bather at Blackpool

1143 "Where's my Little Lad?"

1144 "Wish You were Here!"

1145 Punch and Judy Show

1146 "The Tower Crane" Machine

(Des M. Dempsey and B. Dare. Litho Questa)

1994 (12 Apr). *Centenary of Picture Postcards.* One side band (19p.) or two phosphor bands (others). P 14×14½.

1815	**1142**	19p. new blue, greenish yellow, magenta & black	60	40
1816	**1143**	25p. new blue, greenish yellow, magenta & black	90	60
1817	**1144**	30p. new blue, greenish yellow, magenta & black	1·10	1·50
1818	**1145**	35p. new blue, greenish yellow, magenta & black	1·40	1·75
1819	**1146**	41p. new blue, greenish yellow, magenta & black	1·50	1·75
Set of 5			5·00	5·50
Set of 5 Gutter Pairs			11·00	
First Day Cover				6·00
Presentation Pack (P.O. Pack No. 246)			5·50	
PHQ Cards (set of 5) (160)			5·75	11·50

Special First Day of Issue Postmarks

British Philatelic Bureau, Edinburgh		6·00
Blackpool		6·00

1147 British Lion and French Cockerel over Tunnel

1148 Symbolic Hands over Train

(Des G. Hardie (T **1147**), J.-P. Cousin (T **1148**))

1994 (3 May). *Opening of Channel Tunnel.* Phosphorised paper. P 14×14½.

1820	**1147**	25p. ultramarine, brt orange, scarlet, new blue, emerald, turquoise-blue & silver	75	60
		a. Horiz pair. Nos. 1820/1	1·75	2·00
1821	**1148**	25p. ultramarine, scarlet, new blue, emerald & silver	75	60
1822	**1147**	41p. new blue, brt orange, scarlet, turquoise-blue, emerald, ultramarine & silver	1·00	1·00
		a. Horiz pair. Nos. 1822/3	3·25	2·50
		ab. Imperf (horiz pair)	£6000	
1823	**1148**	41p. ultramarine, scarlet, new blue, emerald & silver	1·00	1·00
Set of 4			4·50	4·75
First Day Cover				5·25
First Day Covers (2) (UK and French stamps)				20·00
Presentation Pack (P.O. Pack No. 247)			5·00	
Presentation Pack (UK and French Stamps)			25·00	
Souvenir Book			50·00	
PHQ Cards (set of 4) (161)			5·75	9·00

Nos. 1820/1 and 1822/3 were printed together, *se-tenant*, in horizontal pairs throughout the sheets.

Stamps in similar designs were also issued by France. These are included in the joint presentation pack and souvenir book.

Special First Day of Issue Postmarks

British Philatelic Bureau, Edinburgh		5·50
Folkestone		8·00

1149 Groundcrew replacing Smoke Canisters on Douglas Boston of 88 Sqn

1150 H.M.S. *Warspite* (battleship) shelling Enemy Positions

1151 Commandos landing on Gold Beach

1152 Infantry regrouping on Sword Beach

1153 Tank and Infantry advancing, Ouistreham

(Des K. Bassford from contemporary photographs. Litho Questa)

1994 (6 June). *50th Anniv of D-Day.* Two phosphor bands. P 14½×14.

1824	**1149**	25p. pink, greenish yellow, blackish lilac, slate-black, brt scarlet & silver-grey	60	60
		a. Horiz strip of 5. Nos. 1824/8	4·25	5·00

1825	**1150**	25p. pink. greenish yellow, blackish lilac, slate-black, brt scarlet & silver-grey	60	60
1826	**1151**	25p. pink. greenish yellow, blackish lilac, slate-black, brt scarlet & silver-grey	60	60
1827	**1152**	25p. pink. greenish yellow, blackish lilac, slate-black, brt scarlet & silver-grey	60	60
1828	**1153**	25p. pink. greenish yellow, blackish lilac, slate-black, brt scarlet & silver-grey	60	60

Set of 5	4·25	5·00
Gutter block of 10	9·50	
First Day Cover		5·50
Presentation Pack (P.O. Pack No. 248)	5·50	
PHQ Cards (set of 5) (162)	5·00	11·50

Nos. 1824/8 were printed together, *se-tenant*, in horizontal strips of five throughout the sheet.

Special First Day of Issue Postmarks

British Philatelic Bureau, Edinburgh	5·50
Portsmouth	5·50

1154 The Old Course, St. Andrews

1155 The 18th Hole, Muirfield

1156 The 15th Hole ("Luckyslap"), Carnoustie

1157 The 8th Hole ("The Postage Stamp"), Royal Troon

1158 The 9th Hole, Turnberry

(Des P. Hogarth)

1994 (5 July). *Scottish Golf Courses.* One phosphor band (19p.) or phosphorised paper (others). P 14½×14.

1829	**1154**	19p. yellow-green, olive-grey, orange-vermilion, apple-green, blue & grey-black	50	40
1830	**1155**	25p. yellow-green, lemon, brt orange, apple-green, blue, magenta & grey-black	75	60
1831	**1156**	30p. yellow-green, yellow, rosine, emerald, blue-green, new blue & grey-black	1·10	1·40
1832	**1157**	35p. yellow-green, yellow, rosine, apple-green, new blue, dull blue & grey-black	1·25	1·40
1833	**1158**	41p. yellow-green, lemon, magenta, apple-green, dull blue, new blue & grey-black	1·40	1·40
Set of 5			4·50	4·75

Set of 5 Gutter Pairs	10·00	
First Day Cover		5·25
Presentation Pack (P.O. Pack No. 249)	5·00	
PHQ Cards (set of 5) (163)	5·75	11·50

Nos. 1829/33 commemorate the 250th anniversary of golf's first set of rules produced by the Honourable Company of Edinburgh Golfers.

Special First Day of Issue Postmarks

British Philatelic Bureau, Edinburgh	5·00
Turnberry	5·50

1159 Royal Welsh Show, Llanelwedd

1160 All England Tennis Championships, Wimbledon

1161 Cowes Week

1162 Test Match, Lord's

1163 Braemar Gathering

(Des M. Cook)

1994 (2 Aug). *The Four Seasons. Summertime.* One phosphor band (19p.) or phosphorised paper (others). P 15×14.

1834	**1159**	19p. black, greenish yellow, brt magenta, brown, yellow-brown & new blue	50	40
1835	**1160**	25p. black, greenish yellow, magenta, reddish violet, yellow-green, myrtle-green & new blue	75	60
1836	**1161**	30p. black, greenish yellow, brt magenta, yellow-ochre, dp slate-blue, blue-green & blue	1·10	1·25
1837	**1162**	35p. black, greenish yellow, magenta, slate-lilac, yellow-green, dp bluish green & brt blue	1·25	1·60
1838	**1163**	41p. black, greenish yellow, brt magenta, dp claret, lt brown, myrtle-green & brt blue	1·40	1·60
Set of 5			4·50	5·00

Set of 5 Gutter Pairs	10·00	
First Day Cover		5·50
Presentation Pack (P.O. Pack No. 250)	5·00	
PHQ Cards (set of 5) (164)	5·75	11·50

Special First Day of Issue Postmarks

British Philatelic Bureau, Edinburgh	5·00
Wimbledon	5·00

1164 Ultrasonic Imaging

1165 Scanning Electron Microscopy

1166 Magnetic Resonance Imaging

1167 Computed Tomography

(Des P. Vermier and J.-P. Tibbles. Gravure Enschedé)

1994 (27 Sept). *Europa. Medical Discoveries.* Phosphorised paper. P 14×14½.

1839	**1164**	25p. greenish yellow, brt magenta, new blue, black & silver	75	60
		a. Imperf (vert pair)	£9250	
1840	**1165**	30p. greenish yellow, brt magenta, new blue, black & silver	1·00	1·25
1841	**1166**	35p. greenish yellow, brt magenta, new blue, black & silver	1·50	1·75
1842	**1167**	41p. greenish yellow, brt magenta, new blue, black & silver	1·75	1·75
Set of 4			4·50	4·75
Set of 4 Gutter Pairs			10·00	
First Day Cover				5·25
Presentation Pack (P.O. Pack No. 251)			5·00	
PHQ Cards (set of 4) (165)			5·75	10·00

Special First Day of Issue Postmarks

British Philatelic Bureau, Edinburgh	5·25
Cambridge	5·25

1168 Mary and Joseph

1169 Three Wise Men

1170 Mary with Doll

1171 Shepherds

1172 Angels

(Des Yvonne Gilbert)

1994 (1 Nov). *Christmas. Children's Nativity Plays.* One phosphor band (19p.) or phosphorised paper (others). P 15×14.

1843	**1168**	19p. turquoise-green, greenish yellow, brt magenta, new blue, dull blue & grey-black	50	40
		a. Imperf (pair)	£175	
1844	**1169**	25p. orange-brown, greenish yellow, brt magenta, new blue, lt blue, bistre & grey-black	75	60
1845	**1170**	30p. lt brown, greenish yellow, brt magenta, blue, turquoise-blue, new blue & brownish grey	1·00	1·50
		a. Imperf (pair)	£25000	
1846	**1171**	35p. dp grey-brown, greenish yellow, brt magenta, turquoise-blue, dull violet-blue, ochre & brown	1·25	1·50
1847	**1172**	41p. blue, greenish yellow, brt magenta, turquoise-blue, lt blue & dp grey	1·50	1·75
Set of 5			4·50	5·25
Set of 5 Gutter Pairs			10·50	
First Day Cover				5·75
Presentation Pack (P.O. Pack No. 252)			5·00	
PHQ Cards (set of 5) (166)			5·75	11·50

Special First Day of Issue Postmarks

British Philatelic Bureau, Edinburgh	5·00
Bethlehem, Llandeilo	5·00

Collectors Pack 1994
1994 (14 Nov). Comprises Nos. 1795/1847.
CP1847a Collectors Pack		48·00

Post Office Yearbook
1994 (14 Nov). Comprises Nos. 1795/9 *and* 1810/47 *in* hardbound book with slip case, illustrated in colour .... 50·00

1173 Sophie (black cat)

1174 Puskas (Siamese) and Tigger (tabby)

1175 Chloe (ginger cat)

1176 Kikko (tortoiseshell) and Rosie (Abyssinian)

1177 Fred (black and white cat)

(Des Elizabeth Blackadder. Litho Questa)

1995 (17 Jan). *Cats.* One phosphor band (19p.) or two phosphor bands (others). P 14½×14.

1848	**1173**	19p. new blue, greenish yellow, magenta, black & brown-red	75	40
1849	**1174**	25p. new blue, greenish yellow, magenta, black & dull yellow-green	75	60

1850	1175	30p. new blue, greenish yellow, magenta, black & yellow-brown......	1·00	1·50
1851	1176	35p. new blue, greenish yellow, magenta, black & yellow..............	1·25	1·50
1852	1177	41p. new blue, greenish yellow, magenta, black & reddish orange ..	1·50	1·50
Set of 5			4·75	5·00
Set of 5 Gutter Pairs............................			11·00	
First Day Cover				5·50
Presentation Pack (P.O. Pack No. 254)............			5·50	
PHQ Cards (set of 5) (167)			6·00	11·50

Special First Day of Issue Postmarks

British Philatelic Bureau, Edinburgh........................	5·50
Kitts Green	5·50

1178 Dandelions   **1179** Chestnut Leaves

1180 Garlic Leaves   **1181** Hazel Leaves

1182 Spring Grass

1995 (14 Mar). *The Four Seasons. Springtime.* Plant Sculptures by Andy Goldsworthy. One phosphor band (19p.) or two phosphor bands (others). *P* 15×14.

1853	1178	19p. silver, greenish yellow, magenta, green & grey-black	75	40
1854	1179	25p. silver, greenish yellow, magenta, new blue & black	75	60
1855	1180	30p. silver, greenish yellow, magenta, new blue & black	1·00	1·50
1856	1181	35p. silver, greenish yellow, magenta, new blue & black	1·25	1·50
1857	1182	41p. silver, greenish yellow, magenta, new blue, blue-green & black	1·50	1·75
Set of 5			4·75	5·25
Set of 5 Gutter Pairs............................			11·00	
First Day Cover				5·75
Presentation Pack (P.O. Pack No. 255)............			5·50	
PHQ Cards (set of 5) (168)			6·00	11·50

Special First Day of Issue Postmarks

British Philatelic Bureau, Edinburgh........................	5·75
Springfield	5·75

1183 "La Danse à la Campagne" (Renoir)

1184 "Troilus and Criseyde" (Peter Brookes)

1185 "The Kiss" (Rodin)

1186 "Girls on the Town" (Beryl Cook)

1187 "Jazz" (Andrew Mockett)

1188 "Girls performing a Kathak Dance" (Aurangzeb period)

1189 "Keppel with her Daughter" (Alice Hughes)

1190 "Children Playing" (L. S. Lowry)

1191 "Circus Clowns" (Emily Firmin and Justin Mitchell)

1192 Decoration from "All the Love Poems of Shakespeare" (Eric Gill)

(Des Newell and Sorrell. Litho Walsall)

1995 (21 Mar). *Greetings Stamps. 'Greetings in Art'.* Two phosphor bands. *P* 14½×14 (with one elliptical hole in each vertical side).

1858	1183	(1st) greenish yellow, new blue, magenta, black & silver	1·25	1·00
		a. Booklet pane. Nos. 1858/67	14·00	14·00
		ab. Silver (Queen's head and "1ST") and phosphor omitted	£16000	
1859	1184	(1st) greenish yellow, new blue, magenta, black & silver	1·25	1·00
1860	1185	(1st) greenish yellow, new blue, magenta, black & silver	1·25	1·00
1861	1186	(1st) greenish yellow, new blue, magenta, black & silver	1·25	1·00
1862	1187	(1st) greenish yellow, new blue, magenta, black & silver	1·25	1·00
1863	1188	(1st) greenish yellow, new blue, magenta, black & silver	1·25	1·00
1864	1189	(1st) purple-brown & silver	1·25	1·00
1865	1190	(1st) greenish yellow, new blue, magenta, black & silver	1·25	1·00
1866	1191	(1st) greenish yellow, new blue, magenta, black & silver	1·25	1·00
1867	1192	(1st) black, greenish yellow & silver	1·25	1·00
Set of 10			14·00	14·00
First Day Cover				15·00
Presentation Pack (P.O. Pack No. G4)............			15·00	
PHQ Cards (set of 10) (GS3)			16·00	30·00

Nos. 1858/67 were issued in £2·50 stamp booklets, No. KX7 (*sold at £2·60 from 8 July 1996*), together with a pane of 20 half stampsized labels

The stamps and labels were attached to the booklet cover by a common gutter margin.

No. 1858ab exists on first day covers bearing the Philatelic Bureau Edinburgh First Day of Issue postmark.

Special First Day of Issue Postmarks

British Philatelic Bureau, Edinburgh ....15·00
Lover ....15·00

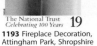

1193 Fireplace Decoration, Attingham Park, Shropshire

1194 Oak Seedling

1195 Carved Table Leg, Attingham Park

1196 St. David's Head, Dyfed, Wales

1197 Elizabethan Window, Little Moreton Hall, Cheshire

(Des T. Evans)

1995 (11–25 Apr). *Centenary of The National Trust.* One phosphor band (19p.), two phosphor bands (25p., 35p.) or phosphorised paper (30p., 41p.). *P* 14×15.

1868	**1193**	19p. grey-green, stone, grey-brown, grey-black & gold..................................	60	40
1869	**1194**	25p. grey-green, greenish yellow, magenta, new blue, gold & black...	80	60
		a. Booklet pane. No. 1869×6 with margins all round (25 Apr)................	4·50	
1870	**1195**	30p. grey-green, greenish yellow, magenta, new blue, gold, black & slate-black..	1·00	1·50
1871	**1196**	35p. grey-green, greenish yellow, magenta, blue, gold & black.............	1·25	1·50
1872	**1197**	41p. grey-green, greenish yellow, brt green, slate-green, gold, blackish brown & black....................................	1·40	1·75
Set of 5			4·50	5·25
Set of 5 Gutter Pairs.......................................			10·50	
First Day Cover..				5·75
Presentation Pack (P.O. Pack No. 256)........			5·00	
PHQ Cards (set of 5) (169)............................			6·00	11·50

Booklet pane No. 1869a comes from the £6 "National Trust" booklet No. DX17.

Special First Day of Issue Postmarks

British Philatelic Bureau, Edinburgh...5·75
Alfriston ....5·75

1198 British Troops and French Civilians celebrating

1199 Symbolic Hands and Red Cross

1200 St. Paul's Cathedral and Searchlights

1201 Symbolic Hand releasing Peace Dove

1202 Symbolic Hands

(Des J. Gorham (Nos. 1873, 1875), J-M. Folon (others))

1995 (2 May). *Europa. Peace and Freedom.* One phosphor band (Nos. 1873/4) or two phosphor bands (others). *P* 14½×14.

1873	**1198**	19p. silver, bistre-brown & grey-black.........	70	50
1874	**1199**	19p. silver, bistre-yellow, brt rose-red, vermilion, brt blue & slate-blue..........	70	50
1875	**1200**	25p. silver, blue & grey-black...........................	1·00	1·00
1876	**1201**	25p. silver, vermilion, brt blue & grey-black..	1·00	1·00
		a. Imperf (vert pair)...................................	£22500	
1877	**1202**	30p. silver, bistre-yellow, brt magenta, pale greenish blue, grey-black & flesh..	1·25	2·25
Set of 5			4·25	4·75
Set of 5 Gutter Pairs.......................................			10·50	
First Day Cover				5·25
Presentation Pack (P.O. Pack No. 257)........			5·00	
PHQ Cards (set of 5) (170)............................			6·00	11·50

Nos. 1873 and 1875 commemorate the 50th anniversary of the end of the Second World War, No. 1874 the 125th anniversary of the British Red Cross Society and Nos. 1876/7 the 50th anniversary of the United Nations.

Nos. 1876/7 include the "EUROPA" emblem.

For No. 1875 with the face value expressed as "1st" see No. **MS**2547.

Special First Day of Issue Postmarks

British Philatelic Bureau, Edinburgh ....5·25
London SW ....5·50

A First Day of Issue handstamp (pictorial) was provided at London EC4 for this issue.

1203 *The Time Machine*

1204 *The First Men in the Moon*

1205 *The War of the Worlds*

1206 *The Shape of Things to Come*

(Des Siobhan Keaney. Litho Questa)

1995 (6 June). *Science Fiction. Novels by H. G. Wells.* Two phosphor bands. P 14½×14.

1878	**1203**	25p. new blue, greenish yellow, magenta, black & rosine	75	60
1879	**1204**	30p. new blue, greenish yellow, black, rosine & violet........................	1·25	1·50
1880	**1205**	35p. rosine, greenish yellow, violet, black & lt blue-green.................	1·25	1·60
1881	**1206**	41p. new blue, greenish yellow, magenta, black & rosine	1·50	1·60
Set of 4			4·25	4·75
Set of 4 Gutter Pairs................................			10·00	
First Day Cover				5·25
Presentation Pack (P.O. Pack No. 258)........			5·00	
PHQ Cards (set of 4) (171)			6·00	11·50

Nos. 1878/81 commemorate the centenary of publication of Wells's *The Time Machine.*

Special First Day of Issue Postmarks

British Philatelic Bureau, Edinburgh................................	5·25
Wells..	5·50

1207 The Swan, 1595

1208 The Rose, 1592

1209 The Globe, 1599

1210 The Hope, 1613

1211 The Globe, 1614

(Des C. Hodges. Litho Walsall)

1995 (8 Aug). *Reconstruction of Shakespeare's Globe Theatre.* Two phosphor bands. P 14½.

1882	**1207**	25p. brownish grey, black, magenta, new blue & greenish yellow.............	60	60
		a. Horiz strip of 5. Nos. 1882/6	4·50	4·75
1883	**1208**	25p. brownish grey, black, magenta, new blue & greenish yellow.............	60	60
1884	**1209**	25p. brownish grey, black, magenta, new blue & greenish yellow.............	60	60
1885	**1210**	25p. brownish grey, black, magenta, new blue & greenish yellow.............	60	60
1886	**1211**	25p. brownish grey, black, magenta, new blue & greenish yellow.............	60	60
Set of 5			4·50	4·75
Gutter Strip of 10...................................			10·50	
First Day Cover				5·50
Presentation Pack (P.O. Pack No. 259)......			5·00	
PHQ Cards (set of 5) (172)			6·00	11·50

Nos. 1882/6 were issued together, *se-tenant*, in horizontal strips of five throughout the sheet with the backgrounds forming a composite design.

Special First Day of Issue Postmarks

British Philatelic Bureau, Edinburgh................................	5·75
Stratford-upon-Avon	5·75

1212 Sir Rowland Hill and Uniform Penny Postage Petition

1213 Hill and Penny Black

1214 Guglielmo Marconi and Early Wireless

1215 Marconi and Sinking of *Titanic* (liner)

(Des The Four Hundred, Eng C. Slania. Recess and litho Harrison)

1995 (5 Sept). *Pioneers of Communications.* One phosphor band (19p.) or phosphorised paper (others). P 14½×14.

1887	**1212**	19p. silver, red & black................................	75	40
1888	**1213**	25p. silver, brown & black.............................	1·00	60
		a. Silver (Queen's head and face value) omitted	£1100	
1889	**1214**	41p. silver, grey-green & black	1·50	1·75
1890	**1215**	60p. silver, dp ultramarine & black...........	1·75	2·25
Set of 4			4·50	4·50
Set of 4 Gutter Pairs................................			10·00	

First Day Cover .... 5·00
Presentation Pack (P.O. Pack No. 260)...................... 5·00
PHQ Cards (set of 4) (173) .... 5·75   11·50
  Nos. 1887/8 mark the birth bicentenary of Sir Rowland Hill and Nos. 1889/90 the centenary of the first radio transmissions.

Special First Day of Issue Postmarks

British Philatelic Bureau, Edinburgh .... 5·00
London EC .... 5·00

1216 Harold Wagstaff

1217 Gus Risman

1218 Jim Sullivan

1219 Billy Batten

1220 Brian Bevan

(Des C. Birmingham)

1995 (3 Oct). *Centenary of Rugby League*. One phosphor band (19p.) or two phosphor bands (others). *P* 14½×14.
1891 **1216** 19p. blue, greenish yellow, magenta,
                     new blue, grey-black & black........... 75   40
1892 **1217** 25p. slate-purple, greenish yellow,
                     magenta, new blue, grey-black &
                     black.. 75   60
1893 **1218** 30p. slate-green, greenish yellow, brt
                     purple, new blue, grey-black &
                     black.. 1·00   1·50
1894 **1219** 35p. slate-black, greenish yellow,
                     magenta, new blue & black............ 1·00   1·60
1895 **1220** 41p. bluish grey, orange-yellow,
                     magenta, new blue, grey-black &
                     black.. 1·50   1·60
Set of 5 .... 4·75   5·25
Set of 5 Gutter Pairs.. 11·00
First Day Cover ....   5·75
Presentation Pack (P.O. Pack No. 261)...................... 5·50
PHQ Cards (set of 5) (174) .... 6·00   11·50

Special First Day of Issue Postmarks

British Philatelic Bureau, Edinburgh......................... 5·75
Huddersfield .... 5·75

  A First Day of Issue handstamp (pictorial) was provided at Headingly, Leeds for this issue.

1221 European Robin in Mouth of Pillar Box

1222 European Robin on Railings and Holly

1223 European Robin on Snow-covered Milk Bottles

1224 European Robin on Road Sign

1225 European Robin on Door Knob and Christmas Wreath

(Des K. Lilly)

1995 (30 Oct). *Christmas. Christmas Robins*. One phosphor band (19p.) or two phosphor bands (others). *P* 15×14.
1896 **1221** 19p. silver, greenish yellow, vermilion,
                     orange-vermilion, bistre & black..... 60   40
1897 **1222** 25p. silver, greenish yellow, scarlet, pale
                     blue, ochre & black...................... 85   60
1898 **1223** 30p. silver, greenish yellow, rose-
                     carmine, lt green, olive-brown &
                     grey.. 1·25   1·50
1899 **1224** 41p. silver, greenish yellow, rose-red,
                     dull blue, bistre & black................ 1·60   1·75
1900 **1225** 60p. silver, orange-yellow, red-orange,
                     bistre & black.............................. 1·75   1·90
Set of 5 .... 5·50   6·00
Set of 5 Gutter Pairs.. 12·00
First Day Cover ....   6·50
Presentation Pack (P.O. Pack No. 262)...................... 6·00
PHQ Cards (set of 5) (175) .... 6·00   11·50
  The 19p. value was re-issued on 3 October 2000 in sheets of 20, each with a *se-tenant* label showing Christmas greetings (*sold for £3·99*) (LS2) or a personal photograph (*sold for £7·99*). These sheets were printed in photogravure by Questa and were sold by the Philatelic Bureau and selected philatelic outlets. Similar sheets were available from 9 October 2001 when the price for a personalised version was increased to £8·75. These could also be purchased, on an experimental basis, from photo-booths at six post offices.

Special First Day of Issue Postmarks

British Philatelic Bureau, Edinburgh .... 6·50
Bethlehem, Llandeilo .... 6·50

Collectors Pack 1995
1995 (30 Oct). Comprises Nos. 1848/1900.
CP1900a Collectors Pack.. 48·00

Post Office Yearbook
1995 (30 Oct). Comprises Nos. 1848/57 and
1868/1900 in hardback book with slip case,
illustrated in colour.. 50·00

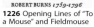

1226 Opening Lines of "To a Mouse" and Fieldmouse

1227 "O my Luve's like a red, red rose" and Wild Rose

1228 "Scots, wha hae wi Wallace bled" and Sir William Wallace

1229 "Auld Lang Syne" and Highland Dancers

(Des Tayburn Design Consultancy. Litho Questa)

1996 (25 Jan). *Death Bicentenary of Robert Burns (Scottish poet)*. One phosphor band (19p.) or two phosphor bands (others). P 14½.

1901	**1226**	19p. cream, bistre-brown & black............	75	40
1902	**1227**	25p. cream, bistre-brown, black, magenta, bistre-yellow & new blue	1·00	60
1903	**1228**	41p. cream, bistre-brown, black, magenta, bistre-yellow & new blue	1·50	2·00
1904	**1229**	60p. cream, bistre-brown, black, magenta, bistre-yellow & new blue	1·75	2·50

Set of 4 .... 4·50 / 5·00
Set of 4 Gutter Pairs.. 10·50
First Day Cover.. 5·50
Presentation Pack (P.O. Pack No. 264)............ 5·00
PHQ Cards (set of 4) (176)................................. 6·00 / 11·50

Special First Day of Issue Postmarks

British Philatelic Bureau, Edinburgh.................................. 5·50
Dumfries .... 5·50

1230 "MORE! LOVE" (Mel Calman)   **1231** "Sincerely" (Charles Barsotti)

1232 "Do you have something for the HUMAN CONDITION?" (Leo Cullum)

1233 "MENTAL FLOSS" (Mel Calman)

1234 "4.55 P.M." (Charles Barsotti)   **1235** "Dear lottery prize winner" (Larry)

1236 "I'm writing to you because...." (Mel Calman)   **1237** "FETCH THIS, FETCH THAT" (Charles Barsotti)

1238 "My day starts before I'm ready for it" (Mel Calman)   **1239** "THE CHEQUE IN THE POST" (Jack Ziegler)

(Des M. Wolff. Litho Walsall)

1996 (26 Feb–11 Nov). *Greetings Stamps. Cartoons.* 'All over' phosphor. P 14½×14 (with one elliptical hole in each vertical side).

1905	**1230**	(1st) black & bright mauve............................	1·25	75
		a. Booklet pane. Nos. 1905/14	12·00	11·00
		p. Two phosphor bands (11 Nov)	3·00	2·50
		pa. Booklet pane. Nos. 1905p/14p..........	45·00	45·00
1906	**1231**	(1st) black & blue-green	1·25	75
		p. Two phosphor bands (11 Nov)	3·00	2·50
1907	**1232**	(1st) black & new blue	1·25	75
		p. Two phosphor bands (11 Nov)	3·00	2·50
1908	**1233**	(1st) black & brt violet	1·25	75
		p. Two phosphor bands (11 Nov)	3·00	2·50
1909	**1234**	(1st) black & vermilion	1·25	75
		p. Two phosphor bands (11 Nov)	3·00	2·50
1910	**1235**	(1st) black & new blue	1·25	75
		p. Two phosphor bands (11 Nov)	3·00	2·50
1911	**1236**	(1st) black & vermilion	1·25	75
		p. Two phosphor bands (11 Nov)	3·00	2·50
1912	**1237**	(1st) black & brt violet	1·25	75
		p. Two phosphor bands (11 Nov)	3·00	2·50
1913	**1238**	(1st) black & blue-green	1·25	75
		p. Two phosphor bands (11 Nov)	3·00	2·50
1914	**1239**	(1st) black & brt mauve	1·25	75
		p. Two phosphor bands (11 Nov)	3·00	2·50

Set of 10 (Nos. 1905/14)................................... 14·00 / 11·00
Set of 10 (Nos. 1905p/14p)............................... 45·00 / 45·00
First Day Cover (1905/14).................................. 12·00
Presentation Pack (1905/14) (P.O. Pack No. G5) .... 16·00
PHQ Cards (set of 10) (GS4).............................. 16·00 / 30·00

Nos. 1905/14 were issued in £2·50 stamp booklets, Nos. KX8/a (*sold at £2·60 from 8 July 1996*), together with a pane of twenty half stamp-sized labels. The stamps and labels were attached to the booklet cover by a common gutter margin.

These designs were re-issued on 18 December 2001 in sheets of 10, each with a *se-tenant* label showing cartoon comments (*sold for £2·95*) (LS6). They were re-issued again on 29 July 2003 in sheets of 20 (*sold for £6·15*) containing two of each design, each stamp accompanied by a half stamp-size label showing a crossword grid (clues printed on the bottom sheet margin) (LS13). Sheets of 20 with personal photographs on the labels and a crossword puzzle in the bottom sheet margin were also available, at £14·95 a sheet from Royal Mail, Edinburgh and Post Office philatelic outlets, or £15 a sheet from photo booths.

All these sheets were printed in lithography by Questa with two phosphor bands and perforated 14½×14 (without elliptical holes), and were available from the bureau and other selected philatelic outlets.

Special First Day of Issue Postmarks

British Philatelic Bureau, Edinburgh...12·00
Titterhill, Haytons Bent, Ludlow...12·00

1240 "Muscovy Duck"   **1241** "Lapwing"

1242 "White-fronted Goose"   **1243** "Bittern"

1244 "Whooper Swan"

(Des Moseley Webb)

1996 (12 Mar). *50th Anniv of the Wildfowl and Wetlands Trust. Bird Paintings by C. F. Tunnicliffe.* One phosphor band (19p.) or phosphorised paper (others). *P* 14×14½.

1915	**1240**	19p. sepia, orange-yellow, brown, pale buff, grey & gold	70	40
1916	**1241**	25p. bistre-brown, greenish yellow, magenta, new blue, pale buff, gold & black	90	60
1917	**1242**	30p. bistre-brown, greenish yellow, magenta, new blue, pale buff, gold & grey-black	1·00	1·25
1918	**1243**	35p. sepia, pale orange, lake-brown, brown-olive, pale buff, gold & grey-black	1·10	1·50
1919	**1244**	41p. sepia, greenish yellow, magenta, new blue, pale buff, gold & grey-black	1·50	1·60
Set of 5			4·75	4·75
Set of 5 Gutter Pairs			10·50	
First Day Cover				5·50
Presentation Pack (P.O. Pack No. 265)			5·50	
PHQ Cards (set of 5) (177)			6·00	11·50

Special First Day of Issue Postmarks

British Philatelic Bureau, Edinburgh ....6·00
Slimbridge, Gloucester ....6·50

1245 The Odeon, Harrogate   **1246** Laurence Olivier and Vivien Leigh in *Lady Hamilton* (film)

1247 Old Cinema Ticket   **1248** Pathé News Still

1249 Cinema Sign, The Odeon, Manchester

(Des The Chase, Gravure Harrison)

1996 (16 Apr). *Centenary of Cinema.* One phosphor band (19p.) or two phosphor bands (others). *P* 14×14½.

1920	**1245**	19p. black, greenish yellow, silver, brt magenta & new blue	50	40
1921	**1246**	25p. black, greenish yellow, silver, brt magenta & new blue	70	60
1922	**1247**	30p. black, greenish yellow, silver, brt magenta & new blue	1·00	1·75
1923	**1248**	35p. black, red & silver	1·25	2·00
1924	**1249**	41p. black, greenish yellow, silver, brt magenta & new blue	1·50	2·25
Set of 5			4·75	6·25
Set of 5 Gutter Pairs			11·00	
First Day Cover				7·00
Presentation Pack (P.O. Pack No. 266)			5·50	
PHQ Cards (set of 5) (178)			6·00	11·50

Special First Day of Issue Postmarks

British Philatelic Bureau, Edinburgh...7·00
London, WC2...7·00

1250 Dixie Dean   **1251** Bobby Moore

1252 Duncan Edwards

1253 Billy Wright

1254 Danny Blanchflower

(Des H. Brown. Litho Questa)

1996 (14 May). *European Football Championship.* One phosphor band (19p.) or two phosphor bands (others). P 14½×14.

1925	**1250**	19p. vermilion, black, pale grey & grey..	50	40
		a. Booklet pane. No. 1925×4 with margins all round	3·25	
1926	**1251**	25p. brt emerald, black, pale grey & grey..	75	60
		a. Booklet pane. No. 1926×4 with margins all round	3·25	
1927	**1252**	35p. orange-yellow, black, pale grey & grey..	1·25	1·75
		a. Booklet pane. Nos. 1927/9, each ×2, with margins all round	8·00	
1928	**1253**	41p. new blue, black, pale grey & grey..	1·50	1·75
1929	**1254**	60p. brt orange, black, pale grey & grey	1·75	2·00
Set of 5			5·50	6·00
Set of 5 Gutter Pairs			12·00	
First Day Cover				6·50
Presentation Pack (P.O. Pack No. 267)			6·00	
PHQ Cards (set of 5) (179)			6·00	11·50

Booklet panes Nos. 1925a, 1926a and 1927a come from the £6·48 "European Football Championship" booklet, No. DX18.

Special First Day of Issue Postmarks

British Philatelic Bureau, Edinburgh...6·50
Wembley ....6·50

1255 Athlete on Starting Blocks

1256 Throwing the Javelin

1257 Basketball

1258 Swimming

1259 Athlete celebrating and Olympic Rings

(Des N. Knight. Litho Questa)

1996 (9 July). *Olympic and Paralympic Games, Atlanta.* Two phosphor bands. P 14½×14.

1930	**1255**	26p. greenish grey, silver, rosine, black, magenta, bistre-yellow & new blue	60	70
		a. Horiz strip of 5. Nos. 1930/4	4·50	4·50
1931	**1256**	26p. greenish grey, silver, rosine, black, magenta, bistre-yellow & new blue	60	70
1932	**1257**	26p. greenish grey, silver, rosine, black, magenta, bistre-yellow & new blue	60	70
1933	**1258**	26p. greenish grey, silver, rosine, black, magenta, bistre-yellow & new blue	60	70
1934	**1259**	26p. greenish grey, silver, rosine, black, magenta, bistre-yellow & new blue	60	70
Set of 5			4·50	4·50
Gutter Strip of 10			10·00	
First Day Cover				5·00
Presentation Pack (P.O. Pack No. 268)			5·00	
PHQ Cards (set of 5) (180)			6·00	11·50

Nos. 1930/4 were printed together, *se-tenant*, in horizontal strips of five throughout the sheet.

For these designs with face value expressed as "1st" see **MS**2554.

Special First Day of Issue Postmarks

British Philatelic Bureau, Edinburgh..5·50
Much Wenlock ....6·00

1260 Prof. Dorothy Hodgkin (scientist)

1261 Dame Margot Fonteyn (ballerina)

1262 Dame Elisabeth Frink (sculptress)

1263 Dame Daphne du Maurier (novelist)

1264 Dame Marea Hartman (sports administrator)

(Des Stephanie Nash Gravure Harrison)

1996 (6 Aug). *Europa. Famous Women.* One phosphor band (20p.) or two phosphor bands (others). P 14½.

1935	**1260**	20p. dull blue-green, brownish grey & black	60	50
1936	**1261**	26p. dull mauve, brownish grey & black	75	60
		a. Imperf (horiz pair)	£875	
1937	**1262**	31p. bronze, brownish grey & black	1·10	1·10
1938	**1263**	37p. silver, brownish grey & black	1·25	1·40
1939	**1264**	43p. gold, brownish grey & black	1·50	1·50
Set of 5			4·75	4·50
Set of 5 Gutter Pairs			11·00	
First Day Cover				5·00
Presentation Pack (P.O. Pack No. 269)			5·50	
PHQ Cards (set of 5) (181)			6·00	11·50

Nos. 1936/7 include the "EUROPA" emblem.

Special First Day of Issue Postmarks

British Philatelic Bureau, Edinburgh	5·50
Fowey	6·00

1265 *Muffin the Mule*

1266 *Sooty*

1267 *Stingray*

1268 *The Clangers*

1269 *Dangermouse*

(Des Tutssels. Gravure Harrison (No. 1940a) or Enschedé (others))

1996 (3 Sept)–**97**. *50th Anniv of Children's Television.* One phosphor band (20p.) or two phosphor bands (others). P 14½×14.

1940	**1265**	20p. dp claret, black, magenta, rosine & greenish yellow	55	30
		a. Perf 15×14 (23.9.97)	2·00	2·00
		ab. Booklet pane. No. 1940a×4 with margins all round	8·00	
1941	**1266**	26p. brt blue, black, dp grey-blue, magenta & greenish yellow	80	40
1942	**1267**	31p. greenish blue, black, new blue, magenta & greenish yellow	1·00	1·50
1943	**1268**	37p. dull violet-blue, black, new blue, magenta & greenish yellow	1·40	1·75
1944	**1269**	43p. brt purple, black, new blue, magenta & greenish yellow	1·60	2·00
Set of 5			4·75	5·50
Set of 5 Gutter Pairs			10·50	
First Day Cover				6·00
Presentation Pack (P.O. Pack No. 270)			5·50	
PHQ Cards (set of 5) (182)			6·00	11·50

Booklet pane No. 1940a comes from the 1997 £6·15 "B.B.C." stamp booklet, No. DX19.

Special First Day of Issue Postmarks

British Philatelic Bureau, Edinburgh	6·00
Alexandra Palace, London	6·00

1270 Triumph TR3

1271 MG TD

1272 Austin-Healey 100

1273 Jaguar XK120

1274 Morgan Plus 4

(Des S. Clay. Gravure Harrison)

1996 (1 Oct). *Classic Sports Cars.* One phosphor band (20p.) or two phosphor bands (others). P 14½.

1945	**1270**	20p. silver, greenish yellow, brt scarlet, vermilion, new blue & black	55	40
1946	**1271**	26p. silver, greenish yellow, magenta, greenish blue & black	1·10	50
		a. Imperf (pair)	£6500	
1947	**1272**	37p. silver, greenish yellow, brt magenta, dp turquoise-blue, new blue & black	1·40	1·90
		a. Imperf (pair)	£2600	
1948	**1273**	43p. silver, greenish yellow, magenta, greenish blue & black	1·60	1·90
		a. Imperf (horiz pair)	£4750	
1949	**1274**	63p. silver, greenish yellow, magenta, greenish blue, stone & black	1·75	2·00
Set of 5			5·75	6·00
Set of 5 Gutter Pairs			13·00	
First Day Cover				6·50
Presentation Pack (P.O. Pack No. 271)			6·50	
PHQ Cards (set of 5) (183)			6·00	11·50

On Nos. 1946/9 the right-hand phosphor band on each stamp is three times the width of that on the left.

Special First Day of Issue Postmarks

British Philatelic Bureau, Edinburgh	6·50
Beaulieu, Brockenhurst	6·50

A pictorial First Day of Issue handstamp was provided at London E1 for this issue.

1275 The Three Kings

1276 The Annunciation

1277 The Journey to Bethlehem

1278 The Nativity

1279 The Shepherds

(Des Laura Stoddart, Gravure Harrison)

1996 (28 Oct). *Christmas.* One phosphor band (2nd) or two phosphor bands (others). P 15×14.

1950	**1275**	(2nd) gold, greenish yellow, magenta, blue, black & lt brown	1·00	60
1951	**1276**	(1st) gold, yellow, cerise, new blue, black & lt brown	1·25	70
1952	**1277**	31p. gold, orange-yellow, cerise, blue, black & lt brown	1·25	1·75
1953	**1278**	43p. gold, greenish yellow, magenta, new blue, grey-black & lt brown	1·25	1·75
1954	**1279**	63p. gold, greenish yellow, magenta, new blue, black & lt brown	1·50	2·00

Set of 5	5·50	6·00
Set of 5 Gutter Pairs	12·50	
First Day Cover		6·50
Presentation Pack (P.O. Pack No. 272)	6·00	
PHQ Cards (set of 5) (184)	6·00	11·50

Special First Day of Issue Postmarks

British Philatelic Bureau, Edinburgh	6·50
Bethlehem, Llandeilo	6·50

Collectors Pack 1996

1996 (28 Oct). Comprises Nos. 1901/54.

CP1954a Collectors Pack	55·00

Post Office Yearbook

1996 (28 Oct). Comprises Nos. 1901/4 and 1915/54 in hardback book with slip case, illustrated in colour .... 55·00

1280 *Gentiana acaulis* (Georg Ehret)

1281 *Magnolia grandiflora* (Ehret)

1282 *Camellia japonica* (Alfred Chandler)

1283 *Tulipa* (Ehret)

1284 *Fuchsia "Princess of Wales"* (Augusta Withers)

1285 *Tulipa gesneriana* (Ehret)

1286 *Gazania splendens* (Charlotte Sowerby)

1287 *Iris latifolia* (Ehret)

1288 *Hippeastrum rutilum* (Pierre-Joseph Redouté)

1289 *Passiflora coerulea* (Ehret)

(Des Tutssels. Litho Walsall)

1997 (6 Jan). *Greeting Stamps. 19th-century Flower Paintings.* Two phosphor bands. P 14½×14 (with one elliptical hole in each vertical side).

1955	**1280**	(1st) greenish yellow, new blue, magenta, black, blue-green & gold	1·25	1·00
		a. Booklet pane. Nos. 1955/64	14·00	14·00
		ab. Gold, blue-green and phosphor omitted	£28000	
1956	**1281**	(1st) greenish yellow, new blue, magenta, black, blue-green & gold	1·25	1·00
1957	**1282**	(1st) greenish yellow, new blue, magenta, black, blue-green & gold	1·25	1·00
1958	**1283**	(1st) greenish yellow, new blue, magenta, black, blue-green & gold	1·25	1·00
1959	**1284**	(1st) greenish yellow, new blue, magenta, black, blue-green & gold	1·25	1·00
1960	**1285**	(1st) greenish yellow, new blue, magenta, black, blue-green & gold	1·25	1·00
1961	**1286**	(1st) greenish yellow, new blue, magenta, black, blue-green & gold	1·25	1·00
1962	**1287**	(1st) greenish yellow, new blue, magenta, black, blue-green & gold	1·25	1·00
1963	**1288**	(1st) greenish yellow, new blue, magenta, black, blue-green & gold	1·25	1·00
1964	**1289**	(1st) greenish yellow, new blue, magenta, black, blue-green & gold	1·25	1·00

Set of 10	14·00	14·00
First Day Cover		15·00
Presentation Pack (P.O. Pack No. G6)	16·00	
PHQ Cards (set of 10) (GS5)	16·00	30·00

Nos. 1955/64 were issued in £2·60 stamp booklets Nos KX9/12 together with a pane of twenty half-sized labels. The stamps and labels were attached to the booklet cover by a common gutter margin.

Nos. 1955/64 were re-issued on 21 January 2003 in *se-tenant* sheets of 20, each accompanied by a label showing further flowers (*sold at* £5·95) (LS11) or personal photographs (*sold at* £14·95). These stamps were printed in lithography by Questa and are without elliptical holes in the perforations.

For booklet stamps in designs as Nos. 1955, 1958 and 1962 and perf 15×14, printed by Enschedé see Nos. 2463/5.

See also Nos. 2942/3.

Special First Day of Issue Postmarks

British Philatelic Bureau, Edinburgh..15·00
Kew, Richmond, Surrey..15·00

Special First Day of Issue Postmarks

British Philatelic Bureau, Edinburgh..10·00
Hampton Court, East Molesey..11·00

1290 "King Henry VIII"   **1291** "Catherine of Aragon"

1292 "Anne Boleyn"   **1293** "Jane Seymour"   **1294** "Anne of Cleves"

1295 "Catherine Howard"   **1296** "Catherine Parr"

(Des Kate Stephens from contemporary paintings. Gravure Harrison)

1997 (21 Jan). *450th Death Anniv of King Henry VIII.* Two phosphor bands. *P* 15 (No. 1965) or 14×15 (others).

1965	**1290**	26p. gold, greenish yellow, brt purple, new blue and black	60	60
		a. Imperf (vert pair)	£10000	
1966	**1291**	26p. gold, greenish yellow, brt carmine, new blue and black	60	60
		a. Horiz strip of 6. Nos. 1966/71	8·00	8·50
1967	**1292**	26p. gold, greenish yellow, brt carmine, new blue and black	60	60
1968	**1293**	26p. gold, greenish yellow, brt carmine, new blue and black	60	60
1969	**1294**	26p. gold, greenish yellow, brt carmine, new blue and black	60	60
1970	**1295**	26p. gold, greenish yellow, brt carmine, new blue and black	60	60
1971	**1296**	26p. gold, greenish yellow, brt carmine, new blue and black	60	60
Set of 7			8·50	9·00
Set of 1 Gutter Pair and a Gutter Strip of 12			17·00	
First Day Cover				9·50
Presentation Pack (P.O. Pack No. 274)			10·00	
PHQ Cards (set of 7) (185)			10·00	18·00

Nos. 1966/71 were printed together, *se-tenant*, in horizontal strips of six throughout the sheet.

1297 St. Columba in Boat   **1298** St. Columba on Iona

1299 St. Augustine with King Ethelbert   **1300** St. Augustine with Model of Cathedral

(Des Claire Melinsky. Gravure Enschedé)

1997 (11 Mar). *Religious Anniversaries.* Two phosphor bands. *P* 14½.

1972	**1297**	26p. greenish yellow, magenta, new blue, grey-black and gold	75	60
		a. Imperf (pair)	£2400	
1973	**1298**	37p. greenish yellow, magenta, new blue, grey-black and gold	1·10	1·50
1974	**1299**	43p. greenish yellow, magenta, new blue, grey-black and gold	1·50	1·50
1975	**1300**	63p. greenish yellow, magenta, new blue, grey-black and gold	2·00	2·10
Set of 4			4·75	5·25
Set of 4 Gutter Pairs			11·50	
First Day Cover				5·75
Presentation Pack (P.O. Pack No. 275)			5·25	
PHQ Cards (set of 4) (186)			5·75	11·50

Nos. 1972/3 commemorate the 1400th death anniversary of St. Columba and Nos. 1974/5 the 1400th anniversary of the arrival of St. Augustine of Canterbury in Kent.

Special First Day of Issue Postmarks

British Philatelic Bureau, Edinburgh ....6·00
Isle of Iona ....6·00

For Nos. 1976/7 see Decimal Machin Definitives section. Nos. 1978/9 are no longer used.

Dracula
1303 *Dracula*

Frankenstein
1304 *Frankenstein*

Dr Jekyll and Mr Hyde
1305 *Dr. Jekyll and Mr. Hyde*

The Hound of the Baskervilles
1306 *The Hound of the Baskervilles*

(Des I. Pollock. Gravure Walsall)

1997 (13 May). *Europa. Tales and Legends. Horror Stories.* Two phosphor bands. P 14×15.

1980	**1303**	26p. grey-black, black, new blue, magenta and greenish yellow..........	1·00	60
1981	**1304**	31p. grey-black, black, new blue, magenta and greenish yellow..........	1·10	1·50
1982	**1305**	37p. grey-black, black, new blue, magenta and greenish yellow..........	1·30	1·75
1983	**1306**	43p. grey-black, black, new blue, magenta and greenish yellow..........	2·00	1·95
Set of 4			5·00	5·50
Set of 4 Gutter Pairs..............................			11·50	
First Day Cover.......................................				6·00
Presentation Pack (P.O. Pack No. 276)....			5·50	
PHQ Cards (set of 4) (187)			5·75	11·50

Nos. 1980/3 commemorate the birth bicentenary of Mary Shelley (creator of Frankenstein) with the 26p. and 31p. values incorporating the "EUROPA" emblem. Each value has features printed in fluorescent ink which are visible under ultra-violet light.

Special First Day of Issue Postmarks

British Philatelic Bureau, Edinburgh..	6·00
Whitby...	6·00

1307 Reginald Mitchell and Supermarine Spitfire MkIIA

1308 Roy Chadwick and Avro Lancaster MkI

1309 Ronald Bishop and de Havilland Mosquito B MkXVI

1310 George Carter and Gloster Meteor T Mk7

1311 Sir Sidney Camm and Hawker Hunter FGA Mk9

(Des Turner Duckworth, Gravure Harrison)

1997 (10 June). *British Aircraft Designers.* One phosphor band (20p.) or two phosphor bands (others). *P* 15×14.

1984	**1307**	20p. silver, greenish yellow, magenta, new blue, black and grey..................	75	50
1985	**1308**	26p. silver, greenish yellow, magenta, new blue, black and grey..................	1·10	1·25
1986	**1309**	37p. silver, greenish yellow, magenta, new blue, black and grey..................	1·40	1·25
1987	**1310**	43p. silver, greenish yellow, magenta, new blue, black and grey..................	1·50	1·60
1988	**1311**	63p. silver, greenish yellow, magenta, new blue, black and grey..................	2·00	2·00
Set of 5			6·00	6·00
Set of 5 Gutter Pairs..............................			14·00	
First Day Cover				6·50
Presentation Pack (P.O. Pack No. 277).....................			6·50	
PHQ Cards (set of 5) (188)			6·00	13·00

See also No. 2868.

Special First Day of Issue Postmarks

British Philatelic Bureau, Edinburgh..	6·50
Duxford, Cambridge	6·50

1312 Carriage Horse and Coachman

1313 Lifeguards Horse and Trooper

1314 Blues and Royals Drum Horse and Drummer

1315 Duke of Edinburgh's Horse and Groom

(Des J.-L. Benard. Litho Walsall)

1997 (8 July). *'All the Queen's Horses'. 50th Anniv of the British Horse Society.* One phosphor band (20p.) or two phosphor bands (others). *P* 14½.

1989	**1312**	20p. scarlet-vermilion, black, magenta, new blue and greenish yellow.........	80	45
1990	**1313**	26p. scarlet-vermilion, black, magenta, new blue and greenish yellow.........	1·10	1·50
1991	**1314**	43p. scarlet-vermilion, black, magenta, new blue and greenish yellow.........	1·50	1·50
1992	**1315**	63p. scarlet-vermilion, black, magenta, new blue and greenish yellow.........	2·00	2·00
Set of 4			5·00	5·25
Set of 4 Gutter Pairs..............................			12·00	
First Day Cover				5·75
Presentation Pack (P.O. Pack No. 278).....................			5·50	
PHQ Cards (set of 4) (189)			5·75	11·50

Special First Day of Issue Postmarks

British Philatelic Bureau, Edinburgh... 6·00
Windsor, Berks .... 6·00

1315a Caernarfon Castle

CASTLE
Harrison plates (Nos. 1611/14)

CASTLE
Enschedé plates (Nos. 1993/6)

Differences between Harrison and Enschedé:
  Harrison- "C" has top serif and tail of letter points to right.
      "A" has flat top. "S" has top and bottom serifs.

  Enschedé- "C" has no top serif and tail of letter points upwards.
      "A" has pointed top. "S" has no serifs.

Harrison plates (Nos. 1611/14) Enschedé plates (Nos. 1993/6)

(Des from photos by Prince Andrew, Duke of York. Eng Inge Madle Recess (Queen's head by silk screen process) Enschedé)

1997 (29 July). Designs as Nos. 1611/14 with Queen's head in silhouette as T **1044,** but re-engraved with differences in inscription as shown above. P 15×14 (with one elliptical hole in each vertical side).

1993	**1315a**	£1·50 deep claret and gold†	12·00	6·00
		a. Gold (Queen's head) omitted	—	£2100
1994	**881**	£2 indigo and gold†	14·00	2·25
		a. Gold (Queen's head) omitted	£900	
1995	**879**	£3 violet and gold†	30·00	3·50
		a. Gold (Queen's head) omitted	£3500	
1996	**882**	£5 deep brown and gold†	35·00	10·00
		a. Gold (Queen's head) omitted	£6000	
Set of 4			80·00	18·00
Set of 4 Gutter Pairs (vert or horiz)			£175	
Presentation Pack (P.O. Pack No. 40)			£150	

† The Queen's head on these stamps is printed in optically variable ink which changes colour from gold to green when viewed from different angles. No. 1996a occurs on R. 5/8 and 6/8 from some sheets.
  See also Nos. 1410/3.

1316 Haroldswick, Shetland

1317 Painswick, Gloucestershire

1318 Beddgelert, Gwynedd

1319 Ballyroney, County Down

(Des T. Millington. Gravure Enschedé)

1997 (12 Aug). *Sub-Post Offices.* One phosphor band (20p.) or two phosphor bands (others). P 14½.

1997	**1316**	20p. greenish yellow, bright magenta, new blue, grey-black, rosine and blue-green	75	50
1998	**1317**	26p. greenish yellow, bright magenta, new blue, grey-black, rosine and blue-green	1·00	1·00
1999	**1318**	43p. greenish yellow, bright magenta, new blue, grey-black, rosine and blue-green	1·50	1·50
2000	**1319**	63p. greenish yellow, bright magenta, new blue, grey-black, rosine and blue-green	2·25	2·25
Set of 4			5·50	5·00
Set of 4 Gutter Pairs			12·00	
First Day Cover				5·75
Presentation Pack (P.O. Pack No. 279)			6·00	
PHQ Cards (set of 4) (190)			5·75	11·50

  Nos. 1997/2000 were issued on the occasion of the Centenary of the National Federation of Sub-Postmasters.

Special First Day of Issue Postmarks

British Philatelic Bureau, Edinburgh .... 6·00
Wakefield ....6·00

PRINTERS. Harrison and Sons Ltd became De La Rue Security Print on 8 September 1997. This was not reflected in the sheet imprints until mid-1998.

Enid Blyton's *Noddy*
1320 Noddy

Enid Blyton's *Famous Five*
1321 Famous Five

Enid Blyton's *Secret Seven*
1322 Secret Seven

Enid Blyton's *Faraway Tree*
1323 Faraway Tree

Enid Blyton's *Malory Towers*
1324 *Malory Towers*

(Des C. Birmingham. Gravure Enschedé)

1997 (9 Sept). *Birth Centenary of Enid Blyton (children's author).* One phosphor band (20p.) or two phosphor bands (others). *P* 14×14½.

2001	**1320**	20p. greenish yellow, magenta, new blue, grey-black and deep grey-blue	50	45
2002	**1321**	26p. greenish yellow, magenta, new blue, grey-black and deep grey-blue	1·00	1·25
2003	**1322**	37p. greenish yellow, magenta, new blue, grey-black and deep grey-blue	1·25	1·25
2004	**1323**	43p. greenish yellow, magenta, new blue, grey-black and deep grey-blue	1·50	2·00
2005	**1324**	63p. greenish yellow, magenta, new blue, grey-black and deep grey-blue	1·75	2·00
Set of 5			5·50	6·00
Set of 5 Gutter Pairs			12·00	
First Day Cover				6·50
Presentation Pack (P.O. Pack No. 280)			6·00	
PHQ Cards (set of 5) (191)			6·00	13·00

Special First Day of Issue Postmarks

British Philatelic Bureau, Edinburgh...6·50
Beaconsfield...6·50

1325 Children and Father Christmas pulling Cracker

1326 Father Christmas with Traditional Cracker

1327 Father Christmas riding Cracker

1328 Father Christmas on Snowball

1329 Father Christmas and Chimney

(Des J. Gorham and M. Thomas (1st), J. Gorham (others) Gravure Harrison)

1997 (27 Oct). *Christmas. 150th Anniv of the Christmas Cracker.* One phosphor band (2nd) or two phosphor bands (others). *P* 15×14.

2006	**1325**	(2nd) gold, greenish yellow, bright magenta, new blue and grey-black	1·00	40
		a. Imperf (pair)	£3000	
2007	**1326**	(1st) gold, greenish yellow, bright magenta, new blue and grey-black	1·25	60
2008	**1327**	31p. gold, greenish yellow, new blue, bright blue and grey-black	1·00	1·50
		a. Imperf (pair)	£4250	
2009	**1328**	43p. gold, greenish yellow, bright magenta, pale new blue and grey-black	1·25	1·75
2010	**1329**	63p. gold, greenish yellow, bright magenta, new blue and grey-black	1·60	2·00
Set of 5			5·50	5·75
Set of 5 Gutter Pairs			12·00	
First Day Cover				6·50
Presentation Pack (P.O. Pack No. 282)			6·00	
PHQ Cards (set of 5) (192)			6·00	13·00

The 1st value was re-issued on 3 October 2000 in sheets of 10, each with a *se-tenant* label showing Christmas greetings (*sold for £2·95*) (LS3) or a personal photograph (*sold for £5·95*). These sheets were printed in photogravure by Questa and were sold by the Philatelic Bureau and selected philatelic outlets. Similar sheets were available from 9 October 2001 when the price for the personalised version was increased to £12·95 for two sheets. These could also be purchased, on an experimental basis, from photo-booths situated at six post offices. From 1 October 2002 the size of the sheet was increased to 20 either with greetings labels (*sold at £5·95*) (LS10) or personal photographs (*sold at £14·95*). These stamps were printed by Questa in lithography and perforated 14½×14.

Special First Day of Issue Postmarks

British Philatelic Bureau, Edinburgh .... 6·50
Bethlehem, Llandeilo .... 6·50

1330 Wedding Photograph, 1947

1331 Queen Elizabeth II and Prince Philip, 1997

(Des D. Driver (20p., 43p.), Lord Snowdon (26p., 63p.) Gravure Harrison)

1997 (13 Nov). *Royal Golden Wedding.* One phosphor band (20p.) or two phosphor bands (others). *P* 15.

2011	**1330**	20p. gold, yellow-brown and grey-black	85	45
		a. Imperf (pair)	£11000	
		b. Face value omitted	£25000	
2012	**1331**	26p. gold, bistre-yellow, magenta, new blue, grey-black and greenish grey	1·10	70
		a. Imperf (vert pair)	£8500	
2013	**1330**	43p. gold, bluish green and grey-black	1·90	2·25
2014	**1331**	63p. gold, bistre-yellow, magenta, new blue, grey-black and lavender-grey	2·50	3·00
Set of 4			5·75	5·75
Set of 4 Gutter Pairs			12·00	
First Day Cover				7·00
Presentation Pack (P.O. Pack No. 281)			6·25	
Souvenir Book (contains Nos. 1668, 1989/92 and 2011/14)			50·00	
PHQ Cards (set of 4) (192)			5·75	11·50

For 26p. and (1st) Machin printed in gold, see Nos. 1672, Y1692, 2295, U2942, U2948/52, U2958, U2964/8, U3002 and U3015.

Set of 6 Gutter Pairs		14·00
First Day Cover		8·00
Presentation Pack (P.O. Pack No. 284)	6·75	
PHQ Cards (set of 6) (194)	6·00	14·00

Special First Day of Issue Postmarks

British Philatelic Bureau, Edinburgh	7·50
London, SW1	8·00

Collectors Pack 1997
1997 (13 Nov). Comprises Nos. 1965/75, 1980/92 and 1997/ 2014.
CP2014a Collectors Pack.......................... 55·00

Post Office Yearbook
1997 (13 Nov). Comprises Nos. 1965/75, 1980/92 and 1997/ 2014 in hardback book with slip case.......... 50·00

1332 Common Dormouse

1333 Lady's Slipper Orchid

1334 Song Thrush

1335 Shining Ram's-horn Snail

1336 Mole Cricket

1337 Devil's Bolete

(Des R. Maude. Litho Questa)

1998 (20 Jan). *Endangered Species.* One side phosphor band (20p.) or two phosphor bands (others). *P* 14×14½.

2015	1332	20p. black, new blue, magenta, greenish yellow, deep blue and pale lavender-grey	60	40
2016	1333	26p. black, new blue, magenta, greenish yellow, deep blue and pale yellow-olive	75	40
2017	1334	31p. black, new blue, magenta, greenish yellow, deep blue and pale bluish grey	1·00	2·00
2018	1335	37p. black, new blue, magenta, greenish yellow, deep blue and pale greenish grey	1·25	1·25
2019	1336	43p. black, new blue, magenta, greenish yellow, deep blue and pale dull mauve	1·40	1·75
2020	1337	63p. black, new blue, magenta, greenish yellow, deep blue and pale grey-brown	1·90	2·25
Set of 6			6·25	7·50

Special First Day of Issue Postmarks

British Philatelic Bureau, Edinburgh	8·00
Selborne, Alton	8·00

1338 Diana, Princess of Wales (photo by Lord Snowdon)

1339 At British Lung Foundation Function, April 1997 (photo by John Stillwell)

1340 Wearing Tiara, 1991 (photo by Lord Snowdon)

1341 On Visit to Birmingham, October 1995 (photo by Tim Graham)

1342 In Evening Dress, 1987 (photo by Terence Donavan)

(Des B. Robinson. Gravure Harrison)

1998 (3 Feb). *Diana, Princess of Wales Commemoration.* Two phosphor bands. *P* 14×15.

2021	1338	26p. purple, greenish yellow, magenta, new blue and black	50	50
		a. Horiz strip of 5. Nos. 2021/5	4·50	4·50
		ab. Imperf (horiz strip of 5. Nos. 2021/5)	£25000	
		ac. Imperf (horiz strip of 4. Nos. 2021/4)	£18000	
		ad. Imperf (horiz strip of 3. Nos. 2021/3)	£12000	
2022	1339	26p. purple, greenish yellow, magenta, new blue and black	50	50
2023	1340	26p. purple, greenish yellow, magenta, new blue and black	50	50
2024	1341	26p. purple, greenish yellow, magenta, new blue and black	50	50
2025	1342	26p. purple, greenish yellow, magenta, new blue and black	50	50
Set of 5			4·50	4·50

Gutter Strip of 10.. 10·00
First Day Cover .... 5·00
Presentation Pack (unnumbered)................................... 16·00
Presentation Pack (Welsh).. 70·00

Nos. 2021/5 were printed together, *se-tenant*, in horizontal strips of five throughout the sheet.

No. 2021ac shows No. 2025 perforated at right only. In addition to the generally issued Presentation Pack a further pack with all text printed in English and Welsh was available.

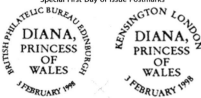

British Philatelic Bureau, Edinburgh .... 5·50
Kensington, London .... 5·50

1343 Lion of England and Griffin of Edward III

1344 Falcon of Plantagenet and Bull of Clarence

1345 Lion of Mortimer and Yale of Beaufort

1346 Greyhound of Richmond and Dragon of Wales

1347 Unicorn of Scotland and Horse of Hanover

(Des J. Matthews. Recess and litho Harrison)

1998 (24 Feb). *650th Anniv of the Order of the Garter. The Queen's Beasts.* Two phosphor bands. *P* 15×14.

2026	**1343**	26p. silver, green, bright blue, carmine-red, vermilion, lemon, grey-black and black	90	90
		a. Horiz strip of 5. Nos. 2026/30........	4·50	4·50
		ab. Missing green (on Nos. 2026, 2028/9) (horiz strip of 5)................	£37000	
		Eay. Horiz strip of 5. Phosphor omitted	25·00	
2027	**1344**	26p. silver, bright blue, carmine-red, vermilion, lemon, grey, grey-black and black	90	90
2028	**1345**	26p. silver, green, bright blue, carmine-red, vermilion, lemon, grey, grey-black and black..............	90	90
2029	**1346**	26p. silver, green, bright blue, carmine-red, vermilion, lemon, grey, grey-black and black..............	90	90
2030	**1347**	26p. silver, green, bright blue, vermilion, lemon, grey, grey-black and black	90	90
Set of 5			4·50	4·50
Gutter Block of 10...			10·00	
First Day Cover				5·25
Presentation Pack (P.O. Pack No. 285)....................			5·00	
PHQ Cards (set of 5) (195)...................................			6·00	13·00

Nos. 2026/30 were printed together, *se-tenant*, in horizontal strips of five throughout the sheet. The phosphor bands on Nos. 2026/30 are only half the height of the stamps and do not cover the silver parts of the designs.

British Philatelic Bureau, Edinburgh......................................5·50
London SW1 ....5·50

1348

(Des G. Knipe, adapted Dew Gibbons Design Group. Gravure Walsall)

1998 (10 Mar). As *T* **157** (Wilding Definitive of 1952–54) but with face values in decimal currency as *T* **1348**. One side phosphor band (20p.) or two phosphor bands (others). *P* 14 (with one elliptical hole in each vertical side).

2031	**1348**	20p. light green (1 band at right)............	70	75
		Ea. Band at left	70	75
		b. Booklet pane. Nos. 2031/Ea each×3 with margins all round........	4·75	
		c. Booklet pane. Nos. 2031/Ea and 2032/3, all×2, and central label with margins all round	10·00	
2032		26p. red-brown	1·00	1·10
		a. Booklet pane. No. 2032×9 with margins all round	9·50	
		b. Booklet pane. Nos. 2032/3, each×3 with margins all round	12·00	
2033		37p. light purple	2·75	2·75
Set of 3 (cheapest)			4·00	4·00
First Day Cover (No. 2031c)				7·00

Nos. 2031/3 were only issued in the 1998 £7·49 Wilding Definitives stamp booklet No. DX20.

For further Wilding designs with decimal face values and on paper watermarked *W* **1565** see Nos. 2258/9, **MS**2326, **MS**2367 and 2378/9.

British Philatelic Bureau, Edinburgh.....................................7·00
London SW1 ....7·00

1349 St. John's Point Lighthouse, County Down

1350 Smalls Lighthouse, Pembrokeshire

1351 Needles Rock Lighthouse, Isle of Wight, c 1900

1352 Bell Rock Lighthouse, Arbroath, mid-19th-century

1353 Original Eddystone
Lighthouse, Plymouth, 1698

(Des D. Davis and J. Boon. Litho Questa)

1998 (24 Mar). *Lighthouses.* One side phosphor band (20p.) or two
phosphor bands (others). P 14½×14.

2034	**1349**	20p. gold, greenish yellow, magenta, new blue and black	50	40
2035	**1350**	26p. gold, greenish yellow, magenta, new blue and black	75	50
2036	**1351**	37p. gold, greenish yellow, magenta, new blue and black	1·10	1·50
2037	**1352**	43p. gold, greenish yellow, magenta, new blue and black	1·50	1·75
2038	**1353**	63p. gold, greenish yellow, magenta, new blue and black	2·10	2·50
Set of 5			5·50	6·00
Set of 5 Gutter Pairs			13·00	
First Day Cover			†	6·50
Presentation Pack (P.O. Pack No. 286)			6·00	
PHQ Cards (set of 5) (196)			6·00	13·00

Nos. 2034/8 commemorate the 300th anniversary of the first
Eddystone Lighthouse and the final year of manned lighthouses.

Special First Day of Issue Postmarks

British Philatelic Bureau, Edinburgh	6·50
Plymouth	6·50

For Nos. 2039/40 see Decimal Machin Definitives section.

1354 Tommy Cooper   **1355** Eric Morecambe

1356 Joyce Grenfell   **1357** Les Dawson

1358 Peter Cook

(Des G. Scarfe. Litho Walsall)

1998 (23 Apr). *Comedians.* One side phosphor band (20p.) or two phosphor bands (others). P 14½×14.

2041	**1354**	20p. vermilion, black, rose-pink, new blue and greenish yellow	50	50
		Ea. Vermilion printed double		£1500
		Eb. Vermilion and black both printed quadruple with rose-pink and new blue both printed double	†	£2500
		Ec. Vermilion and black both printed double	†	£2000
2042	**1355**	26p. vermilion, black, rose-pink and new blue	75	85
		Ea. Vermilion printed double	£600	
		Eb. Vermilion printed triple	£1000	
		Ec. Black printed double, vermilion printed triple	£2500	
		Ed. Black and vermilion printed triple..	£2500	
		Ee. Vermilion and black both printed quadruple	£2500	
2043	**1356**	37p. vermilion, black, rose-pink, new blue and greenish yellow	1·25	1·25
2044	**1357**	43p. vermilion, black, rose-pink, new blue and pale orange	1·50	1·50
2045	**1358**	63p. vermilion, black, deep rose-pink, new blue and greenish yellow	1·75	2·10
		Ea Vermilion printed triple	†	—
Set of 5			5·25	5·50
Set of 5 Gutter Pairs			12·00	
First Day Cover				6·00
Presentation Pack (P.O. Pack No. 287)			6·00	
PHQ Cards (set of 5) (197)			6·00	13·00

Stamps as Type **1356**, but with a face value of 30p., were prepared
but not issued. Mint examples and a first day cover have been
reported (*Price* £2800).

No. 2045Ea is only known on first day cover.

Special First Day of Issue Postmarks

British Philatelic Bureau, Edinburgh	6·50
Morecambe	6·50

1359 Hands forming   **1360** Adult and Child
Heart   holding Hands

1361 Hands forming Cradle   **1362** Hand taking Pulse

(Des V. Frost from photos by A. Wilson. Litho Questa)

1998 (23 June). *50th Anniv of the National Health Service.* One side
phosphor band (20p.) or two phosphor bands (others). P 14×14½.

2046	**1359**	20p. deep claret, black, grey-brown, pale cream and cream	50	50
2047	**1360**	26p. deep grey-green, black, grey-brown, pale cream and cream	90	90
2048	**1361**	43p. deep lilac, black, grey-brown, pale cream and cream	1·50	1·50
2049	**1362**	63p. deep dull blue, black, grey-brown, pale cream and cream	2·10	2·10

Set of 4	4·50	4·50
Set of 4 Gutter Pairs...	11·00	
First Day Cover		5·00
Presentation Pack (P.O. Pack No. 288)...............	5·50	
PHQ Cards (set of 4) (198)	5·75	11·50

British Philatelic Bureau, Edinburgh	5·75
Tredegar, Wales	5·75

1363 *The Hobbit* (J. R. R. Tolkien)   **1364** *The Lion, The Witch and the Wardrobe* (C. S. Lewis)

1365 *The Phoenix and the Carpet* (E. Nesbit)   **1366** *The Borrowers* (Mary Norton)

1367 *Through the Looking Glass* (Lewis Carroll)

(Des P. Malone. Gravure D.L.R.)

1998 (21 July). *Famous Children's Fantasy Novels.* One centre phosphor band (20p.) or two phosphor bands (others). *P* 15×14.

2050	**1363**	20p. silver, greenish yellow, bright magenta, new blue, black and gold	50	50
2051	**1364**	26p. silver, greenish yellow, bright magenta, new blue, black and gold	90	90
		a. Imperf (pair)............................	£4000	
2052	**1365**	37p. silver, greenish yellow, bright magenta, new blue, black and gold	1·25	1·50
2053	**1366**	43p. silver, greenish yellow, bright magenta, new blue, black and gold	1·50	1·50
2054	**1367**	63p. silver, greenish yellow, bright magenta, new blue, black and gold	2·10	2·00
Set of 5			5·75	5·75
Set of 5 Gutter Pairs.................................			13·00	
First Day Cover				6·50
Presentation Pack (P.O. Pack No. 289)......			6·50	
PHQ Cards (set of 5) (199)			6·00	13·00

Nos. 2050/4 commemorate the birth centenary of C. S. Lewis and the death centenary of Lewis Carroll.

The PHQ card showing the Type **1363** design is known incorrectly inscribed "Tolkien".

British Philatelic Bureau, Edinburgh...6·50
Oxford...6·50

1368 Woman in Yellow Feathered Costume   **1369** Woman in Blue Costume and Headdress

1370 Group of Children in White and Gold Robes   **1371** Child in "Tree" Costume

(Des T. Hazael. Gravure Walsall)

1998 (25 Aug). *Europa. Festivals. Notting Hill Carnival.* One centre phosphor band (20p.) or two phosphor bands (others). *P* 14×14½.

2055	**1368**	20p. gold, black, new blue, bright magenta and greenish yellow..........	75	45
		a. Imperf (pair)............................	£1250	
2056	**1369**	26p. gold, grey-black, new blue, bright magenta and greenish yellow..........	95	55
2057	**1370**	43p. gold, grey-black, new blue, bright magenta and bistre-yellow..............	1·50	2·00
2058	**1371**	63p. gold, grey-black, new blue, bright magenta and greenish yellow..........	2·00	2·75
Set of 4			4·75	5·25
Set of 4 Gutter Pairs.................................			11·50	
First Day Cover				5·75
Presentation Pack (P.O. Pack No. 290)......			5·25	
PHQ Cards (set of 4) (200)			5·75	11·50

The 20p. and 26p. incorporate the "EUROPA" emblem.

British Philatelic Bureau, Edinburgh...6·00
London W11...6·50

1372 Sir Malcolm Campbell's *Bluebird*, 1925   **1373** Sir Henry Segrave's *Sunbeam*, 1926

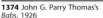

1374 John G. Parry Thomas's *Babs*, 1926

1375 John R. Cobb's *Railton Mobil Special*, 1947

1379 Angel playing Flute

1380 Angel playing Lute

1376 Donald Campbell's *Bluebird CN7*, 1964

1381 Angel praying

(Des Roundel Design Group. Gravure De La Rue)

1998 (29 Sept–13 Oct). *British Land Speed Record Holders*. One phosphor band (20p.) or two phosphor bands (others). *P* 15×14.

2059	**1372**	20p. rosine, greenish yellow, magenta, new blue, black and silver (1 centre band)	50	40
		a. Perf 14½×13½ (1 side band at right) (13.10.98)	1·40	1·20
		aEb. Band at left	1·00	1·00
		ac. Booklet pane. Nos. 2059a and 2059a×2, with margins all round	5·00	
2060	**1373**	26p. rosine, greenish yellow, magenta, new blue, black and silver	75	50
		a. Rosine (face value) omitted	£4750	
		Eb. "2" from face value omitted	£3750	
		Ec. "6" from face value omitted	£3750	
2061	**1374**	30p. rosine, greenish yellow, magenta, new blue, black and silver	1·25	1·50
2062	**1375**	43p. rosine, greenish yellow, magenta, new blue, black and silver	1·50	1·60
2063	**1376**	63p. rosine, greenish yellow, magenta, new blue, black and silver	2·00	2·40
Set of 5			5·50	5·75
Set of 5 Gutter Pairs			13·00	
First Day Cover				6·50
Presentation Pack (P.O. Pack No. 291)			6·25	
PHQ Cards (set of 5) (201)			6·00	13·00

Nos. 2059/63 commemorate the 50th death anniversary of Sir Malcolm Campbell.

Nos. 2060a/Ec occur on the fourth vertical row of several sheets. Other examples show one or other of the figures partially omitted. Nos. 2059a/aEb come from the £6·16 British Land Speed Record Holders stamp booklet, No. DX21, and were printed by Walsall. There are minor differences of design between No. 2059 (sheet stamp printed by De La Rue) and Nos. 2059a/aEb (booklet stamps printed by Walsall), which omit the date and copyright symbol.

Special First Day of Issue Postmarks

British Philatelic Bureau, Edinburgh	6·50
Pendine	6·50

The mis-spelling 'PHILALETIC' in the Bureau datestamp was later corrected; same price, either spelling.

1377 Angel with Hands raised in Blessing

1378 Angel praying

(Des Irene von Treskow. Gravure De La Rue)

1998 (2 Nov). *Christmas. Angels*. One centre phosphor band (20p.) or two phosphor bands (others). *P* 15×14.

2064	**1377**	20p. gold, greenish yellow, magenta, new blue and grey-black	50	50
		a. Imperf (pair)	£1200	
2065	**1378**	26p. gold, greenish yellow, magenta, new blue and grey-black	75	60
		a. Imperf (pair)	£4500	
2066	**1379**	30p. gold, greenish yellow, magenta, new blue and grey-black	1·25	1·50
		a. Imperf (pair)	£1200	
2067	**1380**	43p. gold, greenish yellow, magenta, new blue and grey-black	1·50	1·60
		a. Imperf (pair)	£7000	
2068	**1381**	63p. gold, greenish yellow, magenta, new blue and grey-black	2·00	2·25
Set of 5			5·75	5·75
Set of 5 Gutter Pairs			12·50	
First Day Cover				6·50
Presentation Pack (P.O. Pack No. 292)			6·50	
PHQ Cards (set of 5) (202)			6·00	13·00

Special First Day of Issue Postmarks

British Philatelic Bureau, Edinburgh	6·50
Bethlehem	6·50

Collectors Pack 1998

1998 (2 Nov). Comprises Nos. 2015/30, 2034/8 and 2041/68.
CP2068a Collectors Pack ... 65·00

Post Office Yearbook

1998 (2 Nov). Comprises Nos. 2015/30, 2034/8 and 2041/68 in hardback book with slip case ... 60·00

1382 Greenwich Meridian and Clock (John Harrison's chronometer)

1383 Industrial Worker and Blast Furnace (James Watt's discovery of steam power)

1384 Early Photos of Leaves (Henry Fox-Talbot's photographic experiments)

1385 Computer inside Human Head (Alan Turing's work on computers)

(Des D. Gentleman (20p.), P. Howson (26p.), Z. and Barbara Baran (43p.), E. Paolozzi (63p.), gravure, Questa (63p. No. 2072a), Enschedé (20p.) or De La Rue (others))

1999 (12 Jan – 21 Sept). *Millennium Series. The Inventors' Tale.* One centre phosphor band (20p.) or two phosphor bands (others). *P* 14×14½.

2069	**1382**	20p. silver, deep grey, pale olive-grey, greenish grey, grey-black and bright rose-red	75	70
		a. Imperf (horiz pair)	£4750	
2070	**1383**	26p. silver, black, new blue, bright magenta and greenish yellow	95	1·00
2071	**1384**	43p. silver, greenish yellow, bright crimson, new blue, black and bright magenta	1·50	1·60
2072	**1385**	63p. greenish blue, greenish yellow, cerise, new blue, black and pale lemon	2·25	2·40
		a. Perf 13½×14 (21 Sept)	3·50	3·50
		ab. Booklet pane. No. 2072a×4 with margins all round	10·00	
Set of 4			5·25	5·25
Set of 4 Gutter Pairs			12·00	
First Day Cover (Philatelic Bureau) (Type J, see Introduction)			8·00	
First Day Cover (Greenwich, London SE)			8·00	
Presentation Pack (P.O. Pack No. 294)			7·50	
PHQ Cards (set of 4) (203)			6·00	13·00

No. 2072a comes from the £6·99 World Changers booklet, No. DX23.

Special First Day of Issue Postmark

FIRST DAY OF ISSUE
GREENWICH LONDON SE
12-1-1999

1386 Airliner hugging Globe (International air travel)

1387 Woman on Bicycle (Development of the bicycle)

1388 Victorian Railway Station (Growth of public transport)

1389 Captain Cook and Maori (Captain James Cook's voyages)

(Des G. Hardie (20p.), Sara Fanelli (26p.), J. Lawrence (43p.), A. Klimowski (63p.). Gravure Enschedé (20p., 63p.) or De La Rue (26p.). Litho Enschedé (43p.))

1999 (2 Feb). *Millennium Series. The Travellers' Tale.* One centre phosphor band (20p.) or two phosphor bands (others). *P* 14×14½.

2073	**1386**	20p. silver, vermilion, grey-black, bluish violet, greenish blue and pale grey	75	70
2074	**1387**	26p. silver, greenish yellow, cerise, new blue, black and vermilion	95	1·00
2075	**1388**	43p. grey-black, stone and bronze	1·50	1·60
2076	**1389**	63p. silver, grey-black, new blue, bright magenta and greenish yellow	2·25	2·40
Set of 4			5·25	5·25
Set of 4 Gutter Pairs			12·00	
First Day Cover (Philatelic Bureau) (Type J, see Introduction)			7·00	
First Day Cover (Coventry)			7·00	
Presentation Pack (P.O. Pack No. 295)			7·50	
PHQ Cards (set of 4) (204)			6·00	13·00

Special First Day of Issue Postmark

FIRST DAY OF ISSUE COVENTRY
2-2-1999

For Nos. 2077/9 see Decimal Machins Definitive section

1391 Vaccinating Child (pattern in cow markings) (Jenner's development of smallpox vaccine)

1392 Patient on Trolley (nursing care)

1393 Penicillin Mould (Fleming's discovery of penicillin)

1394 Sculpture of Test-tube Baby (development of in-vitro fertilization)

(Des P. Brookes (20p.), Susan Macfarlane (26p.), M. Dempsey (43p.), A. Gormley (63p.). Gravure Questa.)

1999 (2 Mar – 21 Sept). *Millennium Series. The Patients' Tale.* One centre phosphor band (20p.) or two phosphor bands (others). *P* 13½×14.

2080	**1391**	20p. greenish yellow, bright magenta, new blue, black and silver	75	70
		a. Booklet pane. No. 2080×4 with margins all round (21 Sept)	2·50	
2081	**1392**	26p. greenish yellow, bright magenta, new blue, black, silver and deep turquoise-blue	95	1·00
		a. Imperf (pair)	£8500	
2082	**1393**	43p. greenish yellow, bright magenta, new blue, black, deep bluish green and silver	1·50	1·60
2083	**1394**	63p. greenish yellow, bright magenta, new blue, black, silver and blue-black	2·25	2·40
Set of 4			5·25	5·25
Set of 4 Gutter Pairs			12·00	
First Day Cover (Philatelic Bureau) (Type J, see Introduction)			7·00	
First Day Cover (Oldham)			7·00	
Presentation Pack (P.O. Pack No. 296)			7·00	
PHQ Cards (set of 4) (205)			6·00	13·00

No. 2080a comes from the £6·99 World Changers booklet, No. DX23.

Special First Day of Issue Postmark

1395 Dove and Norman Settler (medieval migration to Scotland)

1396 Pilgrim Fathers and Red Indian (17th-century migration to America)

1397 Sailing Ship and Aspects of Settlement (19th-century migration to Australia)

1398 Hummingbird and Superimposed Stylized Face (20th-century migration to Great Britain)

(Des J. Byrne (20p.), W. McLean (26p.), J. Fisher (43p.), G. Powell (63p.). Litho (20p.) or gravure (others) Walsall)

1999 (6 Apr – 12 May). *Millennium Series. The Settlers' Tale.* One centre phosphor band (20p.) or two phosphor bands (others). *P* 14×14½.

2084	**1395**	20p. gold, silver, black, magenta, blue and greenish yellow	75	70
2085	**1396**	26p. greenish yellow, magenta, new blue, grey-black and silver	95	1·00
		a. Booklet pane. Nos. 2085 and 2089 with margins all round (12 May)	6·50	
2086	**1397**	43p. greenish yellow, magenta, new blue, grey-black, gold and chocolate	2·00	1·75
2087	**1398**	63p. greenish yellow, magenta, new blue, reddish violet, deep reddish violet and gold	3·00	3·00
Set of 4			5·75	5·75
Set of 4 Gutter Pairs			12·00	
First Day Cover (Philatelic Bureau) (Type J, see Introduction)			7·00	
First Day Cover (Plymouth)			7·00	
Presentation Pack (P.O. Pack No. 297)			7·00	
PHQ Cards (set of 4) (206)			8·50	13·00

No. 2085a comes from the £2·60 booklet, No. HBA1.

Imperf pairs of Nos. 2085 and 2089 are known and believed to be of proof status (*Price* £750).

Imperf pairs of No. 2085 with silver and phosphor omitted are known and believed to be of proof status (*Price* £350).

Imperf pairs of No. 2086 are known with gold, chocolate and phosphor omitted and believed to be of proof status (*Price* £350).

Special First Day of Issue Postmark

1399 Woven Threads (woollen industry)

1400 Salts Mill, Saltaire (worsted cloth industry)

1401 Hull on Slipway (shipbuilding)

1402 Lloyd's Building (City of London finance centre)

(Des P. Collingwood (19p.), D. Hockney (26p.), B. Sanderson (44p.), B. Neiland (64p.). Litho (19p.) or gravure (others) De La Rue)

1999 (4 May). *Millennium Series. The Workers' Tale.* One centre phosphor band (19p.) or two phosphor bands (others). P 14×14½.

2088	**1399**	19p. drab, greenish yellow, cerise, new blue, grey-black and bronze	75	70
		a. Bronze (Queen's head) omitted	£750	
		aEy. Bronze and phosphor omitted	£750	
2089	**1400**	26p. silver, greenish yellow, rosine, new blue and grey-black	95	1·00
2090	**1401**	44p. silver, greenish yellow, orangered, bright blue, yellow-brown and grey-black	1·75	1·60
2091	**1402**	64p. silver, greenish yellow, rosine, new blue and grey-black	2·25	2·40
Set of 4			5·25	5·25
Set of 4 Gutter Pairs			12·00	
First Day Cover (Philatelic Bureau) (Type J, see Introduction)			7·00	
First Day Cover (Belfast)			7·50	
Presentation Pack (P.O. Pack No. 298)			7·50	
PHQ Cards (set of 4) (207)			8·50	13·00

For No. 2089, printed by Walsall in photogravure, see booklet pane No. 2085a.

Special First Day of Issue Postmark

1403 Freddie Mercury (lead singer of Queen) ("Popular Music")

1404 Bobby Moore with World Cup, 1966 ("Sport")

1405 Dalek from *Dr. Who* (science-fiction series) ("Television")

1406 Charlie Chaplin (film star) ("Cinema")

(Des P. Blake (19p.), M. White (26p.), Lord Snowdon (44p.),
R. Steadman (64p.). Gravure Enschedé)

1999 (1 June). *Millennium Series. The Entertainers' Tale.* One centre phosphor band (19p.) or two phosphor bands (others). P 14×14½.

2092	**1403**	19p. greenish yellow, bright magenta, new blue, grey-black and gold........	75	70
2093	**1404**	26p. greenish yellow, bright magenta, new blue, grey-black, gold and stone	95	1·00
2094	**1405**	44p. greenish yellow, bright magenta, new blue, grey-black and silver......	1·50	1·60
2095	**1406**	64p. greenish yellow, bright magenta, new blue, grey-black and silver......	2·25	2·40
Set of 4			5·25	5·25
Set of 4 Gutter Pairs..			12·00	
First Day Cover (Philatelic Bureau) (Type J, see Introduction)..				7·00
First Day Cover (Wembley)				7·50
Presentation Pack (P.O. Pack No. 299)............			7·50	
PHQ Cards (set of 4) (208)			8·50	13·00

Special First Day of Issue Postmark

1407 Prince Edward and Miss Sophie Rhys-Jones (from photos by John Swannell)   **1408**

(Adapted J. Gibbs. Gravure De La Rue)

1999 (15 June). *Royal Wedding.* Two phosphor bands. P 15×14.

2096	**1407**	26p. vermilion, black, grey-black and silver	85	85
		a. Imperf (pair).................................	£2800	
2097	**1408**	64p. new blue, black, grey-black and silver	2·50	2·50
Set of 2			3·00	3·00
Set of 2 Gutter Pairs..			7·00	
First Day Cover (Philatelic Bureau)				4·00
First Day Cover (Windsor)				4·50
Presentation Pack (P.O. Pack No. M01)...........			4·00	
PHQ Cards (set of 2) (PSM1)............................			8·50	6·75

Special First Day of Issue Postmarks

1409 Suffragette behind Prison Window (Equal Rights for Women)   **1410** Water Tap (Right to Health)

1411 Generations of School Children (Right to Education)   **1412** "MAGNA CARTA" (Human Rights)

(Des Natasha Kerr (19p.), M. Craig-Martin (26p.), A. Drummond (44p.), A. Kitching (64p.). Gravure De La Rue)

1999 (6 July). *Millennium Series. The Citizens' Tale.* One centre phosphor band (19p.) or two phosphor bands (others). P 14×14½.

2098	**1409**	19p. silver, greenish yellow, cerise, new blue and grey-black	75	70
2099	**1410**	26p. grey-black, new blue, bright mauve, rosine, turquoise-green and apple-green	95	1·00
2100	**1411**	44p. bright blue, greenish yellow, cerise, new blue and grey-black......	1·75	1·60
2101	**1412**	64p. gold, greenish yellow, cerise, new blue and grey-black	2·50	2·40
Set of 4			5·75	5·25
Set of 4 Gutter Pairs..			12·00	
First Day Cover (Philatelic Bureau) (Type J, see Introduction)..				7·00
First Day Cover (Newtown, Powis)				7·50
Presentation Pack (P.O. Pack No. 300)............			7·50	
PHQ Cards (set of 4) (209)			8·50	13·00

Special First Day of Issue Postmark

1413 Molecular Structures (DNA Decoding)   **1414** Galapagos Finch and Fossilized Skeleton (Darwin's Theory of Evolution)

1415 Rotation of Polarized Light by Magnetism (Faraday's work on Electricity)   **1416** Saturn (development of astronomical telescopes)

(Des M. Curtis (19p.), R. Harris Ching (26p.), C. Gray (44p.), from Hubble Space Telescope photograph (64p.). Gravure (19p., 64p.) or litho (26p., 44p.). Questa)

1999 (3 Aug – 21 Sept). *Millennium Series. The Scientists' Tale.* One centre phosphor band (19p.) or two phosphor bands (others). P 13½×14 (19p., 64p.) or 14×14½ (26p., 44p.).

2102	**1413**	19p. bright magenta, greenish yellow, new blue, black and silver	75	70
2103	**1414**	26p. greenish yellow, bright magenta, new blue, black, bronze and reddish violet	1·50	1·00
		a. Imperf (pair).................................	£1800	
		b. Perf 14½×14 (21 Sept)	2·50	2·50

		ba. Booklet pane. No. 2103b×4 with margins all round	8·00	
2104	**1415**	44p. greenish yellow, bright magenta, new blue, black and gold	1·50	1·60
		a. Perf 14½×14 (21 Sept)	2·75	2·75
		ab. Booklet pane. No. 2104a×4 with margins all round	9·00	
2105	**1416**	64p. bright magenta, greenish yellow, new blue, black and silver	2·25	2·40

Set of 4 .... 5·25 5·25
Set of 4 Gutter Pairs .... 13·00
First Day Cover (Philatelic Bureau) (Type J, see Introduction)... 7·00
First Day Cover (Cambridge)................... 7·50
Presentation Pack (P.O. Pack No. 301)..... 7·50
PHQ Cards (set of 4) (210)...................... 8·50 13·00

Nos. 2103b and 2104a come from the £6·99 World Changers booklet, No. DX23.

Special First Day of Issue Postmark

FIRST DAY OF ISSUE CAMBRIDGE
3-8-1999

(Photo De La Rue)

1999 (11 Aug). *Solar Eclipse*. Sheet 89×121 mm. Two phosphor bands. *P* 14×14½.

MS2106 T	**1416**×4 (sold at £2·56)		22·00	22·00
	a. Imperf		£18000	

First Day Cover (Philatelic Bureau).......... 24·00
First Day Cover (Falmouth)....................... 24·00

Special First Day of Issue Postmarks

FIRST DAY OF ISSUE BRITISH PHILATELIC BUREAU EDINBURGH
11-8-1999

FIRST DAY OF ISSUE FALMOUTH
11-8-1999

1417 Upland Landscape (Strip Farming)

1418 Horse-drawn Rotary Seed Drill (Mechanical Farming)

1419 Man peeling Potato (Food Imports)

1420 Aerial View of Combine Harvester (Satellite Agriculture)

(Des D. Tress (19p.), C. Wormell (26p.), Tessa Traeger (44p.), R. Cooke (64p.). Gravure Walsall (No. 2108a) or De La Rue (others))

1999 (7 – 21 Sept). *Millennium Series. The Farmers' Tale*. One centre phosphor band (19p.) or two phosphor bands (others). *P* 14×14½.

2107	**1417**	19p. grey-black, greenish yellow, cerise, new blue and silver	75	70
2108	**1418**	26p. chestnut, orange-brown, violet-blue, grey-black, pale turquoise-green and silver	95	1·00
		a. Booklet pane. No. 2108×2 with margins all round (21 Sept)	6·50	

2109	**1419**	44p. silver, yellow-brown, brown and grey-black	2·00	1·60
2110	**1420**	64p. deep brown, greenish yellow, magenta, new blue and silver	2·50	2·40

Set of 4 .... 5·75 5·25
Set of 4 Gutter Pairs .... 12·00
First Day Cover (Philatelic Bureau) (Type J, see Introduction)... 7·00
First Day Cover (Laxton, Newark).............. 7·50
Presentation Pack (P.O. Pack No. 302)..... 7·50
PHQ Cards (set of 4) (211)...................... 8·50 13·00

The 19p. includes the "EUROPA" emblem. No. 2108a comes from the £2·60 booklet, No. HBA2.

Special First Day of Issue Postmark

FIRST DAY OF ISSUE LAXTON NEWARK
7-9-1999

1421 Robert the Bruce (Battle of Bannockburn, 1314)

1422 Cavalier and Horse (English Civil War)

1423 War Graves Cemetery, The Somme (World Wars)

1424 Soldiers with Boy (Peace-keeping)

(Des A. Davidson (19p.), R. Kelly (26p.), D. McCullin (44p.), C. Corr (64p.). Litho (19p.) or gravure (others) Walsall)

1999 (5 Oct). *Millennium Series. The Soldiers' Tale*. One centre phosphor band (19p.) or two phosphor bands (others). *P* 14×14½.

2111	**1421**	19p. black, stone and silver	75	70
2112	**1422**	26p. lemon, black, grey, silver and gold	95	1·00
2113	**1423**	44p. grey-black, black and silver	2·00	1·60
2114	**1424**	64p. greenish yellow, red-orange, bright magenta, pale new blue, black and bright blue	2·50	2·40

Set of 4 .... 5·75 5·25
Set of 4 Gutter Pairs .... 12·00
First Day Cover (Philatelic Bureau) (Type J, see Introduction)... 7·00
First Day Cover (London SW).................... 7·50
Presentation Pack (P.O. Pack No. 303*)..... 7·50
PHQ Cards (set of 4) (212)...................... 8·50 13·00

*The presentation pack was numbered 302 in error.

Special First Day of Issue Postmark

FIRST DAY OF ISSUE LONDON SW
5-10-1999

1425 "Hark the herald angels sing" and Hymn book (John Wesley)

1426 King James I and Bible (Authorised Version of Bible)

1427 St. Andrews Cathedral, Fife ("Pilgrimage")

1428 Nativity ("First Christmas")

(Des B. Neuenschwander (19p.), Clare Melinsky (26p.), Catherine Yass (44p.), C. Aitchison (64p.). Gravure De La Rue)

1999 (2 Nov). *Millennium Series. The Christians' Tale.* One centre phosphor band (19p.) or two phosphor bands (others). P 14×14½.

2115	**1425**	19p. gold, stone, greenish yellow, bright crimson, deep dull blue, black and yellow-ochre		75	70
		a. Imperf (pair)		£900	
2116	**1426**	26p. gold, greenish yellow, bright scarlet, emerald, dull violet and black		95	1·00
2117	**1427**	44p. gold, greenish yellow, bright magenta, new blue, black and ultramarine		1·50	1·60
2118	**1428**	64p. gold, bistre-yellow, cerise, bright emerald, bistre, slate-blue, pale new blue and black		2·25	2·40
Set of 4				5·25	5·25
Set of 4 Gutter Pairs				12·00	
First Day Cover (Philatelic Bureau) (Type J, see Introduction)					7·00
First Day Cover (St. Andrews, Fife)					7·50
Presentation Pack (P.O. Pack No. 304)				7·50	
PHQ Cards (set of 4) (213)				8·50	13·00

Special First Day of Issue Postmark

1429 "World of the Stage" (Allen Jones)

1430 "World of Music" (Bridget Riley)

1431 "World of Literature" (Lisa Milroy)

1432 "New Worlds" (Sir Howard Hodgkin)

(Gravure Walsall)

1999 (7 Dec). *Millennium Series. The Artists' Tale.* One centre phosphor band (19p.) or two phosphor bands (others). P 14×14½.

2119	**1429**	19p. greenish yellow, bright magenta, new blue, black and silver		75	70
2120	**1430**	26p. lemon, orange, pale new blue, violet-blue and black		95	1·00
2121	**1431**	44p. greenish yellow, bright magenta, new blue, black and gold		1·50	1·60
2122	**1432**	64p. greenish yellow, yellow, bright turquoise-green, bright magenta, new blue, black, gold and silver		2·25	2·40
Set of 4				5·25	5·25
Set of 4 Gutter Pairs				13·00	
First Day Cover (Philatelic Bureau) (Type J, see Introduction)					7·00
First Day Cover (Stratford-upon-Avon)					7·50
Presentation Pack (P.O. Pack No. 305)				7·50	
PHQ Cards (set of 4) (214)				8·50	13·00

Special First Day of Issue Postmark

Collectors Pack 1999

1999 (7 Dec). Comprises Nos. 2069/76, 2080/105 and 2107/22.

CP2122*a* Collectors Pack .... 90·00

Post Office Yearbook

1999 (7 Dec). Comprises Nos. 2069/76, 2080/105 and 2107/22 in hardback book with slip case .... 90·00

1433a (*Illustration reduced. Actual Size* 121×90 *mm*)

(Des D. Gentleman. Gravure De La Rue)

1999 (14 Dec). *Millennium Series. 'Millennium Timekeeper'* Sheet 120×89 mm. Each design silver, deep grey, pale olive-grey, greenish grey, grey-black and bright rose-red. Two phosphor bands. P 14×14½.

MS2123	**1433a**	64p. Clock face and map of North America; 64p. Clock face and map of Asia; 64p. Clock face and map of Middle East; 64p. Clock face and map of Europe	20·00	20·00
First Day Cover (Philatelic Bureau)				21·00
First Day Cover (Greenwich SE)				21·00
Presentation Pack (P.O. Pack No. M02)			22·00	
PHQ Cards (set of 5) (PSM02)			11·00	24·00

No. **MS**2123 also exists overprinted "EARLS COURT, LONDON 22-28 MAY 2000 THE STAMP SHOW 2000" from Exhibition Premium Passes, costing £10, available from 1 March 2000 (*Price* £28).

The five PHQ cards show the four individual stamps and the complete miniature sheet.

Special First Day of Issue Postmarks

For No. 2124 see Decimal Machin Definitives section.

1438 Barn Owl (World Owl Trust, Muncaster)

1439 Night Sky (National Space Science Centre, Leicester)

1440 River Goyt and Textile Mills (Torrs Walkway, New Mills)

1441 Gannets (Seabird Centre, North Berwick)

1442 Millennium Beacon (Beacons across The Land)

1443 Garratt Steam Locomotive No. 143 pulling Train (Rheilffordd Eryri, Welsh Highland Railway)

1444 Lightning (Dynamic Earth Centre, Edinburgh)

1445 Multicoloured Lights (Lighting Croydon's Skyline)

(Litho (44p.), gravure (others) Walsall (No. 2126a/ab) or Questa (others))

2000 (18 Jan)–**02**. *Millennium Projects (1st series).* *'Above and Beyond'* One centre phosphor band (19p.) or two phosphor bands (others). *P* 14×14½ (1st, 44p.) or 13½×14 (others).

2125	**1438**	19p. greenish yellow, magenta, pale new blue, black and silver	1·25	70
		a. Imperf (pair)	£1800	
2126	**1439**	26p. greenish yellow, magenta, pale new blue, black and silver	95	1·00
		aa. Imperf (pair)	£1800	
2126*a*		(1st) greenish yellow, magenta, pale new blue, black and silver (26.5.00)	5·25	4·50
		ab. Booklet pane. Nos. 2126a and 2139 with margins all round	7·00	
		ac. Booklet pane. No. 2126a×4 with margins all round (24.9.02)	15·00	
2127	**1440**	44p. black, bistre-brown, buff and silver	1·75	1·75
2128	**1441**	64p. greenish yellow, magenta, blue, black, silver and orange	2·75	2·75
Set of 4 (ex No. 2126a)			6·00	6·00
Set of 4 Gutter Pairs			13·00	
First Day Cover (Nos. 2125/8) (Philatelic Bureau) (Type J, see Introduction)				7·00
First Day Cover (Nos. 2125/8) (Muncaster, Ravenglass)				7·50
First Day Cover (No. 2126ab) (Philatelic Bureau)				7·50
First Day Cover (No. 2126ab) (Leicester)				7·50
Presentation Pack (P.O. Pack No. 307)			7·00	
PHQ Cards (set of 4) (215)			8·50	13·00

No. 2126ab comes from the £2·70 Millennium booklet, No. HBA3. No. 2162ac comes from the "Across the Universe" sponsored booklet, No. DX29.

Imperforate pairs of No. 2125 with Queen's head in gold, Nos. 2126 and 2139 with inscriptions in an alternative typeface and No. 2128 with inscriptions in silver are all of proof status (*Prices from £200*).

Special First Day of Issue Postmarks

(Gravure De La Rue)

2000 (1 Feb). *Millennium Projects (2nd series).* *'Fire and Light'.* One centre phosphor band (19p.) or two phosphor bands (others). *P* 14×14½.

2129	**1442**	19p. silver, greenish yellow, bright magenta, new blue and black	75	70
2130	**1443**	26p. silver, greenish yellow, bright magenta, new blue and black	1·25	1·00
2131	**1444**	44p. silver, greenish yellow, bright magenta, new blue and black	1·50	1·50
2132	**1445**	64p. silver, greenish yellow, bright magenta, pale greenish blue and black	2·25	2·50
Set of 4			5·50	5·50
Set of 4 Gutter Pairs			13·00	
First Day Cover (Philatelic Bureau) (Type J, see Introduction)				7·00
First Day Cover (Edinburgh 3°10'W)				7·50
Presentation Pack (P.O. Pack No. 308)			7·00	
PHQ Cards (set of 4) (216)			8·50	13·00

Special First Day of Issue Postmark

1446 Queen Victoria and Queen Elizabeth II

(Des J. Matthews. Gravure Walsall)

2000 (15 Feb). *T* **929** redrawn with *1st* face value as *T* **1446**. Two phosphor bands. *P* 14 (with one elliptical hole in each vertical side).

2133	**1446**	(1st) brownish black and cream	2·75	2·75
		l. Booklet pane. No. 2133l×6 with margins all round	12·00	
First Day Cover (No. 2133l) (Philatelic Bureau)				4·00
First Day Cover (No. 2133l) (London SW5)				4·00

No. 2133 was only issued in the £7·50 "Special by Design" booklet, No. DX24. For illustrations of first day cover cancellations see below No. 2124.

For No. 2133 perf 14½×14 see No. 2956.

1447 Beach Pebbles (Turning the Tide, Durham Coast)

1448 Frog's Legs and Water Lilies (National Pondlife Centre, Merseyside)

1449 Cliff Boardwalk (Parc Arfordirol, Llanelli Coast)

1450 Reflections in Water (Portsmouth Harbour Development)

(Litho (44p.), gravure (others) Walsall)

2000 (7 Mar). *Millennium Projects (3rd series). 'Water and Coast'*. One centre phosphor band (19p.) or two phosphor bands (others). P 14×14½.

2134	**1447**	19p. silver, black, dull blue, sage green, olive-grey, orange-yellow and pale grey..........................	75	70
2135	**1448**	26p. new blue, silver, black, greenish yellow and magenta..........................	1·25	1·00
2136	**1449**	44p. black, grey and silver..........................	1·50	1·50
2137	**1450**	64p. black, grey, deep bluish green, greenish blue, cobalt, grey-green and brownish grey	2·25	2·50
Set of 4			5·50	5·50
Set of 4 Gutter Pairs..........................			13·00	
First Day Cover (Philatelic Bureau) (Type J, see Introduction)..........................				7·00
First Day Cover (Llanelli)..........................				7·50
Presentation Pack (P.O. Pack No. 309)..........................			7·00	
PHQ Cards (set of 4) (217)			8·50	13·00

Special First Day of Issue Postmark

1451 Reed Beds, River Braid (ECOS, Ballymena)

1452 South American Leaf-cutter Ants ("Web of Life" Exhibition, London Zoo)

1453 Solar Sensors (Earth Centre, Doncaster)

1454 Hydroponic Leaves (Project SUZY, Teesside)

(Gravure De La Rue)

2000 (4 Apr). *Millennium Projects (4th series). 'Life and Earth'*. One centre phosphor band (2nd) or two phosphor bands (others). P 14×14½.

2138	**1451**	(2nd) silver, greenish yellow, magenta, new blue, black and grey..................	1·00	70
2139	**1452**	(1st) silver, greenish yellow, magenta, new blue and black	1·25	1·00
		a. Imperf (pair).		
2140	**1453**	44p. silver, greenish yellow, magenta, new blue and black	1·50	1·50
2141	**1454**	64p. silver, greenish yellow, magenta, new blue and grey-black..................	2·25	1·50
Set of 4			5·75	5·50
Set of 4 Gutter Pairs..........................			13·00	
First Day Cover (Philatelic Bureau) (Type J, see Introduction)..........................				7·00
First Day Cover (Doncaster)..........................				7·50
Presentation Pack (P.O. Pack No. 310)..........................			7·00	
PHQ Cards (set of 4) (218)			8·50	13·00

For No. 2139 printed by Walsall in photogravure, see booklet pane No. 2126ab.

Types **1453/4** with face values of 45p. and 65p. were prepared, but not issued.

Special First Day of Issue Postmark

1455 Pottery Glaze (Ceramica Museum, Stoke-on-Trent)

1456 Bankside Galleries (Tate Modern, London)

1457 Road Marking (Cycle Network Artworks)

1458 People of Salford (Lowry Centre, Salford)

(Gravure Enschedé)

2000 (2 May). *Millennium Projects (5th series). 'Art and Craft'*. One centre phosphor band (2nd) or two phosphor bands (others). P 14×14½.

2142	**1455**	(2nd) greenish yellow, magenta, new black, silver and grey brown .	1·00	70
2143	**1456**	(1st) greenish yellow, magenta, new blue, black and silver..........................	1·25	1·00
2144	**1457**	45p. greenish yellow, magenta, new blue, black and silver..........................	1·50	1·50
2145	**1458**	65p. greenish yellow, magenta, new blue, black, dull silver and silver	2·25	2·50
Set of 4			5·75	5·50
Set of 4 Gutter Pairs..........................			13·00	
First Day Cover (Philatelic Bureau) (Type J, see Introduction)..........................				7·00
First Day Cover (Salford)				7·50
Presentation Pack (P.O. Pack No. 311)..........................			7·50	
PHQ Cards (set of 4) (219)			8·50	13·00

Special First Day of Issue Postmark

For Nos. **MS**2146/7 see Decimal Machin Definitives section.

1460 Children playing (Millennium Greens Project)

1461 Millennium Bridge, Gateshead

1462 Daisies (Mile End Park, London)

1463 African Hut and Thatched Cottage ("On the Meridian Line" Project)

(Gravure (2nd, 45p.) or litho (1st, 65p.) Walsall)

2000 (6 June). *Millennium Projects (6th series). 'People and Places'.* One centre phosphor band (2nd) or two phosphor bands (others). P 14×14½.

2148	**1460**	(2nd) bistre-yellow, bright magenta, new blue, grey-black and silver	1·00	70
2149	**1461**	(1st) deep ultramarine, silver, black, new blue, bright magenta and greenish yellow	1·25	1·00
2150	**1462**	45p. greenish yellow, magenta, pale new blue, grey-black, silver and deep turquoise-green	1·50	1·50
2151	**1463**	65p. silver, black, new blue, bright magenta and greenish yellow	2·25	2·50
Set of 4			5·75	5·50
Set of 4 Gutter Pairs			13·00	
First Day Cover (Philatelic Bureau) (Type J, see Introduction)				7·00
First Day Cover (Gateshead)				7·50
Presentation Pack (P.O. Pack No. 312)			7·50	
PHQ Cards (set of 4) (220)			8·50	13·00

Special First Day of Issue Postmark

1464 Raising the Stone (Strangford Stone, Killyleagh)

1465 Horse's Hooves (Trans Pennine Trail, Derbyshire)

1466 Cyclist (Kingdom of Fife Cycle Ways, Scotland)

1467 Bluebell Wood (Groundwork's "Changing Places" Project)

(Gravure Walsall (Nos. 2153a, 2155a) or Enschedé (others))

2000 (4 July–18 Sept). *Millennium Projects (7th series). 'Stone and Soil'.* One centre phosphor band (2nd) or two phosphor bands (others). P 14×14½

2152	**1464**	(2nd) brownish black, grey-black and silver	1·00	70
2153	**1465**	(1st) greenish yellow, bright magenta, new blue, grey-black, silver and grey	1·25	1·00
		a. Booklet pane. Nos. 2153 and 2157 with margins all round (18 Sept)	9·00	
2154	**1466**	45p. brownish black, grey-black, black and silver	1·50	1·75
2155	**1467**	65p. greenish yellow, bright magenta, new blue, black and silver	2·50	2·50
		a. Booklet pane. No. 2155×2 with margins all round (18 Sept)	5·00	
Set of 4			5·75	5·75
Set of 4 Gutter Pairs			13·00	
First Day Cover (Philatelic Bureau) (Type J, see Introduction)				7·00
First Day Cover (Killyleagh)				7·50
Presentation Pack (P.O. Pack No. 313)			7·50	
PHQ Cards (set of 4) (221)			8·50	13·00

No. 2153a comes from the £2·70 "Millenium" booklet, No. HBA4. No. 2155a comes from the £7 "Treasury of Trees" booklet, No. DX26.

Special First Day of Issue Postmark

1468 Tree Roots ("Yews for the Millennium" Project)

1469 Sunflower ("Eden" Project, St. Austell)

1470 Sycamore Seeds (Millennium Seed Bank, Wakehurst Place, West Sussex)

1471 Forest, Doire Dach ("Forest for Scotland")

(Gravure Walsall (Nos. 2156a, 2158a, 2159a) or De La Rue (others))

2000 (1 Aug – 18 Sept). *Millennium Projects (8th series). 'Tree and Leaf'.* One centre phosphor band (2nd) or two phosphor bands (others)). P 14×14½.

2156	**1468**	(2nd) silver, greenish yellow, magenta, new blue and black	1·00	70
		a. Booklet pane. No. 2156×4 with margins all round (18 Sept)	4·50	
2157	**1469**	(1st) greenish yellow, magenta, new blue, black and silver	1·25	1·00

2158	1470	45p. black, greenish yellow, magenta, new blue, grey-black and silver.......	1·50	1·60
		a. Booklet pane. No. 2158×4 with margins all round (18 Sept)..............	6·50	
2159	1471	65p. silver, greenish yellow, magenta, new blue and black	2·50	2·50
		a. Booklet pane. No. 2159×2 with margins all round (18 Sept).............	5·50	

Set of 4...	5·75	5·50
Set of 4 Gutter Pairs.......................................	13·00	
First Day Cover (Philatelic Bureau) (Type J, see Introduction)...		7·00
First Day Cover (St Austell)............................		7·50
Presentation Pack (P.O. Pack No. 314)........................	7·50	
PHQ Cards (set of 4) (222)............................	8·50	13·00

Nos. 2156a, 2158a and 2159a come from the £7 Treasury of Trees booklet, No. DX26. For No. 2157 printed by Walsall in photogravure, see booklet pane No. 2153a.

Special First Day of Issue Postmark

1-8-2000

1472 Queen Elizabeth the Queen Mother

1472a Royal Family on Queen Mother's 100th Birthday

(Des J. Gibbs from photo by J. Swannell. Gravure Questa (Nos. 2160, **MS**2161a) or De La Rue (No. **MS**2161))

2000 (4 Aug). *Queen Elizabeth the Queen Mother's 100th Birthday.* Phosphorised paper plus two phosphor bands. *P* 14½.

2160	1472	27p. silver, greenish yellow, magenta, new blue and black	2·50	2·75
		a. Booklet pane. No. 2160×4 with margins all round..................................	9·50	
MS2161	121×89mm.	**1472a** 27p.×4, silver, greenish yellow, magenta, new blue and black............................	11·00	11·00
		a. Booklet pane. As No. **MS**2161, but larger, 150×95 mm, and with additional silver frame	10·00	8·00

First Day Cover (No. 2160a) (Philatelic Bureau)...................		10·00
First Day Cover (No. 2160a) (London SW1)...........................		10·00
First Day Cover (**MS**2161) (Philatelic Bureau)......................		12·00
First Day Cover (**MS**2161) (London SW1)...............................		12·00
Presentation Pack (**MS**2161) (P.O. Pack No. M04)..............	38·00	
PHQ Cards (set of 5) (PSM04)........................	11·00	24·00

No. 2160 was only issued in the £7·08 "The Life of the Century" booklet, No. DX25 and as part of No. **MS**2161/a.

The complete miniature sheet is shown on one of the PHQ cards with the others depicting individual stamps.

Special First Day of Issue Postmarks

THE 100TH YEAR
4-8-2000

Clarence House
4-8-2000

1473 Head of *Gigantiops destructor* (Ant) (Wildscreen at Bristol)

1474 Gathering Water Lilies on Broads (Norfolk and Norwich Project)

1475 X-ray of Hand holding Computer Mouse (Millennium Point, Birmingham)

1476 Tartan Wool Holder (Scottish Cultural Resources Access Network)

(Litho Walsall)

2000 (5 Sept). *Millennium Projects (9th series). 'Mind and Matter'.* One centre phosphor band (2nd) or two phosphor bands (others). *P* 14×14½.

2162	1473	(2nd) black, orange-yellow, slate-green and silver.............................	1·00	70
2163	1474	(1st) black, sage-green, ochre and gold.	1·25	1·00
2164	1475	45p. silver, black, new blue, magenta and greenish yellow....................	1·50	1·75
2165	1476	65p. silver, black, new blue, magenta and greenish yellow....................	2·25	2·50

Set of 4	5·75	5·75
Set of 4 Gutter Pairs	13·00	
First Day Cover (Philatelic Bureau) (Type J, see Introduction)...		7·00
First Day Cover (Norwich)		7·50
Presentation Pack (P.O. Pack No. 315)................................	7·50	
PHQ Cards (set of 4) (223)........................	8·50	13·00

Special First Day of Issue Postmark

5-9-2000

1477 Acrobatic Performers (Millennium Dome)

1478 Football Players (Hampden Park, Glasgow)

1479 Bather (Bath Spa Project)

1480 Hen's Egg under Magnification (Centre for Life, Newcastle)

(Litho (2nd) or gravure (others) Questa)

2000 (3 Oct). *Millennium Projects (10th series).* *'Body and Bone'.* One centre phosphor band (2nd) or two phosphor bands (others). P 14×14½ (2nd) or 13½×14 (others).

2166	**1477**	(2nd) black, slate-blue and silver	1·00	70
2167	**1478**	(1st) magenta, new blue, greenish yellow, black and silver	1·25	1·00
2168	**1479**	45p. mauve, olive-grey, greenish yellow, grey-black and silver	1·50	1·50
2169	**1480**	65p. magenta, pale new blue, greenish yellow, grey-black and silver	2·25	2·50
		Set of 4	5·75	5·75
		Set of 4 Gutter Pairs	13·00	
		First Day Cover (Philatelic Bureau) (Type J, see Introduction)		7·00
		First Day Cover (Glasgow)		7·50
		Presentation Pack (P.O. Pack No. 316)	7·50	
		PHQ Cards (set of 4) (224)	8·50	13·00

Special First Day of Issue Postmark

1481 Virgin and Child Stained Glass Window, St. Edmundsbury Cathedral (Suffolk Cathedral Millennium Project)

1482 Floodlit Church of St. Peter and St. Paul, Overstowey (Church Floodlighting Trust)

1483 12th-cent Latin Gradual (St. Patrick Centre, Downpatrick)

1484 Chapter House Ceiling, York Minster (York Millennium Mystery Plays)

(Gravure De La Rue)

2000 (7 Nov). *Millennium Projects (11th series).* *'Spirit and Faith'.* One centre phosphor band (2nd) or two phosphor bands (others). P 14×14½.

2170	**1481**	(2nd) gold, greenish yellow, cerise, new blue and grey-black	1·00	70
		a. Imperf pair	£875	
2171	**1482**	(1st) gold, greenish yellow, cerise, new blue, bright blue, black and grey-black	1·25	1·00
		a. Imperf (pair)	£1000	
2172	**1483**	45p. deep reddish purple, olive-sepia, red, black and gold	1·50	1·50
2173	**1484**	65p. gold, greenish yellow, cerise, new blue, grey-black and black	2·25	2·50
		Set of 4	5·75	5·50

		Set of 4 Gutter Pairs	13·00	
		First Day Cover (Philatelic Bureau) (Type J, see Introduction)		7·00
		First Day Cover (Downpatrick)		7·50
		Presentation Pack (P.O. Pack No. 317)	7·50	
		PHQ Cards (set of 4) (225)	8·50	13·00

No. 2173 has been reported with the gold omitted, leaving the Queen's head in yellow. It is only known used.

Special First Day of Issue Postmark

Post Office Yearbook

2000 (Nov 7). Comprises Nos. 2125/6, 2127/32, 2134/45, 2148/59 and **MS**2161/77 in hardback book with slip case. ... £100

The last two issues in the Millennium Projects Series were supplied for insertion into the above at a later date.

1485 Church Bells (Ringing in the Millennium)

1486 Eye (Year of the Artist)

1487 Top of Harp (Canolfan Mileniwm, Cardiff)

1488 Silhouetted Figure within Latticework (TS2K Creative Enterprise Centres, London)

(Gravure De La Rue)

2000 (5 Dec). *Millennium Projects (12th series).* *'Sound and Vision'.* One centre phosphor band (2nd) or two phosphor bands (others). P 14×14½.

2174	**1485**	(2nd) silver, greenish yellow, magenta, new blue and black	1·00	70
2175	**1486**	(1st) silver, magenta, blue, black and brownish grey	1·25	1·00
2176	**1487**	45p. silver, greenish yellow, magenta, new blue and black	1·50	1·50
2177	**1488**	65p. black, greenish yellow, magenta, new blue, grey-black and silver	2·25	2·50
		Set of 4	5·75	5·50
		Set of 4 Gutter Pairs	13·00	
		First Day Cover (Philatelic Bureau) (Type J, see Introduction)		7·00
		First Day Cover (Cardiff)		7·50
		Presentation Pack (P.O. Pack No. 318)	7·50	
		PHQ Cards (set of 4) (226)	8·50	13·00

Special First Day of Issue Postmark

Collectors Pack 2000

2000 (Dec 5) Comprises Nos. 2125/6, 2127/32, 2134/45, 2148/59 and **MS**2161/77.

CP2177a Collectors Pack	£100

1489 "Flower" ("Nurture Children")

1490 "Tiger" ("Listen to Children")

1491 "Owl" ("Teach Children")

1492 "Butterfly" ("Ensure Children's Freedom")

(Des Why Not Associates. Gravure De La Rue)

2001 (16 Jan). *New Millennium. Rights of the Child. Face Paintings.* One centre phosphor band (2nd) or two phosphor bands (others). P 14×14½.

2178	**1489**	(2nd) bright violet, greenish yellow, cerise, new blue, rosine, grey-black and silver	1·00	75
2179	**1490**	(1st) lemon, greenish yellow, cerise, new blue, emerald, grey-black and silver	1·25	1·10
2180	**1491**	45p. orange-yellow, greenish yellow, cerise, new blue, pale violet-blue, grey-black and silver	1·60	1·75
2181	**1492**	65p. bright violet, greenish yellow, cerise, new blue, lemon, grey-black and silver	2·40	2·50
Set of 4			5·75	5·75
Set of 4 Gutter Pairs			13·00	
First Day Cover (Philatelic Bureau)				7·00
First Day Cover (Hope, Hope Valley)				7·50
Presentation Pack (P.O. Pack No. 319)			7·50	
PHQ Cards (set of 4) (227)			7·50	10·00

Special First Day of Issue Postmarks

1493 "Love"

1494 "THANKS"

1495 "abc" (New Baby)

1496 "WELCOME"

1497 " Cheers"

(Des Springpoint Design. Gravure Enschedé)

2001 (6 Feb). *Greetings Stamps. 'Occasions'.* Two phosphor bands. P 14×14½.

2182	**1493**	(1st) silver, greenish yellow, magenta, pale greenish blue, black and silver-grey	1·30	1·30
2183	**1494**	(1st) silver, greenish yellow, magenta, pale greenish blue, black and silver-grey	1·30	1·30
2184	**1495**	(1st) silver, greenish yellow, magenta, pale greenish blue, black and silver-grey	1·30	1·30
2185	**1496**	(1st) silver, greenish yellow, magenta, pale greenish blue, black and silver-grey	1·30	1·30
2186	**1497**	(1st) silver, greenish yellow, magenta, pale greenish blue, black and silver-grey	1·30	1·30
Set of 5			6·00	6·00
Set of 5 Gutter Pairs			13·00	
First Day Cover (Philatelic Bureau)				7·50
First Day Cover (Merry Hill, Wolverhampton)				8·00
Presentation Pack (13 Feb) (P.O. Pack No. M05)			10·00	
PHQ Cards (set of 5) (PSM05)			8·50	11·00

The silver-grey backgrounds are printed in Iriodin ink which gives a shiny effect.

Further packs of Nos. 2182/6 were sold from 3 July 2001. These comprised the listed stamps in blocks of ten (from sheets) with an insert describing the occasion (*Price £10 per pack*).

Nos. 2182/6 were re-issued on 1 May 2001 in sheets of 20 printed by Questa in lithography instead of photogravure, in connection with the "customised" stamps scheme. Such sheets contained twenty examples of either Nos. 2182, 2184 or 2185, or ten each of Nos. 2183 and 2186. Sheets with personal photographs printed on the labels were available from Royal Mail in Edinburgh at £12 each. From 5 June 2001 a similar sheet (LS4) containing four of each design in horizontal strips, with postal symbols on the labels, was sold at £5·95.

Special First Day of Issue Postmarks

1498 Dog and Owner on Bench

1499 Dog in Bath

1500 Boxer at Dog Show

1501 Cat in Handbag

1502 Cat on Gate

1503 Dog in Car

1504 Cat at Window

1505 Dog Behind Fence

1506 Cat watching Bird

1507 Cat in Washbasin

(Des johnson banks. Gravure Walsall)

2001 (13 Feb). *Cats and Dogs.* Self-adhesive. Two phosphor bands.
P 15×14 die-cut.

2187	**1498**	(1st) black, grey and silver	1·25	1·00
		a. Sheetlet. Nos. 2187/96	15·00	15·00
		aa. Imperf (sheetlet)	£24000	
		b. Booklet pane. Nos. 2187/96 plus No. 2040×2	30·00	
		ba. Imperf (pane)		
2188	**1499**	(1st) black, grey and silver	1·25	1·00
2189	**1500**	(1st) black, grey and silver	1·25	1·00
2190	**1501**	(1st) black, grey and silver	1·25	1·00
2191	**1502**	(1st) black, grey and silver	1·25	1·00
2192	**1503**	(1st) black, grey and silver	1·25	1·00
2193	**1504**	(1st) black, grey and silver	1·25	1·00
2194	**1505**	(1st) black, grey and silver	1·25	1·00
2195	**1506**	(1st) black, grey and silver	1·25	1·00
2196	**1507**	(1st) black, grey and silver	1·25	1·00
2187/96 *Set of 10*			15·00	15·00
First Day Cover (Philatelic Bureau)				15·00
First Day Cover (Petts Wood, Orpington)				16·00
Presentation Pack (P.O. Pack No. 320)			20·00	
PHQ Cards (set of 10) (228)			14·00	30·00

Nos. 2187/96 were printed together in sheetlets of ten (5×2), with the surplus self-adhesive paper around each stamp retained. The pane has vertical roulettes between rows 2/3 and 4/5 with the design on the reverse of the backing paper similar to Booklet No. PM1.

Special First Day of Issue Postmarks

1508 "RAIN"

1509 "FAIR"

1510 "STORMY"

1511 "VERY DRY"

(Des H. Brown and T. Meeuwissen. Gravure De La Rue)

2001 (13 Mar). *The Weather.* One side phosphor band (19p.) or two phosphor bands (others). P 14½.

2197	**1508**	19p. black, greenish yellow, bright magenta, new blue and gold	70	75
2198	**1509**	27p. black, greenish yellow, bright magenta, new blue and gold	85	1·00
2199	**1510**	45p. black, greenish yellow, bright magenta, new blue and gold	1·50	1·50
2200	**1511**	65p. black, greenish yellow, bright magenta, new blue and gold	2·40	2·50
Set of 4			5·00	5·50
Set of 4 Gutter Pairs			12·00	
First Day Cover (Philatelic Bureau)				7·00
First Day Cover (Fraserburgh)				8·00

Presentation Pack (P.O. Pack No. 321)		14·00
MS2201 105×105 mm. Nos. 2197/200	18·00	18·00
First Day Cover (Philatelic Bureau)		19·00
First Day Cover (Fraserburgh)		20·00
PHQ Cards (set of 5) (229)	8·50	20·00

Nos. 2197/200 show the four quadrants of a barometer dial which are combined on the miniature sheet. The reddish violet on both the 27p. and the miniature sheet is printed in thermochromic ink which changes from reddish violet to light blue when exposed to heat. The PHQ cards depict the four values and the miniature sheet.

Special First Day of Issue Postmarks

1512 Vanguard Class Submarine, 1992

1513 Swiftsure Class Submarine, 1973

1514 Unity Class Submarine, 1939

1515 "Holland" Type Submarine, 1901

1516 White Ensign

1517 Union Jack

1518 Jolly Roger flown by H.M.S. *Proteus* (submarine)

1519 Flag of Chief of Defence Staff

(Des D. Davis. Gravure Questa)

2001 (10 Apr – 22 Oct). *Centenary of Royal Navy Submarine Service.* One centre phosphor band (2nd) or two phosphor bands (others). P 15×14.

(a) Submarines. Ordinary gum.

2202	**1512**	(2nd) black, brownish black, dull purple and gold	1·00	75
		a. Perf 15½×15 (22 Oct)	3·75	3·00
		ab. Booklet pane. Nos. 2202a and 2204a, each×2, with margins all round	12·00	
2203	**1513**	(1st) black, azure, slate-blue and gold	1·25	90
		a. Perf 15½×15 (22 Oct)	3·75	3·00
		b. Imperf (pair)	£2000	
		ab. Booklet pane. Nos. 2203a and 2205a, each×2, with margins all round	12·00	
2204	**1514**	45p. magenta, chrome yellow, new blue, black and gold	1·75	1·60
		a. Perf 15½×15 (22 Oct)	3·75	3·00
2205	**1515**	65p. magenta, chrome yellow, new blue, black and gold	2·40	2·50
		a. Perf 15½×15 (22 Oct)	3·75	3·00
Set of 4			5·75	5·25

Set of 4 Gutter Pairs..	13·00	
First Day Cover (Philatelic Bureau)		7·00
First Day Cover (Portsmouth)		8·00
Presentation Pack (P.O. Pack No. 322)........................	20·00	
PHQ Cards (set of 4) (230)..	7·50	12·00

(b) Flags. Ordinary gum. P 14½.

MS2206 92×97 mm. **1516** (1st) bright scarlet, blue and silver; **1517** (1st) bright scarlet, blue and silver; **1518** (1st) black, blue and silver; **1519** (1st) bright scarlet, blue, greenish yellow, black and silver (22 Oct).. 9·00 9·00

a. Booklet pane. As No. **MS**2206 but larger, 152×96 mm	9·00	
First Day Cover (Tallents House)		11·00
First Day Cover (Rosyth, Dunfermline)		12·00
Presentation Pack (P.O. Pack No. M06)	30·00	
PHQ Cards (set of 5) (PSM07)....................................	12·00	15·00

(c) Self-adhesive. Die-cut P 15½×14 (No. 2207) or 14½ (others).

2207	**1513**	(1st) black, azure, slate-blue and gold (17 Apr)	50·00	40·00
		a. Booklet pane. No. 2207×2 plus No. 2040×4...............................	95·00	
		ab. Booklet pane. Imperf....................	£5250	
2208	**1516**	(1st) bright scarlet, blue and silver (22 Oct).......................................	15·00	15·00
		a. Booklet pane. Nos. 2208/9 plus No. 2040×4...............................	22·00	
		ab. Booklet pane. Imperf....................	—	
2209	**1518**	(1st) black, blue and silver (22 Oct)	15·00	15·00

The five PHQ cards depict the four designs and the complete miniature sheet, **MS**2206.

Nos. 2202a/5a were only issued in the £6·76 "Unseen and Unheard" booklet, No. DX27, and Nos. 2207/9 only come from two different £1·62 self-adhesive booklets, Nos. PM2 and PM4.

Type **1516** was re-issued on 21 June 2005 in sheets of 20, printed in lithography by Cartor and sold at £6·55, containing four vertical rows of five stamps alternated with half stamp-size printed labels showing signal flags (LS25). These sheets with personalised photographs were available at £14·95 from the Royal Mail.

It was subsequently issued, printed in lithography, perf 14½, in booklets DX35 and DX41 (see No. 2581).

Type **1517** was re-issued on 27 July 2004 in sheets of 20, printed in lithography by Walsall and sold at £6·15, containing vertical strips of five stamps alternated with half stamp-size printed labels (LS20). These sheets with personalised photographs were available at £14·95 from the Royal Mail in Edinburgh.

It was subsequently issued, printed in lithography, perf 14½, in booklet DX41 (see No. 2805).

Type **1518** was subsequently issued, printed in lithography, perf 14½, in booklet DX47 (see No. 2970).

Special First Day of Issue Postmarks

1520 Leyland X2 Open-top, London General B Type, Leyland Titan TD1 and AEC Regent 1

1521 AEC Regent 1, Daimler COG5, Utility Guy Arab Mk II and AEC Regent III RT Type

1522 AEC Regent III RT Type, Bristol KSW5G Open-top, AEC Routemaster and Bristol Lodekka FSF6G

1523 Bristol Lodekka FSF6G, Leyland Titan PD3/4, Leyland Atlantean PDR1/1 and Daimler Fleetline CRG6LX-33

1524 Daimler Fleetline CRG6LX-33, MCW Metrobus DR102/43, Leyland Olympian ONLXB/1R and Dennis Trident

(Des M. English. Litho Questa)

2001 (15 May). *150th Anniv of First Double-decker Bus.* 'All-over' phosphor. P 14½×14.

2210	**1520**	(1st) new blue, greenish yellow, magenta, black and grey..................	1·25	1·00
		a. Horiz strip of 5. Nos. 2210/14.......	7·00	7·00
		ab. Imperf (horiz strip of 5)..............	£6250	
		b. Grey omitted	—	
2211	**1521**	(1st) new blue, greenish yellow, magenta, black and grey..................	1·25	1·00
2212	**1522**	(1st) new blue, greenish yellow, magenta, black and grey..................	1·25	1·00
		a. Grey omitted	—	
2213	**1523**	(1st) new blue, greenish yellow, magenta, black and grey..................	1·25	1·00
		a. Grey omitted	—	
2214	**1524**	(1st) new blue, greenish yellow, magenta, black and grey..................	1·25	1·00
		a. Grey omitted	—	

Set of 5	7·00	7·00
Gutter Strip of 10	15·00	
First Day Cover (Philatelic Bureau)		7·50
First Day Cover (Covent Garden, London WC2)		8·00
Presentation Pack (P.O. Pack No. 323)........................	10·00	
PHQ Cards (set of 6) (231)..	14·00	16·00
MS2215 120×105 mm. Nos. 2210/14..........................	10·50	12·00
First Day Cover (Philatelic Bureau)		15·00
First Day Cover (Covent Garden, London WC2)		15·00

Nos. 2210/14 were printed together, *se-tenant*, in horizontal strips of five throughout the sheet. The illustrations of the first bus on No. 2210 and the last bus on No. 2214 continue onto the sheet margins.

In No. **MS**2215 the illustrations of the AEC Regent III RT Type and the Daimler Fleetline CRG6LX-33 appear twice.

The six PHQ cards show the six stamps and **MS**2215.

Special First Day of Issue Postmarks

1525 Toque Hat by Pip Hackett

1526 Butterfly Hat by Dai Rees

1527 Top Hat by Stephen Jones

1528 Spiral Hat by Philip Treacy

(Des Rose Design from photos by N. Knight. Litho Enschedé)

2001 (19 June). *Fashion Hats. 'All-over' phosphor. P* 14½.

2216	**1525**	(1st) greenish yellow, bright magenta, new blue, grey-black and silver........	1·25	90
2217	**1526**	(E) greenish yellow, bright magenta, new blue, grey-black and silver........	1·50	1·25
2218	**1527**	45p. greenish yellow, bright magenta, new blue, grey-black and silver........	1·60	1·60
2219	**1528**	65p. greenish yellow, bright magenta, new blue, grey-black and silver........	2·50	2·50
Set of 4			6·00	5·50
Set of 4 Gutter Pairs			13·00	
First Day Cover (Tallents House)				6·50
First Day Cover (Ascot)				7·00
Presentation Pack (P.O. Pack No. 324).............			7·50	
PHQ Cards (set of 4) (232)			8·50	14·00

Special First Day of Issue Postmarks

1529 Common Frog

1530 Great Diving Beetle

1531 Three-Spined Stickleback

1532 Southern Hawker Dragonfly

(Des J. Gibbs. Gravure De La Rue)

2001 (10 July). *Europa. Pond Life.* Two phosphor bands. *P* 15×14.

2220	**1529**	(1st) black, greenish yellow, bright magenta, new blue, bluish silver and silver................	1·25	1·00
2221	**1530**	(E) black, greenish yellow, bright magenta, new blue, bluish silver and silver................	1·50	1·25
2222	**1531**	45p. black, greenish yellow, bright magenta, new blue, bluish silver, dull silver and silver	1·50	1·50
2223	**1532**	65p. black, greenish yellow, bright magenta, new blue, bluish silver and silver................	2·00	2·25
Set of 4			6·00	5·75
Set of 4 Gutter Pairs			13·00	
First Day Cover (Tallents House)				7·50
First Day Cover (Oundle, Peterborough)				8·00
Presentation Pack (P.O. Pack No. 325).............			7·50	
PHQ Cards (set of 4) (233)			8·50	14·00

The 1st and E values incorporate the "EUROPA" emblem. The bluish silver on all four values is in Iriodin ink and was used as a background for those parts of the design below the water line.

Special First Day of Issue Postmarks

1533 Policeman

1534 Clown

1535 Mr. Punch

1536 Judy

1537 Beadle

1538 Crocodile

(Des K. Bernstein from puppets by Bryan Clarkez)

2001 (4 Sept). *Punch and Judy Show Puppets.* Two phosphor bands. *P* 14×15.

(a) Gravure Walsall. Ordinary gum.

2224	**1533**	(1st) greenish yellow, bright magenta, new blue, grey-black, violet, deep magenta, ultramarine and silver	1·25	1·00
		a. Horiz strip of 6. Nos. 2224/9	6·50	6·50
2225	**1534**	(1st) greenish yellow, bright magenta, new blue, grey-black, violet, deep magenta, ultramarine and silver	1·25	1·00
2226	**1535**	(1st) greenish yellow, bright magenta, new blue, grey-black, violet, deep magenta, ultramarine and silver	1·25	1·00
2227	**1536**	(1st) greenish yellow, bright magenta, new blue, grey-black, violet, deep magenta, ultramarine and silver	1·25	1·00
2228	**1537**	(1st) greenish yellow, bright magenta, new blue, grey-black, violet, deep magenta, ultramarine and silver	1·25	1·00
2229	**1538**	(1st) greenish yellow, bright magenta, new blue, grey-black, violet, deep magenta, ultramarine and silver	1·25	1·00
Set of 6			6·50	6·50
Gutter Block of 12.............			14·00	
First Day Cover (Tallents House)				7·00
First Day Cover (Blackpool)				7·50
Presentation Pack (P.O. Pack No. 326).............			7·00	
PHQ Cards (set of 6) (234)			8·50	18·00

(b) Gravure Questa. Self-adhesive. Die-cut P 14×15½.

2230	**1535**	(1st) greenish yellow, bright magenta, new blue, grey-black, violet, deep magenta, ultramarine and silver (4 Sept)	17·00	17·00
		a. Booklet pane. Nos. 2230/1 plus No. 2040×4.............	30·00	

2231 **1536** (1st) greenish yellow, bright magenta,
new blue, grey-black, violet, deep
magenta, ultramarine and silver
(4 Sept) .... 17·00   17·00

Nos. 2224/9 were printed together, *se-tenant*, as horizontal strips of 6 in sheets of 60 (6×10).

Nos. 2230/1 were only issued in £1·62 stamp booklets, No. PM3.

Imperforate strips of 6 with alternative background colours to 2224, 2228 and 2229 are of proof status (*Price* £3000).

Special First Day of Issue Postmarks

2nd

1539 Carbon 60 Molecule (Chemistry)

1st

1540 Globe (Economic Sciences)

E

1541 Embossed Dove (Peace)

40

1542 Crosses (Physiology or Medicine)

45

1543 Poem "The Addressing of Cats" by T. S. Eliot in Open Book (Literature)

65

1544 Hologram of Boron Molecule (Physics)

(Des P. Vermier. Eng Ing Madle (1st). Litho and silk-screen ptg (2nd), litho and recess (1st), litho and embossed (E), litho (45p.), litho and hologram (65p.) Enschedé)

2001 (2 Oct). *Centenary of Nobel Prizes.* One side phosphor band (2nd) or phosphor frame (others). P 14½.

2232	**1539**	(2nd) black, silver and grey-black	1·00	80
2233	**1540**	(1st) black, silver, dull mauve, blue and rosine	1·50	1·00
2234	**1541**	(E) black, silver and bright green..........	1·50	1·50
2235	**1542**	40p. black, silver, new blue and greenish yellow..	2·00	1·50
2236	**1543**	45p. black, silver, yellow-ochre and pale grey...	3·00	2·00
2237	**1544**	65p. black and silver	5·00	2·50
	Set of 6		12·00	8·00
	Set of 6 Gutter Pairs..		25·00	
	First Day Cover (Tallents House)			9·00
	First Day Cover (Cambridge)...			9·50
	Presentation Pack (P.O. Pack No. 327)..........................		20·00	
	PHQ Cards (set of 6) (235)		10·00	14·00

The grey-black on No. 2232 is printed in thermochromic ink which temporarily changes to pale grey when exposed to heat. The centre of No. 2235 is coated with a eucalyptus scent.

Trials, differing slightly from the issued stamps, are known for all values.

Special First Day of Issue Postmarks

2nd   **1st**

1545 Robins with Snowman   **1546** Robins on Bird Table

E   **45**

1547 Robins skating on Bird Bath   **1548** Robins with Christmas Pudding

65

1549 Robins in Paper Chain Nest

(Des A. Robins and H. Brown. Gravure De La Rue)

2001 (6 Nov). *Christmas. Robins.* Self-adhesive. One centre phosphor band (2nd) or two phosphor bands (others). Die-cut P14½.

2238	**1545**	(2nd) new blue, blue, greenish yellow, bright magenta, vermilion and black...	1·00	80
		a. Booklet pane. No. 2238×24	12·00	
		b. Imperf (pair)...	£950	
2239	**1546**	(1st) red-orange, blue, greenish yellow, bright magenta, new blue and black...	1·25	1·00
		a. Booklet pane. No. 2239×12	8·00	
2240	**1547**	(E) indigo, azure, greenish yellow, bright magenta, new blue, vermilion and black..................	1·50	1·50
2241	**1548**	45p. bright purple, blue, greenish yellow, bright magenta, new blue, vermilion and black..................	2·00	2·00
2242	**1549**	65p. greenish blue, blue, greenish yellow, bright magenta, new blue, vermilion and black..................	3·00	3·00
		a. Imperf (pair) (die-cut perforations and roulettes omitted)	£1500	
		ab. Imperf (pair) (die-cut perforations only omitted)	£750	
		b. Imperf backing paper (pair) (roulettes omitted).............................	£275	
	Set of 5		7·50	7·50
	First Day Cover (Tallents House)			8·50
	First Day Cover (Bethlehem, Llandeilo)			9·00
	Presentation Pack (P.O. Pack No. 328)..........................		8·00	
	PHQ Cards (set of 5) (236)..		11·00	16·00

Nos. 2238/40 were each printed in sheets of 50 with the surplus backing paper around each stamp retained and separated by gauge 9 roulettes.

The 1st value was re-issued on 30 September 2003 in sheets of 20 (*sold at* £6·15) printed in lithography instead of photogravure, each stamp accompanied by a stamp-size label showing a snowman (LS14). Sheets with personal photographs printed on the labels were available from Royal Mail, Edinburgh for £14·95 or photobooths at selected post offices and Safeway stores for £15.

The 2nd and 1st values were re-issued together on 1 November 2005 in sheets of 20, printed in lithography by Cartor (*sold at* £5·60), containing ten 2nd class and ten 1st class, each stamp accompanied by a label showing a snowman (LS27). Separate sheets of 20 2nd class and 20 1st class were available with personalised photographs at £9·95 (2nd) or £14·95 (1st) from Royal Mail.

No. 2238b shows both the die-cut perforations and the roulettes omitted. Stamps from booklet panes Nos. 2238a and 2239a differ from those in sheets by omitting the roulettes in the backing paper between each stamp. Instead there are roulettes after the first and then every alternate horizontal row to assist with the folding of the booklets.

Trials of (2nd) and (1st) stamps in alternative designs are known.

Special First Day of Issue Postmarks

Collectors Pack 2001

2001 (6 Nov). Comprises Nos. 2178/2200, 2202/6, 2210/14, 2216/29 and 2232/42.
CP2242a Collectors Pack.. £110

Post Office Yearbook

2001 (6 Nov). Comprises Nos. 2178/96, **MS**2201/6, 2210/14, 2216/29 and 2232/42 in hardback book with slip case £110

1550 "How the Whale got his Throat"

1551 "How the Camel got his Hump"

1552 "How the Rhinoceros got his Skin"

1553 "How the Leopard got his Spots"

1554 "The Elephant's Child"

1555 "The Sing-Song of Old Man Kangaroo"

1556 "The Beginning of the Armadillos"

1557 "The Crab that played with the Sea"

1558 "The Cat that walked by Himself"

1559 "The Butterfly that stamped"

(Des I. Cohen. Gravure Walsall)

2002 (15 Jan). *Centenary of Publication of Rudyard Kipling's Just So Stories.* Self-adhesive. Two phosphor bands. Die-cut P 15×14.

2243	**1550**	(1st) new blue, magenta, greenish yellow and black...........		1·25	1·00
		a. Sheetlet. Nos. 2243/52		14·00	11·00
2244	**1551**	(1st) new blue, magenta, greenish yellow and black...........		1·25	1·00
2245	**1552**	(1st) new blue, magenta, greenish yellow and black...........		1·25	1·00
2246	**1553**	(1st) new blue, magenta, greenish yellow and black...........		1·25	1·00
2247	**1554**	(1st) new blue, magenta, greenish yellow and black...........		1·25	1·00
2248	**1555**	(1st) new blue, magenta, greenish yellow and black...........		1·25	1·00
2249	**1556**	(1st) new blue, magenta, greenish yellow and black...........		1·25	1·00
2250	**1557**	(1st) new blue, magenta, greenish yellow and black...........		1·25	1·00
2251	**1558**	(1st) new blue, magenta, greenish yellow and black...........		1·25	1·00
2252	**1559**	(1st) new blue, magenta, greenish yellow and black...........		1·25	1·00

Set of 10... 14·00 11·00
First Day Cover (Tallents House)... 12·00
First Day Cover (Burwash, Etchingham).............................. 12·00
Presentation Pack (P.O. Pack No. 330)............................ 16·00
PHQ Cards (set of 10) (237).................................. 10·00 28·00

Nos. 2243/52 were printed together in sheetlets of ten (5×2), with the surplus self-adhesive paper around each stamp retained. The pane shows vertical roulettes between rows 2/3 and 4/5 and has illustrations on the reverse of the backing paper.

Special First Day of Issue Postmarks

1560 Queen Elizabeth II, 1952 (Dorothy Wilding)

1561 Queen Elizabeth II, 1968 (Cecil Beaton)

1562 Queen Elizabeth II, 1978 (Lord Snowdon)

1563 Queen Elizabeth II, 1984 (Yousef Karsh)

1564 Queen Elizabeth II, 1996 (Tim Graham)   **1565**

(Des Kate Stephens. Gravure De La Rue)

2002 (6 Feb). *Golden Jubilee.* Studio portraits of Queen Elizabeth II by photographers named. One centre phosphor band (2nd) or two phosphor bands (others). *W* **1565** (sideways). *P* 14½×14.

2253	**1560**	(2nd) silver, pale turquoise-green, black and deep grey	1·00	80
		a. Watermark upright	4·00	90
		b. Booklet pane. Nos. 2253a/6a with margins all round	13·00	
2254	**1561**	(1st) silver, pale turquoise-green, black and grey-black	1·25	90
		a. Watermark upright	2·50	1·00
		b. Booklet pane. Nos. 2254a/7a with margins all round	15·00	
2255	**1562**	(E) silver, pale turquoise-green, black and grey-black	1·50	1·50
		a. Watermark upright	2·75	1·60
2256	**1563**	45p. silver, pale turquoise-green, black and grey-black	1·75	2·00
		a. Watermark upright	3·50	2·00
2257	**1564**	65p. silver, pale turquoise-green, black and grey-black	2·75	3·00
		a. Watermark upright	6·00	3·00
Set of 5			7·50	7·50
Set of 5 Gutter Pairs			16·00	
First Day Cover (Tallents House)				8·50
First Day Cover (Windsor)				9·00
Presentation Pack (P.O. Pack No. 331)			9·00	
PHQ Cards (set of 5) (238)			4·50	14·00

The turquoise-green is used as an underlay for the black colour on all five values.

Nos. 2253a/7a were only issued in the £7·29 "A Glorious Accesion" booklet, No DX28.

Trials, including dates and with values in a different typeface, are known for all values.

Special First Day of Issue Postmarks

1566

(Des M. Farrar-Bell (2nd), Enid Marx (1st). Gravure Enschedé)

2002 (6 Feb). As *T* **154/5** (Wilding definitive of 1952-54), but with service indicator as *T* **1566**. One centre phosphor band (2nd) or two phosphor bands (1st). *W* **1565**. Uncoated paper. *P* 15×14 (with one elliptical hole in each vertical side).

2258	**1566**	(2nd) carmine-red	1·20	1·20
		Ea. Watermark diagonal	7·50	7·50
		b. Booklet pane. Nos. 2258×4, 2258Ea and 2259×4 with centre blank label and margins all round	18·00	
2259	–	(1st) green	1·40	1·40
First Day Cover (No. 2258b) (Tallents House)				10·00
First Day Cover (No. 2258b) (Windsor)				10·00

Nos. 2258/9 were only issued in the £7·29 "A Gracious Accession" booklet, No. DX28.

No. 2258b contains a block of 8, four of each value, with a blank central label, plus an additional 2nd value shown to the left at such an angle so as to produce a diagonal watermark. First day cover postmarks were as Nos. 2253/7.

1567 Rabbits ("a new baby")   **1568** "LOVE"

1569 Aircraft Sky-writing "hello"   **1570** Bear pulling Potted Topiary Tree (Moving Home)

1571 Flowers ("best wishes")

(Des I. Bilbey (Nos. 2260, 2264), A. Kitching (No. 2261), Hoop Associates (No. 2262) and G. Percy (No. 2263))

2002 (5 Mar)–**03**. *Greetings Stamps. 'Occasions'.* Two phosphor bands.

(a) Litho Questa. Ordinary gum. P 15×14.

2260	**1567**	(1st) greenish yellow, magenta, new blue, black and lilac	1·50	1·10
2261	**1568**	(1st) greenish yellow, magenta, new blue, black and silver	1·50	1·10
2262	**1569**	(1st) greenish yellow, magenta, new blue and black	1·50	1·10
2263	**1570**	(1st) greenish yellow, magenta, new blue and black	1·50	1·10
2264	**1571**	(1st) greenish yellow, magenta, new blue, black and cobalt	1·50	1·10
Set of 5			6·50	5·00
Set of 5 Gutter Pairs			13·00	
First Day Cover (Tallents House)				6·00
First Day Cover (Merry Hill, Wolverhampton)				6·50
Presentation Pack (P.O. Pack No. M07)			7·50	
PHQ Cards (set of 5) (PSM08)			4·50	14·00

(b) Gravure Questa. Self-adhesive. Die-cut P 15×14.

2264a	**1569**	(1st) greenish yellow, magenta, new blue and black (4.3.03)	6·00	6·00
		ab. Booklet pane. No. 2264a×2 plus No. 2295×4	12·00	

Nos. 2260/4 were re-issued on 23 April 2002 in sheets of 20 with half stamp-size labels, with either the five designs *se-tenant* with greetings on the labels (LS7, *sold at* £5·95) or in sheets of one design with personal photographs on the labels (*sold at* £12·95). These stamps, printed by Questa in lithography, were perforated 14 instead of 15×14.

Type **1569** was re-issued in sheets of 20 with half stamp-size *se-tenant* labels all printed in lithography as follows: on 30 January 2004 for Hong Kong Stamp Expo (LS17, Walsall), on 21 April 2005 for Pacific Explorer 2005 World Stamp Expo (LS24, Walsall, P14), on 25 May 2006 for Washington 2006 International Stamp Exhibition (LS30, Cartor, P14), on 14 November 2006 for Belgica 2006 International Stamp Exhibition (LS36, Cartor, P14), on 5 August 2008 for Beijing 2008 Olympic Expo (LS48, Cartor, P14), on 3 August 2009 for Thaipex 09 Stamp Exhibition (LS64, Cartor, P14), on 21 October 2009 for Italia 2009 International Stamp Exhibition (LS66, Cartor, P14) and on 4 December 2009 for MonacoPhil International Stamp Exhibition (LS69, Cartor, P14).

No. 2264a was only issued in £1·62 stamp booklets, No. PM8, in which the surplus self-adhesive paper around each stamp was removed.

Special First Day of Issue Postmarks

1572 Studland Bay, Dorset

1573 Luskentyre, South Harris

1574 Cliffs, Dover, Kent

1575 Padstow Harbour, Cornwall

1576 Broadstairs, Kent

1577 St. Abb's Head, Scottish Borders

1578 Dunster Beach, Somerset

1579 Newquay Beach, Cornwall

1580 Portrush, County Antrim

1581 Sand-spit, Conwy

(Des R. Cooke. Litho Walsall)

2002 (19 Mar). *British Coastlines.* Two phosphor bands. *P* 14½.

2265	**1572**	27p. silver, black, greenish yellow, bright magenta and new blue.........	80	70
		a. Block of 10. Nos. 2265/74..................	8·75	8·75
		b. Silver omitted (block of 10)...............	£12000	
2266	**1573**	27p. silver, black, greenish yellow, bright magenta and new blue.........	80	70
2267	**1574**	27p. silver, black, greenish yellow, bright magenta and new blue.........	80	70
2268	**1575**	27p. silver, black, greenish yellow, bright magenta and new blue.........	80	70
2269	**1576**	27p. silver, black, greenish yellow, bright magenta and new blue.........	80	70
2270	**1577**	27p. silver, black, greenish yellow, bright magenta and new blue.........	80	70
2271	**1578**	27p. silver, black, greenish yellow, bright magenta and new blue.........	80	70
2272	**1579**	27p. silver, black, greenish yellow, bright magenta and new blue.........	80	70
2273	**1580**	27p. silver, black, greenish yellow, bright magenta and new blue.........	80	70
2274	**1581**	27p. silver, black, greenish yellow, bright magenta and new blue.........	80	70

Set of 10..........	8·75	8·75
Gutter Block of 20..........	19·00	
First Day Cover (Tallents House)		10·00

First Day Cover (Poolewe, Achnasheen)		11·00
Presentation Pack (P.O. Pack No. 332)........................	10·50	
PHQ Cards (set of 10) (239).................................	9·25	28·00

Nos. 2265/74 were printed together, *se-tenant,* in blocks of ten (5×2) throughout the sheet.

Special First Day of Issue Postmarks

1582 Slack Wire Act

1583 Lion Tamer

1584 Trick Tri-cyclists

1585 Krazy Kar

1586 Equestrienne

(Des R. Fuller. Gravure Questa)

2002 (10 Apr*). *Europa. Circus.* One centre phosphor band (2nd) or two phosphor bands (others). *P* 14½.

2275	**1582**	(2nd) greenish yellow, magenta, new blue, black, bright orange, emerald and silver	1·00	80
2276	**1583**	(1st) greenish yellow, magenta, new blue, black, bright orange, emerald and silver	1·25	1·00
		a. Imperf (vert pair)	£3500	
2277	**1584**	(E) greenish yellow, magenta, new blue, black, bright orange, emerald and silver	1·50	1·25
		a. Imperf (pair)..	£4000	
2278	**1585**	45p. greenish yellow, magenta, new blue, black, bright orange, emerald and silver	1·75	1·50
2279	**1586**	65p. greenish yellow, magenta, new blue, black, bright orange, emerald and silver	2·75	2·25

Set of 5	6·50	6·25
Set of 5 Gutter Pairs..........	14·00	
First Day Cover (Tallents House)		7·00
First Day Cover (Clowne, Chesterfield)		8·00
Presentation Pack (P.O. Pack No. 333).....................	7·50	
PHQ Cards (set of 5) (240)...............................	4·50	14·00

The 1st and E values incorporate the "EUROPA" emblem.

* Due to the funeral of the Queen Mother, the issue of Nos. 2275/9 was delayed from 9 April, the date which appears on first day covers.

Special First Day of Issue Postmarks

1592 Comet (1952)

1587 Queen Elizabeth
the Queen Mother

(Des J. Gorham from photographs by N. Parkinson (1st), Dorothy
Wilding (E), B. Park (45p.), Rita Martin (65p.). Gravure De La Rue)

2002 (25 Apr). *Queen Elizabeth the Queen Mother Commemoration.* Vert
designs as *T* **955/8** with changed face values and showing both
the Queen's head and frame in black as in *T* **1587**. Two phosphor
bands. P 14×15.

2280	**1587**	(1st) black, greenish yellow, magenta, new blue and grey-black	1·25	85
2281	**956**	(E) black and indigo	1·50	1·10
2282	**957**	45p. black, greenish yellow, magenta, new blue and grey-black	1·50	1·50
2283	**958**	65p. black, stone and sepia	2·00	2·25
Set of 4			5·50	5·50
Set of 4 Gutter Pairs			13·00	
First Day Cover (Tallents House)				7·00
First Day Cover (London SW1)				8·00
Presentation Pack (P.O. Pack No. M08)			7·00	

(Des Roundel)

2002 (2 May). *50th Anniv of Passenger Jet Aviation. Airliners.* One centre
phosphor band (2nd) or two phosphor bands (others). P 14½.

(a) Gravure De La Rue. Ordinary gum.

2284	**1588**	(2nd) greenish yellow, bright magenta, new blue, black and silver	1·00	70
2285	**1589**	(1st) greenish yellow, bright magenta, new blue, black and silver	1·25	1·00
2286	**1590**	(E) greenish yellow, bright magenta, new blue, black and silver	1·50	1·50
2287	**1591**	45p. greenish yellow, bright magenta, new blue, black and silver	2·00	2·00
2288	**1592**	65p. greenish yellow, bright magenta, new blue, black and silver	3·00	3·00
Set of 5			8·00	7·50
Set of 5 Gutter Pairs			17·00	
First Day Cover (Tallents House)				8·00
First Day Cover (Heathrow Airport, London)				9·00
Presentation Pack (P.O. Pack No. 334)			10·00	
MS2289 120×105 mm. Nos. 2284/8			12·00	11·00
First Day Cover (Tallents House)				12·00
First Day Cover (Heathrow Airport, London)				12·00
PHQ Cards (set of 6) (241)			5·25	18·00

(b) Gravure Questa. Self-adhesive. Die-cut P 14½.

2290	**1589**	(1st) greenish yellow, bright magenta, new blue, black and silver	7·00	7·00
		a. Booklet pane. No. 2040×4 and No. 2290×2	15·00	

No. 2290 was only issued in £1·62 stamp booklets, No. PM5.
See also No. 2897.

Special First Day of Issue Postmarks

Special First Day of Issue Postmarks

1588 Airbus A340-600 (2002)   1589 Concorde (1976)

1593 Crowned Lion with
Shield of St. George

1590 Trident (1964)   1591 VC10 (1964)

1594 Top Left Quarter of
English Flag, and Football

1595 Top Right Quarter of
English Flag, and Football

1596 Bottom Left Quarter of English Flag, and Football

1597 Bottom Right Quarter of English Flag, and Football

(Des Sedley Place (No. 2291), H. Brown (No. **MS**2292). Gravure Walsall)

2002 (21 May). *World Cup Football Championship, Japan and Korea.* Two phosphor bands. P 14½×**14**.

(a) Ordinary gum.

2291	**1593**	(1st) deep turquoise-blue, scarlet-vermilion and silver	2·50	2·50
		Gutter Pair	6·00	

MS2292 145×74 mm. No. 2291; **1594** (1st) deep turquoise-blue, indigo, deep blue, black, silver, scarlet-vermilion and pale bluish grey; **1595** (1st) deep turquoise-blue, indigo, deep blue, black, silver, scarlet-vermilion and pale bluish grey; **1596** (1st) deep turquoise-blue, indigo, deep blue, black, silver, scarlet-vermilion and pale bluish grey; **1597** (1st) deep turquoise-blue, indigo, deep blue, black, silver, scarlet-vermilion and pale bluish grey. P 14½ or 15×14 (square) or 15×14 (horiz) ... 7·50 7·50

First Day Cover (**MS**2292) (Tallents House)	8·50
First Day Cover (**MS**2292) (Wembley)	8·50
Presentation Pack (**MS**2292) (P. O. Pack No. 335)	8·50
PHQ Cards (set of 6) (242)	5·25 15·00

(b) Self–adhesive. Die–cut P 15×14.

2293	**1594**	(1st) deep turquoise-blue, indigo, deep blue, black, silver, scarlet-vermilion and pale bluish grey	6·00	6·00
		a. Booklet pane. Nos. 2293/4 plus No. 2040×4	14·00	14·00
2294	**1595**	(1st) deep turquoise-blue, indigo, deep blue, black, silver, scarlet-vermilion and pale bluish grey	6·00	6·00

The complete miniature sheet is shown on one of the PHQ cards with the others depicting individual stamps from No. **MS**2292 and No. 2291.

Nos. 2293/4 were only issued in £1·62 stamp booklets, No. PM6.

Stamps as Type **1597** also exist in sheets of 20 with *se-tenant* labels, printed in lithography by Questa (LS8). Such sheets, with the labels showing match scenes or supporters, were available at £5·95 from philatelic outlets, or with personal photographs at £12·95 from Royal Mail in Edinburgh.

Stamps as Type **1593** but with "WORLD CUP 2002" inscription omitted were issued on 17 May 2007 in sheets of 20 with *se-tenant* labels showing scenes from Wembley Stadium, printed in lithography by Cartor (LS39).

Special First Day of Issue Postmarks

For Nos. 2295/8 see Decimal Machin Definitives section.

1598 Swimming

1599 Running

1600 Cycling

1601 Long Jumping

1602 Wheelchair Racing

(Des Madeleine Bennett. Gravure Enschedé)

2002 (16 July). *17th Commonwealth Games, Manchester.* One side phosphor band (2nd) or two phosphor bands (others). P 14½.

2299	**1598**	(2nd) greenish yellow, magenta, greenish blue, black, silver and new blue	1·00	80
2300	**1599**	(1st) greenish yellow, magenta, new blue, black and silver	1·25	1·00
2301	**1600**	(E) greenish yellow, magenta, new blue, black and silver	1·50	1·25
2302	**1601**	47p. greenish yellow, magenta, new blue, black and silver	1·50	1·50
2303	**1602**	68p. greenish yellow, magenta, new blue, black and silver	2·00	2·25

Set of 5	6·50	6·00
Set of 5 Gutter Pairs	14·00	
First Day Cover (Tallents House)		7·00
First Day Cover (Manchester)		8·00
Presentation Pack (P.O. Pack No. 336)	7·50	
PHQ Cards (set of 5) (243)	4·75	16·00

On Nos. 2300/3 the phosphor bands appear at the right and the centre of each stamp.

Special First Day of Issue Postmarks

1603 Tinkerbell	**1604** Wendy, John and Michael Darling in front of Big Ben

1605 Crocodile and Alarm Clock	**1606** Captain Hook

1607 Peter Pan

(Des Tutssels. Gravure De La Rue)

2002 (20 Aug). *150th Anniv of Great Ormond Street Children's Hospital. Peter Pan* by Sir James Barrie. One centre phosphor band (2nd) or two phosphor bands (others). P 15×14.

2304	**1603**	(2nd) gold, deep ultramarine, greenish yellow and grey-black	1·00	80
2305	**1604**	(1st) gold, purple, greenish yellow, deep violet and grey-black	1·25	1·00

2306	**1605**	(E) gold, blue-green, greenish yellow, bright carmine, new blue grey-black and orange-brown	1·50	1·25
2307	**1606**	47p. gold, pale new blue, greenish yellow, bright carmine and grey-black	1·50	1·50
2308	**1607**	68p. gold, bright rose-red, orange-brown, emerald and grey-black	2·00	2·25

Set of 5	6·50	6·00
Set of 5 Gutter Pairs	14·00	
First Day Cover (Tallents House)		7·00
First Day Cover (Hook)		8·00
Presentation Pack (P.O. Pack No. 337)	7·50	
PHQ Cards (set of 5) (244)	4·75	15·00

Special First Day of Issue Postmarks

1608 Millennium Bridge, 2001   **1609** Tower Bridge, 1894

1610 Westminster Bridge, 1864   **1611** "Blackfriars Bridge, c1800" (William Marlow)

1612 "London Bridge, c1670" (Wenceslaus Hollar)

(Des Sarah Davies and R. Maude)

2002 (10 Sept). **Bridges of London.** One centre phosphor band (2nd) or two phosphor bands (others).

(a) Litho Questa. Ordinary gum. P 15×14.

2309	**1608**	(2nd) greenish yellow, magenta, new blue and black	1·00	80
2310	**1609**	(1st) grey-brown, black, brown-purple and pale grey-brown	1·25	80
2311	**1610**	(E) greenish yellow, magenta, new blue, black and reddish brown	2·00	1·50
2312	**1611**	47p. greenish yellow, magenta, new blue and black	2·50	2·00
2313	**1612**	68p. greenish yellow, magenta, new blue, black and reddish brown	3·50	3·00

Set of 5	9·00	8·50
Set of 5 Gutter Pairs	20·00	
First Day Cover (Tallents House)		9·00
First Day Cover (London SE1)		10·00
Presentation Pack (P.O. Pack No. 338)	45·00	
PHQ Cards (set of 5) (245)	4·00	12·00

(b) Gravure Questa. Self-adhesive. Die-cut P 15×14.

2314	**1609**	(1st) grey-brown, black, brown-purple and pale grey-brown	6·00	6·00
		a. Booklet pane. No. 2314×2, and No. 2295×4	14·00	

No. 2314 was only issued in £1·62 stamp booklets in which the surplus self-adhesive paper around each stamp was removed, No. PM7.

Special First Day of Issue Postmarks

1613a Galaxies and Nebulae (*Illustration reduced. Actual size* 120×89 mm)

(Des Rose Design. Gravure Questa)

2002 (24 Sept). **Astronomy.** *Sheet* 120×89 mm. Multicoloured. Two phosphor bands. P 14½×14.

MS2315 **1613a** (1st) Planetary nebula in Aquila; (1st) Seyfert 2 galaxy in Pegasus; (1st) Planetary nebula in Norma; (1st) Seyfert 2 galaxy in Circinus	6·00	6·00
a. Booklet pane. As No. **MS**2315, but larger, 150×95 mm	6·00	
First Day Cover (Tallents House)		7·00
First Day Cover (Star, Glenrothes)		7·00
Presentation Pack (P.O. Pack No. 339)	20·00	
PHQ Cards (set of 5) (246)	4·75	18·00

Booklet pane No. **MS**2315a comes from the £6·83 "Across the Universe" booklet No. DX29. The five PHQ cards depict the four designs and the complete miniature sheet.

Special First Day of Issue Postmarks

1614 Green Pillar Box, 1857   **1615** Horizontal Aperture Box, 1874

1616 Air Mail Box, 1934   **1617** Double Aperture Box, 1939

1618 Modern Style
Box, 1980

(Des Silk Pearce. Eng C. Slania. Recess and litho Enschedé)

2002 (8 Oct). *150th Anniv. of the First Pillar Box.* One centre phosphor band (2nd) or two phosphor bands (others). *P* 14×14½.

2316	**1614**	(2nd) greenish black, new blue, bright magenta, greenish yellow, grey and silver..........	1·00	80
2317	**1615**	(1st) deep blue, new blue, bright magenta, greenish yellow, grey and silver..........	1·25	1·00
2318	**1616**	(E) deep blue, new blue, bright magenta, greenish yellow, grey and silver..........	1·75	1·75
2319	**1617**	47p. brown-purple, new blue, bright magenta, greenish yellow, grey and silver..........	2·00	2·50
2320	**1618**	68p. deep brown-red, new blue, bright magenta, greenish yellow, grey and silver..........	2·50	3·00

Set of 5	7·50	8·00
Set of 5 Gutter Pairs	16·00	
First Day Cover (Tallents House)		9·00
First Day Cover (Bishops Caundle, Sherborne)		9·00
Presentation Pack (P.O. Pack No. 340)	8·00	
PHQ Cards (set of 5) (247)	4·75	16·00

Special First Day of Issue Postmarks

1619 Blue Spruce Star   **1620** Holly

1621 Ivy   **1622** Mistletoe

1623 Pine Cone

(Des Rose Design. Gravure De La Rue)

2002 (5 Nov). *Christmas.* Self-adhesive. One centre phosphor band (2nd) or two phosphor bands (others). Die-cut p 14½×14.

2321	**1619**	(2nd) lilac, greenish yellow, bright carmine, new blue and black	1·00	80
		a. Booklet pane. No. 2321×24	6·75	
		b. Imperf (pair)	80·00	
2322	**1620**	(1st) greenish grey, greenish yellow, bright carmine, new blue and black	1·25	80
		a. Booklet pane. No. 2322×12	4·75	
		b. Imperf (pair)	£325	
2323	**1621**	(E) dull mauve, greenish yellow, bright carmine, new blue and black	1·50	1·50
2324	**1622**	47p. silver, greenish yellow, bright carmine, new blue and black	2·00	1·75
2325	**1623**	68p. light blue, greenish yellow, bright carmine, new blue and black	3·00	2·75

Set of 5	8·00	7·00
First Day Cover (Tallents House)		8·00
First Day Cover (Bethlehem, Llandeilo)		9·00
Presentation Pack (P.O. Pack No. 341)	8·50	
PHQ Cards (set of 5) (248)	4·75	16·00

Nos. 2321/5 were each printed in sheets of 50, with the surplus backing paper around each stamp retained, separated by gauge 9 roulettes. Nos. 2321b and 2322b show both the die-cut perforations and the roulettes omitted.

Special First Day of Issue Postmarks

Collectors Pack 2002

2002 (5 Nov). Comprises Nos. 2243/57, 2260/4, 2265/88, **MS**2292, 2299/313 and **MS**2315/25.

CP2325a Collectors Pack	£110

Post Office Yearbook

2002 (5 Nov). Comprises Nos. 2243/57, 2260/4, 2265/88, 2291/2, 2299/313 and **MS**2315/25 in hardback book with slip case £100

1623a

(Des Rose Design. Gravure De La Rue)

2002 (5 Dec). *50th Anniv of Wilding Definitives* (1st issue). Sheet 124×70 mm, printed on pale cream. One centre phosphor band (2nd) or two phosphor bands (others). W **1565**. *P* 15×14 (with one elliptical hole in each vertical side).

MS2326	**1623a** 1p. orange-red; 2p. ultramarine; 5p. red-brown; (2nd) carmine-red; (1st) green; 33p. brown; 37p. magenta; 47p. bistre-brown; 50p. green and label showing national emblems	10·00	10·00
	a. Imperf	£8000	

First Day Cover (Tallents House)		11·00
First Day Cover (Windsor)		12·00
Presentation Pack (P.O. Pack No. 59)	65·00	
PHQ Cards (set of 5) (D21)	3·00	12·00

The five PHQ cards depict the 1st, 2nd, 33p., 37p. and 47p. stamps.

Special First Day of Issue Postmarks

1624 Barn Owl landing

1625 Barn Owl with folded Wings and Legs down

1626 Barn Owl with extended Wings and Legs down

1627 Barn Owl in Flight with Wings lowered

1628 Barn Owl in Flight with Wings raised

1629 Kestrel with Wings folded

1630 Kestrel with Wings fully extended upwards

1631 Kestrel with Wings horizontal

1632 Kestrel with wings partly extended downwards

1633 Kestrel with wings fully extended downwards

(Des J. Gibbs from photographs by S. Dalton. Litho Walsall)

2003 (14 Jan).*Birds of Prey.* Phosphor background. P 14½.

2327	**1624**	(1st) brownish grey, black, greenish yellow, magenta and new blue	1·25	1·00
		a. Block of 10. Nos. 2327/36..................	14·00	14·00
		ab. Brownish grey and phosphor omitted	£3000	
2328	**1625**	(1st) brownish grey, black, greenish yellow, magenta and new blue	1·25	1·00
2329	**1626**	(1st) brownish grey, black, greenish yellow, magenta and new blue	1·25	1·00
2330	**1627**	(1st) brownish grey, black, greenish yellow, magenta and new blue	1·25	1·00
2331	**1628**	(1st) brownish grey, black, greenish yellow, magenta and new blue	1·25	1·00
2332	**1629**	(1st) brownish grey, black, greenish yellow, magenta and new blue	1·25	1·00
2333	**1630**	(1st) brownish grey, black, greenish yellow, magenta and new blue	1·25	1·00
2334	**1631**	(1st) brownish grey, black, greenish yellow, magenta and new blue	1·25	1·00
2335	**1632**	(1st) brownish grey, black, greenish yellow, magenta and new blue	1·25	1·00
2336	**1633**	(1st) brownish grey, black, greenish yellow, magenta and new blue	1·25	1·00

Set of 10..	14·00	14·00
Gutter Block of 20..	28·00	
First Day Cover (Talents House)		12·00
First Day Cover (Hawkshead Ambleside)...........		12·00
Presentation Pack (P.O. Pack No. 343)	15·00	
PHQ Cards (set of 10) (249).............................	9·25	28·00

Nos. 2327/36 were printed together, *se-tenant*, in blocks of ten (5×2) throughout the sheet.

No. 2327ab shows the owl white on Nos. 2327/31, and the face value with Queen's head omitted on Nos. 2332/6.

Special First Day of Issue Postmarks (applied in silver)

1634 "Gold star, See me, Playtime"

1635 "I♥U, XXXX, S.W.A.L.K."

1636 "Angel, Poppet, Little terror"

1637 "Yes, No, Maybe"

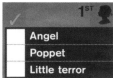

1638 "Oops!, Sorry, Will try harder"

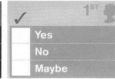

1639 "I did it!, You did it!, We did it!"

(Des UNA, Sara Wiegand and M. Exon. Litho Questa)

2003 (4 Feb). *Greetings Stamps. Occasions.* Two phosphor bands. P 14½×14.

2337	**1634**	(1st) lemon and new blue	1·25	1·00
		a. Block of 6. Nos. 2337/42..................	8·00	6·50
		b. Imperf (block of 6).............................	£4750	
2338	**1635**	(1st) red and deep ultramarine	1·25	1·00
2339	**1636**	(1st) purple and bright yellow-green	1·25	1·00
2340	**1637**	(1st) bright yellow-green and red............	1·25	1·00
2341	**1638**	(1st) deep ultramarine and lemon............	1·25	1·00
2342	**1639**	(1st) new blue and purple..........................	1·25	1·00

Set of 6..	8·00	6·50
Gutter Block of 12...	17·00	
First Day Cover (Talents House)		7·50
First Day Cover (Merry Hill, Wolverhampton)...		7·50
Presentation Pack (P.O. Pack No. M09)	10·00	
PHQ Cards (set of 6) (PSM09)	5·25	18·00

Nos. 2337/42 were printed together, *se-tenant*, in blocks of six (3×2) throughout the sheet.

Nos. 2337/42 were also issued in sheets of 20 (containing four of Nos. 2338 and 2340 and three each of the others) with *se-tenant* labels (LS12). Such sheets with the labels showing printed faces were available at £5·95 from philatelic outlets, or with personalised photographs at £14·95 from Royal Mail in Edinburgh.

1640 Completing the
Genome Jigsaw

1641 Ape with Moustache
and Scientist

1642 DNA Snakes and
Ladders

1643 "Animal Scientists"

1644 Genome Crystal Ball

(Des Williams Murray Hamm and P. Brookes. Litho Enschedé)

2003 (25 Feb). *50th Anniv of Discovery of DNA.* One centre phosphor
band (2nd) or two phosphor bands (others). *P* 14½.

2343	**1640**	(2nd)	azure, black, new blue, magenta and greenish yellow..........................	1·00	80
			a. Booklet pane. Nos. 2343/4, each×2, with margins all round.......	4·00	
2344	**1641**	(1st)	bright apple-green, black, new blue, magenta and greenish yellow	1·25	1·00
2345	**1642**	(E)	yellow-orange, black, new blue, magenta and greenish yellow..........	1·50	1·25
			a. Booklet pane. No. 2345×4 with margins all round...................	5·50	
2346	**1643**	47p.	bistre-yellow, black, new blue, magenta and greenish yellow..........	1·50	1·50
2347	**1644**	68p.	lavender, black, new blue, magenta and greenish yellow..........	2·00	2·25

Set of 5	6·50	6·00
Set of 5 Gutter Pairs..	15·00	
First Day Cover (Tallents House)		7·50
First Day Cover (Cambridge)		8·00
Presentation Pack (P.O. Pack No. 344)............	9·00	
PHQ Cards (set of 5) (250)	4·75	18·00

Booklet panes Nos. 2343a and 2345a come from the £6·99
"Microcosmos" booklet, No. DX30.

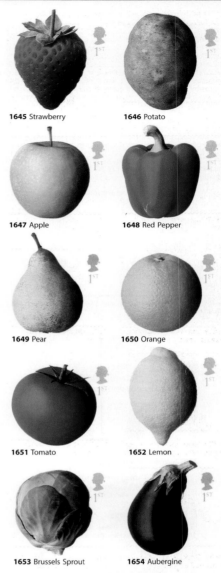

1645 Strawberry

1646 Potato

1647 Apple

1648 Red Pepper

1649 Pear

1650 Orange

1651 Tomato

1652 Lemon

1653 Brussels Sprout

1654 Aubergine

(Des johnson banks. Gravure Walsall)

2003 (25 Mar). *Fruit and Vegetables.* Self-adhesive. Two phosphor bands.
P 14½×14 die-cut (without teeth around protruding tops or bot-
toms of the designs).

2348	**1645**	(1st)	greenish yellow, magenta, new blue, black and silver............................	1·25	1·00
			a. Sheetlet. Nos. 2348/57 and pane of decorative labels................................	14·00	
			ab. Imperf (block of 10)	£4600	
2349	**1646**	(1st)	greenish yellow, magenta, new blue, black and silver............................	1·25	1·00
2350	**1647**	(1st)	greenish yellow, magenta, new blue, black and silver............................	1·25	1·00
2351	**1648**	(1st)	greenish yellow, magenta, new blue, black and silver............................	1·25	1·00
2352	**1649**	(1st)	greenish yellow, magenta, new blue, black and silver............................	1·25	1·00
2353	**1650**	(1st)	greenish yellow, magenta, new blue, black and silver............................	1·25	1·00
2354	**1651**	(1st)	greenish yellow, magenta, new blue, black and silver............................	1·25	1·00
2355	**1652**	(1st)	greenish yellow, magenta, new blue, black and silver............................	1·25	1·00
2356	**1653**	(1st)	greenish yellow, magenta, new blue, black and silver............................	1·25	1·00

2357	**1654**	(1st) greenish yellow, magenta, new blue, black and silver	1·25	1·00
		Set of 10	14·00	10·00
		First Day Cover (Tallents House)		12·00
		First Day Cover (Pear Tree, Derby)		12·00
		Presentation Pack (P.O. Pack No. 345)	20·00	
		PHQ Cards (set of 10) (251)	9·25	25·00

Nos. 2348/57 were printed together in sheets of ten with the surplus self-adhesive paper around each stamp retained. The stamp pane is accompanied by a similar-sized pane of self-adhesive labels showing ears, eyes, mouths, hats, etc which are intended for the adornment of fruit and vegetables depicted. This pane is separated from the stamps by a line of roulettes.

Nos. 2348/57 were re-issued on 7th March 2006 in sheets of 20, containing two of each of the ten designs accompanied by *se-tenant* labels with speech bubbles and stickers showing eyes, hats, etc. in the sheet margin (LS29). These sheets were printed in lithography by Cartor and *sold for £6·55.*

No. 2355 was also available in sheets of 20 with personal photographs on the labels at £14·95 per sheet from Royal Mail, Edinburgh.

Special First Day of Issue Postmarks

For Nos. 2357a/59 (Overseas Booklet Stamps) see Decimal Machin Definitives sections

1656 Amy Johnson (pilot) and Bi-plane

1657 Members of 1953 Everest Team

1658 Freya Stark (traveller and writer) and Desert

1659 Ernest Shackleton (Antarctic explorer) and Wreck of *Endurance*

1660 Francis Chichester (yachtsman) and *Gipsy Moth IV*

1661 Robert Falcon Scott (Antarctic explorer) and Norwegian Expedition at the Pole

(Des H. Brown)

2003 (29 Apr). *Extreme Endeavours (British Explorers).* One centre phosphor band (2nd) or two phosphor bands (others). P 15×14½.

(a) Gravure Questa. Ordinary gum.

2360	**1656**	(2nd) gold, black, magenta, greenish yellow and new blue	1·00	80
2361	**1657**	(1st) gold, black, magenta, greenish yellow and new blue	1·25	1·00
2362	**1658**	(E) gold, black, magenta, greenish yellow and new blue	1·50	1·50
2363	**1659**	42p. gold, black, magenta, greenish yellow and new blue	1·75	1·75
2364	**1660**	47p. gold, black, magenta, greenish yellow and new blue	2·00	2·00
2365	**1661**	68p. gold, black, magenta, greenish yellow and new blue	2·50	2·50
		Set of 6	8·00	8·50
		Set of 6 Gutter Pairs	17·00	
		First Day Cover (Tallents House)		10·00
		First Day Cover (Plymouth)		10·00
		Presentation Pack (P.O. Pack No. 346)	10·00	
		PHQ Cards (set of 6) (252)	3·25	14·00

(b) Gravure De La Rue. Self-adhesive. Die-cut P 14½.

2366	**1657**	(1st) gold, black, magenta, greenish yellow and new blue	5·00	5·00
		a. Booklet pane. No. 2366×2 plus No. 2295×4	12·00	

The phosphor bands on Nos. 2361/5 are at the centre and right of each stamp.

No. 2366 was only issued in £1·62 stamp booklets, No. PM9, in which the surplus self-adhesive paper around each stamp was removed.

Gummed perforated trials with alternative face values and/or designs are known (*Price from £500*).

Special First Day of Issue Postmarks

1661a

Des Rose Design. Gravure De La Rue)

2003 (20 May). *50th Anniv of Wilding Definitives* (2nd issue). Sheet 124×70 mm, , printed on pale cream. One centre phosphor band (20p.) or two phosphor bands (others). W **1565.** P 15×14 (with one elliptical hole in each vertical side).

MS2367 **1661a**	4p. deep lilac; 8p. ultramarine; 10p. reddish purple; 20p. bright green; 28p. bronze-green; 34p. brown-purple; (E) chestnut; 42p. Prussian blue; 68p. grey-blue and label showing national emblems	11·00	12·00
	First Day Cover (Tallents House)		13·00
	First Day Cover (Windsor)		14·00
	Presentation Pack (P.O. Pack No. 61)	15·00	

Special First Day of Issue Postmarks

1662 Guardsmen in Coronation Procession

1663 East End Children reading Coronation Party Poster

1664 Queen Elizabeth II in Coronation Chair with Bishops of Durham and Bath and Wells

1665 Children in Plymouth working on Royal Montage

1666 Queen Elizabeth II in Coronation Robes (photograph by Cecil Beaton)

1667 Children's Race at East End Street Party

1668 Coronation Coach passing through Marble Arch

1669 Children in Fancy Dress

1670 Coronation Coach outside Buckingham Palace

1671 Children eating at London Street Party

(Des Kate Stephens. Gravure De La Rue (sheets) or Walsall (booklets))

2003 (2 June). *50th Anniv of Coronation.* W **1565**. Two phosphor bands. P 14½×14.

2368	**1662**	(1st) greenish yellow, bright magenta, new blue, grey-black, deep turquoise-blue and gold	1·25	1·00
		a. Block of 10. Nos. 2368/77	14·00	12·00
		b. Booklet pane. Nos. 2368, 2370, 2373 and 2375 with margins all round	5·00	
2369	**1663**	(1st) black and gold	1·25	1·00
		b. Booklet pane. Nos. 2369, 2372, 2374 and 2377 with margins all round	5·00	
2370	**1664**	(1st) greenish yellow, bright magenta, new blue, grey-black, deep turquoise-blue and gold	1·25	1·00
2371	**1665**	(1st) black and gold	1·25	1·00

2372	**1666**	(1st) greenish yellow, bright magenta, new blue, grey-black and deep turquoise-blue	1·25	1·00
2373	**1667**	(1st) black and gold	1·25	1·00
2374	**1668**	(1st) greenish yellow, bright magenta, new blue, grey-black, deep turquoise-blue and gold	1·25	1·00
2375	**1669**	(1st) black and gold	1·25	1·00
2376	**1670**	(1st) greenish yellow, bright magenta, new blue, grey-black, deep turquoise-blue and gold	1·25	1·00
2377	**1671**	(1st) black and gold	1·25	1·00
Set of 10			14·00	12·00
Gutter Block of 20			30·00	
First Day Cover (Tallents House)				12·00
First Day Cover (London SW1)				13·00
Presentation Pack (P.O. Pack No. 347)			20·00	
PHQ Cards (set of 10) (253)			9·25	20·00

Nos. 2368/77 were printed together, *se-tenant*, as blocks of ten (5×2) in sheets of 60 (2 panes of 30). No. 2372 does not show a silhouette of the Queen's head in gold as do the other nine designs.

Booklet pane Nos. 2368b/9b come from the £7·46 "A perfect Coronation" booklet, No. DX31.

Special First Day of Issue Postmarks

(Gravure Walsall)

2003 (2 June). *50th Anniv of Coronation.* Booklet stamps. Designs as T **160** (Wilding definitive of 1952) and **163** (Coronation commemorative of 1953), but with values in decimal currency as T **1348**. W **1565**. Two phosphor bands. P 15×14 (with one elliptical hole in each vertical side for Nos. 2378/9).

2378	**160**	47p. bistre-brown	5·00	4·00
		a. Booklet pane. Nos. 2378/9, each×2, and 2380 with margins all round	75·00	
2379		68p. grey-blue	5·00	4·00
2380	**163**	£1 deep yellow-green	60·00	55·00
Set of 3			60·00	55·00

Nos. 2378/80 were only issued in the £7·46 "A Perfect Coronation" booklet, No. DX31. Stamps as Nos. 2378/9, but on pale cream, were also included in the Wilding miniature sheets, Nos. **MS**2326 or **MS**2367. A £1 design as No. 2380, but on phosphorised paper, was previously included in the "Stamp Show 2000" miniature sheet, No. **MS**2147.

1672 Prince William in September 2001 (Brendan Beirne)

1673 Prince William in September 2000 (Tim Graham)

1674 Prince William in September 2001 (Camera Press)

1675 Prince William in September 2001 (Tim Graham)

(Des Madeleine Bennett. Gravure Walsall)

2003 (17 June). *21st Birthday of Prince William of Wales.* Phosphor backgrounds. P 14½.

2381	**1672**	28p. silver, black, grey-black and light green	1·00	80
2382	**1673**	(E) dull mauve, grey-black and light green	2·25	1·50
2383	**1674**	47p. greenish grey, grey-black, black and light green	2·75	2·00

2384	**1675**	68p. sage-green, black and bright green	4·00	2·50
Set of 4			9·00	6·00
Set of 4 Gutter Pairs			19·00	
First Day Cover (Tallents House)				8·00
First Day Cover (Cardiff)				8·00
Presentation Pack (P.O. Pack No. 348)			20·00	
PHQ Cards (set of 4) (254)			7·50	20·00

Special First Day of Issue Postmarks

1676 Loch Assynt, Sutherland

1677 Ben More, Isle of Mull

1678 Rothiemurchus, Cairngorms

1679 Dalveen Pass, Lowther Hills

1680 Glenfinnan Viaduct, Lochaber

1681 Papa Little, Shetland Islands

(Des Phelan Barker. Gravure De La Rue)

2003 (15 July). *A British Journey: Scotland.* One centre phosphor band (2nd) or two phosphor bands (others). P 14½.

(a) Ordinary gum.

2385	**1676**	(2nd) silver, black, bright magenta, greenish yellow and new blue	1·00	90
2386	**1677**	(1st) silver, black, bright magenta, greenish yellow and new blue	1·25	1·00
2387	**1678**	(E) silver, black, bright magenta, greenish yellow and new blue	1·50	1·25
2388	**1679**	42p. silver, black, bright magenta, greenish yellow and new blue	1·25	1·50
2389	**1680**	47p. silver, black, bright magenta, greenish yellow and new blue	1·50	2·00
2390	**1681**	68p. silver, black, bright magenta, greenish yellow and new blue	2·00	2·50
Set of 6			7·00	8·50
Set of 6 Gutter Pairs			15·00	
First Day Cover (Tallents House)				10·00
First Day Cover (Baltasound, Unst, Shetland)				10·00
Presentation Pack (P.O. Pack No. 349)			9·50	
PHQ Cards (set of 6) (255)			3·00	14·00

(b) Self-adhesive. Die-cut P 14½.

2391	**1677**	(1st) silver, black, bright magenta, greenish yellow and new blue	6·00	6·00
		a. Booklet pane. No. 2391×2, and No. 2295×4	12·00	

Perforated trials of this set with alternative face values or designs are known.

No. 2391 was only issued in £1·68 stamp booklets, No. PM10, in which the surplus self-adhesive paper around each stamp was removed.

Special First Day of Issue Postmarks

1682 "The Station" (Andrew Davidson)

1683 "Black Swan" (Stanley Chew)

1684 "The Cross Keys" (George Mackenney)

1685 "The Mayflower" (Ralph Ellis)

1686 "The Barley Sheaf" (Joy Cooper)

(Des Elmwood. Gravure De La Rue)

2003 (12 Aug). *Europa. British Pub Signs.* Two phosphor bands. P 14×14½.

2392	**1682**	(1st) silver, black, magenta, greenish yellow and new blue	1·25	70
		a. Booklet pane. No. 2392×4 with margins all round (16.3.04)	3·75	
2393	**1683**	(E) silver, black, magenta, greenish yellow and new blue	2·00	2·00
2394	**1684**	42p. silver, black, magenta, greenish yellow and new blue	1·50	1·50
2395	**1685**	47p. silver, black, magenta, greenish yellow and new blue	1·75	2·00
2396	**1686**	68p. silver, black, magenta, greenish yellow and new blue	2·00	2·25
Set of 5			7·50	8·00
Set of 5 Gutter Pairs			16·00	
First Day Cover (Tallents House)				9·00
First Day Cover (Cross Keys, Hereford)				9·00
Presentation Pack (P.O. Pack No. 350)			11·00	
PHQ Cards (set of 5) (256)			3·00	12·00

The 1st and E values include the "EUROPA" emblem. No. 2392a comes from the £7·44 "Letters by Night" booklet, No. DX32.

Special First Day of Issue Postmarks

1687 Meccano Constructor Biplane, *c.1931*

1688 Wells-Brimtoy Clockwork Double-decker Omnibus, *c.1938*

1689 Hornby M1 Clockwork Locomotive and Tender, *c.1948*

1690 Dinky Toys Ford Zephyr, *c.1956*

1691 Mettoy Friction Drive Space Ship *Eagle*, *c.1960*

(Des Trickett and Webb)

2003 (18 Sept). *Classic Transport Toys.* Two phosphor bands.

(a) Gravure Enschedé. Ordinary gum. P 14½×14.

2397	**1687**	(1st)	silver, blue-black, black, new blue, magenta and greenish yellow..........	1·25	70
2398	**1688**	(E)	silver, blue-black, black, new blue, magenta and greenish yellow..........	1·50	1·25
2399	**1689**	42p.	silver, blue-black, black, new blue, magenta and greenish yellow..........	1·50	1·50
2400	**1690**	47p.	silver, blue-black, black, new blue, magenta and greenish yellow..........	1·75	1·75
2401	**1691**	68p.	silver, blue-black, black, new blue, magenta and greenish yellow..........	2·50	2·50

Set of 5	7·50	7·00
Set of 5 Gutter Pairs..........	16·00	
First Day Cover (Tallents House)		10·00
First Day Cover (Toye, Downpatrick)		10·00
Presentation Pack (P.O. Pack No. 351)..........	12·00	
PHQ Cards (set of 6) (257)	3·00	14·00
MS2402 115×105mm.Nos. 2397/401	8·00	8·50
First Day Cover		11·00

(b) Gravure De La Rue. Self-adhesive. Die-cut P 14½×14.

2403	**1687**	(1st)	silver, blue-black, black, new blue, magenta and greenish yellow..........	6·00	6·00
			a. Booklet pane. No. 2403×2 and No. 2295×4	12·00	

The complete miniature sheet is shown on one of the PHQ cards with the others depicting individual stamps.

No. 2403 was only issued in £1·68 stamp booklets, No. PM11, in which the surplus self-adhesive paper around each stamp was removed.

1692 Coffin of Denytenamun, Egyptian, *c.*900BC

1693 Alexander the Great, Greek, *c.*200BC

1694 Sutton Hoo Helmet, Anglo-Saxon, *c.*AD600

1695 Sculpture of Parvati, South Indian, *c.*AD1550

1696 Mask of Xiuhtecuhtli, Mixtec-Aztec, *c.*AD1500

1697 Hoa Hakananai'a, Easter Island, *c.*AD1000

(Des Rose Design. Gravure Walsall)

2003 (7 Oct). *250th Anniv of the British Museum.* One side phosphor band (2nd), two phosphor bands ((1st), (E), 47p.) or phosphor background at left and band at right (42p., 68p.). *P* 14×14½.

2404	**1692**	(2nd)	brownish grey, black, greenish yellow, magenta and pale new blue	1·00	70
2405	**1693**	(1st)	brownish grey, black, greenish yellow, magenta and pale new blue	1·25	90
2406	**1694**	(E)	brownish grey, black, greenish yellow, magenta and pale new blue	1·50	1·25
2407	**1695**	42p.	brownish grey, black, greenish yellow, magenta and pale new blue	1·50	1·50
2408	**1696**	47p.	brownish grey, black, greenish yellow, magenta and pale new blue	2·00	2·00
2409	**1697**	68p.	brownish grey, black, greenish yellow, magenta and pale new blue	2·75	2·75

Set of 6	9·00	8·00
Set of 6 Gutter Pairs..........	19·00	
First Day Cover (Tallents House)		10·00
First Day Cover (London WC1)		10·00
Presentation Pack (P.O. Pack No. 352)..........	11·00	
PHQ Cards (set of 6) (258)	3·00	14·00

Special First Day of Issue Postmarks

Special First Day of Issue Postmarks

1698 Ice Spiral

1699 Icicle Star

1700 Wall of Ice Blocks

1701 Ice Ball

1702 Ice Hole

1703 Snow Pyramids

(Des D. Davis. Gravure De La Rue)

2003 (4 Nov). *Christmas. Ice Sculptures by Andy Goldsworthy.* Self-adhesive. One side phosphor band (2nd), 'all-over' phosphor (1st) or two bands (others). Die-cut P 14½×14.

2410	**1698**	(2nd) magenta, greenish yellow, new blue and black	1·00	70
		a. Booklet pane. No. 2410×24	21·00	
2411	**1699**	(1st) magenta, greenish yellow, new blue and black	1·25	90
		a. Booklet pane. No. 2411×12	11·00	
2412	**1700**	(E) magenta, greenish yellow, new blue and black	1·50	1·50
2413	**1701**	53p. magenta, greenish yellow, new blue and black	2·00	2·00
2414	**1702**	68p. magenta, greenish yellow, new blue and black	2·50	2·50
2415	**1703**	£1.12 magenta, greenish yellow, new blue and black	3·00	3·00
Set of 6			10·00	9·50
First Day Cover (Tallents House)				11·00
First Day Cover (Bethlehem, Llandeilo)				11·00
Presentation Pack (P.O. Pack No. 353)			12·00	
PHQ Cards (set of 6) (259)			4·00	14·00

Nos. 2410/15 were each printed in sheets of 50 with the surplus backing paper around each stamp removed.

The 2nd and 1st class were also issued in separate sheets of 20 printed in lithography instead of photogravure, each stamp accompanied by a half stamp-size *se-tenant* label showing either ice sculptures (2nd) or animals (1st) (LS15/16). Both sheets have the backing paper around each stamp retained. The 2nd class sheet was sold for £4·20 and the 1st class for £6·15. These sheets were also available with personal photographs instead of labels at £9·95 (2nd) or £14·95 (1st) from Royal Mail, Edinburgh or £15 from photo-booths at selected post offices and Safeway stores.

Special First Day of Issue Postmarks

Collectors Pack 2003

2003 (4 Nov). Comprises Nos. 2327/57, 2360/5, 2368/77, 2381/90, 2392/401 and 2404/15

CP2415a Collectors Pack		£120

Post Office Yearbook

2003 (4 Nov). Comprises Nos. 2327/57, 2360/5, 2368/77, 2381/90, 2392/401 and 2404/15 in hardback book with slipcase | £100

1704 (*Illustration reduced. Actual size 115×88 mm*)

(Des Why Not Associates. Litho Walsall)

2003 (19 Dec). *England's Victory in Rugby World Cup Championship, Australia.* Sheet 115×85 mm. Multicoloured. Two phosphor bands. P 14.

MS2416 **1704** (1st) England flags and fans; (1st) England team standing in circle before match; 68p. World Cup trophy; 68p. Victorious England players after match | 14·00 | 14·00

First Day Cover (Tallents House)		15·00
First Day Cover (Twickenham)		15·00
Presentation Pack (P.O. Pack No. M9B)	18·00	

Special First Day of Issue Postmarks

1705 *Dolgoch*, Rheilffordd Talyllyn Railway, Gwynedd

1706 CR Class 439, Bo'ness and Kinneil Railway, West Lothian

1707 GCR Class 8K, Leicestershire

1708 GWR Manor Class *Bradley Manor*, Severn Valley Railway, Worcestershire

1709 SR West Country Class *Blackmoor Vale*, Bluebell Railway, East Sussex

1710 BR Standard Class, Keighley and Worth Valley Railway, Yorkshire

(Des Roundel. Litho De La Rue)

2004 (13 Jan–16 Mar). *Classic Locomotives.* One side phosphor band (20p.) or two phosphor bands (others). P 14½.

2417	**1705**	20p. greenish yellow, magenta, new blue, silver and black	65	65
2418	**1706**	28p. greenish yellow, magenta, new blue, silver and black	90	90
		a. Booklet pane. Nos. 2418/20 with margins all round (16 Mar)	3·50	
2419	**1707**	(E) greenish yellow, magenta, new blue, silver and black	1·50	1·20
2420	**1708**	42p. greenish yellow, magenta, new blue, silver and black	1·50	1·50
2421	**1709**	47p. greenish yellow, magenta, new blue, silver and black	2·00	2·00
		a. Imperf (pair)	£3750	
2422	**1710**	68p. greenish yellow, magenta, new blue, silver and black	3·00	3·50
Set of 6			8·00	8·50
Set of 6 Gutter Pairs			17·00	
First Day Cover (Tallents House)				10·00
First Day Cover (York)				10·00
Presentation Pack (P.O. Pack No. 355)			25·00	
PHQ Cards (set of 7) (260)			8·50	15·00
MS2423 190×67 mm. Nos. 2417/22			25·00	25·00
First Day Cover (Tallents House)				26·00
First Day Cover (York)				26·00

No. 2418a comes from the £7·44 "Letters by Night" booklet, No. DX32.

The seven PHQ cards depict the six individual stamps and the miniature sheet.

1711 Postman   **1712** Face

1713 Duck   **1714** Baby

1715 Aircraft

(Des S. Kambayashi. Litho De La Rue)

2004 (3 Feb). *Occasions.* Two phosphor bands. P 14½×14.

2424	**1711**	(1st) bright mauve and black	1·25	1·00
		a. Horiz strip of 5. Nos. 2424/8	7·00	6·00
		ab. Imperf strip of 5		

2425	**1712**	(1st) magenta and black	1·25	1·00
2426	**1713**	(1st) lemon and black	1·25	1·00
2427	**1714**	(1st) pale turquoise-green and black	1·25	1·00
2428	**1715**	(1st) bright new blue and black	1·25	1·00
Set of 5			7·00	6·00
Gutter Block of 10			15·00	
First Day Cover (Tallents House)				8·00
First Day Cover (Merry Hill, Wolverhampton)				8·00
Presentation Pack (P.O. Pack No. M10)			8·00	
PHQ Cards (set of 5) (PSM10)			4·75	12·00

Nos. 2424/8 were printed together, *se-tenant*, as horizontal strips of five in sheets of 25 (5×5). Nos. 2424/8 were also issued in sheets of 20 containing vertical strips of the five designs alternated with half stamp-size labels (LS18). These sheets with printed labels were available at £6·15 from philatelic outlets, or with personalised photographs at £14·95 from Royal Mail in Edinburgh.

1716 Map showing Middle Earth   **1717** Forest of Lothlórien in Spring

1718 Dust-jacket for *The Fellowship of the Ring*   **1719** Rivendell

1720 The Hall at Bag End   **1721** Orthanc

1722 Doors of Durin   **1723** Barad-dûr

1724 Minas Tirith

1725 Fangorn Forest

(Des HGV Design. Litho Walsall)

2004 (26 Feb). *50th Anniv of Publication of The Fellowship of the Ring and The Two Towers by J. R. R. Tolkien.* Two phosphor bands. P 14½.

2429	**1716**	(1st) pale stone, sepia, black, greenish yellow, magenta and new blue	1·25	1·00
		a. Block of 10. Nos. 2429/38	14·00	12·00
2430	**1717**	(1st) pale stone, sepia, black, greenish yellow, magenta and new blue	1·25	1·00
2431	**1718**	(1st) pale stone, sepia, black, greenish yellow, magenta and new blue	1·25	1·00
2432	**1719**	(1st) pale stone, sepia, black, greenish yellow, magenta and new blue	1·25	1·00
2433	**1720**	(1st) pale stone, sepia, black, greenish yellow, magenta and new blue	1·25	1·00
2434	**1721**	(1st) pale stone, sepia, black, greenish yellow, magenta and new blue	1·25	1·00
2435	**1722**	(1st) pale stone, sepia, black, greenish yellow, magenta and new blue	1·25	1·00
2436	**1723**	(1st) pale stone, sepia, black, greenish yellow, magenta and new blue	1·25	1·00
2437	**1724**	(1st) pale stone, sepia, black, greenish yellow, magenta and new blue	1·25	1·00
2438	**1725**	(1st) pale stone, sepia, black, greenish yellow, magenta and new blue	1·25	1·00
Set of 10			14·00	12·00
Gutter Block of 20			30·00	
First Day Cover (Tallents House)				13·00
First Day Cover (Oxford)				13·00
Presentation Pack (P.O. Pack No. 356)			20·00	
PHQ Cards (set of 10) (261)			9·75	18·00

Nos. 2429/38 were printed together, *se-tenant*, in blocks of ten (5×2) throughout the sheet.

Special First Day of Issue Postmarks

1726 Ely Island, Lower Lough Erne

1727 Giant's Causeway, Antrim Coast

1728 Slemish, Antrim Mountains

1729 Banns Road, Mourne Mountains

1730 Glenelly Valley, Sperrins

1731 Islandmore, Strangford Lough

(Des Phelan Barker. Gravure Enschedé (sheets) or De La Rue (booklet))

2004 (16 Mar). *A British Journey: Northern Ireland.* One side phosphor band (2nd) or two phosphor bands (others). P 14½.

(a) Ordinary gum.

2439	**1726**	(2nd) silver, black, new blue, magenta and greenish yellow	1·00	75
2440	**1727**	(1st) silver, black, new blue, magenta and greenish yellow	1·25	90
2441	**1728**	(E) silver, black, new blue, magenta and greenish yellow	1·50	1·20
2442	**1729**	42p. silver, black, new blue, magenta and greenish yellow	1·30	1·30
2443	**1730**	47p. silver, black, new blue, magenta and greenish yellow	1·50	1·50
2444	**1731**	68p. silver, black, new blue, magenta and greenish yellow	2·20	2·20
Set of 6			8·00	7·00
Set of 6 Gutter Pairs			17·00	
First Day Cover (Tallents House)				9·00
First Day Cover (Garrison, Enniskillen)				9·00
Presentation Pack (P.O. Pack No. 357)			12·00	
PHQ Cards (set of 6) (262)			5·75	14·00

(b) Self-adhesive. Die-cut P 14½.

2445	**1727**	(1st) silver, black, new blue, magenta and greenish yellow	6·00	6·00
		a. Booklet pane. No. 2445×2 and No. 2295×4	12·00	
		ab. Imperf (pane)	£5000	

No. 2445 was only issued in £1·68 stamp booklets No. PM12 in which the surplus self-adhesive paper around each stamp was removed.

Special First Day of Issue Postmarks

1732 "Lace 1 (trial proof) 1968" (Sir Terry Frost)

1733 "Coccinelle" (Sonia Delaunay)

(Des Rose Design. Gravure Walsall)

2004 (6 Apr). *Centenary of the Entente Cordiale. Contemporary Paintings.* Two phosphor bands. P 14×14½.

2446	**1732**	28p. grey, black and rosine	1·00	85
2447	**1733**	57p. grey, black, grey-brown, rosine, new blue, orange-yellow and bright crimson	2·25	2·00
Set of 2			3·00	2·75
Set of 2 Gutter Pairs			7·00	
Set of 2 Traffic Light Gutter Blocks of 4			15·00	
First Day Cover (Tallents House)				3·75
First Day Cover (London SW1)				3·75
First Day Cover (UK and French stamps)				10·00
Presentation Pack (P.O. Pack No. 358)			25·00	
Presentation Pack (UK and French stamps)			25·00	
PHQ Cards (set of 2) (263)			3·50	6·00

Stamps in similar designs were issued by France and these are included in the joint Presentation Pack.

Special First Day of Issue Postmarks

Special First Day of Issue Postmarks

1734 "RMS *Queen Mary 2*, 2004" (Edward D. Walker)

1735 "SS *Canberra*, 1961" (David Cobb)

1740 *Dianthus Allwoodii* Group

1741 Dahlia "Garden Princess"

1736 "RMS *Queen Mary*, 1936" (Charles Pears)

1737 "RMS *Mauretania*, 1907" (Thomas Henry)

1742 Clematis "Arabella"

1743 Miltonia "French Lake"

1738 "SS *City of New York*, 1888" (Raphael Monleaon y Torres)

1739 "PS *Great Western*, 1838" (Joseph Walter)

1744 Lilium "Lemon Pixie"

1745 Delphinium "Clifford Sky"

(Des J. Gibbs. Gravure De La Rue)

2004 (13 Apr). Ocean Liners. Two phosphor bands. P 14½×14.

(a) Ordinary gum.

2448	**1734**	(1st) gold, black, magenta, greenish yellow and new blue	1·25	90
2449	**1735**	(E) gold, black, magenta, greenish yellow and new blue	1·50	1·30
		a. Imperf (pair)	£1000	
2450	**1736**	42p. gold, black, magenta, greenish yellow and new blue	1·30	1·30
2451	**1737**	47p. gold, black, magenta, greenish yellow and new blue	1·50	1·50
2452	**1738**	57p. gold, black, magenta, greenish yellow and new blue	1·80	1·80
2453	**1739**	68p. gold, black, magenta, greenish yellow and new blue	2·20	2·20
Set of 6			9·00	9·00
Set of 6 Gutter Pairs			20·00	
First Day Cover (Tallents House)				11·00
First Day Cover (Southampton)				11·00
Presentation Pack (P.O. Pack No. 359)			11·00	
PHQ Cards (set of 7) (264)			6·75	20·00
MS2454 114×104mm. Nos. 2448/53			20·00	18·00
First Day Cover (Tallents House)				19·00
First Day Cover (Southampton)				19·00

(b) Self-adhesive. Die-cut P 14½×14.

2455	**1734**	(1st) gold, black, magenta, greenish yellow and new blue	6·00	6·00
		a. Booklet pane. No. 2455×2 and No. 2295×4	12·00	

Nos. 2448/55 commemorate the introduction to service of the *Queen Mary 2*.

The complete miniature sheet is shown on one of the PHQ cards with the others depicting individual stamps. No. 2455 was only issued in £1·68 stamp booklets No. PM13 in which the surplus self-adhesive paper around each stamp was removed.

No. **MS**2454 is known to exist with a face value of "53" on No. 2452. It is known perforated and imperforate. See also No. 2614.

(Des Rose Design. Gravure Enschedé)

2004 (25 May). *Bicentenary of the Royal Horticultural Society* (1st issue). One side phosphor band (2nd) or 'all-over' phosphor (others). P 14½.

2456	**1740**	(2nd) sage-green, black, new blue, magenta and greenish yellow	1·00	80
		a. Booklet pane. Nos. 2456, 2458/9 and 2461 with margins all round	5·50	
2457	**1741**	(1st) sage-green, black, new blue, magenta and greenish yellow	1·25	1·00
		a. Booklet pane. Nos. 2457 and 2460, each×2, with margins all round	4·75	
2458	**1742**	(E) sage-green, black, new blue, magenta and greenish yellow	1·50	1·30
2459	**1743**	42p. sage-green, black, new blue, magenta and greenish yellow	2·00	2·00
2460	**1744**	47p. sage-green, black, new blue, magenta and greenish yellow	2·50	2·50
2461	**1745**	68p. sage-green, black, new blue, magenta and greenish yellow	3·50	3·50
Set of 6			11·00	10·00
Set of 6 Gutter Pairs			23·00	
First Day Cover (Tallents House)				12·00
First Day Cover (Wisley, Woking)				12·00
Presentation Pack (P.O. Pack No. 360)			12·00	
PHQ Cards (set of 7) (265)			6·75	20·00
MS2462 115×105 mm. Nos. 2456/61			14·00	14·00
First Day Cover (Tallents House)				16·00
First Day Cover (Wisley, Woking)				16·00

Booklet panes Nos. 2456a/7a come from the £7·23 "Glory of the Garden" booklet, No. DX33. The complete miniature sheet is shown on one of the PHQ cards with the others depicting individual stamps.

The 1st class stamp was also issued in sheets of 20, printed in lithography by Walsall and *sold at* £6·15, containing vertical strips of five stamps alternated with printed labels giving information about dahlias (LS19). These sheets with personalised photographs were available at £14·95 from the Royal Mail in Edinburgh.

Special First Day of Issue Postmarks

(Litho Enschedé)

2004 (25 May). *Bicentenary of the Royal Horticultural Society* (2nd issue). Booklet stamps. Designs as Nos. 1955, 1958 and 1962 (1997 Greeting Stamps 19th-century Flower Paintings). Two phosphor bands. *P* 15×14 (with one elliptical hole in each vert side.)

2463	**1280**	(1st) greenish yellow, new blue, magenta, black, blue-green and gold	8·00	8·00
		a. Booklet pane. Nos. 2463, 2464×2 and 2465 with margins all round	29·00	
2464	**1283**	(1st) greenish yellow, new blue, magenta, black, blue-green and gold	4·00	4·00
2465	**1287**	(1st) greenish yellow, new blue, magenta, black, blue-green and gold	8·00	8·00
Set of 3			18·00	18·00

On Nos. 2463/5 the phosphor bands appear at the left and the centre of each stamp. Nos. 2463/5 were only issued in the £7·23 Glory of the Garden booklet, No. DX33.

1746 Barmouth Bridge

1747 Hyddgen, Plynlimon

1748 Brecon Beacons

1749 Pen-pych, Rhondda Valley

1750 Rhewl, Dee Valley

1751 Marloes Sands

(Des Phelan Barker. Gravure De La Rue)

2004 (15 June). *A British Journey: Wales.* One centre phosphor band (2nd), 'all-over' phosphor (1st) or two phosphor bands (others). *P* 14½.

(a) Ordinary gum.

2466	**1746**	(2nd) silver, black, magenta, greenish yellow and new blue	1·00	80
		a. Imperf (pair)	£1150	
2467	**1747**	(1st) silver, black, magenta, greenish yellow and new blue	1·25	1·00
		a. Imperf (pair)	£1150	
2468	**1748**	40p. silver, black, magenta, greenish yellow and new blue	1·75	1·50
2469	**1749**	43p. silver, black, magenta, greenish yellow and new blue	2·00	2·00
2470	**1750**	47p. silver, black, magenta, greenish yellow and new blue	2·50	3·00
		a. Imperf (pair)	£800	
2471	**1751**	68p. silver, black, magenta, greenish yellow and new blue	3·50	4·00
		a. Imperf (pair)	£1100	
Set of 6			10·00	11·00

Set of 6 Gutter Pairs	22·00	
First Day Cover (Tallents House)		12·00
First Day Cover (Llanfair)		12·00
Presentation Pack (P.O. Pack No. 361)	11·00	
PHQ Cards (set of 6) (266)	5·75	12·00

(b) Self-adhesive. Die-cut P 14½.

2472	**1747**	(1st) silver, black, magenta, greenish yellow and new blue	8·00	8·00
		a. Booklet pane. No. 2472×2 and No. 2295×4	18·00	

The 1st and 40p. values include the "EUROPA" emblem.

Imperf pairs of Type **1748** and Type **1749** with alternative face values are of proof status. (*Price* £1000 *per pair*).

No. 2472 was only issued in £1·68 stamp booklets, No. PM14, in which the surplus self-adhesive paper around each stamp was removed.

Special First Day of Issue Postmarks

1752 Sir Rowland Hill Award

1753 William Shipley (Founder of Royal Society of Arts)

1754 "RSA" as Typewriter Keys and Shorthand

1755 Chimney Sweep

1756 "Gill Typeface"

1757 "Zero Waste"

(Des D. Birdsall. Litho Walsall)

2004 (10 Aug). *250th Anniv of the Royal Society of Arts.* Two phosphor bands. *P* 14.

2473	**1752**	(1st) silver, vermilion, blackish-brown and black	1·25	95
2474	**1753**	40p. silver, vermilion, grey-black, blackish-brown and black	1·30	1·30
2475	**1754**	43p. silver, new blue, vermilion and black	1·40	1·40
2476	**1755**	47p. silver, vermilion, blackish-brown and black	1·50	1·50
2477	**1756**	57p. silver, vermilion and black	2·20	2·20
2478	**1757**	68p. silver, vermilion and black	3·00	3·00
Set of 6			10·00	10·00

Set of 6 Gutter Pairs	22·00	
First Day Cover (Tallents House)		12·00
First Day Cover (London WC2)		12·00
Presentation Pack (P.O. Pack No. 362)	11·00	
PHQ Cards (set of 6) (267)	5·75	14·00

Special First Day of Issue Postmarks

1758 Pine Marten

1759 Roe Deer

1760 Badger

1761 Yellow-necked Mouse

1762 Wild Cat

1763 Red Squirrel

1764 Stoat

1765 Natterer's Bat

1766 Mole

1767 Fox

(Des Kate Stephens. Gravure Enschedé)

2004 (16 Sept). *Woodland Animals*. Two phosphor bands. *P* 14½.

2479	1758	(1st) ochre, black, bright new blue, magenta and lemon	1·25	1·00
		a. Block of 10. Nos. 2479/88	14·00	12·00
2480	1759	(1st) ochre, black, bright new blue, magenta and lemon	1·25	1·00
2481	1760	(1st) ochre, black, bright new blue, magenta and lemon	1·25	1·00
2482	1761	(1st) ochre, black, bright new blue, magenta and lemon	1·25	1·00
2483	1762	(1st) ochre, black, bright new blue, magenta and lemon	1·25	1·00
2484	1763	(1st) ochre, black, bright new blue, magenta and lemon	1·25	1·00
2485	1764	(1st) ochre, black, bright new blue, magenta and lemon	1·25	1·00
2486	1765	(1st) ochre, black, bright new blue, magenta and lemon	1·25	1·00
2487	1766	(1st) ochre, black, bright new blue, magenta and lemon	1·25	1·00
2488	1767	(1st) ochre, black, bright new blue, magenta and lemon	1·25	1·00
		Set of 10	14·00	12·00
		Gutter Block of 20	30·00	
		First Day Cover (Tallents House)		13·00
		First Day Cover (Woodland, Bishop Auckland)		14·00
		Presentation Pack (P.O. Pack No. 363)	16·00	
		PHQ Cards (set of 10) (268)	9·75	18·00

Nos. 2479/88 were printed together, *se-tenant*, in blocks of ten (5×2) throughout sheets of 30.

Special First Day of Issue Postmarks

1768 Pte. McNamara, 5th Dragoon Guards, Heavy Brigade charge, Battle of Balaklava

1769 Piper Muir, 42nd Regt of Foot, amphibious assault on Kerch

1770 Sgt. Maj. Edwards, Scots Fusilier Guards, gallant action, Battle of Inkerman

1771 Sgt. Powell, 1st Regt of Foot Guards, Battles of Alma and Inkerman

1772 Sgt. Maj. Poole, Royal Sappers and Miners, defensive line, Battle of Inkerman

1773 Sgt. Glasgow, Royal Artillery, gun battery besieged Sevastopol

(Des Atelier Works. Litho Walsall)

2004 (12 Oct). *150th Anniv of the Crimean War*. One centre phosphor band (2nd) or two phosphor bands (others). P 14.

2489	**1768**	(2nd) greyish silver, brownish grey, black and grey-black	1·00	80
		a. Greyish silver and phosphor omitted	£1300	
2490	**1769**	(1st) greyish silver, brownish grey, black and grey-black	1·25	1·00
2491	**1770**	40p. greyish silver, brownish grey, black and grey-black	2·00	2·00
2492	**1771**	57p. greyish silver, brownish grey, black and grey-black	2·50	2·50
		a. Imperf	£850	
2493	**1772**	68p. greyish silver, brownish grey, black and grey-black	2·75	3·00
		a. Imperf	£2500	
2494	**1773**	£1·12 greyish silver, brownish grey, black and grey-black	4·50	5·00
Set of 6			12·00	13·00
Set of 6 Gutter Pairs			25·00	
Set of 6 Traffic Light Gutter Pairs			30·00	
First Day Cover (Tallents House)				14·00
First Day Cover (London SW3)				14·00
Presentation Pack (P.O. Pack No. 364)			14·00	
PHQ Cards (set of 6) (269)			5·75	16·00

Nos. 2489/94 show "Crimean Heroes" photographs taken in 1856.

Special First Day of Issue Postmarks

1774 Father Christmas on Snowy Roof   **1775** Celebrating the Sunrise

1776 On Roof in Gale   **1777** With Umbrella in Rain

1778 On Edge of Roof with Torch   **1779** Sheltering behind Chimney

(Des R. Briggs. Gravure De La Rue)

2004 (2 Nov). *Christmas*. One centre phosphor band (2nd) or two phosphor bands (others). P 14½×14.

(a) Self-adhesive.

2495	**1774**	(2nd) magenta, greenish yellow, new blue and black	1·00	80
		a. Booklet pane. No. 2495×24	16·00	
2496	**1775**	(1st) magenta, greenish yellow, new blue and black	1·25	1·00
		a. Booklet pane. No. 2496×12	11·00	
2497	**1776**	40p. magenta, greenish yellow, new blue and black	1·30	1·30
2498	**1777**	57p. magenta, greenish yellow, new blue and black	1·80	1·80
2499	**1778**	68p. magenta, greenish yellow, new blue and black	2·20	2·20

2500	**1779**	£1·12 magenta, greenish yellow, new blue and black	3·75	3·75
Set of 6			11·00	12·00
First Day Cover (Tallents House)				13·50
First Day Cover (Bethlehem, Llandeilo)				13·50
Presentation Pack (P.O. Pack No. 365)			12·50	
PHQ Cards (set of 7) (270)			6·75	18·00

(b) Ordinary gum.

MS2501	115×105 mm. As Nos. 2495/500	12·00	13·00
First Day Cover (Tallents House)			14·00
First Day Cover (Bethlehem, Llandeilo)			14·00

Nos. 2495/500 were each printed in sheets of 50 with the surplus backing paper around each stamp removed.

The seven PHQ cards depict the six individual stamps and the miniature sheet.

The 2nd and 1st class were also issued together in sheets of 20, *sold at* £5·40, containing ten 2nd class and ten 1st class, each value arranged in vertical rows of five alternated with rows of half stamp-size labels showing Father Christmas (LS21). Separate sheets of 20 2nd class and 20 1st class were available with personalised photographs at £9·95 (2nd class) or £14·95 (1st class) from Royal Mail, Edinburgh. These sheets were printed in lithography instead of photogravure and had the backing paper around the stamps retained.

Trials are known showing alternative face values.

Special First Day of Issue Postmarks

Collectors Pack 2004

2004 (2 Nov). Comprises Nos. 2417/22, 2424/44, 2446/53, 2456/61, 2466/71 and 2473/500.
CP2500a Collectors Pack £120

Post Office Yearbook

2004 (2 Nov). Comprises Nos. 2417/22, 2424/44, 2446/53, 2456/61, 2466/71 and 2473/500 in hardback book with slipcase £110

1780 British Saddleback Pigs   **1781** Khaki Campbell Ducks

1782 Clydesdale Mare and Foal   **1783** Dairy Shorthorn Cattle

1784 Border Collie Dog   **1785** Light Sussex Chicks

1786 Suffolk Sheep

1787 Bagot Goat

1788 Norfolk Black Turkeys

1789 Embden Geese

(Des C. Wormell. Gravure Enschedé)

2005 (11 Jan). *Farm Animals*. Two phosphor bands. *P* 14½.

2502	**1780**	(1st) grey, grey-black, new blue, magenta and greenish yellow..........	1·25	1·00
		a. Block of 10. Nos. 2502/11......................	14·00	12·00
2503	**1781**	(1st) grey, grey-black, new blue, magenta and greenish yellow..........	1·25	1·00
2504	**1782**	(1st) grey, grey-black, new blue, magenta and greenish yellow..........	1·25	1·00
2505	**1783**	(1st) grey, grey-black, new blue, magenta and greenish yellow..........	1·25	1·00
2506	**1784**	(1st) grey, grey-black, new blue, magenta and greenish yellow..........	1·25	1·00
2507	**1785**	(1st) grey, grey-black, new blue, magenta and greenish yellow..........	1·25	1·00
2508	**1786**	(1st) grey, grey-black, new blue, magenta and greenish yellow..........	1·25	1·00
2509	**1787**	(1st) grey, grey-black, new blue, magenta and greenish yellow..........	1·25	1·00
2510	**1788**	(1st) grey, grey-black, new blue, magenta and greenish yellow..........	1·25	1·00
2511	**1789**	(1st) grey, grey-black, new blue, magenta and greenish yellow..........	1·25	1·00

Set of 10... 14·00 12·00
Gutter Block of 20.. 30·00
Traffic Light Gutter Block of 20........................ 30·00
First Day Cover (Tallents House) .... 13·00
First Day Cover (Paddock, Huddersfield)......... 13·00
Presentation Pack (P.O. Pack No. 367)............ 15·00
PHQ Cards (set of 10) (271)............................. 9·75 18·00

Nos. 2502/11 were printed together, *se-tenant*, in blocks of ten (5×2) throughout sheets of 30. Nos. 2502/11 were also issued in sheets of 20, containing two of each of the ten designs, arranged in vertical strips of five alternated with printed labels showing black/white illustrations of farm scenes (LS 22). These sheets were printed in lithography by Walsall and sold for £6·15.

They were also available with personal photographs on the labels at £14·95 per sheet from Royal Mail, Edinburgh.

Special First Day of Issue Postmarks

1790 Old Harry Rocks, Studland Bay

1791 Wheal Coates, St. Agnes

1792 Start Point, Start Bay

1793 Horton Down, Wiltshire

1794 Chiselcombe, Exmoor

1795 St. James's Stone, Lundy

(Des J. Phelan and Lissa Barker. Gravure De La Rue)

2005 (8 Feb). *A British Journey: South West England*. One centre phosphor band (2nd) or two phosphor bands (others). *P* 14½.

2512	**1790**	(2nd) silver, black, magenta, greenish yellow and new blue............................	1·00	80
2513	**1791**	(1st) silver, black, magenta, greenish yellow and new blue............................	1·25	90
2514	**1792**	40p. silver, black, magenta, greenish yellow and new blue............................	1·50	1·75
2515	**1793**	43p. silver, black, magenta, greenish yellow and new blue............................	1·75	2·00
2516	**1794**	57p. silver, black, magenta, greenish yellow and new blue............................	2·50	2·50
2517	**1795**	68p. silver, black, magenta, greenish yellow and new blue............................	3·50	3·00

Set of 6 .... 10·00 10·00
Set of 6 Gutter Pairs... 21·00
First Day Cover (Tallents House) .... 12·00
First Day Cover (The Lizard, Helston)............... 12·00
Presentation Pack (P.O. Pack No. 368)............ 11·00
PHQ Cards (set of 6) (262)............................... 6·00 14·00

Perforated examples of Type **1794** are known with face value of 47p are known (price £3000).

Special First Day of Issue Postmarks

1796 "Mr Rochester"

1797 "Come to Me"

1798 "In the Comfort of her Bonnet"

1799 "La Ligne des Rats"

1800 "Refectory"

1801 "Inspection"

(Des P. Willberg. Litho Walsall)

2005 (24 Feb). *150th Death Anniv of Charlotte Brontë*. Illustrations of scenes from *Jane Eyre* by Paula Rego. One centre phosphor band (2nd), or two phosphor bands (others). P 14×14½.

2518	**1796**	(2nd) silver, sage-green, brownish grey and black	1·00	80
		a. Booklet pane. Nos. 2518/19, both×2, with margins all round	4·00	
2519	**1797**	(1st) silver, lemon, magenta, new blue and black	1·25	1·00
2520	**1798**	40p. silver, lemon, magenta, new blue and black	1·50	1·50
		a. Booklet pane. Nos. 2520/3 with margins all round	13·00	
2521	**1799**	57p. silver, brownish grey and black	3·00	2·50
2522	**1800**	68p. silver, pale brownish grey, lemon, magenta, new blue and black	3·75	3·00
2523	**1801**	£1.12 silver, brownish grey and black	4·50	3·50
Set of 6			12·00	11·00
Set of 6 Gutter Pairs			25·00	
Set of 6 Traffic Light Gutter Blocks of 4			48·00	
First Day Cover (Tallents House)				12·00
First Day Cover (Haworth, Keighley)				12·00
Presentation Pack (P.O. Pack No. 369)			13·00	
PHQ Cards (set of 7) (273)			6·00	18·00
MS2524 114×105 mm. Nos. 2518/23			12·00	11·00
First Day Cover (Tallents House)				12·00
First Day Cover (Haworth, Keighley)				12·00

Booklet panes Nos. 2518a and 2520a come from the £7·43 "The Brontë Sisters" booklet, No. DX34. The complete miniature sheet is shown on one of the PHQ cards with the others depicting individual stamps.

Special First Day of Issue Postmarks

FERNDEAN MANOR
24.2.2005

HAWORTH PARSONAGE
24.2.2005

1802 Spinning Coin

1803 Rabbit out of Hat Trick

1804 Knotted Scarf Trick

1805 Card Trick

1806 Pyramid under Fez Trick

(Des G. Hardie and Tatham Design. Gravure Walsall)

2005 (15 Mar). ·*Centenary of the Magic Circle*. Two phosphor bands. P 14½×14.

2525	**1802**	(1st) brownish grey, bright blue, yellow-orange and black	1·25	80
2526	**1803**	40p. brownish grey, turquoise-green, bright violet, yellow-orange and black	1·00	90
2527	**1804**	47p. brownish grey, bright mauve, bright violet, turquoise-green, yellow-orange and black	2·50	2·75
2528	**1805**	68p. brownish grey, turquoise-green, rosine and black	3·00	3·00
2529	**1806**	£1.12 brownish grey, bright mauve, new blue, lilac, reddish violet and black	3·50	3·50
Set of 5			10·00	11·00
Set of 5 Gutter Pairs			21·00	
First Day Cover (Tallents House)				12·00
First Day Cover (London NW1)				12·00
Presentation Pack (P.O. Pack No. 370)			15·00	
PHQ Cards (set of 5) (274)			5·00	12·00

Nos. 2525/9 are each printed with instructions for the illusion or trick on the stamp. No. 2525 can be rubbed with a coin to reveal the "head" or "tail" of a coin. The two versions, which appear identical before rubbing, are printed in alternate rows of the sheet, indicated by the letters H and T in the side margins of the sheet. Nos. 2526 and 2528 each show optical illusions. The bright mauve on No. 2527 and the bright mauve, new blue, and lilac on No. 2529 are printed in thermochromic inks which fade temporarily when exposed to heat, making the pyramid under the centre fez visible.

The 1st class stamp was also issued in sheets of 20, printed in lithography instead of photogravure and sold at £6·15, containing vertical rows of five stamps alternated with half stamp-size printed labels illustrating magic tricks (LS23). These sheets were also available with personal photographs on the labels at £14·95 per sheet from Royal Mail, Edinburgh.

Special First Day of Issue Postmarks

THE CASTLES DEFINITIVES

1806a First Castles Definitives (*Illustration reduced. Actual size 127×73 mm*)

(Des Sedley Place. Recess and litho Enschedé)

2005 (22 Mar). *50th Anniv of First Castles Definitives*. Printed on pale cream. 'All-over' phosphor. P 11×11½.

MS2530	**1806a**	50p. brownish-black; 50p. black; £1 dull vermilion; £1 royal blue	10·00	10·00
First Day Cover (Tallents House)				12·00
First Day Cover (Windsor)				12·00
Presentation Pack (P.O. Pack No. 69)			15·00	
PHQ Cards (set of 5) (D28)			5·00	12·00

The five PHQ cards depict the whole miniature sheet and the four stamps it contains.

Special First Day of Issue Postmarks

1807 Royal Wedding (*Illustration reduced.*
Actual size 85×115 mm)

(Des Rose Design. Litho Enschedé)

2005 (9 Apr). *Royal Wedding.* Sheet 85×115 mm. Multicoloured. 'All-over'
phosphor. *P* 13½×14.

MS2531 30p.×2 Prince Charles and Mrs Camilla Parker Bowles laughing; 68p.×2 Prince Charles and Mrs Camilla Parker Bowles smiling into camera	8·00
First Day Cover (Tallents House)	10·00
First Day Cover (Windsor)	10·00
Presentation Pack (P.O. Pack No. M10)	18·00

No. **MS**2531 was officially issued on 9th April. It was originally
intended for issue on 8th April, and many post offices put it on sale
on that day. Royal Mail first day covers were dated 8th April, but could
be ordered with a 9th April Windsor handstamp. Our prices cover
either date.

Special First Day of Issue Postmarks

1808 Hadrian's Wall, England

1809 Uluru-Kata Tjuta
National Park, Australia

1810 Stonehenge, England

1811 Wet Tropics of
Queensland, Australia

1812 Blenheim Palace,
England

1813 Greater Blue
Mountains Area, Australia

1814 Heart of Neolithic
Orkney, Scotland

1815 Purnululu National
Park, Australia

(Des J. Godfrey. Litho Enschedé)

2005 (21 Apr). *World Heritage Sites.* One side phosphor band (2nd) or
two phosphor bands (others). *P* 14½.

2532	**1808**	2nd silver, black, magenta, new blue and greenish yellow.............................	1·00	80
		a. Horiz pair. Nos. 2532/3...............	2·00	1·60
2533	**1809**	2nd silver, black, magenta, new blue and greenish yellow.............................	1·00	80
2534	**1810**	1st silver, black, magenta, new blue and greenish yellow.............................	1·25	90
		a. Horiz pair. Nos. 2534/5...............	2·50	2·00
2535	**1811**	1st silver, black, magenta, new blue and greenish yellow.............................	1·25	90
2536	**1812**	47p. silver, black, magenta, new blue and greenish yellow.............................	1·00	1·00
		a. Horiz pair. Nos. 2536/7...............	2·00	2·25
2537	**1813**	47p. silver, black, magenta, new blue and greenish yellow.............................	1·00	1·00
2538	**1814**	68p. silver, black, magenta, new blue and greenish yellow.............................	1·50	1·50
		a. Horiz pair. Nos. 2538/9...............	3·00	3·00
2539	**1815**	68p. silver, black, magenta, new blue and greenish yellow.............................	1·50	1·50
Set of 8			8·50	8·00
Set of 4 Gutter Strips of 4			20·00	
Set of 4 Traffic Light Gutter Blocks of 8..................			42·00	
First Day Cover (Tallents House)				11·00
First Day Cover (Blenheim Palace, Woodstock)				12·00
First Day Covers (2) (UK and Australian stamps)				22·00
Presentation Pack (P.O. Pack No. 371)			10·00	
Presentation Pack (UK and Australian stamps)			16·00	
PHQ Cards (set of 8) (275).......................................			7·00	14·00

The two designs of each value were printed together, *se-tenant*, in
horizontal pairs in sheets of 30 (6×5).

Stamps in these designs were also issued by Australia and these
are included in the joint Presentation Pack.

Special First Day of Issue Postmarks

1816 Ensign of the Scots
Guards, 2002

1817 Queen taking the
salute as Colonel-in-Chief of
the Grenadier Guards, 1983

1818 Trumpeter of the Household Cavalry, 2004

1819 Welsh Guardsman, 1990s

1820 Queen riding side-saddle, 1972

1821 Queen and Duke of Edinburgh in carriage, 2004

(Des A. Altmann. Litho Walsall)

2005 (7 June). *Trooping the Colour.* One phosphor band (2nd), two phosphor bands (others). P 14½.

2540	**1816**	(2nd) silver, greenish yellow, bright carmine, new blue and black	1·00	80
2541	**1817**	(1st) silver, greenish yellow, bright carmine, new blue and black	1·25	1·00
2542	**1818**	42p. silver, greenish yellow, bright carmine, new blue and black	1·00	1·20
2543	**1819**	60p. silver, greenish yellow, bright carmine, new blue and black	2·00	2·00
2544	**1820**	68p. silver, greenish yellow, bright carmine, new blue and black	2·50	2·50
2545	**1821**	£1·12 silver, greenish yellow, bright carmine, new blue and black	3·50	3·50

Set of 6	10·00	10·00
Set of 6 Gutter Pairs	21·00	
First Day Cover (Tallents House)		12·00
First Day Cover (London SW1)		12·00
Presentation Pack (P.O. Pack No. 372)	14·00	
PHQ Cards (set of 7) (276)	5·00	20·00
MS2546 115×105 mm. Nos. 2540/5	11·00	11·00
First Day Cover (Tallents House)		12·00
First Day Cover (London SW1)		12·00

The seven PHQ cards show the six stamps and **MS**2546.

1822 End of the War (*Illustration reduced. Actual size 115×105 mm*)

(Des J. Matthews. Gravure Enschedé)

2005 (5 July). *60th Anniv of End of the Second World War.* Sheet 115×105 mm containing design as *T* **1200** (1995 Peace and Freedom) but with service indicator and No. 1668×5. Two phosphor bands. P 15×14 (with one elliptical hole in each vert side) (1668) or 14½×14 (other).

MS2547	**1822**	(1st) gold×5; (1st) silver, blue and grey-black	7·50	7·00
First Day Cover (Tallents House)				8·00
First Day Cover (Peacehaven, Newhaven)				8·00

1823 Norton F.1, Road Version of Race Winner (1991)

1824 BSA Rocket 3, Early Three Cylinder "Superbike" (1969)

1825 Vincent Black Shadow, Fastest Standard Motorcycle (1949)

1826 Triumph Speed Twin, Two Cylinder Innovation (1938)

1827 Brough Superior, Bespoke Luxury Motorcycle (1930)

1828 Royal Enfield, Small Engined Motor Bicycle (1914)

(Des I. Chilvers and M. English. Litho Walsall)

2005 (19 July). *Motorcycles.* Two phosphor bands. P 14×14½.

2548	**1823**	(1st) silver, greenish yellow, bright crimson, new blue and black	1·25	1·00
2549	**1824**	40p. silver, greenish yellow, bright crimson, new blue and black	90	1·00
2550	**1825**	42p. silver, greenish yellow, bright crimson, new blue and black	1·25	1·00
2551	**1826**	47p. silver, greenish yellow, bright crimson, new blue and black	1·75	2·00
2552	**1827**	60p. silver, greenish yellow, bright crimson, new blue and black	2·50	2·50
2553	**1828**	68p. silver, greenish yellow, bright crimson, new blue and black	3·00	3·00

Set of 6	9·00	9·00
Set of 6 Gutter Pairs	19·00	
First Day Cover (Tallents House)		11·00
First Day Cover (Solihull)		11·00
Presentation Pack (P.O. Pack No. 373)	13·00	
PHQ Cards (set of 6) (277)	5·00	14·00

Special First Day of Issue Postmarks

1834 Woman eating Chips   **1835** Teenage Boy eating Apple

(Des Catell Ronca and Rose Design. Gravure Enschedé)

2005 (23 Aug). *Europa. Gastronomy.* Changing Tastes in Britain. One side phosphor band (2nd) or two phosphor bands (others). P 14½.

2555	**1830**	(2nd) olive-grey, grey-black, new blue, magenta and greenish yellow	1·00	80
2556	**1831**	(1st) olive-grey, grey-black, new blue, magenta and greenish yellow	1·25	1·00
2557	**1832**	42p. olive-grey, grey-black, new blue, magenta and greenish yellow	1·30	1·40
2558	**1833**	47p. olive-grey, grey-black, new blue, magenta and greenish yellow	1·50	1·60
2559	**1834**	60p. olive-grey, grey-black, new blue, magenta and greenish yellow	2·00	1·90
2560	**1835**	68p. olive-grey, grey-black, new blue, magenta and greenish yellow	2·50	2·20
Set of 6			8·00	8·00
Set of 6 Gutter Pairs			17·00	
First Day Cover (Tallents House)				10·00
First Day Cover (Cookstown)				10·00
Presentation Pack (P.O. Pack No. 374)			9·00	
PHQ Cards (set of 6) (278)			5·00	12·00

The 1st snd 42p values include the 'EUROPA' emblem.

1829 London 2012 Host City (*Illustration reduced. Actual size 115×105 mm*)

(Des CDT Design. Litho Walsall)

2005 (5 Aug). *London's Successful Bid for Olympic Games*, **2012**. Sheet 115×105 mm containing designs as T **1255/9**, but with service indicator. Multicoloured. Two phosphor bands. P 14½.

MS2554	**1829**	(1st) Athlete celebrating×2; (1st) Throwing the javelin; (1st) Swimming; (1st) Athlete on starting blocks; (1st) Basketball	6·50	6·50
First Day Cover (Tallents House)				8·00
First Day Cover (London E15)				8·00
Presentation Pack (P.O. Pack No. M11)			12·00	

Stamps from **MS2554** are all inscribed "London 2012—Host City" and have imprint date "2005". The design as Type **1259** omits the Olympic rings.

Special First Day of Issue Postmarks

1830 African Woman eating Rice   **1831** Indian Woman drinking Tea

1832 Boy eating Sushi   **1833** Woman eating Pasta

Special First Day of Issue Postmarks

1836 *Inspector Morse*   **1837** *Emmerdale*

1838 *Rising Damp*   **1839** *The Avengers*

1840 *The South Bank Show*   **1841** *Who Wants to be a Millionaire*

(Des Kate Stephens. Litho D.L.R.)

2005 (15 Sept). *50th Anniversary of Independent Television.* Classic ITV Programmes. One side phosphor band (2nd) or two phosphor bands (others). *P* 14½×14.

2561	**1836**	(2nd) new blue, magenta, greenish yellow and brownish-black.............	1·00	1·00
2562	**1837**	(1st) new blue, magenta, greenish yellow and brownish-black.............	1·25	1·00
2563	**1838**	42p. new blue, magenta, greenish yellow and brownish-black.............	1·30	1·40
2564	**1839**	47p. new blue, magenta, greenish yellow and brownish-black.............	1·40	1·50
2565	**1840**	60p. new blue, magenta, greenish yellow and brownish-black.............	2·00	1·90
2566	**1841**	68p. new blue, magenta, greenish yellow and brownish-black.............	2·20	2·20
Set of 6			8·00	8·00
Set of 6 Gutter Pairs...			17·00	
First Day Cover (Tallents House)				10·00
First Day Cover (London SE19)				10·00
Presentation Pack (P.O. Pack No. 375)............................			9·00	
PHQ Cards (set of 6) (279)			5·00	12·00

The 1st class stamps were also issued in sheets of 20 sold at £6·55, printed in lithography by Walsall, containing four vertical rows of five stamps alternated with half stamp-size labels (LS26). These sheets with personalised photographs were available at £14·95 from the Royal Mail.

Special First Day of Issue Postmarks

1843 Cricket Scenes (*Illustration reduced. Actual size* 115×90 *mm*)

(Des Why Not Associates. Litho Cartor)

2005 (6 Oct). *England's Ashes Victory.* Sheet 115×90 mm. Multicoloured. Two phosphor bands. *P* 14½×14.

MS2573	**1843**	(1st) England team with Ashes trophy; (1st) Kevin Pietersen, Michael Vaughan and Andrew Flintoff on opening day of First Test, Lords; 68p. Michael Vaughan, Third Test, Old Trafford; 68p. Second Test cricket, Edgbaston	7·50	7·50
First Day Cover (Tallents House)				9·00
First Day Cover (London SE11)				9·00
Presentation Pack (P.O. Pack No. M12)			10·00	

Special First Day of Issue Postmarks

1842 Gazania splendens (Charlotte Sowerby)

1842a "LOVE"

(Gravure Walsall)

2005 (4 Oct). *Smilers Booklet stamps* (1st series). Designs as Types **992, 1221, 1286, 1517** and **1569** but smaller, 20×23 mm and inscribed '1st' as *T* **1842/a.** Self-adhesive. Two phosphor bands. Die-cut. P 15×14.

2567	**1842**	(1st) multicoloured..................................	2·50	2·50
		a. Booklet pane. Nos. 2567/72	14·00	
2568	**1569**	(1st) multicoloured..................................	2·50	2·50
2569	**1842a**	(1st) multicoloured..................................	2·50	2·50
2570	**1517**	(1st) multicoloured..................................	2·50	2·50
2571	**992**	(1st) multicoloured..................................	2·50	2·50
2572	**1221**	(1st) multicoloured..................................	2·50	2·50
Set of 6			14·00	14·00
First Day Cover (Tallents House) (Type K, see Introduction).......................................				15·00
First Day Cover (Windsor) (Type K)................................				15·00

Nos. 2567/72 were only issued in stamp booklets, Nos. QA1 and QA2, in which the surplus backing paper around each stamp was removed.

Stamps in these designs in separate sheets printed in lithography by Cartor were available with personal photographs on the labels at £14·95 *per sheet* from Royal Mail, Edinburgh.

Nos. 2567/72 were issued on 4 July 2006 in sheets of 20 with *se-tenant* greetings labels, No. LS32, printed by Cartor in lithography instead of photogravure and sold at £6·95 *per sheet.*

Nos. 2568/70 were re-issued on 15 January 2008 in sheets of 20 with circular labels printed in lithography by Cartor and sold at £7·35 (LS45). These sheets were perforated with one elliptical hole on each vert side.

These three designs were available in separate sheets of 10 (*sold at* £8·95) or 20 (*sold at* £14·95) with personal photographs on the labels from Royal Mail, Edinburgh).

No. 2572 was issued on 8 May 2010 with other greetings stamps in sheets of 20 with *se-tenant* greetings labels, printed in lithography by Cartor, No. LS73, and sold for £10 *per sheet.* These sheets were printed with one elliptical hole in each vertical side.

For stamp as No. 2569 with one elliptical hole in each vertical side see No. 2693.

For stamps as Nos. 2567/8 and 2570 with one elliptical hole in each vertical side see Nos. 2819/21.

1844 *Entreprente* with dismasted British *Belle Isle*

1845 Nelson wounded on Deck of HMS *Victory*

1846 British Cutter *Entreprente* attempting to rescue Crew of burning French *Achille*

1847 Cutter and HMS *Pickle* (schooner)

1848 British Fleet attacking in Two Columns

1849 Franco/Spanish Fleet putting to Sea from Cadiz

(Des D. Davis. Litho Cartor)

2005 (18 Oct). *Bicentenary of the Battle of Trafalgar* (1st issue). Scenes from 'Panorama of the Battle of Trafalgar' by William Heath. Two phosphor bands. *P* 15×14½.

2574	**1844**	(1st) gold, deep bluish-green, greenish yellow, magenta, new blue and black...........	1·25	1·00
		a. Horiz pair. Nos. 2574/5..........	2·50	2·25
		b. Booklet pane. Nos. 2574, 2576 and 2578.........	3·75	
2575	**1845**	(1st) gold, deep bluish-green, greenish yellow, magenta, new blue and black...........	1·25	1·00
		b. Booklet pane. Nos. 2575, 2577 and 2579.........	3·75	
2576	**1846**	42p. gold, deep bluish-green, greenish yellow, magenta, new blue and black...........	1·00	1·10
		a. Horiz pair. Nos. 2576/7.........	2·50	2·75
2577	**1847**	42p. gold, deep bluish-green, greenish yellow, magenta, new blue and black...........	1·00	1·10
2578	**1848**	68p. gold, deep bluish-green, greenish yellow, magenta, new blue and black...........	1·25	1·50
		a. Horiz pair. Nos. 2578/9.........	4·00	4·00
2579	**1849**	68p. gold, deep bluish-green, greenish yellow, magenta, new blue and black...........	1·25	1·50
Set of 6			8·00	8·50
Set of 3 Gutter Strips of 4			18·00	
First Day Cover (Tallents House)				10·00
First Day Cover (Portsmouth)				10·00
Presentation Pack (P.O. Pack No. 376)			10·00	
PHQ Cards (set of 7) (280)			7·00	20·00
MS2580 190×68 mm. Nos. 2574/9			10·00	11·00
First Day Cover (Tallents House)				12·00
First Day Cover (Portsmouth)				12·00

Nos. 2574/5, 2576/7 and 2578/9 were each printed together, *se-tenant*, in horizontal pairs throughout the sheets, each pair forming a composite design.

The phosphor bands are at just left of centre and at right of each stamp.

Booklet panes Nos. 2574b/5b come from the £7·26 Battle of Trafalgar booklet, No. DX35. The seven PHQ cards depict the six individual stamps and the miniature sheet.

Special First Day of Issue Postmarks

(Litho Cartor or De La Rue)

2005 (18 Oct). *Bicentenary of the Battle of Trafalgar* (2nd issue). Booklet stamp. Design as Type **1516** (2001 White Ensign from Submarine Centenary). Two phosphor bands. *P* 14½.

2581	**1516**	(1st) multicoloured..........	5·00	5·00
		a. Booklet pane. No. 2581×3 with margins all round..........	16·00	

No. 2581 was issued in the £7·26 Trafalgar Bicentenary booklet, No. DX35, printed by Cartor, the £7·40 James Bond booklet, No. DX41, which was printed by De La Rue (see booklet pane No. 2805a) and the £7·93 Royal Navy Uniforms booklet, No. DX47.

1850 Black Madonna and Child from Haiti

1851 "Madonna and Child" (Marianne Stokes)

1852 "The Virgin Mary with the Infant Christ"

1853 Choctaw Virgin Mother and Child (Fr. John Giuliani)

1854 "Madonna and the Infant Jesus" (from India)

1855 "Come let us adore Him" (Dianne Tchumut)

(Des Irene Von Treskow. Gravure De La Rue)

2005 (1 Nov). *Christmas. Madonna and Child Paintings.* One side phosphor band (2nd) or two phosphor bands (others). *P* 14½×14.

(a) Self-adhesive

2582	**1850**	(2nd) silver, magenta, greenish yellow, new blue and black............	1·00	80
		a. Booklet pane. No. 2582×24............	22·00	
2583	**1851**	(1st) silver, magenta, greenish yellow, new blue and black............	1·25	1·00
		a. Booklet pane. No. 2583×12............	13·50	
2584	**1852**	42p. silver, magenta, greenish yellow, new blue and black............	1·30	1·40
2585	**1853**	60p. silver, magenta, greenish yellow, new blue and black............	1·80	1·90
2586	**1854**	68p. silver, magenta, greenish yellow, new blue and black............	2·00	2·20
2587	**1855**	£1·12 silver, magenta, greenish yellow, new blue and black............	3·40	3·60
Set of 6			9·50	10·00
First Day Cover (Tallents House)				12·00
First Day Cover (Bethlehem, Llandeilo)				13·00
Presentation Pack (P.O. Pack No. 377)			11·00	
PHQ Cards (set of 7) (281)			4·00	16·00

The seven PHQ cards depict the six individual stamps and the miniature sheet.

(b) Ordinary gum

MS2588 115×102 mm. As Nos. 2582/7		10·50	11·00
First Day Cover (Tallents House)			12·00
First Day Cover (Bethlehem, Llandeilo)			13·00

Special First Day of Issue Postmarks

Collectors Pack

2005 (1 Nov). Comprises Nos. 2502/23, 2525/9. **MS**2531/45, 2548/53, 2555/66, 2574/9 and 2582/7.

CP2587a Collectors Pack £110

Post Office Yearbook

2005 (1 Nov). Comprises Nos. 2502/23, 2525/9, **MS**2531/45, 2548/53, 2555/66, 2574/9 and 2582/7.

YB2587a Yearbook .... 95·00

Miniature Sheet Collection

2005 (1 Nov). Comprises Nos. **MS**2524, **MS**2530/1, **MS**2546/7, **MS**2554, **MS**2573, **MS**2580 and **MS**2588.

MS2588a Miniature Sheet Collection............ 75·00

1856 *The Tale of Mr. Jeremy Fisher* (Beatrix Potter)

1857 *Kipper* (Mick Inkpen)

1858 *The Enormous Crocodile* (Roald Dahl)

1859 *More About Paddington* (Michael Bond)

1860 *Comic Adventures of Boots* (Satoshi Kitamura)

1861 *Alice's Adventures in Wonderland* (Lewis Carroll)

1862 *The Very Hungry Caterpillar* (Eric Carle)

1863 *Maisy's ABC* (Lucy Cousins)

(Des Rose Design. Litho D.L.R.)

2006 (10 Jan). *Animal Tales.* One side phosphor band (2nd) or two phosphor bands (others). P 14½.

2589	**1856**	(2nd) brownish-black, new blue, magenta, greenish yellow and black	90	75
		a. Horiz pair. Nos. 2589/90	1·75	1·60
2590	**1857**	(2nd) brownish-black, new blue, magenta, greenish yellow and black	90	75
2591	**1858**	(1st) brownish-black, new blue, magenta, greenish yellow and black	1·25	1·00
		a. Horiz pair. Nos. 2591/2	2·50	2·25
2592	**1859**	(1st) brownish-black, new blue, magenta, greenish yellow and black	1·25	1·00
2593	**1860**	42p. brownish-black, new blue, magenta, greenish yellow and black	90	1·10
		a. Horiz pair. Nos. 2593/4	4·00	4·00
2594	**1861**	42p. brownish-black, new blue, magenta, greenish yellow and black	90	1·10
2595	**1862**	68p. brownish-black, new blue, magenta, greenish yellow and black	1·25	1·60
		a. Horiz pair. Nos. 2595/6	5·00	5·00
2596	**1863**	68p. brownish-black, new blue, magenta, greenish yellow and black	1·25	1·60
Set of 8			12·00	11·50
Set of 4 Gutter Blocks of 4			25·00	
Set of 4 Traffic Light Gutter Blocks of 8			50·00	
First Day Cover (Tallents House)				13·00
First Day Cover (Mousehole, Penzance, Cornwall)				13·00
First Day Cover (Nos. 2595/6 UK and US stamps)				9·00
Presentation Pack (P.O. Pack No. 379)			13·00	
PHQ Cards (set of 8) (282)			7·00	16·00

Nos. 2589/90, 2591/2, 2593/4 and 2595/6 were printed together, se-tenant, in horizontal pairs in sheets of 60 (2 panes 6×5).

A design as No. 2592 but self-adhesive was issued in sheets of 20, printed in lithography by Cartor *sold at* £6·55, containing four vertical rows of five stamps alternated with printed labels (LS28). This sheet was also available with personal photographs on the labels at £14·95 from Royal Mail.

No. 2595 contains two die-cut holes.

Special First Day of Issue Postmarks

1864 Carding Mill Valley, Shropshire

1865 Beachy Head, Sussex

1866 St. Paul's Cathedral, London

1867 Brancaster, Norfolk

1868 Derwent Edge, Peak District

1869 Robin Hood's Bay, Yorkshire

1870 Buttermere, Lake District

1871 Chipping Campden, Cotswolds

1872 St. Boniface Down, Isle of Wight

1873 Chamberlain Square, Birmingham

(Des Phelan Barker Design Consultants. Gravure D.L.R.)

2006 (7 Feb). *A British Journey: England.* Two phosphor bands. P 14½.

2597	**1864**	(1st) silver, black, rosine, greenish yellow and new blue	1·25	1·00

		a. Block of 10. Nos. 2597/2606		14·00	12·00
2598	**1865**	(1st) silver, black, rosine, greenish yellow and new blue		1·25	1·00
2599	**1866**	(1st) silver, black, rosine, greenish yellow and new blue		1·25	1·00
2600	**1867**	(1st) silver, black, rosine, greenish yellow and new blue		1·25	1·00
2601	**1868**	(1st) silver, black, rosine, greenish yellow and new blue		1·25	1·00
2602	**1869**	(1st) silver, black, rosine, greenish yellow and new blue		1·25	1·00
2603	**1870**	(1st) silver, black, rosine, greenish yellow and new blue		1·25	1·00
2604	**1871**	(1st) silver, black, rosine, greenish yellow and new blue		1·25	1·00
2605	**1872**	(1st) silver, black, rosine, greenish yellow and new blue		1·25	1·00
2606	**1873**	(1st) silver, black, rosine, greenish yellow and new blue		1·25	1·00
Set of 10				14·00	12·00
Gutter Block of 20				30·00	
First Day Cover (Tallents House)					13·00
First Day Cover (Tea Green, Luton)					13·00
Presentation Pack (P.O. Pack No. 380)				15·00	
PHQ Cards (set of 10) (283)				9·00	18·00

Nos. 2597/606 were printed together, *se-tenant*, as blocks of ten (5×2) in sheets of 60 (2 panes of 30).

First Day of Issue Postmarks

1874 Royal Albert Bridge

1875 Box Tunnel

1876 Paddington Station

1877 PSS *Great Eastern* (paddle steamer)

1878 Clifton Suspension Bridge Design

1879 Maidenhead Bridge

(Des Hat-trick Design. Litho Enschedé)

2006 (23 Feb). *Birth Bicentenary of Isambard Kingdom Brunel (engineer)* (1st issue). Phosphor-coated paper (42p.) or two phosphor bands (others). P 14×13½.

2607	**1874**	(1st) silver, black, new blue, magenta and greenish yellow		1·25	80
		a. Booklet pane. Nos. 2607, 2609 and 2612		5·00	
2608	**1875**	40p. silver, black, new blue, magenta and greenish yellow		1·10	1·10
		a. Booklet pane. Nos. 2608 and 2610/11		5·00	
2609	**1876**	42p. silver, black, new blue, magenta and greenish yellow		1·10	1·10
2610	**1877**	47p. silver, black, new blue, magenta and greenish yellow		1·50	1·50
		a. Booklet pane. No. 2610 and No. 2614×2		23·00	
2611	**1878**	60p. silver, black, new blue, magenta and greenish yellow		2·00	1·75
2612	**1879**	68p. silver, black, new blue, magenta and greenish yellow		2·50	2·25
Set of 6				7·50	7·50
Set of 6 Gutter Pairs				16·00	
First Day Cover (Tallents House)					9·00
First Day Cover (Bristol)					10·00
Presentation Pack (P.O. Pack No. 381)				10·00	
PHQ Cards (set of 7) (284)				6·00	14·00
MS2613 190×65 mm. Nos. 2607/12				8·50	8·50
		a. Imperforate		—	
First Day Cover (Tallents House)					9·00
First Day Cover (Bristol)					10·00

The phosphor bands on Nos. 2607/8 and 2610/12 are at just left of centre and at right of each stamp.

Booklet panes Nos. 2607a/8a and 2610a come from the £7·40 Isambard Kingdom Brunel booklet, No. DX36. The complete miniature sheet is shown on one of the PHQ Cards with the others depicting individual stamps.

First Day of Issue Postmarks

(Litho Enschedé)

2006 (23 Feb). *Birth Bicentenary of Isambard Kingdom Brunel* (2nd issue). Booklet stamp. Design as Type **1739** ('PS *Great Western*') from 2004 Ocean Liners). Two phosphor bands. P 14½×14.

2614	**1739**	68p. multicoloured		12·00	12·50

No. 2614 was only issued in the £7·40 Isambard Kingdom Brunel booklet, No. DX36.

1880 Sabre-tooth Cat   **1881** Giant Deer

1882 Woolly Rhino   **1883** Woolly Mammoth

1884 Cave Bear

(Des A. Davidson and H. Brown. Litho Enschedé)

2006 (21 Mar). *Ice Age Animals.* Two phosphor bands. P 14½.

2615	**1880**	(1st) black and silver	1·25	1·00
2616	**1881**	42p. black and silver	1·00	1·00
2617	**1882**	47p. black and silver	2·00	2·00
2618	**1883**	68p. black and silver	2·25	2·25
2619	**1884**	£1·12 black and silver	3·25	3·25
Set of 5			8·50	8·50
Set of 5 Gutter Pairs			18·00	
First Day Cover (Tallents House)				10·00
First Day Cover (Freezywater, Enfield)				10·00
Presentation Pack (P.O. Pack No. 382)			12·00	
PHQ Cards (set of 5) (285)			4·00	12·00

Special First Day of Issue Postmarks

1885 On *Britannia*, 1972

1886 At Royal Windsor Horse Show, 1985

1887 At Heathrow Airport, 2001

1888 As Young Princess Elizabeth with Duchess of York, 1931

1889 At State Banquet, Ottawa, 1951

1890 Queen in 1960

1891 As Princess Elizabeth, 1940

1892 With Duke of Edinburgh, 1951

(Des Sedley Place. Gravure Enschedé)

2006 (18 Apr). *80th Birthday of Queen Elizabeth II.* One side phosphor band (No. 2620), one centre phosphor band (No. 2621) or two phosphor bands (others). P 14½.

2620	**1885**	(2nd) black, turquoise-green and grey	1·00	1·00
		a. Horiz pair. Nos. 2620/1	2·25	2·25
2621	**1886**	(2nd) black, turquoise-green and grey	1·00	1·00
2622	**1887**	(1st) black, turquoise-green and grey	1·25	1·10
		a. Horiz pair. Nos. 2622/3	2·50	2·40
2623	**1888**	(1st) black, turquoise-green and grey	1·25	1·10
2624	**1889**	44p. black, turquoise-green and grey	1·00	1·25
		a. Horiz pair. Nos. 2624/5	2·75	2·75
2625	**1890**	44p. black, turquoise-green and grey	1·00	1·25
2626	**1891**	72p. black, turquoise-green and grey	1·50	2·00
		a. Horiz pair. Nos. 2626/7	4·50	4·50
2627	**1892**	72p. black, turquoise-green and grey	1·50	2·00
Set of 8			11·00	11·00
Set of 4 Gutter Strips of 4			23·00	
First Day Cover (Tallents House)				12·00
First Day Cover (Windsor)				12·00
Presentation Pack (P.O. Pack No. 383)			12·00	
PHQ Cards (set of 8) (286)			7·00	16·00

Nos. 2620/1, 2622/3, 2624/5 and 2626/7 were each printed together, *se-tenant*, as horizontal pairs in sheets of 60 (2 panes 6×5).

Special First Day of Issue Postmarks

1893 England (1966)

1894 Italy (1934, 1938, 1982)

1895 Argentina (1978, 1986)

1896 Germany (1954, 1974, 1990)

1897 France (1998)

1898 Brazil (1958, 1962, 1970, 1994, 2002)

(Des Madeleine Bennett. Litho Walsall)

2006 (6 June). *World Cup Football Championship, Germany. World Cup Winners.* Two phosphor bands. P 14½.

2628	**1893**	(1st) lemon, deep brownish grey, greenish yellow, bright magenta, new blue and black	1·25	1·00
2629	**1894**	42p. lemon, deep brownish grey, greenish yellow, bright magenta, new blue and black	1·25	1·10

2630	**1895**	44p. lemon, deep brownish grey, greenish yellow, bright magenta, new blue and black	1·25	1·25
2631	**1896**	50p. lemon, deep brownish grey, greenish yellow, bright magenta, new blue and black	2·00	2·00
2632	**1897**	64p. lemon, deep brownish grey, greenish yellow, bright magenta, new blue and black	3·00	3·00
2633	**1898**	72p. lemon, deep brownish grey, greenish yellow, bright magenta, new blue and black	3·50	3·50
Set of 6			11·00	10·50
Set of 6 Gutter Pairs			23·00	
First Day Cover (Tallents House)				12·00
First Day Cover (Balls Park, Hertford)				12·00
Presentation Pack (P.O. Pack No. 384)			12·00	
PHQ Cards (set of 6) (287)			5·00	12·00

The 1st class stamp was also issued in sheets of 20, sold for £6·95, printed in lithography by Cartor, containing four vertical rows of five stamps alternated with labels showing scenes from the 1966 World Cup final (LS31).

Special First Day of Issue Postmarks

1899 30 St. Mary Axe, London

1900 Maggie's Centre, Dundee

1901 Selfridges, Birmingham

1902 Downland Gridshell, Chichester

1903 An Turas, Isle of Tiree

1904 The Deep, Hull

(Des Roundel. Gravure Walsall)

2006 (20 June). *Modern Architecture.* Two phosphor bands. P 14½.

2634	**1899**	(1st) greenish yellow, magenta, new blue and black	1·25	1·00
2635	**1900**	42p. greenish yellow, magenta, new blue and black	1·10	1·10
2636	**1901**	44p. greenish yellow, magenta, new blue and black	1·25	1·25
2637	**1902**	50p. greenish yellow, magenta, new blue and black	2·00	2·00
2638	**1903**	64p. greenish yellow, magenta, new blue and black	3·00	3·00
2639	**1904**	72p. greenish yellow, magenta, new blue and black	3·50	3·50
Set of 6			11·00	10·50
Set of 6 Gutter Pairs			23·00	

First Day Cover (Tallents House)		12·00
First Day Cover (London EC3)		12·00
Presentation Pack (P.O. Pack No. 385)	13·00	
PHQ Cards (set of 6) (288)	5·00	12·00

Special First Day of Issue Postmarks

1905 "Sir Winston Churchill" (Walter Sickert)

1906 "Sir Joshua Reynolds" (self-portrait)

1907 "T. S. Eliot" (Patrick Heron)

1908 "Emmeline Pankhurst" (Georgina Agnes Brackenbury)

1909 Virginia Woolf (photo by George Charles Beresford)

1910 Bust of Sir Walter Scott (Sir Francis Leggatt Chantry)

1911 "Mary Seacole" (Albert Charles Challen)

1912 "William Shakespeare" (attrib to John Taylor)

1913 "Dame Cicely Saunders" (Catherine Goodman)

1914 "Charles Darwin" (John Collier)

(Des P. Willberg. Gravure De La Rue)

2006 (18 July). *150th Anniversary of National Portrait Gallery, London.* Two phosphor bands. P 14½.

2640	**1905**	(1st) silver, black, magenta, greenish yellow and new blue	1·25	1·00
		a. Block of 10. Nos. 2640/9	14·00	12·00
2641	**1906**	(1st) silver, black, magenta, greenish yellow and new blue	1·25	1·00
2642	**1907**	(1st) silver, black, magenta, greenish yellow and new blue	1·25	1·00
2643	**1908**	(1st) silver, black, magenta, greenish yellow and new blue	1·25	1·00
2644	**1909**	(1st) silver, black, magenta, greenish yellow and new blue	1·25	1·00
2645	**1910**	(1st) silver, black, magenta, greenish yellow and new blue	1·25	1·00
2646	**1911**	(1st) silver, black, magenta, greenish yellow and new blue	1·25	1·00
2647	**1912**	(1st) silver, black, magenta, greenish yellow and new blue	1·25	1·00
2648	**1913**	(1st) silver, black, magenta, greenish yellow and new blue	1·25	1·00
2649	**1914**	(1st) silver, black, magenta, greenish yellow and new blue	1·25	1·00
Set of 10			14·00	12·00
Gutter Block of 20			28·00	
Traffic Light Gutter Block of 20			30·00	
First Day Cover (Tallents House)				13·00
First Day Cover (London WC2)				13·00
Presentation Pack (P.O. Pack No. 386)			15·00	
PHQ Cards (set of 10) (289)			9·00	18·00

Nos. 2640/9 were printed together, *se-tenant*, as blocks of ten (5×2) in sheets of 60 (2 panes of 30).

Special First Day of Issue Postmarks

FIRST DAY OF ISSUE ROYAL MAIL TALLENTS HOUSE EDINBURGH 18.7.2006

FIRST DAY OF ISSUE LONDON WC2 18.7.2006

For Nos. 2650/7 and **MS**2658 see Decimal Machin Definitives section.

1918 Corporal Agansing Rai

1919 Boy Seaman Jack Cornwell

1920 Midshipman Charles Lucas

1921 Captain Noel Chavasse

1922 Captain Albert Ball

1923 Captain Charles Upham

(Des Atelier Works. Litho Enschedé)

2006 (21 Sept). *150th Anniv of the Victoria Cross* (1st issue). One side phosphor band. P 14½×14.

2659	**1918**	(1st) gold, black, new blue, magenta and greenish yellow	1·25	1·10
		a. Horiz pair. Nos. 2659/60	2·50	2·25
		b. Booklet pane. Nos. 2659, 2661 and 2663	4·50	
		ba. Booklet pane. Bronze and phosphor omitted	£18000	

2660	**1919**	(1st) gold, black, new blue. magenta and greenish yellow	1·25	1·10
		b. Booklet pane. Nos. 2660, 2662 and 2664	4·50	
		ba. Booklet pane. Bronze and phosphor omitted	£18000	
2661	**1920**	64p. gold, black, new blue. magenta and greenish yellow	1·25	1·50
		a. Horiz pair. Nos. 2661/2	3·00	3·00
2662	**1921**	64p. gold, black, new blue. magenta and greenish yellow	1·25	1·50
2663	**1922**	72p. gold, black, new blue. magenta and greenish yellow	2·00	2·25
		a. Horiz pair. Nos. 2663/4	4·00	4·50
2664	**1923**	72p. gold, black, new blue. magenta and greenish yellow	2·00	2·25
Set of 6			8·50	8·50
Set of 3 Gutter Strips of 4			19·00	
First Day Cover (Tallents House)				10·00
First Day Cover (Cuffley, Potters Bar, Herts)				10·00
Presentation Pack (P.O. Pack No. 387)			10·00	
MS2665 190×67 mm. Nos. 2659/64 and 2666			11·00	11·00
		a. Imperforate	—	
First Day Cover (Tallents House)				13·00
First Day Cover (Cuffley, Potters Bar, Herts)				13·00
PHQ Cards (set of 7) (290)			7·00	18·00

Nos. 2659/60, 2661/2 and 2663/4 were each printed together, *se-tenant,* as horizontal pairs in sheets of 60 (2 panes 6×5).

Booklet panes Nos. 2659b/60b come from the £7·44 Victoria Cross booklet No. DX37.

The seven PHQ Cards depict the six individual stamps and the miniature sheet.

Special First Day of Issue Postmarks

ROYAL MAIL TALLENTS HOUSE "Who would true valour see, Let him come hither..." JOHN BUNYAN FIRST DAY OF ISSUE EDINBURGH 21-9-2006

CUFFLEY POTTERS BAR HERTS "I only did my job" WILLIAM LEEFE ROBINSON VC FIRST DAY OF ISSUE 21-9-2006

(Litho Enschedé)

2006 (21 Sept). *150th Anniv of the Victoria Cross* (2nd issue). Booklet stamp. Design as No. 1517 (1990 Gallantry Awards). 'All-over' phosphor. P 14×14½.

2666	**959**	20p. grey-black, pale stone, stone, bistre-brown and bright carmine	10·00	10·00
		a. Booklet pane. Nos. 2666×4	35·00	35·00

No. 2666 was only issued in No. **MS**2665 and in the £7·44 Victoria Cross booklet, No. DX37.

1924 Sitar Player and Dancer

1925 Reggae Bass Guitarist and African Drummer

1926 Fiddler and Harpist

1927 Sax Player and Blues Guitarist

1928 Maraca Player and Salsa Dancers

(Des CDT Design. Litho Cartor)

2006 (3 Oct). *Europa. Integration. Sounds of Britain.* 'All-over' phosphor. P 14½.

2667	**1924**	(1st) silver, greenish yellow, magenta, new blue and black	1·25	1·00
2668	**1925**	42p. silver, greenish yellow, magenta, new blue and black	1·25	1·25
2669	**1926**	50p. silver, greenish yellow, magenta, new blue and black	1·25	1·50
2670	**1927**	72p. silver, greenish yellow, magenta, new blue and black	1·75	1·75
2671	**1928**	£1·19 silver, greenish yellow, magenta, new blue and black	2·50	3·00
Set of 5			7·50	7·50
Set of 5 Gutter Pairs			16·00	
Set of 5 Traffic Light Gutter Blocks of 4			38·00	
First Day Cover (Tallents House)				9·00
First Day Cover (Rock, Kidderminster, Worcs)				9·00
Presentation Pack (P.O. Pack No. 388)			9·00	
PHQ Cards (set of 5) (291)			4·50	10·00

The 1st class and 50p. values include the "EUROPA" emblem.

Special First Day of Issue Postmarks

1929 "New Baby" (Alison Carmichael) **1930** "Best Wishes" (Alan Kitching) **1931** "THANK YOU" (Alan Kitching)

1932 Balloons (Ivan Chermayeff) **1933** Firework (Kam Tang) **1934** Champagne, Flowers and Butterflies (Olaf Hajek)

(Des NB Studio. Gravure Walsall)

2006 (17 Oct). *Smilers Booklet stamps (2nd series). Occasions.* Self-adhesive. Two phosphor bands. Die-cut P 15×14.

2672	**1929**	(1st) chrome-yellow	1·40	1·20
		a. Booklet pane. Nos. 2672/7	9·00	7·00
2673	**1930**	(1st) multicoloured	1·40	1·20
2674	**1931**	(1st) scarlet-vermilion, rosine and yellow	1·40	1·20
2675	**1932**	(1st) multicoloured	1·40	1·20
2676	**1933**	(1st) multicoloured	1·40	1·20
2677	**1934**	(1st) multicoloured	1·40	1·20
Set of 6			9·00	7·00
First Day Cover (Tallents House)				8·00
First Day Cover (Grinshill, Shrewsbury)				8·00
Presentation Pack (P.O. Pack No. M13)			18·00	
PHQ Cards (set of 6) (D29)			5·00	12·00

Nos. 2672/7 were issued in £1·92 stamp booklets, No. QA3, in which the surplus backing paper around each stamp was removed.

Nos. 2672/7 were also issued in sheets of 20, No. LS33, containing four of Nos. 2672 and 2677 and three of each of the other designs, each stamp accompanied by a *se-tenant* greetings label. These sheets were printed by Cartor in lithography instead of photogravure and sold at £6·95 each.

These designs were available in separate sheets with personal photographs printed on the labels from Royal Mail in Edinburgh at £14·95 each.

Stamps as No. 2672 but perforated with one elliptical hole on each vertical side were issued on 28 October 2008 in sheets of 20 with circular *se-tenant* Peter Rabbit labels, No. LS50. These sheets were printed by Cartor in lithography instead of photogravure and sold for £7·95 each.

Similar sheets of ten stamps and ten *se-tenant* labels were sold in £7·95 packs.

No. 2674 was issued on 8 May 2010 with other greetings stamps in sheets of 20 with *se-tenant* greetings labels printed in lithography by Cartor, No. LS73, sold for £10 pre sheet. These sheets were printed with one elliptical hole in each vertical side.

Special First Day of Issue Postmarks

1935 Snowman **1936** Father Christmas **1937** Snowman

1938 Father Christmas **1939** Reindeer **1940** Christmas Tree

(Des T. Kiuchi, Rose Design and CDT Design. Gravure De La Rue)

2006 (7 Nov). *Christmas.* One centre phosphor band (No. 2678) or two phosphor bands (others). P 15×14.

(a) Self-adhesive.

2678	**1935**	(2nd) silver, magenta, greenish yellow, new blue and black	1·00	90
		a. Booklet pane. No. 2678×12	11·00	
2679	**1936**	(1st) silver, magenta, greenish yellow, new blue and black	1·25	1·00
		a. Booklet pane. No. 2679×12	14·00	
2680	**1937**	(2nd Large) silver, deep new blue, magenta, greenish yellow, new blue and black	1·50	1·25
2681	**1938**	(1st Large) silver, gold, magenta, greenish yellow, new blue and black	2·00	1·40
2682	**1939**	72p. silver, magenta, greenish yellow, new blue and black	3·25	3·25
2683	**1940**	£1·19 silver, magenta, greenish yellow, new blue and black	6·00	4·50
Set of 6			12·00	12·00
First Day Cover (Tallents House)				13·00
First Day Cover (Bethlehem, Llandeilo)				13·00
Presentation Pack (P.O. Pack No. 389)			13·00	
PHQ Cards (set of 7) (292)			3·00	18·00

(b) Ordinary gum.

MS2684	115×102 mm. As Nos. 2678/83	12·00	12·00
First Day Cover (Tallents House)			13·00
First Day Cover (Bethlehem, Llandeilo)			13·00

The seven PHQ Cards depict the six individual stamps and the miniature sheet.

The 2nd and 1st class stamps were also issued together in sheets of 20 sold at £6, printed in lithography by Cartor, containing ten 1st class and ten 2nd class stamps, each value arranged in vertical rows of five alternated with rows of printed labels (LS34). Separate sheets of 20 1st or 20 2nd class were available with personalised photographs at £9·95 (2nd class) and £14·95 (1st class) and in 2010 the same designs with one elliptical hole on each vertical side were available from Royal Mail, Edinburgh. All these sheets had the backing paper around the stamps retained.

Special First Day of Issue Postmarks

1941 Lest We Forget (*Illustration reduced. Actual size 124×71 mm*)

(Des Hat-trick Design. Gravure De La Rue)

2006 (9 Nov). *Lest We Forget* (1st issue). 90th Anniversary of the Battle of the Somme. Sheet 124×71 mm containing new stamp as No. 2883 and designs as Nos. EN17 (Type I), NI102, S120 and W109. Two phosphor bands. P 14½ (1st) or 15×14 (with one elliptical hole in each vertical side) (72p).

MS2685 **1941** (1st) Poppies on barbed wire stems;			
72p.×4 As Nos. EN17 (Type I), NI102, S120 and W109...	9·00	9·00
First Day Cover (Tallents House)		10·00
First Day Cover (London SW1)		10·00
Presentation Pack (P.O. Pack No. 390)	12·00	

No. **MS**2685 (including the Northern Ireland stamp) is printed in gravure.

The 1st class stamp was also issued in sheets of 20 with *se-tenant* labels showing war memorials, printed in lithography by Cartor (LS35).

See also Nos. **MS**2796 and **MS**2886.

Special First Day of Issue Postmarks

Collectors Pack

2006 (9 Nov). Comprises Nos. 2589/612, 2615/49, 2659/64, 2667/71, 2678/83 and **MS**2685.

CP2685*a* Collectors Pack £120

Post Office Yearbook

2006 (9 Nov). Comprises Nos. 2589/612, 2615/49, 2659/64, 2667/71, 2678/83 and **MS**2685.

YB2685*a* Yearbook £100

Miniature Sheet Collection

2006 (30 Nov). Comprises Nos. **MS**2613, **MS**2658, **MS**2665, **MS**2684/5, **MS**S153 and **MS**W143.

MS2685*a* Miniature Sheet Collection.................... 75·00

1942 "with the beatles"   **1943** "Sgt Pepper's Lonely Hearts Club Band"

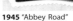

1944 "Help!"   **1945** "Abbey Road"

1946 "Revolver"   **1947** "Let It Be"

1948 Beatles Memorabilia (*Illustration reduced. Actual size 115×89 mm*)

(Des johnson banks)

2007 (9 Jan). *The Beatles. Album Covers*. Two phosphor bands.

(a) Self-adhesive. Gravure Walsall. Die-cut irregular P 13½–14½.

2686	**1942**	(1st) silver, greenish yellow, bright magenta, new blue and black	1·25	1·00
		a. Horiz pair. Nos. 2686/7	2·75	
2687	**1943**	(1st) silver, greenish yellow, bright magenta, new blue and black	1·25	1·00
2688	**1944**	64p. silver, greenish yellow, bright magenta, new blue and black	1·50	1·50
		a. Horiz pair. Nos. 2688/9	3·25	
2689	**1945**	64p. silver, greenish yellow, bright magenta, new blue and black	1·50	1·50
2690	**1946**	72p. greenish yellow, bright magenta, new blue and black	1·80	1·80
		a. Horiz pair. Nos. 2690/1	4·00	
2691	**1947**	72p. greenish yellow, bright magenta, new blue and black	1·80	1·80
Set of 6			9·00	8·00
First Day Cover (Tallents House)				10·00
First Day Cover (Liverpool)				11·00
Presentation Pack (Nos. 2686/**MS**2692) (P.O. Pack No. 392)			16·00	
PHQ Cards (set of 11) (293)			9·00	20·00

(b) Ordinary gum. Litho Walsall. P 14.

MS2692 115×89 mm. **1948** (1st) Guitar; (1st) Yellow Submarine lunch-box and key-rings; (1st) Record "Love Me Do"; (1st) Beatles tea tray and badges .... 5·00 5·00
First Day Cover (Tallents House) .... 7·00
First Day Cover (Liverpool) .... 8·00

Nos. 2686/91 are all die-cut in the shape of a pile of records.

Nos. 2686/7, 2688/9 and 2690/1 were each printed together in sheets of 60 (2 panes of 30), with the two designs alternating horizontally and the surplus backing paper around each stamp removed.

Nos. 2686/92 commemorate the 50th anniversary of the first meeting of Paul McCartney and John Lennon.

The complete miniature sheet is on one of the eleven PHQ cards, with the others depicting individual stamps, including those from **MS**2692.

Special First Day of Issue Postmarks

(Gravure Walsall)

2007 (16 Jan)-**08**. *Smilers* Booklet stamp (3rd series). 'LOVE' design as No. 2569. Self-adhesive. Two phosphor bands. Die-cut P 15×14 (with one elliptical hole in each vertical side).

2693	**1842a**	(1st) multicoloured..	10·00	10·00
		a. Booklet pane. No. 2655×5 and		
		No. 2693..	24·00	
		b. Booklet pane. No. 2693×2 with		
		two attached labels and No.		
		2295×4 (15.1.08)	15·00	

No. 2693 was issued in stamp booklets, Nos. SA1 and SA2, in which the surplus backing paper around each stamp was removed.

No. 2693 was reissued on 8 May 2010 with other greetings stamps in sheets of 20 with *se-tenant* greetings labels printed in lithography by Cartor, No. LS73, sold for £10 per sheet.

Nos. 2694/8 are left vacant.

1949 Moon Jellyfish   **1950** Common Starfish

1951 Beadlet Anemone   **1952** Bass

1953 Thornback Ray   **1954** Lesser Octopus

1955 Common Mussels   **1956** Grey Seal

1957 Shore Crab   **1958** Common Sun Star

(Des A. Ross. Litho Walsall)

2007 (1 Feb). *Sea Life*. Two phosphor bands. P 14½.

2699	**1949**	(1st) greyish silver, greenish yellow, magenta, new blue and black.......	1·25	90
		a. Block of 10. Nos. 2699/708	14·00	12·00
2700	**1950**	(1st) greyish silver, greenish yellow, magenta, new blue and black.......	1·25	90
2701	**1951**	(1st) greyish silver, greenish yellow, magenta, new blue and black.......	1·25	90
2702	**1952**	(1st) greyish silver, greenish yellow, magenta, new blue and black.......	1·25	90
2703	**1953**	(1st) greyish silver, greenish yellow, magenta, new blue and black.......	1·25	90
2704	**1954**	(1st) greyish silver, greenish yellow, magenta, new blue and black.......	1·25	90
2705	**1955**	(1st) greyish silver, greenish yellow, magenta, new blue and black.......	1·25	90
2706	**1956**	(1st) greyish silver, greenish yellow, magenta, new blue and black.......	1·25	90
2707	**1957**	(1st) greyish silver, greenish yellow, magenta, new blue and black.......	1·25	90
2708	**1958**	(1st) greyish silver, greenish yellow, magenta, new blue and black.......	1·25	90
Set of 10...			14·00	12·00
Gutter Block of 20..			29·00	
First Day Cover (Tallents House).............................				13·00
First Day Cover (Seal Sands, Middlesbrough, Cleveland)...				13·00
Presentation Pack (P.O. Pack No. 393).....................			16·00	
PHQ Cards (set of 10) (294)......................................			8·00	18·00

Nos. 2699/708 were printed together, *se-tenant*, as blocks of ten (5×2) in sheets of 60 (2 panes of 30).

Special First Day of Issue Postmarks

1959 Saturn Nebula C55   **1960** Eskimo Nebula C39

1961 Cat's Eye Nebula C6   **1962** Helix Nebula C63

1963 Flaming Star Nebula C31   **1964** The Spindle C53

(Des D. Davis. Gravure Walsall)

2007 (13 Feb). *50th Anniv of 'The Sky at Night' (TV programme)*. Nebulae. Self-adhesive. Two phosphor bands. Die-cut P 14½×14.

2709	**1959**	(1st) greenish yellow, magenta, new blue and black.................................	1·25	90
		a. Horiz pair. Nos. 2709/10...................	2·50	
2710	**1960**	(1st) greenish yellow, magenta, new blue and black.................................	1·25	90
2711	**1961**	50p. greenish yellow, magenta, new blue and black.................................	1·20	1·20
		a. Horiz pair. Nos. 2711/12...................	2·75	
2712	**1962**	50p. greenish yellow, magenta, new blue and black.................................	1·20	1·20

2713	**1963**	72p. greenish yellow, magenta, new blue and black...........	1·70	1·70
		a. Horiz pair. Nos. 2713/14..........	4·00	
2714	**1964**	72p. greenish yellow, magenta, new blue and black...........	1·70	1·70
Set of 6			8·50	7·00
First Day Cover (Tallents House)				9·00
First Day Cover (Star, Glenrothes, Fife)				9·00
Presentation Pack (P.O. Pack No. 394)...........			10·00	
PHQ Cards (set of 6) (295)..............................			4·50	14·00

Nos. 2709/10, 2711/12 and 2713/14 were each printed together in sheets of 60 (2 panes of 30), with the two designs alternating horizontally and the surplus backing paper around each stamp removed.

Special First Day of Issue Postmarks

1965 Iron Bridge (Thomas Telford)

1966 Steam Locomotive and Railway Tracks

1967 Map of British Isles and Australia (telephone)

1968 Camera and Television (John Logie Baird)

1969 Globe as Web (email and internet)

1970 Couple with Suitcases on Moon (space travel)

(Des P. Willberg. Gravure De La Rue)

2007 (1 Mar). *World of Invention* (1st issue). Self-adhesive. Two phosphor bands. Die-cut P 14½×14.

2715	**1965**	(1st) olive-grey, magenta, greenish yellow, new blue and black...........	1·25	90
		a. Horiz pair. Nos. 2715/16..........	3·00	
2716	**1966**	(1st) olive-grey, magenta, greenish yellow, new blue and black...........	1·25	90
2717	**1967**	64p. olive-grey, magenta, greenish yellow, new blue and black...........	1·25	1·25
		a. Horiz pair. Nos. 2717/18..........	3·00	
2718	**1968**	64p. olive-grey, magenta, greenish yellow, new blue and black...........	1·25	1·25
2719	**1969**	72p. olive-grey, magenta, greenish yellow, new blue and black...........	2·00	2·25
		a. Horiz pair. Nos. 2719/20..........	4·50	
2720	**1970**	72p. olive-grey, magenta, greenish yellow, new blue and black...........	2·00	2·25
Set of 6			9·50	8·00
First Day Cover (Tallents House)				10·00
First Day Cover (Pont Menai, Menai Bridge, Gwynedd) ..				10·00
Presentation Pack (P.O. Pack No. 395)...........			11·00	
PHQ Cards (set of 7) (296)..............................			4·50	14·00

Nos. 2715/16, 2717/18 and 2719/20 were each printed together in sheets of 60 (2 panes of 30), with the two designs alternating horizontally and the surplus backing paper around each stamp removed.

The seven PHQ Cards depict the six individual stamps and **MS**2727.

Special First Day of Issue Postmarks

(Gravure De La Rue)

2007 (1 Mar). *World of Invention* (2nd issue). Two phosphor bands. P 14½×14.

2721	**1965**	(1st) multicoloured........................	1·25	90
		a. Booklet pane. Nos. 2721/4.........	7·00	
		b. Booklet pane. Nos. 2721/2 and 2725/6	10·00	
2722	**1966**	(1st) multicoloured........................	1·25	90
2723	**1967**	64p. multicoloured........................	2·50	2·50
2724	**1968**	64p. multicoloured........................	2·50	2·50
2725	**1969**	72p. multicoloured........................	4·50	4·50
2726	**1970**	72p. multicoloured........................	4·50	4·50
Set of 6			15·00	15·00
MS2727 115×104 mm. Nos. 2721/6			15·00	15·00
First Day Cover (Tallents House)				16·00
First Day Cover (Pont Menai, Menai Bridge, Gwynedd) .				16·00

Nos. 2721/6 were only issued in the £7·49 World of Invention booklet, No. DX38 and in No. **MS**2727.

1971 William Wilberforce and Anti-slavery Poster

1972 Olaudah Equiano and Map of Slave Trade Routes

1973 Granville Sharp and Slave Ship

1974 Thomas Clarkson and Diagram of Slave Ship

1975 Hannah More and Title Page of *The Sorrows of Yamba*

1976 Ignatius Sancho and Trade/Business Card

(Des Howard Brown. Litho Cartor)

2007 (22 Mar). *Bicentenary of the Abolition of the Slave Trade.* Two phosphor bands. P 14½.

2728	**1971**	(1st) grey-brown, pale stone, olive-bistre, bright reddish violet, deep blue-green and black..................	1·25	90
		a. Horiz pair. Nos. 2728/9............	2·50	2·50
		ab. Gold and phosphor omitted..........	£3500	
2729	**1972**	(1st) grey-brown, pale stone, olive-bistre, bright reddish violet, deep blue-green and black..................	1·25	90

2730	**1973**	50p. grey-brown, pale stone, light blue, cinnamon, deep blue-green and black	1·20	1·20
		a. Horiz pair. Nos. 2730/1	2·60	2·60
2731	**1974**	50p. grey-brown, pale stone, light blue, cinnamon, deep blue-green and black	1·20	1·20
2732	**1975**	72p. grey-brown, pale stone, sage-green, brown-lilac, deep blue-green and black	1·80	1·80
		a. Horiz pair. Nos. 2732/3	4·00	4·00
2733	**1976**	72p. grey-brown, pale stone, sage-green, brown-lilac, deep blue-green and black	1·80	1·80

Set of 6	8·00	8·00
Set of 3 Gutter Strips of 4	17·00	
Set of 3 Traffic Light Gutter Strips of 4	19·00	
First Day Cover (Tallents House)		10·00
First Day Cover (Hull)		10·00
Presentation Pack (P.O. Pack No. 396)	10·00	
PHQ Cards (set of 6) (297)	4·50	14·00

Nos. 2728/9, 2730/1 and 2732/3 were each printed together, se-tenant, in horizontal pairs throughout the sheets.

Set of 6 Gutter Pairs	18·00	
First Day Cover (Tallents House)		10·00
First Day Cover (Blackpool)		10·00
Presentation Pack (P.O. Pack No. 397)	12·00	
PHQ Cards (set of 6) (298)	4·50	14·00

See also No. 2848.

Special First Day of Issue Postmarks

Special First Day of Issue Postmarks

1977 Ice Cream Cone

1978 Sandcastle

1979 Carousel Horse

1980 Beach Huts

1981 Deckchairs

1982 Beach Donkeys

(Des Phelan Barker. Gravure De La Rue)

2007 (15 May). *Beside the Seaside* Two phosphor bands. *P* 14½.

2734	**1977**	1st magenta, greenish yellow, new blue and black	1·25	90
2735	**1978**	46p. magenta, greenish yellow, new blue and black	1·20	1·10
2736	**1979**	48p. magenta, greenish yellow, new blue and black	1·30	1·30
2737	**1980**	54p. magenta, greenish yellow, new blue and black	1·40	1·40
2738	**1981**	69p. magenta, greenish yellow, new blue and black	1·80	1·80
2739	**1982**	78p. magenta, greenish yellow, new blue and black	2·00	2·00
Set of 6			8·00	8·00

1983 Wembley Stadium (*Illustration reduced. Actual size* 113×103 *mm*)

(Des Roundel. Gravure De La Rue)

2007 (17 May). *New Wembley Stadium, London.* Sheet 113×103 mm containing design as Type **1593** but with *WORLD CUP 2002* inscription omitted, and Nos. EN6a and EN**18**, each×2. One centre phosphor band (2nd) or two phosphor bands (others). *P* 14½×14 (1st) or 15×14 (with one elliptical hole in each vertical side) (2nd, 78p.).

MS2740	**1983**	(1st) As Type **1593**; (2nd) No. EN6a×2; 78p. No. EN18×2 and one central stamp-size label	8·00	8·00
First Day Cover (Tallents House)				9·00
First Day Cover (Wembley)				9·00

The design as Type **1593** omits the "WORLD CUP 2002" inscription at the left of the stamp.

Special First Day of Issue Postmarks

1984 Arnold Machin

1985 1967 4d. Machin

1986 The Machin Definitives (*Illustration reduced. Actual size 127×73 mm*)

(Des Jeffery Matthews and Together Design.
Gravure and embossed De La Rue)

2007 (5 June). *40th Anniv of the First Machin Definitives.* All-over phosphor (1st) or two phosphor bands (others). *P* 14½ (1st) or 15×14 (with one elliptical hole in each vertical side) (£1).

2741	**1984**	(1st) multicoloured	4·50	4·50
		a. Booklet pane. Nos. 2741/2,		
		each×2, with margins all round	17·00	
2742	**1985**	(1st) multicoloured	4·50	4·50
MS2743	127×73mm	**1986** Nos. 2741/2, Y1743 and		
		Y1744	12·00	12·00
		a. Imperf	£8500	

First Day Cover (**MS**2743) (Tallents House) .... 13·00
First Day Cover (**MS**2743) (Windsor) .... 13·00
First Day Cover (**MS**2743) (Stoke-on-Trent) .... 13·00
Presentation Pack (**MS**2743) (P.O. Pack No. 398) .... 14·00
PHQ Cards (set of 3) (Nos. 2741/**MS**2743) (299) .... 3·00 14·00

Nos. 2741/2 were only issued in the £7·66 The Machin — The Making of a Masterpiece booklet, No. DX39 and in No. **MS**2743. Stamps as Type **1984** but with phosphor frames were issued in sheets of 20 with *se-tenant* labels showing the 1967–9 Machin definitives (LS40). These sheets were sold for £7·35.

Special First Day of Issue Postmarks

1987 Stirling Moss in Vanwall 2.5L, 1957

1988 Graham Hill in BRM P57, 1962

1989 Jim Clark in Lotus 25 Climax, 1963

1990 Jackie Stewart in Tyrrell 006/2, 1973

1991 James Hunt in McLaren M23, 1976

1992 Nigel Mansell in Williams FW11, 1986

(Des True North. Litho Cartor)

2007 (3 July). *Grand Prix. Racing Cars.* Two phosphor bands. *P* 14½.

2744	**1987**	(1st) grey-brown, greenish yellow,		
		magenta, new blue and black	1·25	90
2745	**1988**	(1st) grey-brown, greenish yellow,		
		magenta, new blue and black	1·25	90
2746	**1989**	54p. grey-brown, greenish yellow,		
		magenta, new blue and black	1·50	1·50
2747	**1990**	54p. grey-brown, greenish yellow,		
		magenta, new blue and black	1·50	1·50
2748	**1991**	78p. grey-brown, greenish yellow,		
		magenta, new blue and black	2·00	2·00
2749	**1992**	78p. grey-brown, greenish yellow,		
		magenta, new blue and black	2·00	2·00

Set of 6 .... 8·50 8·00
Set of 6 Gutter Pairs .... 19·00
First Day Cover (Tallents House) .... 10·00
First Day Cover (Silverstone, Towcester, Northants) .... 11·00
Presentation Pack (P.O. Pack No. 399) .... 11·00
PHQ Cards (set of 6) (300) .... 4·50 14·00

Nos. 2744/9 commemorate the 50th anniversary of Stirling Moss' Victory in the British Grand Prix and the centenary of the opening of Brooklands race track.

Special First Day of Issue Postmarks

1993 Harry Potter and the Philosopher's Stone

1994 Harry Potter and the Chamber of Secrets

1995 Harry Potter and the Prisoner of Azkaban

1996 Harry Potter and the Goblet of Fire

1997 Harry Potter and the Order of the Phoenix

1998 Harry Potter and the Half-Blood Prince

1999 Harry Potter and the Deathly Hallows

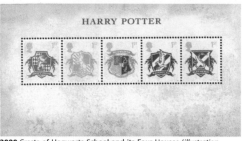

2000 Crests of Hogwarts School and its Four Houses (*illustration reduced. Actual size 123×70 mm*)

(True North. Litho Walsall)

2007 (17 July). *Publication of Final Book in the Harry Potter Series.*

(a) Book Covers. "All-over" phosphor. P 14½.

2750	**1993**	(1st) gold, greenish yellow, magenta, new blue and black	1·25	90
		a. Horiz strip of 7. Nos. 2750/6	9·00	8·00
2751	**1994**	(1st) gold, greenish yellow, magenta, new blue and black	1·25	90
2752	**1995**	(1st) gold, greenish yellow, magenta, new blue and black	1·25	90
2753	**1996**	(1st) gold, greenish yellow, magenta, new blue and black	1·25	90
2754	**1997**	(1st) gold, greenish yellow, magenta, new blue and black	1·25	90
2755	**1998**	(1st) gold, greenish yellow, magenta, new blue and black	1·25	90
2756	**1999**	(1st) gold, greenish yellow, magenta, new blue and black	1·25	90
Set of 7			9·00	8·00
Gutter Block of 14			20·00	
Traffic Light Gutter Block of 14			22·00	
First Day Cover (Tallents House)				9·00
First Day Cover (Broom, Alcester, Warwickshire)				9·00
Presentation Pack (Nos. 2750/7) (P.O. Pack No. M16)			17·00	
PHQ Cards (set of 13) (HP)			11·00	27·00

(b) Crests of Hogwarts School and its Four Houses. Multicoloured. Two phosphor bands. P 15×14.

MS2757	123×70 mm. **2000** (1st) Gryffindor; (1st) Hufflepuff; (1st) Hogwarts; (1st) Ravenclaw; (1st) Slytherin	6·00	6·00
First Day Cover (Tallents House)			7·50
First Day Cover (Broom, Alcester, Warwickshire)			8·00

Nos. 2750/6 were printed together, *se-tenant*, as horizontal strips of seven stamps in sheets of 56 (2 panes 7×4).

The complete miniature sheet is shown on one of the thirteen PHQ cards with the others depicting individual stamps including those from **MS2757**.

Stamps as those within **MS2757** but self-adhesive were issued in sheets of 20 containing the five designs *se-tenant* with labels depicting either magic spells (LS41, *sold for* £7·35) or personal photographs (*sold for* £14·95). The magic spells labels are printed in thermochromic ink which fades temporarily when exposed to heat, revealing the meaning of the spells.

2003 Scout planting Tree

2004 Adult Volunteer teaching Scout Archery

2005 Scouts learning gliding

2006 Scouts from Many Nations

(Des Gez Fry and The Work Room. Litho Enschedé)

2007 (26 July). *Europa. Centenary of Scouting and 21st World Scout Jamboree, Chelmsford, Essex.* Two phosphor bands. P 14½×14.

2758	**2001**	(1st) silver, black, new blue, magenta and greenish yellow	1·25	90
2759	**2002**	46p. silver, black, new blue, magenta and greenish yellow	1·20	1·20
2760	**2003**	48p. silver, black, new blue, magenta and greenish yellow	1·20	1·20
2761	**2004**	54p. silver, black, new blue, magenta and greenish yellow	1·40	1·40
2762	**2005**	69p. silver, black, new blue, magenta and greenish yellow	1·80	1·80
2763	**2006**	78p. silver, black, new blue, magenta and greenish yellow	2·00	2·00
Set of 6			8·00	8·00
Set of 6 Gutter Pairs			18·00	
First Day Cover (Tallents House)				10·00
First Day Cover (Brownsea Island, Poole, Dorset)				10·00
Presentation Pack (P.O. Pack No. 400)			10·00	
PHQ Cards (set of 6) (301)			4·50	14·00

The 1st class and 48p. values include the "EUROPA" emblem.

Special First Day of Issue Postmarks

Special First Day of Issue Postmarks

2007 White-tailed Eagle   **2008** Bearded Tit

2001 Scout and Camp Fire

2002 Scouts Rock climbing

2009 Red Kite   **2010** Cirl Bunting

2011 Marsh Harrier

2012 Avocet

2017 NCO, Royal Military Police, 1999

2018 Tank Commander, 5th Royal Tank Regiment, 1944

2013 Bittern

2014 Dartford Warbler

2019 Observer, Royal Field Artillery, 1917

2020 Rifleman, 95th Rifles, 1813

2015 Corncrake

2016 Peregrine Falcon

2021 Grenadier, Royal Regiment of Foot of Ireland, 1704

2022 Trooper, Earl of Oxford's Horse, 1661

(Des Kate Stephens. Litho Da La Rue)

2007 (4 Sept). *Action for Species* (1st series). Birds. Two phosphor bands. P 14½.

2764	**2007**	(1st) stone, new blue, magenta, greenish yellow and black	1·25	90
		a. Block of 10. Nos. 2764/73	14·00	10·00
2765	**2008**	(1st) stone, new blue, magenta, greenish yellow and black	1·25	90
2766	**2009**	(1st) stone, new blue, magenta, greenish yellow and black	1·25	90
2767	**2010**	(1st) stone, new blue, magenta, greenish yellow and black	1·25	90
2768	**2011**	(1st) stone, new blue, magenta, greenish yellow and black	1·25	90
2769	**2012**	(1st) stone, new blue, magenta, greenish yellow and black	1·25	90
2770	**2013**	(1st) stone, new blue, magenta, greenish yellow and black	1·25	90
2771	**2014**	(1st) stone, new blue, magenta, greenish yellow and black	1·25	90
2772	**2015**	(1st) stone, new blue, magenta, greenish yellow and black	1·25	90
2773	**2016**	(1st) stone, new blue, magenta, greenish yellow and black	1·25	90
Set of 10			14·00	10·00
Gutter Block of 20			30·00	
First Day Cover (Tallents House)				11·00
First Day Cover (Dartford)				11·00
Presentation Pack (P.O. Pack No. 401)			15·00	
PHQ Cards (set of 10) (302)			9·00	18·00

Nos. 2764/73 were printed together, *se-tenant*, as blocks of ten (5×2) in sheets of 60 (2 panes of 30).

(Des Graham Turner and Atelier Works. Litho Enschedé)

2007 (20 Sept). *Military Uniforms* (1st series). British Army Uniforms. Two phosphor bands. P 14½.

2774	**2017**	(1st) silver, black, new blue, magenta and greenish yellow	1·25	90
		a. Horiz strip of 3. Nos. 2774/6	4·00	4·00
		b. Booklet pane. Nos. 2774/6 with margins all round	4·50	
2775	**2018**	(1st) silver, black, new blue, magenta and greenish yellow	1·25	90
2776	**2019**	(1st) silver, black, new blue, magenta and greenish yellow	1·25	90
2777	**2020**	78p. silver, black, new blue, magenta and greenish yellow	2·00	2·00
		a. Horiz strip of 3. Nos. 2777/9	7·00	7·00
		b. Booklet pane. Nos. 2777/9 with margins all round	7·00	7·00
2778	**2021**	78p. silver, black, new blue, magenta and greenish yellow	2·00	2·00
2779	**2022**	78p. silver, black, new blue, magenta and greenish yellow	1·70	1·70
Set of 6			10·00	10·00
Set of 2 Gutter blocks of 6			22·00	
Set of 2 Traffic Light Gutter blocks of 6			24·00	
First Day Cover (Tallents House)				11·00
First Day Cover (Boot, Holmrook, Cumbria)				12·00
Presentation Pack (P.O. Pack No. 402)			12·00	
PHQ Cards (set of 6) (303)			4·50	14·00

Nos. 2774/6 and 2777/9 were each printed together, *se-tenant*, in horizontal strips of three stamps in sheets of 60 (2 panes 6×5).

Booklet panes Nos. 2774b and 2777b come from the £7·66 British Army Uniforms booklet, No., DX40.

Special First Day of Issue Postmarks

Special First Day of Issue Postmarks

"I Seen 'im Serve the Queen in a Suit o' Rifle-Green" Rudyard Kipling

2023 Leaving St. Paul's Cathedral after Thanksgiving Service, 2006

2024 Inspecting King's Troop Royal Horse Artillery, Regents Park, 1997

2025 At Garter Ceremony, Windsor, 1980

2026 At Royal Ascot, 1969

2027 At Premiere of *The Guns of Navarone*, 1961

2028 At Clydebank, 1947

2029 Photographs of the Royal Family (*illustration reduced. Actual size 115×89 mm*)

(Des Studio David Hillman)

2007 (16 Oct). *Diamond Wedding of Queen Elizabeth II and Duke of Edinburgh.*

(a) Ordinary gum. Litho Cartor. 'All-over' phosphor. P 14½×14.

2780	**2023**	(1st) blackish-brown and black	1·25	90
		a. Horiz pair. Nos. 2780/1	2·50	2·00
2781	**2024**	(1st) blackish-brown and black	1·25	90
2782	**2025**	54p. blackish-brown and black	1·40	1·40
		a. Horiz pair. Nos. 2782/3	3·00	3·00
2783	**2026**	54p. blackish-brown and black	1·40	1·40
2784	**2027**	78p. blackish-brown and black	2·00	2·00
		a. Horiz pair. Nos. 2784/5	4·50	4·50
2785	**2028**	78p. blackish-brown and black	2·00	2·00
Set of 6			9·00	9·00
Set of 3 Gutter blocks of 4			19·00	
First Day Cover (Tallents House)			11·00	
First Day Cover (Windsor, Berks)			11·00	
Presentation Pack (Nos. 2780/**MS**2786) (P.O. Pack No. 403)			17·00	
PHQ Cards (set of 11) (304)			9·00	27·00

(b) Self-adhesive. Gravure Walsall. Two phosphor bands. P 14½.

MS2786 115×89 mm. (1st) Royal family, Balmoral, 1972; (1st) Queen and Prince Philip, Buckingham Palace, 2007; 69p. Royal family, Windsor Castle, 1965; 78p. Princess Elizabeth, Prince Philip, Prince Charles and Princess Anne, Clarence House, 1951 — 6·00 / 6·00

First Day Cover (Tallents House) — 7·00
First Day Cover (Windsor, Berks) — 7·00

Nos. 2780/1, 2782/3 and 2784/5 were each printed together, *se-tenant*, in horizontal pairs throughout the sheets.

The complete miniature sheet is shown on one of the eleven PHQ cards with the others depicting individual stamps including those from **MS**2786.

Special First Day of Issue Postmarks

2030 *Madonna and Child* (William Dyce), c 1827

2031 *The Madonna of Humility* (Lippo di Dalmasio), c 1390–1400)

(Des Peter Willberg. Gravure De La Rue)

2007 (6 Nov). *Christmas* (1st issue). Paintings of the Madonna and Child. Self-adhesive. One centre phosphor band (2nd) or two phosphor bands (1st). Die-cut P 15×14 (with one elliptical hole in each vertical side).

2787	**2030**	(2nd) gold, magenta, greenish yellow, new blue and black	1·00	80
2788	**2031**	(1st) gold, magenta, greenish yellow, new blue and black	1·25	90
First Day Cover (Tallents House)			4·00	
First Day Cover (Bethlehem, Llandeilo)			4·00	

2032 Angel playing Trumpet ("PEACE")

2033 Angel playing Lute ("GOODWILL")

2034 Angel playing Trumpet ("PEACE")

2035 Angel playing Lute ("GOODWILL")

2036 Angel playing Flute ("JOY")

2037 Angel playing Tambourine ("GLORY")

(Des Marco Ventura and Rose Design. Gravure De La Rue)

2007 (6 Nov). *Christmas* (2nd issue). Angels. One centre phosphor band (2789) or two phosphor bands (others). P 15×14.

(a) Self-adhesive

2789	**2032**	(2nd) gold, magenta, greenish yellow, new blue and black	1·00	80
		a. Booklet pane. No. 2789×12	11·00	
2790	**2033**	(1st) gold, magenta, greenish yellow, new blue and black	1·25	90
		a. Booklet pane. No. 2790×12	14·00	
2791	**2034**	(2nd Large) gold, magenta, greenish yellow, new blue and black	1·50	1·00
2792	**2035**	(1st Large) gold, magenta, greenish yellow, new blue and black	2·00	2·00
2793	**2036**	78p. gold, magenta, greenish yellow, new blue and black	2·00	2·00
2794	**2037**	£1·24 gold, magenta, greenish yellow, new blue and black	3·50	3·50

Set of 6	10·00	10·00
First Day Cover (Tallents House)................		10·00
First Day Cover (Bethlehem, Llandeilo)		10·00
Presentation Pack *(Nos. 2787/94) (P.O. Pack No. 404)*.......	14·00	
PHQ Cards *(set of 9) (305)*.....................	8·00	18·00

(b) Ordinary gum.

MS2795 115×102 mm. As Nos. 2789/94............	10·00	10·00
First Day Cover (Tallents House)................		11·00
First Day Cover (Bethlehem, Llandeilo)		11·00

The phosphor bands on Nos. 2791/2 are at the centre and right of each stamp.

The PHQ cards depict Nos. 2787/94 and **MS**2795.

The 2nd class, 1st class and 78p. stamps were also issued together in sheets of 20 sold at £8·30 containing eight 1st class, eight 2nd class and four 78p. stamps, arranged in vertical strips of five stamps alternated with printed labels (LS42). Separate sheets of 20 1st, 20 2nd or 10 78p. were available with personalised photographs from Royal Mail, Edinburgh. These were sold at £9·95 for 20 2nd or £14·95 for 20 1st or 10 78p. All these sheets were printed in lithography by Cartor and had the backing paper around the stamps retained.

Special First Day of Issue Postmarks

2038 Lest We Forget (*Illustration reduced. Actual size 124×70 mm*)

(Des Hat-trick design. Litho De La Rue)

2007 (8 Nov). *Lest We Forget* (2nd issue). 90th Anniv. of the Battle of Passchendaele. Sheet 124×70 mm containing new stamp as No. 2884 and designs as Nos. EN18, NI128, S121 and W110. Two phosphor bands. 14½ (1st) or 15×14 (with one elliptical hole in each vertical side) (78p.).

MS2796	**2038**	(1st) Soldiers in poppy flower;
78p.×4 As Nos. EN18, NI128, S121 and W110.............	10·00	10·00
First Day Cover (Tallents House)................		11·00
First Day Cover (London SW1)...................		11·00
Presentation Pack *(P.O. Pack No. 405)*..........	12·00	

No. **MS**2796 (including the England, Northern Ireland, Scotland and Wales stamps) is printed in lithography.

A single example of the "Soldiers in Poppy" stamp from **MS**2796 is known with the silver (Queen's head and value) omitted.

The 1st class stamp was also issued in sheets of 20 with *se-tenant* labels showing soldiers and their letters home, printed in lithography by Cartor and sold at £7·35 (LS43).

Special First Day of Issue Postmarks

Collectors Pack

2007 (8 Nov). Comprises Nos. 2686/92, 2699/720, 2728/39, **MS**2743/94 and **MS**2796.

| CP2796*a* Collectors Pack .... | £190 |

Post Office Yearbook

2007 (8 Nov). Comprises Nos. 2686/92, 2699/720, 2728/39, **MS**2743/94 and **MS**2796.

| YB2796*a* Yearbook............................... | £130 |

Miniature Sheet Collection

2007 (8 Nov). Comprises Nos. **MS**2692, **MS**2727, **MS**2740, **MS**2743, **MS**2757, **MS**2786 and **MS**2795/6.

| **MS**2796*a* Miniature Sheet Collection................. | 75·00 |

2039 Casino Royale

2040 Dr. No

2041 Goldfinger

2042 Diamonds are Forever

2043 For Your Eyes Only

2044 From Russia with Love

(Des A2. Litho De La Rue)

2008 (8 Jan). *Birth Centenary of Ian Fleming* (author of James Bond books). Book Covers. Two phosphor bands. P 14½×14.

2797	**2039**	(1st) gold, new blue, magenta, greenish yellow and black..............	1·25	90
		a. Booklet pane. Nos. 2797, 2799 and 2801 with margins all round	5·00	
2798	**2040**	(1st) gold, new blue, magenta, greenish yellow and black..............	1·25	90
		a. Booklet pane. Nos. 2798, 2800 and 2802 with margins all round	5·00	
		aa. Phosphor omitted................	£1350	
2799	**2041**	54p. gold, new blue, magenta, greenish yellow and black..............	1·40	1·40
2800	**2042**	54p. gold, new blue, magenta, greenish yellow and black..............	1·40	1·40
2801	**2043**	78p. gold, new blue, magenta, greenish yellow and black..............	2·00	2·00
2802	**2044**	78p. gold, new blue, magenta, greenish yellow and black..............	2·00	2·00
Set of 6...		8·50	8·00
Set of 6 Gutter Pairs...........................		19·00	
First Day Cover (Tallents House)			10·00
First Day Cover (London SE1)..................			10·00
Presentation Pack *(P.O. Pack No. 407)*.........		11·00	
PHQ Cards *(set of 7) (306)*....................		6·00	20·00
MS2803 189×68 mm. Nos. 2797/2802............		9·00	9·00
First Day Cover (Tallents House)			11·00
First Day Cover (London SE1)..................			11·00

Booklet panes Nos. 2797a/8a come from the £7·40 Ian Fleming's James Bond booklet, No. DX41.

No. 2804 is vacant.

(Litho De La Rue)

2008 *(8 Jan). Ian Fleming's James Bond.* Booklet stamp. Design as Type **1517** (2001 Union Jack from Submarine Centenary). Two phosphor bands. *P* 14½.

2805	1517	(1st) multicoloured	4·25	4·25

a. Booklet pane.
Nos. 2581 and 2805, each×2,
with margins all round .... 12·00

No. 2805 was issued in the £7·40 Ian Fleming's James Bond booklet, No. DX41. It had previously been issued in Post Office Label sheet LS20.

For White Ensign stamp from booklet No. DX41 see No. 2581.

2045 Assistance Dog carrying Letter (Retriever "Rowan")

2046 Mountain Rescue Dog (Cross-bred "Merrick")

2047 Police Dog (German Shepherd "Max")

2048 Customs Dog (Springer Spaniel "Max")

2049 Sheepdog (Border Collie "Bob")

2050 Guide Dog (Labrador "Warwick")

(Des Redpath Design. Litho Cartor)

2008 *(5 Feb). Working Dogs.* Two phosphor bands. *P* 14½.

2806	2045	(1st) multicoloured	1·25	90
2807	2046	46p. multicoloured	1·20	1·20
2808	2047	48p. multicoloured	1·20	1·20
2809	2048	54p. multicoloured	1·40	1·40
2810	2049	69p. multicoloured	1·80	1·80
2811	2050	78p. multicoloured	2·00	2·00

Set of 6 .... 8·00 8·00
Set of 6 Gutter Pairs .... 18·00
First Day Cover (Tallents House) .... 10·00
First Day Cover (Hound Green, Basingstoke, Hants) .... 10·00
Presentation Pack (P.O. Pack No. 408) .... 10·00
PHQ Cards (set of 6) (307) .... 4·50 14·00
The 1st class value includes the "EUROPA" emblem.

2051 Henry IV (1399–1413)
2052 Henry V (1413–1422)
2053 Henry VI (1422–1461 & 1470–1)

2054 Edward IV (1461–1470 & 1471–1483)
2055 Edward V (1483)
2056 Richard III (1483–1485)

2057 The Age of Lancaster and York (*Illustration reduced. Actual size 123×70 mm*)

(Des Atelier Works. Litho Cartor)

2008 *(28 Feb). Kings and Queens* (1st issue). Houses of Lancaster and York. Two phosphor bands. *P* 14½.

2812	2051	(1st) slate, greenish yellow, magenta, new blue and black	1·25	90
2813	2052	(1st) slate, greenish yellow, magenta, new blue and black	1·25	90
2814	2053	54p. slate, greenish yellow, magenta, new blue and black	1·40	1·40
2815	2054	54p. slate, greenish yellow, magenta, new blue and black	1·40	1·40
2816	2055	69p. slate, greenish yellow, magenta, new blue and black	1·80	1·80
2817	2056	69p. slate, greenish yellow, magenta, new blue, and black	1·80	1·80

Set of 6 .... 8·00 8·00
Set of 6 Gutter Pairs .... 18·00
Set of 6 Traffic Light Gutter Blocks of 4 .... 38·00
First Day Cover (Tallents House) .... 10·00
First Day Cover (Tewkesbury) .... 10·00
Presentation Pack (P.O. Pack No. 409) (2812/**MS**2818) ..... 17·00
PHQ Cards (set of 11) (308) .... 9·00 27·00

MS2818 123×70 mm. **2057** (1st) Owain Glyn Dwr ("Parliament"), 1404; (1st) Henry V's triumph at Battle of Agincourt, 1415; 78p. Yorkist victory at Battle of Tewkesbury, 1471; 78p. William Caxton, first English printer, 1477 .... 7·00 7·00
First Day Cover (Tallents House) .... 8·00
First Day Cover (Tewkesbury) .... 8·00

The complete miniature sheet is shown on one of the eleven PHQ cards with the others depicting individual stamps including those from **MS**2818.

(Gravure Walsall)

2008 (28 Feb). *Smilers* Booklet stamps (4th series). As Nos. 2567/8, 2570 and 2675/7. Self-adhesive. Two phosphor bands. Die-cut P 15×14 (with one elliptical hole in each vertical side).

2819	**1569**	(1st) multicoloured......................		8·00	8·00
		a. Booklet pane. Nos. 2819/24		42·00	
2820	**1842**	(1st) multicoloured......................		8·00	8·00
2821	**1517**	(1st) multicoloured......................		8·00	8·00
2822	**1932**	(1st) multicoloured......................		8·00	8·00
2823	**1933**	(1st) multicoloured......................		8·00	8·00
2824	**1934**	(1st) multicoloured......................		8·00	8·00
Set of 6				42·00	42·00

Nos. 2819/24 were issued in £2·04 booklets, No. QA4, in which the surplus backing paper around each stamp was removed.

Similar sheets of ten stamps and ten *se-tenant* labels were only sold in packs for £7·95 each.

No. 2819 was re-issued again on 8 May 2010 for London 2010 Festival of Stamps in sheets of 20 (No. LS72) printed in lithography by Cartor and originally sold for £8·50 per sheet.

Nos. 2820 and 2822 were each issued on 28 October 2008 in separate sheets of 20, Nos. LS51/3, with circular *se-tenant* labels showing the Almond Blossom fairy (2820), Mr. Men or Noddy (2822). These sheets were printed in lithography by Cartor and originally sold for £9·95 per sheet.

Nos. 2819, 2820 and 2822 were issued again on 30 April 2009 in separate sheets of 20, Nos. LS60/3, with circular *se-tenant* labels showing Jeremy Fisher (2820), Wild Cherry fairy (2820), Little Miss Sunshine or Big Ears (2822). These sheets were issued for £8·50 per sheet.

Similar sheets of ten stamps and ten *se-tenant* labels were sold in £7·95 packs.

Nos. 2821/3 were issued on 8 May 2010 with other greetings stamps in sheets of 20 with *se-tenant* greetings labels, No. LS73 sold for £10 per sheet.

No. 2821 was issued on 12 February 2011 in sheets of 20 with *se-tenant* labels for Indipex International Stamp Exhibition, No. LS76, sold at £8·50 per sheet.

No. 2819 was issued in sheets of 20 with *se-tenant* labels on 28 July 2011 for Philanippon '11 World Stamp Exhibition, Yokohama (LS77), on 18 June 2012 for Indonesia 2012 International Stamp Exhibition, Jakarta (LS81), on 10 May 2013 for Australia 2013 World Stamp Exhibition, Melbourne (LS86) on 2 August 2013 for Bangkok 2013 World Stamp Exhibition, Thailand (LS87) and on 13 May 2015 for Europhilex London 2015 Exhibition (LS95).

No. 2823 was issued in sheets of 20 with *se-tenant* labels on 20 January 2012 for Lunar New Year, Year of the Dragon (LS80), on 7 February 2013 for Year of the Snake (LS84), 10 December 2013 for Year of the Horse (LS89) and on 9 November 2015 for Year of the Monkey (LS98).

All the above sheets were printed by Cartor (known from late 2013 onwards as International Security Printers) in lithography instead of photogravure.

2058 Lifeboat, Barra

2059 Lifeboat approaching Dinghy, Appledore

2060 Helicopter Winchman, Portland

2061 Inshore lifeboat, St Ives

2062 Rescue Helicopter, Lee-on-Solent

2063 Launch of Lifeboat, Dinbych-y-Pysgod, Tenby

(Des Hat-trick Design. Litho Walsall)

2008 (13 Mar). *Rescue at Sea*. 'All-over' phosphor. P 14½×14*.

2825	**2058**	(1st) bright orange, greenish yellow, magenta, new blue and black.......	1·25	90
2826	**2059**	46p. bright orange, greenish yellow, magenta, new blue and black.......	1·20	1·20
2827	**2060**	48p. bright orange, greenish yellow, magenta, new blue and black.......	1·20	1·20
2828	**2061**	54p. bright orange, greenish yellow, magenta, new blue and black.......	1·40	1·40
2829	**2062**	69p. bright orange, greenish yellow, magenta, new blue and black.......	1·80	1·80
2830	**2063**	78p. bright orange, greenish yellow, magenta, new blue and black.......	2·00	2·00
Set of 6.			8·00	8·00
Set of 6 Gutter Pairs..			18·00	
First Day Cover (Tallents House)				10·00
First Day Cover (Poole, Dorset)				10·00
Presentation Pack (P.O. Pack No. 411)			10·00	
PHQ Cards (set of 6) (309)			4·50	14·00

* Nos. 2825/30 have interrupted perforations along the top and bottom edges of the stamps, the gaps in the perforations forming the three dots and three dashes that spell out "SOS" in morse code.

Special First Day of Issue Postmarks

2064 *Lysandra bellargus* (Adonis blue*)*

2065 *Coenagrion mercuriale* (southern damselfly)

2066 *Formica rufibarbis* (red-barbed ant)

2067 *Pareulype berberata* (barberry carpet moth)

2068 *Lucanus cervus* (stag beetle)

2069 *Cryptocephalus coryli* (hazel pot beetle)

2070 *Gryllus campestris* (field cricket)

2071 *Hesperia comma* (silver-spotted skipper)

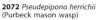

2072 *Pseudepipona herrichii* (Purbeck mason wasp)

2073 *Gnorimus nobilis* (noble chafer)

2076 Gloucester Cathedral

2077 St. David's Cathedral

(Des Andrew Ross. Litho De La Rue)

2008 (15 Apr). *Action for Species* (2nd series). Insects. Phosphor background. P 14½.

2831	**2064**	(1st) brownish grey, new blue, magenta, greenish yellow and black......	1·25	90
		a. Block of 10. Nos. 2831/40........	14·00	10·00
2832	**2065**	(1st) brownish grey, new blue, magenta, greenish yellow and black......	1·25	90
2833	**2066**	(1st) brownish grey, new blue, magenta, greenish yellow and black......	1·25	90
2834	**2067**	(1st) brownish grey, new blue, magenta, greenish yellow and black......	1·25	90
2835	**2068**	(1st) brownish grey, new blue, magenta, greenish yellow and black......	1·25	90
2836	**2069**	(1st) brownish grey, new blue, magenta, greenish yellow and black......	1·25	90
2837	**2070**	(1st) brownish grey, new blue, magenta, greenish yellow and black......	1·25	90
2838	**2071**	(1st) brownish grey, new blue, magenta, greenish yellow and black......	1·25	90
2839	**2072**	(1st) brownish grey, new blue, magenta, greenish yellow and black......	1·25	90
2840	**2073**	(1st) brownish grey, new blue, magenta, greenish yellow and black......	1·25	90
Set of 10			14·00	10·00
Gutter Block of 20			30·00	
First Day Cover (Tallents House)				11·00
First Day Cover (Crawley, W. Sussex)				11·00
Presentation Pack (P.O. Pack No. 412)			16·00	
PHQ Cards (set of 10) (310)			9·00	16·00

Nos. 2831/40 were printed together, *se-tenant*, as blocks of ten (5×2) in sheets of 60 (2 panes of 30).

2078 Westminster Cathedral

2079 St. Magnus Cathedral, Kirkwall, Orkney

ST PAUL'S CATHEDRAL
BENEATH LIES BURIED THE FOUNDER OF THIS CHURCH AND CITY,
CHRISTOPHER WREN, WHO LIVED MORE THAN 90 YEARS,
NOT FOR HIMSELF BUT FOR THE PUBLIC GOOD.
READER, IF YOU SEEK HIS MONUMENT, LOOK AROUND YOU.

2080 St. Paul's Cathedral (*Illustration reduced. Actual size* 115×89 mm)

(Des Howard Brown. Litho Enschedé)

2008 (13 May). *Cathedrals*. 'All-over' phosphor. P 14½.

2841	**2074**	(1st) black, blackish brown, brownish black and brownish grey......	1·25	90
2842	**2075**	48p. black, brownish black, blackish brown and brownish grey......	1·20	1·20
2843	**2076**	50p. black, brownish black, blackish brown and brownish grey......	1·30	1·30
2844	**2077**	56p. black, brownish black, blackish brown and brownish grey......	1·40	1·40
2845	**2078**	72p. black, brownish black, blackish brown and brownish grey......	1·80	1·80
2846	**2079**	81p. black, brownish black, blackish brown and brownish grey......	2·00	2·00
Set of 6			8·00	8·00
Set of 6 Gutter Pairs......			17·00	
Set of 6 Traffic Light Gutter Pairs			20·00	
First Day Cover (Tallents House)				10·00
First Day Cover (London EC4)				10·00
Presentation Pack (P.O. Pack No. 413) (2841/**MS**2847)......			20·00	
PHQ Cards (set of 11) (311)			9·00	27·00

MS2847 115×89 mm. (1st) multicoloured; (1st) multicoloured; 81p. multicoloured; 81p. multicoloured.

P 14½×14......		7·00	7·00
First Day Cover (Tallents House)			8·00
First Day Cover (London EC4)			8·00

No. **MS**2847 commemorates the 300th anniversary of St. Paul's Cathedral.

The complete miniature sheet is shown on one of the eleven PHQ cards with the others depicting individual stamps including those from **MS**2847.

2074 Lichfield Cathedral

2075 Belfast Cathedral

(Gravure Walsall)

2008 (13 May). *Beside the Seaside* (2nd series). As Type 1977 but self-adhesive. Two phosphor bands. Die-cut P 14½.

2848	**1977**	(1st) multicoloured.....................................	4·50	4·50
		a. Booklet pane. No. 2848×2 and		
		No. 2295×4............................	18·00	

No. 2848 was only issued in £2·16 booklets, No. PM15, in which the surplus self-adhesive paper was removed from around the 1st class gold stamps (No. 2295), but retained from around No. 2848.

2081 *Carry on Sergeant*

2082 *Dracula*

2083 *Carry on Cleo*

2084 *The Curse of Frankenstein*

2085 *Carry on Screaming*

2086 *The Mummy*

(Des Elmwood. Litho Walsall)

2008 (10 June). *Posters for Carry On and Hammer Horror Films.* Two phosphor bands. *P* 14.

2849	**2081**	(1st) silver, greenish yellow, magenta, new blue and black	1.25	90
2850	**2082**	48p. silver, greenish yellow, magenta, new blue and black	1·20	1·20
2851	**2083**	50p. silver, greenish yellow, magenta, new blue and black	1·30	1·30
2852	**2084**	56p. silver, greenish yellow, magenta, new blue and black	1·40	1·40
2853	**2085**	72p. silver, greenish yellow, magenta, new blue and black	1·80	1·80
2854	**2086**	81p. silver, greenish yellow, magenta, new blue and black	2·00	2·00

Set of 6 .... 8·00 | 8·00
Set of 6 Gutter Pairs.. 18·00
First Day Cover (Tallents House) .... 10·00
First Day Cover (Bray, Maidenhead, Berks) .... 10·00
Presentation Pack (P.O. Pack No. 414)............. 10·00
PHQ Cards (set of 6) (312).................... 4·50 | 14·00
PHQ Cards ('brick wall' background) and Stamps Set .... 9·00

Nos. 2849/54 commemorate the 50th anniversary of *Dracula* and the first *Carry On* film (*Carry on Sergeant*).

2087 Red Arrows, Dartmouth Regatta Airshow, 2006

2088 RAF Falcons Parachute Team, Biggin Hill, 2006

2089 Spectator watching Red Arrows, Farnborough, 2006

2090 Prototype Avro Vulcan Bombers and Avro 707s, Farnborough, 1953

2091 Parachutist Robert Wyndham on Wing of Avro 504, 1933

2092 Air Race rounding the Beacon, Hendon, *c.* 1912

(Des Roundel. Gravure De La Rue)

2008 (17 July). *Air Displays.* Two phosphor bands. *P* 14½×14.

2855	**2087**	(1st) olive-grey, bright magenta, greenish yellow, new blue and black...	1·25	90
2856	**2088**	48p. olive-grey, bright magenta, greenish yellow, new blue and black...	1·20	1·20
2857	**2089**	50p. olive-grey, bright magenta, greenish yellow, new blue and black...	1·30	1·30
2858	**2090**	56p. olive-grey, bright magenta, greenish yellow, new blue and black...	1·40	1·40
2859	**2091**	72p. olive-grey, bright magenta, greenish yellow, new blue and black...	1·80	1·80
2860	**2092**	81p. olive-grey, bright magenta, greenish yellow, new blue and black...	2·00	2·00

Set of 6 .... 8·00 | 8·00
Set of 6 Gutter Pairs.. 18·00
First Day Cover (Tallents House) .... 10·00
First Day Cover (Farnborough, Hants) .... 10·00
Presentation Pack (P.O. Pack No. 415)............. 11·00
PHQ Cards (set of 6) (313) .... 4·50 | 13·00

The 1st class stamp was also issued in sheets of 20 with *se-tenant* labels, printed in lithography by Cartor, and sold for £7·75 per sheet (LS47).

2093 Landmarks of Beijing and London (*Illustration reduced. Actual size 115×76 mm*)

(Des Why Not Associates. Litho Walsall)

2008 (22 Aug). *Handover of Olympic* Flag from Beijing to London. Sheet 115×76 mm. Multicoloured. Phosphorised paper. *P* 14½.

MS2861	2093	(1st) National Stadium, Beijing; (1st) London Eye; (1st) Tower of London; (1st) Corner Tower of the Forbidden City, Beijing....	7·00	7·00
		a. UV varnish (Olympic Rings) omitted	£8750	
		First Day Cover (Tallents House)		8·00
		First Day Cover (London E15).........................		8·00
		Presentation Pack (P.O. Pack No. M17)	9·00	
		PHQ Cards (set of 5) (OGH)	4·00	15·00

The Olympic rings overprinted on **MS**2861 are in silk-screen varnish.

The five PHQ cards show the four individual stamps and the complete miniature sheet.

Stamps in these designs were also issued by China.

Special First Day of Issue Postmarks

2094 Drum Major, RAF Central Band, 2007

2095 Helicopter Rescue Winchman, 1984

2096 Hawker Hunter Pilot, 1951

2097 Lancaster Air Gunner, 1944

2098 WAAF Plotter, 1940

2099 Pilot, 1918

(Des Graham Turner and Atelier Works. Litho Walsall)

2008 (18 Sept). *Military Uniforms* (2nd series). RAF Uniforms. Two phosphor bands. *P* 14.

2862	2094	(1st) silver, greenish yellow, bright magenta, new blue and black.......	1·25	90
		a. Horiz strip of 3. Nos. 2862/4	4·00	4·00

		b. Booklet pane. Nos. 2862/4 with margins all round..............	4·00	
2863	2095	(1st) silver, greenish yellow, bright magenta, new blue and black......	1·25	90
2864	2096	(1st) silver, greenish yellow, bright magenta, new blue and black......	1·25	90
2865	2097	81p. silver, greenish yellow, bright magenta, new blue and black......	2·00	2·00
		a. Horiz strip of 3. Nos. 2865/7	7·00	7·00
		b. Booklet pane. Nos. 2865/7 with margins all round..............	7·00	
2866	2098	81p. silver, greenish yellow, bright magenta, new blue and black......	2·00	2·00
2867	2099	81p. silver, greenish yellow, bright magenta, new blue and black......	2·00	2·00
Set of 6			10·00	10·00
Set of 2 Gutter Strips of 6			21·00	
Set of 2 Traffic Light Gutter Blocks of 12			42·00	
First Day Cover (Tallents House)				11·00
First Day Cover (Hendon, London NW9)				11·00
Presentation Pack (P.O. Pack No. 416)			12·00	
PHQ Cards (set of 6) (314)			5·00	14·00

Nos. 2862/4 and 2865/7 were each printed together, *se-tenant*, as horizontal strips of three stamps in sheets of 60 (2 panes 6×5).

Booklet panes Nos. 2862b and 2865b come from the £7·15 Pilot to Plane, RAF Uniforms booklet No. DX42.

Special First Day of Issue Postmarks

(Litho Walsall)

2008 (18 Sept). *'Pilot to Plane'. RAF Uniforms.* Booklet stamps. Designs as Types 1307 (Spitfire from 1997 British Aircraft Designers) and 2087 (Red Arrows from 2008 Air Displays). Two phosphor bands. *P* 14.

2868	1307	20p. multicoloured..........................	4·00	4·00
		a. Booklet pane. Nos. 2868/9, each×2, with margins all round.....	14·00	
2869	2087	(1st) multicoloured..........................	4·00	4·00

Nos. 2868/9 were only issued in the £7·15 Pilot to Plane, RAF Uniforms booklet, No. DX42.

2100 Millicent Garrett Fawcett (suffragist)

2101 Elizabeth Garrett Anderson (physician – women's health)

2102 Marie Stopes (family planning pioneer)

2103 Eleanor Rathbone (family allowance campaigner)

2104 Claudia Jones (civil rights activist)

2105 Barbara Castle (politician – Equal Pay Act)

(Des Together Design. Gravure Walsall)

2008 (14 Oct). *Women of Distinction.* 'All-over' phosphor. *P* 14×14½.

2870	2100	(1st) grey-black, grey, gold and black..	1·25	90
2871	2101	48p. grey-black, grey, gold and black..	1·20	1·20

2872	**2102**	50p. grey-black, grey, gold and black..	1·30	1·30
2873	**2103**	56p. grey-black, grey, gold and black..	1·40	1·40
2874	**2104**	72p. grey-black, grey, gold and black..	1·80	1·80
2875	**2105**	81p. grey-black, grey, gold and black..	2·00	2·00
	Set of 6		8·00	8·00
	Set of 6 Gutter Pairs		17·00	
	First Day Cover (Tallents House)			9·00
	First Day Cover (Aldeburgh, Suffolk)			9·00
	Presentation Pack (P.O. Pack No. 417)		10·00	
	PHQ Cards (set of 6) (315)		4·50	13·00

Special First Day of Issue Postmarks

2106 Ugly Sisters from *Cinderella* **2107** Genie from *Aladdin* **2108** Ugly Sisters from *Cinderella*

2109 Captain Hook from *Peter Pan* **2110** Genie from *Aladdin* **2111** Wicked Queen from *Snow White*

(Des Steve Haskins. Gravure De La Rue)

2008 (4 Nov). Christmas. One centre band (2876) or two phosphor bands (others). P 15×14.

(a) Self-adhesive

2876	**2106**	(2nd) bright magenta, greenish yellow, new blue and black	1·25	70
		a. Booklet pane. No. 2876×12	11·00	
2877	**2107**	(1st) bright magenta, greenish yellow, new blue and black	1·40	1·00
		a. Booklet pane. No. 2877×12	14·00	
2878	**2108**	(2nd Large) deep new blue, bright magenta, greenish yellow, new blue and black	1·75	1·25
2879	**2109**	50p. bright magenta, greenish yellow, new blue and black	1·75	1·40
2880	**2110**	(1st Large) gold, bright magenta, greenish yellow, new blue and black	2·40	1·60
2881	**2111**	81p. bright magenta, greenish yellow, new blue and black	2·40	2·25
	Set of 6		10·00	7·50
	First Day Cover (Tallents House)			8·50
	First Day Cover (Bethlehem, Llandeilo)			8·50
	Presentation Pack (P.O. Pack No. 418)		12·00	
	PHQ Cards (set of 7) (316)		6·00	24·00

(b) Ordinary gum

MS2882 114×102 mm. As Nos. 2876/81		10·00	10·00
First Day Cover (Tallents House)			11·00
First Day Cover (Bethlehem, Llandeilo)			11·00

The phosphor bands on Nos. 2878/9 are at the centre and right of each stamp.

The seven PHQ cards depict the six stamps and **MS**2882.

The 2nd class, 1st class and 81p. stamps were also issued together in sheets of 20, sold for £8·85, containing eight 1st class, eight 2nd class and four 81p. stamps, arranged in vertical strips of five stamps alternated with printed labels (LS54). Separate sheets of ten 1st, 20 1st, 20 2nd or ten 81p. stamps were available with personalised photographs from Royal Mail, Edinburgh. These were sold at £7·50 for ten 1st, £8·50 for 20 and £13·50 for 20 1st or ten 81p. These sheets were printed in lithography by Cartor and had the backing paper around the stamps retained.

Special First Day of Issue Postmarks

2112 Poppies on Barbed Wire Stem **2113** Soldiers in Poppy Flower

2114 Soldier's Face in Poppy Flower

2115 Lest We Forget (*Illustration reduced. Actual size* 124×70 mm)

(Des Hat-trick design. Litho De La Rue)

2008 (6 Nov). 'Lest We Forget' (3rd issue). 90th Anniv of the Armistice. Two phosphor bands. P 14½ (1st) or 15×14 (with one elliptical hole in each vertical side) (81p.).

2883	**2112**	(1st) silver, new blue, bright magenta, greenish yellow and black	2·00	90
		a. Horiz strip of 3. Nos. 2883/5	6·00	6·00
2884	**2113**	(1st) silver, new blue, bright magenta, greenish yellow and black	2·00	90
2885	**2114**	(1st) silver, new blue, bright magenta, greenish yellow and black	2·00	90
	Set of 3		6·00	6·00
	Gutter Strip of 6		13·00	
	Traffic Light Gutter Block of 12		25·00	
MS2886 124×70 mm. **2115** No. 2885 and as Nos. EN19, NI129, S122 and W111			12·00	12·00
	First Day Cover (Tallents House)			13·00
	First Day Cover (London SW1)			13·00
	Presentation Pack (P.O. Pack No. 419)		14·00	
	PHQ Cards (set of 6) (317)		4·75	14·00

Nos. 2883/5 were printed together, *se-tenant*, in horizontal strips of three stamps in sheets of 30.

No. **MS**2886 (including the Northern Ireland, Scotland and Wales stamps) is printed in lithography.

The six PHQ cards depict Nos. **MS**2685, **MS**2796 and 2883/**MS**2886.

The 1st class stamp, Type **2114**, was also issued in sheets of 20 with *se-tenant* labels showing artifacts from the trenches, printed in lithography by Cartor and sold at £7·75 (LS55).

No. 2885 has the two phosphor bands shaped around each side of the poppy.

A Miniature Sheet Collection containing Nos. **MS**2685, **MS**2796, **MS**2886 and a replica embroidered postcard in a folder was sold for £26·95.

Collectors Pack
2008 (6 Nov). Comprises Nos. 2797/802, 2806/**MS**2818, 2825/**MS**2847, 2849/67, 2870/81, **MS**2886 and **MS**NI152
CP2886a Collectors Pack £140

Post Office Yearbook
2008 (6 Nov). Comprises Nos. 2797/802, 2806/**MS**2818, 2825/**MS**2847, 2849/67, 2870/81, **MS**2886 and **MS**NI152/3
YB2886a Yearbook £125

Miniature Sheet Collection
2008 (6 Nov). Comprises Nos. **MS**2803, **MS**2818, **MS**2847, **MS**2861, **MS**2882, **MS**2886 and **MS**NI110/11
MS2886a Miniature Sheet Collection................................... 75·00

2116 Supermarine Spitfire
(R. J. Mitchell)

2117 Mini Skirt (Mary Quant)

2118 Mini (Sir Alec Issigonis)

2119 Anglepoise Lamp
(George Carwardine)

2120 Concorde
(Aérospatiale-BAC)

2121 K2 Telephone Kiosk
(Sir Giles Gilbert Scott)

2122 Polypropylene Chair
(Robin Day)

2123 Penguin Books (Edward Young)

London Underground Map
Designed by Harry Beck

2124 London Underground Map (based on original design by Harry Beck)

Routemaster Bus
Design team led by AAM Durrant

2125 Routemaster Bus (design team led by AAM Durrant)

(Des HGV Design. Litho Cartor)

2009 (13 Jan). *British Design Classics* (1st series). Phosphor background. P 14½.

2887	2116	(1st) silver, greenish yellow, bright magenta, new blue and black......	1·25	90
		a. Block of 10. Nos. 2887/96................	14·00	12·00
		ab. Black printed treble.................	£10000	
		b. Booklet pane. Nos. 2887, 2889 and 2896×2...................................	5·00	
2888	2117	(1st) silver, greenish yellow, bright magenta, new blue and black......	1·25	90
		a. Booklet pane. Nos. 2888, 2890, 2892 and 2893/5................	7·00	
2889	2118	(1st) silver, greenish yellow, bright magenta, new blue and black......	1·25	90
2890	2119	(1st) silver, greenish yellow, bright magenta, new blue and black......	1·25	90
2891	2120	(1st) silver, greenish yellow, bright magenta, new blue and black......	1·25	90
		a. Booklet pane. Nos. 2891 and 2897, each×2...................	20·00	
2892	2121	(1st) silver, greenish yellow, bright magenta, new blue and black......	1·25	90
2893	2122	(1st) silver, greenish yellow, bright magenta, new blue and black......	1·25	90
2894	2123	(1st) silver, greenish yellow, bright magenta, new blue and black......	1·25	90
2895	2124	(1st) silver, greenish yellow, bright magenta, new blue and black......	1·25	90
2896	2125	(1st) silver, greenish yellow, bright magenta, new blue and black......	1·25	90

Set of 10.. 14·00 12·00
Gutter Block of 20.. 28·00
First Day Cover (Tallents House)................................ 13·00
First Day Cover (Longbridge, Birmingham).................. 13·00
Presentation Pack (P.O. Pack No. 421)...................... 16·00
PHQ Cards (set of 10) (318)........................... 9·00 20·00

Nos. 2887/96 were printed together, *se-tenant*, in blocks of ten (2×5) throughout sheets of 30 stamps.

Booklet panes Nos. 2887b/8a and 2891a come from the £7·68 British Design Classics booklet, No. DX44.

No. 2889 was also issued in sheets of 20 with *se-tenant* labels, perforated 14×14½, on 13 January 2009. No. LS56, sold at £7·75 per sheet.

No. 2891 was also issued on 2 March 2009 in sheets of 20 with *se-tenant* labels, No. LS57, and sold at £7·75 per sheet.

No. 2887 was also issued on 15 September 2010 in sheets of 20 with *se-tenant* labels, No. LS74, sold at £8·50 per sheet.

The above sheets were all printed in lithography by Cartor and perforated 14×14½.

For self-adhesive versions of these stamps see Nos. 2911/5b..

(Litho Cartor)

2009 (13 Jan). *British Design Classics* (2nd series). Booklet stamp. Design as No. 2285 (Concorde from 2002 Passenger Jet Aviation). Two phosphor bands. P 14½.

2897 **1589** (1st) multicoloured...................................... 10·00 9·50
No. 2897 was only issued in the £7·68 British Design Classics booklet, No. DX44.

2126 Charles Darwin

2127 Marine Iguana

2128 Finches

2129 Atoll

2130 Bee Orchid

2131 Orang-utan

2132 Fauna and Map of the Galapagos Islands (*Illustration reduced. Actual size 115×89 mm*)

(Des Hat-trick design (Nos. 2898/903) or Howard Brown (**MS**2904)

2009 (12 Feb). *Birth Bicentenary of Charles Darwin (naturalist and evolutionary theorist)* (1st issue).

(a) *Self-adhesive. Gravure De La Rue. 'All-over' phosphor. P 14.*

2898	**2126**	(1st) black, new blue, greenish yellow and bright magenta	1·25	90
2899	**2127**	48p. black, new blue, greenish yellow and bright magenta	1·20	1·20
2900	**2128**	50p. black, new blue, greenish yellow and bright magenta	1·30	1·30
2901	**2129**	56p. black, new blue, greenish yellow and bright magenta	1·40	1·40
2902	**2130**	72p. black, new blue, greenish yellow and bright magenta	1·80	1·80
2903	**2131**	81p. black, new blue, greenish yellow and bright magenta	2·00	2·00
Set of 6			8·00	8·00
First Day Cover (Tallents House)				10·00
First Day Cover (Shrewsbury)				10·00
Presentation Pack (P.O. Pack No. 423) (2898/**MS**2904)			18·00	
PHQ Cards (set of 11) (320)			9·00	20·00

(b) *Ordinary gum. Litho De La Rue. Two phosphor bands. P 14.*

MS2904 115×89 mm. (1st) Flightless cormorant; (1st) Giant tortoise and cactus finch; 81p. Marine iguana; 81p. Floreana mockingbird		8·00	8·00
a. Booklet pane. No. **MS**2904 150×96 mm		8·00	
First Day Cover (Tallents House)			9·00
First Day Cover (Shrewsbury)			9·00

Nos. 2898/903 have "jigsaw" perforations on the two vertical sides.

Booklet pane No. 2904a comes from the £7·75 Charles Darwin booklet No. DX45.

The complete miniature sheet is shown on one of the eleven PHQ cards with the others depicting individual stamps, including those from the miniature sheet.

Special First Day of Issue Postmarks

(Gravure De La Rue)

2009 (12 Feb). *Birth Bicentenary of Charles Darwin (naturalist and evolutionary theorist)* (2nd issue). Phosphorised paper. P 14.

2905	**2126**	(1st) multicoloured	4·50	4·50
		a. Booklet pane. Nos. 2905 and 2909/10	20·00	
2906	**2127**	48p. multicoloured	5·00	5·00
		a. Booklet pane. Nos. 2906/8	20·00	
2907	**2128**	50p. multicoloured	5·50	5·50
2908	**2129**	56p. multicoloured	6·00	6·00
2909	**2130**	72p. multicoloured	6·50	6·50
2910	**2131**	81p. multicoloured	7·00	7·00
Set of 6			30·00	30·00

Nos. 2905/10 were only issued in the £7·75 Charles Darwin booklet, No. DX45. They also have "Jigsaw" perforations on both vertical sides.

For Nos. U2911/37, U2941/74, U2981/85 U2991/5 and U3001/20 see Decimal Machin Definitives section.

(Gravure Walsall)

2009 (10 Mar)–**2010**. *British Design Classics* (3rd series). Booklet stamps. Designs as Nos. 2887/9, 2891/2 and 2896. Self-adhesive. Phosphor background. Die-cut perf 14½.

2911	**2121**	(1st) multicoloured	4·25	4·25
		a. Booklet pane. Nos. 2911/12 and U2949×4	12·00	
2912	**2125**	(1st) multicoloured	4·25	4·25
2913	**2118**	(1st) multicoloured (21.4.09)	4·25	3·00
		a. Booklet pane. No. 2913×2 and U2949×4	12·00	
2914	**2120**	(1st) multicoloured (18.8.09)	4·25	3·00
		a. Booklet pane. No. 2914×2 and U2949×4	12·00	
2915	**2117**	(1st) multicoloured (17.9.09)	4·25	3·00
		a. Booklet pane. No. 2915×2 and U2949×4	12·00	
2915b	**2116**	(1st) multicoloured (15.9.10)	4·25	3·00
		ba. Booklet pane. No. 2915b×2 and U2965×4	12·00	
Set of 6			23·00	19·00

Nos. 2911/15b were only issued in booklets, Nos. PM16/17, PM19/20 and PM25, initially sold for £2·16 (PM16) or £2·34 (PM17, PM19/20) or £2·46 (PM25).

2133 Matthew Boulton and Factory (manufacturing)

2134 James Watt and Boulton & Watt Condensing Engine (steam engineering)

2135 Richard Arkwright and Spinning Machine (textiles)

2136 Josiah Wedgwood and Black Basalt Teapot and Vase (ceramics)

2137 George Stephenson and *Locomotion* (railways)

2138 Henry Maudslay and Table Engine (machine making)

2139 James Brindley and Bridgewater Canal Aqueduct (canal engineering)

2140 John McAdam (road building)

2143 Edward VI (1547–53)

2144 Lady Jane Grey (1553)

2145 Mary I (1553–8)

2146 Elizabeth I (1558–1603)

(Des Webb and Webb. Litho Enschedé)

2009 (10 Mar). *Pioneers of the Industrial Revolution*. 'All-over' phosphor. P 14×14½.

2916	2133	(1st) gold, black, new blue, bright magenta and greenish yellow.......	1·25	90
		a. Horiz pair. Nos. 2916/17	2·75	2·75
2917	2134	(1st) gold, black, new blue, bright magenta and greenish yellow.......	1·25	90
2918	2135	50p. gold, black, new blue, bright magenta and greenish yellow.......	1·30	1·30
		a. Horiz pair. Nos. 2918/19	3·00	3·00
2919	2136	50p. gold, black, new blue, bright magenta and greenish yellow.......	1·30	1·30
2920	2137	56p. gold, black, new blue, bright magenta and greenish yellow.......	1·40	1·40
		a. Horiz pair. Nos. 2920/1	3·00	3·00
2921	2138	56p. gold, black, new blue, bright magenta and greenish yellow.......	1·40	1·40
2922	2139	72p. gold, black, new blue, bright magenta and greenish yellow.......	1·80	1·80
		a. Horiz pair. Nos. 2922/3	4·00	4·00
2923	2140	72p. gold, black, new blue, bright magenta and greenish yellow.......	1·80	1·80

Set of 8	11·50	11·50
Set of 4 Gutter Strips of 4	24·00	
First Day Cover (Tallents House)		13·00
First Day Cover (Steam Mills, Cinderford)		13·00
Presentation Pack (P.O. Pack No. 425)......................	14·00	
PHQ Cards (set of 8) (321)......................	6·00	16·00

Nos. 2916/17, 2918/19, 2920/1 and 2922/3 were each printed together, *se-tenant*, as horizontal pairs in sheets of 60 (2 panes 6×5).

Special First Day of Issue Postmarks

2141 Henry VII (1485–1509)

2142 Henry VIII (1509–47)

2147 The Age of the Tudors (*Illustration reduced. Actual size 123×70 mm*)

(Des Atelier Works. Litho Cartor)

2009 (21 Apr). *Kings and Queens* (2nd issue). The House of Tudor. Two phosphor bands. P 14.

2924	2141	(1st) blackish olive, greenish yellow, bright magenta, new blue and black........	1·25	90
2925	2142	(1st) blackish olive, greenish yellow, bright magenta, new blue and black........	1·25	90
2926	2143	62p. blackish olive, greenish yellow, bright magenta, new blue and black........	1·60	1·60
2927	2144	62p. blackish olive, greenish yellow, bright magenta, new blue and black........	1·60	1·60
		a. Imperf (pair)........	£6000	
2928	2145	81p. blackish olive, greenish yellow, bright magenta, new blue and black........	2·10	2·10
2929	2146	81p. blackish olive, greenish yellow, bright magenta, new blue and black........	2·10	2·10

Set of 6	9·00	9·00
Set of 6 Gutter Pairs......................	19·00	
Set of 6 Traffic Light Gutter Blocks of 4	40·00	
First Day Cover (Tallents House)		10·00
First Day Cover (London SE10)		10·00
Presentation Pack (P.O. Pack No. 426) (2924/**MS**2930)......	18·00	
PHQ Cards (set of 11) (322)	9·00	22·00

MS2930 123×70 mm. **2147** (1st) *Mary Rose* (galleon), 1510; (1st) Field of Cloth of Gold Royal Conference, 1520; 90p. Royal Exchange (centre of commerce), 1565; 90p. Francis Drake (circumnavigation), 1580.....

	7·00	7·00
First Day Cover (Tallents House)		8·00
First Day Cover (London SE10)		8·00

The complete miniature sheet is shown on one of the eleven PHQ cards with the others depicting individual stamps including those from **MS**2930.

The PHQ Card for the Royal Exchange design has the inscription for Sir Francis Drake and *vice versa*.

21.4.09   21.4.09

2148 *Allium sphaerocephalon*
(round-headed leek)

2149 *Luronium natans*
(floating water-plantain)

2150 *Cypripedium calceolus*
(lady's slipper orchid)

2151 *Polygala amarella*
(dwarf milkwort)

2152 *Saxifraga hirculus*
(marsh saxifrage)

2153 *Stachys germanica*
(downy woundwort)

2154 *Euphorbia serrulata*
(upright spurge)

2155 *Pyrus cordata*
(Plymouth pear)

2156 *Polygonum maritimum*
(Sea knotgrass)

2157 *Dianthus armeria*
(Deptford pink)

2158 Royal Botanic Gardens, Kew (*Illustration reduced. Actual size* 115×89 mm)

(Des Studio Dempsey. Litho Cartor)

2009 (19 May). *Action for Species* (3rd series). Plants.

(a) Phosphor background. P 14½

2931	**2148**	(1st) brownish grey, greenish yellow, bright magenta, new blue and black	1·25	90
		a. Block of 10. Nos. 2931/40	14·00	10·00
2932	**2149**	(1st) brownish grey, greenish yellow, bright magenta, new blue and black	1·25	90
2933	**2150**	(1st) brownish grey, greenish yellow, bright magenta, new blue and black	1·25	90
2934	**2151**	(1st) brownish grey, greenish yellow, bright magenta, new blue and black	1·25	90
2935	**2152**	(1st) brownish grey, greenish yellow, bright magenta, new blue and black	1·25	90
2936	**2153**	(1st) brownish grey, greenish yellow, bright magenta, new blue and black	1·25	90
2937	**2154**	(1st) brownish grey, greenish yellow, bright magenta, new blue and black	1·25	90
2938	**2155**	(1st) brownish grey, greenish yellow, bright magenta, new blue and black	1·25	90
2939	**2156**	(1st) brownish grey, greenish yellow, bright magenta, new blue and black	1·25	90
2940	**2157**	(1st) brownish grey, greenish yellow, bright magenta, new blue and black	1·25	90

Set of 10	14·00	10·00
Gutter Block of 10	16·00	
First Day Cover (Tallents House)		12·00
First Day Cover (Kew, Richmond)		12·00
Presentation Pack (P.O. Pack No. 427) (2931/**MS**2941)	22·00	
PHQ Cards (set of 15) (323)	12·00	30·00

(b) 250th Anniv of Royal Botanic Gardens, Kew. Multicoloured. Two phosphor bands. P 14×14½.

MS2941 115×89 mm. **2158** (1st) Palm House, Kew Gardens; (1st) Millennium Seed Bank, Wakehurst Place; 90p. Pagoda, Kew Gardens; 90p. Sackler Crossing, Kew Gardens	7·00 7·00
First Day Cover (Tallents House)	8·00
First Day Cover (Kew, Richmond)	8·00

Nos. 2931/40 were printed together, *se-tenant*, as blocks of ten (5×2) in sheets of 60 (2 panes of 30).

The complete miniature sheet is shown on one of the 15 PHQ cards with the others depicting individual stamps including those from **MS**2941.

(Gravure Walsall)

2009 (21 May). *50th Anniv of NAFAS (National Association of Flower Arrangement Societies). Booklet stamps. Designs as Nos. 1958 and 1962 (1997 Greeting Stamps 19th-century Flower Paintings). Self-adhesive. Two phosphor bands. Die-cut P 14 (with one elliptical hole in each vert side).*

2942	**1287**	(1st) multicoloured	4·00	4·00
		a. Booklet pane. Nos. 2942/3 and U2949×4	15·00	
2943	**1283**	(1st) multicoloured	4·00	4·00

Nos. 2942/3 were only issued in stamp booklets, No. PM18.

2159 Dragon

2160 Unicorn

2161 Giant

2162 Pixie

2163 Mermaid

2164 Fairy

(Des Dave McKean and Morgan Radcliffe. Gravure De La Rue)

2009 (16 June). *Mythical Creatures.* 'All-over' phosphor. P 14½.

2944	**2159**	(1st) bright magenta, greenish yellow, new blue and black	1·25	90
2945	**2160**	(1st) bright magenta, greenish yellow, new blue and black	1·25	90
2946	**2161**	62p. bright magenta, greenish yellow, new blue and black	1·60	1·60
2947	**2162**	62p. bright magenta, greenish yellow, new blue and black	1·60	1·60
2948	**2163**	90p. bright magenta, greenish yellow, new blue and black	2·25	2·25
2949	**2164**	90p. bright magenta, greenish yellow, new blue and black	2·25	2·25
Set of 6			9·00	9·00
Set of 6 Gutter Pairs			19·00	
First Day Cover (Tallents House)				10·00
First Day Cover (Dragonby, Scunthorpe)				10·00
Presentation Pack (P.O. Pack No. 428)			11·00	
PHQ Cards (set of 6) (324)			5·00	12·00

2165 George V Type B Wall Letter Box, 1933–6

2166 Edward VII Ludlow Letter Box, 1901–10

2167 Victorian Lamp Letter Box, 1896

2168 Elizabeth II Type A Wall Letter Box, 1962–3

2169 Post Boxes (*Illustration reduced. Actual size* 145×74 mm)

(Des Elmwood. Litho Cartor)

2009 (18 Aug). *Post Boxes.* 'All-over' phosphor. P 14.

2950	**2165**	(1st) multicoloured	1·50	1·50
		a. Booklet pane. Nos. 2950/3 with margins all round	8·50	
2951	**2166**	56p. multicoloured	2·00	2·00
2952	**2167**	81p. multicoloured	2·50	2·50
2953	**2168**	90p. multicoloured	2·75	2·75
Set of 4			8·50	8·50
MS2954 145×74 mm 2169 Nos. 2950/3			8·50	8·50
First Day Cover (Tallents House)				9·00
First Day Cover (Wakefield, W. Yorkshire)				9·00
Presentation Pack (P.O. Pack No. 430)			10·00	
PHQ Cards (set of 5) (325)			4·00	10·00

Nos. 2950/3 were only issued in the £8·18 Treasures of the Archive booklet, No. DX46 and in No. **MS**2954.

The five PHQ cards show the four individual stamps and the miniature sheet.

Type **2165** was also issued in sheets of 20 with *se-tenant* labels showing post boxes, No. LS65, sold for £8·35 per sheet.

(Litho Cartor)

2009 (18 Aug). *Treasures of the Archive* (1st series). Booklet stamps. Designs as Types 929 (1990 150th anniv of the Penny Black) and 1446 (with redrawn 1st face value). Printed in lithography. Two phosphor bands. P 14½×14 (with one elliptical hole in each vert side).

2955	**929**	20p. brownish-black and grey-brown	2·75	2·75
		a. Booklet pane. Nos. 2955/6, each×4 with central label and margins all round	16·00	

2956   (1st) brownish-black and grey-brown ..... 2·75   2·75
Nos. 2955/6 were only issued in the £8·18 Treasures of the Archive booklet, No. DX46.
For No. 2956 perf 14 see No. 2133.
Also see Nos. 1478 and **MS**1501.

(Litho Cartor)

2009 (18 Aug). *Treasures of the Archive* (2nd series). Booklet stamps. Design as Type 919 (1989 Lord Mayor's Show). 'All-over' phosphor. *P* 14.
2957   **919**   20p. multicoloured.. 4·50   4·50
                    a. Booklet pane. No. 2957×4 with
                       margins all round...................................   16·00
No. 2957 was only issued in the £8·18 Treasures of the Archive booklet, No. DX46.

Special First Day of Issue Postmarks

2176 Flight Deck
Officer, 2009

2177 Captain, 1941

2170 Firefighting

2171 Chemical Fire

2178 Second Officer
WRNS, 1918

2179 Able Seaman,
1880

2172 Emergency Rescue

2173 Flood Rescue

2180 Royal Marine,
1805

2181 Admiral, 1795

2174 Search and Rescue

2175 Fire Safety

(Des Rose Design. Gravure De La Rue)

2009 (1 Sept). *Fire and Rescue Service*. 'All-over' phosphor. *P* 14×14½.
2958   **2170**   (1st) pale greenish yellow, bright
                     magenta, greenish yellow, new
                     blue and black................................ 1·25   90
2959   **2171**   54p. pale greenish yellow, bright
                     magenta, greenish yellow, new
                     blue and black................................ 1·40   1·40
2960   **2172**   56p. pale greenish yellow, bright
                     magenta, greenish yellow, new
                     blue and black................................ 1·40   1·40
2961   **2173**   62p. pale greenish yellow, bright
                     magenta, greenish yellow, new
                     blue and black................................ 1·60   1·60
2962   **2174**   81p. pale greenish yellow, bright
                     magenta, greenish yellow, new
                     blue and black................................ 2·00   2·00
2963   **2175**   90p. pale greenish yellow, bright
                     magenta, greenish yellow, new
                     blue and black................................ 2·25   2·25
Set of 6 .... 10·00   10·00
Set of 6 Gutter Pairs.. 21·00
First Day Cover (Tallents House) ....   11·00
First Day Cover (Hose, Melton Mowbray) ....   11·00
Presentation Pack (P.O. Pack No. 429)................ 12·00
PHQ Cards (set of 6) (326) .... 5·00   12·00

(Des Graham Turner and Atelier Works. Litho Cartor)

2009 (17 Sept). *Military Uniforms* (3rd series). Royal Navy Uniforms. Phosphor background. *P* 14.
2964   **2176**   (1st) silver, greenish yellow, magenta,
                     new blue and black .... 1·25   90
                     a. Horiz strip of 3. Nos. 2964/6 .... 4·00   4·00
                     b. Booklet pane. Nos. 2964/6 with
                        margins all round............................. 4·00
2965   **2177**   (1st) silver, greenish yellow, magenta,
                     new blue and black .... 1·25   90
2966   **2178**   (1st) silver, greenish yellow, magenta,
                     new blue and black .... 1·25   90
2967   **2179**   90p. silver, greenish yellow, magenta,
                     new blue and black .... 2·25   2·25
                     a. Horiz strip of 3. Nos. 2967/9 .... 7·00   7·00
                     b. Booklet pane. Nos. 2967/9 with
                        margins all round............................. 7·00
2968   **2180**   90p. silver, greenish yellow, magenta,
                     new blue and black .... 2·25   2·25
2969   **2181**   90p. silver, greenish yellow, magenta,
                     new blue and black .... 2·25   2·25
Set of 6 .... 10·00   10·00
Set of 2 Gutter Strips of 6 .... 21·00

Set of 2 Traffic Light Gutter Blocks of 12	42·00	
First Day Cover (Tallents House)		11·00
First Day Cover (Portsmouth)		11·00
Presentation Pack (P.O. Pack No. 431)	12·00	
PHQ Cards (set of 6) (327)	5·00	12·00

Nos. 2964/6 and 2967/9 were each printed together, *se-tenant*, as horizontal strips of three in sheets of 60 (2 panes 6×5).

Booklet panes Nos. 2964b and 2967b were from the £7·93 Royal Navy Uniforms booklet, No. DX47.

Special First Day of Postmarks

(Litho Cartor)

2009 (17 Sept). *Royal Navy Uniforms.* Booklet stamp. Design as Type 1518 (Jolly Roger flag from 2001 Submarine Centenary). Two phosphor bands. P 14½.

2970	**1518**	(1st) multicoloured....................	5·00	5·00
		a. Booklet pane. Nos. 2970 and		
		2581, each×2 with margins all		
		round		12·00

No. 2970 was only issued in the £7·93 Royal Navy Uniforms booklet, No. DX47.

2182 Fred Perry 1909–95 (lawn tennis champion)

2183 Henry Purcell 1659–95 (composer and musician)

2184 Sir Matt Busby 1909–94 (footballer and football manager)

2185 William Gladstone 1809–98 (statesman and Prime Minister)

2186 Mary Wollstonecraft 1759–97 (pioneering feminist)

2187 Sir Arthur Conan Doyle 1859–1930 (writer and creator of Sherlock Holmes)

2188 Donald Campbell 1921–67 (water speed record broken 1959)

2189 Judy Fryd 1909–2000 (campaigner and founder of MENCAP)

2190 Samuel Johnson 1709–84 (lexicographer, critic and poet)

2191 Sir Martin Ryle 1918–84 (radio survey of the Universe 1959)

(Des Together Design. Litho Cartor)

2009 (8 Oct). *Eminent Britons.* Phosphor background. P 14½.

2971	**2182**	(1st) silver, greenish yellow, magenta, new blue and black	1·25	90
		a. Horiz strip of 5. Nos. 2971/5	7·00	7·00
2972	**2183**	(1st) silver, greenish yellow, magenta, new blue and black	1·25	90
2973	**2184**	(1st) silver, greenish yellow, magenta, new blue and black	1·25	90
2974	**2185**	(1st) silver, greenish yellow, magenta, new blue and black	1·25	90
2975	**2186**	(1st) silver, greenish yellow, magenta, new blue and black	1·25	90
2976	**2187**	(1st) silver, greenish yellow, magenta, new blue and black	1·25	90
		a. Horiz strip of 5. Nos. 2976/80.......	7·00	7·00
2977	**2188**	(1st) silver, greenish yellow, magenta, new blue and black	1·25	90
2978	**2189**	(1st) silver, greenish yellow, magenta, new blue and black	1·25	90
2979	**2190**	(1st) silver, greenish yellow, magenta, new blue and black	1·25	90
2980	**2191**	(1st) silver, greenish yellow, magenta, new blue and black	1·25	90
Set of 10..			13·00	13·00
Set of 2 Gutter Strips of 10....................			28·00	
First Day Cover (Tallents House)				14·00
First Day Cover (Britannia, Bacup, Lancashire).................				12·00
Presentation Pack (P.O. Pack No. 432)..................			15·00	
PHQ Cards (set of 10) (328)			9·00	20·00

Nos. 2971/5 and 2976/80 were each printed together, *se-tenant*, as horizontal strips of five stamps in sheets of 50 (2 panes 5×5).

No. 2980 includes the "EUROPA" emblem.

Special First Day of Issue Postmarks

2192 Canoe Slalom

2193 Paralympic Games Archery

2194 Athletics: Track

2195 Diving

2196 Paralympic Games Boccia

2197 Judo

Special First Day of Issue Postmarks

22.10.2009

22.10.2009

2198 Paralympic Games Dressage

2199 Badminton

2202 Angel playing Lute (William Morris), Church of St. James, Staveley, Kendal, Cumbria

2203 Madonna and Child (Henry Holiday), Church of Ormesby St. Michael, Great Yarmouth, Norfolk

2204 Angel playing Lute (William Morris), Church of St. James, Staveley, Kendal, Cumbria

2200 Weightlifting

2201 Basketball

2205 Joseph (Henry Holiday), Parish Church of St. Michael, Minehead, Somerset

2206 Madonna and Child (Henry Holiday), Church of St. Michael, Ormesby, Great Yarmouth, Norfolk

2207 Wise Man (Sir Edward Burne-Jones), Church of St. Mary the Virgin, Rye, East Sussex

2208 Shepherd (Henry Holiday), St. Mary's Church, Upavon, Wiltshire

(Des John Royle (2981), George Hardie (2982), Nathalie Guinamard (2983), Julian Opie (2984), David Doyle (2985), Paul Slater (2986), Andrew Davidson (2987), David Holmes (2988), Guy Billout (2989), Huntley Muir (2990) and Studio David Hillman (all). Litho Cartor)

2009 (22 Oct)–**2012**. *Olympic and Paralympic Games, London (2012)* (1st issue). 'All-over' phosphor. P 14½.

2981	**2192**	(1st) grey, greenish yellow, bright magenta, new blue and black......	1·25	90
		a. Horiz strip of 5. Nos. 2981/5	7·00	7·00
2982	**2193**	(1st) grey, greenish yellow, bright magenta, new blue and black......	1·25	90
		b. Booklet pane. Nos. 2982 and 2987 with margins all round (27.7.12)	3·00	
2983	**2194**	(1st) grey, greenish yellow, bright magenta, new blue and black......	1·25	90
		b. Booklet pane. Nos. 2983 and 3104 with margins all round (27.7.12)	3·00	
2984	**2195**	(1st) grey, greenish yellow, bright magenta, new blue and black......	1·25	90
		b. Booklet pane. Nos. 2984 and 3196 with margins all round (27.7.12)	3·00	
2985	**2196**	(1st) grey, greenish yellow, bright magenta, new blue and black......	1·25	90
2986	**2197**	(1st) grey, greenish yellow, bright magenta, new blue and black......	1·25	90
		a. Horiz strip of 5. Nos. 2986/90.......	7·00	7·00
2987	**2198**	(1st) grey, greenish yellow, bright magenta, new blue and black......	1·25	90
2988	**2199**	(1st) grey, greenish yellow, bright magenta, new blue and black......	1·25	90
2989	**2200**	(1st) grey, greenish yellow, bright magenta, new blue and black......	1·25	90
2990	**2201**	(1st) grey, greenish yellow, bright magenta, new blue and black......	1·25	90
Set of 10...			13·00	13·00
Set of 2 Gutter Strips of 10..................................			27·00	
First Day Cover (Tallents House)				14·00
First Day Cover (Badminton, Glos)				14·00
Presentation Pack (P.O. Pack No. M18)...............			15·00	
PHQ Cards (set of 10) (OXPG1)			9·00	20·00

Nos. 2981/5 and 2986/90 were each printed together, *se-tenant*, as horizontal strips of five stamps in sheets of 50 (2 panes 5×5).

(Des Andrew Ross. Gravure De La Rue)

2009 (3 Nov). *Christmas. Stained Glass Windows.* One centre band (**2202**) or two phosphor bands (others). P 14½×14 (with one elliptical hole in each vert side).

(a) Self-adhesive

2991	**2202**	(2nd) gold, bright magenta, greenish yellow, new blue, and black..........	1·00	60
		a. Booklet pane. No. 2991×12	11·00	
2992	**2203**	(1st) gold, bright magenta, greenish yellow, new blue and black..........	1·25	85
		a. Booklet pane. No. 2992×12	14·00	
2993	**2204**	(2nd Large) gold, bright magenta, greenish yellow, new blue and black..	1·50	1·10
2994	**2205**	56p. gold, bright magenta, greenish yellow, new blue and black..........	1·40	1·40
2995	**2206**	(1st Large) gold, bright magenta, greenish yellow, new blue and black..	2·00	1·25
2996	**2207**	90p. gold, bright magenta, greenish yellow, new blue and black..........	2·25	2·25
2997	**2208**	£1·35 gold, bright magenta, greenish yellow, new blue and black..........	3·50	3·00
Set of 7...			12·00	11·00
First Day Cover (Tallents House)				11·00
First Day Cover (Bethlehem, Llandeilo)................				12·00
Presentation Pack (P.O. Pack No. 433).................			14·00	
PHQ Cards (set of 8) (328)...................................			6·00	16·00

(b) Ordinary gum.

MS2998 115×102 mm. As Nos. 2991/7................		12·00	11·00
First Day Cover (Tallents House)			12·00
First Day Cover (Bethlehem, Llandeilo)................			12·00

The eight PHQ cards show the seven stamps and **MS**2998.

The 2nd class, 1st class, 56p and 90p stamps were also issued together in sheets of 20 (No. LS67), sold for £9, containing eight 2nd class, eight 1st class, two 56p and two 90p stamps, each stamp accompanied by a *se-tenant* label (LS67).

Separate sheets of 20 2nd, 20 1st, ten 1st, ten 56p and ten 90p were available with personal photographs from Royal Mail, Edinburgh. These were sold at £7·50 for ten 1st, £9·50 for 20 2nd or ten 56p or £13·50 for 20 1st or ten 90p.

All these sheets were printed in lithography by Cartor and had the backing paper around the stamps retained.

For the 2nd class stamp with ordinary gum see No. 3186a.

Special First Day of Issue Postmarks

For Nos. U2981/6 see Decimal Machin Definitives section.

Collectors Pack

2009 (3 Nov). Comprises Nos. 2887/96, 2898/**MS**2904, 2916/**MS**2941, 2944/9, **MS**2954, 2958/69, 2971/97, **MS**S157 and **MS**W147.
CP2998a Collectors Pack £120

Post Office Yearbook

2009 (3 Nov). Comprises Nos. 2887/96, 2898/**MS**2904, 2916/**MS**2941, 2944/9, **MS**2954, 2958/69 and 2971/97, **MS**S157 and **MS**W147.
YB2998a Yearbook £130

Miniature Sheet Collection

2009 (3 Nov). Comprises Nos. **MS**2904, **MS**2930, **MS**2941, **MS**2954, **MS**2998, **MS**S157 and **MS**W147.
MS2998a Miniature Sheet Collection..................................... 70·00

2209 *The Division Bell* (Pink Floyd)

2210 *A Rush of Blood to the Head* (Coldplay)

2211 *Parklife* (Blur)

2212 *Power Corruption and Lies* (New Order)

2213 *Let It Bleed* (Rolling Stones)

2214 *London Calling* (The Clash)

2215 *Tubular Bells* (Mike Oldfield)

2216 *IV* (Led Zeppelin)

2217 *Screamadelica* (Primal Scream)

2218 *The Rise and Fall of Ziggy Stardust and the Spiders from Mars* (David Bowie)

(Des Studio Dempsey)

2010 (7 Jan). *Classic Album Covers* (1st issue). 'All-over' phosphor.

(a) Self-adhesive. Gravure De La Rue. Die-cut P 14½ (interrupted)

2999	**2209**	(1st)	black, new blue, greenish yellow, bright magenta and silver..............	1·25	90
			a. Horiz strip of 5. Nos. 2999/3003...	7·00	—
3000	**2210**	(1st)	black, new blue, greenish yellow, bright magenta and silver..............	1·25	90
3001	**2211**	*(1st)	black, new blue, greenish yellow, bright magenta and silver..............	1·25	90
3002	**2212**	(1st)	black, new blue, greenish yellow, bright magenta and silver..............	1·25	90
3003	**2213**	(1st)	black, new blue, greenish yellow, bright magenta and silver..............	1·25	90
3004	**2214**	(1st)	black, new blue, greenish yellow, bright magenta and silver..............	1·25	90
			a. Horiz strip of 5. Nos. 3004/8	7·00	—
3005	**2215**	(1st)	black, new blue, greenish yellow, bright magenta and silver..............	1·25	90
3006	**2216**	(1st)	black, new blue, greenish yellow, bright magenta and silver..............	1·25	90
3007	**2217**	(1st)	black, new blue, greenish yellow, bright magenta and silver..............	1·25	90
3008	**2218**	(1st)	black, new blue, greenish yellow, bright magenta and silver..............	1·25	90
Set of 10..				13·00	13·00
First Day Cover (Tallents House)					14·00
First Day Cover (Oldfield, Keighley)					15·00
Presentation Pack (P.O. Pack No. 435)..........................				15·00	
PHQ Cards (set of 10) (330)..				9·00	22·00

Nos. 2999/3003 and 3004/8 were each printed together, as horizontal strips of five stamps in sheets of 50 (2 panes of 25).

The right-hand edges of Nos. 2999/3008 are all cut around to show the vinyl disc protruding from the open edge of the album cover.

Special First Day of Issue Postmarks

2010 (7 Jan). *Classic Album Covers* (2nd issue). 'All-over' phosphor. Litho Cartor. P 14½ (interrupted).

3009	**2213**	(1st)	multicoloured............................	2·40	2·40
			a. Booklet pane. Nos. 3009/14	14·00	
3010	**2216**	(1st)	multicoloured............................	2·40	2·40
3011	**2218**	(1st)	multicoloured............................	2·40	2·40
3012	**2212**	(1st)	multicoloured............................	2·40	2·40
3013	**2217**	(1st)	multicoloured............................	2·40	2·40
3014	**2209**	(1st)	multicoloured............................	2·40	2·40
3015	**2215**	(1st)	multicoloured............................	2·40	2·40
			a. Booklet pane. Nos. 3015/18	10·00	
3016	**2214**	(1st)	multicoloured............................	2·40	2·40
3017	**2211**	(1st)	multicoloured............................	2·40	2·40
3018	**2210**	(1st)	multicoloured............................	2·40	2·40
3009/18 Set of 10..				22·00	22·00
MS3019 223×189 mm. Nos. 3009/18........................				35·00	35·00
First Day Cover (Tallents House)					32·00
First Day Cover (Oldfield, Keighley)					32·00

Nos. 3009/18 were only issued in the £8·06 Classic Album Covers booklet, No. DX48 and in No. **MS**3019.

The right-hand edges of Nos. 3009/18 and the miniature sheet **MS**3019 are all cut around in an imperforate section to show the vinyl disc protruding from the open edge of the album cover.

A miniature sheet containing No. 3014×10 The Division Bell (Pink Floyd) was issued on 6 March 2010 and sold for £4·75 per sheet.

(Gravure Walsall)

2010 (7 Jan–25 Feb). *Olympic and Paralympic Games, London* (2012) (2nd issue). Booklet stamps. Designs as Nos. 2982/3, 2986 and 2990. Self-adhesive. 'All-over' phosphor. Die-cut P 14½.

3020	**2197**	(1st)	multicoloured............................	4·75	4·75
			a. Booklet pane. Nos. 3020/1 and U2949×4......................	13·00	

3021	**2193**	(1st) multicoloured..................................	4·75	4·75
3022	**2194**	(1st) multicoloured (25 Feb)	4·75	4·75
		a. Booklet pane. Nos. 3022/3 and		
		U2965×4....................................	13·00	
3023	**2201**	(1st) multicoloured (25 Feb)	4·75	4·75
Set of 4			17·00	17·00

Nos. 3020/1 and 3022/3 were only issued in separate booklets, Nos. PM21/2, each sold for £2·34.

2219 Smilers (*Illustration reduced. Actual size 124×71 mm*)

(Des Hat-trick Design. Litho Cartor)

2010 (26 Jan). *Business and Consumer Smilers.* Sheet 124×71 mm. Multicoloured. Two phosphor bands. P 14½×14 (with one elliptical hole in each vertical side).

MS3024	**2219**	(1st) Propellor driven airplane (Andrew Davidson); (1st) Vintage sports roadster (Andrew Davidson); (1st) Recreation of crown seal (Neil Oliver); (1st) Birthday cake (Annabel Wright); (1st) Steam locomotive (Andrew Davidson); (1st) Ocean liner (Andrew Davidson); (1st) As Type **2112**; (1st) Birthday present (Annabel Wright); (Europe up to 20 grams) Bird carrying envelope (Lucy Davey); (Worldwide up to 20 grams) "Hello" in plane vapour trail (Lucy Davey)................................	17·00	17·00
First Day Cover (Tallents House)				19·00
First Day Cover (Happy Valley, Malvern)				19·00
Presentation Pack (P.O. Pack No. M19)			19·00	
PHQ Cards (set of 11) (D31)...			9·00	22·00

MS3024 was sold for £4·58.

The eleven PHQ cards show the ten individual stamps and the complete miniature sheet.

Stamps in designs as within **MS**3024 but self-adhesive were available printed together, *se-tenant*, in sheets of 20 containing two of each design with greetings labels (No. LS70), sold for £9·70 per sheet.

The (1st) birthday cake, (1st) birthday present, Europe and Worldwide designs were also available in separate sheets with personal photographs.

A stamp as the crown seal design in **MS**3024 but self-adhesive was issued on 15 September 2011 in sheets of 20 with postmark labels for the 350th Anniversary of the Postmark, No. LS78 sold for £9·50.

The other 1st class designs were for the business customised service.

Stamps as the (1st) birthday cake (×4), (1st) birthday present (×4), Europe bird carrying envelope (×2) and Worldwide "Hello" in plane vapour trail (×2) designs but self-adhesive were issued together with Nos. 2572, 2674, 2693 and 2821/3 on 8 May 2010 in sheets of 20 stamps with *se-tenant* greetings labels printed in lithography by Cartor, No. LS73, and sold for £10 per sheet.

Special First Day of Issue Postmarks

2220 Girlguiding UK (*Illustration reduced. Actual size 190×67 mm*)

(Des Together Design. Litho Cartor)

2010 (2 Feb). *Centenary of Girlguiding.* Sheet 190×67 mm. Multicoloured. Phosphor background. P 14×14½.

MS3025	**2220**	(1st) Rainbows; 56p. Brownies; 81p. Guides; 90p. Senior Section members............................	8·00	7·00
First Day Cover (Tallents House)				8·00
First Day Cover (Guide, Blackburn)				8·00
Presentation Pack (P.O. Pack No. 436).........................			12·00	
PHQ Cards (set of 5) (331)...			4·00	10·00

The five PHQ cards show the four individual stamps and the complete miniature sheet.

Special First Day of Issue Postmarks

2221 Sir Robert Boyle (chemistry)	**2222** Sir Isaac Newton (optics)

2223 Benjamin Franklin (electricity)	**2224** Edward Jenner (pioneer of smallpox vaccination)

2225 Charles Babbage (computing)	**2226** Alfred Russel Wallace (theory of evolution)

2227 Joseph Lister (antiseptic surgery)	**2228** Ernest Rutherford (atomic structure)

2229 Dorothy Hodgkin (crystallography)	**2230** Sir Nicholas Shackleton (earth sciences)

(Des Hat-trick Design. Litho Cartor)

2010 (25 Feb). *350th Anniv of the Royal Society.* 'All-over' phosphor. *P* 14½.

3026	**2221**	(1st) greenish yellow, bright magenta, new blue and black	1·25	90
		a. Block of 10. Nos. 3026/35	15·00	13·00
		b. Booklet pane. Nos. 3026, 3030/1 and 3035 with margins all round	5·00	
3027	**2222**	(1st) greenish yellow, bright magenta, new blue and black	1·25	90
		a. Booklet pane. Nos. 3027/8 and 3033×2 with margins all round	5·00	
3028	**2223**	(1st) greenish yellow, bright magenta, new blue and black	1·25	90
3029	**2224**	(1st) greenish yellow, bright magenta, new blue and black	1·25	90
		a. Booklet pane. Nos. 3029×2, 3032 and 3034 with margins all round	5·00	
3030	**2225**	(1st) greenish yellow, bright magenta, new blue and black	1·25	90
3031	**2226**	(1st) greenish yellow, bright magenta, new blue and black	1·25	90
3032	**2227**	(1st) greenish yellow, bright magenta, new blue and black	1·25	90
3033	**2228**	(1st) greenish yellow, bright magenta, new blue and black	1·25	90
3034	**2229**	(1st) greenish yellow, bright magenta, new blue and black	1·25	90
3035	**2230**	(1st) greenish yellow, bright magenta, new blue and black	1·25	90
Set of 10			15·00	13·00
Gutter Block of 20			32·00	
First Day Cover (Tallents House)				14·00
First Day Cover (London SW1)				14·00
Presentation Pack (P.O. Pack No. 437)			17·00	
PHQ Cards (set of 10) (332)			9·00	20·00

Nos. 3026/35 were printed together, *se-tenant*, as blocks of ten (5×2) in sheets of 60 (2 panes of 30).

Booklet panes Nos. 3026b/7a and 3029a come from the £7·72 The Royal Society booklet, No. DX49.

Special First Day of Issue Postmarks

2231 "Pixie" (mastiff cross)   **2232** "Button"

2233 "Herbie" (mongrel)   **2234** "Mr. Tumnus"

2235 "Tafka" (border collie)   **2236** "Boris" (bulldog cross)

2237 "Casey" (lurcher)   **2238** "Tigger"

2239 "Leonard" (Jack Russell cross)   **2240** "Tia" (terrier cross)

(Des CDT Design. Litho Cartor)

2010 (11 Mar). *150th Anniv of Battersea Dogs and Cats Home.* Phosphor background. *P* 14½.

3036	**2231**	(1st) gold, greenish yellow, bright magenta, new blue and black	1·25	90
		a. Block of 10. Nos. 3036/45	15·00	13·00
3037	**2232**	(1st) gold, greenish yellow, bright magenta, new blue and black	1·25	90
3038	**2233**	(1st) gold, greenish yellow, bright magenta, new blue and black	1·25	90
3039	**2234**	(1st) gold, greenish yellow, bright magenta, new blue and black	1·25	90
3040	**2235**	(1st) gold, greenish yellow, bright magenta, new blue and black	1·25	90
3041	**2236**	(1st) gold, greenish yellow, bright magenta, new blue and black	1·25	90
3042	**2237**	(1st) gold, greenish yellow, bright magenta, new blue and black	1·25	90
3043	**2238**	(1st) gold, greenish yellow, bright magenta, new blue and black	1·25	90
3044	**2239**	(1st) gold, greenish yellow, bright magenta, new blue and black	1·25	90
3045	**2240**	(1st) gold, greenish yellow, bright magenta, new blue and black	1·25	90
Set of 10			15·00	13·00
Gutter Block of 20			32·00	
First Day Cover (Tallents House)				14·00
First Day Cover (London SW8)				14·00
Presentation Pack (P.O. Pack No. 438)			17·00	
PHQ Cards (set of 10) (333)			9·00	20·00

Nos. 3036/45 were printed together, *se-tenant*, as blocks of ten (5×2) in sheets of 60 (2 panes of 30).

Special First Day of Issue Postmarks

2241 James I (1406–37)   **2242** James II (1437–60)

2243 James III (1460–88)

2244 James IV (1488–1513)

2245 James V (1513–42)

2246 Mary (1542–67)

2247 James VI (1567–1625)

2248 The Age of the Stewarts (*Illustration reduced. Actual size 123×70 mm*)

(Des Atelier Works. Litho Cartor)

2010 (23 Mar). *Kings and Queens* (3rd issue). House of Stewart. Two phosphor bands. *P* 14.

3046	**2241**	(1st) indigo, greenish yellow, bright magenta, new blue and black.......	1·25	90
3047	**2242**	(1st) indigo, greenish yellow, bright magenta, new blue and black.......	1·25	90
3048	**2243**	(1st) indigo, greenish yellow, bright magenta, new blue and black.......	1·25	90
3049	**2244**	(62p.) indigo, greenish yellow, bright magenta, new blue and black.......	1·60	1·60
3050	**2245**	(62p.) indigo, greenish yellow, bright magenta, new blue and black.......	1·60	1·60
3051	**2246**	(81p.) indigo, greenish yellow, bright magenta, new blue and black.......	2·00	2·00
3052	**2247**	(81p.) indigo, greenish yellow, bright magenta, new blue and black.......	2·00	2·00
Set of 7			10·00	10·00
Set of 7 Gutter Pairs			21·00	
Set of 7 Traffic Light Gutter Blocks of 4			42·00	
First Day Cover (Tallents House)				11·00
First Day Cover (Linlithgow, West Lothian)				11·00
Presentation Pack (P.O. Pack No. 439) (3046/**MS**3053)			18·00	
PHQ Cards (set of 12) (334)			10·00	24·00

MS3053 123×70 mm. **2248** (1st) Foundation of the University of St. Andrews, 1413; (1st) Foundation of the College of Surgeons, Edinburgh, 1505; 81p. Foundation of Court of Session, 1532; 81p. John Knox (Reformation, 1559)...... 6·50 / 6·50

First Day Cover (Tallents House)		7·50
First Day Cover (Linlithgow, West Lothian)		7·50

The complete miniature sheet is shown on one of the twelve PHQ cards with the others depicting individual stamps including those from **MS**3053.

Special First Day of Issue Postmarks

2249 Humpback Whale (*Megaptera novaeangliae*)

2250 Wildcat (*Felis silvestris*)

2251 Brown Long-eared Bat (*Plecotus auritus*)

2252 Polecat (*Mustela putorius*)

2253 Sperm Whale (*Physeter macrocephalus*)

2254 Water Vole (*Arvicola terrestris*)

2255 Greater Horseshoe Bat (*Rhinolophus ferrumequinum*)

2256 Otter (*Lutra lutra*)

2257 Dormouse (*Muscardinus avellanarius*)

2258 Hedgehog (*Erinaceus europaeus*)

(Des Jason Godfrey. Litho Cartor)

2010 (13 Apr). *Action for Species* (4th series). Mammals. 'All-over' phosphor. *P* 14½.

3054	**2249**	(1st) greenish yellow, bright magenta, new blue and black	1·25	1·00
		a. Block of 10. Nos. 3054/63	14·00	12·00
3055	**2250**	(1st) greenish yellow, bright magenta, new blue and black	1·25	1·00
3056	**2251**	(1st) greenish yellow, bright magenta, new blue and black	1·25	1·00

3057	**2252**	(1st) greenish yellow, bright magenta, new blue and black	1·25	1·00
3058	**2253**	(1st) greenish yellow, bright magenta, new blue and black	1·25	1·00
3059	**2254**	(1st) greenish yellow, bright magenta, new blue and black	1·25	1·00
3060	**2255**	(1st) greenish yellow, bright magenta, new blue and black	1·25	1·00
3061	**2256**	(1st) greenish yellow, bright magenta, new blue and black	1·25	1·00
3062	**2257**	(1st) greenish yellow, bright magenta, new blue and black	1·25	1·00
3063	**2258**	(1st) greenish yellow, bright magenta, new blue and black	1·25	1·00

Set of 10..	14·00	12·00
Gutter Block of 20...................................	30·00	
First Day Cover (Tallents House)		13·00
First Day Cover (Batts Corner, Farnham)...		13·00
Presentation Pack (P.O. Pack No. 440)...	16·00	
PHQ Cards (set of 10) (335)..................	9·00	20·00

Nos. 3054/63 were printed together, *se-tenant*, as blocks of ten (5×2) in sheets of 60 (2 panes of 30).

Special First Day of Issue Postmarks

No. 3064, T **2259** is vacant.

2260 King George V and Queen Elizabeth II (1st); Two portraits of King George V (£1) (*Illustration reduced. Actual size 141×74 mm*)

(Des Sedley Place. Litho Cartor)

2010 (6 May). *London 2010 Festival of Stamps and Centenary of Accession of King George V* (1st issue). 'All-over' phosphor. P 14½×14.

MS3065 141×74 mm **2260** (1st) rosine; £1 blackish brown, grey-brown and silver	4·50	4·50
First Day Cover (Tallents House)		5·50
First Day Cover (Sandringham, Norfolk)......		5·50

A miniature sheet as No. **MS**3065 but inscr 'BUSINESS DESIGN CENTRE, LONDON 8–15 MAY 2010' along the top right margin was only available at London 2010 Festival of Stamps (Price £15).

The eight PHQ cards depict the individual stamps from **MS**3065 and **MS**3072 and the complete miniature sheets.

Special First Day of Issue Postmarks

2261 King George V and Queen Elizabeth II

2262 1924 British Empire Exhibition 1½d. Brown Stamp

2263 1924 British Empire Exhibition 1d. Scarlet Stamp

2264 Two Portraits of King George V

2265 1913 £1 Green 'Sea Horses' Design Stamp

2266 1913 10s. Blue 'Sea Horses' Design Stamp

2267 (*Illustration reduced. Actual size 115×90 mm*)

(Des Sedley Place. Litho Cartor (Nos. 3066 and 3069) or recess and litho Enschedé (others))

2010 (6–8 May). *London 2010 Festival of Stamps and Centenary of Accession of King George V* (2nd issue). 'All-over' phosphor. P 14½×14.

3066	**2261**	(1st) rosine (6 May)...............................	1·25	1·00
		a. Booklet pane. Nos. 3066 and 3069, each×3 with margins all round (8 May)	10·00	
3067	**2262**	(1st) multicoloured (8 May)....................	1·25	1·00
		a. Booklet pane. Nos. 3067/8, each×2	4·50	
3068	**2263**	(1st) multicoloured (8 May)....................	1·25	1·00
3069	**2264**	£1 blackish brown, grey-brown and silver (8 May)	2·50	2·50
3070	**2265**	£1 multicoloured (8 May)........................	2·50	2·50
		a. Booklet pane. Nos. 3070/1 with margins all round	4·50	
3071	**2266**	£1 multicoloured (8 May)........................	2·50	2·50
3066/71		*Set of 6*	10·00	10·00
Gutter Pair (No. 3066)			3·00	
MS3072 115×90 mm **2267** Nos. 3067/8 and 3070/1 (8 May)			7·50	7·50
First Day Cover (**MS**3072) (Tallents House)				8·50
First Day Cover (**MS**3072) (London N1)				8·50
Presentation Pack (**MS**3065 and **MS**3072) (P.O. Pack No. 441)..			13·00	
PHQ Cards (set of 8) (336)...................................			7·00	16·00

No. 3066 was also issued as a sheet stamp on 6 May 2010.

Nos. 3066/71 come from the £11·15 "King George V" booklet, No. DX50.

Nos. 3066 and 3069 also come from **MS**3065, issued on 6 May 2010.

Nos. 3067/8 and 3070/1 also come from **MS**3072, issued on 8 May 2010.

For presentation pack and PHQ cards for No. **MS**3072 see under **MS**3065.

The thirteen PHQ cards depict Nos. 3074/85 and the complete miniature sheet **MS**3086.

Booklet panes Nos. 3074a and 3076a come from the £9·76 "Britain Alone" booklet, No. DX51.

Special First Day of Issue Postmarks

For No. **MS**3073 see Decimal Machin Definitives section

2269 Winston Churchill

2270 Land Girl

2271 Home Guard

2272 Evacuees

2273 Air Raid Wardens

2274 Woman working in Factory

2275 Royal Broadcast by Princess Elizabeth and Princess Margaret

2276 Fire Service

(Des Why Not Associates. Litho Cartor)

2010 (13 May). *Britain Alone* (1st issue). 'All-over' phosphor. *P* 14½.

3074	**2269**	(1st) pale stone, pale bistre and black.	1·25	1·00
		a. Booklet pane. Nos. 3074/5 and 3079/80 with margins all round...	5·50	
3075	**2270**	(1st) pale stone, pale bistre and black.	1·25	1·00
3076	**2271**	60p. pale stone, pale bistre and black.	1·50	1·50
		a. Booklet pane. Nos. 3076/8 and 3081...	6·50	
3077	**2272**	60p. pale stone, pale bistre and black.	1·50	1·50
3078	**2273**	67p. pale stone, pale bistre and black.	1·70	1·70
3079	**2274**	67p. pale stone, pale bistre and black.	1·70	1·70
3080	**2275**	97p. pale stone, pale bistre and black.	2·40	2·40
3081	**2276**	97p. pale stone, pale bistre and black.	2·40	2·40
Set of 8			12·00	12·00
Set of 8 Gutter Pairs			25·00	
First Day Cover (Tallents House)				13·00
First Day Cover (Dover, Kent)				13·00
Presentation Pack (P.O. Pack No. 442) (3074/81 and MS3086)			25·00	
PHQ Cards (set of 13) (337)			11·00	29·00

Special First Day of Issue Postmarks

2277 Evacuation of British Soldiers from Dunkirk

2278 Vessels from Upper Thames Patrol in 'Operation Little Ships'

2279 Rescued Soldiers on Board Royal Navy Destroyer, Dover

2280 Steamship and Other Boat loaded with Troops

2281 Evacuation of British Troops from Dunkirk, 1940
(*Illustration reduced. Actual size* 115×89 *mm*)

(Des Why Not Associates. Litho Cartor)

2010 (13 May). *Britain Alone* (2nd issue). 'All-over' phosphor. *P* 14½.

3082	**2277**	(1st) pale stone, pale bistre and black.	2·00	2·00
		a. Booklet pane. Nos. 3082/5 with margins all round	12·00	
3083	**2278**	60p. pale stone, pale bistre and black.	3·00	3·00
3084	**2279**	88p. pale stone, pale bistre and black.	4·00	4·00
3085	**2280**	97p. pale stone, pale bistre and black.	4·00	4·00
3082/5 Set of 4			12·00	12·00
MS3086 115×89 mm. **2281** Nos. 3082/5			7·50	7·50
First Day Cover (**MS**3086) (Tallents House)				8·50
First Day Cover (**MS**3086) (Dover, Kent)				8·50

Nos. 3082/5 were only issued in the £9·76 "Britain Alone" booklet, No. DX51, and in No. **MS**3086.

For Nos. U3001/20 see Decimal Machin Definitives section

2282 James I (1603–25)

2283 Charles I (1625–49)

2284 Charles II (1660–85)

2285 James II (1685–8)

2286 William III (1689–1702)

2287 Mary II (1689–94)

2288 Anne (1702–14)

2289 The Age of the Stuarts (*Illustration reduced. Actual size 123×70 mm*)

(Des Atelier Works. Litho Cartor)

2010 (15 June). *Kings and Queens* (4th issue). House of Stuart. Two phosphor bands. P 14.

3087	**2282**	(1st) reddish-brown, greenish yellow, bright magenta, new blue and black	1·25	1·00
3088	**2283**	(1st) reddish-brown, greenish yellow, bright magenta, new blue and black	1·25	1·00
3089	**2284**	60p. reddish-brown, greenish yellow, bright magenta, new blue and black	1·50	1·50
3090	**2285**	60p. reddish-brown, greenish yellow, bright magenta, new blue and black	1·50	1·50
3091	**2286**	67p. reddish-brown, greenish yellow, bright magenta, new blue and black	1·70	1·70

3092	**2287**	67p. reddish-brown, greenish yellow, bright magenta, new blue and black	1·70	1·70
3093	**2288**	88p. reddish-brown, greenish yellow, bright magenta, new blue and black	2·25	2·25
Set of 7			10·00	10·00
Set of 7 Gutter Pairs			21·00	
Set of 7 Traffic Light Gutter Blocks of 4			42·00	
First Day Cover (Tallents House)				11·00
First Day Cover (Royal Oak, Filey)				11·00
Presentation Pack (P.O. Pack No. 443) (3087/93 and MS3094)			19·00	
PHQ Cards (set of 12) (338)			10·00	24·00

MS3094 123×70 mm. **2289** (1st) William Harvey (discovery of blood circulation, 1628); 60p. Civil War Battle of Naseby, 1645; 88p. John Milton (*Paradise Lost*, 1667); 97p. Castle Howard (John Vanbrugh, 1712).. 7·50 7·50

First Day Cover (Tallents House)		8·50
First Day Cover (Royal Oak, Filey)		8·50

The complete miniature sheet is shown on one of the twelve PHQ cards with the others depicting individual stamps including those from **MS**3094.

Special First Day of Issue Postmarks

(Gravure Walsall)

2010 (15 June). *Mammals*. Booklet stamps. Designs as Nos. 3061 and 3063. Self-adhesive. Die-cut P 14½.

3095	**2256**	(1st) multicoloured	4·75	4·25
		a. Booklet pane. Nos. 3095/6 and No. U2965×4	13·00	
3096	**2258**	(1st) multicoloured	4·75	4·25

Nos. 3095/6 were only issued in booklets, No. PM23.

2290 Paralympic Games: Rowing

2291 Shooting

2292 Modern Pentathlon

2293 Taekwondo

2294 Cycling

2295 Paralympic Games: Table Tennis

2296 Hockey

2297 Football

2298 Paralympic Games: Goalball

2299 Boxing

(Des Marion Hill (3097), David Hillman (3098), Katherine Baxter (3099), James Fryer (3100), Matthew Dennis (3101), Michael Craig Martin (3102), Darren Hopes (3103), Alex Williamson (3104), Tobatron (3105), Stephen Ledwidge (3106), Studio David Hillman (all). Litho Cartor)

2010 (27 July). *Olympic and Paralympic Games, London (2012)* (3rd issue). 'All-over' phosphor. P 14½.

3097	**2290**	(1st) grey, greenish yellow, bright magenta, new blue and black.......	1·25	1·00
		a. Horiz strip of 5. Nos. 3097/101	6·25	5·50
3098	**2291**	(1st) grey, greenish yellow, bright magenta, new blue and black.......	1·25	1·00
3099	**2292**	(1st) grey, greenish yellow, bright magenta, new blue and black.......	1·25	1·00
3100	**2293**	(1st) grey, greenish yellow, bright magenta, new blue and black.......	1·25	1·00
3101	**2294**	(1st) grey, greenish yellow, bright magenta, new blue and black.......	1·25	1·00
3102	**2295**	(1st) grey, greenish yellow, bright magenta, new blue and black.......	1·25	1·00
		a. Horiz strip of 5. Nos. 3102/6	6·25	5·50
3103	**2296**	(1st) grey, greenish yellow, bright magenta, new blue and black.......	1·25	1·00
3104	**2297**	(1st) grey, greenish yellow, bright magenta, new blue and black.......	1·25	1·00
3105	**2298**	(1st) grey, greenish yellow, bright magenta, new blue and black.......	1·25	1·00
3106	**2299**	(1st) grey, greenish yellow, bright magenta, new blue and black.......	1·25	1·00

Set of 10........................ 12·00 10·00
Set of 2 Gutter Strips of 10 .... 25·00
First Day Cover (Tallents House) .... 11·00
First Day Cover (Rowington, Warwick) .... 11·00
Presentation Pack (P.O. Pack No. 444).................... 13·00
PHQ Cards (set of 10) (339)......... 9·00 20·00

Nos. 3097/101 and 3102/6 were each printed together, *se-tenant*, in horizontal strips of five stamps in sheets of 50 (2 panes 5×5).

Special First Day of Issue Postmarks

(Gravure Walsall)

2010 (27 July - 12 Oct). *Olympic and Paralympic Games, London (2012)* (4th issue). Booklet stamps. Designs as Nos. 3097, 3101/2 and 3104. Self-adhesive. 'All-over' phosphor. Die-cut perf 14½.

3107	**2290**	(1st) multicoloured	3·75	3·25
		a. Booklet pane. Nos. 3107/8 and Nos. U2965×4..................	12·00	
3108	**2295**	(1st) multicoloured	3·75	3·25
3108a	**2297**	(1st) multicoloured (12 Oct)..................	3·75	3·25
		ab. Booklet pane. Nos. 3108a/b and U2965×4..................	12·00	
3108b	**2294**	(1st) multicoloured (12 Oct)..................	3·75	3·25

Set of 4 .... 13·00 12·00

Nos. 3107/8 and 3108a/b were only issued in two separate stamp booklets, Nos. PM24 and PM26, each originally sold for £2·46.

2300 LMS Coronation Class Locomotive, Euston Station, 1938

2301 BR Class 9F Locomotive *Evening Star*, Midsomer Norton, 1962

2302 GWR King Class Locomotive *King William IV*, near Teignmouth, 1935

2303 LNER Class A1 Locomotive *Royal Lancer*, 1929

2304 SR King Arthur Class Locomotive *Sir Mador de la Porte*, Bournmouth Central Station, 1935–9

2305 LMS NCC Class WT No. 2, Larne Harbour, c. 1947

(Des Delaney Design Consultants. Gravure De La Rue)

2010 (19 Aug). *Great British Railways.* 'All-over' phosphor. P 14.

3109	**2300**	(1st) gold, bluish grey and black............	1·25	1·00
3110	**2301**	(1st) gold, bluish grey and black............	1·25	1·00
3111	**2302**	67p. gold, bluish grey and black............	1·70	1·70
3112	**2303**	67p. gold, bluish grey and black............	1·70	1·70
3113	**2304**	97p. gold, bluish grey and black............	2·50	2·50
3114	**2305**	97p. gold, bluish grey and black............	2·50	2·50

Set of 6 .... 10·00 10·00
Set of 6 Gutter Pairs................ 21·00
First Day Cover (Tallents House) .... 11·00
First Day Cover (Swindon).......................... 11·00
Presentation Pack (P.O. Pack No. 445)................ 12·00
PHQ Cards (set of 6) (340) .... 5·00 12·00

Special First Day of Issue Postmarks

2306 Heart-regulating Beta Blockers (Sir James Black, 1962)

2307 Antibiotic Properties of Penicillin (Sir Alexander Fleming, 1928)

2308 Total Hip Replacement Operation (Sir John Charnley, 1962)

2309 Artificial Lens Implant Surgery (Sir Harold Ridley, 1949)

2310 Malaria Parasite transmitted by Mosquitoes (proved by Sir Ronald Ross, 1897)

2311 Computed Tomography Scanner (Sir Godfrey Hounsfield, 1971)

(Des Howard Brown. Litho Cartor)

2010 (16 Sept). *Medical Breakthroughs*. 'All-over' phosphor. P 14×14½.

3115	**2306**	(1st) grey-black, greenish yellow, bright magenta, new blue and black	1·25	1·00
3116	**2307**	58p. grey-black, greenish yellow, bright magenta, new blue and black	1·50	1·50
3117	**2308**	60p. grey-black, greenish yellow, bright magenta, new blue and black	1·50	1·50
3118	**2309**	67p. grey-black, greenish yellow, bright magenta, new blue and black	1·70	1·70
3119	**2310**	88p. grey-black, greenish yellow, bright magenta, new blue and black	2·25	2·25
3120	**2311**	97p. grey-black, greenish yellow, bright magenta, new blue and black	2·50	2·50
Set of 6			9·50	9·50
Set of 6 Gutter Pairs			20·00	
First Day Cover (Tallents House)				11·00
First Day Cover (Paddington, London W2)				11·00
Presentation Pack (P.O. Pack No. 446)			11·00	
PHQ Cards (set of 6) (341)			5·00	12·50

First Day of Issue Postmarks

2312 Winnie the Pooh and Christopher Robin (*Now we are Six*)

2313 Winnie the Pooh and Piglet (*The House at Pooh Corner*)

2314 Winnie the Pooh and Rabbit (*Winnie the Pooh*)

2315 Winnie the Pooh and Eeyore (*Winnie the Pooh*)

2316 Winnie the Pooh and Friends (*Winnie the Pooh*)

2317 Winnie the Pooh and Tigger (*The House at Pooh Corner*)

2318 Winnie the Pooh

(Des Magpie Studio. Litho Cartor)

2010 (12 Oct). *Europa. Children's Books*. Winnie the Pooh by A. A. Milne. Book Illustrations by E. H. Shepard. 'All-over' phosphor. P 14×14½.

3121	**2312**	(1st) yellow-brown, pale stone and black	1·25	1·00
3122	**2313**	58p. yellow-brown, pale stone and black	1·40	1·40
3123	**2314**	60p. yellow-brown, pale stone and black	1·50	1·50
3124	**2315**	67p. yellow-brown, pale stone and black	1·70	1·70
3125	**2316**	88p. yellow-brown, pale stone and black	2·25	2·25
3126	**2317**	97p. yellow-brown, pale stone and black	2·40	2·40
Set of 6			9·50	9·50
Set of 6 Gutter Pairs			20·00	
First Day Cover (Tallents House)				11·00
First Day Cover (Hartfield, East Sussex)				11·00
Presentation Pack (P.O. Pack No. 447) (Nos. 3121/6 and MS3127)			19·00	
PHQ Cards (set of 11) (342)			9·00	22·00

MS3127 115×89 mm. **2318** (1st) Winnie the Pooh and Christopher Robin (from *Now we are Six*); 60p. Christopher Robin reads to Winnie the Pooh (from *Winnie the Pooh*); 88p. Winnie the Pooh and Christopher Robin sailing in umbrella (from *Winnie the Pooh*); 97p. Christopher Robin (putting on wellingtons) and Pooh (from *Winnie the Pooh*). P 14½.

	7·50	7·50
First Day Cover (Tallents House)		8·50
First Day Cover (Hartfield, East Sussex)		8·50

Stamps from **MS**3127 show lines from poem "We Too" by A. A. Milne: "Wherever I am, there's always Pooh" (1st); "There's always Pooh and Me. Whatever I do, he wants to do" (60p.); "Where are you going to-day?" says Pooh: "Well that's very odd 'cos I was too" (88p.); "Let's go together," says Pooh, says he. "Let's go together," says Pooh (97p.).

The 1st class value includes the "EUROPA" emblem.

The eleven PHQ cards show the six stamps, the four individual stamps within **MS**3127 and the complete miniature sheet.

Special First Day of Issue Postmarks

2319 Wallace and Gromit Carol singing

2320 Gromit posting Christmas Cards

2321 Wallace and Gromit Carol singing

2322 Wallace and Gromit decorating Christmas Tree

2323 Gromit posting Christmas Cards

2324 Gromit carrying Christmas Pudding

2325 Gromit wearing Oversized Sweater

(Gravure De La Rue)

2010 (2 Nov). *Christmas with Wallace and Gromit.* One centre band (3128) or two bands (others). P 14½×14 (with one elliptical hole in each vert side).

(a) Self-adhesive

3128	**2319**	(2nd) bright magenta, greenish yellow, new blue and black	1·00	75
		a. Booklet pane. No. 3128×12	11·00	
3129	**2320**	(1st) bright magenta, greenish yellow, new blue and black	1·25	1·00
		a. Booklet pane. No. 3129×12	14·00	
3130	**2321**	(2nd) bright magenta, greenish yellow, Large) new blue and black	1·50	1·50
3131	**2322**	60p. bright magenta, greenish yellow, new blue and black	1·50	1·50
3132	**2323**	(1st bright magenta, greenish yellow, Large) new blue and black	2·00	2·00
3133	**2324**	97p. bright magenta, greenish yellow, new blue and black	2·40	2·40
3134	**2325**	£1·46 bright magenta, greenish yellow, new blue and black	3·50	3·50
Set of 7			12·00	11·00
First Day Cover (Tallents House)				12·00
First Day Cover (Bethlehem, Llandeilo)				12·00
Presentation Pack (P.O. Pack No. 448)			14·00	
PHQ Cards (set of 8) (343)			6·00	17·00

(b) Ordinary gum

MS3135 115×102 mm. Nos. 3128/34		12·00	12·00
First Day Cover (Tallents House)			13·00
First Day Cover (Bethlehem, Llandeilo)			13·00

The eight PHQ cards show the seven individual stamps and the miniature sheet.

The 2nd class, 1st class, 60p and 97p stamps were also issued together in sheets of 20 (No. LS75) sold for £9·30, containing eight 2nd class, eight 1st class, two 60p and two 97p stamps, each stamp accompanied by a *se-tenant* label.

Separate sheets of 20 2nd, 20 1st, ten 1st, ten 60p and ten 97p were available with personal photographs on the labels from Royal Mail, Edinburgh. These were sold at £7·80 for ten 1st, £9·95 for 20 2nd or ten 60p, £13·95 for 20 1st and £14·50 for ten 97p.

All these sheets were printed in lithography by Cartor and had the backing paper around the stamps retained.

Collectors Pack

2010 (2 Nov). Comprises Nos. 2999/3008, **MS**3025/63, **MS**3065, **MS**3072, 3074/81, **MS**3086/94, 3097/106 and 3109/34.

CP3135a	Collectors Pack	£145

Post Office Yearbook

2010 (2 Nov). Comprises Nos. 2999/3008, **MS**3025/63, **MS**3065, **MS**3072, 3074/81, **MS**3086/94, 3097/106 and 3109/34.

YB3135a	Yearbook	£140

Miniature Sheet Collection

2010 (2 Nov). Comprises Nos. **MS**3024, **MS**3025, **MS**3053, **MS**3065, **MS**3072, **MS**3086, **MS**3094, **MS**3127 and **MS**3135.

MS3135a	Miniature Sheet Collection	60·00

2326 *Joe 90* **2327** *Captain Scarlet*

2328 Thunderbird 2 (*Thunderbirds*) **2329** *Stingray*

2330 *Fireball XL5* **2331** *Supercar*

2332 Thunderbird 4; Thunderbird 3; Thunderbird 2; Thunderbird 1 (*Illustration reduced. Actual size 116×89 mm*)

(Des GBH)

2011 (11 Jan). *F.A.B. The Genius of Gerry Anderson* (producer of TV programmes). 'All-over' phosphor.

(a) Ordinary gum. Litho Cartor. P 14

3136	**2326**	(1st) greenish yellow, bright magenta, new blue and black	1·25	1·00
		a. Horiz strip of 3. Nos. 3136/8	4·00	4·00
3137	**2327**	(1st) greenish yellow, bright magenta, new blue and black	1·25	1·00

3138	2328	(1st) greenish yellow, bright magenta, new blue and black	1·25	1·00
3139	2329	97p. brownish grey, greenish yellow, bright magenta, new blue and black	2·40	2·40
		a. Horiz strip of 3. Nos. 3139/41	8·00	8·00
3140	2330	97p. brownish grey, greenish yellow, bright magenta, new blue and black	2·40	2·40
3141	2331	97p. brownish grey, greenish yellow, bright magenta, new blue and black	2·40	2·40
Set of 6			11·00	11·00
Set of 2 Gutter Strips of 6			23·00	
First Day Cover (Tallents House)				12·00
First Day Cover (Slough)				12·00
Presentation Pack (P.O. Pack No. 450) (Nos. 3136/41 and **MS**3142)			19·00	
PHQ Cards (set of 11) (344)			9·00	22·00

(b) Microlenticular Cartor and Outer Aspect Ltd, New Zealand. P 14

MS3142		116×89 mm. **2332** 41p., 60p., 88p., 97p. multicoloured	8·00	8·00
MS3142a		Error imperforate	—	
First Day Cover (Tallents House)				9·00
First Day Cover (Slough)				9·00

(c) Self-adhesive. Gravure Walsall. Die-cut P 14

3143	2328	(1st) multicoloured	3·50	3·50
		a. Booklet pane. No. 3143×2 and U2965×4	12·00	

Nos. 3136/8 and 3139/41 were each printed together, *se-tenant*, as horizontal strips of three stamps in sheets of 60 (2 panes 6×5).

The stamps within **MS**3142 use microlenticular technology to show each vehicle's launch sequences when the miniature sheet is tilted. One example of **MS**3142a is known on a first day cover.

The complete miniature sheet is shown on one of the eleven PHQ cards with the others depicting individual stamps including those from **MS**3142.

No. 3143 was only issued in booklets, No. PM27, sold for £2·46.

Special First Day of Issue Postmarks

2333 Classic Locomotives of England

(Des Delaney Design Consultants. Litho Cartor)

2011 (1 Feb). *Classic Locomotives* (1st series). England. Sheet 180×74 mm. Multicoloured. 'All-over' phosphor. *P* 14.

MS3144	2333	(1st) BR Dean Goods No. 2532; 60p. Peckett R2 *Thor*; 88p. Lancashire and Yorkshire Railway 1093 No. 1100; 97p. BR WD No. 90662	7·50	7·50
First Day Cover (Tallents House)				8·50
First Day Cover (Liverpool)				8·50
Presentation Pack (P.O. Pack No. 451)			8·00	
PHQ Cards (set of 5) (345)			4·00	10·00

The five PHQ cards show the four individual stamps and the complete miniature sheet.

Special First Day of Issue Postmarks

2334 Oliver

2335 Blood Brothers

2336 We Will Rock You

2337 Spamalot

2338 Rocky Horror Show

2339 Me and My Girl

2340 Return to the Forbidden Planet

2341 Billy Elliot

(Des Webb and Webb. Litho Cartor)

2011 (24 Feb). *Musicals*. 'All-over' phosphor. P 14.

3145	2334	(1st) greenish yellow, bright magenta, new blue and black	1·25	1·00
3146	2335	(1st) greenish yellow, bright magenta, new blue and black	1·25	1·00
3147	2336	(1st) greenish yellow, bright magenta, new blue and black	1·25	1·00
3148	2337	(1st) greenish yellow, bright magenta, new blue and black	1·25	1·00
3149	2338	97p. greenish yellow, bright magenta, new blue and black	2·40	2·40
3150	2339	97p. greenish yellow, bright magenta, new blue and black	2·40	2·40
3151	2340	97p. greenish yellow, bright magenta, new blue and black	2·40	2·40
3152	2341	97p. greenish yellow, bright magenta, new blue and black	2·40	2·40
Set of 8			13·00	13·00
Set of 8 Gutter Pairs			27·00	
Set of 8 Traffic Light Gutter Pairs			29·00	
First Day Cover (Tallents House)				14·00
First Day Cover (Dancers End, Tring)				14·00
Presentation Pack (P.O. Pack No. 452)			15·00	
PHQ Cards (set of 8) (346)			6·00	17·00

Special First Day of Issue Postmarks

(Gravure Walsall)

2011 (24 Feb). *50th Anniv. of the British Heart Foundation.* Booklet stamp. Design as No. 3115. Self-adhesive. 'All-over' phosphor. Die-cut P 14×14½.

3153	**2306**	(1st) multicoloured	3·00	3·00
		a. Booklet pane. No. 3153×2 and U2965×4	9·00	

No. 3153 was only issued in booklets, No. PM28, sold for £2·46.

2342 Rincewind (Terry Pratchett's *Discworld*)

2343 Nanny Ogg (Terry Pratchett's *Discworld*)

2344 Michael Gambon as Dumbledore (J. K. Rowling's *Harry Potter*)

2345 Ralph Fiennes as Lord Voldemort (J. K. Rowling's *Harry Potter*)

2346 Merlin (Arthurian Legend)

2347 Morgan Le Fay (Arthurian Legend)

2348 Aslan (C. S. Lewis's *Narnia*)

2349 Tilda Swinton as The White Witch (C. S. Lewis's *Narnia*)

(Des So Design Consultants. Gravure De La Rue)

2011 (8 Mar). *Magical Realms.* 'All-over' phosphor. P 14½.

3154	**2342**	(1st) brownish grey, bright magenta, greenish yellow, new blue and black	1·25	1·00
		a. Vert pair. Nos. 3154/5	2·60	2·60
3155	**2343**	(1st) brownish grey, bright magenta, greenish yellow, new blue and black	1·25	1·00
3156	**2344**	(1st) brownish grey, bright magenta, greenish yellow, new blue and black	1·25	1·00
		a. Vert pair. Nos. 3156/7	2·60	2·60
3157	**2345**	(1st) brownish grey, bright magenta, greenish yellow, new blue and black	1·25	1·00
3158	**2346**	60p. brownish grey, bright magenta, greenish yellow, new blue and black	1·50	1·50
		a. Vert pair. Nos. 3158/9	3·25	3·25
3159	**2347**	60p. brownish grey, bright magenta, greenish yellow, new blue and black	1·50	1·50
3160	**2348**	97p. brownish grey, bright magenta, greenish yellow, new blue and black	2·40	2·40
		a. Vert pair. Nos. 3160/1	5·00	5·00

3161	**2349**	97p. brownish grey, bright magenta, greenish yellow, new blue and black	2·40	2·40
Set of 8			12·00	12·00
Set of 4 Gutter Strips of 4			25·00	
First Day Cover (Tallents House)				13·00
First Day Cover (Merlins Bridge, Haverfordwest)				13·00
Presentation Pack (P.O. Pack No. 453)			14·00	
Presentation Pack ('Heroes and Villains' containing Nos. 3156/7, each×5) (2 Dec)			15·00	
PHQ Cards (set of 8) (347)			6·00	18·00

Nos. 3154/5, 3156/7, 3158/9 and 3160/1 were each printed together, *se-tenant*, as vertical pairs in sheets of 60 (2 panes 5×6).

Special First Day of Issue Postmarks

(postmark illustrations)

FIRST DAY OF ISSUE ROYAL MAIL TALLENTS HOUSE EDINBURGH 8.3.2011

MERLINS BRIDGE HAVERFORDWEST FIRST DAY OF ISSUE 8.3.2011

For Nos. U2991/5 see Decimal Machin Definitives section

2350 African Elephant **2351** Mountain Gorilla

2352 Siberian Tiger **2353** Polar Bear

2354 Amur Leopard **2355** Iberian Lynx

2356 Red Panda **2357** Black Rhinoceros

2358 African Wild Dog

2359 Golden Lion Tamarin

Special First Day of Issue Postmarks

22.3.2011

2360 Wildlife of the Amazon Rainforest (*Illustration reduced. Actual size 115×89 mm*)

2361 David Tennant as *Hamlet*, 2008

2362 Antony Sher as Prospero, *The Tempest*, 2009

2363 Chuk Iwuji as *Henry VI*, 2006

2364 Paul Schofield as *King Lear*, 1962

2365 Sara Kestelman as Titania, *A Midsummer Night's Dream*, 1970

2366 Ian McKellen and Francesca Annis as *Romeo and Juliet*, 1976

(Des Janice Nicholson and Rose Design (**MS**3172) or Rose Design Consultants (others). Litho Cartor)

2011 (22 Mar). *50th Anniv of the WWF.* 'All-over' phosphor. *P* 14 (**MS**3172/a) or 14½ (others).

3162	**2350**	(1st) greenish yellow, bright magenta, new blue and black	1·25	1·00
		a. Horiz strip of 5. Nos. 3162/6	7·00	7·00
		b. Booklet pane. Nos. 3162/3 and 3170/1 with margins all round	5·00	
3163	**2351**	(1st) greenish yellow, bright magenta, new blue and black	1·25	1·00
3164	**2352**	(1st) greenish yellow, bright magenta, new blue and black	1·25	1·00
		b. Booklet pane. Nos. 3164/9 with margins all round	7·50	
3165	**2353**	(1st) greenish yellow, bright magenta, new blue and black	1·25	1·00
3166	**2354**	(1st) greenish yellow, bright magenta, new blue and black	1·25	1·00
3167	**2355**	(1st) greenish yellow, bright magenta, new blue and black	1·25	1·00
		a. Horiz strip of 5. Nos. 3167/71	7·00	7·00
3168	**2356**	(1st) greenish yellow, bright magenta, new blue and black	1·25	1·00
3169	**2357**	(1st) greenish yellow, bright magenta, new blue and black	1·25	1·00
3170	**2358**	(1st) greenish yellow, bright magenta, new blue and black	1·25	1·00
3171	**2359**	(1st) greenish yellow, bright magenta, new blue and black	1·25	1·00
Set of 10			12·50	12·50
Set of 2 Gutter Strips of 10			26·00	
First Day Cover (Tallents House)				13·00
First Day Cover (Godalming, Surrey)				13·00
Presentation Pack (P.O. Pack No. 454) (Nos. 3162/71 and **MS**3172)			22·00	
PHQ Cards (set of 15) (348)			12·00	30·00

MS3172 115×89 mm. **2360** (1st) Spider monkey; 60p. Hyacinth macaw; 88p. Poison dart frog; 97p. Jaguar ..... 7·50 7·50
  a. Booklet pane. No. **MS**3172 but 125×96 mm with line of roulettes at left ..... 7·50

First Day Cover (Tallents House)			8·50
First Day Cover (Godalming, Surrey)			8·50

Nos. 3162/6 and 3167/71 were each printed together, *se-tenant*, as horizontal strips of five stamps in sheets of 50 (2 panes 5×5).

Booklet panes Nos. 3162b, 3164b and **MS**3172a come from the £9·05 "WWF" booklet, No. DX52.

The complete miniature sheet is shown on one of the fifteen PHQ cards with the others depicting individual stamps including those from **MS**3172.

The 1st class value from **MS**3172 includes the "EUROPA" emblem.

2367 The Four Theatres of the Royal Shakespeare Company, Stratford-upon-Avon (*Illustration reduced. Actual size 115×89 mm*)

(Des Hat-trick. Gravure (Nos. 3173/8) or litho (**MS**3179) Walsall (Nos. 3173/8) or Cartor (**MS**3179))

2011 (21 Apr). *50th Anniv of the Royal Shakespeare Company.* 'All-over' phosphor. *P* 14½ (Nos. 3173/8) or 14 (**MS**3179).

3173	**2361**	(1st) black, brownish black and bright scarlet	1·25	1·00
3174	**2362**	66p. black, brownish black and bright scarlet	1·70	1·70
3175	**2363**	68p. black, brownish black and bright scarlet	1·70	1·70
3176	**2364**	76p. black, brownish black and bright scarlet	1·90	1·90

3177	**2365**	£1 black, brownish black and bright scarlet	2·50	2·50
3178	**2366**	£1·10 black, brownish black and bright scarlet	2·75	2·75

Set of 6	10·50	10·50
Set of 6 Gutter Pairs	22·00	
First Day Cover (Tallents House)		12·00
First Day Cover (Stratford-upon-Avon)		12·00
Presentation Pack (*P.O. Pack No. 455*) (Nos. 3173/8 and **MS**3179)	20·00	
PHQ Cards (set of 11) (349)	9·00	22·00

MS3179 115×89 mm. **2367** (1st) Janet Suzman as Ophelia, *Hamlet*, 1965, Royal Shakespeare Theatre; 68p. Patrick Stewart in *Antony and Cleopatra*, 2006, Swan Theatre; 76p. Geoffrey Streatfield in *Henry V*, 2007, The Courtyard Theatre; £1 Judy Dench as Lady Macbeth, 1976, The Other Place .... 7·50 7·50

First Day Cover (Tallents House)	8·50
First Day Cover (Stratford-upon-Avon)	8·50

The 11 PHQ cards show the six stamps, the four individual stamps within **MS**3179 and the complete miniature sheet.

2368 Prince William and Miss Catherine Middleton (*Illustration reduced. Actual size 115×89 mm*)

(Litho Walsall)

2011 (21 Apr). *Royal Wedding.* Official Engagement Portraits by Mario Testino. Sheet 115×89 mm. 'All-over' phosphor. P 14½×14.

MS3180 **2368** (1st)×2 Prince William and Miss Catherine Middleton embracing; £1·10×2 Formal portrait of Prince William and Miss Catherine Middleton in Council Chamber, St. James's Palace ..... 8·50 8·50

First Day Cover (Tallents House)	9·50
First Day Cover (London SW1)	9·50
Presentation Pack (*P.O. Pack No. M20*)	13·00
Commemorative Document	15·00

2369 "Cray" (fabric print by William Morris), 1884

2370 "Cherries" (detail from panel by Philip Webb), 1867

2371 "Seaweed" (wallpaper pattern by John Henry Dearle), 1901

2372 "Peony" (ceramic tile design by Kate Faulkner), 1877

2373 "Acanthus" (tile by William Morris and William De Morgan), 1876

2374 "The Merchant's Daughter" (detail of stained glass window by Edward Burne-Jones), 1864

(Des Kate Stephens. Litho Cartor or Walsall (booklet stamps))

2011 (5 May). *150th Anniv of Morris and Company (designers and manufacturers of textiles, wallpaper and furniture)* (1st issue). 'All-over' phosphor. P 14×14½.

3181	**2369**	(1st) greenish yellow, bright magenta, new blue and black	1·25	1·00
		a. Booklet pane. Nos. 3181 and 3183/5 with margins all round	7·75	
3182	**2370**	(1st) greenish yellow, bright magenta, new blue and black	1·25	1·00
		a. Booklet pane. Nos. 3182 and 3186, each×2, with margins all round	8·00	
3183	**2371**	76p. greenish yellow, bright magenta, new blue and black	1·90	1·90
3184	**2372**	76p. greenish yellow, bright magenta, new blue and black	1·90	1·90
3185	**2373**	£1·10 greenish yellow, bright magenta, new blue and black	2·75	2·75
3186	**2374**	£1·10 greenish yellow, bright magenta, new blue and black	2·75	2·75

Set of 6	11·00	11·00
Set of 6 Gutter Pairs	22·00	
First Day Cover (Tallents House)		12·00
First Day Cover (Walthamstow)		12·00
Presentation Pack (*P.O. Pack No. 456*)	12·00	
PHQ Cards (set of 6) (350)	5·00	16·00

Nos. 3181/6 were also issued in premium booklets, No. DY1, sold for £9·99.

2011 (5 May). *150th Anniv of Morris and Company* (2nd issue). Design as Type 2202 (2009 Christmas. Stained-glass Windows). One centre band. *P* 14½×14 (with one elliptical hole in each vert side).

3186*a*	**2202**	(2nd) multicoloured	3·00	3·00
		ab. Booklet pane. No. 3186*a*×4 with central label and margins all round	11·00	

No. 3186*a* was only issued in premium booklets, No. DY1, sold for £9·99.

2375 Thomas the Tank Engine

2376 James the Red Engine

2377 Percy the Small Engine

2378 Daisy (diesel railcar)

2379 Toby the Tram Engine

2380 Gordon the Big Engine

2381 Book Illustrations by John T. Kenny (76p.) or C. Reginald Dalby (others) *(Illustration reduced. Actual size* 115×89 *mm)*

"Goodbye, Bertie," called Thomas

2382 "Goodbye, Bertie", called Thomas (from *Tank Engine Thomas Again*)

(Des Elmwood. Litho Cartor)

2011 (14 June). *Thomas the Tank Engine.* 'All-over' phosphor.

(a) Ordinary gum. P 14 (**MS**3193) *or* 14½×14 *(others)*

3187	**2375**	(1st) greenish yellow, bright magenta, new blue and black	1·25	1·00
3188	**2376**	66p. greenish yellow, bright magenta, new blue and black	1·70	1·70
3189	**2377**	68p. greenish yellow, bright magenta, new blue and black	1·70	1·70
3190	**2378**	76p. greenish yellow, bright magenta, new blue and black	1·90	1·90
3191	**2379**	£1 greenish yellow, bright magenta, new blue and black	2·50	2·50
3192	**2380**	£1·10 greenish yellow, bright magenta, new blue and black	2·75	2·75
		Set of 6	11·00	11·00
		Set of 6 Gutter Pairs	23·00	
		First Day Cover (Tallents House)		12·00
		First Day Cover (Box, Corsham, Wiltshire)		12·00
		Presentation Pack (P.O. Pack No. 457) (Nos. 3187/92 and **MS**3193)	20·00	
		PHQ Cards (set of 11) (351)	9·00	22·00

MS3193 115×89 mm. **2381** (1st) "Goodbye, Bertie", called Thomas (from *Tank Engine Thomas Again*); 68p. James was more dirty than hurt (from *Toby the Tram Engine*); 76p. "Yes, Sir", Percy shivered miserably (from *The Eight Famous Engines*); £1 They told Henry, "We shall leave you there for always" (from *The Three Railway Engines*) ..... 7·50 ..... 7·50

First Day Cover (Tallents House) ..... 8·50
First Day Cover (Box, Corsham, Wiltshire) ..... 8·50

(b) Self-adhesive. Die-cut perf 14

3194	**2382**	(1st) multicoloured	3·75	3·75
		a. Booklet pane. Nos. 3194×2 and U2965×4	10·00	

Nos. 3187/92 show scenes from TV series *Thomas and Friends*, and Nos. **MS**3193/4 book illustrations from *The Railway Series*.

No. 3194 was only issued in stamp booklets, No. PM29, originally sold for £2·76.

The 11 PHQ cards show the six stamps, the four individual stamps within **MS**3193 and the complete miniature sheet.

Special First Day of Issue Postmarks

2383 Paralympic Games: Sailing

2384 Athletics: Field

2385 Volleyball

2386 Wheelchair Rugby

2387 Wrestling

2388 Wheelchair Tennis

2389 Fencing

2390 Gymnastics

2391 Triathlon

2392 Handball

(Des Lara Harwood and Heart (3195), Anthony Pike and The Art Market (3196), Ben Dalling (3197), Matthew Hollings and Illustration Ltd (3198), Daniel Stolle and Anna Goodson Management (3199), David McConochie and The Art Market (3200), Lyndon Hayes and Dutch Uncle Agency (3201), Kathy Wyatt (3202), Adam Simpson and Heart (3203), David Cutter and Folio (3204). Litho Cartor)

2011 (27 July). *Olympic and Paralympic Games, London (2012)* (5th issue). 'All-over' phosphor. P 14½.

3195	**2383**	(1st) grey, greenish yellow, bright magenta, new blue and black.......	1·25	1·00
		a. Horiz strip of 5. Nos. 3195/9	6·25	5·50
3196	**2384**	(1st) grey, greenish yellow, bright magenta, new blue and black.......	1·25	1·00
3197	**2385**	(1st) grey, greenish yellow, bright magenta, new blue and black.......	1·25	1·00
3198	**2386**	(1st) grey, greenish yellow, bright magenta, new blue and black.......	1·25	1·00
3199	**2387**	(1st) grey, greenish yellow, bright magenta, new blue and black.......	1·25	1·00
3200	**2388**	(1st) grey, greenish yellow, bright magenta, new blue and black.......	1·25	1·00
		a. Horiz strip of 5. Nos. 3200/4	6·25	5·50
3201	**2389**	(1st) grey, greenish yellow, bright magenta, new blue and black.......	1·25	1·00
3202	**2390**	(1st) grey, greenish yellow, bright magenta, new blue and black.......	1·25	1·00
3203	**2391**	(1st) grey, greenish yellow, bright magenta, new blue and black.......	1·25	1·00
3204	**2392**	(1st) grey, greenish yellow, bright magenta, new blue and black.......	1·25	1·00
Set of 10			12·00	10·00
Set of 2 Gutter Strips of 10			25·00	
First Day Cover (Tallents House)				11·00
First Day Cover (Rugby, Warks)				11·00
Presentation Pack (P.O. Pack No. 458)			14·00	
PHQ Cards (set of 10) (352)			9·00	20·00
MS3204*a* 210×300 mm. Nos. 2981/90, 3097/106 and 3195/3204			50·00	55·00

Nos. 3195/9 and 3200/4 were each printed together, *se-tenant*, in horizontal strips of five stamps in sheets of 50 (2 panes 5×5).

Special First Day of Issue Postmarks

(Gravure Walsall)

2011 (27 July–15 Sept). *Olympic and Paralympic Games (2012)* (6th issue). Booklet stamps. Designs as Nos. 3195, 3198 and 3201/2 . Self-adhesive. 'All-over' phosphor. Die-cut P 14½×14.

3205	**2386**	(1st) multicoloured..................................	3·75	3·50
		a. Booklet pane. Nos. 3205/6 and U2965×4.................................	10·00	
3206	**2383**	(1st) multicoloured..................................	3·75	3·50
3206*a*	**2390**	(1st) multicoloured (15 Sept)...............	3·75	3·50
		ab. Booklet pane. Nos. 3206a/b and U2965×4.................................	10·00	
3206*b*	**2389**	(1st) multicoloured (15 Sept)...............	3·75	3·50

Nos. 3205/6 and 3206a/b were only issued in two separate stamp booklets, Nos. PM30 and PM32, each originally sold for £2·76.

2393 The Sovereign's Sceptre with Cross

2394 St. Edward's Crown

2395 Rod and Sceptre with Doves

2396 Queen Mary's Crown

2397 The Sovereign's Orb

2398 Jewelled Sword of Offering

2399 Imperial State Crown

2400 Coronation Spoon

(Des Purpose. Litho Cartor)

2011 (23 Aug). *Crown Jewels.* Phosphor background. P 14×14½.

3207	**2393**	(1st) silver, greenish yellow, magenta, new blue and black	1·25	1·00
3208	**2394**	(1st) silver, greenish yellow, magenta, new blue and black	1·25	1·00
3209	**2395**	68p. silver, greenish yellow, magenta, new blue and black	1·70	1·70
3210	**2396**	68p. silver, greenish yellow, magenta, new blue and black	1·70	1·70
3211	**2397**	76p. silver, greenish yellow, magenta, new blue and black	1·90	1·90
3212	**2398**	76p. silver, greenish yellow, magenta, new blue and black	1·90	1·90
3213	**2399**	£1·10 silver, greenish yellow, magenta, new blue and black	2·75	2·75
3214	**2400**	£1·10 silver, greenish yellow, magenta, new blue and black	2·75	2·75
Set of 8			14·00	14·00
Set of 8 Gutter Pairs			29·00	
First Day Cover (Tallents House)				15·00
First Day Cover (London EC3)				15·00
Presentation Pack (P.O. Pack No. 459)			16·00	
PHQ Cards (set of 8) (353)			7·00	21·00

Special First Day of Issue Postmarks

2401 BR Dean Goods No. 2532

(Gravure Walsall)

2011 (23 Aug). *Classic Locomotives*. Booklet stamp. Design as 1st class
stamp within **MS3144**. Self-adhesive. Die-cut P 14.

3215	**2401**	(1st) black and gold	5·00	5·00
		a. Booklet pane. No. 3215×2 and U2965×4	11·00	

No. 3215 was only issued in booklets, No. PM31, originally sold for
£2·76.

2402 Pilot Gustav Hamel receiving Mailbag

2403 Gustav Hamel in Cockpit

2404 Pilot Clement Greswell and Blériot Monoplane

2405 Delivery of First Airmail to Postmaster General at Windsor

2406 First United Kingdom Aerial Post, 9 September 1911 (*Illustration
reduced. Actual size 146×74 mm*)

(Des Robert Maude and Sarah Davies. Litho Cartor)

2011 (9 Sept). *Centenary of First United Kingdom Aerial Post* (1st issue).
'All-over' phosphor. P 14.

3216	**2402**	(1st) purple-black and pale grey-lilac...	1·25	1·10
		a. Booklet pane. Nos. 3216×2 and 3219, with margins all round	5·50	
3217	**2403**	68p. brownish black and stone	1·70	1·70
		a. Booklet pane. Nos. 3217×2 and 3218	7·00	
3218	**2404**	£1 deep sepia and pale grey-brown.	2·50	2·50
3219	**2405**	£1·10 black and pale grey	2·75	2·75
Set of 4			7·50	7·50
MS3220 146×74 mm. **2406** Nos. 3216/19			7·50	7·50

First Day Cover (Tallents House)	9·00
First Day Cover (Hendon, London NW4)	9·00
Presentation Pack (P.O. Pack No. 460)	9·00
PHQ Cards (set of 5) (354)	4·50 12·00

Nos. 3216/19 were only issued in £9·99 stamp booklets, No. DY2, and
in **MS**3220.

The five PHQ cards show the four individual stamps and the
complete miniature sheet.

Special First Day of Issue Postmarks

2407 Windsor Castle

(Recess and litho Cartor)

2011 (9 Sept). *Centenary of First United Kingdom Aerial Post* (2nd issue).
P 11×11½.

3221	**2407**	50p. black on cream	5·00	5·00
		a. Booklet pane. No. 3221×4, with margins all round	16·00	

No. 3221 was only issued in £9·97 stamp booklets, No. DY2.

For No. **MS**3222 see Decimal Machin Definitives section

2409 George I (1714-27)

2410 George II (1727-60)

2411 George III (1760-1820)

2412 George IV (1820-30)

2413 William IV (1830-7)

2414 Victoria (1837-1901)

2415 The Age of the Hanoverians (*Illustration reduced. Actual size
123×70 mm*)

(Des Atelier Works. Litho Cartor)

2011 (15 Sept). Kings and Queens (5th issue). House of Hanover. Two phosphor bands. *P* 14.

3223	**2409**	(1st) brownish-black, greenish yellow, bright magenta, new blue and black	1·25	1·10
3224	**2410**	(1st) brownish-black, greenish yellow, bright magenta, new blue and black	1·25	1·10
3225	**2411**	76p. brownish-black, greenish yellow, bright magenta, new blue and black	1·90	1·90
3226	**2412**	76p. brownish-black, greenish yellow, bright magenta, new blue and black	1·90	1·90
3227	**2413**	£1·10 brownish-black, greenish yellow, bright magenta, new blue and black	2·75	2·75
3228	**2414**	£1·10 brownish-black, greenish yellow, bright magenta, new blue and black	2·75	2·75

Set of 6	11·00	11·00
Set of 6 Gutter Pairs	23·00	
Set of 6 Traffic Light Gutter Blocks of 4	48·00	
First Day Cover (Tallents House)		13·00
First Day Cover (London SW1)		13·00
Presentation Pack (P.O. Pack No. 461) (Nos. 3223/8 and **MS**3229)	20·00	
PHQ Cards (set of 11) (355)	9·00	20·00

MS3229 123×70 mm. **2415** (1st) Robert Walpole (first Prime Minister), 1721; 68p. Ceiling by Robert Adam, Kedleston Hall, 1763; 76p. Penny Black (uniform postage), 1840; £1 Queen Victoria (Diamond Jubilee), 1897 .... 7·50 7·50

First Day Cover (Tallents House)		8·50
First Day Cover (London SW1)		8·50

The complete miniature sheet is shown on one of the 11 PHQ cards with the others depicting individual stamps including those from **MS**3229.

Special First Day of Issue Postmarks

ROYAL MAIL TALLENTS HOUSE
FIRST DAY OF ISSUE EDINBURGH
15.9.2011

FIRST DAY OF ISSUE LONDON SW1
15.9.2011

2416 Angel of the North

2417 Blackpool Tower

2418 Carrick-a-Rede, Co. Antrim

2419 Downing Street

2420 Edinburgh Castle

2421 Forth Railway Bridge

2422 Glastonbury Tor

2423 Harlech Castle

2424 Ironbridge

2425 Jodrell Bank

2426 Kursaal, Southend, Essex

2427 Lindisfarne Priory

(Des Robert Maude and Sarah Davies. Litho Cartor)

2011 (13 Oct). UK A-Z (1st series). 'All-over' phosphor. *P* 14½.

3230	**2416**	(1st) pale brownish grey, greenish yellow, bright magenta, new blue and black	1·40	1·25
		a. Horiz strip of 6. Nos. 3230/5	8·00	7·00
3231	**2417**	(1st) pale brownish grey, greenish yellow, bright magenta, new blue and black	1·40	1·25
3232	**2418**	(1st) pale brownish grey, greenish yellow, bright magenta, new blue and black	1·40	1·25
3233	**2419**	(1st) pale brownish grey, greenish yellow, bright magenta, new blue and black	1·40	1·25
3234	**2420**	(1st) pale brownish grey, greenish yellow, bright magenta, new blue and black	1·40	1·25
3235	**2421**	(1st) pale brownish grey, greenish yellow, bright magenta, new blue and black	1·40	1·25
3236	**2422**	(1st) pale brownish grey, greenish yellow, bright magenta, new blue and black	1·40	1·25
		a. Horiz strip of 6. Nos. 3236/41	8·00	7·00
3237	**2423**	(1st) pale brownish grey, greenish yellow, bright magenta, new blue and black	1·40	1·25
3238	**2424**	(1st) pale brownish grey, greenish yellow, bright magenta, new blue and black	1·40	1·25
3239	**2425**	(1st) pale brownish grey, greenish yellow, bright magenta, new blue and black	1·40	1·25
3240	**2426**	(1st) pale brownish grey, greenish yellow, bright magenta, new blue and black	1·40	1·25
3241	**2427**	(1st) pale brownish grey, greenish yellow, bright magenta, new blue and black	1·40	1·25

Set of 12	16·00	13·00
Set of 2 Gutter Strips of 12	32·00	
Set of 2 Traffic Light Gutter Strips of 24	60·00	
First Day Covers (2) (Tallents House)		14·00
First Day Covers (2) (Blackpool)		14·00
Presentation Pack (P.O. Pack No. 462)	18·00	
PHQ Cards (set of 12) (356)	10·00	20·00

Nos. 3230/5 and 3236/41 were each printed together, *se-tenant*, as horizontal strips of six stamps in sheets of 60 (2 panes of 30).

Special First Day of Issue Postmarks

Special First Day of Issue Postmarks

2428 Joseph visited by the Angel (Matthew 1:21)

2429 Madonna and Child (Matthew 1:23)

2430 Joseph visited by the Angel (Matthew 1:21)

2431 Madonna and Child (Matthew 1:23)

2432 Baby Jesus in the Manger (Luke 2:7)

2433 Shepherds visited by the Angel (Luke 2:10)

2434 Wise Men and Star (Matthew 2:10)

(Des Peter Malone/The Artworks and Together Design. Gravure De La Rue)

2011 (8 Nov). *Christmas. 400th Anniv of the King James Bible.* One centre band (3242) or two phosphor bands (others). P 14½×14 (with one elliptical hole in each vert side).

(a) Self-adhesive

3242	**2428**	(2nd) gold, bright magenta, greenish yellow, new blue and black............	1·00	75
		a. Booklet pane. No. 3242×12	11·00	
3243	**2429**	(1st) gold, bright magenta, greenish yellow, new blue and black............	1·25	1·00
		a. Booklet pane. No. 3243×12	14·00	
3244	**2430**	(2nd) gold, bright magenta, greenish Large) yellow, new blue and black............	1·50	1·25
3245	**2431**	(1st) gold, bright magenta, greenish Large) yellow, new blue and black............	2·00	1·50
3246	**2432**	68p. gold, bright magenta, greenish yellow, new blue and black............	1·70	1·70
3247	**2433**	£1·10 gold, bright magenta, greenish yellow, new blue and black............	2·75	2·75
3248	**2434**	£1·65 gold, bright magenta, greenish yellow, new blue and black............	4·00	4·00

Set of 7	13·00	13·00
First Day Cover (Tallents House)............		14·00
First Day Cover (Bethlehem, Llandeilo)............		14·00
Presentation Pack (P.O. Pack No. 463)............	15·00	
PHQ Cards (set of 8) (357)............	5·50	20·00

(b) Ordinary gum

MS3249	116×102 mm. As Nos. 3242/8............	13·00	13·00
First Day Cover (Tallents House)............			14·00
First Day Cover (Bethlehem, Llandeilo)............			14·00

The eight PHQ cards show the seven individual stamps and the miniature sheet.

The 2nd class, 1st class, 68p., and £1·10 stamps were also issued in sheets of 20 (No. LS79) printed in lithography and sold for £10·45, containing eight 2nd class, eight 1st class, two 68p. and two £1·10 stamps, each stamp accompanied by a *se-tenant* label with a verse from the King James Bible.

Separate sheets of 20 2nd, ten 1st, ten 68p. and ten £1·10 were available with personal photographs on the labels from Royal Mail, Edinburgh. These were sold at £8·30 for ten 1st, £10·95 for 20 2nd, £10·75 for ten 68p. or £15·80 for ten £1·10.

Collectors Pack

2011 (8 Nov). Comprises Nos. 3136/42, **MS**3144/52, 3154/93, 3195/3204, 3207/14, **MS**3220 and 3223/48.

CP3244a	Collectors Pack	£165

Post Office Yearbook

2011 (8 Nov). Comprises Nos. 3136/42, **MS**3144/52, 3154/93, 3195/3204, 3207/14, **MS**3220 and 3223/48.

YB3244a	Yearbook	£165

Miniature Sheet Collection

2011 (8 Nov). Comprises Nos. **MS**3142, **MS**3144, **MS**3172, **MS**3179/80, **MS**3193, **MS**3220, **MS**3229 and **MS**3249.

MS3244a	Miniature Sheet Collection............	£130

2435 Paralympic Games Emblem

2436 Olympic Games Emblem

(Gravure Walsall (booklets) or De La Rue (others))

2012 (5 Jan). *Olympic and Paralympic Games* (7th issue). Self-adhesive. Two phosphor bands. Die-cut P 14½×14 (with one elliptical hole on each vert side).

3250	**2435**	(1st) black and orange-red............		
			1·90	1·25
		a. Booklet pane. Nos. 3250/1, each×3	10·00	
3251	**2436**	(1st) black and orange-red............		
			1·90	1·25
3252	**2435**	(Worldwide up to 20g) black, bright scarlet and greenish blue....		
			3·00	3·00
3253	**2436**	(Worldwide up to 20g) black, bright scarlet and greenish blue....		
			3·00	3·00

Set of 4	9·00	8·00
First Day Cover (Tallents House)............		10·00
First Day Cover (Sennen, Penzance, Cornwall)............		10·00
Presentation Pack (P.O. Pack No. D92)............	13·00	
PHQ Cards (set of 4) (D32)............	2·75	9·00

Nos. 3250/1 were printed together in sheets of 50 (2 panes 5×5), with the two designs alternating horizontally and vertically. The upper pane had No. 3250 at top left and contained 13 of No. 3250 and 12 of No. 3251. The lower pane had No. 3251 at top left and contained 13 of No. 3251 and 12 of No. 3250.

Nos. 3250/1 were also issued in stamp booklets, No. MB9/10, originally sold for £2·76.

Booklet pane 3250a exists in two versions which differ in the order of the stamps within the block of six.

Nos. 3252/3 were printed together in sheets of 25 (5×5) with the two designs alternating horizontally and vertically. There were two versions of the sheets of 25, one having No. 3252 at top left and containing 13 of No. 3252 and 12 of No. 3253, and the other having No. 3253 at top left and containing 13 of No. 3253 and 12 of No. 3252.

Nos. 3250/3 were also issued on 27 June 2012 in sheets of 20 containing Nos. 3250/1, each×8, and Nos. 3252/3, each×2, all with *se-tenant* labels showing Games venues (No. LS82). These sheets were printed in lithography by Cartor.

Special First Day of Issue Postmarks

2437 *Charlie and the Chocolate Factory*

2438 *Fantastic Mr. Fox*

2439 *James and the Giant Peach*

2445 *Sophie sitting on Buckingham Palace Window-sill*

2446 *The BFG and Sophie at Writing Desk*

2440 *Matilda*

2441 *The Twits*

2442 *The Witches*

(Des Magpie Studio. Litho Cartor)

2012 (10 Jan). *Roald Dahl's Children's Stories* (1st issue). Book Illustrations by Quentin Blake. 'All-over' phosphor. P 14.

3254	**2437**	(1st) gold, greenish yellow, bright magenta, new blue and black.......	1·25	1·00
		a. Booklet pane. Nos. 3254 and 3256/7 with margins all round	4·75	
3255	**2438**	66p. gold, greenish yellow, bright magenta, new blue and black.......	1·70	1·70
		a. Booklet pane. Nos. 3255 and 3258/9 with margins all round	6·75	
3256	**2439**	68p. gold, greenish yellow, bright magenta, new blue and black.......	1·70	1·70
3257	**2440**	76p. gold, greenish yellow, bright magenta, new blue and black.......	1·90	1·90
3258	**2441**	£1 gold, greenish yellow, bright magenta, new blue and black.......	2·50	2·50
3259	**2442**	£1·10 gold, greenish yellow, bright magenta, new blue and black.......	2·75	2·75
Set of 6			11·00	11·00
Set of 6 Gutter Pairs......			23·00	
Set of 6 Traffic Light Gutter Blocks of 4......			48·00	
First Day Cover (Tallents House)				12·00
First Day Cover (Great Missenden, Bucks)				12·00
Presentation Pack (P.O. Pack No. 465) (Nos. 3254/9 and MS3264)......			20·00	
PHQ Cards (set of 11) (358)......			7·50	17·00

2447 *Roald Dahl's The BFG (Illustration reduced. Actual size 114×89 mm)*

(Des Magpie Studio. Litho Cartor)

2012 (10 Jan). *Roald Dahl's Children's Stories* (2nd issue). Book Illustrations by Quentin Blake. 'All-over' phosphor. P 14×14½.

3260	**2443**	(1st) multicoloured......	2·00	2·00
		a. Booklet pane. Nos. 3260/3	12·00	
3261	**2444**	68p. multicoloured......	3·25	3·25
3262	**2445**	76p. multicoloured......	3·50	3·50
3263	**2446**	£1 multicoloured......	3·75	3·75
Set of 4			12·00	12·00
MS3264 115×89 mm. **2447** Nos. 3260/3			12·00	12·00
First Day Cover (Tallents House)				13·00
First Day Cover (Great Missenden, Bucks)				13·00

Nos. 3260/3 were only issued in £11·47 premium booklets, No. DY3, and in **MS**3264.

The complete miniature sheet is shown on one of the eleven PHQ cards with the others showing individual stamps including those from **MS**3264.

No. **MS**3264 commemorates the 30th anniv of the publication of *The BFG*.

Special First Day of Issue Postmarks

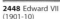

2443 *The BFG carrying Sophie in his Hand*

2444 *The BFG wakes up the Giants*

2448 *Edward VII (1901-10)*

2449 *George V (1910-36)*

2450 *Edward VIII (1936)*

2451 *George VI (1936-52)*

2452 *Elizabeth II (1952-)*

2453 The Age of the Windsors (*Illustration reduced. Actual size 123×70 mm*)

(Des Atelier Works. Litho Cartor)

2012 (2 Feb). *Kings and Queens* (6th issue). House of Windsor. Two phosphor bands. P 14.

3265	**2448**	(1st) light brown, greenish yellow, bright magenta, new blue and black	1·45	1·25
3266	**2449**	68p. light brown, greenish yellow, bright magenta, new blue and black	2·00	2·00
3267	**2450**	76p. light brown, greenish yellow, bright magenta, new blue and black	2·25	2·25
3268	**2451**	£1 light brown, greenish yellow, bright magenta, new blue and black	2·75	2·75
3269	**2452**	£1·10 light brown, greenish yellow, bright magenta, new blue and black	3·25	3·25
Set of 5			10·00	10·00
Set of 5 Gutter Pairs			19·00	
Set of 5 Traffic Light Gutter Blocks of 4			42·00	
First Day Cover (Tallents House)				11·00
First Day Cover (Windsor, Berkshire)				11·00
Presentation Pack (P.O. Pack No. 466) (Nos. 3265/9 and MS3270)			21·00	
PHQ Cards (set of 10) (359)			6·75	14·00

MS3270 123×70 mm. **2453** (1st) Scott Expedition to South Pole, 1912; 68p. Queen Elizabeth the Queen Mother and King George VI in bomb damaged street, *c.* 1940; 76p. England's winning World Cup football team, 1966; £1 Channel Tunnel, 1996............ 10·00 | 10·00

First Day Cover (Tallents House)		11·00
First Day Cover (Windsor, Berkshire)		11·00

The complete miniature sheet is shown on one of the ten PHQ cards with the others depicting individual stamps including those from **MS**3270.

No. 3271 is vacant.

Special First Day of Issue Postmarks

2.2.2012   2.2.2012

For Nos. U3271/8 see Decimal Machin Definitives section

2454 Diamond Jubilee (*Illustration reduced. Actual size 146×74 mm*)

(Des Sedley Place. Gravure Walsall)

2012 (6 Feb). *Diamond Jubilee*. (2nd issue). Two phosphor bands. P 14½×14 (with one elliptical hole in each vertical side).

MS3272 146×74 mm. **2454** (1st)×6 Portrait from photograph by Dorothy Wilding; 1960 £1 Banknote portrait by Robert Austin; 1971 £5 Banknote portrait by Harry Eccleston; 1953 Coinage portrait by Mary Gillick; 1971 decimal coin portrait by Arnold Machin; As No. U3271............ 12·00 | 12·00

First Day Cover (Tallents House)		13·00
First Day Cover (London SW1)		13·00
Presentation Pack (P.O. Pack No. 93)	14·00	
PHQ Cards (set of 7) (D33)	4·75	14·00
Commemorative Document	14·00	

The 1st class slate-blue Machin stamp from **MS**3272 has an iridescent overprint reading "DIAMOND JUBILEE" and the source code "MMND".

The seven PHQ cards show the six individual stamps and the complete miniature sheet.

Special First Day of Issue Postmarks

2455 Coventry Cathedral, 1962 (Sir Basil Spence, architect)

2456 Frederick Delius (1862-1934, composer)

2457 "Orange Tree" Embroidery (Mary "May" Morris 1862-1938, designer and textile artist)

2458 Odette Hallowes (1912-95, SOE agent in occupied France)

2459 Steam Engine, 1712 (Thomas Newcomen, inventor of atmospheric steam engine)

2460 Kathleen Ferrier (1912-53, contralto)

2461 Interior of Palace of Westminster (Augustus Pugin 1812-52, Gothic revival architect and designer)

2462 Montagu Rhodes James (1862-1936 scholar and author)

2463 Bombe Code Breaking Machine (Alan Turing 1912-54, mathematician and World War II code breaker)

2464 Joan Mary Fry (1862-1955 relief worker and social reformer)

(Des Purpose. Litho Cartor)

2012 (23 Feb). *Britons of Distinction.* 'All-over' phosphor. P 14½.

3273	**2455**	(1st) greenish yellow, bright magenta, new blue and black	1·25	1·10
		a. Horiz strip of 5. Nos. 3273/7	6·25	5·50
3274	**2456**	(1st) greenish yellow, bright magenta, new blue and black	1·25	1·10
3275	**2457**	(1st) greenish yellow, bright magenta, new blue and black	1·25	1·10
3276	**2458**	(1st) greenish yellow, bright magenta, new blue and black	1·25	1·10
3277	**2459**	(1st) greenish yellow, bright magenta, new blue and black	1·25	1·10
3278	**2460**	(1st) greenish yellow, bright magenta, new blue and black	1·25	1·10
		a. Horiz strip of 5. Nos. 3278/82	6·25	5·50
3279	**2461**	(1st) greenish yellow, bright magenta, new blue and black	1·25	1·10
3280	**2462**	(1st) greenish yellow, bright magenta, new blue and black	1·25	1·10
3281	**2463**	(1st) greenish yellow, bright magenta, new blue and black	1·25	1·10
3282	**2464**	(1st) greenish yellow, bright magenta, new blue and black	1·25	1·10
Set of 10			12·00	10·00
Set of 2 Gutter Strips of 10			25·00	
First Day Cover (Tallents House)				12·00
First Day Cover (Coventry)				12·00
Presentation Pack (P.O. Pack No. 467)			14·00	
PHQ Cards (set of 10) (360)			6·75	18·00

Nos. 3273/7 and 3278/82 were each printed together, *se-tenant*, as horizontal strips of five stamps in sheets of 50 (2 panes 5×5).

No. 3281 also comes from booklet pane No. 3679b in £14·60 Inventive Britain booklet, No. DY12.

Special First Day of Issue Postmarks

2465 Classic Locomotives of Scotland (*Illustration reduced. Actual size* 180×74 mm)

(Des Delaney Design Consultants. Litho Cartor)

2012 (8 Mar). *Classic Locomotives* (2nd series). Scotland. Sheet 180×74 mm. 'All-over' phosphor. P 14.

MS3283	**2465**	(1st) BR Class D34 Nos. 62471 *Glen Falloch* and 62496 *Glen Loy* at Ardlui, 9 May 1959; 68p. BR Class D40 No. 62276 *Andrew Bain* at Macduff, July 1950; £1 Andrew Barclay No. 807 *Bon Accord* propelling wagons along Miller Street, Aberdeen, June 1962; £1·10 BR Class 4P No. 54767 *Clan Mackinnon* pulling fish train, Kyle of Lochalsh, October 1948	8·00	8·00
First Day Cover (Tallents House)				9·00
First Day Cover (Glasgow)				9·00
Presentation Pack (P.O. Pack No. 468)			9·00	
PHQ Cards (set of 5) (361)			3·25	10·00

The five PHQ cards show the four individual stamps and the complete miniature sheet.

Special First Day of Issue Postmarks

2466 The Dandy and Desperate Dan

2467 The Beano and Dennis the Menace

2468 Eagle and Dan Dare

2469 The Topper and Beryl the Peril

2470 Tiger and Roy of the Rovers

2471 Bunty and the Four Marys

2472 Buster and Cartoon Character Buster

2473 Valiant and the Steel Claw

2474 Twinkle and Nurse Nancy

2475 2000 AD and Judge Dredd

(Des The Chase. Litho Cartor)

2012 (20 Mar). *Comics.* 'All-over' phosphor. P 14½.

3284	**2466**	(1st) greenish yellow, bright magenta, new blue and black	1·25	1·10
		a. Horiz strip of 5. Nos. 3284/8	6·25	5·50
3285	**2467**	(1st) greenish yellow, bright magenta, new blue and black	1·25	1·10

3286	**2468**	(1st) greenish yellow, bright magenta, new blue and black	1·25	1·10
3287	**2469**	(1st) greenish yellow, bright magenta, new blue and black	1·25	1·10
3288	**2470**	(1st) greenish yellow, bright magenta, new blue and black	1·25	1·10
3289	**2471**	(1st) greenish yellow, bright magenta, new blue and black	1·25	1·10
		a. Horiz strip of 5. Nos. 3289/93	6·25	5·50
3290	**2472**	(1st) greenish yellow, bright magenta, new blue and black	1·25	1·10
3291	**2473**	(1st) greenish yellow, bright magenta, new blue and black	1·25	1·10
3292	**2474**	(1st) greenish yellow, bright magenta, new blue and black	1·25	1·10
3293	**2475**	(1st) greenish yellow, bright magenta, new blue and black	1·25	1·10
Set of 10			12·00	11·00
Set of 2 Gutter Strips of 5			25·00	
First Day Cover (Tallents House)				12·00
First Day Cover (Dundee)				12·00
Presentation Pack (P.O. Pack No. 469)			14·00	
PHQ Cards (set of 10)			6·75	17·00

Special First Day of Issue Postmarks

2476 Manchester Town Hall

2477 Narrow Water Castle, Co. Down

2478 Old Bailey, London

2479 Portmeirion, Wales

2480 The Queen's College, Oxford

2481 Roman Baths, Bath

2482 Stirling Castle, Scotland

2483 Tyne Bridge, Newcastle

2484 Urquhart Castle, Scotland

2485 Victoria and Albert Museum, London

2486 White Cliffs of Dover

2487 Station X, Bletchley Park, Buckinghamshire

2488 York Minster

2489 London Zoo

(Des Robert Maude and Sarah Davies. Litho Cartor)

2012 (10 Apr). *UK A–Z* (2nd series). 'All-over' phosphor. *P* 14½.

3294	**2476**	(1st) pale brownish grey, greenish yellow, bright magenta, new blue and black	1·25	1·10
		a. Horiz strip of 6. Nos. 3294/9	7·50	6·50
3295	**2477**	(1st) pale brownish grey, greenish yellow, bright magenta, new blue and black	1·25	1·10
3296	**2478**	(1st) pale brownish grey, greenish yellow, bright magenta, new blue and black	1·25	1·10
3297	**2479**	(1st) pale brownish grey, greenish yellow, bright magenta, new blue and black	1·25	1·10
3298	**2480**	(1st) pale brownish grey, greenish yellow, bright magenta, new blue and black	1·25	1·10
3299	**2481**	(1st) pale brownish grey, greenish yellow, bright magenta, new blue and black	1·25	1·10
3300	**2482**	(1st) pale brownish grey, greenish yellow, bright magenta, new blue and black	1·25	1·10
		a. Horiz strip of 6. Nos. 3300/5	7·50	6·50
3301	**2483**	(1st) pale brownish grey, greenish yellow, bright magenta, new blue and black	1·25	1·10
3302	**2484**	(1st) pale brownish grey, greenish yellow, bright magenta, new blue and black	1·25	1·10
3303	**2485**	(1st) pale brownish grey, greenish yellow, bright magenta, new blue and black	1·25	1·10
3304	**2486**	(1st) pale brownish grey, greenish yellow, bright magenta, new blue and black	1·25	1·10
3305	**2487**	(1st) pale brownish grey, greenish yellow, bright magenta, new blue and black	1·25	1·10
3306	**2488**	(1st) pale brownish grey, greenish yellow, bright magenta, new blue and black	1·25	1·10
		a. Horiz pair. Nos. 3306/7	2·50	2·20
3307	**2489**	(1st) pale brownish grey, greenish yellow, bright magenta, new blue and black	1·25	1·10
Set of 14			14·00	12·00
Set of 2 Gutter Strips of 12 and 1 Gutter Strip of 4			30·00	
Set of 2 Traffic Light Gutter Strips of 24 and 1 Gutter Block of 8			60·00	
First Day Covers (2) (Tallents House)				14·00

First Day Covers (2) (Dover, Kent)..................................... 14·00
Presentation Pack (P.O. Pack No. 470).............................. 16·00
PHQ Cards (set of 14) (363).. 9·50 20·00
MS3308 297×210 mm. Nos. 3230/41 and 3294/307 .... 80·00 80·00

Nos. 3294/9 and 3300/5 were each printed together, *se-tenant*, as horizontal strips of six stamps in sheets of 60 (2 panes 6×5).

Nos. 3306/7 were printed together, *se-tenant*, as horizontal pairs in sheets of 60 (2 panes 6×5).

No. 3303 includes the 'EUROPA' emblem.

No. 3305 also comes from booklet pane No. 3679b in £14·60 Inventive Britain booklet No DY12.

Special First Day of Issue Postmarks

2498 Suit by Paul Smith, 2003

2499 'Black Raven' by Alexander McQueen, 2009

(Des Johnson Banks. Litho Cartor)

2012 (15 May). *Great British Fashion.* Phosphor background. P 14½×14.

3309	**2490**	(1st) silver, greenish yellow, bright magenta, new blue and black	1·25	1·25
		a. Horiz strip of 5. Nos. 3309/13	6·50	6·50
3310	**2491**	(1st) silver, greenish yellow, bright magenta, new blue and black	1·25	1·25
3311	**2492**	(1st) silver, greenish yellow, bright magenta, new blue and black	1·25	1·25
3312	**2493**	(1st) silver, greenish yellow, bright magenta, new blue and black	1·25	1·25
3313	**2494**	(1st) silver, greenish yellow, bright magenta, new blue and black	1·25	1·25
3314	**2495**	(1st) silver, greenish yellow, bright magenta, new blue and black	1·25	1·25
		a. Horiz strip of 5. Nos. 3314/18	6·50	6·50
3315	**2496**	(1st) silver, greenish yellow, bright magenta, new blue and black	1·25	1·25
3316	**2497**	(1st) silver, greenish yellow, bright magenta, new blue and black	1·25	1·25
3317	**2498**	(1st) silver, greenish yellow, bright magenta, new blue and black	1·25	1·25
3318	**2499**	(1st) silver, greenish yellow, bright magenta, new blue and black	1·25	1·25

Set of 10 .... 12·00 12·00
Set of 2 Gutter Strips of 10 .... 25·00
Set of 2 Traffic Light Gutter Strips of 20 .... 50·00
First Day Cover (Tallents House)............................... 14·00
First Day Cover (London W1) .... 14·00
Presentation Pack (P.O. Pack No. 471)............... 15·00
PHQ Cards (set of 10) (364)................................ 6·75 20·00

Nos. 3309/13 and 3314/18 were each printed together, *se-tenant*, as horizontal strips of five stamps in sheets of 50 (2 panes 5×5).

Special First Day of Issue Postmarks

2490 Skirt Suit by Hardy Amies, late 1940s

2491 Outfit by Norman Hartnell, 1950s

2492 Jacket designed by John Pearce for Granny Takes a Trip Boutique, 1960s

2493 Print by Celia Birtwell for Outfit by Ossie Clark, late 1960s

2494 Suit designed for Ringo Starr by Tommy Nutter

2495 Outfit by Jean Muir, late 1970s/early 1980s

2496 'Royal' Dress by Zandra Rhodes, 1981

2497 Harlequin dress by Vivienne Westwood, 1993

2500 Queen Elizabeth II at Golden Jubilee Service, St. Paul's Cathedral, London, 2002

2501 Queen Elizabeth II Trooping the Colour, 1967

2502 Queen Elizabeth II inspecting 2nd Battalion Royal Welsh, Tidworth, 1 March 2007

2503 First Christmas Television Broadcast, 1957

2504 Silver Jubilee Walkabout, 1977

2505 Queen Elizabeth II in Garter Ceremony Procession, 1997

2506 Queen Elizabeth II addressing the UN General Assembly, 1957

2507 Queen Elizabeth II at Commonwealth Games, Brisbane, Australia, 1982

(Des Kate Stephens. Gravure De La Rue (A3319/20, A3323/6) or Enschedé (A3321/2), Litho Walsall (B3319/26) or gravure Walsall (3327))

2012 (31 May). *Diamond Jubilee* (3rd issue). 'All-over' phosphor.

(a) Sheet stamps. Ordinary gum. gravure. P 14×14½.

A3319	**2500**	(1st) grey, bright magenta, greenish yellow, new blue and black...........	1·25	1·10
		a. Horiz pair. Nos. A3319/20	2·50	2·50
A3320	**2501**	(1st) black and brownish grey	1·25	1·10
A3321	**2502**	77p. grey, black, bright magenta, greenish yellow, new blue and grey-black...........	1·90	1·90
		a. Horiz pair. Nos. A3321/2..............	3·75	3·75
A3322	**2503**	77p. black and brownish grey	1·90	1·90
A3323	**2504**	87p.black and brownish grey	2·25	2·25
		a. Horiz pair. Nos. A3323/4..............	4·50	4·50
A3324	**2505**	87p. grey, bright magenta, greenish yellow, new blue and black...........	2·25	2·25
A3325	**2506**	£1·28 black and brownish grey	3·25	3·25
		a. Horiz pair. Nos. A3325/6..............	6·50	6·50
A3326	**2507**	£1·28 grey, bright magenta, greenish yellow, new blue and black...........	3·25	3·25
Set of 8..			16·00	16·00
Set of 4 Gutter Strips of 4			32·00	
First Day Cover (Tallents House).....................				18·00
First Day Cover (Windsor, Berkshire)...............				18·00
Presentation Pack (P.O. Pack No. 472).............			21·00	
PHQ Cards (Set of 8) (365).............................			5·50	21·00

(b) Booklet stamps. Ordinary gum. Litho. P 14×14½.

B3319	**2500**	(1st) grey, bright magenta, greenish yellow, new blue and black...........	1·50	1·50
		b. Booklet pane. Nos. B3319 and B3323/5 with margins all round..	8·50	
B3320	**2501**	(1st) black and brownish grey	1·50	1·50
		b. Booklet pane. Nos. B3320/1 with margins all round	3·25	
B3321	**2502**	77p. black, bright magenta, greenish yellow, new blue and grey-black...........	1·90	1·90
B3322	**2503**	77p. black and brownish grey	1·90	1·90
		b. Booklet pane. Nos. B3322 and B3326 with margins all round......	4·75	
B3323	**2504**	87p. black and brownish grey	2·25	2·25
B3324	**2505**	87p. grey, bright magenta, greenish yellow, new blue and black...........	2·25	2·25
B3325	**2506**	£1·28 black and brownish grey	3·25	3·25
B3326	**2507**	£1·28 grey, bright magenta, greenish yellow, new blue and black...........	3·25	3·25
Set of 8..			16·00	16·00

(c) Self-adhesive booklet stamp. gravure. Die-cut P 14.

3327	**2500**	(1st) grey, bright magenta, greenish yellow, new blue and black...........	3·75	3·25
		a. Booklet pane. No. 3327×2 and No. U3274×4	11·00	

Nos. A3319/20, A3321/2, A3323/4 and A3325/6 were printed together, *se-tenant*, as horizontal pairs in sheets of 60 (2 panes 6×5).

Nos. B3319/26 come from £12·77 booklets, No. DY4.

No. 3327 was only issued in stamp booklets, No. PM33, originally sold for £3·60.

Special First Day of Issue Postmarks

(Des Sedley Place. Gravure Walsall)

2012 (31 May). *Diamond Jubilee* (4th issue). As Nos. U3272/4 (3328) or as Type **159** but redrawn with 1st value indicator (3329). Iridescent overprint reading 'DIAMOND JUBILEE' (3328). Two phosphor bands. P 14½×14 (with one elliptical hole in each vert side).

3328		(1st) slate-blue ("MPND")..	4·50	3·75
		a. Booklet pane. Nos. 3328/9, each×4, with central label and margins all round...........	12·00	
3329		(1st) light brown	4·50	3·75
First Day Cover (No. 3328a), (Tallents House or Windsor) ...				15·00

No. 3328 has the source code "MPND".

Nos. 3328/9 were issued in £12·27 booklets, No. DY4.

Similar stamps were issued in **MS**3272.

2508 Mr Bumble *(Oliver Twist)*

2509 Mr Pickwick *(The Pickwick Papers)*

2510 The Marchioness *(The Old Curiosity Shop)*

2511 Mrs Gamp *(Martin Chuzzlewit)*

2512 Captain Cuttle *(Dombey and Son)*

2513 Mr Micawber *(David Copperfield)*

2514 Scenes from *Nicholas Nickleby, Bleak House, Little Dorrit and A Tale of Two Cities (Illustration reduced. Actual size 190×67 mm)*

(Des Howard Brown. Litho Cartor)

2012 (19 June). *Birth Bicentenary of Charles Dickens.* Illustrations from Character Sketches from Charles Dickens, c. 1890 by Joseph Clayton Clarke ('Kyd') (3330/5) or Book Illustrations by Hablot Knight Browne ('Phiz') (**MS**3336). One centre band (2nd) or 'all-over' phosphor (others). P 14 (3330/5) or 14×14½ (**MS**3336).

3330	**2508**	(2nd) gold, greenish yellow, bright magenta, new blue and black	1·00	1·00
3331	**2509**	(1st) gold, greenish yellow, bright magenta, new blue and black	1·25	1·10

3332	**2510**	77p. gold, greenish yellow, bright magenta, new blue and black	1·90	1·90
3333	**2511**	87p. gold, greenish yellow, bright magenta, new blue and black	2·25	2·25
3334	**2512**	£1.28 gold, greenish yellow, bright magenta, new blue and black	3·25	3·25
3335	**2513**	£1.90 gold, greenish yellow, bright magenta, new blue and black	4·75	4·75

Set of 6 .... 13·00 13·00
Set of 6 Gutter Pairs .... 27·00
Set of 6 Traffic Light Gutter Blocks of 4 .... 55·00
First Day Cover (Tallents House)........................ 15·00
First Day Cover (Portsmouth) .... 15·00
Presentation Pack (P.O. Pack No. 473) (Nos. 3330/5 and
MS3336).. 22·00
PHQ Cards (set of 11) (366)............................ 7·50 20·00
MS3336 190×67 mm. **2514** (1st)×4 Nicholas Nickleby caning headmaster Wackford Squeers (Nicholas Nickleby); Mrs. Bagnet is charmed with Mr. Bucket (Bleak House); Amy Dorrit introduces Maggy to Arthur Clennam (Little Dorrit); Charles Darnay arrested by French revolutionaries (A Tale of Two Cities) .... 6·00 6·00
First Day Cover (Tallents House)........................ 8·00
First Day Cover (Portsmouth) .... 8·00

The complete miniature sheet is shown on one of the eleven PHQ cards with the others depicting individual stamps including those from **MS**3336.

(Litho Cartor)

2012 (19 July). Olympic and Paralympic Games (8th issue). Designs as Nos. 3250/3. Two phosphor bands. P 14½×14 (with one elliptical hole in each vert side).

3337	**2436**	(1st) black and orange-red.....................	5·00	5·00
		a. Booklet pane. Nos. 3337/8, each×3, and 3339/40 with central label and margins all round	40·00	
3338	**2435**	(1st) black and orange-red.....................	5·00	5·00
3339	**2436**	(Worldwide up to 20g) black, bright scarlet and greenish blue.	11·00	10·00
3340	**2435**	(Worldwide up to 20g) black, bright scarlet and greenish blue.	11·00	10·00

Set of 4 .... 28·00 25·00
First Day Cover (No. 3337a) (Tallents House) .... 26·00
First Day Cover (No. 3337a) (London E20) .... 26·00

Nos. 3339/40 were for use on Worldwide Mail up to 20g.
Nos. 3337/40 were only issued in £10·71 stamp booklets, No. DY5.

2515 Sports and London Landmarks (Illustration reduced. Actual size 192×75 mm)

(Des Hat-trick design. Litho Cartor)

2012 (27 July). Welcome to London, Olympic Games. Sheet 192×75 mm. 'All-over' phosphor. P 14½.
MS3341 **2515** (1st) Fencer and Tower Bridge; (1st) Athletes in race and Olympic Stadium; £1·28 Diver and Tate Modern; £1·28 Cyclist and London Eye .... 9·50 9·50
First Day Cover (Tallents House)........................ 11·00
First Day Cover (London E20) .... 11·00
Presentation Pack (P.O. Pack No. 474)..................... 12·00
PHQ Cards (set of 5) (367)............................ 3·50 14·00

The five PHQ Cards show the four individual stamps and the complete miniature sheet.

2516 Helen Glover and Heather Stanning (rowing: women's pairs)

2517 Bradley Wiggins (cycling: road, men's time trial)

2518 Tim Baillie and Etienne Stott (canoe slalom: men's canoe double (C2))

2519 Peter Wilson (shooting: shotgun men's double trap)

2520 Philip Hindes, Chris Hoy and Jason Kenny (cycling: track men's team sprint)

2521 Katherine Grainger and Anna Watkins (rowing: women's double sculls)

2522 Steven Burke, Ed Clancy, Peter Kennaugh and Geraint Thomas (cycling: track men's team pursuit)

2523 Victoria Pendleton (cycling: track women's keirin)

2524 Alex Gregory, Tom James, Pete Reed and Andrew Triggs Hodge (rowing: men's fours)

2525 Katherine Copeland and Sophie Hosking (rowing: lightweight women's double sculls)

2526 Dani King, Joanna Rowsell and Laura Trott (cycling: track women's team pursuit)

2527 Jessica Ennis (athletics: combined women's heptathlon)

2528 Greg Rutherford (athletics: field men's long jump)

2529 Mo Farah (athletics: track men's 10,000m)

2530 Ben Ainslie (sailing: Finn men's heavyweight dinghy)

2531 Andy Murray (tennis: men's singles)

2532 Scott Brash, Peter Charles, Ben Maher and Nick Skelton (equestrian: jumping team)

2533 Jason Kenny (cycling: track men's sprint)

2534 Alistair Brownlee (men's triathlon)

2535 Carl Hester, Laura Bechtolsheimer and Charlotte Dujardin (equestrian: dressage team)

2536 Laura Trott (cycling: track women's omnium)

2537 Chris Hoy (cycling: track men's keirin)

2538 Charlotte Dujardin (equestrian: dressage individual)

2539 Nicola Adams (boxing: women's fly weight)

2540 Jade Jones (taekwondo: women's under 57kg)

2541 Ed McKeever (canoe sprint: men's kayak single (K1) 200m)

2542 Mo Farah (athletics: track men's 5000m)

2543 Luke Campbell (boxing: men's bantam weight)

2544 Anthony Joshua (boxing: men's super heavy weight)

(Des True North and Royal Mail. Litho with digital overprint Walsall and six regional printers)

2012 (2–13 Aug). *British Gold Medal Winners at London Olympic Games.* Self-adhesive. Two phosphor panels. Die-cut P15×14½.

3342	**2516**	(1st) multicoloured	2·25	2·75
		a. Sheetlet. No. 3342×6..................	9·50	10·50
3343	**2517**	(1st) multicoloured	2·25	2·75
		a. Sheetlet. No. 3343×6..................	9·50	10·50
3344	**2518**	(1st) multicoloured (3 Aug)............	2·25	2·75
		a. Sheetlet. No. 3344×6..................	9·50	10·50
3345	**2519**	(1st) multicoloured (3 Aug)............	2·25	2·75
		a. Sheetlet. No. 3345×6..................	9·50	10·50
3346	**2520**	(1st) multicoloured (3 Aug)............	2·25	2·75
		a. Sheetlet. No. 3346×6..................	9·50	10·50
3347	**2521**	(1st) multicoloured (4 Aug)............	2·25	2·75
		a. Sheetlet. No. 3347×6..................	9·50	10·50
3348	**2522**	(1st) multicoloured (4 Aug)............	2·25	2·75
		a. Sheetlet. No. 3348×6..................	9·50	10·50
3349	**2523**	(1st) multicoloured (4 Aug)............	2·25	2·75
		a. Sheetlet. No. 3349×6..................	9·50	10·50
3350	**2524**	(1st) multicoloured (5 Aug)............	2·25	2·75
		a. Sheetlet. No. 3350×6..................	9·50	10·50
3351	**2525**	(1st) multicoloured (5 Aug)............	2·25	2·75
		a. Sheetlet. No. 3351×6..................	9·50	10·50
		ab. Black ptg double......................		
3352	**2526**	(1st) multicoloured (5 Aug)............	2·25	2·75
		a. Sheetlet. No. 3352×6..................	9·50	10·50
3353	**2527**	(1st) multicoloured (5 Aug)............	2·25	2·75
		a. Sheetlet. No. 3353×6..................	9·50	10·50
3354	**2528**	(1st) multicoloured (5 Aug)............	2·25	2·75
		a. Sheetlet. No. 3354×6..................	9·50	10·50
3355	**2529**	(1st) multicoloured (5 Aug)............	2·25	2·75
		a. Sheetlet. No. 3355×6..................	9·50	10·50
3356	**2530**	(1st) multicoloured (6 Aug)............	2·25	2·75
		a. Sheetlet. No. 3356×6..................	9·50	10·50
3357	**2531**	(1st) multicoloured (6 Aug)............	2·25	2·75
		a. Sheetlet. No. 3357×6..................	9·50	10·50
3358	**2532**	(1st) multicoloured (7 Aug)............	2·25	2·75
		a. Sheetlet. No. 3358×6..................	9·50	10·50
3359	**2533**	(1st) multicoloured (7 Aug)............	2·25	2·75
		a. Sheetlet. No. 3359×6..................	9·50	10·50
3360	**2534**	(1st) multicoloured (8 Aug)............	2·25	2·75
		a. Sheetlet. No. 3360×6..................	9·50	10·50
3361	**2535**	(1st) multicoloured (8 Aug)............	2·25	2·75
		a. Sheetlet. No. 3361×6..................	9·50	10·50
3362	**2536**	(1st) multicoloured (8 Aug)............	2·25	2·75
		a. Sheetlet. No. 3362×6..................	9·50	10·50
3363	**2537**	(1st) multicoloured (8 Aug)............	2·25	2·75
		a. Sheetlet. No. 3363×6..................	9·50	10·50
3364	**2538**	(1st) multicoloured (10 Aug)............	2·25	2·75
		a. Sheetlet. No. 3364×6..................	9·50	10·50
3365	**2539**	(1st) multicoloured (10 Aug)............	2·25	2·75
		a. Sheetlet. No. 3365×6..................	9·50	10·50
3366	**2540**	(1st) multicoloured (10 Aug)............	2·25	2·75
		a. Sheetlet. No. 3366×6..................	9·50	10·50
3367	**2541**	(1st) multicoloured (12 Aug)............	2·25	2·75
		a. Sheetlet. No. 3367×6..................	9·50	10·50
		ab. Black printed double..................		
3368	**2542**	(1st) multicoloured (12 Aug)............	2·25	2·75
		a. Sheetlet. No. 3368×6..................	9·50	10·50
		ab. Black printed double..................		
3369	**2543**	(1st) multicoloured (12 Aug)............	2·25	2·75
		a. Sheetlet. No. 3369×6..................	9·50	10·50
3370	**2544**	(1st) multicoloured (13 Aug)............	2·25	2·75
		a. Sheetlet. No. 3370×6..................	9·50	10·50

Set of 29 Single Stamps	60·00	75·00
3342a/70a *Set of* 29 sheetlets..........................	£260	£260
First Day Covers (Nos. 3342a/70a) (29) (Tallents House)		
(London E20)...		£350
First Day Cover (any gold medal stamp (Tallents House))		
(London E20)...		10·00
First Day Cover (any gold medal stamp) (London E20)....		10·00

The self-adhesive base sheetlets for Nos. 3342/70 were produced by Walsall with the image, name and event of the winning athletes digitally printed by regional printers in six different locations: Attleborough, Edinburgh, London, Preston, Solihull and Swindon. Nos. 3368/70 were not produced by the Preston printer due to machinery breakdown. Post office sheets comprised four sheetlets of six stamps (3×2), the sheetlets being separated by roulettes. The four sheetlets

had one of the following inscriptions on the left margin: emblem 'TEAM GB' and Olympic rings; 'The XXX Olympiad'; barcode; Sheet number, Issue date and Printer location. Individual stamps had to be cut from the sheetlets using scissors.

2545 Paralympic Sports and London Landmarks (*Illustration reduced. Actual size* 193×75 *mm*)

(Des Pearce Marchbank. Litho Cartor)

2012 (29 Aug). *Welcome to London, Paralympic Games.* Sheet 193×75 mm. 'All-over' phosphor. *P* 14½.

MS3371 **2545** (1st) Athlete wearing running blades and Olympic Stadium; (1st) Wheelchair basketball player and Palace of Westminster; £1·28 Powerlifter, Millennium Bridge and St. Paul's Cathedral; £1·28 Cyclist and London Eye...	9·50	9·50
First Day Cover (Tallents House)........................		11·50
First Day Cover (London E20)............................		11·50
Presentation Pack (P.O. Pack No. 475)..............	12·00	
PHQ Cards (set of 5) (368)................................	3·50	14·00

The five PHQ Cards show the four individual stamps and the complete miniature sheet.

Special First Day of Issue Postmarks

2546 Sarah Storey (cycling: track women's C5 pursuit)

2547 Jonathan Fox (swimming: men's 100m backstroke, S7)

2548 Mark Colbourne (cycling: track men's C1 pursuit)

2549 Hannah Cockroft (athletics: track women's 100m, T34)

2550 Neil Fachie and Barney Storey (cycling: men's B 1km time trial)

2551 Richard Whitehead (athletics: track men's 200m, T42)

2552 Natasha Baker (equestrian: individual championship test, grade II)

2553 Sarah Storey (cycling: track – women's C4-5 500m time trial)

2554 Ellie Simmonds (swimming: women's 400m freestyle, S6)

2555 Pamela Relph, Naomi Riches, James Roe, David Smith and Lily van den Broecke (rowing: mixed coxed four, LTAmix4+)

2556 Aled Davies (athletics: field men's discus, F42)

2557 Anthony Kappes and Craig MacLean (cycling: track men's B sprint)

2558 Jessica-Jane Applegate (swimming: women's 200m freestyle, S14)

2559 Sophie Christiansen (equestrian: individual championship test, grade 1a)

2560 David Weir (athletics: track men's 5000m, T54)

2561 Natasha Baker (equestrian: individual freestyle test, grade II)

2562 Ellie Simmonds (swimming: women's 200m individual medley, SM6)

2563 Mickey Bushell (athletics: track men's 100m, T53)

2564 Danielle Brown (archery: women's individual compound, open)

2565 Heather Frederiksen (swimming: women's 100m backstroke, S8)

2566 Sophie Christiansen (equestrian: individual freestyle test, grade 1a)

2567 David Weir (athletics: track men's 1500m, T54)

2568 Sarah Storey (cycling: road women's C5 time trial)

2569 Ollie Hynd (swimming: men's 200m individual medley, SM8)

2570 Sophie Christiansen, Deb Criddle, Lee Pearson and Sophie Wells (equestrian team, open)

2571 Helena Lucas (sailing: single-person keelboat, 2.4mR)

2572 Sarah Storey (cycling: road women's C4-5 road race)

2573 Josef Craig (swimming: men's 400m freestyle, S7)

2574 Hannah Cockroft (athletics: track women's 200m, T34)

2575 David Weir (athletics: track men's 800m, T54)

2576 Jonnie Peacock (athletics: track men's 100m, T44)

2577 Josie Pearson (athletics: field women's discus, F51/52/53)

2578 David Stone (cycling: road mixed T1-2 road race)

2579 David Weir (athletics: road men's marathon, T54)

(Des True North and Royal Mail. Litho with digital overprint Walsall and six regional printers)

2012 (31 Aug–10 Sept). *British Gold Medal Winners at London Paralympic Games.* Self-adhesive. Two phosphor panels. Die-cut P 15×14½.

3372	**2546**	(1st) multicoloured	2·00	2·00
		a. Sheetlet. No. 3372×2......................	4·00	4·00
3373	**2547**	(1st) multicoloured (1 Sept)	2·00	2·00
		a. Sheetlet. No. 3373×2......................	4·00	4·00
3374	**2548**	(1st) multicoloured (3 Sept)...................	2·00	2·00
		a. Sheetlet. No. 3374×2......................	4·00	4·00
3375	**2549**	(1st) multicoloured (3 Sept)...................	2·00	2·00
		a. Sheetlet. No. 3375×2......................	4·00	4·00
3376	**2550**	(1st) multicoloured (3 Sept)...................	2·00	2·00
		a. Sheetlet. No. 3376×2......................	4·00	4·00
3377	**2551**	(1st) multicoloured (3 Sept)...................	2·00	2·00
		a. Sheetlet. No. 3377×2......................	4·00	4·00
3378	**2552**	(1st) multicoloured (3 Sept)...................	2·00	2·00
		a. Sheetlet. No. 3378×2......................	4·00	4·00
3379	**2553**	(1st) multicoloured (3 Sept)...................	2·00	2·00
		a. Sheetlet. No. 3379×2......................	4·00	4·00
3380	**2554**	(1st) multicoloured (3 Sept)...................	2·00	2·00
		a. Sheetlet. No. 3380×2......................	4·00	4·00
3381	**2555**	(1st) multicoloured (4 Sept)...................	2·00	2·00
		a. Sheetlet. No. 3381×2......................	4·00	4·00
3382	**2556**	(1st) multicoloured (4 Sept)...................	2·00	2·00
		a. Sheetlet. No. 3382×2......................	4·00	4·00
3383	**2557**	(1st) multicoloured (4 Sept)...................	2·00	2·00
		a. Sheetlet. No. 3383×2......................	4·00	4·00
3384	**2558**	(1st) multicoloured (4 Sept)...................	2·00	2·00
		a. Sheetlet. No. 3384×2......................	4·00	4·00
3385	**2559**	(1st) multicoloured (4 Sept)...................	2·00	2·00
		a. Sheetlet. No. 3385×2......................	4·00	4·00
3386	**2560**	(1st) multicoloured (4 Sept)...................	2·00	2·00
		a. Sheetlet. No. 3386×2......................	4·00	4·00
3387	**2561**	(1st) multicoloured (4 Sept)...................	2·00	2·00
		a. Sheetlet. No. 3387×2......................	4·00	4·00
3388	**2562**	(1st) multicoloured (4 Sept)...................	2·00	2·00
		a. Sheetlet. No. 3388×2......................	4·00	4·00
3389	**2563**	(1st) multicoloured (5 Sept)...................	2·00	2·00
		a. Sheetlet. No. 3389×2......................	4·00	4·00
3390	**2564**	(1st) multicoloured (5 Sept)...................	2·00	2·00
		a. Sheetlet. No. 3390×2......................	4·00	4·00
3391	**2565**	(1st) multicoloured (5 Sept)...................	2·00	2·00
		a. Sheetlet. No. 3391×2......................	4·00	4·00
3392	**2566**	(1st) multicoloured (5 Sept)...................	2·00	2·00
		a. Sheetlet. No. 3392×2......................	4·00	4·00
3393	**2567**	(1st) multicoloured (7 Sept)...................	4·00	4·00
		a. Sheetlet. No. 3393×2......................	8·00	8·00
3394	**2568**	(1st) multicoloured (7 Sept)...................	4·00	4·00
		a. Sheetlet. No. 3394×2......................	8·00	8·00
3395	**2569**	(1st) multicoloured (7 Sept)...................	4·00	4·00
		a. Sheetlet. No. 3395×2......................	8·00	8·00
3396	**2570**	(1st) multicoloured (7 Sept)...................	4·00	4·00
		a. Sheetlet. No. 3396×2......................	8·00	8·00
3397	**2571**	(1st) multicoloured (8 Sept)...................	2·00	2·00
		a. Sheetlet No. 3397×2......................	4·00	4·00
3398	**2572**	(1st) multicoloured (8 Sept)...................	2·00	2·00
		a. Sheetlet. No. 3398×2......................	4·00	4·00
3399	**2573**	(1st) multicoloured (8 Sept)...................	2·00	2·00

		a. Sheetlet. No. 3399×2	4·00	4·00
3400	**2574**	(1st) multicoloured (8 Sept)	2·00	2·00
		a. Sheetlet. No. 3400×2	4·00	4·00
3401	**2575**	(1st) multicoloured (10 Sept)	2·00	2·00
		a. Sheetlet. No. 3401×2	4·00	4·00
3402	**2576**	(1st) multicoloured (10 Sept)	2·00	2·00
		a. Sheetlet. No. 3402×2	4·00	4·00
3403	**2577**	(1st) multicoloured (10 Sept)	2·00	2·00
		a. Sheetlet. No. 3403×2	4·00	4·00
3404	**2578**	(1st) multicoloured (10 Sept)	2·00	2·00
		a. Sheetlet. No. 3404×2	4·00	4·00
3405	**2579**	(1st) multicoloured (10 Sept)	2·00	2·00
		a. Sheetlet. No. 3405×2	4·00	4·00

Set of 34	70·00	70·00
3372a/3405a *Set of 34 sheetlets*	£140	£140
First Day Covers (Nos. 3372a/3405a) (34) (Tallents House)		£200
First Day Covers (Nos. 3372a/3405a) (34) (London E20)		£190
First Day Cover (any gold medal stamp) (Tallents House)		10·00
First Day Cover (any gold medal stamp) (London E20)		10·00

The self-adhesive base sheetlets for Nos. 3372/405 were produced by Walsall with the image, name and event of the winning athletes digitally printed by regional printers in six different locations: Attleborough, Edinburgh, London, Preston, Solihull and Swindon. These sheetlets of 16 stamps were divided by roulettes into eight panes of two stamps (1×2). The left margins were inscribed as follows (reading downwards): emblem and 'ParalympicsGB'; 'London 2012 Paralympic Games'; barcode; Sheet number, Issue date and Printer location.

Nos. 3372, 3373 and 3405 were each printed in separate sheetlets of 16 stamps. Nos. 3374/7, 3381/4, 3385/8, 3389/92, 3393/6, 3397/400 and 3401/4 were printed in sheetlets of 16 containing four stamps of each design. The sheetlets of 16 containing Nos. 3378/80 contained four each of Nos. 3378/9 and eight of No. 3380.

2580 Scenes from Olympic and Paralympic Games (*Illustration reduced. Actual size 192×75 mm*)

Des The Chase. Litho Walsall.

2012 (27 Sept). *Memories of London 2012 Olympic and Paralympic Games.* Sheet 192×75 mm. 'All-over' phosphor. P 14½.

MS3406 **2580** (1st) Procession of athletes, Paralympic Games; (1st) Games makers and Olympic Stadium; £1·28 Opening ceremony of Paralympic Games; £1·28 Olympic Games closing ceremony and handover to Rio	9·50	9·50
First Day Cover (Tallents House)		11·00
First Day Cover (London E20)		11·00
Presentation Pack (P.O. Pack No. 476)	19·00	
PHQ Cards (set of 5) (369)	3·50	14·00

The five PHQ Cards show the four individual stamps and the complete miniature sheet.

Special First Day of Issue Postmarks

2581 BR Class D34 Nos. 62471 *Glen Falloch* and 62496 *Glen Loy* at Ardlui, 9 May 1959

(Gravure Walsall)

2012 (27 Sept). *Classic Locomotives of Scotland.* Booklet stamp. Design as 1st class stamp within **MS**3283. Self-adhesive. 'All-over' phosphor. Die-cut 14.

3407	**2581**	(1st) multicoloured	3·75	3·25

a. Booklet pane. No. 3407×2 and U3274×4	12·00	

No. 3407 was only issued in booklets, No. PM34, originally sold for £3·60.

2582 Sun and Particles ejected from Solar Surface seen from SOHO Observatory

2583 Venus with Clouds in Southern Hemisphere seen from *Venus Express*

2584 Ice in Martian Impact Crater seen from *Mars Express*

2585 Surface of Asteroid Lutetia seen from *Rosetta Probe*

2586 Saturn and its Rings seen from *Cassini Satellite*

2587 Titan (Saturn's largest moon) seen from *Huygens Probe*

(Des Osborne Ross Design. Litho Cartor)

2012 (16 Oct). *Space Science.* 'All-over' phosphor. P 14.

3408	**2582**	(1st) greenish yellow, bright magenta, new blue and black	1·25	1·10
3409	**2583**	(1st) greenish yellow, bright magenta, new blue and black	1·25	1·10
3410	**2584**	77p. greenish yellow, bright magenta, new blue and black	1·90	1·90
3411	**2585**	77p. black	1·90	1·90
3412	**2586**	£1·28 greenish yellow, bright magenta, new blue and black	3·25	3·25
3413	**2587**	£1·28 greenish yellow, bright magenta, new blue and black	3·25	3·25

Set of 6	11·50	11·50
Set of 6 Gutter Pairs	24·00	
First Day Cover (Tallents House)		13·00
First Day Cover (Star, Gaerwen Gwynnedd)		13·00
Presentation Pack (P.O. Pack No. 477)	13·00	
PHQ Cards (set of 6) (370)	5·00	12·00

Special First Day of Issue Postmarks

2588 Poppies on Barbed Wire Stems

(Des Hat-trick Design. Gravure Walsall)

2012 (23 Oct). *Lest We Forget* (4th issue). Self-adhesive. Two phosphor bands. P 14½×14 (with one elliptical hole in each vert side).
3414	**2588**	(1st) silver, black, new blue, greenish yellow and bright magenta	3·50	3·50

2589 Reindeer with Decorated Antlers

2590 Santa with Robin

2591 Reindeer with Decorated Antlers

2592 Snowman and Penguin

2593 Santa with Robin

2594 Robin with Star Decoration in Beak

2595 Cat and Mouse decorating Christmas Tree

(Des Axel Scheffler and Webb and Webb Design. Gravure Walsall (3415a, 3416a) or De La Rue (others))

2012 (6 Nov). *Christmas.* Illustrations by Axel Scheffler. One centre band (3415) or two phosphor bands (others). P 14½×14 (with one elliptical hole in each vert side).

(a) Self-adhesive.
3415	**2589**	(2nd) gold, bright magenta, greenish yellow, new blue and black..........	1·00	90
		a. Booklet pane. No. 3415×12	12·00	
3416	**2590**	(1st) gold, bright magenta, greenish yellow, new blue and black..........	1·25	1·10
		a. Booklet pane. No. 3416×12	15·00	
3417	**2591**	(2nd Large) gold, bright magenta, greenish yellow, new blue and black.......................	1·50	1·50
3418	**2592**	87p. gold, bright magenta, greenish yellow, new blue and black..........	2·25	2·25
3419	**2593**	(1st Large) gold, bright magenta, greenish yellow, new blue and black.......................	2·00	2·00
3420	**2594**	£1·28 gold, bright magenta, greenish yellow, new blue and black..........	3·25	3·25
3421	**2595**	£1·90 gold, bright magenta, greenish yellow, new blue and black	4·75	4·75
Set of 7			14·00	14·00
First Day Cover (Tallents House)				16·00
First Day Cover (Bethlehem, Llandeilo)				16·00
Presentation Pack (P.O. Pack No. 478)			29·00	
PHQ Cards (set of 8) (371)			5·50	18·00

(b) Ordinary gum.
MS3422	115×102 mm. As Nos. 3415/21		14·00	14·00
First Day Cover (Tallents House)				16·00
First Day Cover (Bethlehem, Llandeilo)				16·00

The eight PHQ cards depict the seven individual stamps and the miniature sheet.

The 2nd class, 1st class, 87p. and £1·28 stamps were also issued in sheets of 20 (LS83) containing eight 2nd class, eight 1st class, two 87p. and two £1·28 stamps, each with a *se-tenant* label. These sheets were printed in lithography and sold for £13·10 each.

Separate sheets of 20 2nd, 20 1st, ten 1st, ten 87p. and ten £1·28 were available with personal photographs on the labels from Royal Mail, Edinburgh. These were sold at £13·99 for 20 2nd, £18·25 for 20 1st, £9·99 for ten 1st, £13·55 for ten 87p. and £18·50 for ten £1·28.

The 1st class stamp printed in lithography, from either Post Office label sheets or 'Personalised Smilers' sheets is known with the black printing double.

Special First Day of Issue Postmarks

Collectors Pack
2012 (6 Nov). Comprises Nos. 3254/9, **MS**3264/70, **MS**3272/307, 3309/18, A3319/26, 3330/6, **MS**3341, **MS**3371, **MS**3406, 3408/13 and 3415/21
CP3422a Collectors Pack £200

Post Office Yearbook
2012 (6 Nov). Comprises Nos. 3254/9, **MS**3264/70, **MS**3272/307, 3309/18, A3319/26, 3330/6, **MS**3341, **MS**3371, **MS**3406, 3408/13 and 3415/21
YB3422a Yearbook £325

Miniature Sheet Collection
2012 (6 Nov). Comprises Nos. **MS**3264, **MS**3270, **MS**3272, **MS**3283, **MS**3336, **MS**3341, **MS**3371, **MS**3406 and **MS**3422
MS3422a Miniature Sheet Collection....................... 60·00

2596 Steam Locomotive on Metropolitan Railway, 1863

2597 Navvies excavating 'Deep Cut' Tube Tunnel, 1898

2598 Commuters in Carriage, 1911

2599 Boston Manor Art Deco Station, 1934

2600 Train on 'Deep Cut' Line, 1938

2601 Canary Wharf Station, 1999

2602 Classic London Underground Posters

(Des NB Studios (**MS**3429) or Hat-trick Design (others). Litho Cartor (3423/9) or photo Walsall (3430))

2013 (9 Jan). *150th Anniv of the London Underground.* One centre band (2nd) or 'all-over' phosphor (others).

(a) Ordinary gum. P 14½.
3423	**2596**	(2nd) greenish yellow, bright magenta, new blue and black	1·00	90
3424	**2597**	(2nd) greenish yellow, bright magenta, new blue and black	1·00	90

3425	**2598**	(1st) greenish yellow, bright magenta, new blue and black	1·25	1·10
3426	**2599**	(1st) greenish yellow, bright magenta, new blue and black	1·25	1·10
3427	**2600**	£1·28 greenish yellow, bright magenta, new blue and black	2·75	2·50
3428	**2601**	£1·28 greenish yellow, bright magenta, new blue and black	2·75	2·50

Set of 6 .... 10·00 9·00
Set of 6 Gutter Pairs.......................... 20·00
First Day Cover (Tallents House)........................ 11·00
First Day Cover (London W2) .... 11·00
Presentation Pack (P.O. Pack No. 480) (Nos. 3423/8 and
MS3429).......................... 18·00
PHQ Cards (set of 11) (372).............................. 7·50 17·00

MS3429 184×74 mm. **2602** (1st) Golders Green, 1908, By Underground to fresh air (Maxwell Armfield), 1915 and Summer Sales (Mary Koop), 1925; 77p. For the Zoo (Charles Paine), 1921, Power (Edward McKnight-Kauffer), 1931 and The Seen (James Fitton), 1948; 87p. A train every 90 seconds (Abram Games), 1937, Thanks to the Underground (Zero (Hans Schleger)), 1935 and Cut travelling time, Victoria Line (Tom Eckersley), 1969; £1·28 The London Transport Collection (Tom Eckersley), 1975, London Zoo (Abram Games), 1976 and The Tate Gallery by Tube (David Booth), 1987 .... 7·00 7·00
First Day Cover (Tallents House).......................... 9·00
First Day Cover (London W2) .... 9·00

(b) Self-adhesive. Die-cut P 14½.

3430	**2599**	(1st) multicoloured	3·50	3·00
		a. Booklet pane. Nos. 3430×2 and U2968b×4	12·00	

Special First Day of Issue Postmarks

2603 Elinor and Marianne Dashwood *(Sense and Sensibility)*

2604 Elizabeth Bennet and Portrait of Mr. Darcy *(Pride and Prejudice)*

2605 Fanny Price *(Mansfield Park)*

2606 Emma Woodhouse and Mr. Knightley *(Emma)*

2607 Catherine Morland *(Northanger Abbey)*

2608 Anne Elliot and Captain Wentworth *(Persuasion)*

(Des Angela Barrett and Webb and Webb. Litho Cartor)

2013 (21 Feb). Bicentenary of the Publication of Jane Austen's Pride and Prejudice. 'All-over' phosphor. P 14.

3431	**2603**	(1st) greenish yellow, bright magenta, new blue and black	1·25	1·10
3432	**2604**	(1st) greenish yellow, bright magenta, new blue and black	1·25	1·10
3433	**2605**	77p. greenish yellow, bright magenta, new blue and black	1·75	1·75
3434	**2606**	77p. greenish yellow, bright magenta, new blue and black	1·75	1·75
3435	**2607**	£1·28 greenish yellow, bright magenta, new blue and black	2·75	2·50
3436	**2608**	£1·28 greenish yellow, bright magenta, new blue and black	2·75	2·50

Set of 6 .... 11·00 10·00
Set of 6 Gutter Pairs.......................... 23·00
Set of 6 Traffic Light Gutter Pairs .... 26·00
First Day Cover (Tallents House)........................ 12·00
First Day Cover (Steventon, Basingstoke) .... 12·00
Presentation Pack (P.O. Pack No. 481)................... 13·00
PHQ Cards (set of 6) (373) .... 4·00 16·00

Special First Day of Issue Postmarks

2609 The Eleventh Doctor *(Matt Smith, from 2010)*

2610 The Tenth Doctor *(David Tennant, 2005-10)*

2611 The Ninth Doctor *(Christopher Eccleston, 2005)*

2612 The Eighth Doctor *(Paul McGann, 1996)*

2613 The Seventh Doctor *(Sylvester McCoy, 1987-9)*

2614 The Sixth Doctor *(Colin Baker, 1984-6)*

2615 The Fifth Doctor *(Peter Davison, 1982-4)*

2616 The Fourth Doctor *(Tom Baker, 1974-81)*

2617 The Third Doctor (Jon Pertwee, 1970-4)

2618 The Second Doctor (Patrick Troughton, 1966-9)

2619 The First Doctor (William Hartnell, 1963-6)

2620 Tardis

2621 *Dr. Who* 1963-2013

(Des GBH. Litho Cartor (3437/47) and **MS**3451a or gravure Walsall (3448/50) or Enschedé (**MS**3451))

2013 (26 Mar). *50th Anniv of Doctor Who* (TV programme) (1st issue). 'All-over' phosphor.

(a) Ordinary gum. 'All-over' phosphor. P 14.

3437	**2609**	(1st) greenish yellow, bright magenta, new blue and black	1·25	1·10
		a. Horiz strip of 3. Nos. 3437/9	3·75	3·25
		b. Booklet pane. Nos. 3437/9	4·25	
3438	**2610**	(1st) greenish yellow, bright magenta, new blue and black	1·25	1·10
3439	**2611**	(1st) greenish yellow, bright magenta, new blue and black	1·25	1·10
3440	**2612**	(1st) greenish yellow, bright magenta, new blue and black	1·25	1·10
		a. Horiz strip of 4. Nos. 3440/3	5·00	4·25
		b. Booklet pane. Nos. 3440/3	5·75	
3441	**2613**	(1st) greenish yellow, bright magenta, new blue and black	1·25	1·10
3442	**2614**	(1st) greenish yellow, bright magenta, new blue and black	1·25	1·10
3443	**2615**	(1st) greenish yellow, bright magenta, new blue and black	1·25	1·10
3444	**2616**	(1st) greenish yellow, bright magenta, new blue and black	1·25	1·10
		a. Horiz strip of 4. Nos. 3444/7	5·00	4·25
		b. Booklet pane. Nos. 3444/7	5·75	
3445	**2617**	(1st) greenish yellow, bright magenta, new blue and black	1·25	1·10
3446	**2618**	(1st) black and new blue	1·25	1·10
3447	**2619**	(1st) black and new blue	1·25	1·10
Set of 11			13·50	12·00
Set of 1 Gutter Strip of 3 and 2 Gutter Strips of 8			27·00	
First Day Covers (2) (Tallents House)				18·00
First Day Covers (2) (Cardiff)				18·00
Presentation Pack (P.O. Pack No. 482) (Nos. 3437/47 and **MS**3451)			19·00	
PHQ Cards (set of 17)			11·50	25·00

(b) Self-adhesive. One centre band (2nd) or two bands (1st). Die-cut P14½ (2nd) or 14½×14 (with one elliptical hole in each vert side) (1st).

3448	**2609**	(1st) multicoloured	5·50	5·00
		a. Booklet pane. No. 3448, 3449×4 and 3450	18·00	
3449	**2620**	(1st) multicoloured	2·50	2·00

3450	**2619**	(1st) multicoloured	5·50	5·00

MS3451 115×89 mm. **2621** (2nd) Dalek; (2nd) The Ood; (2nd) Weeping Angel; (2nd) Cyberman; (1st) TARDIS

		6·00	6·00
	a. Booklet pane. As No. **MS**3451 but 119×96 mm, with line of roulettes at left	7·00	
First Day Cover (Tallents House)			7·25
First Day Cover (Cardiff)			7·25

Nos. 3437/9 were printed together, *se-tenant*, as horizontal strips of three stamps in sheets of 48 (2 panes 6×4).

Nos. 3440/3 and 3444/7 were each printed together, *se-tenant*, as horizontal strips of four stamps in sheets of 48 (2 panes 4×6).

Nos. 3448/50 were issued in stamp booklets, No. PM36, sold for £3·60.

The 1st class TARDIS stamp from the booklet pane **MS**3451a differs from the same design in the miniature sheet by being perforated 15 all round.

The *design area* of No. 3449 measures 17½ × 21½ mm, slightly larger than the same TARDIS design (Type **2620**) from the miniature sheet and premium booklet pane (**MS**3451/a) which measures 17 × 21mm. (All are 20 × 24 measured *perf to perf* edge).

The 1st class TARDIS stamp was also issued in sheets of 20, each stamp accompanied by a *se-tenant* label (LS85). These sheets were printed in lithography.

Special First Day of Issue Postmarks

(Des GBH. Litho Cartor)

2013 (26 Mar). *50th Anniv of Doctor Who* (TV programme) (2nd issue). As No. 3449 but ordinary gum. Two phosphor bands. P 14½×14 with one elliptical hole in each vertical side

3452	**2620**	(1st) multicoloured	3·50	3·00

No. 3452 only comes from pane No. U3012a in the £13·37 premium booklet, No. DY6.

2622 Norman Parkinson (1913-90, portrait and fashion photographer)

2623 Vivien Leigh (1913-67, actress)

2624 Peter Cushing (1913-94, actor)

2625 David Lloyd George (1863-1945, Prime Minister 1916-22)

2626 Elizabeth David (1913-92, cookery writer)

2627 John Archer (1863-1932, politician and civil rights campaigner)

2628 Benjamin Britten
(1913-76, composer and
pianist)

2629 Mary Leakey
(1913-96, archaeologist and
anthropologist)

2630 Bill Shankly
(1913-81, football player and
manager)

2631 Richard Dimbleby
(1913-65, journalist and
broadcaster)

(Des Together Design. Litho Cartor)

2013 (16 Apr). *Great Britons.* 'All-over' phosphor. *P* 14½.

3453	**2622**	(1st) silver, greenish yellow, bright magenta, new blue and black........	1·25	1·10
		a. Horiz strip of 5. Nos. 3453/7	6·25	5·50
3454	**2623**	(1st) silver, greenish yellow, bright magenta, new blue and black........	1·25	1·10
3455	**2624**	(1st) silver, greenish yellow, bright magenta, new blue and black........	1·25	1·10
3456	**2625**	(1st) silver, greenish yellow, bright magenta, new blue and black........	1·25	1·10
3457	**2626**	(1st) silver, greenish yellow, bright magenta, new blue and black........	1·25	1·10
3458	**2627**	(1st) silver, greenish yellow, bright magenta, new blue and black........	1·25	1·10
		a. Horiz strip of 5. Nos. 3458/62..........	6·25	5·50
3459	**2628**	(1st) silver, greenish yellow, bright magenta, new blue and black........	1·25	1·10
3460	**2629**	(1st) silver, greenish yellow, bright magenta, new blue and black........	1·25	1·10
3461	**2630**	(1st) silver, greenish yellow, bright magenta, new blue and black........	1·25	1·10
3462	**2631**	(1st) silver, greenish yellow, bright magenta, new blue and black........	1·25	1·10
Set of 10..			11·00	10·00
Set of 2 Gutter Strips of 10........................			23·00	
First Day Cover (Tallents House)...............				12·00
First Day Cover (Great Ness, Shrewsbury)............				12·00
Presentation Pack (P.O. Pack No. 483)...............			12·00	
PHQ Cards (set of 10) (375)			7·00	18·00

Nos. 3453/7 and 3458/62 were each printed together, *se-tenant*, as
horizontal strips of five stamps in sheets of 50 (2 panes 5×5).

Special First Day of Issue Postmarks

"I have been
impelled
by
curiosity."
Mary Leakey
· 16.4.2013 ·

'Liberty
has restraints
but no
frontiers.'
David Lloyd George
· 16.4.2013 ·

2632 Jimmy Greaves
(England)

2633 John Charles
(Wales)

2634 Gordon Banks
(England)

2635 George Best
(Northern Ireland)

2636 John Barnes
(England)

2637 Kevin Keegan
(England)

2638 Denis Law
(Scotland)

2639 Bobby Moore
(England)

2640 Bryan Robson
(England)

2641 Dave Mackay
(Scotland)

2642 Bobby Charlton
(England)

(Des Andrew Kinsman and True North. Litho Cartor (3463/74)
or gravure Walsall (3475/6))

2013 (9 May) –**14**. *Football Heroes* (1st issue). 'All-over' phosphor.

(a) Ordinary gum. P 14½.

3463	**2632**	(1st) greenish yellow, bright magenta, new blue and black	1·50	1·40
		a. Horiz strip of 5. Nos. 3463/7	7·50	7·00
3464	**2633**	(1st) greenish yellow, bright magenta, new blue and black	1·50	1·40
3465	**2634**	(1st) greenish yellow, bright magenta, new blue and black	1·50	1·40
3466	**2635**	(1st) greenish yellow, bright magenta, new blue and black	1·50	1·40
3467	**2636**	(1st) greenish yellow, bright magenta, new blue and black	1·50	1·40
3468	**2637**	(1st) greenish yellow, bright magenta, new blue and black	1·50	1·40
		a. Horiz strip of 6. Nos. 3468/73.......	9·00	8·25
3469	**2638**	(1st) greenish yellow, bright magenta, new blue and black	1·50	1·40
3470	**2639**	(1st) greenish yellow, bright magenta, new blue and black	1·50	1·40
3471	**2640**	(1st) greenish yellow, bright magenta, new blue and black	1·50	1·40
3472	**2641**	(1st) greenish yellow, bright magenta, new blue and black	1·50	1·40
3473	**2642**	(1st) greenish yellow, bright magenta, new blue and black	1·50	1·40

Set of 11			15·00	14·00
Set of 1 Gutter Strip of 12 and 1 Gutter Strip of 10			29·00	
First Day Cover (Tallents House)				15·00
First Day Cover (Wembley, Middlesex)				15·00
Presentation Pack (P.O. Pack 484)			16·00	
PHQ Cards (set of 12) (376)			8·00	20·00
MS3474 192×74 mm. Nos. 3463/73			15·00	15·00
First Day Cover				16·00

(b) Self-adhesive. Die-cut P 14½.

3475	**2635**	(1st) multicoloured	4·00	3·25
		a. Booklet pane. Nos. 3475/6 and		
		U2968b×4	12·00	
3476	**2639**	(1st) multicoloured	4·00	3·25
3477	**2633**	(1st) multicoloured (20.2.14)	4·00	3·25
		a. Booklet pane. Nos. 3477/8 and		
		U2968b×4	12·00	
3478	**2641**	(1st) multicoloured (20.2.14)	4·00	3·25

Nos. 3463/7 were printed together, se-tenant, as horizontal strips of five stamps in sheets of 30 (5×6).

Nos. 3468/73 were printed together, se-tenant, as horizontal strips of six stamps in sheets of 30 (6×5).

Nos. 3475/6 and 3477/8 were issued in separate booklets, Nos. PM37 and PM41, both sold for £3·60.

Nos. 3463/87 commemorate the 150th anniversary of the Football Association and the 140th Anniversary of the Scottish Football Association.

Special First Day of Issue Postmarks

(Litho Cartor)

2013 (9 May). *Football Heroes* (2nd issue). Self-adhesive. 'All-over'. phosphor. Die-cut P 14½×14.

3479	**2632**	(1st) multicoloured	2·50	2·00
		a. Booklet pane. Nos. 3479/83	12·50	
3480	**2633**	(1st) multicoloured	2·50	2·00
3481	**2637**	(1st) multicoloured	2·50	2·00
3482	**2638**	(1st) multicoloured	2·50	2·00
3483	**2639**	(1st) multicoloured	2·50	2·00
3484	**2634**	(1st) multicoloured	2·50	2·00
		a. Booklet pane. Nos. 3484/9	14·00	
3485	**2635**	(1st) multicoloured	2·50	2·00
3486	**2636**	(1st) multicoloured	2·50	2·00
3487	**2640**	(1st) multicoloured	2·50	2·00
3488	**2641**	(1st) multicoloured	2·50	2·00
3489	**2642**	(1st) multicoloured	2·50	2·00
Set of 11			25·00	20·00

Nos. 3479/89 were issued in £11·11 premium booklets, No. DY7.

No. 3490 is vacant.

2646 Preliminary Oil Sketch for The Coronation of Queen Elizabeth II (Terence Cuneo), 1953

2647 Queen Elizabeth II in Garter Robes (Nicky Philipps), 2012

2648 Portrait by Andrew Festing, 1999

2649 Portrait by Pietro Annigoni, 1955

2650 Portrait by Sergei Pavlenko, 2000

2651 Her Majesty Queen Elizabeth II (Richard Stone), 1992

(Gravure Walsall)

2013 (30 May). *60th Anniversary of the Coronation*. Six Decades of Royal Portraits. Phosphor band at left (2nd) or 'all-over' phosphor (others). P 14.

3491	**2646**	(2nd) gold, black, new blue, greenish yellow and bright magenta	1·00	90
3492	**2647**	(1st) gold, black, new blue, greenish yellow and bright magenta	1·25	1·10
3493	**2648**	78p. gold, black, new blue, greenish yellow and bright magenta	1·75	1·75
3494	**2649**	88p. gold, black, new blue, greenish yellow and bright magenta	2·00	2·00
3495	**2650**	£1·28 gold, black, new blue, greenish yellow and bright magenta	2·75	2·50
3496	**2651**	£1·88 gold, black, new blue, greenish yellow and bright magenta	3·75	3·75
Set of 6			11·50	11·00
Set of 6 Gutter Pairs			24·00	
Set of 6 Traffic Light Gutter Blocks of 4			50·00	
First Day Cover (Tallents House)			13·00	
First Day Cover (London SW1)			13·00	
Presentation Pack (P.O. Pack No. 485)			13·00	
PHQ Cards (set of 6) (377)			4·00	15·00
Commemorative Document (Nos. 3491/2) (2 June)			15·00	

Special First Day of Issue Postmarks

2652 UTA Class W No. 103 *Thomas Somerset* with Belfast Express, Downhill, near Castlerock, c.1950

2653 Classic Locomotives of Northern Ireland

(Des Delaney Design Consultants. Gravure Walsall (3497) or litho Cartor (**MS**3498))

2013 (18 June). *Classic Locomotives* (3rd series). Northern Ireland. 'All-over' phosphor.

(a) Self-adhesive. Die-cut P .

3497	**2652**	(1st) black, grey and gold	3·75	3·25
		a. Booklet pane. No. 3497×2 and		
		U2968b×4	12·00	

(b) Ordinary gum. Sheet 180×74 mm. P 14.
MS3498 **2653** (1st) As Type 2652; 78p. UTA SG3 No. 35; 88p. Peckett No. 2; £1·28 CDRJC Class 5 No. 4 .... 8·00 8·00
First Day Cover (Tallents House) .... 9·00
First Day Cover (Belfast) .... 9·00
Presentation Pack (P.O. Pack No. 486) .... 8·50
PHQ Cards (set of 5) (378) .... 3·50 10·00

No. 3497 was issued in booklets, No. PM38, sold for £3·60.
The five PHQ cards show the four individual stamps and the complete miniature sheet.

Special First Day of Issue Postmarks

2654 Comma
(Polygonia c-album)

2655 Orange-tip
(Anthocharis cardamines)

2656 Small Copper
(Lycaena phlaeas)

2657 Chalkhill Blue
(Polyommatus coridon)

2658 Swallowtail
(Papilio machaon)

2659 Purple Emperor
(Apatura iris)

2660 Marsh Fritillary
(Euphydryas aurinia)

2661 Brimstone
(Gonepteryx rhamni)

2662 Red Admiral
(Vanessa atalanta)

2663 Marbled White
(Melanargia galathea)

(Des Richard Lewington and Marc & Anna. Litho Cartor (3499/508) or gravure (3509/10) Walsall)

2013 (11 July). Butterflies. 'All-over' phosphor.

(a) Ordinary paper. P 14×14½.
3499 **2654** (1st) silver, greenish yellow, bright magenta, new blue and black.......... 1·25 1·10
 a. Horiz strip of 5. Nos. 3499/503 .... 6·00 5·25
3500 **2655** (1st) silver, greenish yellow, bright magenta, new blue and black.......... 1·25 1·10
3501 **2656** (1st) .... 1·25 1·10
3502 **2657** (1st) .... 1·25 1·10
3503 **2658** (1st) .... 1·25 1·10
3504 **2659** (1st) .... 1·25 1·10
 a. Horiz strip of 5. Nos. 3504/8 .... 6·00 5·25
3505 **2660** (1st) .... 1·25 1·10
3506 **2661** (1st) .... 1·25 1·10
3507 **2662** (1st) .... 1·25 1·10
3508 **2663** (1st) .... 1·25 1·10
Set of 10 .... 11·00 10·00
Set of 2 Gutter Strips of 10 .... 23·00
First Day Cover (Tallents House) .... 12·00
First Day Cover (Lulworth Camp, Wareham, Dorset) .... 12·00
Presentation Pack (P.O. Pack No. 487) .... 13·00
PHQ Cards (set of 10) (379) .... 6·75 18·00

(b) Self-adhesive. Die-cut P 14×14½.
3509 **2657** (1st) multicoloured.......... 3·75 3·25
 a. Booklet pane. Nos. 3509/10 and U2968b×4 .... 12·00
3510 **2654** (1st) multicoloured.......... 3·75 3·25

Nos. 3499/503 and 3504/8 were each printed together, *se-tenant*, as horizontal strips of five stamps in sheets of 50 (2 panes 5×5).

Nos. 3509/10 were issued in stamp booklets, No. PM39, sold for £3·60.

Special First Day of Issue Postmarks

2664 Andy Murray's Wimbledon Victory

(Litho Walsall)

2013 (8 Aug). Andy Murray, Men's Singles Champion, Wimbledon. Sheet 192×75 mm. 'All-over' phosphor. P 14½.
MS3511 **2664** (1st) Andy Murray kissing Wimbledon Trophy; (1st) Andy Murray serving; £1·28 In action; £1·28 Holding Trophy.......... 8·50 8·50
First Day Cover (Tallents House) .... 8·50
First Day Cover (Wimbledon, SW19) .... 8·50
Presentation Pack (P.O. Pack No. M21) .... 9·25

Special First Day of Issue Postmarks

2665 Jaguar E-Type, 1961

2666 Rolls-Royce Silver Shadow, 1965

2667 Aston Martin DB5, 1963

2668 MG MGB, 1962

2669 Morgan Plus 8, 1968

2670 Lotus Esprit, 1976

2671 'The Workhorses'

(Des Why Not Associates (3512/17) or Robert Maude
and Sarah Davies (**MS**3518). Litho Cartor)

2013 (13 Aug). British Auto Legends. 'All-over' phosphor. *P* 13½
(3512/17) or 14 (**MS**3518).

3512	**2665**	(1st) silver, greenish yellow, bright magenta, new blue and black..........	1·25	1·10
		a. Horiz strip of 3. Nos. 3512/14...........	3·50	3·25
3513	**2666**	(1st) silver, greenish yellow, bright magenta, new blue and black..........	1·25	1·10
3514	**2667**	(1st) silver, greenish yellow, bright magenta, new blue and black..........	1·25	1·10
3515	**2668**	£1·28 silver, greenish yellow, bright magenta, new blue and black..........	2·75	2·50
		a. Horiz strip of 3. Nos. 3515/17...........	8·00	7·25

3516	**2669**	£1·28 silver, greenish yellow, bright magenta, new blue and black..........	2·75	2·50
3517	**2670**	£1·28 silver, greenish yellow, bright magenta, new blue and black..........	2·75	2·50
Set of 6..			11·00	10·00
Set of 2 Gutter Strips of 6....................................			24·00	
First Day Cover (Tallents House)..........................				12·00
First Day Cover (Alwalton, Peterborough)..........				12·00
Presentation Pack (P.O. Pack No. 488) (Nos. 3512/7 and **MS**3518)..			17·00	
PHQ Cards (set of 11) (380)..................................			7·50	18·00

MS3518 180×74 mm. **2671** (1st)×4 Morris Minor Royal
Mail van (1953-71); Austin FX4 (1958-97) London taxi;
Ford Anglia 105E (1959-67) police car; Coastguard
Land Rover Defender 110 (from 1990) (all 40×30 mm) 6·00 6·00

First Day Cover (Tallents House)................................ 7·00
First Day Cover (Alwalton, Peterborough)............... 7·00

Nos. 3512/14 and 3515/17 were each printed together, *se-tenant*, as
horizontal strips of three stamps in sheets of 60 (2 panes 6×5).

The 1st value from **MS**3518 is inscr 'EUROPA'.

The complete miniature sheet is shown on one of the eleven PHQ
cards with the others depicting individual stamps including those from
the miniature sheet.

Special First Day of Issue Postmarks

2672 East Indiaman *Atlas*, 1813   **2673** Royal Mail Ship *Britannia*, 1840

2674 Tea Clipper *Cutty Sark*, 1870   **2675** Cargo Liner *Clan Matheson*, 1919

2676 Royal Mail Ship *Queen Elizabeth*, 1940   **2677** Bulk Carrier *Lord Hinton*, 1986

(Des Silk Pearce. Litho Enschedé (booklet panes) or Cartor (others))

2013 (19 Sept). *Merchant Navy* (1st issue). 'All-over' phosphor. *P* 14.

3519	**2672**	(1st) bluish grey, greenish yellow, bright magenta, new blue and black.........	1·25	1·10
		a. Booklet pane. Nos. 3519/21 with margins all round.....................	4·25	
3520	**2673**	(1st) bluish grey, greenish yellow, bright magenta, new blue and black.........	1·25	1·10
3521	**2674**	(1st) bluish grey, greenish yellow, bright magenta, new blue and black.........	1·25	1·10
3522	**2675**	£1·28 bluish grey, greenish yellow, bright magenta, new blue and black.........	2·75	2·50
		a. Booklet pane. Nos. 3522/4 with margins all round.....................	9·00	
3523	**2676**	£1·28 bluish grey, greenish yellow, bright magenta, new blue and black.........	2·75	2·50
3524	**2677**	£1·28 bluish grey, greenish yellow, bright magenta, new blue and black.........	2·75	2·50
Set of 6..			11·00	10·00

Set of 6 Gutter Pairs..	23·00	
First Day Cover (Tallents House)...............................	12·00	
First Day Cover (Clydebank).....................................	12·00	
Presentation Pack (P.O. Pack No. 489) (Nos. 3519/24 and		
MS3529)...	17·00	
PHQ Cards (set of 11) (381).......................................	6·75	18·00

Nos. 3519a and 3522a were only issued in the £11·19 Merchant Navy booklet, No DY8.

The complete miniature sheet is shown on one of the eleven PHQ cards with the others depicting individual stamps including those from **MS**3529.

Special First Day of Issue Postmarks

2678 Destroyer HMS *Vanoc* escorting Atlantic Convoy

2679 Merchant Ship passing the Naval Control Base in the Thames Estuary

2680 Sailors clearing Ice from the Decks of HMS *King George V* in Arctic Waters

2681 Naval Convoy of 24 Merchant Ships in the North Sea

2682 Second World War Atlantic and Arctic Convoys

(Des Silk Pearce. Litho Enschedé)

2013 (19 Sept). *Merchant Navy* (2nd issue). 'All-over' phosphor. *P* 14.

3525	**2678**	(1st) multicoloured..........................	1·40	1·40
		a. Booklet pane. Nos. 3525/8............	5·00	
3526	**2679**	(1st) multicoloured..........................	1·40	1·40
3527	**2680**	(1st) multicoloured..........................	1·40	1·40
3528	**2681**	(1st) multicoloured..........................	1·40	1·40
Set of 4			5·00	5·00
MS3529	**2682**	115×89 mm. Nos. 3525/8............	5·00	5·00
First Day Cover				6·00

Nos. 3525/8 were only issued in the £11·19 Merchant Navy booklet, No. DY8, and in **MS**3529.

2683 Royal Mail Van

(Gravure Walsall)

2013 (19 Sept). *Royal Mail Transport: By Land and Sea.* Self-adhesive booklet stamps. Die-cut P 14.

3530	**2683**	(1st) multicoloured..........................	4·50	4·00
		a. Nos. 3530/1 and No. U2968b×4......	13·00	
3531	**2673**	(1st) multicoloured..........................	4·50	4·00

The design of No. 3530 is as the Royal Mail van stamp within **MS**3518, and it is also inscr 'EUROPA'.

Nos. 3530/1 were only issued in booklets, No. PM40, originally sold for £3.60.

No. 3530 includes the 'EUROPA' emblem.

2684 Polacanthus

2685 Ichthyosaurus

2686 Iguanodon

2687 Ornithocheirus

2688 Baryonyx

2689 Dimorphodon

2690 Hypsilophodon

2691 Cetiosaurus

2692 Megalosaurus

2693 Plesiosaurus

(Des John Sibbick (illustrator) and Why Not Associates. Gravure Walsall)

2013 (10 Oct). *Dinosaurs.* Self-adhesive. 'All-over' phosphor. Die-cut P 13½×14 (with no teeth around protruding parts at top or foot of the designs).

3532	**2684**	(1st) black, new blue, greenish yellow,		
		bright magenta and grey....................	1·25	1·10
		a. Horiz strip of 5. Nos. 3532/6..........	6·00	
3533	**2685**	(1st) black, new blue, greenish yellow,		
		bright magenta and grey....................	1·25	1·10

3534	**2686**	(1st) black, new blue, greenish yellow, bright magenta and grey	1·25	1·10
3535	**2687**	(1st) black, new blue, greenish yellow, bright magenta and grey	1·25	1·10
3536	**2688**	(1st) black, new blue, greenish yellow, bright magenta and grey	1·25	1·10
3537	**2689**	(1st) black, new blue, greenish yellow, bright magenta and grey	1·25	1·10
		a. Horiz strip of 5. Nos. 3537/41	6·00	
3538	**2690**	(1st) black, new blue, greenish yellow, bright magenta and grey	1·25	1·10
3539	**2691**	(1st) black, new blue, greenish yellow, bright magenta and grey	1·25	1·10
3540	**2692**	(1st) black, new blue, greenish yellow, bright magenta and grey	1·25	1·10
3541	**2693**	(1st) black, new blue, greenish yellow, bright magenta and grey	1·25	1·10
Set of 10			11·00	10·00
First Day Cover (Tallents House)				12·00
First Day Cover (Lyme Regis, Dorset)				12·00
Presentation Pack (P.O. Pack 490)			15·00	
PHQ Cards (set of 10) (382)			6·75	15·00

Nos. 3532/6 and 3537/41 were each printed together as horizontal strips of five stamps in sheets of 50 (2 panes 5×5).

Special First Day of Issue Postmarks

2694 Madonna and Child (Francesco Granacci)

2695 Virgin and Child with the Young St. John the Baptist (detail) (Antoniazzo Romano)

2696 Madonna and Child (Francesco Granacci)

2697 St. Roch Praying to the Virgin for an End to the Plague (detail) (Jacques-Louis David)

2698 Virgin and Child with the Young St. John the Baptist (detail) (Antoniazzo Romano)

2699 La Vierge au Lys (William-Adolphe Bouguereau)

2700 Theotokos, Mother of God (Fadi Mikhail)

(Des Robert Maude and Sarah Davies. Gravure Walsall (3542a, 3543a) or De La Rue (others))

2013 (5 Nov). *Christmas. Madonna and Child Paintings.* One centre band (3542) or two bands (others). P 14½×15.

(a) Self-adhesive.

3542	**2694**	(2nd) bright magenta, greenish yellow, new blue and black	1·00	90
		a. Booklet pane. No. 3542×12	12·00	
3543	**2695**	(1st) bright magenta, greenish yellow, new blue and black	1·25	1·10
		a. Booklet pane. No. 3543×12	15·00	
3544	**2696**	(2nd Large) bright magenta, greenish yellow, new blue and black	1·50	1·50
3545	**2697**	88p. bright magenta, greenish yellow, new blue and black	2·00	2·00
3546	**2698**	(1st Large) bright magenta, greenish yellow, new blue and black	2·00	2·00
3547	**2699**	£1·28 bright magenta, greenish yellow, new blue and black	2·75	2·50
3548	**2700**	£1·88 bright magenta, greenish yellow, new blue and black	3·75	3·75
Set of 7			13·00	12·00
First Day Cover (Tallents House)				14·00
First Day Cover (Bethlehem, Llandeilo)				14·00
Presentation Pack (P.O. Pack No. 491)			15·00	
PHQ Cards (set of 8) (383)			5·50	18·00

(b) Ordinary gum.

MS3549	146×74 mm. As Nos. 3542/8		14·00	14·00
First Day Cover				15·00

The eight PHQ cards show the seven individual stamps and the complete miniature sheet.

The 2nd class, 1st class, 88p., £1·28 and £1·88 stamps were also issued in sheets of 20 containing eight 2nd class, eight 1st class, two 88p, one £1·28 and one £1·88 stamps, each stamp accompanied by a *se-tenant* label. These sheets were printed in lithography and sold for £13·62 each.

Separate sheets of 20 2nd, ten 1st, ten 88p. and ten £1·28 were available with personal photographs on the labels from Royal Mail, Edinburgh. These were sold at £14·50 for 20 2nd, £10·20 for ten 1st, £14·45 for ten 88p. and £18·50 for ten £1·28.

Special First Day of Issue Postmarks

2701 Angels (Rosie Hargreaves)

2702 Santa (Molly Robson)

(Gravure Walsall)

2013 (5 Nov). *Children's Christmas.* Self-adhesive. One phosphor band at right (2nd) or two phosphor bands (1st). Die-cut P 14½.

3550	**2701**	(2nd) multicoloured	3·50	2·00
3551	**2702**	(1st) multicoloured	4·00	2·50
First Day Cover (Tallents House)				6·00
First Day Cover (Bethlehem, Llandeilo)				6·00
Presentation Pack (P.O. Pack No. M22)			8·00	

Special First Day of Issue Postmarks

2713 Peppa Pig   **2714** Shaun the Sheep

Collectors Pack

2013 (5 Nov). Comprises Nos. 3423/9, 3431/47, **MS**3451, 3453/73, 3491/6, **MS**3498/508, **MS**3511/24, **MS**3529, 3532/48 and 3550/1

CP3551*a* Collectors Pack.. £175

Post Office Yearbook

2013 (5 Nov). Comprises Nos. 3423/9, 3431/47, **MS**3451, 3453/73, 3491/6, **MS**3498/508, **MS**3511/24, **MS**3529, 3532/48 and 3550/1

YB3551*a* Yearbook... £180

Miniature Sheet Collection

2013 (5 Nov). Comprises Nos. **MS**3429, **MS**3451, **MS**3474, **MS**3498, **MS**3511, **MS**3518, **MS**3529 and **MS**3549

MS3551*a* Miniature Sheet Collection......................... 50.00

(Des Interabang. Gravure Walsall)

2014 (7 Jan). *Classic Children's TV*. 'All-over' phosphor. Self-adhesive. Die-cut P 15.

3552	**2703**	(1st)	greenish yellow, bright magenta, new blue and black	1·25	1·10
			a. Horiz strip of 6. Nos. 3552/7	7·25	
3553	**2704**	(1st)	greenish yellow, bright magenta, new blue and black	1·25	1·10
3554	**2705**	(1st)	greenish yellow, bright magenta, new blue and black	1·25	1·10
3555	**2706**	(1st)	greenish yellow, bright magenta, new blue and black	1·25	1·10
3556	**2707**	(1st)	greenish yellow, bright magenta, new blue and black	1·25	1·10
3557	**2708**	(1st)	greenish yellow, bright magenta, new blue and black	1·25	1·10
3558	**2709**	(1st)	greenish yellow, bright magenta, new blue and black	1·25	1·10
			a. Horiz strip of 6. Nos. 3558/63............	7·25	
3559	**2710**	(1st)	greenish yellow, bright magenta, new blue and black	1·25	1·10
3560	**2711**	(1st)	greenish yellow, bright magenta, new blue and black	1·25	1·10
3561	**2712**	(1st)	greenish yellow, bright magenta, new blue and black	1·25	1·10
3562	**2713**	(1st)	greenish yellow, bright magenta, new blue and black	1·25	1·10
3563	**2714**	(1st)	greenish yellow, bright magenta, new blue and black	1·25	1·10
Set of 12.........				11·00	12·00
Set of 2 Gutter Strips of 12.........				27·00	
First Day Cover (Tallents House).........					14·00
First Day Cover (Wimbledon, London SW19).........					14·00
Presentation Pack (P.O. Pack No. 493).........				15·00	
PHQ Cards (set of 12) (384).........				8·00	20·00

Nos. 3552/7 and 3558/63 were each printed together, *se-tenant*, in horizontal strips of six stamps in sheets of 60 (6×10).

2703 Andy Pandy

2704 Ivor the Engine

2705 Dougal (*The Magic Roundabout*)

2706 Windy Miller (*Camberwick Green*)

2707 Mr. Benn

2708 Great Uncle Bulgaria (*The Wombles*)

2709 Bagpuss

2710 Paddington Bear

2711 Postman Pat

2712 Bob the Builder

Special First Day of Issue Postmarks

2715 Riding for the Disabled Association

2716 The King's Troop Ceremonial Horses

2717 Dray Horses

2718 Royal Mews Carriage Horses

2719 Police Horses

2720 Forestry Horse

(Des Michael Denny and Harold Batten. Litho Cartor)

2014 (4 Feb). *Working Horses*. 'All-over' phosphor. *P* 14.
3564	**2715**	(1st) pale grey, greenish yellow, bright magenta, new blue and black		1·25	1·10
3565	**2716**	(1st) pale grey, greenish yellow, bright magenta, new blue and black		1·25	1·10
3566	**2717**	88p. pale grey, greenish yellow, bright magenta, new blue and black		2·00	2·00
3567	**2718**	88p. pale grey, greenish yellow, bright magenta, new blue and black		2·00	2·00
3568	**2719**	£1·28 pale grey, greenish yellow, bright magenta, new blue and black		2·75	2·50
3569	**2720**	£1·28 pale grey, greenish yellow, bright magenta, new blue and black		2·75	2·50

Set of 6 ... 11·00 10·00
Set of 6 Gutter Pairs ... 23·00
First Day Cover (Tallents House) ... 12·00
First Day Cover (Horseheath, Cambridge) ... 12·00
Presentation Pack (P.O. Pack No. 494) ... 13·00
PHQ Cards (set of 6) (385) ... 4·00 16·00

Special First Day of Issue Postmarks

2721 BR Dean Goods No. 2532

2722 BR D34 Nos. 62471 & 62496

2723 UTA Class W No. 103 *Thomas Somerset* with Belfast Express, Downhill, near Castlerock, *c.*1950

2724 LMS No. 7720

2725 Peckett R2 *Thor*

2726 BR D40 No. 62276

2727 UTA SG3 No. 35

2728 Hunslet No. 589 *Blanche*

2729 Classic Locomotives of Wales *(Illustration reduced)*

(Des Delaney Design Consultants. Litho Enschedé (booklet))

2014 (20 Feb). *Classic Locomotives* (4th and 5th series). Wales (**MS**3578) and United Kingdom. 'All-over' phosphor. *P* 14.
3570	**2721**	(1st) multicoloured		1·50	1·50
		a. Booklet pane. Nos. 3570 and 3574, each×2 with margins all round	6·00		
3571	**2722**	(1st) multicoloured		1·50	1·50
		a. Booklet pane. Nos. 3571 and 3575, each×2 with margins all round	6·25		
3572	**2723**	(1st) multicoloured		1·50	1·50
		a. Booklet pane. Nos. 3572 and 3576, each×2 with margins all round	6·75		
3573	**2724**	(1st) multicoloured		1·50	1·50
		a. Booklet pane. Nos. 3573 and 3577, each×2 with margins all round	6·75		
3574	**2725**	60p. multicoloured		1·50	1·50
3575	**2726**	68p. multicoloured		1·75	1·75
3576	**2727**	78p. multicoloured		2·00	2·00
3577	**2728**	78p. multicoloured		2·00	2·00

Set of 8 ... 12·00 12·00
MS3578 180×74 mm. **2729** No. 3573; No. 3577; 88p. W&LLR No. 822 *The Earl*; £1.28 BR 5600 No. 5652 ... 7·50 7·50
First Day Cover (Tallents House) ... 9·50
First Day Cover (Porthmadog) ... 9·50
Presentation Pack (P.O. Pack No. 495) ... 9·00
PHQ Cards (set of 5) (386) ... 3·50 11·00
Nos. 3570/7 were issued only in £13·97 Classic Locomotives booklets, No. DY9, or also in **MS**3578 (Nos. 3573 and 3577).
The five PHQ cards show the four individual stamps and the complete miniature sheet.

Special First Day of Issue Postmarks

2730 Roy Plomley (1914-85, broadcaster and writer)

2731 Barbara Ward (1914-81, economist and broadcaster)

2732 Joe Mercer (1914-90, football player and manager)

2733 Kenneth More (1914-82, stage and screen actor)

2734 Dylan Thomas (1914-53, poet and writer)

2735 Sir Alec Guinness (1914-2000, stage and screen actor)

2736 Noorunissa Inayat Khan (1914-44, SOE agent in occupied France)

2737 Max Perutz (1914-2002, molecular biologist and Nobel laureate)

2738 Joan Littlewood (1914-2002, theatre director and writer)

2739 Abram Games (1914-96, graphic designer)

(Des Purpose. Litho Cartor)

2014 (25 Mar). *Remarkable Lives.* 'All-over' phosphor. P 14½.

3579	**2730**	(1st) greenish yellow, bright magenta, new blue and black		1·25	1·10
		a. Horiz strip of 5. Nos. 3579/83		6·00	5·25
3580	**2731**	(1st) greenish yellow, bright magenta, new blue and black		1·25	1·10
3581	**2732**	(1st) greenish yellow, bright magenta, new blue and black		1·25	1·10
3582	**2733**	(1st) greenish yellow, bright magenta, new blue and black		1·25	1·10
3583	**2734**	(1st) greenish yellow, bright magenta, new blue and black		1·25	1·10
3584	**2735**	(1st) greenish yellow, bright magenta, new blue and black		1·25	1·10
		a. Horiz strip of 5. Nos. 3584/8		6·00	5·25
3585	**2736**	(1st) greenish yellow, bright magenta, new blue and black		1·25	1·10
3586	**2737**	(1st) greenish yellow, bright magenta, new blue and black		1·25	1·10
3587	**2738**	(1st) greenish yellow, bright magenta, new blue and black		1·25	1·10
3588	**2739**	(1st) greenish yellow, bright magenta, new blue and black		1·25	1·10

Set of 10	11·00	10·00
Set of 2 Gutter Strips of 10	23·00	
First Day Cover (Tallents House)		12·00
First Day Cover (Swansea)		12·00
Presentation Pack (P.O. Pack No. 496)	13·00	
PHQ Cards (set of 10) (387)	6·75	20·00

Nos. 3579/83 and 3584/8 were each printed together, *se-tenant*, as horizontal strips of five stamps in sheets of 50 (2 panes 5×5).

Special First Day of Issue Postmarks

2740 Buckingham Palace, 2014

2741 Buckingham Palace, c. 1862

2742 Buckingham Palace, 1846

2743 Buckingham House, 1819

2744 Buckingham House, 1714

2745 Buckingham House, c. 1700

2746 The Grand Staircase

2747 The Throne Room

(Des Howard Brown (sheet stamps). Litho ISP Cartor (3589/94) or Enschedé (booklet panes 3589b/94b) or gravure ISP Walsall (3595/6))

2014 (15 Apr). *Buckingham Palace, London* (1st issue). 'All-over' phosphor.

(a) Ordinary gum. P 14½.

3589	**2740**	(1st) gold, greenish yellow, bright magenta, new blue and black		1·25	1·10
		a. Horiz strip of 3. Nos. 3589/91		3·75	3·25
		b. Perf 14×13½		1·50	1·50
		ba. Booklet pane. Nos. 3589b and 3590b, each×2 with margins all round		5·50	

3590	**2741**	(1st) gold, greenish yellow, bright magenta, new blue and black......	1·25	1·10
		b. Perf 14×13½	1·50	1·50
3591	**2742**	(1st) gold, greenish yellow, bright magenta, new blue and black......	1·25	1·10
		b. Perf 14×13½	1·50	1·50
		ba. Booklet pane. Nos. 3591b/4b with margins all round	5·50	
3592	**2743**	(1st) gold, greenish yellow, bright magenta, new blue and black......	1·25	1·10
		a. Horiz strip of 3. Nos. 3592/4	3·50	3·00
		b. Perf 14×13½	1·50	1·50
3593	**2744**	(1st) gold, greenish yellow, bright magenta, new blue and black......	1·25	1·10
		b. Perf 14×13½	1·50	1·50
3594	**2745**	(1st) gold, greenish yellow, bright magenta, new blue and black......	1·25	1·10
		b. Perf 14×13½	1·50	1·50
Set of 6 (Nos. 3589/94)....................................			7·00	6·00
Set of 2 Gutter Strips of 6...........................			15·00	
Set of 6 (Nos. 3589b/94b)........................			8·00	8·00
First Day Cover (Tallents House)				9·50
First Day Cover (London SW1).....................				9·50
Presentation Pack (P.O. Pack No. 497)			14·00	
PHQ Cards (set of 11) (388).......................			7·50	15·00

(b) Self-adhesive. Die-cut P 14.

3595	**2746**	(1st) multicoloured................................	3·75	3·25
		a. Booklet pane. Nos. 3595/6 and U2968b×4	12·00	
3596	**2747**	(1st) multicoloured................................	3·75	3·25

Nos. 3589/91 and 3592/4 were each printed together, *se-tenant*, as horizontal strips of three stamps in sheets of 36 (2 panes 3×6).

Nos. 3589b/94b come from £11·39 premium booklets, No. DY10.

Nos. 3595/6 were issued in stamp booklets, No. PM42, originally sold for £3·72.

The complete miniature sheet is shown on one of the eleven PHQ cards with the others depicting individual stamps including those from **MS**3601.

Special First Day of Issue Postmarks

2748 The Blue Drawing Room

2749 The Green Drawing Room

2750 Buckingham Palace

(Des Robert Maude and Sarah Davies (**MS**3601). Litho Enschedé)

2014 (15 Apr). *Buckingham Palace, London* (2nd issue). 'All-over' phosphor. P 14.

3597	**2747**	(1st) multicoloured................................	1·50	1·50
		a. Booklet pane. Nos. 3597/3600 with margins all round and roulettes at left.....................	5·50	
3598	**2746**	(1st) multicoloured................................	1·50	1·50
3599	**2748**	(1st) multicoloured................................	1·50	1·50

3600	**2749**	(1st) multicoloured................................	1·50	1·50
Set of 4			5·50	5·50
MS3601 146×74 mm. **2750** Nos. 3597/3600			5·50	5·50
MS3601a *Imperf*			£12000	
First Day Cover (Tallents House)				7·00
First Day Cover (London SW1).....................				7·00

Nos. 3597/3600 come from £11·39 premium booklets, No. DY10 and **MS**3601.

2751 *A Matter of Life and Death* (1946)

2752 *Lawrence of Arabia* (1962)

2753 *2001 A Space Odyssey* (1968)

2754 *Chariots of Fire* (1981)

2755 *Secrets and Lies* (1996)

2756 *Bend It Like Beckham* (2002)

2757 Films by GPO Film Unit

(Des Johnson Banks (3602/7) or Magpie Studio (**MS**3608). Litho ISP Cartor (3602/7) or Enschedé (**MS**3608))

2014 (13 May). *Great British Films.* 'All-over' phosphor. P 14½ (3602/7) or 14 (**MS**3608).

3602	**2751**	(1st) silver, greenish yellow, bright magenta, new blue and black......	1·25	1·10
		a. Horiz strip of 3. Nos. 3602/4	3·50	3·00
3603	**2752**	(1st) silver, greenish yellow, bright magenta, new blue and black......	1·25	1·10
3604	**2753**	(1st) silver, greenish yellow, bright magenta, new blue and black......	1·25	1·10
3605	**2754**	£1·28 silver, greenish yellow, bright magenta, new blue and black......	2·75	2·50
		a. Horiz strip of 3. Nos. 3605/7	8·00	7·25
3606	**2755**	£1·28 silver, greenish yellow, bright magenta, new blue and black......	2·75	2·50
3607	**2756**	£1·28 silver, greenish yellow, bright magenta, new blue and black......	2·75	2·50
Set of 6				11·00	9·50
Set of 2 Gutter Strips of 6				23·00	
First Day Cover (Tallents House)					11·00
First Day Cover (Blackheath London SE3)..........					11·00
Presentation Pack (P.O. Pack No. 498)				17·00	
PHQ Cards (set of 11) (389)				7·50	19·00

MS3608 115×89 mm. **2757** (1st)×4 *Night Mail* (1936) directed by Harry Watt and Basil Wright; *Love on the Wing* (1938) directed by Norman McLaren; *A Colour Box* (1935) directed by Len Lye; *Spare Time* (1939) directed by Humphrey Jennings.......... 5·50 5·50

First Day Cover (Tallents House) .... 7·00
First Day Cover (Blackheath London SE3).......... 7·00

Nos. 3602/4 and 3605/7 were each printed together, *se-tenant*, as horizontal strips of three stamps in sheets of 36 (2 panes 3×6).

The complete miniature sheet is shown on one of the eleven PHQ cards with the others depicting individual stamps including those from **MS**3608.

Special First Day of Issue Postmarks

2758 Herring

2759 Red Gurnard

2760 Dab

2761 Pouting

2762 Cornish Sardine

2763 Common Skate

2764 Spiny Dogfish

2765 Wolffish

2766 Sturgeon

2767 Conger Eel

(Des Kate Stephens. Litho ISP Cartor)

2014 (5 June). *Sustainable Fish* (Nos. 3609/13) *and Threatened Fish* (Nos. 3614/18). 'All-over' phosphor. P 14×14½.

3609	**2758**	(1st) azure, greenish yellow, bright magenta, new blue and black.......	1·25	1·10
		a. Horiz strip of 5. Nos. 3609/13.......	6·00	5·25
3610	**2759**	(1st) azure, greenish yellow, bright magenta, new blue and black.......	1·25	1·10
3611	**2760**	(1st) azure, greenish yellow, bright magenta, new blue and black.......	1·25	1·10
3612	**2761**	(1st) azure, greenish yellow, bright magenta, new blue and black.......	1·25	1·10
3613	**2762**	(1st) azure, greenish yellow, bright magenta, new blue and black.......	1·25	1·10
3614	**2763**	(1st) azure, greenish yellow, bright magenta, new blue and black.......	1·25	1·10
		a. Horiz strip of 5. Nos. 3614/18.......	6·00	5·25
3615	**2764**	(1st) azure, greenish yellow, bright magenta, new blue and black.......	1·25	1·10
3616	**2765**	(1st) azure, greenish yellow, bright magenta, new blue and black.......	1·25	1·10
3617	**2766**	(1st) azure, greenish yellow, bright magenta, new blue and black.......	1·25	1·10
3618	**2767**	(1st) azure, greenish yellow, bright magenta, new blue and black.......	1·25	1·10
Set of 10..........				11·00	9·50
Set of 2 Gutter Strips of 10				23·00	
First Day Cover (Tallents House)					11·00
First Day Cover (Fishguard)					11·00
Presentation Pack (P.O. Pack No. 499)				13·00	
PHQ Cards (set of 10) (390)				6·75	19·00

Nos. 3609/13 and 3614/18 were each printed together, *se-tenant*, as horizontal strips of five in sheets of 50 (2 panes 5×5).

Special First Day of Issue Postmarks

Special First Day of Issue Postmarks

2768 Judo

2769 Swimming

2774 Poppy (Fiona Strickland)

2775 Lines from *For the Fallen* (Laurence Binyon)

2770 Marathon

2771 Squash

2776 Private William Cecil Tickle

2777 *A Star Shell* (C. R. W. Nevinson)

2772 Netball

2773 Para-athlete Cycling

2778 *The Response* (sculpture by William Goscombe John)

2779 Princess Mary's Gift Box Fund

(Des Nanette Hoogslag (illustration) and Howard Brown. Litho ISP Cartor (3619/24) or gravure ISP Walsall (3625))

2014 (17 July). *Commonwealth Games, Glasgow.* One phosphor band (3619) or two bands (others).

(a) Ordinary gum. P 14×14½.

3619	**2768**	(2nd) deep grey-green, greenish yellow, bright magenta, new blue and black	1·00	90
3620	**2769**	(1st) deep grey-green, greenish yellow, bright magenta, new blue and black	1·25	1·10
3621	**2770**	97p. deep grey-green, greenish yellow, bright magenta, new blue and black	2·00	2·00
3622	**2771**	£1·28 deep grey-green, greenish yellow, bright magenta, new blue and black	2·75	2·50
3623	**2772**	£1·47 deep grey-green, greenish yellow, bright magenta, new blue and black	3·25	3·25
3624	**2773**	£2·15 deep grey-green, greenish yellow, bright magenta, new blue and black	4·25	4·25
Set of 6			14·50	14·00
Set of 6 Gutter Pairs			29·00	
First Day Cover (Tallents House)				15·00
First Day Cover (Glasgow)				15·00
Presentation Pack (P.O. Pack No. 500)			15·00	
PHQ Cards (set of 6) (391)			4·00	17·00

(b) Self-adhesive. Die-cut P 14×14½.

3625	**2769**	(1st) deep grey-green, greenish yellow, bright magenta, new blue and black	3·75	3·25
		a. Booklet pane. Nos. 3625×2 and U2968b×4	12·00	

The phosphor band on No. 3619 is at centre right of the stamps.
No. 3625 was issued in stamp booklets, No. PM43, originally sold for £3·72.

(Des Hat-trick Design. Litho ISP Cartor (3626/31) or Enschedé (booklet panes 3626a, 3629a))

2014 (28 July). *Centenary of the First World War* (1st issue). 'All-over' phosphor (3627, 3629) or two bands (others). P 14½.

3626	**2774**	(1st) deep grey-green, greenish yellow, bright magenta, new blue and black	1·25	1·10
		a. 'All-over' phosphor	1·50	1·50
		b. Booklet pane. Nos. 3626a, 3627, 3628a with margins all round	3·75	
3627	**2775**	(1st) deep grey-green, greenish yellow, bright magenta, new blue and black	1·25	1·10
3628	**2776**	(1st) deep grey-green, greenish yellow, bright magenta, new blue and black	1·25	1·10
		a. 'All-over' phosphor	1·50	1·50
3629	**2777**	£1·47 greenish yellow, bright magenta, new blue and black	3·25	3·25
		b. Booklet pane. Nos. 3629, 3630a, 3631a with margins all round	9·50	
3630	**2778**	£1·47 greenish yellow, bright magenta, new blue and black	3·25	3·25
		a. 'All-over' phosphor	3·50	3·50
3631	**2779**	£1·47 deep grey-green, greenish yellow, bright magenta, new blue and black	3·25	3·25
		a. 'All-over' phosphor	3·50	3·50
Set of 6			12·00	12·00
Set of 6 Gutter Pairs			27·00	
First Day Cover (Tallents House)				14·00
First Day Cover (Newcastle upon Tyne)				14·00
Presentation Pack (P.O. Pack No. 501)			13·50	
PHQ Cards (set of 6) (392)			4·00	18·00

Nos. 3626a, 3628a, 3630a and 3631a only come from premium booklets, No. DY11.

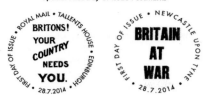

(Gravure ISP Walsall)

2014 (18 Aug). *Sustainable Fish and Threatened Fish* (2nd issue). Designs as Nos. 3613/14. Self-adhesive. Die-cut P 14×14½.

3632	**2763**	(1st) multicoloured......................	3·75	3·25
		a. Booklet pane. Nos. 3632/3 and U2968b×4	12·00	
3633	**2762**	(1st) multicoloured......................	3·75	3·25

Nos. 3632/3 were issued in stamp booklets, No. PM44, originally sold for £3·72.

(Gravure ISP Walsall)

2014 (18 Sept). *Classic Locomotives of Wales.* Booklet stamp as *T* **2724**. 'All-over' phosphor. Self-adhesive. Die-cut P 14.

3634	**2724**	(1st) multicoloured......................	3·75	3·25
		a. Booklet pane. No. 3634×2 and U2968b×4	12·00	

No. 3634 was only issued in booklets, No. PM45, originally sold for £3·72.

(Des Why Not Associates. Litho ISP Cartor (3635/40) or Enschedé (**MS**3641))

2014 (18 Sept). *Seaside Architecture.* Two bands (3635/40) or 'All-over' phosphor (**MS**3641). P 14.

3635	**2780**	(1st) greenish yellow, bright magenta, new blue and black...........	1·25	1·10
3636	**2781**	(1st) greenish yellow, bright magenta, new blue and black...........	1·25	1·10
3637	**2782**	97p. greenish yellow, bright magenta, new blue and black...........	2·00	2·00
3638	**2783**	97p. greenish yellow, bright magenta, new blue and black...........	2·00	2·00
3639	**2784**	£1·28 greenish yellow, bright magenta, new blue and black...........	2·75	2·50
3640	**2785**	£1·28 greenish yellow, bright magenta, new blue and black...........	2·75	2·50
Set of 6			11·00	10·00
Set of 6 Gutter Pairs.......................................			23·00	
First Day Cover (Tallents House)				12·00
First Day Cover (Eastbourne)				12·00
Presentation Pack (P.O. Pack No. 502)			13·00	
PHQ Cards (set of 11) (393)			7·50	19·00

MS3641 125×89 mm. **2786** (1st) Llandudno Pier; (1st) Worthing Pier; £1·28 Dunoon Pier; £1·28 Brighton Pier. ....

	8·00	8·00
First Day Cover (Tallents House)		10·00
First Day Cover (Eastbourne)		10·00

The complete miniature sheet is shown on one of the eleven PHQ cards with the others depicting individual stamps including those from the miniature sheet.

2780 Eastbourne Bandstand

2781 Tinside Lido, Plymouth

2782 Bangor Pier

2783 Southwold Lighthouse

2784 Blackpool Pleasure Beach

2785 Bexhill-on-Sea Shelter

2786 British Piers

2787 Margaret Thatcher

2788 Harold Wilson

2789 Clement Attlee

2790 Winston Churchill

2791 William Gladstone

2792 Robert Peel

2793 Charles Grey   **2794** William Pitt the Younger

(Des Together. Litho ISP Cartor)

2014 (14 Oct). *Prime Ministers.* 'All-over' phosphor. P 14½.

3642	**2787**	(1st) silver, greenish yellow, bright magenta, new blue and black......	1·25	1·10
		a. Horiz strip of 4. Nos. 3642/5	5·00	4·25
3643	**2788**	(1st) silver, greenish yellow, bright magenta, new blue and black......	1·25	1·10
3644	**2789**	(1st) silver, greenish yellow, bright magenta, new blue and black......	1·25	1·10
3645	**2790**	(1st) silver, greenish yellow, bright magenta, new blue and black......	1·25	1·10
3646	**2791**	97p. silver, greenish yellow, bright magenta, new blue and black......	2·00	2·00
		a. Horiz strip of 4. Nos. 3646/9	8·00	8·00
3647	**2792**	97p. silver, greenish yellow, bright magenta, new blue and black......	2·00	2·00
3648	**2793**	97p. silver, greenish yellow, bright magenta, new blue and black......	2·00	2·00
3649	**2794**	97p. silver, greenish yellow, bright magenta, new blue and black......	2·00	2·00
Set of 8			12·00	12·00
Set of 2 Gutter strips of 4			26·00	
First Day Cover (Tallents House)				14·00
First Day Cover (London SW1)				14·00
Presentation Pack (P.O. Pack No. 503)			14·00	
PHQ Cards (set of 8) (394)			5·50	19·00

Nos. 3642/5 and 3646/9 were each printed together, *se-tenant*, as horizontal strips of four stamps in sheets of 48 (2 panes 4×6).

Special First Day of Issue Postmarks

2795 Collecting the Christmas Tree

2796 Posting Christmas Cards

2797 Collecting the Christmas Tree

2798 Posting Christmas Cards

2799 Building a Snowman

2800 Carol Singing

2801 Ice Skating

(Des True North. Gravure Walsall (3650a, 3651a) or De La Rue (others))

2014 (4 Nov). *Christmas.* Illustrations by Andrew Bannecker. One centre band (3650) or two bands (others). P 14½×15.

(a) Self-adhesive

3650	**2795**	(2nd) bright magenta, greenish yellow, new blue and black	1·00	90
		a. Booklet pane. No. 3650×12	12·00	
3651	**2796**	(1st) bright magenta, greenish yellow, new blue and black	1·25	1·10
		a. Booklet pane. No. 3651×12	15·00	
3652	**2797**	(2nd) bright magenta, greenish yellow, Large) new blue and black	1·50	1·50
3653	**2798**	(1st) bright magenta, greenish yellow, Large) new blue and black	2·00	2·00
3654	**2799**	£1·28 bright magenta, greenish yellow, new blue and black	2·75	2·50
3655	**2800**	£1·47 bright magenta, greenish yellow, new blue and black	3·25	3·25
3656	**2801**	£2·15 bright magenta, greenish yellow, new blue and black	4·25	4·25
Set of 7			15·00	15·00
First Day Cover (Tallents House)				17·00
First Day Cover (Bethlehem, Llandeilo)				17·00
Presentation Pack (Po. pack No. 504)			17·00	
Stamp Cards (395)			5·25	20·00

(b) Ordinary gum

MS3657 156×74 mm. Nos. 3650/6		15·00	15·00
First Day Cover (Tallents House)			19·00
First Day Cover (Bethlehem, Llandeilo)			19·00

The 2nd class, 1st class, £1·28 and £1·47 stamps were also issued in sheets of 20 containing eight 2nd class, eight 1st class, two £1·28 and two £1·47 stamps, each stamp accompanied by a *se-tenant* label. These sheets were printed in lithography and sold for £15·20 per sheet.

Separate sheets of 20 2nd, 20 1st, ten 1st, ten £1·28 and ten £1·47 were available with personal photographs on the labels from Royal Mail, Edinburgh. These were sold at £14·50 for 20 2nd, £18·65 for 20 1st, £10·20 for ten 1st, £18·50 for ten £1·28 and £21·85 for ten £1·47.

Special First Day of Issue Postmarks

Collectors Pack
2014 (4 Nov). Comprises Nos. 3552/69, **MS**3578/94, **MS**3601/24, 3626/31, 3635/56.
CP3657a Collectors Pack ....
£150

Post Office Yearbook
2014 (4 Nov). Comprises Nos. 3552/69, **MS**3578/94, **MS**3601/24, 3626/31, 3635/56.
YB3657a Yearbook ....
£175

Miniature Sheet Collection
2004 (4 Nov). Comprises Nos. **MS**3578, **MS**3601, **MS**3608, **MS**3641 and **MS**3657.
MS3657a Miniature Sheet Collection .... 35·00

2802 The White Rabbit

2803 Down the Rabbit Hole

2804 Drink Me

2805 The White Rabbit's House

2806 The Cheshire-Cat

2807 A Mad Tea-Party

2808 The Queen of Hearts

2809 The Game of Croquet

2812 Happy Birthday (NB Studio)

2813 Well Done (Webb & Webb Design Ltd)

2814 Wedding (Caroline Gardner Ltd)

2815 Love (Rebecca Sutherland)

2810 Alice's Evidence

2811 A Pack of Cards

2816 Mum (The Chase)

2817 New Baby (NB Studio)

(Grahame Baker-Smith (illustration) and Godfrey Design. Litho ISP Cartor (3658/67) or gravure ISP Walsall (3668/9))

2015 (6 Jan). *Alice in Wonderland.* One phosphor band at right (2nd) or two phosphor bands (others).

(a) Ordinary gum. P 14½

3658	2802	(2nd) greenish yellow, bright magenta, new blue and black	1·00	90
		a. Vert pair. Nos. 3658/9	2·00	1·75
3659	2803	(2nd) greenish yellow, bright magenta, new blue and black	1·00	90
3660	2804	(1st) greenish yellow, bright magenta, new blue and black	1·25	1·10
		a. Vert pair. Nos. 3660/1	2·50	2·25
3661	2805	(1st) greenish yellow, bright magenta, new blue and black	1·25	1·10
3662	2806	81p. greenish yellow, bright magenta, new blue and black	1·75	1·50
		a. Vert pair. Nos. 3662/3	3·50	3·50
3663	2807	81p. greenish yellow, bright magenta, new blue and black	1·75	1·50
3664	2808	£1·28 greenish yellow, bright magenta, new blue and black	2·75	2·50
		a. Vert pair. Nos. 3664/5	5·50	5·00
3665	2809	£1·28 greenish yellow, bright magenta, new blue and black	2·75	2·50
3666	2810	£1·47 greenish yellow, bright magenta, new blue and black	3·25	3·25
		a. Vert pair. Nos. 3666/7	6·50	6·50
3667	2811	£1·47 greenish yellow, bright magenta, new blue and black	3·25	3·25
Set of 10			20·00	18·50
Set of 5 Gutter Strips of 4			40·00	
First Day Cover (Tallents House)				23·00
First Day Cover (Oxford)				23·00
Presentation Pack (P.O. Pack No. 506)			21·00	
PHQ Cards (Set of 10) (396)			6·75	25·00

(b) Self-adhesive. Die-cut P 14½

3668	2804	(1st) multicoloured	2·00	1·75
		a. Booklet pane. Nos. 3668/9 and U2968b×4	12·00	
3669	2805	(1st) multicoloured	2·00	1·75

Nos. 3658/9, 3660/1, 3662/3, 3664/5 and 3666/7 were each printed together, *se-tenant*, as vertical pairs in sheets of 60 (2 panes 5×6).

Nos. 3658/67 commemorate the 150th anniversary of the Publication of *Alice's Adventures in Wonderland* by Lewis Carroll.

Nos. 3668/9 were only issued in booklets, No. PM46, originally sold for £3.72.

2818 Grandparent (NB Studio)

2819 Dad (Webb & Webb Design Ltd)

(Des Jenny Bowers and NB Studio. Gravure ISP Walsall (3670/7) or litho ISP Cartor (**MS**3678))

2015 (20 Jan). *Smilers* (5th series). Two phosphor bands.

(a) Self-adhesive booklet stamps. Die-cut P 14½×14 *(with one elliptical hole in each vert side)*

3670	2812	(1st) multicoloured	1·25	1·10
		a. Booklet pane. Nos. 3670×2, 3671, 3672/3 each×2, 3674, 3675×2 and 3676/7	15·00	
3671	2813	(1st) multicoloured	1·25	1·10
3672	2814	(1st) multicoloured	1·25	1·10
3673	2815	(1st) multicoloured	1·25	1·10
3674	2816	(1st) multicoloured	1·25	1·10
3675	2817	(1st) multicoloured	1·25	1·10
3676	2818	(1st) multicoloured	1·25	1·10
3677	2819	(1st) multicoloured	1·25	1·10

(b) Ordinary gum. P 14½×14 *(with one elliptical hole in each vert side)*

MS3678	134×70 mm. As Nos. 3670/7	10·00	10·00
	First Day Cover (Tallents House)		13·00
	First Day Cover (Greetwell, Lincoln)		13·00
	Presentation Pack (P.O. Pack No. M23)	12·00	
	PHQ Cards (set of 9) (D34)	6·75	17·00

Nos. 3670/7 were issued in booklets of 12, No. QB1, originally sold for £7·44.

Nos. 3670/7 were also issued in sheets of 20 with *se-tenant* greetings labels, No. LS93, printed by Cartor in lithography and originally sold at £12·90 per sheet.

The complete miniature sheet is shown on one of the nine PHQ cards with the others depicting individual stamps.

2820 Colossus - world's first electronic digital computer

2821 World Wide Web - revolutionary global communications system

2822 Catseyes - light-reflecting road safety innovation

2823 Fibre Optics - pioneering rapid-data-transfer technology

2824 Stainless Steel - non-corrosive, versatile, 100% recyclable alloy

2825 Carbon Fibre - high-strength, lightweight, composite material

2826 DNA Sequencing - revolution in understanding the genome

2827 i-LIMB - bionic hand with individually powered digits

(Des GBH. Litho ISP Cartor)

2015 (19 Feb). *Inventive Britain.* Two phosphor bands. P 14½.

3679	2820	(1st) greenish yellow, bright magenta, new blue and black	1·25	1·10
		a. Horiz pair. Nos. 3679/80	2·50	2·25
		b. Booklet pane. Nos. 3305, 3281×2 and 3679 with margins all round	5·00	
		c. Booklet pane. Nos. 3679/80, 3683 and 3686	8·50	
3680	2821	(1st) greenish yellow, bright magenta, new blue and black	1·25	1·10
3681	2822	81p. greenish yellow, bright magenta, new blue and black	1·75	1·50
		a. Horiz pair. Nos. 3681/2	3·50	3·00
		b. Booklet pane. Nos. 3681/2 and 3684/5 with margins all round	9·50	
3682	2823	81p. greenish yellow, bright magenta, new blue and black	1·75	1·50
3683	2824	£1·28 greenish yellow, bright magenta, new blue and black	2·75	2·50
		a. Horiz pair. Nos. 3683/4	5·50	5·00
3684	2825	£1·28 greenish yellow, bright magenta, new blue and black	2·75	2·50
3685	2826	£1·47 greenish yellow, bright magenta, new blue and black	3·25	3·25
		a. Horiz pair. Nos. 3685/6	6·50	6·50
3686	2827	£1·47 greenish yellow, bright magenta, new blue and black	3·25	3·25

Set of 8 .... 18·00 16·50
Set of 4 Gutter Blocks of 4 .... 36·00
First Day Cover (Tallents House) .... 21·00
First Day Cover (Harlow) .... 21·00
Presentation Pack (P.O. Pack No. 507) .... 19·00

Nos. 3679/80, 3681/2, 3683/4 and 3685/6 were each printed together, *se-tenant*, as horizontal pairs in sheets of 60 (2 panes 6×5).

Nos. 3679b/c and 3681b were only issued in the £14.60 Inventive Britain booklet, No. DY12.

Special First Day of Issue Postmarks

2828 Tarr Steps, River Barle
2829 Row Bridge, Mosedale Beck

2830 Pulteney Bridge, River Avon
2831 Craigellachie Bridge, River Spey

2832 Menai Suspension Bridge, Menai Strait
2833 High Level Bridge, River Tyne

2834 Royal Border Bridge, River Tweed
2835 Tees Transporter Bridge, River Tees

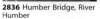

2836 Humber Bridge, River Humber

2837 Peace Bridge, River Foyle

(Des GBH. Litho ISP Cartor)

2015 (5 Mar). *Bridges.* Two phosphor bands. P 14½×14.

3687	**2828**	(1st) greenish yellow, bright magenta, new blue and black	1·25	1·10
		a. Horiz strip of 5. Nos. 3687/91	6·25	5·50
3688	**2829**	(1st) greenish yellow, bright magenta, new blue and black	1·25	1·10
3689	**2830**	(1st) greenish yellow, bright magenta, new blue and black	1·25	1·10
3690	**2831**	(1st) greenish yellow, bright magenta, new blue and black	1·25	1·10
3691	**2832**	(1st) greenish yellow, bright magenta, new blue and black	1·25	1·10
3692	**2833**	(1st) greenish yellow, bright magenta, new blue and black	1·25	1·10
		a. Horiz strip of 5. Nos. 3692/6	6·25	5·50
3693	**2834**	(1st) greenish yellow, bright magenta, new blue and black	1·25	1·10
3694	**2835**	(1st) greenish yellow, bright magenta, new blue and black	1·25	1·10
3695	**2836**	(1st) greenish yellow, bright magenta, new blue and black	1·25	1·10
3696	**2837**	(1st) greenish yellow, bright magenta, new blue and black	1·25	1·10
Set of 10			12·50	11·00
Set of 2 Gutter Strips of 10			25·00	
Set of 2 Traffic Light Gutter Strips of 10			28·00	
First Day Cover (Tallents House)				15·00
First Day Cover (Bridge, Canterbury)				15·00
Presentation Pack (P.O. Pack No. 508)			13·50	
PHQ Cards (set of 10) (398)			6·75	20·00

Nos. 3687/91 and 3692/6 were each printed together, *se-tenant*, as horizontal strips of five stamps in sheets of 50 (2 panes 5×5).

Special First Day of Issue Postmarks

2838 Spike Milligan

2839 The Two Ronnies

2840 Billy Connolly

2841 Morecambe and Wise

2842 Norman Wisdom

2843 Lenny Henry

2844 Peter Cook and Dudley Moore

2845 Monty Python

2846 French and Saunders

2847 Victoria Wood

(Des The Chase. Litho ISP Cartor (3697/3706) or gravure ISP Walsall 3707/8)

2015 (1 Apr). *Comedy Greats.* Two phosphor bands.

(a) Ordinary gum. P 14.

3697	**2838**	(1st) greenish yellow, bright magenta, new blue and black	1·25	1·10
		a. Horiz strip of 5. Nos. 3697/701	6·25	5·50
3698	**2839**	(1st) greenish yellow, bright magenta, new blue and black	1·25	1·10
3699	**2840**	(1st) greenish yellow, bright magenta, new blue and black	1·25	1·10
3700	**2841**	(1st) greenish yellow, bright magenta, new blue and black	1·25	1·10
3701	**2842**	(1st) greenish yellow, bright magenta, new blue and black	1·25	1·10
3702	**2843**	(1st) greenish yellow, bright magenta, new blue and black	1·25	1·10
		a. Horiz strip of 5. Nos. 3702/6	6·25	5·50
3703	**2844**	(1st) greenish yellow, bright magenta, new blue and black	1·25	1·10
3704	**2845**	(1st) greenish yellow, bright magenta, new blue and black	1·25	1·10
3705	**2846**	(1st) greenish yellow, bright magenta, new blue and black	1·25	1·10
3706	**2847**	(1st) greenish yellow, bright magenta, new blue and black	1·25	1·10
Set of 10			12·50	11·00
Set of 2 Gutter Strips of 10			25·00	
First Day Cover (Tallents House)				15·00
First Day Cover (Laughterton, Lincoln)				15·00
Presentation Pack (P.O. Pack No. 509)			13·00	
PHQ Cards (set of 10) (399)			6·75	20·00

(b) Self-adhesive. Die-cut P 14.

3707	**2842**	(1st) multicoloured	2·00	1·75
		a. Booklet pane. Nos. 3707/8 and U2968b×4	12·00	
3708	**2841**	(1st) multicoloured	2·00	1·75

Nos. 3697/701 and 3702/6 were each printed together, *se-tenant*, as horizontal strips of five stamps in sheets of 50 (2 panes 5×5).

Nos. 3707/8 were issued in stamp booklets, No. PM47, sold for £3·72.

Special First Day of Issue Postmarks

2848 Penny Black

2849 'Penny Black' and 1840 2d. blue

(Des Sedley Place. Gravure ISP Walsall (3709)
or litho ISP Cartor (**MS**3710))

2015 (6 May). *175th Anniv of the Penny Black* Two phosphor bands.
(a) Self-adhesive booklet stamps. *Die-cut perf* 14½×14 (with one elliptical hole in each vert side).

3709 **2848** (1st) cinnamon and black .... 2·00 1·75

(b) *Ordinary gum.* P 14½×14 (*with one elliptical hole in each vert side*).

MS3710 156×74 mm. (1st) Penny Black×2; (1st) 1840 2d. 5·00 5·00
blue×2 ....
First Day Cover (Tallents House) .... 6·00
First Day Cover (Bath) .... 6·00
Presentation Pack (P.O. Pack No. 510)........................ 6·00
PHQ Cards (set of 3) (400) .... 2·00 6·25

No. 3709 was issued in booklets of six, No. MB13.
The three PHQ cards show the two individual stamps and the complete miniature sheet.
Designs as No. 3709 and (1st) Twopenny Blue as within **MS**3710 were also issued in sheets of 20 (No. LS94) containing ten 1st class Penny Black and ten 1st class Twopenny Blue, each stamp accompanied by a *se-tenant* label. These sheets were printed in lithography by ISP Cartor and originally sold for £12.90.
Sheets of ten or 20 1st Penny Black were available with personal photographs on the labels from Royal Mail Edinburgh, sold for £10.20 (ten) or £18.65 (20).
Miniature sheets as No. **MS**3710 with a special inscription were available only at Europhilex 2015.

2852 Rifleman Kulbir Thapa **2853** The Kensingtons at Laventie (*Eric Kennington*)

2854 'A British Soldier visits his Comrade's Grave on the Cliffs near Cape Helles', Gallipoli (*posed photo by Ernest Brooks*) **2855** London Irish Rifles' Football from Loos

(Des hat-trick design. Litho ISP Cartor)

2015 (14 May). *Centenary of the First World War* (2nd issue). Two phosphor bands. P 14½.

3711	**2850**	(1st) olive-grey, greenish yellow, bright magenta, new blue and black..........	1·25	1·10
		a. Booklet pane. Nos. 3711/13 with margins all round.............	3·75	
3712	**2851**	(1st) olive-grey, greenish yellow, bright magenta, new blue and black..........	1·25	1·10
3713	**2852**	(1st) olive-grey, greenish yellow, bright magenta, new blue and black..........	1·25	1·10
3714	**2853**	£1.52 olive-grey, greenish yellow, bright magenta, new blue and black..........	3·25	3·25
		a. Booklet pane. Nos. 3714/16 with margins all round.............	9·75	
3715	**2854**	£1.52 olive-grey, greenish yellow, bright magenta, new blue and black..........	3·25	3·25
3716	**2855**	£1.52 olive-grey, greenish yellow, bright magenta, new blue and black..........	3·25	3·25
Set of 6			13·50	13·00
Set of 6 Gutter Pairs			27·00	
First Day Cover (Tallents House)				14·50
First Day Cover (Winchester)				14·50
Presentation Pack (P.O. Pack No. 511)			14·00	
PHQ Cards (set of 6) (401)			4·00	17·50

Nos. 3711a and 3714a were only issued in £13.96 premium booklets, No DY13.

Special First Day of Issue Postmarks

Special First Day of Issue Postmarks

2850 Poppies (*Howard Hodgkin*)

2851 All the Hills and Vales Along (*Charles Hamilton Sorley*)

2856 Magna Carta, 1215

2857 Simon de Montfort's Parliament, 1265

2858 Bill of Rights, 1689

2859 American Bill of Rights, 1791

2860 Universal Declaration of Human Rights, 1948

2861 Charter of the Commonwealth, 2013

(Des Howard Brown. Litho ISP Cartor)

2015 (2 June). *800th Anniv of the Magna Carta.* Two phosphor bands. *P* 14½.

3718	**2856**	(1st) gold, pale stone, carmine, greenish grey and black	1·25	1·10
3719	**2857**	(1st) gold, pale stone, carmine, greenish grey and black	1·25	1·10
3720	**2858**	£1.33 gold, pale stone, carmine, greenish grey and black	2·75	2·50
3721	**2859**	£1.33 gold, pale stone, carmine, greenish grey and black	2·75	2·50
3722	**2860**	£1.52 gold, pale stone, carmine, greenish grey and black	3·25	3·25
3723	**2861**	£1.52 gold, pale stone, carmine, greenish grey and black	3·25	3·25
Set of 6			14·50	13·50
Set of 6 Gutter Pairs			29·00	
First Day Cover (Tallents House)				16·00
First Day Cover (London NW1)				16·00
Presentation Pack (P.O. Pack No. 512)			16·00	
PHQ Cards (set of 6) (402)			4·00	19·00

Special First Day of Issue Postmarks

2862 The Defence of Hougoumont

2863 The Scots Greys during the Charge of the Union Brigade

2864 The French Cavalry's Assault on Allied Defensive Squares

2865 The Defence of La Haye Sainte by the King's German Legion

2866 The Capture of Plancenoit by the Prussians

2867 The French Imperial Guard's Final Assault

(Des Silk Pearce. Litho ISP Cartor)

2015 (18 June). *Bicentenary of the Battle of Waterloo* (1st issue). Two phosphor bands. *P* 14½.

3724	**2862**	(1st) greenish yellow, bright magenta, new blue and black	1·25	1·10
		a. Booklet pane. Nos. 3724 and 3729 with margins all round	4·50	
3725	**2863**	(1st) greenish yellow, bright magenta, new blue and black	1·25	1·10
		a. Booklet pane. Nos. 3725/8 with margins all round	9·00	
3726	**2864**	£1 greenish yellow, bright magenta, new blue and black	2·25	2·00
3727	**2865**	£1 greenish yellow, bright magenta, new blue and black	2·25	2·00
3728	**2866**	£1.52 greenish yellow, bright magenta, new blue and black	3·25	3·25
3729	**2867**	£1.52 greenish yellow, bright magenta, new blue and black	3·25	3·25
Set of 6			13·50	12·50
Set of 6 Gutter Pairs			27·00	
First Day Cover (Tallents House)				14·50
First Day Cover (Waterloo, Liverpool)				14·50
Presentation Pack (P.O. Pack No. 513)			16·00	
PHQ Cards (set of 11) (403)			7·50	21·00

Nos. 3724a and 3725a were only issued in the £14.47 premium booklets, No. DY14

The eleven PHQ cards depict the individual stamps, including those from **MS**3734, and the complete miniature sheet.

Special First Day of Issue Postmarks

2873 Battle of Britain

(Des Supple Studio (stamps) and The Team (miniature sheet). Litho ISP Cartor)

2015 (16 July). *75th Anniv of the Battle of Britain.* Sheet 190×74 mm. All-over phosphor. *P* 14.

MS3735 **2873** (1st) Pilots scramble to their Hurricanes; (1st) Supermarine Spitfires of 610 Squadron, Biggin Hill, on patrol; (1st) Armourer Fred Roberts replaces ammunition boxes on Supermarine Spitfire; £1.33 Spotters of the Auxiliary Territorial Service looking for enemy aircraft; £1.33 Operations Room at Bentley Priory; £1.33 Pilots of 32 Squadron await orders, RAF Hawkinge,

Kent	12·00	12·00
First Day Cover (Tallents House)		13·00
First Day Cover (London NW9)		13·00
Presentation Pack (P.O. Pack No. 514)	12·50	
PHQ Cards (set of 7) (404)	4·75	17·00

The seven PHQ cards show the six individual stamps and the complete miniature sheet.

2868 15th Infantry Regiment, IV Corps, Prussian Army

2869 Light Infantry, King's German Legion, Anglo-Allied Army

2870 92nd Gordon Highlanders, Anglo-Allied Army

2871 Grenadiers, Imperial Guard, French Army

Special First Day of Issue Postmarks

2872 Soldiers and Battle of Waterloo Map

(Des Chris Collingwood (illustrations) and Webb and Webb Design Ltd. Litho ISP Cartor)

2015 (18 June). *Bicentenary of the Battle of Waterloo* (2nd issue). Two phosphor bands. *P* 14.

3730	**2868**	(1st) multicoloured	1·50	1·50
		a. Booklet pane. Nos. 3730/3 with margins all round and roulettes at left	9·00	
3731	**2869**	(1st) multicoloured	1·50	1·50
3732	**2870**	£1.33 multicoloured	3·00	3·00
3733	**2871**	£1.33 multicoloured	3·00	3·00
MS3734	156×74 mm.	**2872** Nos. 3730/3	8·00	8·00
First Day Cover (Tallents House)				9·50
First Day Cover (Waterloo, Liverpool)				9·50

Nos. 3730/3 come from £14.47 premium booklets, No. DY14, and **MS**3734.

(Des Hat-trick Design. Litho ISP Cartor)

2015 (14 May). *Centenary of the First World War.* Premium Booklet stamp. As No. 3414 but ordinary gum. Phosphor background. *P* 14½×14 (with one elliptical hole in each vertical side).

3717	**2588**	(1st) multicoloured	1·50	1·50

No. 3717 only comes from pane No. U3010c in the £13.96 premium booklet, No. DY13.

2874 Scabious Bee (*Andrena hattorfiana*) on Field Scabious (*Knautia arvensis*)

2875 Great Yellow Bumblebee (*Bombus distinguendus*) on Bird's-foot Trefoil (*Lotus corniculatus*)

2876 Northern Colletes Bee (*Colletes floralis*) on Wild Carrot (*Daucus carota*)

2877 Bilberry Bumblebee (*Bombus monticola*) on Bilberry (*Vaccinium myrtillus*)

2878 Large Mason Bee (*Osmia xanthomelana*) on Horseshoe Vetch (*Hippocrepis comosa*)

2879 Potter Flower Bee (*Anthophora retusa*) on Ground Ivy (*Glechoma hederacea*)

2880 The Honeybee

(Des Richard Lewington (illustration) and Anna Ekelund (3736/41) or Andy English (illustration) and Interabang (**MS**3742). Litho ISP Cartor (3736/42) or gravure ISP Walsall (3743))

2015 (18 Aug). *Bees*. (a) Ordinary gum. One centre band (3736), two phosphor bands (3737/41) or phosphor background (**MS**3742). *P* 14×14½.

3736	**2874**	(2nd) silver, greenish yellow, bright magenta, new blue and black..........	1·00	90
3737	**2875**	(1st) silver, greenish yellow, bright magenta, new blue and black..........	1·25	1·10
3738	**2876**	£1 silver, greenish yellow, bright magenta, new blue and black..........	2·25	2·00
3739	**2877**	£1.33 silver, greenish yellow, bright magenta, new blue and black..........	2·75	2·50
3740	**2878**	£1.52 silver, greenish yellow, bright magenta, new blue and black..........	3·25	3·25
3741	**2879**	£2.25 silver, greenish yellow, bright magenta, new blue and black..........	4·50	4·50
Set of 6			15·00	14·00
Set of 6 Gutter Pairs..			30·00	
First Day Cover (Tallents House)				16·00
First Day Cover (St Bees)				16·00
Presentation Pack (P.O. Pack No. 515).......			24·00	
PHQ Cards (set of 7) (405)			7·50	22·00
MS3742 191×74 mm. **2880** (1st) Waggle dance; (1st) Pollination; £1.33 Making honey; £1.33 Tending young			8·00	8·00
First Day Cover (Tallents House)				9·00
First Day Cover (St Bees)				9·00

(b) Self-adhesive. Two phosphor bands. Die-cut perf 14×14½.

3743	**2875**	(1st) multicoloured	2·00	1·75
		a. Booklet pane. Nos. 3743×2 and U2968b×4	12·00	

No. 3743 was issued in stamp booklets, No. PM48, originally sold for £3.78.

The seven PHQ cards depict the six individual stamps and the complete miniature sheet.

Special First Day of Issue Postmarks

2881 'Long to Reign Over Us'

(Des Sedley Place. Recess and gravure FNMT (Spain))

2015 (9 Sept) *Long to Reign Over Us* (2nd issue). Two phosphor bands. *P* 14½×14 (with one elliptical hole in each vertical side) (Machin) or 14 (others).

MS3747 194×75 mm. **2881** (1st) William Wyon's City Medal depicting Queen Victoria; (1st) Portrait of Queen Elizabeth II from photo by Dorothy Wilding; As No. U3744; £1.52 Badge of the House of Windsor depicting Round Tower of Windsor Castle; £1.52 Device from The Queen's Personal Flag .... 10·00 10·00

First Day Cover (Tallents House)		11·00
First Day Cover (Windsor)............................		11·00
Presentation Pack (P.O. Pack No. 516).......	10·50	
PHQ Cards (set of 6) (406)	4·00	14·00

Stamps from **MS**3747 all have an iridescent overprint reading 'LONG TO REIGN OVER US'.

The 1st class bright lilac stamp from **MS**3747 has a source code 'REIGM' and date code '015R' within this iridescent overprint.

The PHQ cards depict the five individual stamps and the complete miniature sheet.

Special First Day of Issue Postmarks

2882 Tackle
2883 Scrum

2884 Try
2885 Conversion

2886 Pass
2887 Drop Goal

2888 Ruck
2889 Line-Out

(Des Hat-trick design and Geoff Appleton (illustrations). Litho ISP Cartor (3748/55) or gravure ISP Walsall (3756/7))

2015 (18 Sept). *Rugby World Cup*. Two phosphor bands. (a) Ordinary gum. *P* 14.

3748	**2882**	(2nd) greenish yellow, bright magenta, new blue and black	1·00	90
		a. Horiz pair. Nos. 3748/9...................	2·00	1·75
3749	**2883**	(2nd) greenish yellow, bright magenta, new blue and black	1·00	90
3750	**2884**	(1st) greenish yellow, bright magenta, new blue and black	1·25	1·10
		a. Horiz pair. Nos. 3750/1...................	2·50	2·25
3751	**2885**	(1st) greenish yellow, bright magenta, new blue and black	1·25	1·10
3752	**2886**	£1 greenish yellow, bright magenta, new blue and black	2·25	2·00
		a. Horiz pair. Nos. 3752/3...................	4·50	4·00
3753	**2887**	£1 greenish yellow, bright magenta, new blue and black	2·25	2·00
3754	**2888**	£1.52 greenish yellow, bright magenta, new blue and black	3·25	3·25
		a. Horiz pair. Nos. 3754/5...................	6·50	6·50
3755	**2889**	£1.52 greenish yellow, bright magenta, new blue and black	3·25	3·25
Set of 8			15·00	14·50
Set of 4 Gutter Blocks of 4..........................			30·00	
First Day Cover (Tallents House)				17·00

First Day Cover (Rugby)				17·00
Presentation Pack (P.O. Pack No. 517)............................			16·00	
PHQ Cards (set of 8) (407)			5·50	21·00

(b) Self-adhesive. Die-cut perf 14.

3756	**2884**	(1st) new magenta, greenish yellow, black and gold..........................	2·00	1·75
		a. Booklet pane. Nos. 3756/7 and U3746×4....................................	12·00	
3757	**2885**	(1st) new blue, bright magenta, greenish yellow, black and gold	2·00	1·75

Nos. 3748/9, 3750/1, 3752/3 and 3754/5 were each printed together, *se-tenant*, as horizontal pairs in sheets of 60 (2 panes 6×5).

Nos. 3756/7 were issued in stamp booklets, No. PM49, originally sold for £3.78.

Special First Day of Issue Postmarks

2890 Darth Vader   **2891** Yoda

2892 Obi-Wan Kenobi   **2893** Stormtrooper

2894 Han Solo   **2895** Rey

2896 Princess Leia   **2897** The Emperor

2898 Luke Skywalker   **2899** Boba Fett

2900 Finn   **2901** Kylo Ren

2902 Star Wars

(Des Malcolm Tween (illustrations) and Interabang (3758/69) or GBH (**MS**3770). Litho ISP Cartor).

2015 (20 Oct–17 Dec). *Star Wars* (1st issue). Two phosphor bands and fluorescent emblems (3758/**69**) or 'All-over' phosphor (**MS**3770). (a) Ordinary gum. *P* 14½.

3758	**2890**	(1st) greenish yellow, bright magenta, new blue and black	1·25	1·10
		a. Horiz strip of 6. Nos. 3758/63......	7·50	6·50
		b. Booklet pane. Nos. 3758, 3760, 3763 and 3767/9 with margins all round (17 Dec)	7·50	
3759	**2891**	(1st) greenish yellow, bright magenta, new blue and black	1·25	1·10
		b. Booklet pane. Nos. 3759, 3761/2 and 3764/6 with margins all round (17 Dec)	7·50	
3760	**2892**	(1st) greenish yellow, bright magenta, new blue and black	1·25	1·10
3761	**2893**	(1st) greenish yellow, bright magenta, new blue and black	1·25	1·10
3762	**2894**	(1st) greenish yellow, bright magenta, new blue and black	1·25	1·10
3763	**2895**	(1st) greenish yellow, bright magenta, new blue and black	1·25	1·10
3764	**2896**	(1st) greenish yellow, bright magenta, new blue and black	1·25	1·10
		a. Horiz strip of 6. Nos. 3764/9	7·50	6·50
3765	**2897**	(1st) greenish yellow, bright magenta, new blue and black	1·25	1·10
3766	**2898**	(1st) greenish yellow, bright magenta, new blue and black	1·25	1·10
3767	**2899**	(1st) greenish yellow, bright magenta, new blue and black	1·25	1·10
3768	**2900**	(1st) greenish yellow, bright magenta, new blue and black	1·25	1·10
3769	**2901**	(1st) greenish yellow, bright magenta, new blue and black	1·25	1·10
Set of 12..			15·00	13·00
Set of 2 Gutter Strips of 12............			30·00	
First Day Cover (Tallents House)				16·00
First Day Cover (Elstree, Borehamwood) ..				16·00
Presentation Pack (P.O. Pack No. 518)........			24·00	
PHQ Cards (set of 19) (408)............			13·00	30·00

MS3770 204×75 mm. (1st) X-wing Starfighter (60×21 mm, p 14½×14); (1st) TIE fighters (35×36 mm, p 14); (1st) X-wing Starfighters (60×21 mm, p 14½×14); (1st) AT-AT Walkers (41×30 mm, p 14); (1st) TIE fighters (27×37 mm, p 14); (1st) *Millennium Falcon* (60×30 mm, p 14½)..............

	7·50	7·50
First Day Cover (Tallents House)		8·50
First Day Cover (Elstree, Borehamwood)		8·50

Nos. 3758/63 and 3764/9 were each printed together, *se-tenant*, as horizontal strips of six stamps in sheets of 60 (2 panes 6×5).

Nos. 3758/69 all show fluorescent emblems under UV light. Nos. 3758, 3761 and 3765 show the symbol of the Galactic Empire, Nos. 3759/60 show the Jedi Order symbol, 3762, 3764 and 3766 show the Rebel Alliance symbol, Nos. 3763 and 3768/9 show the logo for the new film *Star Wars The Force Awakens* and No. 3767 shows the Mandalorian Crest.

Nos 3758b and 3759b were only issued in £16.99 premium booklets, No. DY15.

The 19 PHQ cards depict the individual stamps including those from **MS**3770 and the complete miniature sheet.

Designs as Nos. 3758/9 and 3761/2 but self-adhesive were issued in sheets of ten with *se-tenant* labels showing film stills (No. LS96), each sheet containing Nos. 3758/9, each ×3, and Nos. 3761/2, each×2. These sheets were originally sold for £6.80 each.

The four designs were also available from Royal Mail, Edinburgh in separate sheets of ten with personal photographs on the labels, originally sold for £10.20 per sheet.

Special First Day of Issue Postmarks

2903 The Journey to Bethlehem

2904 The Nativity

2905 The Journey to Bethlehem

2906 The Nativity

2907 The Animals of the Nativity

2908 The Shepherds

2909 The Three Wise Men

2910 The Annunciation

(Des David Holmes (illustrations) and Studio David Hillman. Gravure ISP Walsall (3771a, 3772a) or De La Rue (others))

2015 (3 Nov). Christmas. One centre band (3771) or two bands (others). *P* 14½×15.

(a) Self-adhesive.

3771	**2903**	(2nd) multicoloured............................	1·00	90
		a. Booklet pane. No. 3771×12	12·00	
3772	**2904**	(1st) multicoloured.............................	1·25	1·10
		a. Booklet pane. No. 3772×12	15·00	
3773	**2905**	(2nd Large) multicoloured	1·50	1·50
3774	**2906**	(1st Large) multicoloured	2·00	2·00
3775	**2907**	£1.00 multicoloured..........................	2·25	2·00
3776	**2908**	£1.33 multicoloured..........................	2·75	2·50
3777	**2909**	£1.52 multicoloured..........................	3·25	3·25
3778	**2910**	£2.25 multicoloured..........................	4·50	4·50
Set of 8			18·00	17·00
First Day Cover (Tallents House).......................				20·00
First Day Cover (Bethlehem, Llandeilo).............				20·00
Presentation Pack (P.O. Pack No. 519)...............			19·00	
PHQ Cards (set of 9) (409)			6·00	25·00

(b) Ordinary gum.

MS3779	190×74 mm. As Nos. 3771/8..........	18·00	18·00
First Day Cover (Tallents House).......................			20·00
First Day Cover (Bethlehem, Llandeilo).............			20·00

The nine PHQ cards show the eight individual stamps and the complete miniature sheet.

The 2nd class, 1st class, £1, £1.33, £1.52 and £2.25 stamps were also issued in sheets of 20 (No. LS97) containing 8 2nd class, 8 1st class and one each of £1, £1.33, £1.52 and £2.25 stamps, each stamp accompanied by a *se-tenant* label with a verse from the King James Bible. These sheets were printed in lithography by ISP Cartor and originally sold for £15.96.

Special First Day of Issue Postmarks

Collectors Pack

2015 (3 Nov). Comprises Nos. 3658/67, **MS**3678/706, **MS**3710/29, **MS**3734, **MS**3735/42, **MS**3747/55 and 3758/78

CP3779a Collectors Pack...£175

Post Office Yearbook

2015 (3 Nov). Comprises Nos. 3658/67, **MS**3678/706, **MS**3710/29, **MS**3734, **MS**3735/**42**, **MS**3747/55 and 3758/78

YB3779a Yearbook £200

Miniature Sheet Collection

2015 (3 Nov). Comprises **MS**3678, **MS**3710, **MS**3734, **MS**3735, **MS**3742, **MS**3747, **MS**3770 and **MS**3779

MS3779a.. 60.00

2911 X-wing Starfighter

2912 AT-AT Walkers

2913 TIE fighters   **2914** TIE fighters

2915 X-wing Starfighters

2916 *Millennium Falcon*

(Des GBH. Litho ISP Cartor)

2015 (17 Dec). *Star Wars* (2nd issue). Self-adhesive. 'All-over' phosphor. *Die-cut perf* 14½×14 (3780, 3784), 14 (3781/3 or 14½ (3785).

3780	**2911**	(1st) multicoloured.................................	1·50	1·50
		a. Booklet pane. Nos. 3780/2.................	4·50	
3781	**2912**	(1st) multicoloured.................................	1·50	1·50
3782	**2913**	(1st) multicoloured.................................	1·50	1·50

3783	**2914**	(1st) multicoloured......................	1·50	1·50
		a. Booklet pane. Nos. 3783/5..............	4·50	
3784	**2915**	(1st) multicoloured......................	1·50	1·50
3785	**2916**	(1st) multicoloured......................	1·50	1·50
Set of 6			9·00	9·00

Nos. 3780/5 were only issued in £16.99 Star Wars booklets, No. DY15, or **MS**3770.

2917 Union Flag

(Litho ISP Cartor)

2015 (17 Dec). *Star Wars* (3rd issue). As No. 2570 but ordinary gum. Two phosphor bands. *P* 14½×14 (with one elliptical hole in each vert side).

| 3786 | **2917** | (1st) multicoloured...................... | 1·50 | 1·50 |

No. 3786 comes from booklet pane No. U3014ab from £16.99 Star Wars booklet, No. DY15.

2918 Entering the Antarctic Ice, December 1914

2919 *Endurance* Frozen in Pack Ice, January 1915

2920 Striving to Free *Endurance*, February 1915

2921 Trapped in a Pressure Crack, October 1915

2922 Patience Camp, December 1915 – April 1916

2923 Safe Arrival at Elephant Island, April 1916

2924 Setting out for South Georgia, April 1916

2925 Rescue of *Endurance* Crew, August 1916

(Des Robert Maude and Sarah Davies. Litho ISP Cartor)

2016 (7 Jan). *Shackleton and the Endurance Expedition*. Two phosphor bands. *P* 14×14½.

3787	**2918**	(1st) bluish grey, grey and black	1·25	1·10
		Horiz pair. Nos. 3787/8..................	2·50	2·25
3788	**2919**	(1st) bluish grey, grey and black	1·25	1·10
3789	**2920**	£1 bluish grey, grey and black	2·25	2·00
		Horiz pair. Nos. 3789/90..................	4·50	4·00
3790	**2921**	£1 bluish grey, grey and black	2·25	2·00
3791	**2922**	£1.33 bluish grey, grey and black	2·75	2·50
		Horiz pair. Nos. 3791/2..................	5·50	5·00
3792	**2923**	£1.33 bluish grey, grey and black	2·75	2·50
3793	**2924**	£1.52 bluish grey, grey and black	3·25	3·25

		Horiz pair. Nos. 3793/4..................	6·50	6·50
3794	**2925**	£1.52 bluish grey, grey and black	3·25	3·25
Set of 8			19·00	17·50
First Day Cover (Tallents House)			21·00	
First Day Cover (Plymouth)			21·00	
Presentation Pack (P.O. Pack 521)			20·00	
PHQ Cards (set of 8) (410)			5·50	25·00

Nos. 3787/8, 3789/90, 3791/2 and 3793/4 were each printed together, *se-tenant*, as horizontal pairs in sheets of 60 (2 panes 6×5).

Special First Day of Issue Postmarks

2926 Sir Brian Tuke, Master of the Posts

2927 Mail Packet off Eastbourne (*Capt. Victor Howes*)

2928 Penfold Pillar Box

2929 River Post

2930 Mail Coach

2931 Medway Mail Centre

2932 Classic GPO Posters

(Des Atelier Works (3795/800) or Purpose (**MS**3801). Litho ISP Cartor)

2016 (17-18 Feb). *Royal Mail 500* (1st issue). Two phosphor bands. P 14½×14 (3795/800) or 14 (**MS**3801)

3795	**2926**	(1st) gold, greenish yellow, bright magenta, new blue and black..........	1·25	1·10
		a. Booklet pane. Nos. 3795 and 3797/8 with margins all round (18 Feb)..	5·75	
3796	**2927**	(1st) gold, greenish yellow, bright magenta, new blue and black..........	1·25	1·10
		a. Booklet pane. Nos. 3796 and 3799/800 with margins all round (18 Feb)	7·75	
3797	**2928**	(1st) gold, greenish yellow, bright magenta, new blue and black..........	1·25	1·10
3798	**2929**	£1.52 gold, greenish yellow, bright magenta, new blue and black..........	3·25	3·25
3799	**2930**	£1.52 gold, greenish yellow, bright magenta, new blue and black..........	3·25	3·25
3800	**2931**	£1.52 gold, greenish yellow, bright magenta, new blue and black..........	3·25	3·25
Set of 6		....	13·00	12·50
First Day Cover (Tallents House)				15·00
First Day Cover (London WC1)				15·00
Presentation Pack (P.O. Pack No. 522)			22·00	
PHQ Cards (set of 11) (411)			7·50	21·00

MS3801 125×89 mm. (1st) 'QUICKEST WAY BY AIR MAIL' (Edward McKnight Kauffer, 1935); (1st) 'ADDRESS your letters PLAINLY' (Hans Schleger, 1942); £1.33 'pack your parcels carefully' (Hans Unger, 1950); £1.33 'STAMPS IN BOOKS SAVE TIME' (Harry Stevens, 1960).

	8·00	8·00
First Day Cover (Tallents House)		9·00
First Day Cover (London WC1)		9·00

Nos. 3795/**MS**3801 commemorate 500 years of a regular, organised postal service.

MS3801 additionally inscribed "Spring Stampex, 17-20 February 2016" was only available at that exhibition.

The complete miniature sheet is shown on one of the eleven PHQ cards with the others depicting individual stamps including those from the miniature sheet.

Special First Day of Issue Postmarks

2016 (17-18 Feb). *Royal Mail 500* (2nd issue). P 14.

3802	**2933**	(1st) multicoloured..............................	1·50	1·50
		a. Booklet pane. Nos. 3802/5 with margins all round and roulettes at left (18 Feb)................	9·00	
3803	**2934**	(1st) multicoloured..............................	1·50	1·50
3804	**2935**	£1.33 multicoloured............................	3·00	3·00
3805	**2936**	£1.33 multicoloured............................	3·00	3·00
Set of 4		....	9·00	9·00

Nos. 3802/5 come from No. **MS**3801 and £16.36 premium booklets, No. DY16.

2937 Penny Red

2938 Twopenny Blue

(Des Atelier Works (3807/9). Gravure ISP Walsall (3806) or litho ISP Cartor (3807/9))

2016 (18 Feb). *175th Anniversary of the Penny Red.* Two phosphor bands.

(a) Self-adhesive booklet stamp. Die-cut perf 14½×14 (with one elliptical hole in each vert side)

3806	**2937**	(1st) buff and Indian red	1·25	1·10

(b) Ordinary gum. P 14½×14 (with one elliptical hole in each vert side)

3807	**2848**	(1st) multicoloured.............................	1·50	1·50
		a. Booklet pane. No. 3807×2 and 3808/9, each ×3	12·00	
3808	**2937**	(1st) multicoloured.............................	1·50	1·50
3809	**2938**	(1st) multicoloured.............................	1·50	1·50
First Day Cover (Tallents House) (3807a)				13·00
First Day Cover (London WC1) (3807a)				13·00

No. 3806 comes from booklets of six, No. MB15.

Nos. 3807/9 come from £16.36 500 Years of Royal Mail premium booklets, No. DY16.

No. 3806 was also issued in sheets of 20 with attached labels showing the 'Rainbow Trials' from which the Penny Red evolved (No. LS99). These sheets were printed in lithography by ISP Cartor and originally sold for £13.10 each.

Sheets of ten or 20 of these Penny Red stamps were available from Royal Mail with personal photographs on the labels for £10.20 (10) or £18.65 (20).

Special First Day of Issue Postmarks

2933 'QUICKEST WAY BY AIR MAIL' (Edward McKnight Kauffer, 1935)

2934 'ADDRESS your letters PLAINLY' (Hans Schleger, 1942)

2935 'STAMPS IN BOOKS SAVE TIME' (Harry Stevens, 1960)

2936 'pack your parcels carefully' (Hans Unger, 1950)

(Litho ISP Cartor)

2939 Nicholas Winton (1909-2015)

2940 Sue Ryder (1924-2000)

2941 John Boyd Orr (1880-1971)

2942 Eglantyne Jebb (1876-1928)

2943 Joseph Rowntree
(1836-1925)

2944 Josephine Butler
(1828-1906)

(Hat-trick Design. Litho ISP Cartor)

2016 (15 Mar). *British Humanitarians*. Two phosphor bands. P 14½.

3810	**2939**	(1st) black....................	1·25	1·10
		a. Horiz strip of 3. Nos. 3810/12............	3·75	3·25
3811	**2940**	(1st) black....................	1·25	1·10
3812	**2941**	(1st) black....................	1·25	1·10
3813	**2942**	£1.33 black....................	2·75	2·50
		a. Horiz strip of 3. Nos. 3813/15............	8·25	7·50
3814	**2943**	£1.33 black....................	2·75	2·50
3815	**2944**	£1.33 black....................	2·75	2·50
Set of 6			11·50	10·50
Set of 2 Gutter Strips of 6			23·00	
First Day Cover (Tallents House)				13·00
First Day Cover (Winton, Northallerton)..................				13·00
Presentation Pack (P.O. Pack No. 523)			12·50	
PHQ Cards (set of 6) (412)			4·00	15·00

Nos. 3810/12 and 3813/15 were each printed together, *se-tenant*, as horizontal strips of three stamps in sheets of 60 (2 panes 6×5).

Special First Day of Issue Postmarks

2945 'to thine own self be true' (*Hamlet*)

COWARDS DIE MANY TIMES BEFORE THEIR DEATHS · THE **VALIANT** NEVER TASTE of DEATH BUT ONCE·
2946 'cowards die many times before their deaths. The valiant never taste of death but once.' (*Julius Caesar*)

Love is a smoke made with the fume of sighs
2947 'Love is a smoke made with the fume of sighs' (*Romeo and Juliet*)

THE FOOL DOTH THINK HE IS WISE, BUT THE WISE MAN KNOWS HIMSELF TO BE A FOOL.
2948 'The fool doth think he is wise, but the wise man knows himself to be a fool.' (*As You Like It*)

THERE WAS A STAR DANCED, and under that — WAS I — BORN.
2949 'There was a star danced, and under that was I born.' (*Much Ado About Nothing*)

BUT IF THE WHILE I THINK ON THEE, DEAR FRIEND, ALL LOSSES ARE RESTORED AND SORROWS END.
2950 'But if the while I think on thee, dear friend, all losses are restored and sorrows end.' (*Sonnet 30*)

LOVE comforteth like sunshine after rain
2951 'LOVE comforteth like sunshine after rain' (*Venus and Adonis*)

WE ARE SUCH STUFF AS DREAMS ARE MADE ON; AND OUR LITTLE LIFE IS ROUNDED WITH A SLEEP.
2952 'We are such stuff as dreams are made on; and our little life is rounded with a sleep.' (*The Tempest*)

Life's but a walking shadow, a poor player That struts and frets his hour upon the stage
2953 'Life's but a walking shadow, a poor player That struts and frets his hour upon the stage' (*Macbeth*)

I wasted time, and now doth time waste me
2954 'I wasted time, and now doth time waste me' (*Richard II*)

(Des The Chase. Litho ISP Cartor)

2016 (5 Apr). *400th Death Anniv of William Shakespeare*. Two phosphor bands. P 14½.

3816	**2945**	(1st) carmine, pale grey-brown and black	1·25	1·10
		a. Horiz strip of 5. Nos. 3816/20............	6·25	6·25
3817	**2946**	(1st) carmine, pale grey-brown and black....................	1·25	1·10
3818	**2947**	(1st) carmine, pale grey-brown and black....................	1·25	1·10
3819	**2948**	(1st) carmine, pale grey-brown and black....................	1·25	1·10
3820	**2949**	(1st) carmine, pale grey-brown and black....................	1·25	1·10
3821	**2950**	(1st) carmine, pale grey-brown and black	1·25	1·10
		b. Horiz strip of 5. Nos. 3821/5............	6·25	6·25
3822	**2951**	(1st) carmine, pale grey-brown and black....................	1·25	1·10
3823	**2952**	(1st) carmine, pale grey-brown and black....................	1·25	1·10
3824	**2953**	(1st) carmine, pale grey-brown and black....................	1·25	1·10
3825	**2954**	(1st) carmine, pale grey-brown and black....................	1·25	1·10
3816/25 *Set of 10*			12·50	12·50
Set of 2 Gutter Strips of 10			25·00	
First Day Cover (Tallents House)				14·50
First Day Cover (Stratford-upon-Avon)				14·50
Presentation Pack (P.O. Pack No. 524)			14·50	
PHQ Cards (set of 10)			6·75	19·00

Nos. 3816/20 and 3821/5 were each printed together, *se-tenant*, as horizontal strips of five stamps in sheets of 50 (2 panes 5×5).

Special First Day of Issue Postmarks

Decimal Machin Definitives

Denominated stamps, PVA, PVAD or gum arabic, 'standard' perforations

356a   **357** (Value redrawn)

(Des after plaster cast by Arnold Machin. Recess B.W.)

1970 (17 June)–**72.** Decimal Currency. Chalk-surfaced paper or phosphorised paper (10p.). *Perf* 12.

829	**356a**	10p. cerise	50	75
830		20p. olive-green	60	25
		Ea. Thinner uncoated paper*		
831		50p. deep ultramarine	1·50	40
		Ea. Thinner uncoated paper*	60·00	
831*b*	**357**	£1 bluish black (6.12.72)	3·50	80
Set of 4			5·50	2·00
First Day Cover (829/31)				2·75
First Day Cover (831b)				3·00
Presentation Pack No. 18 (829/31)			10·00	
Presentation Pack No. 38 (790 or 831b), 830/1)			17·00	

* These are not as apparent as uncoated photogravure issues where there is normally a higher degree of chalk-surfacing. The 20p. is known only as a block of four with Plate No. 5. The 50p. comes from Plate No. 9.

The 10p. on phosphorised paper continued the experiments which started with the Machin 1s.6d. When the experiment had ended a quantity of the 50p. value was printed on the phosphorised paper to use up the stock. These stamps were issued on 1 February 1973, but they cannot be distinguished from No. 831 by the naked eye. (*Price £2*).

A £1 was also issued in 1970, but it is difficult to distinguish it from the earlier No. 790. In common with the other 1970 values it was issued in sheets of 100.

A whiter paper was introduced in 1973. The £1 appeared on 27 Sept. 1973, the 20p. on 30 Nov. 1973 and the 50p. on 20 Feb. 1974.

Imperforate examples of No. 831*b* are believed to be printer's waste.

Special First Day of Issue Postmarks

British Philatelic Bureau, Edinburgh (Type C) (Nos. 829/31)	4·00
Windsor, Berks (Type C) (Nos. 829/31)	8·00
Philatelic Bureau, Edinburgh (Type E) (No. 831*b*)	4·00
Windsor, Berks (Type E) (No. 831*b*)	10·00

"X" NUMBERS. The following definitive series has been allocated "X" prefixes to the catalogue numbers to avoid renumbering all subsequent issues.

NO VALUE INDICATED. Stamps as Types **367/a** inscribed "2nd" or "1st" are listed as Nos. 1445/52, 1511/16, 1664/72, 2039/40 and 2295.

ELLIPTICAL PERFORATIONS. These were introduced in 1993 and stamps showing them will be found listed as Nos. Y1667 etc.

367   **367a**

Printing differences

Litho   Photo

(*Illustrations enlarged ×6*)

Litho. Clear outlines to value and frame of stamp.
Photo. Uneven lines to value and frame formed by edges of screen.

Two types of the 3p., 10p. and 26p. (Nos. X930/c, X886/b and X971/b)

Figures of face value as I (all ptgs of 3p. bright magenta except the multi-value coil No. 930cl and sheets from 21.1.92 onwards, 10p. orange-brown except 1984 "Christian Heritage" £4 booklet and 26p. rosine except 1987 £1.04 barcode booklet).

Figures of face value narrower as in II (from coil No. X930cl and in sheets from 21.1.92 (3p.), 1984 "Christian Heritage" £4 booklet (10p.) or 1987 £1.04 barcode booklet (26p.)). This catalogue includes changes of figure styles on these stamps where there is no other listable difference. Similar changes have also taken place on other values, but only in conjuction with listed colour, paper or perforation changes.

1971 (15 Feb)–**96.** Decimal Currency. *T* **367.** Chalk-surfaced paper.
(*a*) *Photo Harrison (except for some printings of Nos. X879 and X913 in sheets produced by Enschedé and issued on 12 Dec 1979 (8p.) and 19 Nov 1991 (18p.)). With phosphor bands.* P 15×14.

X841		½p. turquoise-blue (2 bands)	10	10
	a.	Imperf (pair)†	£3500	
	Ey.	Phosphor omitted	4·00	
	l.	Booklet pane. No. X841×2 se-tenant vert with X849×2	6·00	
	lEy.	Booklet pane. Phosphor omitted	£225	
	la.	Booklet pane. No. X841×2 se-tenant horiz with X849×2 (14.7.71)	1·00	
	laEy.	Booklet pane. Phosphor omitted	£375	
	m.	Booklet pane. No. X841×5 plus label	2·75	
	mEy.	Booklet pane. Phosphor omitted	£120	
	n.	Coil strip. No. X849Eg, X841Eg×2 and X844Eg×2	3·50	
	nEy.	Coil strip. Phosphor omitted	45·00	
	nEv.	Coil strip. PVA gum. No. X849, X841×2 and X844×2 (4.74)	80	
	nEvy.	Coil strip. Phosphor omitted	18·00	
	o.	Booklet pane. No. X841, X851, X852, X852Ea, each×3 (24.5.72)	13·00	
	oEy.	Booklet pane. Phosphor omitted	£1600	
	p.	Booklet pane. No. X841×3, X842 and X852×2 (24.5.72)	60·00	
	pEy.	Booklet pane. Phosphor omitted		
	q.	Coil strip. No. X870, X849, X844 and X841×2 (3.12.75)	1·00	
	r.	Booklet pane. No. X841×2, X844×3 and X870 (10.3.76)	75	
	s.	Booklet pane. No. X841×2, X844×2, X873×2 and X881×4 (8½p. values at right) (26.1.77)	3·50	
	sa.	Ditto, but No. X873Ea and 8½p. values at left	3·50	
	t.	Booklet pane. No. X841, X844, X894×3 and X902 (14p. value at right) (26.1.81)	2·00	
	tEy.	Booklet pane. Phosphor omitted	65·00	
	ta.	Booklet pane. No. X841, X844, X894Ea×3 and X902 (14p. value at left)	1·90	
	taEy.	Booklet pane. Phosphor omitted	65·00	

	u. Booklet pane. No. X841, X857×4 and X899×3 (12½p. values at left) (1.2.82)	3·00	
	ua. Ditto, but No. X899Ea and 12½p. values at right	3·00	
	Eg. Gum arabic (from coil strip, and on 22.9.72 from sheets)	40	
	Egy. Phosphor omitted	70·00	
X842	½p. turquoise-blue (1 side band at left) (24.5.72)	55·00	30·00
X843	½p. turquoise-blue (1 centre band) (14.12.77)	40	25
	l. Coil strip. No. X843×2, X875 and X845×2 (14.12.77)	85	
	m. Booklet pane. No. X843×2, X845×2 and X875 plus label (8.2.78)	60	
	mEy. Booklet pane. Phosphor omitted	45·00	
X844	1p. crimson (2 bands)	10	15
	a. Imperf (vert coil)		
	b. Pair, one imperf 3 sides (vert coil)		
	c. Imperf (pair)	£1700	
	Ey. Phosphor omitted	5·00	
	l. Booklet pane. No. X844×2 *se-tenant* vert with X848×2	6·00	
	m. Ditto, but *se-tenant* horiz (14.7.71)	1·00	
	mEy. Booklet pane. Phosphor omitted	£300	
	n. Booklet pane. No. X844×2, X876×3 and X883×3 (9p. values at right) (13.6.77)	4·75	
	na. Ditto, but No. X876Ea and 9p. values at left	2·75	
	Eg. Gum arabic (from coil strip)	50	
	Egy. Phosphor omitted	70·00	
X845	1p. crimson (1 centre band) (14.12.77)	35	30
	l. Booklet pane. No. X879 and X845×2 plus label (17.10.79)	60	
	m. Coil strip. No. X879 and X845×2 plus 2 labels (16.1.80)	85	
	n. Booklet pane. No. X845×2, X860 and X898 each×3 (5.4.83)	6·50	
	nEy. Booklet pane. Phosphor omitted	22·00	
	p. Booklet pane. No. X845×3, X863×2 and X900×3 (3.9.84)	4·00	
	pEy. Booklet pane. Phosphor omitted	£250	
	q. Booklet pane. No. X845×2 and X896×4 (29.7.86)	9·00	
	s. Booklet pane. No. X845, X867×2 and X900×3 (20.10.86)	6·00	
	sa. Ditto, but with vertical edges of pane imperf (29.9.87)	3·00	
	saEy. Booklet pane. Phosphor omitted	£225	
X846	1p. crimson ("all-over") (10.10.79)	30	40
X847	1p. crimson (1 side band at left) (20.10.86) .	1·50	1·75
	Ea. Band at right (3.3.87)	4·00	4·25
	l. Booklet pane. No. X847, X901 and X912×2 (20.10.86)	4·00	
	lEy. Booklet pane. Phosphor omitted	£110	
	m. Booklet pane. No. X847Ea, X901×2, X912×5 and X918 with margins all round (3.3.87)	20·00	
X848	1½p. black (2 bands)	20	30
	a. Uncoated paper*	£130	
	b. Imperf (pair)		
	c. Imperf 3 sides (horiz pair)		
	Ey. Phosphor omitted	60·00	
X849	2p. myrtle-green (2 bands)	15	20
	a. Imperf (horiz pair)	£3500	
	Ey. Phosphor omitted	12·00	
	l. Booklet pane. No. X849×2, X880×2 and X886×3 plus label (10p. values at right) (28.8.79)	2·50	
	la. Ditto, but No. X880Ea and 10p. values at left	2·50	
	m. Booklet pane. No. X849×3, X889×2 and X895×2 plus label (12p. values at right) (4.2.80)	2·50	
	mEy. Booklet pane. Phosphor omitted	55·00	
	ma. Booklet pane. No. X849×3, X889Ea×2 and X895×2 plus label (12p. values at left)	2·50	
	maEy. Booklet pane. Phosphor omitted	55·00	
	n. Booklet pane. No. X849, X888×3, X889Ea and X895×4 with margins all round (16.4.80)	4·25	
	nEy. Booklet pane. Phosphor omitted	55·00	
	o. Booklet pane. No. X849×6 with margins all round (16.4.80)	1·40	
	oEy. Booklet pane. Phosphor omitted	60·00	
	p. Booklet pane. No. X849, X857, X898, X899×3 and X899Ea×3 with margins all round (19.5.82)	6·00	
	pEy. Booklet pane. Phosphor omitted	£150	
	Eg. Gum arabic (from coil strip)	2·25	
	Egy. Phosphor omitted	£225	
X850	2p. myrtle-green ("all-over") (10.10.79)	25	30

X851	2½p. magenta (1 centre band)	20	15
	a. Imperf (pair)†	£375	
	Ey. Phosphor omitted	10·00	
	l. Booklet pane. No. X851×5 plus label	4·50	
	lEy. Booklet pane. Phosphor omitted	55·00	
	m. Booklet pane. No. X851×4 plus two labels	5·00	
	mEy. Booklet pane. Phosphor omitted	£425	
	n. Booklet pane. No. X851×3, X852Ea×3 and X855×6 (24.5.72)	8·00	
	nEy. Booklet pane. Phosphor omitted		
	Eg. Gum arabic (13.9.72)	30	
X852	2½p. magenta (1 band at left)	1·50	1·75
	l. Booklet pane. No. X852×2 and X855×4.	6·00	
	lEy. Booklet pane. Phosphor omitted	£160	
	Ea. Band at right (24.5.72)	1·50	1·75
X853	2½p. magenta (2 bands) (21.5.75)	50	1·00
X854	2½p. rose-red (2 bands) (26.8.81)	55	75
	l. Booklet pane. No. X854×3, X862×2 and X894×3 (11½p. values at left)	5·25	
	la. Ditto, but No. X894Ea and 11½p. values at right	7·00	
X855	3p. ultramarine (2 bands)	20	25
	a. Imperf (coil strip of 5)	£3000	
	b. Imperf (pair)†	£400	
	c. Uncoated paper*	45·00	
	Ey. Phosphor omitted	5·00	
	l. Booklet pane. No. X855×5 plus label	2·50	
	lEy. Booklet pane. Phosphor omitted	£375	
	n. Booklet pane. No. X855×12 (24.5.72)	5·00	
	nEy. Booklet pane. Phosphor omitted	£250	
	Eg. Gum arabic (23.8.72)	1·00	
	Egy. Phosphor omitted	10·00	
X856	3p. ultramarine (1 centre band) (10.9.73)	15	20
	a. Imperf (pair)†	£350	
	b. Imperf between (vert pair)†	£475	
	c. Imperf horiz (vert pair)†	£300	
	Eg. Gum arabic	50	
X857	3p. bright magenta (Type I) (2 bands) (1.2.82)	35	45
	Ey. Phosphor omitted	£160	
X858	3½p. olive-grey (2 bands) (*shades*)	25	30
	a. Imperf (pair)	£600	
	Ey. Phosphor omitted	12·00	
	Eb. *Bronze-green* (18.7.73)	25	30
	Eby. Phosphor omitted	12·00	
X859	3½p. olive-grey (1 centre band) (24.6.74)	30	35
X860	3½p. purple-brown (1 centre band) (5.4.83) ...	1·40	1·40
	Ey. Phosphor omitted	10·00	
X861	4p. ochre-brown (2 bands)	40	50
	a. Imperf (pair)†	£2400	
	Ey. Phosphor omitted	38·00	
	Eg. Gum arabic (1.11.72)	75	
X862	4p. greenish blue (26.8.81)	2·00	2·50
X863	4p. greenish blue (1 centre band) (3.9.84) ...	1·50	1·90
	Ey. Phosphor omitted	90·00	
X864	4p. greenish blue (1 band at right) (8.1.85).	3·75	3·75
	Ea. Band at left	3·75	3·75
	l. Booklet pane. No. X864, X864Ea, X901×2, X901Ea×2, X909×2 and X920 with margins all round (8.1.85)	18·00	
	lEy. Booklet pane. Phosphor omitted	£2600	
X865	4½p. grey-blue (2 bands) (24.10.73)	25	30
	a. Imperf (pair)	£525	
	Ey. Phosphor omitted	11·00	
X866	5p. pale violet (2 bands)	20	20
	a. Imperf (pair)	£240	
X867	5p. claret (1 centre band) (20.10.86)	2·50	2·75
	Ey. Phosphor omitted	85·00	
X868	5½p. violet (2 bands) (24.10.73)	55	65
X869	5½p. violet (1 centre band) (17.3.75)	25	30
	a. Uncoated paper*	£400	
	Ey. Phosphor omitted	22·00	
X870	6p. light emerald (2 bands)	25	40
	a. Uncoated paper*	20·00	
	Ey. Phosphor omitted	75·00	
	Eg. Gum arabic (6.6.73)	2·50	
X871	6½p. greenish blue (2 bands) (4.9.74)	70	80
X872	6½p. greenish blue (1 centre band) (24.9.75)	25	20
	a. Imperf (vert pair)	£450	
	b. Uncoated paper*	£225	
	Ey. Phosphor omitted	15·00	
X873	6½p. greenish blue (1 band at right) (26.1.77)	1·10	1·40
	Ea. Band at left	1·10	1·40
X874	7p. purple-brown (2 bands) (15.1.75)	30	35
	a. Imperf (pair)	£1200	
	Ey. Phosphor omitted	4·00	
X875	7p. purple-brown (1 centre band) (13.6.77).	25	30
	a. Imperf (pair)	£140	

	l. Booklet pane. No. X875 and X883, each×10 (15.11.78)	4·50	
X876	7p. purple-brown (1 band at right) (13.6.77)	80	1·00
	Ea. Band at left	80	1·00
X877	7½p. pale chestnut (2 bands)	30	40
	Ey. Phosphor omitted	22·00	
X878	8p. rosine (2 bands) (24.10.73)	30	30
	a. Uncoated paper*	15·00	
X879	8p. rosine (1 centre band) (20.8.79)	30	30
	a. Uncoated paper*	£900	
	b. Imperf (pair)	£1400	
	Ey. Phosphor omitted	£475	
	l. Booklet pane. No. X879 and X886, each×10 (14.11.79)	5·00	
X880	8p. rosine (1 band at right) (28.8.79) ††	1·10	1·40
	Ea. Band at left	1·10	1·40
X881	8½p. light yellowish green (2 bands) (*shades*) (24.9.75)	30	30
	a. Imperf (pair)	£1700	
	Eb. *Yellowish green* (24.3.76)	35	35
	Ey. Phosphor omitted	6·00	
X882	9p. yellow-orange and black (2 bands)	45	55
	Ey. Phosphor omitted	£110	
X883	9p. deep violet (2 bands) (25.2.76)	35	30
	a. Imperf (pair)	£325	
	Ey. Phosphor omitted	4·50	
X884	9½p. purple (2 bands) (25.2.76)	75	1·00
	Ey. Phosphor omitted	24·00	
X885	10p. orange-brown and chestnut (2 bands) (11.8.71)	35	45
	a. Orange-brown omitted	£200	
	b. Imperf (horiz pair)	£4000	
	Ey. Phosphor omitted	12·00	
X886	10p. orange-brown (Type I) (2 bands) (25.2.76)	35	30
	a. Imperf (pair)	£375	
	Ey. Phosphor omitted	3·00	
	b. Type II (4.9.84)	22·00	22·00
	bEy. Phosphor omitted	£2000	
	bl. Booklet pane. No. X886b, X901Ea and X909×7 with margins all round	32·00	
	blEy. Booklet pane. Phosphor omitted	£4000	
X887	10p. orange-brown (Type I) ("all-over") (3.10.79)	35	45
X888	10p. orange-brown (Type I) (1 centre band) (4.2.80)	35	25
	a. Imperf (pair)	£375	
	l. Booklet pane. No. X888×9 with margins all round (16.4.80)	3·75	
	lEy. Booklet pane. Phosphor omitted	55·00	
	m. Booklet pane. No. X888 and X895, each×10 (12.11.80)	5·50	
X889	10p. orange-brown (Type I) (1 band at right) (4.2.80)	1·10	1.50
	Ea. Band at left	1·00	1·20
X890	10½p. yellow (2 bands) (25.2.76)	60	75
X891	10½p. deep dull blue (2 bands) (26.4.78)	80	1·00
X892	11p. brown-red (2 bands) (25.2.76)	40	40
	a. Imperf (pair)	£3750	
	Ey. Phosphor omitted	5·00	
X893	11½p. drab (1 centre band) (14.1.81)	40	35
	a. Imperf (pair)	£340	
	Ey. Phosphor omitted	7·00	
	l. Booklet pane. No. X893 and X902, each×10 (11.11.81)	8·50	
X894	11½p. drab (1 band at right) (26.1.81)	65	80
	Ea. Band at left	65	80
	l. Booklet pane. No. X894/Ea, each×2 & X902×6 (6.5.81)	6·50	
X895	12p. yellowish green (2 bands) (4.2.80)	55	65
	Ey. Phosphor omitted	8·00	
	l. Booklet pane. No. X895×9 with margins all round (16.4.80)	4·00	
	lEy. Booklet pane. Phosphor omitted	45·00	
X896	12p. bright emerald (1 centre band) (29.10.85)	45	45
	a. Imperf (pair)	£2200	
	Ey. Phosphor omitted	12·00	
	l. Booklet pane. No. X896×9 with margins all round (18.3.86)	4·75	
	lEy. Booklet pane. Phosphor omitted	£225	
	Eu. Underprint Type 4 (29.10.85)	55	
X897	12p. bright emerald (1 band at right) (14.1.86)	80	85
	Ea. Band at left	80	85
	l. Booklet pane. No. X897/Ea, each×2 and X909×6 (12p. values at left) (14.1.86)	6·00	
	la. Ditto, but 12p. values at right	6·00	

	m. Booklet pane. No. X897/Ea, each×3, X909×2 and X919 with margins all round (18.3.86)	23·00	
	mEy. Booklet pane. Phosphor omitted	£1800	
X898	12½p. light emerald (1 centre band) (27.1.82)	45	40
	a. Imperf (pair)	£120	
	Ey. Phosphor omitted	6·50	
	Eu. Underprint Type 1 (10.11.82)	60	
	Euy. Phosphor omitted	75·00	
	Ev. Underprint Type 2 (9.11.83)	60	
	l. Booklet pane. No. X898Eu and X907Eu, each×10 (10.11.82)	10·00	
X899	12½p. light emerald (1 band at right) (1.2.82)	70	75
	Ea. Band at left	70	75
	l. Booklet pane. No. X899/Ea, each×2 and X907×6 (1.2.82) ††	5·00	
	lEy. Booklet pane. Phosphor omitted	£3600	
	m. Booklet pane. No. X899/Ea, each×3 with margins all round (19.5.82)	3·25	
	mEy. Booklet pane. Phosphor omitted	45·00	
	n. Booklet pane. No. X899/Ea, each×2, and X908×6 (12½p. values at left) (5.4.83)	8·50	
	na. Ditto, but 12½p. values at right	8·00	
X900	13p. pale chestnut (1 centre band) (28.8.84)	40	40
	a. Imperf (pair)	£775	
	Eu. Underprint Type 2 (2.12.86)	90	
	Ey. Phosphor omitted	6·50	
	l. Booklet pane. No. X900×9 with margins all round (8.1.85)	4·50	
	lEy. Booklet pane. Phosphor omitted	£425	
	m. Booklet pane. No. X900×6 with margins all round (3.3.87)	3·75	
	n. Booklet pane. No. X900×4 with margins all round (4.8.87)	3·00	
	o. Booklet pane. No. X900×10 with margins all round (4.8.87)	7·00	
X901	13p. pale chestnut (1 band at right) (3.9.84)	50	60
	Ea. Band at left	50	60
	l. Booklet pane. No. X901/Ea, each×2, and X909×6 (13p. values at left) ††	5·00	
	la. Ditto, but 13p. values at right	5·00	
	m. Booklet pane. No. X901/Ea, each×3 with margins all round (4.9.84)	4·50	
	mEy. Booklet pane. Phosphor omitted	£325	
	n. Booklet pane. No. X901Ea and X912×5 (20.10.86)	4·50	
	na. Ditto, but with vertical edges of pane imperf (29.9.87)	4·75	
X902	14p. grey-blue (2 bands) (26.1.81)	1·00	1·00
	Ey. Phosphor omitted	30·00	
X903	14p. deep blue (1 centre band) (23.8.88)	45	50
	a. Imperf (pair)	£500	
	Ey. Phosphor omitted	9·00	
	l. Booklet pane. No. X903×4 with margins all round	6·00	
	lEy. Booklet pane. Phosphor omitted	£110	
	m. Booklet pane. No. X903×10 with margins all round	9·50	
	n. Booklet pane. No. X903×4 with horizontal edges of pane imperf (11.10.88)	6·50	
	p. Booklet pane. No. X903×10 with horizontal edges of pane imperf (11.10.88)	9·00	
	pEy. Booklet pane. Phosphor omitted	£160	
	q. Booklet pane. No. X903×4 with three edges of pane imperf (24.1.89)	32·00	
	qEy. Booklet pane. Phosphor omitted	35·00	
X904	14p. deep blue (1 band at right) (5.9.88)	4·00	4·00
	l. Booklet pane. No. X904 and X914×2 plus label	8·00	
	lEy. Booklet pane. Phosphor omitted	15·00	
	m. Booklet pane. No. X904×2 and X914×4 with vertical edges of pane imperf	6·50	
	mEy. Booklet pane. Phosphor omitted	£850	
X905	15p. bright blue (1 centre band) (26.9.89)	65	65
	a. Imperf (pair)	£625	
	Ey. Phosphor omitted	14·00	
X906	15p. brt blue (1 band at left) (2.10.89)	4·00	4·00
	Ea. Band at right (20.3.90)	4·75	4·75
	l. Booklet pane. No. X906×2 and X916 plus label	10·00	
	lEy. Booklet pane. Phosphor omitted	£550	
	m. Booklet pane. No. X906Ea, X916, X922, 1446, 1448, 1468Ea, 1470 and 1472 plus label with margins all round (20.3.90)	20·00	
X907	15½p. pale violet (2 bands) (1.2.82)	70	80
	aEy. Phosphor omitted	7·00	
	Eu. Underprint Type 1 (10.11.82)	80	
	l. Booklet pane. No. X907×6 with margins all round (19.5.82)	4·00	

	lEy. Booklet pane. Phosphor omitted..............	85·00	
	m. Booklet pane. No. X907×9 with		
	margins all round (19.5.82)..........	5·25	
	mEy. Booklet pane. Phosphor omitted..............	50·00	
X908	16p. olive-drab (2 bands) (5.4.83)........	1·40	1·60
	Ey. Phosphor omitted..................................	£110	
X909	17p. grey-blue (2 bands) (3.9.84).........	60	60
	aEy. Phosphor omitted.............................	£240	
	Eu. Underprint Type 4 (4.11.85).............	70	
	Euy. Phosphor omitted.............................	22·00	
	l. Booklet pane. No. X909Eu×3 plus label		
	(4.11.85)..	2·50	
	lEy. Booklet pane. Phosphor omitted..............	65·00	
	Ela. Booklet pane. No. X909×3 plus label		
	(12.8.86)..	3·00	
X910	17p. deep blue (1 centre band) (4.9.90).........	80	85
	a. Imperf (pair)......................................	£1700	
X911	17p. deep blue (1 band at right) (4.9.90)......	5·50	5·50
	Ea. Band at left....................................	2·75	2·75
	Ey. Phosphor omitted.............................	12·00	
	l. Booklet pane. No. X911 and X911Ea×2		
	plus label..	7·50	
	lEy. Booklet pane. Phosphor omitted..............	55·00	
	m. Booklet pane. No. X911×2 and X917×3		
	plus three labels with vertical edges of		
	pane imperf.......................................	4·25	
	mEy. Booklet pane. Phosphor omitted..............	75·00	
X912	18p. deep olive-grey (2 bands) (20.10.86).......	70	80
	Ey. Phosphor omitted.............................	30·00	
X913	18p. bright green (1 centre band) (10.9.91) ...	60	60
	a. Imperf (pair)......................................	£525	
	Ey. Phosphor omitted.............................	28·00	
X914	19p. brt orange-red (2 bands) (5.9.88)...........	1·50	1·50
	Ey. Phosphor omitted.............................	4·00	
X915	20p. dull purple (2 bands) (25.2.76)...........	1·20	1·20
X916	20p. brownish black (2 bands) (2.10.89).......	2·75	3·00
	Ey. Phosphor omitted.............................	£550	
X917	22p. brt orange-red (2 bands) (4.9.90)...........	1·50	1·25
	Ey. Phosphor omitted.............................	22·00	
X917a	25p. rose-red (2 bands) (6.2.96)................	12·00	12·00
X918	26p. rosine (Type I) (2 bands) (3.3.87).........	15·00	16·00
X919	31p. purple (2 bands) (18.3.86)................	15·00	15·00
	Ey. Phosphor omitted.............................	£1600	
X920	34p. ochre-brown (2 bands) (8.1.85)..........	9·00	9·50
	Ey. Phosphor omitted.............................	£1600	
X921	50p. ochre-brown (2 bands) (2.2.77)..........	2·00	75
X922	50p. ochre (2 bands) (20.3.90)................	5·50	6·00
	(b) Photo Harrison. On phosphorised paper. P 15×14.		
X924	½p. turquoise-blue (10.12.80)................	10	20
	a. Imperf (pair)......................................	£150	
	l. Coil strip. No. X924 and X932×3		
	(30.12.81)...	75	
X925	1p. crimson (12.12.79)..........................	10	15
	a. Imperf (pair)......................................	£1600	
	l. Coil strip. No. X925 and X932Ea×3		
	(14.8.84)...	90	
	m. Booklet pane. No. X925 and X969,		
	each×2 (10.9.91)................................	2·00	
X926	2p. myrtle-green (face value as T **367**)		
	(12.12.79)...	15	20
	a. Imperf (pair)......................................	£3000	
X927	2p. deep green (face value as T **367a**)		
	(26.7.88)...	25	25
	a. Imperf (pair)......................................	£3000	
	l. Booklet pane. No. X927×2 and X969×4		
	plus 2 labels with vert edges of pane		
	imperf (10.9.91).................................	3·25	
X928	2p. myrtle-green (face value as T **367a**)		
	(5.9.88)...	9·00	9·00
	l. Coil strip. No. X928 and X932Ea×3..........	9·50	
X929	2½p. rose-red (14.1.81).........................	25	40
	l. Coil strip. No. X929 and X930×3 (6.81) ..	1·00	
X930	3p. brt magenta (Type I) (22.10.80)...........	20	25
	a. Imperf (horiz pair)..............................	£2000	
	b. Booklet pane. No. X930, X931×2		
	and X949×6 with margins all round		
	(14.9.83)...	6·50	
	c. Type II (10.10.89)................................	90	1·30
	cl. Booklet pane. No. X930c and X933×3	2·25	
X931	3½p. purple-brown (30.3.83)................	60	70
X932	4p. greenish blue (30.12.81)................	45	60
	Ea. Pale greenish blue (14.8.84)	45	60
X933	4p. new blue (26.7.88).........................	20	25
	a. Imperf (pair)......................................	£3000	
	l. Coil strip. No. X933×3 and X935		
	(27.11.90)...	1·40	
	m. Coil strip. No. X933 and X935, each×2		
	(1.10.91)...	1·00	
	n. Coil strip. No. X933 and X935×3		
	(31.1.95)...	1·25	
X934	5p. pale violet (10.10.79)	55	65
X935	5p. dull red-brown (26.7.88)	25	30

	a. Imperf (pair)......................................	£5000	
X936	6p. yellow-olive (10.9.91)....................	30	40
X937	7p. brownish red (29.10.85).................	1·50	1·60
X938	8½p. yellowish green (24.3.76)..............	1·50	1·75
X939	10p. orange-brown (Type I) (11.79).........	35	35
X940	10p. dull orange (Type II) (4.9.90)..........	40	35
X941	11p. brown-red (27.8.80).....................	2·00	2·00
X942	11½p. ochre-brown (15.8.79)................	65	75
X943	12p. yellowish green (30.1.80)..............	45	45
X944	13p. olive-grey (15.8.79)......................	1·20	1·20
X945	13½p. purple-brown (30.1.80)...............	90	90
X946	14p. grey-blue (14.1.81)......................	50	50
X947	15p. ultramarine (15.8.79)....................	60	60
X948	15½p. pale violet (14.1.81)...................	60	50
	a. Imperf (pair)......................................	£300	
X949	16p. olive-drab (30.3.83).....................	55	55
	a. Imperf (pair)......................................	£200	
	Eu. Underprint Type 3 (10.8.83).............	80	
	l. Booklet pane. No. X949×9 with		
	margins all round (14.9.83)................	5·00	
X950	16½p. pale chestnut (27.1.82)................	90	1·00
X951	17p. light emerald (30.1.80).................	90	1·00
X952	17p. grey-blue (30.3.83)......................	45	45
	a. Imperf (pair)......................................	£400	
	Eu. Underprint Type 3 (5.3.85)...............	80	
	l. Booklet pane. No. X952×6 with		
	margins all round (4.9.84).................	4·50	
	m. Booklet pane. No. X952×9 with		
	margins all round (8.1.85).................	6·00	
X953	17½p. pale chestnut (30.1.80)...............	1·00	1·10
X954	18p. deep violet (14.1.81)....................	80	90
X955	18p. deep olive-grey (28.8.84)..............	75	60
	a. Imperf (pair)......................................	£150	
	l. Booklet pane. No. X955×9 with		
	margins all round (3.3.87).................	7·50	
	m. Booklet pane. No. X955×4 with		
	margins all round (4.8.87).................	3·50	
	n. Booklet pane. No. X955×10 with		
	margins all round (4.8.87).................	8·00	
X956	19p. bright orange-red (23.8.88)............	80	60
	a. Imperf (pair)......................................	£500	
	l. Booklet pane. No. X956×4 with		
	margins all round..............................	7·00	
	m. Booklet pane. No. X956×10 with		
	margins all round..............................	12·00	
	n. Booklet pane. No. X956×4 with		
	horizontal edges of pane imperf		
	(11.10.88)...	8·50	
	o. Booklet pane. No. X956×10 with		
	horizontal edges of pane imperf		
	(11.10.88)...	12·00	
	q. Booklet pane. No. X956×4 with three		
	edges of pane imperf (24.1.89)...........	32·00	
X957	19½p. olive-grey (27.1.82)....................	2·25	2·25
X958	20p. dull purple (10.10.79)	1·00	75
X959	20p. turquoise-green (23.8.88)..............	75	70
X960	20p. brownish black (26.9.89)..............	75	75
	a. Imperf (pair)......................................	£1100	
	l. Booklet pane. No. X960×5 plus label		
	with vertical edges of pane imperf		
	(2.10.89)...	6·25	
X961	20½p. ultramarine (30.3.83).................	1·40	1·40
	a. Imperf (pair)......................................	£2200	
X962	22p. blue (22.10.80)...........................	1·20	1·20
	a. Imperf (pair)......................................	£325	
X963	22p. yellow-green (28.8.84)..................	1·00	1·00
	a. Imperf (horiz pair)..............................	£2700	
X964	22p. bright orange-red (4.9.90).............	90	80
	a. Imperf (pair)......................................	£875	
X965	23p. brown-red (30.3.83).....................	1·25	1·10
	a. Imperf (horiz pair)..............................	£2000	
X966	23p. bright green (23.8.88)..................	1·60	1·60
X967	24p. violet (28.8.84)...........................	1·40	1·50
X968	24p. Indian red (26.9.89).....................	2·00	2·25
	a. Imperf (horiz pair)..............................	£4000	
X969	24p. chestnut (10.9.91).......................	80	80
	a. Imperf (pair)......................................	£280	
X970	25p. purple (14.1.81)..........................	1·00	1·00
X971	26p. rosine (Type I) (27.1.82)...............	1·10	80
	a. Imperf (horiz pair)..............................	£975	
	b. Type II (4.8.87)..................................	6·00	7·00
	bl. Booklet pane. No. X971b×4 with		
	margins all round..............................	22·00	
X972	26p. drab (4.9.90)...............................	1·50	1·25
X973	27p. chestnut (23.8.88).......................	1·25	1·25
	l. Booklet pane. No. X973×4 with		
	margins all round..............................	12·50	
	m. Booklet pane. No. X973×4 with		
	horizontal edges of pane imperf		
	(11.10.88)...	30·00	
X974	27p. violet (4.9.90).............................	1·50	1·25
X975	28p. deep violet (30.3.83)....................	1·25	1·25

	a. Imperf (pair)	£2400	
X976	28p. ochre (23.8.88)	1·40	1·25
X977	28p. deep bluish grey (10.9.91)	1·40	1·50
	a. Imperf (pair)	£3000	
X978	29p. ochre-brown (27.1.82)	2·00	2·00
X979	29p. deep mauve (26.9.89)	1·75	1·75
X980	30p. deep olive-grey (26.9.89)	1·25	1·25
X981	31p. purple (30.3.83)	1·25	1·25
	a. Imperf (pair)	£1900	
X982	31p. ultramarine (4.9.90)	1·60	1·75
X983	32p. greenish blue (23.8.88)	1·90	1·75
	a. Imperf (pair)	£3000	
X984	33p. light emerald (4.9.90)	1·75	1·60
X985	34p. ochre-brown (28.8.84)	1·75	1·75
X986	34p. deep bluish grey (26.9.89)	2·00	2·0
X987	34p. deep mauve (10.9.91)	1·75	1·75
X988	35p. sepia (23.8.88)	1·60	1·60
	a. Imperf (pair)	£3000	
X989	35p. yellow (10.9.91)	1·75	1·60
X990	37p. rosine (26.9.89)	2·00	1·75
X991	39p. bright mauve (10.9.91)	1·75	1·75
X991*a*	50p. ochre (21.1.92)	5·00	2·00
	ab. Imperf (pair)	£2600	

(c) Photo Harrison. On ordinary paper. P 15×14.

X992	50p. ochre-brown (21.5.80)	1·75	70
	a. Imperf (pair)	£875	
X993	50p. ochre (13.3.90)	5·00	2·00
X994	75p. grey-black (face value as T **367a**) (26.7.88)	3·25	1·50

(d) Litho J.W. P. 14.

X996	4p. greenish blue (2 bands) (30.1.80)	50	55
	Ey. Phosphor omitted	£1600	
X997	4p. greenish blue (phosphorised paper) (11.81)	45	40
X998	20p. dull purple (2 bands) (21.5.80)	1·50	1·50
X999	20p. dull purple (phosphorised paper) (11.81)	1·20	1·20

(e) Litho Questa. P. 14 (Nos. X1000, X1003/4 and X1023) or 15×14 (others).

X1000	2p. emerald-green (face value as T **367**) (phosphorised paper) (21.5.80)	40	45
	a. Perf 15×14 (10.7.84)	35	35
X1001	2p. brt green and dp green (face value as T **367a**) (phosphorised paper) (23.2.88)	75	80
X1002	4p. greenish blue (phosphorised paper) (13.5.86)	80	90
X1003	5p. light violet (phosphorised paper) (21.5.80)	60	75
X1004	5p. claret (phosphorised paper) (27.1.82)	75	75
	a. Perf 15×14 (21.2.84)	65	60
X1005	13p. pale chestnut (1 centre band) (9.2.88)	85	1·00
	l. Booklet pane. No. X1005×6 with margins all round	4·75	
X1006	13p. pale chestnut (1 side band at right) (9.2.88)	75	75
	Ea. Band at left	75	75
	l. Booklet pane. No. X1006/Ea each×3, X1010, X1015 and X1021 with margins all round	30·00	
	lEa. Grey-green (on 18p.) ptg double	£3800	
X1007	14p. deep blue (1 centre band) (11.10.88)	2·00	2·00
X1008	17p. deep blue (1 centre band) (19.3.91)	1·00	1·00
	Ey. Phosphor omitted	£240	
	l. Booklet pane. No. X1008×6 with margins all round	5·00	
	lEy. Booklet pane. Phosphor omitted	£1400	
X1009	18p. deep olive-grey (phosphorised paper) (9.2.88)	1·00	1·10
	l. Booklet pane. No. X1009×9 with margins all round	10·00	
	m. Booklet pane. No. X1009×6 with margins all round	5·50	
X1010	18p. deep olive-grey (2 bands) (9.2.88)	8·00	8·00
X1011	18p. bright green (1 centre band) (27.10.92)	1·00	1·20
	l. Booklet pane. No. X1011×6 with margins all round	5·00	
X1012	18p. bright green (1 side band at right) (27.10.92)	1·80	2·00
	Ea. Band at left (10.8.93)	1·80	2·00
	Ey. Phosphor omitted	£850	
	l. Booklet pane. No. X1012×2, X1018×2, X1022×2, 1451a, 1514a and centre label with margins all round	12·00	
	lEa. Bright blue (on 2nd) ptg treble		
	lEy. Phosphor omitted	£7000	
	m. Booklet pane. No. X1012Ea, X1020, X1022 and 1451aEb, each×2, with centre label and margins all round (10.8.93)	13·00	
	mEy. Booklet pane. Phosphor omitted	£4000	
X1013	19p. bright orange-red (phosphorised paper) (11.10.88)	2·20	2·00

X1014	20p. dull purple (phosphorised paper) (13.5.86)	1·75	1·75
X1015	22p. yellow-green (2 bands) (9.2.88)	9·00	9·00
X1016	22p. bright orange-red (phosphorised paper) (19.3.91)	1·00	90
	l. Booklet pane. No. X1016×9 with margins all round	9·00	
	m. Booklet pane. No. X1016×6, X1019×2 and centre label with margins all round	10·00	
X1017	24p. chestnut (phosphorised paper) (27.10.92)	90	1·10
	l. Booklet pane. No. X1017×6 with margins all round	5·50	
X1018	24p. chestnut (2 bands) (27.10.92)	2·00	2·00
	Ey. Phosphor omitted	£950	
X1019	33p. light emerald (phosphorised paper) (19.3.91)	2·75	2·75
X1020	33p. lt emerald (2 bands) (25.2.92)	1·75	1·75
	Ey. Phosphor omitted	£750	
X1021	34p. bistre-brown (2 bands) (23.8.88)	8·00	8·00
X1022	39p. brt mauve (2 bands) (27.10.92)	2·00	2·00
	Ey. Phosphor omitted	£950	
X1023	75p. black (face value as T **367**) (ordinary paper) (30.1.80)	3·00	1·50
	a. Perf 15×14 (21.2.84)	4·00	2·25
X1024	75p. brownish grey and black (face value as T **367a**) (ordinary paper) (23.2.88)	10·00	10·50

(f) Litho Walsall. P. 14.

X1050	2p. deep green (phosphorised paper) (9.2.93)	1·50	1·50
	l. Booklet pane. No. X1050×2 and X1053×4 plus 2 labels with vert edges of pane imperf	7·50	
X1051	14p. deep blue (1 side band at right) (25.4.89)	5·25	5·25
	Ey. Phosphor omitted	£280	
	l. Booklet pane. No. X1051×2 and X1052×4 with vertical edges of pane imperf	14·00	
	lEy. Booklet pane. Phosphor omitted	£975	
X1052	19p. bright orange-red (2 bands) (25.4.89)	3·00	3·00
	Ey. Phosphor omitted	£240	
X1053	24p. chestnut (phosphorised paper) (9.2.93)	1·40	1·40
X1054	29p. dp mauve (2 bands) (2.10.89)	3·25	3·25
	l. Booklet pane. No. X1054×4 with three edges of pane imperf	15·00	
X1055	29p. deep mauve (phosphorised paper) (17.4.90)	4·50	4·50
	l. Booklet pane. No. X1055×4 with three edges of pane imperf	17·00	
X1056	31p. ultramarine (phosphorised paper) (17.9.90)	1·50	1·50
	l. Booklet pane. No. X1056×4 with horizontal edges of pane imperf	7·00	
X1057	33p. light emerald (phosphorised paper) (16.9.91)	1·75	1·75
	l. Booklet pane. No. X1057×4 with horiz edges of pane imperf	6·00	
X1058	39p. bright mauve (phosphorised paper) (16.9.91)	2·25	2·25
	l. Booklet pane. No. X1058×4 with horiz edges of pane imperf	8·00	

*See footnote after No. 744.

†These come from sheets with gum arabic.

††Examples of Booklet panes Nos. X899l, X901l and X901la are known on which the phosphor bands were printed on the wrong values in error with the result that the side bands appear on the 15½p. or 17p. and the two bands on the 12½p. or 13p. Similarly examples of the 1p. with phosphor band at right instead of left and of the 13p. with band at left instead of right, exist from 50p. booklet pane No. X847l.

Nos. X844a/b come from a strip of eight of the vertical coil. It comprises two normals, one imperforate at sides and bottom, one completely imperforate, one imperforate at top, left and bottom and partly perforated at right due to the bottom three stamps being perforated twice. No. X844b is also known from another strip having one stamp imperforate at sides and bottom.

Nos. X848b/c come from the same sheet, the latter having perforations at the foot of the stamps only.

Multi-value coil strips Nos. X924l, X925l, X928l, X929l, X930cl and X933l/n were produced by the Post Office for use by a large direct mail marketing firm. From 2 September 1981 No. X929l was available from the Philatelic Bureau, Edinburgh, and, subsequently from a number of other Post Office counters. Later multi-value coil strips were sold at the Philatelic Bureau and Post Office philatelic counters.

In addition to booklet pane No. X1012m No. X1020 also comes from the *se-tenant* pane in the Wales £6 booklet. This pane is listed under No. W49a in the Wales Regional section.

PANES OF SIX FROM STITCHED BOOKLETS. Nos. X841m, X851l/m and X855l include one or two printed labels showing commercial advertisements. These were originally perforated on all four sides, but from the August 1971 editions of the 25p. and 30p. booklets (Nos. DH42, DQ59) and December 1971 edition of the 50p. (No. DT4) the line of perforations between the label and the binding margin was omitted. Similar panes, with the line of perforations omitted, exist for the 3p., 3½p. and 4½p. values (Nos. X856, X858 and X865), but these are outside the scope of this listing as the labels are blank.

PART-PERFORATED SHEETS. Since the introduction of the "Jumelle" press in 1972 a number of part perforated sheets, both definitives and commemoratives, have been discovered. It is believed that these occur when the operation of the press is interrupted. Our listings invariably show a number of "blind" perforations, where the pins have failed to cut the paper. Our listings of imperforate errors from these sheets are for pairs showing no traces whatsoever of the perforations. Examples showing "blind" perforations are outside the scope of this catalogue.

In cases where perforation varieties affect *se-tenant* stamps, fuller descriptions will be found in Vols. 4 and 5 of the *G.B. Specialised Catalogue.*

WHITE PAPER. From 1972 printings appeared on fluorescent white paper giving a stronger chalk reaction than the original ordinary cream paper.

PHOSPHOR OMITTED ERRORS. It should be noted that several values listed with phosphor omitted errors also exist on phosphorised paper. These errors can only be identified with certainty by checking for an "afterglow", using a short-wave ultraviolet lamp.

"ALL-OVER" PHOSPHOR. To improve mechanised handling most commemoratives from the 1972 Royal Silver Wedding 3p. value to the 1979 Rowland Hill Death Centenary set had the phosphor applied by printing cylinder across the entire surface of the stamp, giving a matt effect. Printings of the 1, 2 and 10p. definitives, released in October 1979, also had "all-over" phosphor, but these were purely a temporary expedient pending the adoption of phosphorised paper. Nos. X883, X890 and X921 have been discovered with "all-over" phosphor in addition to the normal phosphor bands. These errors are outside the scope of this catalogue.

PHOSPHORISED PAPER. Following the experiments on Nos. 743c and 829 a printing of the 4½p. definitive was issued on 13 November 1974, which had, in addition to the normal phosphor bands, phosphor included in the paper coating. Because of difficulties in identifying this phosphorised paper with the naked eye this printing is not listed separately in this catalogue.

No. X938 was the first value printed on phosphorised paper without phosphor bands and was a further experimental issue to test the efficacy of this system. From 15 August 1979 phosphorised paper was accepted for use generally, this paper replacing phosphor bands on values other than those required for the second-class mail.

Stamps on phosphorised paper show a shiny surface instead of the matt areas of those printed with phosphor bands.

DEXTRIN GUM. From 1973 printings in photogravure appeared with PVA gum to which dextrin had been added. Because this is virtually colourless a bluish green colouring matter was added to distinguish it from the earlier pure PVA.

The 4p., 5p. (light violet), 20p. and 75p. printed in lithography exist with PVA and PVAD gum. From 1988 Questa printings were with PVAD gum, but did not show the bluish green additive.

VARNISH COATING. Nos. X841 and X883 exist with and without a varnish coating. This cannot easily be detected without the use of an ultra-violet lamp as it merely reduces the fluorescent paper reaction.

POSTAL FORGERIES. In mid-1993 a number of postal forgeries of the 24p. chestnut were detected in the London area. These forgeries, produced by lithography, can be identified by the lack of phosphor in the paper, screening dots across the face value and by the perforations which were applied by a line machine gauging 11.

First Day Covers

15.2.71	½p., 1p., 1½p., 2p., 2½p., 3p., 3½p., 4p., 5p., 6p., 7½p., 9p. (X841, X844, X848/9, X851, X855, X858, X861, X866, X870, X877, X882) (Covers carry "POSTING DELAYED BY THE POST OFFICE STRIKE 1971"cachet)	2·50
11.8.71	10p. (X885)	1·50
24.5.72	Wedgwood *se-tenant* pane ½p., 2½p. (X841p)	25·00
24.10.73	4½p., 5½p., 8p. (X865, X868, X878)	1·50
4.9.74	6½p. (X871)	1·50
15.1.75	7p. (X874)	1·00
24.9.75	8½p. (X881)	1·50
25.2.76	9p., 9½p., 10p., 10½p., 11p., 20p. (X883/4, X886, X890, X892, X915)	3·50
2.2.77	50p. (X921)	1·75
26.4.78	10½p. (X891)	1·20
15.8.79	11½p., 13p., 15p. (X942, X944, X947)	1·75
30.1.80	4p., 12p., 13½p., 17p., 17½p., 75p. (X996, X943, X945, X951, X953, X1023)	3·25
16.4.80	Wedgwood *se-tenant* pane 2p., 10p., 12p. (X849n)	2·25
22.10.80	3p., 22p. (X930, X962)	1·50
14.1.81	2½p., 11½p., 14p., 15½p., 18p., 25p. (X929, X893, X946, X948, X954, X970)	2·00
27.1.82	5p., 12½p., 16½p., 19½p., 26p., 29p. (X1004, X898, X950, X957, X971, X978)	3·50
19.5.82	Stanley Gibbons *se-tenant* pane 2p., 3p., 12½p. (X849p)	3·00
30.3.83	3½p., 16p., 17p., 20½p., 23p., 28p., 31p. (X931, X949, X952, X961, X965, X975, X981)	5·00

14.9.83	Royal Mint *se-tenant* pane 3p., 3½p., 16p. (X930b)	4·00
28.8.84	13p., 18p., 22p., 24p., 34p. (X900, X955, X963, X967, X985)	3·00
4.9.84	Christian Heritage *se-tenant* pane 10p., 13p., 17p. (X886bl)	20·00
8.1.85	*The Times se-tenant* pane 4p., 13p., 17p., 34p. (X864l)	9·50
29.10.85	7p., 12p. (X937, X896)	3·00
18.3.86	British Rail *se-tenant* pane 12p., 17p., 31p. (X897m)	12·00
3.3.87	P & O *se-tenant* pane 1p., 13p., 18p., 26p. (X847m)	9·00
9.2.88	*Financial Times se-tenant* pane 13p., 18p., 22p., 34p. (X1006l)	15·00
23.8.88	14p., 19p., 20p., 23p., 27p., 28p., 32p., 35p. (X903, X956, X959, X966, X973, X976, X983, X988)	6·00
26.9.89	15p., 20p., 24p., 29p., 30p., 34p., 37p. (X905, X960, X968, X979/80, X986, X990)	5·00
20.3.90	London Life *se-tenant* pane 15p., (2nd), 20p., (1st), 15p., 20p., 29p. (X906m)	10·00
4.9.90	10p., 17p., 22p., 26p., 27p., 31p., 33p. (X910, X940, X964, X972, X982, X984)	5·50
19.3.91	Alias Agatha Christie *se-tenant* pane 22p., 33p. (X1016m)	8·00
10.9.91	6p., 18p., 24p., 28p., 34p., 35p., 39p. (X936, X913, X969, X977, X987, X989, X991)	6·00
27.10.92	Tolkien *se-tenant* pane 18p., (2nd), 24p., (1st), 39p. (X1012l)	8·00
10.8.93	Beatrix Potter *se-tenant* pane 18p., (2nd), 33p., 39p. (X1012m)	12·00

Post Office Presentation Packs

15.2.71	P.O. Pack No. 26. ½p. (2 bands), 1p. (2 bands), 1½p. (2 bands), 2p. (2 bands), 2½p. magenta (1 centre band), 3p. ultramarine (2 bands), 3½p. olive-grey (2 bands), 4p. ochre-brown (2 bands), 5p. pale violet (2 bands), 6p. light emerald (2 bands), 7½p. (2 bands), 9p. yellow-orange and black (2 bands). (*Nos.* X841, X844, X848/9, X851, X855, X858, X861, X866, X870, X877, X882)	5·00
15.4.71**	"Scandinavia 71". Contents as above	30·00
25.11.71	P.O. Pack No. 37. ½p. (2 bands), 1p. (2 bands), 1½p. (2 bands), 2p. (2 bands), 2½p. magenta (1 centre band), 3p. ultramarine (2 bands) or (1 centre band), 3½p. olive-grey (2 bands) or (1 centre band) 4p. ochre-brown (2 bands), 4½p. (2 bands), 5p. pale violet (2 bands), 5½p. (2 bands) or (1 centre band), 6p. (2 bands), 6½p. (2 bands) or (1 centre band), 7p. (2 bands), 7½p. (2 bands), 8p (2 bands), 9p. yellow-orange and black (2 bands), 10p. orange-brown and chestnut (2 bands). (*Nos.* X841, X844, X848/9, X851, X855 or X856, X858 or X859, X861, X865/6, X868 or X869, X870, X871 or X872, X874, X877/8, X882, X885)	30·00
	Later issues of this Pack contained the alternatives	
2.2.77	P.O. Pack No. 90. ½p. (2 bands), 1p. (2 bands), 1½p (2 bands), 2p. (2 bands), 2½p. magenta (1 centre band), 3p. ultramarine (2 bands), 5p. pale violet (2 bands), 6½p. (1 centre band), 7p. (2 bands) or (1 centre band), 7½p. (2 bands), 8p. (2 bands), 8½p. (2 bands), 9p. deep violet (2 bands), 9½p. (2 bands), 10p. orange-brown (2 bands), 10½p. yellow (2 bands), 11p. (2 bands), 20p. dull purple (2 bands), 50p. ochre-brown (2 bands) (*Nos.* X841, X844, X848/9, X851, X856, X866, X872, X874 or X875, X877/8, X881, X883/4, X886, X890, X892, X915, X921)	5·00
28.10.81	P.O. Pack No. 129a. 10½p. deep dull blue (2 bands), 11½p. (1 centre band), 2½p. (phos paper), 3p. (phos paper), 11½p. (phos paper), 12p. (phos paper), 13p. (phos paper), 13½p. (phos paper), 14p. (phos paper), 15p. (phos paper), 15½p. (phos paper), 17p. light emerald (phos paper), 17½p. (phos paper), 18p. deep violet (phos paper), 22p. blue (phos paper), 25p. (phos paper), 4p. greenish blue (litho, 2 bands), 75p. (litho) (Nos. X891, X893, X929/30, X942/8, X951, X953/4, X962, X970, X996, X1023)	20·00
3.8.83	P.O. Pack No. 1. 10p. orange-brown (1 centre band), 12½p. (1 centre band), ½p. (phos paper), 1p. (phos paper), 3p. (phos paper), 3½p. (phos paper), 16p. (phos paper), 16½p. (phos paper), 17p. grey-blue (phos paper), 20½p. (phos paper), 23p. brown-red (phos paper), 26p. prosine (phos paper), 28p. deep violet (phos paper), 31p. purple (phos paper), 50p (ord paper), 2p. (litho phos paper), 4p. (litho phos paper), 5p. claret (litho phos paper), 20p. (litho phos paper), 75p. (litho) (*Nos.* X888, X898, X924/5, X930/1, X949/50, X952, X961, X965, X971, X975, X981, X992, X997, X999, X1000, X1004, X1023)	40·00

23.10.84	P.O. Pack No. 5. 13p. (1 centre band), ½p. (phos paper), 1p. (phos paper), 3p. (phos paper), 10p. orange-brown (phos paper), 16p. (phos paper), 17p. grey-blue (phos paper), 18p. dp olive-grey (phos paper), 22p. yellow-green (phos paper), 24p. violet (phos paper), 26p. rosine (phos paper), 28p. deep violet (phos paper), 31p. purple (phos paper), 34p. ochre-brown (phos paper), 50p. (ord paper), 2p. (litho phos paper), 4p. (litho phos paper), 5p. claret (litho phos paper), 20p. (litho phos paper), 75p. (litho) (*Nos.* X900, X924/5, X930, X939, X949, X952, X955, X963, X967, X971, X975, X981, X985, X992, X1000a, X997, X1004a, X999, X1023a)			36·00
3.3.87	P.O. Pack No. 9. 12p. (1 centre band), 13p. (1 centre band), 1p. (phos paper), 3p. (phos paper), 7p. (phos paper), 10p. orange-brown (phos paper), 17p. grey-blue (phos paper), 18p. dp olive-grey (phos paper), 22p. yellow-green (phos paper), 24p. violet (phos paper), 26p. rosine (phos paper), 28p. deep violet (phos paper), 31p. purple (phos paper), 34p. ochre-brown (phos paper), 50p. (ord paper), 2p. (litho phos paper), 4p. (litho phos paper), 5p. claret (litho phos paper), 20p. (litho phos paper), 75p. (litho) (*Nos.* X896, X900, X925, X930, X937, X939, X952, X955, X963, X967, X971, X975, X981, X985, X992, X1000a, X997, X1004a, X999, X1023a)			40·00
23.8.88	P.O. Pack No. 15. 14p. (1 centre band), 19p. (phos paper), 20p. turquoise-green (phos paper), 23p. bright green (phos paper), 27p. chestnut (phos paper), 28p. ochre (phos paper), 32p. (phos paper), 35p. sepia (phos paper) (*Nos.* X903, X956, X959, X966, X973, X976, X983, X988)			12·00
26.9.89	P.O. Pack No. 19. 15p. (centre band), 20p. brownish black (phos paper), 24p. Indian red (phos paper), 29p. deep mauve (phos paper), 30p. (phos paper), 34p. deep bluish grey (phos paper), 37p. (phos paper) (*Nos.* X905, X960, X968, X979/80, X986, X990)			10·00
4.9.90	P.O. Pack No. 22. 10p. dull orange (phos paper), 17p. (centre band), 22p. bright orange-red (phos paper), 26p. drab (phos paper), 27p. violet (phos paper), 31p. ultramarine (phos paper), 33p. (phos paper) (*Nos.* X940, X910, X964, X972, X974, X9 82, X984)			9·00
14.5.91	P.O. Pack No. 24. 1p. (phos paper), 3p. (phos paper), 4p. new blue (phos paper), 5p. dull red-brown (phos paper), 10p. dull orange (phos paper), 17p. (centre band), 20p. turquoise-green (phos paper), 22p. bright orange-red (phos paper), 26p. drab (phos paper), 27p. violet (phos paper), 30p. (phos paper), 31p. ultramarine (phos paper), 32p. (phos paper), 33p. (phos paper), 37p. (phos paper), 50p. (ord paper), 75p. (ord paper). (*Nos.* X925, X927, X930, X933, X935, X940, X910, X959, X964, X972, X974, X980, X982/4, X990, X993/4)			30·00
10.9.91	P.O. Pack No. 25. 6p (phos paper), 18p. (centre band), 24p. chestnut (phos paper), 28p. deep bluish grey (phos paper), 34p. deep mauve (phos paper), 35p. yellow (phos paper), 39p. (phos paper) (*Nos.* X913, X936, X969, X977, X987, X989, X991)			9·00

**The "Scandinavia 71" was a special pack produced for sale during a visit to six cities in Denmark, Sweden and Norway by a mobile display unit between 15 April and 20 May 1971. The pack gives details of this tour and also lists the other stamps which were due to be issued in 1971, the text being in English. A separate insert gives translations in Danish, Swedish and Norwegian. The pack was also available at the Philatelic Bureau, Edinburgh.

For stamps of this design inscribed "2nd" and "1st" see Nos. 1445/52 and 1511/16, and for stamps with one elliptical perforation hole on each vertical side see Nos. 1664/72, Y1667/1803, 2039/40, 2295/8, 2650/7, U2941/74 and 3271/8.

508

1977 (2 Feb)–**87**. *Perf* 14×15.

1026	**508**	£1 brt yellow-green and blackish olive	3·00	25
		a. Imperf (pair)	£1700	
1026b		£1.30 pale drab and deep greenish blue (3.8.83)	5·50	6·00

1026c		£1.33 pale mauve and grey-black (28.8.84)	7·50	8·00
1026d		£1.41 pale drab and deep greenish blue (17.9.85)	8·50	8·50
1026e		£1.50 pale mauve and grey-black (2.9.86)	6·00	5·00
1026f		£1.60 pale drab and deep greenish blue (15.9.87)	6·50	7·00
1027		£2 light emerald and purple-brown	9·00	50
		a. Imperf (pair)	£4000	
1028		£5 salmon and chalky blue	22·00	3·00
		a. Imperf (vert pair)	£15000	
Set of 8			60·00	32·00
Set of 8 Gutter Pairs			£140	
Set of 8 Traffic Light Gutter Pairs			£170	

	Gutter pairs		
	Plain	*Traffic Light*	*First Day Covers*
1026, 1027/8	70·00	75·00	14·00
1026b	13·00	20·00	6·50
1026c	16·00	22·00	8·00
1026d	18·00	25·00	9·00
1026e	13·00	17·00	6·50
1026f	14·00	18·00	8·50

Presentation Pack (*P.O. Pack No.* 91 (small size)) (1026, 1027/8)		48·00
Presentation Pack (*P.O. Pack No.* 13 (large size)) (1026, 1027/8)		£180
Presentation Pack (*P.O. Pack No.* 14) (large size) (1026f)		22·00

Special First Day of Issue Postmarks
(for illustrations see Introduction)

Philatelic Bureau, Edinburgh (Type F) (£1, £2, £5)	16·00
Windsor, Berks (Type F) (£1, £2, £5)	20·00
Philatelic Bureau, Edinburgh (Type F) (£1.30)	7·00
Windsor, Berks (Type F) (£1.30)	10·00
British Philatelic Bureau, Edinburgh (Type F) (£1.33)	8·50
Windsor, Berks (Type F) (£1.33)	10·00
British Philatelic Bureau, Edinburgh (Type G) (£1.41)	9·50
Windsor, Berks (Type G) (£1.41)	9·50
British Philatelic Bureau, Edinburgh (Type G) (£1.50)	7·00
Windsor, Berks (Type G) (£1.50)	7·00
British Philatelic Bureau, Edinburgh (Type G) (£1.60)	9·00
Windsor, Berks (Type G) (£1.60)	9·00

Decimal Machin Index

(Denominated stamps with 'standard' perforations)

Those booklet stamps shown below with an * after the catalogue number do not exist with perforations on all four sides, but show one or two sides imperforate.

Value.	Process	Colour	Phosphor	Cat. No.	Source
½p.	photo	turquoise-blue	2 bands	X841/Eg	(a) with P.V.A. gum–sheets, 5p. m/v coil (X841nEv), 10p.m/v coil (X841q), 10p. booklets (DN46/75, FA1/3), 25p. booklets (DH39/52), 50p. booklets (DT1/12, FB1, FB14/16, FB19/23), £1 Wedgwood booklet (DX1) (b) with gum arabic—sheets, 5p. m/v coil (X841n)
½p.	photo	turquoise-blue	1 band at left	X842	£1 Wedgwood booklet (DX1)
½p.	photo	turquoise-blue	1 centre band	X843	10p. m/v coil (X843l), 10p. booklets (FA4/9)
½p.	photo	turquoise-blue	phos paper	X924	sheets, 12½p. m/v coil (X924l)
1p.	photo	crimson	2 bands	X844/Eg	(a) with P.V.A. gum—sheets, vertical coils, 5p. m/v coil (X841nEv), 10p. m/v coil (X841q), 10p. booklets (DN46/75, FA1/3), 50p. booklets (FB1/8, FB14/16) (b) with gum arabic—vertical coils, 5p. m/v coil (X841n)
1p.	photo	crimson	1 centre band	X845	10p. m/v coils (X843l, X845m), 10p. booklets (FA4/11), 50p. booklets (FB24/30, 34/36, 43/6, 48, 50)
1p.	photo	crimson	"all-over"	X846	sheets
1p.	photo	crimson	phos paper	X925	sheets, horizontal and vertical coils, 13p. m/v coil (X925l), 50p. booklet (FB59/66)
1p.	photo	crimson	1 band at left	X847	50p. booklets (FB37/42, 47, 49)
1p.	photo	crimson	1 band at right	X847Ea	£5 P. & O. booklet (DX8)
1½p.	photo	black	2 bands	X848	sheets, 10p. booklets (DN46/75)
2p.	photo	myrtle-green	2 bands	X849/Eg	(a) with P.V.A. gum—sheets, 5p. m/v coil (X841nEv), 10p. m/v coil (X841q), 10p. booklets (DN46/75), 50p. booklets (FB9/13), £3 Wedgwood booklet (DX2), £4 SG booklet (DX3) (b) with gum arabic—5p. m/v coil (X841n)
2p.	photo	myrtle-green	"all-over"	X850	sheets
2p.	photo	myrtle-green	phos paper	X926	sheets
2p.	photo	myrtle-green	phos paper	X928	14p. m/v coil (X928l)
2p.	litho	emerald-green	phos paper	X1000/a	sheets
2p.	litho	brt grn and dp grn	phos paper	X1001	sheets
2p.	photo	dp green	phos paper	X927	sheets, £1 booklets (FH23/7)
2p.	litho	dp green	phos paper	X1050*	£1 booklets (FH28/30)
2½p.	photo	magenta	1 centre band	X851/Eg	(a) with P.V.A. gum—sheets, horizontal and vertical coils, 25p. booklets (DH39/52), 50p. booklets (DT1/12), £1 Wedgwood booklet (DX1) (b) with gum arabic—sheets, horizontal coils
2½p.	photo	magenta	1 side band	X852/Ea	(a) band at left—50p. booklets (DT1/12), £1 Wedgwood booklet (DX1) (b) band at right—£1 Wedgwood booklet (DX1)
2½p.	photo	magenta	2 bands	X853	sheets
2½p.	photo	rose-red	phos paper	X929	sheets, 11½p. m/v coil (X929l)
2½p.	photo	rose-red	2 bands	X854	50p. booklets (FB17/18)
3p.	photo	ultramarine	2 bands	X855/Eg	(a) with P.V.A. gum—sheets, horizontal and vertical coils, 30p. booklets (DQ56/72), 50p. booklets (DT1/12), £1 Wedgwood booklet (DX1) (b) with gum arabic—sheets, vertical coils
3p.	photo	ultramarine	1 centre band	X856/Eg	(a) with P.V.A. gum—sheets, horizontal and vertical coils, 30p. booklets (DQ73/4), 50p. booklets (DT13/14) (b) with gum arabic—sheets
3p.	photo	brt magenta	phos paper	X930	Type I. sheets, 11½p. m/v coil (X929l), £4 Royal Mint booklet (DX4)
3p.	photo	brt magenta	phos paper	X930c	Type II. sheets (from 21.1.92), 15p. m/v coil (X930cl)
3p.	photo	brt magenta	2 bands	X857	Type I. 50p. booklets (FB19/23), £4 SG booklet (DX3)
3½p.	photo	olive-grey	2 bands	X858/Eb	sheets, horizontal and vertical coils, 35p. booklets (DP1/3), 50p. booklets (DT13/14)
3½p.	photo	olive-grey	1 centre band	X859	sheet, horizontal coils, 35p. booklet (DP4), 85p. booklet (DW1)
3½p.	photo	purple-brown	phos paper	X931	sheets, £4 Royal Mint booklet (DX4)
3½p.	photo	purple-brown	1 centre band	X860	50p. booklets (FB24/6)
4p.	photo	ochre-brown	2 bands	X861/Eg	(a) with P.V.A. gum—sheets. (b) with gum arabic—sheets
4p.	litho	greenish blue	2 bands	X996	sheets
4p.	photo	greenish blue	2 bands	X862	50p. booklets (FB17/18)
4p.	litho	greenish blue	phos paper	X997	sheets J.W. ptg.
				X1002	sheets Questa ptg.
4p.	photo	greenish blue	phos paper	X932	12½p. m/v coil (X924l)
				X932Ea	13p. m/v coil (X925l), 14p. m/v coil (X928l)
4p.	photo	greenish blue	1 centre band	X863	50p. booklets (FB27/30)
4p.	photo	greenish blue	1 side band	X864/Ea	(a) band at right—£5 Times booklet (DX6) (b) band at left—£5 Times booklet (DX6)
4p.	photo	new blue	phos paper	X933	sheets, 15p. m/v coil (X930cl), 17p. m/v coil (X933l), 18p. m/v coil (X933m), 19p. m/v coil (X933n)
4½p.	photo	grey-blue	2 bands	X865	sheets, horizontal coils, 45p. booklets (DS1/2), 85p. booklet (DW1)
5p.	photo	pale violet	2 bands	X866	sheets
5p.	photo	pale violet	phos paper	X934	sheets
5p.	litho	lt violet	phos paper	X1003	sheets

Value.	Process	Colour	Phosphor	Cat. No.	Source
5p.	litho	claret	phos paper	X1004/a	sheets
5p.	photo	claret	1 centre band	X867	50p. booklets (FB35/36, 43/6, 48, 50)
5p.	photo	dull red-brown	phos paper	X935	sheets, 17p. m/v coil (X933l), 18p. m/v coil (X933m), 19p m/v coil (X933n)
5½p.	photo	violet	2 bands	X868	sheets
5½p.	photo	violet	1 centre band	X869	sheets
6p.	photo	lt emerald	2 bands	X870/Eg	(a) with P.V.A. gum—sheets, 10p. m/v coil (X841q), 10p. booklets (FA1/3) (b) with gum arabic—sheets
6p.	photo	yellow-olive	phos paper	X936	sheets
6½p.	photo	greenish blue	2 bands	X871	sheets
6½p.	photo	greenish blue	1 centre band	X872	sheets, horizontal and vertical coils, 65p. booklet (FC1)
6½p.	photo	greenish blue	1 side band	X873/Ea	(a) band at right—50p. booklet (FB1A). (b) band at left—50p. booklet (FB1B)
7p.	photo	purple-brown	2 bands	X874	sheets
7p.	photo	purple-brown	1 centre band	X875	sheets, horizontal and vertical coils, 10p. m/v coil (X843l), 10p. booklets (FA4/9), 70p. booklets (FD1/8), £1.60 Christmas booklet (FX1)
7p.	photo	purple-brown	1 side band	X876/Ea	(a) band at right—50p. booklets (FB2A/8A) (b) band at left—50p. booklets (FB2B/8B)
7p.	photo	brownish red	phos paper	X937	sheets
7½p.	photo	pale chestnut	2 bands	X877	sheets
8p.	photo	rosine	2 bands	X878	sheets
8p.	photo	rosine	1 centre band	X879	sheets, vertical coils, 10p. m/v coil (X845m), 10p. booklets (FA10/11), 80p. booklet (FE1), £1.80 Christmas booklet (FX2)
8p.	photo	rosine	1 side band	X880/Ea	(a) band at right—50p. booklets (FB9A/10A) (b) band at left—50p. booklets (FB9B/10B)
8½p	photo	lt yellowish green	2 bands	X881	sheets, horizontal and vertical coils, 50p. booklet (FB1), 85p. booklet (FF1)
8½p.	photo	yellowish green	phos paper	X938	sheets
9p.	photo	yellow-orange and black	2 bands	X882	sheets
9p.	photo	dp violet	2 bands	X883	sheets, horizontal and vertical coils, 50p. booklets (FB2/8), 90p. booklets (FG1/8), £1.60 Christmas booklet (FX1)
9½p	photo	purple	2 bands	X884	sheets
10p.	recess	cerise	phos paper	829	sheets
10p.	photo	orange-brown and chestnut	2 bands	X885	sheets
10p.	photo	orange-brown	2 bands	X886	Type I. sheets, 50p. booklets (FB9/10), £1.80 Christmas booklet (FX2)
10p.	photo	orange-brown	2 bands	X886b	Type II. £4 Christian Heritage booklet (DX5)
10p.	photo	orange-brown	"all-over"	X887	Type I. sheets, vertical coils, £1 booklet (FH1)
10p.	photo	orange-brown	phos paper	X939	Type I. sheets
10p.	photo	orange-brown	1 centre band	X888	Type I. sheets, vertical coils, £1 booklets (FH2/4), £2.20 Christmas booklet (FX3), £3 Wedgwood booklet (DX2)
10p.	photo	orange-brown	1 side band	X889/Ea	Type I. (a) band at right—50p. booklets (FB11A/13A) (b) band at left—50p. booklets (FB11B/13B), £3 Wedgwood booklet (DX2)
10p.	photo	dull orange	phos paper	X940	sheets
10½p.	photo	yellow	2 bands	X890	sheets
10½p.	photo	dp dull blue	2 bands	X891	sheets
11p.	photo	brown-red	2 bands	X892	sheets
11p.	photo	brown-red	phos paper	X941	sheets
11½p	photo	ochre-brown	phos paper	X942	sheets
11½p	photo	drab	1 centre band	X893	sheets, vertical coils, £1.15 booklets (FI1/4), £2.55 Christmas booklet (FX4)
11½p	photo	drab	1 side band	X894/Ea	(a) band at right—50p. booklets (FB14A/18A), £1.30 booklets (FL1/2) (b) band at left—50p. booklets FB14B/18B), £1.30 booklets (FL1/2)
12p.	photo	yellowish green	phos paper	X943	sheets, vertical coils, £1.20 booklets (FJ1/3)
12p.	photo	yellowish green	2 bands	X895	50p. booklets (FB11/13), £2.20 Christmas booklet (FX3), £3 Wedgwood booklet (DX2)
12p.	photo	brt emerald	1 centre band	X896	sheets, horizontal and vertical coils, 50p. booklet (FB34), £1.20 booklets (FJ4/6), £5 British Rail booklet (DX7)
12p.	photo	brt emerald	1 side band	X897/ Ea	(a) band at right—£1.50 booklets (FP1/3), £5 British Rail booklet (DX7) (b) band at left—£1.50 booklets (FP1/3), £5 British Rail booklet (DX7)
12p.	photo	brt emerald	1 centre band Underprint T.4	X896Eu	sheets
12½p.	photo	lt emerald	1 centre band	X898	sheets, vertical coils, 50p. booklets (FB24/6), £1.25 booklets (FK1/8), £4 SG booklet (DX3)
12½p.	photo	lt emerald	1 centre band Underprint T.1	X898Eu	£2.80 Christmas booklet (FX5)
12½p.	photo	lt emerald	1 centre band Underprint T.2	X898Ev	£2.50 Christmas booklet (FX6)
12½p.	photo	lt emerald	1 side band	X899/Ea	(a) band at right—50p. booklets (FB19A/23A), £1.43 booklets (FN1/6), £1.46 booklets (FO1/3), £4 SG booklet (DX3), £4 Royal Mint booklet (DX4) (b) band at left—50p. booklets (FB19B/23B), £1.43 booklets (FN1/6), £1.46 booklets (FO1/3), £4 SG booklet (DX3), £4 Royal Mint booklet (DX4)
13p.	photo	olive-grey	phos paper	X944	sheets
13p.	photo	pale chestnut	1 centre band	X900	sheets, horizontal and vertical coils, 50p. booklets (FB27/30, 35/6, 43/6, 48, 50), 52p. booklet (GA1), £1.30 booklets (FL3/14, GI1), £5 Times booklet (DX6), £5 P & O booklet (DX8)
13p.	photo	pale chestnut	1 centre band Underprint T.2	X900Eu	£1.30 Christmas booklet (FX9)
13p.	photo	pale chestnut	1 side band	X901/Ea	(a) band at right—50p. booklets (FB37/42, 47, 49), £1.54 booklets (FQ1/4), £4 Christian Heritage booklet (DX5), £5 Times booklet (DX6), £5 P & O booklet (DX8) (b) band at left—£1 booklets (FH6/13), £1.54 booklets (FQ1/4), £4 Christian Heritage booklet (DX5), £5 Times booklet (DX6)
13p.	litho	pale chestnut	1 centre band	X1005	£5 Financial Times booklet (DX9)

Value.	Process	Colour	Phosphor	Cat. No.	Source
13p.	litho	pale chestnut	1 side band	X1006/Ea	£5 Financial Times booklet (DX9)
13½p.	photo	purple-brown	phos paper	X945	sheets
14p.	photo	grey-blue	phos paper	X946	sheets, vertical coils, £1.40 booklets (FM1/4)
14p.	photo	grey-blue	2 bands	X902	50p. booklets (FB14/16), £1.30 booklets (FL1/2), £2.55 Christmas booklet (FX4)
14p.	photo	dp blue	1 centre band	X903	sheets, horizontal and vertical coils, 56p. booklets (GB1/4), £1.40 booklets (FM5/6, GK1, 3)
14p.	photo	dp blue	1 band at right	X904	50p. booklets (FB51/4), £1 booklets (FH14/15 and 17)
14p.	litho	dp blue	1 centre band	X1007	£1.40 booklets (GK2, 4)
14p.	litho	dp blue	1 band at right	X1051*	£1 booklet (FH16)
15p.	photo	ultramarine	phos paper	X947	sheets
15p.	photo	brt blue	1 centre band	X905	sheets, horizontal and vertical coils
15p.	photo	brt blue	1 side band	X906/Ea	(a) band at left—50p. booklet (FB55)
					(b) band at right—£5 London Life booklet (DX11)
15½p.	photo	pale violet	phos paper	X948	sheets, vertical coils, £1.55 booklets (FR1/4)
15½p.	photo	pale violet	2 bands	X907	£1.43 booklets (FN1/6), £4 SG booklet (DX3)
15½p.	photo	pale violet	2 bands Underprint T.1	X907Eu	£2.80 Christmas booklet (FX5)
16p.	photo	olive-drab	phos paper	X949	sheets, vertical coils, £1.60 booklets (FS1, 3/4), £4 Royal Mint booklet (DX4)
16p.	photo	olive-drab	phos paper Underprint T.3	X949Eu	£1.60 booklet (FS2)
16p.	photo	olive-drab	2 bands	X908	£1.46 booklets (FO1/3)
16½p.	photo	pale chestnut	phos paper	X950	sheets
17p.	photo	lt emerald	phos paper	X951	sheets
17p.	photo	grey-blue	phos paper	X952	sheets, vertical coils, £1 booklet (FH5), £1.70 booklets (FT1, 3 & 5/7), £4 Christian Heritage booklet (DX5), £5 Times booklet (DX6), £5 British Rail booklet (DX7)
17p.	photo	grey-blue	phos paper Underprint T.3	X952Eu	£1.70 booklet (FT2)
17p.	photo	grey-blue	2 bands	X909	50p. booklet (FB33a), £1.50 booklets (FP1/3), £1.54 booklets (FQ1/4), £4 Christian Heritage booklet (DX5), £5 Times booklet (DX6), £5 British Rail booklet (DX7)
17p.	photo	grey-blue	2 bands Underprint T.4	X909Eu	50p. booklets (FB31/3)
17p.	photo	dp blue	1 centre band	X910	sheets, vertical coils
17p.	photo	dp blue	1 side band	X911/Ea	(a) band at right—50p. booklet (FB57/8), £1 booklet (FH21/2)
					(b) band at left—50p. booklet (FB57/8)
17p.	litho	dp blue	1 centre band	X1008	£6 Alias Agatha Christie booklet (DX12)
17½p.	photo	pale chestnut	phos paper	X953	sheets
18p.	photo	dp violet	phos paper	X954	sheets
18p.	photo	dp olive-grey	phos paper	X955	sheets, vertical coils, 72p. booklet (GC1), £1.80 booklets (FU1/8, GO1), £5 P & O booklet (DX8)
18p.	photo	dp olive-grey	2 bands	X912	50p. booklets (FB37/42, 47, 49), £1 booklet (FH6/13), £5 P & O booklet (DX8)
18p.	litho	dp olive-grey	phos paper	X1009	£5 Financial Times booklet (DX9)
18p.	litho	dp olive-grey	2 bands	X1010	£5 Financial Times booklet (DX9)
18p.	photo/gravure	brt green	1 centre band	X913	sheets, vertical coils
18p.	litho	brt green	1 centre band	X1011	£6 Tolkien booklet (DX14)
18p.	litho	brt green	1 side band	X1012/Ea	(a) band at right—£6 Tolkien booklet (DX14).
					(b) band at left—£6 (£5.64) Beatrix Potter booklet (DX15)).
19p.	photo	brt orange-red	phos paper	X956	sheets, vertical coils, 76p. booklets (GD1/4), £1.90 booklets (FV1/2, GP1, 3)
19p.	photo	brt orange-red	2 bands	X914	50p. booklets (FB51/4), £1 booklets (FH14/15, 17)
19p.	litho	brt orange-red	phos paper	X1013	£1.90 booklets (GP2, 4)
19p.	litho	brt orange-red	2 bands	X1052*	£1 booklet (FH16)
19½p	photo	olive-grey	phos paper	X957	sheets
20p.	recess	olive-green	none	830	sheets
20p.	photo	dull purple	2 bands	X915	sheets
20p.	photo	dull purple	phos paper	X958	sheets
20p.	litho	dull purple	2 bands	X998	sheets
20p.	litho	dull purple	phos paper	X999	sheets J.W. ptg.
				X1014	sheets Questa ptg.
20p.	photo	turquoise-green	phos paper	X959	sheets
20p.	photo	brownish black	phos paper	X960	sheets, horizontal and vertical coils, £1 booklet (FH18)
20p.	photo	brownish black	2 bands	X916	50p. booklet (FB55), £5 London Life booklet (DX11)
20½p.	photo	ultramarine	phos paper	X961	sheets
22p.	photo	blue	phos paper	X962	sheets
22p.	photo	yellow-green	phos paper	X963	sheets
22p.	litho	yellow-green	2 bands	X1015	£5 Financial Times booklet (DX9)
22p.	photo	brt orange-red	2 bands	X917*	£1 booklet (FH21/2)
22p.	photo	brt orange-red	phos paper	X964	sheets, vertical coils
22p.	litho	brt orange-red	phos paper	X1016	£6 Alias Agatha Christie booklet (DX12)
23p.	photo	brown-red	phos paper	X965	sheets
23p.	photo	brt green	phos paper	X966	sheets
24p.	photo	violet	phos paper	X967	sheets
24p.	photo	Indian red	phos paper	X968	sheets
24p.	photo	chestnut	phos paper	X969	sheets, vertical coils, 50p. booklets (FB59/66), £1 booklets (FH23/7)
24p.	litho	chestnut	phos paper	X1017	£6 Tolkien booklet (DX14) (Questa ptg)
				X1053*	£1 booklet (FH28/30) Walsall ptg
24p.	litho	chestnut	2 bands	X1018	£6 Tolkien booklet (DX14)
25p.	photo	purple	phos paper	X970	sheets
25p.	photo	rose-red	2 bands	X917a	horizontal coils
26p.	photo	rosine	phos paper	X971	Type I. sheets
26p.	photo	rosine	2 bands	X918	Type I. £5 P & O booklet (DX8)
26p.	photo	rosine	phos paper	X971b	Type II. £1.04 booklet (GE1)

Value.	Process	Colour	Phosphor	Cat. No.	Source
26p.	photo	drab	phos paper	X972	sheets
27p.	photo	chestnut	phos paper	X973	sheets, £1.08 booklets (GF1/2)
27p.	photo	violet	phos paper	X974	sheets
28p.	photo	dp violet	phos paper	X975	sheets
28p.	photo	ochre	phos paper	X976	sheets
28p.	photo	dp bluish grey	phos paper	X977	sheets
29p.	photo	ochre-brown	phos paper	X978	sheets
29p.	photo	dp mauve	phos paper	X979	sheets
29p.	litho	dp mauve	2 bands	X1054*	£1.16 booklet (GG1)
29p.	litho	dp mauve	phos paper	X1055*	£1.16 booklet (GG2)
30p.	photo	dp olive-grey	phos paper	X980	sheets
31p.	photo	purple	phos paper	X981	sheets
31p.	photo	purple	2 bands	X919	£5 British Rail booklet (DX7)
31p.	photo	ultramarine	phos paper	X982	sheets
31p.	litho	ultramarine	phos paper	X1056*	£1.24 booklet (GH1)
32p.	photo	greenish blue	phos paper	X983	sheets
33p.	photo	lt emerald	phos paper	X984	sheets, vertical coils
33p.	litho	lt emerald	phos paper	X1019	£6 Alias Agatha Christie booklet (DX12)
33p.	litho	lt emerald	phos paper	X1057*	£1.32 booklet (GJ1)
33p.	litho	lt emerald	2 bands	X1020	£6 Wales booklet (DX13), £6 (£5.64) Beatrix Potter booklet (DX15)
34p.	photo	ochre-brown	phos paper	X985	sheets
34p.	photo	ochre-brown	2 bands	X920	£5 Times booklet (DX6)
34p.	litho	bistre-brown	2 bands	X1021	£5 Financial Times booklet (DX9)
34p.	photo	dp bluish grey	phos paper	X986	sheets
34p.	photo	dp mauve	phos paper	X987	sheets
35p.	photo	sepia	phos paper	X988	sheets
35p.	photo	yellow	phos paper	X989	sheets
37p.	photo	rosine	phos paper	X990	sheets
39p.	photo	brt mauve	phos paper	X991	sheets, vertical coils
39p.	litho	brt mauve	phos paper	X1058*	78p. booklet (GD4a), £1.56 booklet (GM1)
39p.	litho	brt mauve	2 bands	X1022	£6 Tolkien booklet (DX14), £6 (£5.64) Beatrix Potter booklet (DX15)
50p.	recess	dp ultramarine	none or phos paper	831/Ea	sheets
50p.	photo	ochre-brown	2 bands	X921	sheets
50p.	photo	ochre-brown	none	X992	sheets
50p.	photo	ochre	2 bands	X922	£5 London Life (DX11)
50p.	photo	ochre	none	X993	sheets
50p.	photo	ochre	phos paper	X991a	sheets
75p.	litho	black	none	X1023/a	sheets
75p.	litho	brownish grey and black	none	X1024	sheets
75p.	photo	grey-black	none	X994	sheets
£1	recess	bluish black	none	831b	sheets
£1	photo	brt yellow-green and blackish olive	none	1026	sheets
£1.30	photo	drab and dp greenish blue	none	1026b	sheets
£1.33	photo	pale mauve and grey-black	none	1026c	sheets
£1.41	photo	drab and dp greenish blue	none	1026d	sheets
£1.50	photo	pale mauve and grey-black	none	1026e	sheets
£1.60	photo	pale drab and dp greenish blue	none	1026f	sheets
£2	photo	lt emerald and purple-brown	none	1027	sheets
£5	photo	salmon and chalky blue	none	1028	sheets

For 1st and 2nd class no value indicated (NVI) stamps, see Nos. 1445/52, 1511/16 and 1664/71.

For table covering Machin stamps with elliptical perforations see after Nos. Y1667, etc, in 1993.

Photo/Gravure stamps were printed from both photogravure and computer engraved (Gravure) cylinders.

DECIMAL MACHIN MULTI-VALUE COIL INDEX

The following is a simplified checklist of horizontal multi-value coils, to be used in conjunction with the main listing as details of stamps listed there are not repeated.

Strip Value	Date	Contents	Cat No.
5p.	15.2.71	½p.×2, 1p.×2, 2p.	X841n
10p.	3.12.75	½p.×2, 1p., 2p., 6p.	X841q
10p.	14.12.77	½p.×2, 1p.×2, 7p.	X843l
10p.	16.1.80	1p.×2, 8p. plus 2 labels	X845m
11½p.	6.81	2½p., 3p.×3	X929l
12½p.	30.12.81	½p., 4p.×3	X924l
13p.	14.8.84	1p., 4p.×3	X925l
14p.	5.9.88	2p., 4p.×3	X928l
15p.	10.10.89	3p., 4p.×3	X930cl
17p.	27.11.90	4p.×3, 5p.	X933l
18p.	1.10.91	4p.×2, 5p.×2	X933m
19p.	31.1.95	4p., 5p.×3	X933n

Abbreviations used in the diagrams: 2B = 2 bands, CB = centre band, LB = left band and RB = right band. The shaded squares represent printed labels.
Panes completed by unprinted white labels are outside the scope of this catalogue.

Unless otherwise stated the panes were printed in photogravure. Some panes exist in photogravure and lithography and these are separately identified and listed. Imperforate or straight edges are described under the appropriate illustration.

X8411 (2 bands)

2	2
½	½

X8411a (2 bands)

2	½
2	½

X841m (2 bands)

½	½	½
(label)	½	½

X841o — £1 Wedgwood

2½ RB	½ 2B	2½ LB	2½ CB
2½ RB	½ 2B	2½ LB	2½ CB
2½ RB	½ 2B	2½ LB	2½ CB

X841p — £1 Wedgwood

½ 2B	2½ LB
½ 2B	2½ LB
½ 2B	½ LB

X841r (2 bands)

½	½
6	1
1	1

X841s

½ 2B	½ 2B
1 2B	8½ 2B
1 2B	8½ 2B
6½ RB	8½ 2B
6½ RB	8½ 2B

X841sa

½ 2B	½ 2B
8½ 2B	1 2B
8½ 2B	1 2B
8½ 2B	6½ 2B
8½ 2B	6½ LB

X841t

11½ RB	½ 2B
11½ RB	1 2B
11½ RB	14 2B

X841ta

½ 2B	11½ LB
1 2B	11½ LB
14 2B	11½ LB

X841u

½ 2B	3 2B
12½ RB	3 2B
12½ RB	3 2B
12½ RB	3 2B

X841ua

3 2B	½ 2B
3 2B	12½ LB
3 2B	12½ LB
3 2B	12½ LB

X843m (centre band)

½	(label)
½	1
7	1

X844l (2 bands)

1	1
1½	1½

X844m (2 bands)

1½	1
1½	1

X844n

1 2B	1 2B
7 RB	9 2B
7 RB	9 2B
7 RB	9 2B

X844na

1 2B	1 2B
9 2B	7 LB
9 2B	7 LB
9 2B	7 LB

X845l

(label)	1
8	1

X845n (centre band)

1	1
3½	12½
3½	12½
3½	12½

X845p (centre band)

1	1
1	13
4	13
4	13

X845q (centre band)

1	1
12	12
12	12

X845s/sa (centre band) — X845sa imperf at left and right

1	13
5	13
5	13

X847l

1 LB	13 RB
18 2B	18 2B

X847m — £5 P & O

13 RB	18 2B	18 2B
1 RB	18 2B	26 2B
13 RB	18 2B	18 2B

X849l

(label)	2 2B
2 2B	10 2B
8 RB	10 2B
8 RB	10 2B

X849la

2 2B	(label)
10 2B	2 2B
10 2B	8 LB
10 2B	8 LB

X849m

(label)	2 RB
2 2B	2 2B
10 RB	12 2B
10 RB	12 2B

X849ma

2 2B	(label)
2 2B	2 2B
12 2B	10 LB
12 2B	10 LB

X849n — £3 Wedgwood

12 2B	10 LB	10 CB
12 2B	2 2B	10 CB
12 2B	12 2B	10 CB

X849o (2 bands) — £3 Wedgwood

2	2
2	2
2	2

X849p — £4 Stanley Gibbons

12½ RB	12½ LB	12½ CB
12½ RB	3 2B	12½ LB
12½ RB	2 2B	12½ LB

X851l
(centre band)

X851m
(centre band)

X851n
£1 Wedgwood

X852l

X854l

X854la

X855l
(2 bands)

X864l
£5 The Times

X875l
Christmas 1978

X879l
Christmas 1979

X886bl
£4 Christian Heritage

X888l (centre band)
£3 Wedgwood

X888m
Christmas 1980

X893l
Christmas 1981

X894l
Margin at left or right

X895l (2 bands)
Wedgwood

X896l (centre band)
£5 British Rail

X897l

X897la

X897m
£5 British Rail

X898l
Christmas 1982

X899l
Margin at left or right

X899m

12½ RB	12½ LB
12½ RB	12½ LB
12½ RB	12½ LB

X899m
£4 Stanley Gibbons
£4 Royal Mint

X899n

16 2B	16 2B	16 2B	16 2B	16 2B
12½ LB	12½ RB	12½ LB	12½ RB	16 2B

X899n

X899na

16 2B	16 2B	16 2B	16 2B	16 2B
16 2B	12½ LB	12½ RB	12½ LB	12½ RB

X899na

X900l (centre band)

13	13	13
13	13	13
13	13	13

X900l (centre band)
£5 The Times
£5 P & O

X900m

13	13
13	13
13	13

X900m, (photo), X1005l (litho)
(centre band)
£5 P & O (X900m)
£5 Financial times (X 1005l)

X900n (centre band)

13	13
13	13

X900n (centre band)
52p. Barcode booklet

X900o (centre band)

13	13	13	13	13
13	13	13	13	13

X900o (centre band)
£1.30 Barcode Booklet

X901l

17 2B	17 2B	17 2B	17 2B	17 2B
13 LB	13 RB	13 LB	13 RB	17 2B

X901l

X901la

17 2B	17 2B	17 2B	17 2B	17 2B
17 2B	13 LB	13 RB	13 LB	13 RB

X901la

X901m

13 RB	13 LB
13 RB	13 LB
13 RB	13 LB

X901m
£4 Christian Heritage

X901n/na

13 LB	18 2B
18 2B	18 2B
18 2B	18 2B

X901n/na
901na imperf
at left and right

X903l (centre band)

14	14
14	14

X903l (centre band)
56p. Barcode Booklet

X903m (centre band)

14	14	14	14	14
14	14	14	14	14

X903m
(centre band)
£1.40 Barcode Booklet

X903n, X903q (centre band)

14	14
14	14

X903n, X903q
(centre band)
56p. Barcode Booklet
X903n imperf at top
and bottom
X903q imperf 3 sides

X903p (centre band)

14	14	14	14
14	14	14	14

X903p (centre band)
£1.40 Barcode Booklet
Imperf at top and bottom

X904l

	19 2B
14 RB	19 2B

X904l

X904m (photo)

14 RB	19 2B
14 RB	19 2B
19 2B	19 2B

X904m (photo)
X1051l (litho)
Imperf at left
and right

X906l

	15 LB
20 LB	15 LB

X906l

X906m

2ND RB	50 2B	1ST 2B
15 RB		20 2B
15 RB	29 2B	20 2B

X906m
£5 London Life
The stamps in the bottom row are
Penny Black Anniversary definitives
(Nos 1468Ea,1470 and 1472)

X907l

15½	15½
15½	15½
15½	15½

X907l
(2 bands)
£4 Stanley Gibbons

X907m

15½	15½	15½
15½	15½	15½
15½	15½	15½

X907m
(2 bands)
£4 Stanley Gibbons

X909l

	17
17	17

X909l (2 bands)
and underprint
X909Ela (as
X909l but with-
out underprint)

X911l

	17 LB
17 RB	17 LB

X911l

X911m

	22 2B
17 RB	22 2B
17 RB	22 2B

X911m
Imperf at left
and right

X925m

1	1
24	24

X925m
(phosphorised
paper)

X927l

2	2
24	24
24	24

X927l (photo)
X1050l (litho)
(phosphorised
paper) Imperf
at left and right

X930b

16	16	16
3½	3	3½
16	16	16

X930b
(phosphorised paper)
£4 Royal mint

X949l
(phosphorised paper)
£4 Royal Mint

X952l
(phosphorised paper)
£4 Christian Heritage
£5 The Times £5 British Rail
X1008l (centre band)
£6 Agatha Christie

X952m
(phosphorised paper)
£5 The Times
£5 British Rail

X955l (photo), **X1009l** (litho)
(phosphorised paper)
£5 P & O (X955l)
£5 Financial Times (X1009l)

X955m
(phosphorised paper)
72p. Barcode Booklet

X955n
(phosphorised paper)
£1.80 Barcode Booklet

X956l
(phosphorised paper)
76p. Barcode Booklet

X956m
(phosphorised paper)
£1.90 Barcode Booklet

X956n, X956q
(phosphorised paper)
76p. Barcode Booklet
X956n imperf at top
and bottom
X956q imperf on
three sides

X956o
(phosphorised paper)
£1.90 Barcode Booklet Imperf
at top and bottom

X960l
(phosphorised
paper)
Imperf at left
and right

X971bl
(phosphorised paper)
£1.04 Barcode Booklet

X973l
(phosphorised paper)
£1.08 Barcode
Booklet

X973m
(phosphorised
paper)
£1.08 Barcode
Booklet
Imperf at top and
bottom

X1006l (litho)
£5 Financial Times

X1009m (litho)
(phosphorised paper)
£5 Financial Times
X1011l (litho) (centre band)
£6 Tolkien

X1012l (litho)
£6 Tolkien

X1012m (litho)
£6 (£5.64) Beatrix Potter

X1016l (litho)
(phosphorised paper)
£6 Agatha Christie

X1016m (litho)
(phosphorised paper)
£6 Agatha Christie

X1017l (litho)
(phosphorised paper)
£6 Tolkien

X1054l (litho), **X1055l** (litho)
(X1054l 2 bands)
(X1055l phosphorised paper)
£1.16 Barcode Booklet
Imperf on three sides

X1056l (litho)
(phosphorised paper)
£1.24 Barcode Booklet
Imperf top and bottom

X1057l
(phosphorised paper)
£1.32 Barcode Booklet
Imperf top and bottom

X1058l
(phosphorised paper)
£1.56 Barcode Booklet
Imperf top and bottom

N.V.I. stamps, PVA Gum, "standard" perforations

913

914

1989 (22 Aug)–**1993.** Booklet Stamps.

(a) Photo Harrison. P 15×14.

1445	**913**	(2nd) brt blue (1 centre band)	1·25	1·50
		a. Booklet pane. No. 1445×10 with		
		horizontal edges of pane imperf....	12·50	
		b. Booklet pane. No. 1445×4 with		
		three edges of pane imperf		
		(28.11.89).................................	23·00	
1446		(2nd) brt blue (1 band at right) (20.3.90)	3·50	3·75
1447	**914**	(1st) brownish black (phosphorised		
		paper).................................	1·75	1·50
		a. Booklet pane. No. 1447×10 with		
		horizontal edges of pane imperf....	15·00	
		b. Booklet pane. No. 1447×4 with		
		three edges of pane imperf		
		(5.12.89).................................	35·00	
1448		(1st) brownish black (2 phosphor		
		bands) (20.3.90)	3·75	3·75

First Day Cover (Nos. 1445, 1447)..................... 5·00

(b) Litho Walsall. P 14.

1449	**913**	(2nd) brt blue (1 centre band)	1·00	1·00
		a. Imperf between (vert pair)		
		b. Booklet pane. No. 1449×4 with		
		three edges of pane imperf	7·00	
		c. Booklet pane. No. 1449×4 with		
		horiz edges of pane imperf		
		(6.8.91).................................	3·50	
		d. Booklet pane. No. 1449×10 with		
		horiz edges of pane imperf		
		(6.8.91).................................	7·50	
1450	**914**	(1st) blackish brown (2 phosphor		
		bands).................................	2·50	2·75
		a. Booklet pane. No. 1450×4 with		
		three edges of pane imperf	8·50	
		Ey. Phosphor omitted........................	£650	

(c) Litho Questa. P 15×14.

1451	**913**	(2nd) brt blue (1 centre band) (19.9.89) ..	1·00	1·00
		Ey. Phosphor omitted........................	£160	
1451a		(2nd) brt blue (1 band at right) (25.2.92)	3·25	3·25
		aEb. Band at left (10.8.93)	2·50	2·50
		al. Booklet pane. Nos. 1451aEb and		
		1514a, each×3, with margins all		
		round (10.8.93)	17·00	
		Ey. Phosphor omitted........................	£950	
1452	**914**	(1st) brownish black (phosphorised		
		paper) (19.9.89)	2·50	2·75

First Day Cover (Nos. 1445, 1447)..................... 5·00

Nos. 1445, 1447 and 1449/52 were initially sold at 14p. (2nd) and 19p. (1st), but these prices were later increased to reflect new postage rates.

Nos. 1446 and 1448 come from the *se-tenant* pane in the London Life £5 Booklet. This pane is listed under No. X906m in the Decimal Machin section.

No. 1451a comes from the *se-tenant* panes in the Wales and Tolkien £6 booklet. These panes are listed under Nos. X1012l and W49a (Wales Regionals). No. 1451aEb comes from the £6 (£5.64) Beatrix Potter booklet.

Nos. 1445, 1447 and 1449/50 do not exist perforated on all four sides, but come with either one or two adjacent sides imperforate.

No. 1450Ey comes from a pane in which one stamp was without phosphor bands due to a dry print.

For illustrations showing the differences between photogravure and lithography see Type **367**.

For similar designs, but in changed colours, see Nos. 1511/16, for those with elliptical perforations, Nos. 1664/71, and for self-adhesive versions Nos. 2039/40 and 2295.

Special First Day of Issue Postmarks
(for illustrations see Introduction)

Philatelic Bureau Edingburgh (Type G) (in red)............................6·00
Windsor, Berks (Type G) (in red)..6·00

1990 (7 Aug)–**92.** Booklet stamps. As *T* **913/14**, but colours changed.

(a) Photo Harrison. P 15×14.

1511	**913**	(2nd) deep blue (1 centre band)..................	1·50	1·50
		a. Booklet pane. No. 1511×10 with		
		horiz edges of pane imperf................	12·00	
1512	**914**	(1st) brt orange-red (phosphorised		
		paper).................................	1·50	1·50
		a. Booklet pane. No. 1512×10 with		
		horiz edges of pane imperf................	10·00	

(b) Litho Questa. P 15×14.

1513	**913**	(2nd) deep blue (1 centre band).................	2·50	2·75
1514	**914**	(1st) brt orange-red (phosphorised		
		paper)	1·50	1·00
1514a		(1st) brt orange-red (2 bands) (25.2.92) ...	3·25	3·25
		aEy. Phosphor omitted....................	£775	

(c) Litho Walsall. P 14.

1515	**913**	(2nd) deep blue (1 centre band).................	1·50	1·20
		a. Booklet pane. No. 1515×4 with		
		horiz edges of pane imperf................	3·75	
		b. Booklet pane. No. 1515×10 with		
		horiz edges of pane imperf................	8·50	
1516	**914**	(1st) brt orange-red (phosphorised		
		paper)	1·20	1·20
		a. Booklet pane. No. 1516×4 with		
		horiz edges of pane imperf................	4·00	
		b. Booklet pane. No. 1516×10 with		
		horiz edges of pane imperf................	8·00	
		c. Perf 13	6·00	6·50
		ca. Booklet pane. No. 1516c×4 with		
		horiz edges of pane imperf................	18·00	

First Day Cover (Nos. 1515/16)..................... 5·00

Nos. 1511/14 and 1515/16 were initially sold at 15p. (2nd) and 20p. (1st), but these prices were later increased to reflect new postage rates.

No. 1514a comes from the *se-tenant* panes in the £6 Wales, £6 Tolkien and £5.64 Beatrix Potter booklets. These panes are listed under Nos. X1012l, 1451al and W49a (Wales Regionals). No. 1514a exists with phosphor omitted (*Price £700 unused*).

No. 1516c was caused by the use of an incorrect perforation comb.

Nos. 1511/12 and 1515/16 do not exist with perforations on all four sides, but come with either the top or the bottom edge imperforate.

For similar stamps with elliptical perforations see Nos. 1664/72.

Special First Day of Issue Postmarks
(For illustration see Introduction)

Philatelic Bureau, Edinburgh (Type G)..5·50
Windsor, Berks (Type G) ....7·00

FLUORESCENT PHOSPHOR BANDS. Following the introduction of new automatic sorting machinery in 1991 it was found necessary to substantially increase the signal emitted by the phosphor bands. This was achieved by adding a fluorescent element to the phosphor which appears yellow under U.V. light. This combination was first used on an experimental sheet printing of the 18p., No. X913, produced by Enschedé in 1991. All values with phosphor bands from the elliptical perforations issue, including the No Value Indicated design, originally showed this yellow fluor.

From mid-1995 printings of current sheet and booklet stamps began to appear with the colour of the fluorescent element changed to blue. As such differences in fluor colour can only be identified by use of a U.V. lamp they are outside the scope of this catalogue, but full details will be found in the *Great Britain Specialised Catalogue Volume 4.*

The first commemorative/special stamp issue to show the change to blue fluor was the Centenary of Rugby League set, Nos. 1891/5.

COMPUTER-ENGRAVED CYLINDERS. In 1991 Enschedé introduced a new method of preparing photogravure cylinders for Great Britain stamps. This new method utilised computer-engraving instead of the traditional acid-etching and produced cylinders without the minor flaws which had long been a feature of the photogravure process. Such cylinders were first used on Great Britain stamps for the printing of the 18p. released on 19 November 1991 (see No. X913).

Harrison and Sons continued to use the acid-etching method until mid-1996 after which most Machin values, including N.V.I.'s, were produced from computer-engraved cylinders using a very similar process to that of Enschedé. Some values exist in versions from both cylinder production methods and can often be identified by minor differences. Such stamps are, however, outside the scope of this listing, but full details can be found in the current edition of the *Great Britain Specialised Catalogue Volume 4.*

For commemoratives stamps the first Harrison issue to use computer-engraved cylinders was the Centenary of Cinema set (Nos. 1920/4).

When Walsall introduced photogravure printing in 1997 their cylinders were produced using a similar computer-engraved process.

N.V.I. stamps, PVA gum, elliptical perforations

1093a

1993 (6 Apr)–**2008**. As T **913**/14, and **1093a**. Perf 14 (No. 1665) or 15×14 (others) (both with one elliptical hole in each vertical side).

(a) *Photo*
Harrison – No. 1666
Questa – Nos. 1664a, 1667a
Walsall – No. 1665
Harrison/De La Rue, Questa or Walsall – No. 1667
Harrison/De La Rue, Enschedé, Questa or Walsall – Nos. 1664, 1668, 1669

1664	**913**	(2nd) brt blue (1 centre band) (7.9.93)	1·50	1·30
		a. Perf 14 (1.12.98)	1·50	1·30
		b. Imperf (pair)	£1400	
		l. Booklet pane. Nos. 1664 and 1667×3 plus 4 labels ("postcode" on top right label) (27.4.00)	4·50	
		la. As No. 1664l, but inscr "postcodes" on top right label (17.4.01)	5·50	
		m. Booklet pane. Nos. 1664×2 and 1667×6 (27.4.00)	12·00	
		n. Booklet pane. Nos. 1664 and 1669, each×4, with central label and margins all round (6.2.02)	12·00	
		o. Booklet pane. Nos. 1664 and 1668, each×4, with central label and margins all round (2.6.03)	11·00	
		p. Booklet pane. Nos. 1664×4, Y1709×2 and Y1715×2, with central label and margins all round (24.2.05)	10·00	
1665		(2nd) bright blue (1 band at right) (13.10.98)	2·75	2·75
		Ec. Band at left	2·25	2·25
		l. Booklet pane. Nos. 1665×3 and NI81b, S91a and W80a with margins all round	7·50	
1666	**914**	(1st) brt orange-red (phosphorised paper)	1·80	1·50
1667		(1st) brt orange-red (2 phosphor bands) (4.4.95)	1·80	1·30
		Ey. Phosphor omitted	£225	
		a. Perf 14 (1.12.98)	2·00	1·80
		l. Booklet pane. No. 1667×8 with centre label and margins all round (16.2.99)	12·00	
		m. Booklet pane. No. 1667×4 plus commemorative label at right (12.5.99)	4·50	
1668		(1st) gold (2 phosphor bands) (21.4.97)	1·60	1·60
		a. Imperf (pair)	£175	
		l. Booklet pane. Nos. 1668 and Y1692, each×4, and centre label with margins all round (23.9.97)	9·00	
		m. Booklet pane. Nos. 1668/9, each×4, with centre label and margins all round (24.9.02)	12·00	
		o. Booklet pane. Nos. 1668 and Y1704, each×4, with centre label and margins all round (16.3.04)	10·00	
		p. Booklet pane. Nos. 1668×4, Y1715×2 and Y1723×2, with centre label and margins all round (25.5.04)	9·75	
		q. Booklet pane. Nos. 1668×4, Y1726×2 and Y1736×2, with centre label and margins all round (18.10.05)	9·50	
		r. Booklet pane. Nos. 1668×4, Y1701×2 and Y1711×2, with centre label and margins all round (23.2.06)	9·50	
1669	**1093a**	(E) deep blue (2 phosphor bands) (19.1.99)	2·00	1·50

(b) *Litho Questa or Walsall* (1670), *Enschedé, Questa or Walsall* (1671) or *De La Rue or Walsall* (1672).

1670	**913**	(2nd) brt blue (1 centre band)	1·50	90
		Ey. Phosphor omitted	£175	
		l. Booklet pane. Nos. 1670 and 1672, each×4, with central label and margins all round (18.9.08)	5·75	
1671	**914**	(1st) brt orange-red (2 phosphor bands)	1·80	1·00
		Ey. Phosphor omitted	£200	
		l. Booklet pane. No. 1671×4 plus commemorative label at left (27.7.94)	8·50	

		la. Ditto, but with commemorative label at right (16.5.95)	6·00	
		lEy. Phosphor omitted	£400	
		m. Pane. No. 1671 with margins all round (roul 8 across top corners of pane) (Boots logo on margin) (17.8.94)	2·50	
		mEy. Phosphor omitted	£1500	
		ma. Without Boots logo above stamp (11.9.95)	1·25	
		mb. Ditto, but roul 10 across top corners of pane (20.2.97)	1·40	
		n. Booklet pane. No. 1671×9 with margins all round (16.2.99)	9·00	
1672		(1st) gold (2 phosphor bands) (8.1.08)	3·00	3·00
		Ey. Phosphor omitted	£1800	
		l. Booklet pane. No. 1672×8 with centre label and margins all round	20·00	

For details of sheets, booklets, etc containing these stamps see Decimal Machin Index following the "Y" numbers.

Nos. 1664/71 were issued in booklet panes showing perforations on all four edges.

On 6 September 1993 Nos. 1670/71 printed in lithography by Questa were made available in sheets from post offices in Birmingham, Coventry, Falkirk and Milton Keynes. These sheet stamps became available nationally on 5 October 1993. On 29 April 1997 No. 1664 printed in photogravure by Walsall became available in sheets. On the same date Nos. 1664 and 1667 were issued in coils printed by Harrison. Sheets of No. 1667 were printed by Walsall from 18 November 1997.

No. 1665 exists with the phosphor band at the left or right of the stamp from separate panes of the £6.16 Speed stamp booklet No. DX21. For pane containing No. 1665Ec see No. Y1676al.

No. 1668 was originally printed by Harrisons in booklets and Walsall in sheets and booklets for The Queen's Golden Wedding and issued on 21 April 1997. It was printed in coils by Enschedé (5.10.02), when gold became the accepted colour for 1st class definitives, and later in sheets and coils by De La Rue.

Booklet pane No. 1668m was issued on 24 September 2002 in the £6·83 "Across the Universe" booklet, No. DX29. It was issued again with a different central label on 25 February 2003 in the £6·99 "Microcosmos" booklet, No. DX30.

No. 1669 was intended for the basic European air mail rate, initially 30p., and was at first only available from Barcode booklet No. HF1, printed by Walsall. It appeared in sheets printed by De La Rue on 5 October 1999.

No. 1671m, printed by Questa, was provided by the Royal Mail for inclusion in single pre-packed greetings cards. The pane shows large margins at top and sides with lines of roulette gauging 8 stretching from the bottom corners to the mid point of the top edge. Examples included with greetings cards show the top two corners of the pane folded over. Unfolded examples were available from the British Philatelic Bureau and from other Post Office philatelic outlets. The scheme was originally limited to Boots and their logo appeared on the pane margin. Other card retailers subsequently participated and later supplies omitted the logo.

A further printing by Enschedé in 1997 showed the roulettes gauging 10 (No. 1671mb). Blank pieces of gummed paper have been found showing the perforation and rouletting of No. 1671mb, but no printing.

No. 1672 was only issued in the following booklets: £7.40 Ian Fleming's "James Bond" (DX41), "Pilot to Plane" (DX42) and "Charles Darwin" (DX45).

For illustration of differences between lithography and gravure see below Types **367** and **367a**.

For self-adhesive stamps in these colours see Nos. 2039/40 and 2295/6.

POSTAL FORGERIES. In mid-1994 a number of postal forgeries of the 2nd bright blue printed in lithography were detected after having been rejected by the sorting equipment. These show the Queen's head in bright greenish blue, have a fluorescent, rather than a phosphor, band and show matt, colourless gum on the reverse. These forgeries come from booklets of ten which also have forged covers.

COMMEMORATIVE BOOKLET PANES. Booklets of four 1st Class stamps with *se-tenant* commemorative label were issued for the following anniversaries or events:
300th Anniversary of the Bank of England (No. 1671l)
Birth Centenary of R. J. Mitchell (No. 1671la)
70th Birthday of Queen Elizabeth II (No. 1671la)
"Hong Kong '97" International Stamp Exhibition (No. 1671la)
Commonwealth Heads of Government Meeting, Edinburgh (No. 1671la)
50th Birthday of Prince of Wales (No. 1671la)
50th Anniversary of Berlin Airlift (No. 1667m)
Rugby World Cup (No. 1667m)

First Day Covers

21.4.97	1st (No. 1668), 26p. (Y1692) (Type G) (Philatelic Bureau or Windsor)	3·50
23.9.97	B.B.C. label pane 1st×4, 26p×4 (No. 1668l), (Philatelic Bureau or London W1)	12·00
19.1.99	E (No. 1669) (Type G) (Philatelic Bureau or Windsor)	3·50

16.2.99	"Profile on Print" label pane 1st×8 (No. 1671n) (see Nos. 2077/9) (Philatelic Bureau or London SW1)	5·50
6.2.02	"A Gracious Accession" label pane 2nd×4 and E×4 (No. 1664n) (see Nos. 2253/7) (Tallents House or Windsor)	5·00
24.9.02	"Across the Universe" label pane 1st×4, E×4 (No. 1668m) (Tallents House or Star, Glenrothes)	5·00
25.2.03	"Microcosmos" label pane 1st×4, E×4 (No. 1668n) (Tallents House or Cambridge)	5·00
2.6.03	"A Perfect Coronation" label pane 2nd×4, 1st×4 (No. 1664o) (Tallents House or London SW1)	4·00
16.3.04	"Letters by Night: A Tribute to the Travelling Post Office" label pane 1st×4, 37p×4 (No. 1680o) (Tallents House or London NW10)	11·00
25.5.04	"The Glory of the Garden" label pane 1st×4, 42p×2, 47p×2 (No. 1668p) (Tallents House or Wisley, Woking	11·00
24.2.05	The Brontë Sisters label pane 2nd×4, 39p.×2, 42p.×2 (No. 1664p) (Tallents House or Haworth, Keighley)	5·00
18.10.05	Bicentenary of the Battle of Trafalgar label pane 1st×4, 50p.×2 and 68p.×2 (No. 1668q) (Tallents House and Portsmouth)	8·50
23.2.06	Birth Bicentenary of Isambard Kingdom Brunel label pane 1st×4, 35p.×2 and 40p.×2 (No. 1668r) (Tallents House or Bristol)	7·00
8.1.08	James Bond label pane 1st×8 (No. 1672a) (Tallents House or London SE1)	12·00
18.9.08	"Pilot to Plane" RAF Uniforms label pane 2nd×4 and 1st×4 (No.1670l) (Tallents House or Hendon, London NW9)	8·00

1390

1999 (16 Feb).

(a) Embossed and litho Walsall. Self-adhesive.
Die-cut perf 14×15.

| 2077 | **1390** | (1st) grey (face value) (Queen's head in colourless relief) (phosphor background around head) .... | 3·00 | 2·75 |
| | | I. Booklet pane. No. 2077×4 with margins all round................................... | 10·00 | |

(b) Eng C. Slania. Recess Enschedé. P 14×14½.

| 2078 | **1390** | (1st) grey-black (2 phosphor bands)........ | 3·00 | 2·75 |
| | | I. Booklet pane. No. 2078×4 with margins all round................................... | 10·00 | |

(c) Typo Harrison. P 14×15.

2079	**1390**	(1st) black (2 phosphor bands)	3·00	2·75
		Ey. Phosphor omitted................................	£1800	
		I. Booklet pane. No. 2078×4 with margins all round...................................	10·00	
		LEy. Booklet pane.Phosphor omitted		

Set of 3	8·00	7·50
First Day Covers (3 covers with Nos. 2077l, 2078l, 2079l) (Philatelic Bureau)		12·00
First Day Covers (3 covers with Nos. 2077l, 2078l, 2079l) (London SW1)		12·00

Nos. 2077/9 were only issued in the £7.54 "Profile on Print" booklet, No. DX22.

NVI Stamps. Panes with "standard" perforations

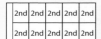

2nd	2nd	2nd	2nd	2nd
2nd	2nd	2nd	2nd	2nd

1445a (bright blue, photo)
Imperf at top and bottom

2nd	2nd
2nd	2nd

1445b (bright blue, photo)
Imperf at top and bottom

2nd	2nd
2nd	2nd

1449b (bright blue, litho)
Imperf at top and bottom and right

2nd	2nd
2nd	2nd

1449c (bright blue, litho)
Imperf at top and bottom

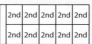

2nd	2nd	2nd	2nd	2nd
2nd	2nd	2nd	2nd	2nd

1449d (bright blue, litho)
Imperf at top and bottom

2nd	2nd	2nd	2nd	2nd
2nd	2nd	2nd	2nd	2nd

1511a (deep blue, photo)
Imperf at top and bottom

2nd	2nd
2nd	2nd

1515a (deep blue, litho)
Imperf at top and bottom

2nd	2nd	2nd	2nd	2nd
2nd	2nd	2nd	2nd	2nd

1515b (deep blue, litho)
Imperf at top and bottom

1st	1st	1st	1st	1st
1st	1st	1st	1st	1st

1447a (black, photo)
Imperf at top and bottom

1st	1st
1st	1st

1447b (black, litho)
Imperf at top and bottom

1st	1st
1st	1st

1450a (black, litho)
Imperf at top and bottom and right

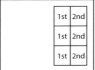

1st	2nd
1st	2nd
1st	2nd

1451al (litho)
£6 (£5.64) Beatrix Potter

1st	1st	1st	1st	1st
1st	1st	1st	1st	1st

1512a (orange, photo)
Imperf at top and bottom

1st	1st
1st	1st

1516a (orange, litho P 14)
Imperf at top and bottom

1st	1st
1st	1st

1516a (orange, litho, P 13))
Imperf at top and bottom

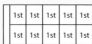

1st	1st	1st	1st	1st
1st	1st	1st	1st	1st

1516b (orange, litho)
Imperf at top and bottom

NVI Stamps. Panes with elliptical perforations the shaded squares represent printed labels.

post-code

2nd	1st
1st	1st

1664l

post-codes

2nd	1st
1st	1st

1664la

2nd	2nd
1st	1st
1st	1st
1st	1st

1664m

	E	2nd	E
	2nd		2nd
	E	2nd	E

1664n
£7.29 A Gracious Accession

1st	1st	1st
1st		1st
1st	1st	1st

1667l
£7.54 Profile in Print

1st	1st	
1st	1st	Label

1667m (photo)

1st	26	1st
26		26
1st	26	1st

1668l
£6.15 Celebrating 75 Years of the BBC

1st	E	1st
E		E
1st	E	1st

1668m
£6.83 Across the Universe

37	1st	37
1st		1st
37	1st	37

1668o (photo)
£7.44 Letters by Night

1st	42	1st
47		47
1st	42	1st

1668p
£7.23 The Glory of the Garden

1st	50	1st
68		68
1st	50	1st

1668q
£7.26 Bicentenary of the Battle of Trafalgar

1st	35	1st
40		40
1st	35	1st

1668r
£7.40 Isambard Kingdom Brunel

1st	2nd	1st
2nd		2nd
1st	2nd	1st

1670l
£7.15 Pilot to Plane

Label	1st	1st
	1st	1st

1671l

1st	1st	Label
1st	1st	

1671la (litho)

1st	1st	1st
1st	1st	1st
1st	1st	1st

1671n
£7.54 Profile on Print

1st	1st	1st
1st		1st
1st	1st	1st

1672l
£7.40 Ian Fleming's James Bond

1st	5	1st
5		5
1st	5	1st

Y1670l
£7.49 World of Invention

Denominated stamps, PVA gum, elliptical perforations

II Normal figures of face value   III Open '4' and open lower curve of '5'

1993 (27 Apr)–**2012**. As Nos. X**841**, etc, but *Perf* 15×14 (with one elliptical hole in each vertical side).

(a) Photo

Enschedé: – 20p. (Y1684), 29p., 35p. (Y1698), 36p., 38p. (Y1706), 41p. (Y1712), 43p. (Y1716)
Harrison: – 20p. (Y1686), 25p. (Y1689), 26p. (Y1692), 35p. (Y1699), 41p. (Y1713), 43p. (Y1717)
Walsall: – 10p. (Y1676a), 19p. (Y1683), 38p. (Y1707a), 43p. (Y1717a).
Enschedé or Harrison/De La Rue: – 4p., 5p., 6p., 25p. (Y1690), 31p., 39p. (Y1708), £1 (Y1743)
Enschedé, Harrison/De La Rue or Questa: – 1p.
Enschedé, Harrison/De La Rue, Questa or Walsall: – 2p.
Enschedé, Harrison/De La Rue or Walsall: – 10p. (Y1676), 30p., 37p. (Y1703), 42p., 50p. (Y1726), 63p.
Harrison/De La Rue or Questa: – 19p. (Y1682), 20p. (Y1685), 26p. (Y1691)
De La Rue or Walsall: – 38p. (Y1707), 39p. (Y1709), 40p. (Y1710), 64p., 65p., 68p.
De La Rue: – 7p., 8p., 9p., 12p., 14p., 15p., 16p., 17p., 20p. (Y1687), 22p., 33p., 34p., 35p. (Y1700), 37p. (Y1704/5), 41p. (Y1714), 43p. (Y1718), 44p., 45p., 48p., 49p., 50p., (Y1727), 56p., 60p., 62p., 67p., 72p., 78p., 81p., 88p., 90p., 97p., £1 (Y1744), £1.46, £1.50, £2, £3, £5
Enschedé or De La Rue: – 35p. (Y1701), 40p. (Y1711), 46p., 47p., 54p.

Y1667	**367**	1p. crimson (2 bands) (8.6.93)	30	25
		l. Booklet pane. Nos. Y1667×2, Y1685 and Y1691×3 plus 2 labels (1.12.98)	20·00	
		m. Booklet pane. Nos. Y1667/8, Y1682 and Y1691×3 plus 2 labels (26.4.99)	6·50	
		n. Booklet pane. Nos. Y1667×4, Y1682×3 and Y1691 with central label and margins all round (21.9.99)	5·50	
		o. Booklet pane. Nos. Y1667×4, Y1722×4 and Y1728×2 with central label and margins all round (20.9.07)	6·00	
Y1668		2p. dp green (2 bands) (11.4.95)	30	30
		a. Imperf (pair)	£2500	
		l. Booklet pane. Nos. Y1668×4 and Nos. Y1722 and Y1724, each×2 with centre label and margins all round (5.6.07)	4·25	
		m. Booklet pane. Nos. Y1668 ×2, Y1676 ×2 and U3005 ×4 with central label and margins all round (10.1.12)	12·00	
Y1669		4p. new blue (2 bands) (14.12.93)	30	30
		a. Imperf	£1700	
Y1670		5p. dull red-brown (Type II) (2 bands) (8.6.93)	30	35
		l. Booklet pane. Nos. Y1670 and 2651, each ×4, with centre label and margins all round (1.3.07)	5·50	
Y1671		6p. yellow-olive (2 bands)	30	35
		Ey. Phosphor omitted	£180	
Y1672		7p. grey (2 bands) (20.4.99)	2·75	2·75
		a. Imperf (pair)		
Y1673		7p. bright magenta (2 bands) (1.4.04)	75	80
		a. Imperf (pair)	£240	
Y1674		8p. yellow (2 bands)	35	35
Y1675		9p. yellow-orange (2 bands) (5.4.05)	30	20
Y1676		10p. dull orange (2 bands) (8.6.93)	35	35
		aa. Imperf pair	£1400	
		a. Perf 14 (13.10.98)	2·00	2·00
		al. Booklet pane. Nos. Y1676a×2, 1665Ec and Y1717a, each×3, with centre label and margins all round	12·00	
Y1677		12p. greenish blue (2 bands) (1.8.06)	1·00	1·25
Y1678		14p. rose-red (2 bands) (1.8.06)	50	55
Y1679		15p. bright magenta (2 bands) (1.4.08)	60	65
Y1680		16p. pale cerise (2 bands) (27.3.07)	60	65
Y1681		17p. brown-olive (2 bands) (31.3.09)	60	65
		a. Imperf (pair)	£2600	
Y1682		19p. bistre (1 centre band) (26.10.93)	40	45
		a. Imperf (pair)	£550	

		l. Booklet pane. Nos. Y1682 and Y1691×7 (26.4.99)	13·00	
		lEy. Phosphor omitted	£140	
Y1683		19p. bistre (1 band at right) (*p* 14) (15.2.00)	2·75	2·75
		l. Booklet pane. Nos. Y1683×4 and Y1707a×2 with margins all round	22·00	
Y1684		20p. turquoise-green (2 bands) (14.12.93)	80	80
Y1685		20p. brt green (1 centre band) (25.6.96)	50	50
		a. Imperf (horiz pair)	£350	
		l. Booklet pane. Nos. Y1685 and Y1691×7 (1.12.98)	22·00	
Y1686		20p. brt green (1 band at right) (23.9.97)	3·00	3·00
		l. Booklet pane. Nos. Y1686 and Y1691, each×3 with margins all round	10·00	
Y1687		20p. brt green (2 bands) (20.4.99)	75	75
		a. Imperf (pair)	£425	
Y1688		22p. drab (2 bands) (31.3.09)	1·30	1·30
Y1689		25p. rose-red (phosphorised paper) (26.10.93)	70	70
		a. Imperf (pair)	£1000	
		l. Booklet pane. No. Y1689×2 plus 2 labels (1.11.93)	2·00	
Y1690		25p. rose-red (2 bands) (20.12.94)	70	70
		Ey. Phosphor omitted	24·00	
		l. Booklet pane. No. Y1690×2 plus 2 labels (6.6.95)	3·50	
Y1691		26p. red-brown (2 bands) (25.6.96)	70	70
		a. Imperf (pair)	£650	
Y1692		26p. gold (2 bands) (21.4.97)	1·10	1·10
		ba. Imperf (horiz pair)	£2750	
Y1693		29p. grey (2 bands) (26.10.93)	1·25	1·25
Y1694		30p. dp olive-grey (2 bands) (27.7.93)	1·10	1·10
		a. Imperf (pair)	£1400	
Y1695		31p. dp mauve (2 bands) (25.6.96)	1·20	1·20
Y1696		33p. grey-green (2 bands) (25.4.00)	1·50	1·50
Y1697		34p. yellow-olive (2 bands) (6.5.03)	4·00	4·00
Y1698		35p. yellow (2 bands) (17.8.93)	1·50	1·50
Y1699		35p. yellow (phosphorised paper) (1.11.93)	10·00	10·00
Y1700		35p. sepia (2 bands) (1.4.04)	1·30	1·30
		a. Imperf (pair)	£375	
Y1701		35p. yellow-olive (5.4.05) (1 centre band)	90	90
Y1702		36p. brt ultramarine (2 bands) (26.10.93)	1·75	1·75
Y1703		37p. brt mauve (2 bands) (25.6.96)	1·40	1·40
Y1704		37p. grey-black (2 bands) (4.7.02)	1·50	1·50
Y1705		37p. brown-olive (1 centre band) (28.3.06)	1·75	1·50
Y1706		38p. rosine (2 bands) (26.10.93)	1·50	1·50
		a. Imperf (pair)	£375	
Y1707		38p. ultramarine (2 bands) (20.4.99)	2·00	2·00
		a. Perf 14 (15.2.00)	8·00	8·00
Y1708		39p. brt magenta (2 bands) (25.6.96)	1·50	1·50
		a. Imperf (pair)	£1700	
Y1709		39p. grey (2 bands) (1.4.04)	1·50	1·50
		a. Imperf (pair)	£325	
Y1710		40p. dp azure (2 bands) (25.4.00)	1·40	1·40
Y1711		40p. turquoise-blue (2 bands) (1.4.04)	1·40	1·40
		a. Imperf (pair)	£850	
Y1712		41p. grey-brown (2 bands) (26.10.93)	1·75	1·75
Y1713		41p. drab (phosphorised paper) (1.11.93)	10·00	10·00
Y1714		41p. rosine (2 bands) (25.4.00)	1·40	1·40
Y1715		42p. dp olive-grey (2 bands) (4.7.02)	1·40	1·40
Y1716		43p. dp olive-brown (2 bands) (25.6.96)	1·75	1·75
Y1717		43p. sepia (2 bands) (8.7.96)	2·50	2·50
		a. Perf 14 (13.10.98)	2·50	2·50
Y1718		43p. emerald (2 bands) (1.4.04)	1·40	1·40
		a. Imperf (pair)	£300	
Y1719		44p. grey-brown (2 bands) (20.4.99)	5·00	5·00
Y1720		44p. deep bright blue (2 bands) (28.3.06)	1·50	1·50
Y1721		45p. brt mauve (2 bands) (25.4.00)	1·50	1·50
Y1722		46p. yellow (2 bands) (5.4.05)	1·20	1·20
Y1723		47p. turquoise-green (2 bands) (4.7.02)	1·75	1·75
Y1724		48p. bright mauve (2 bands) (27.3.07)	1·20	1·20
Y1725		49p. red-brown (2 bands) (28.3.06)	2·25	2·25
Y1726		50p. ochre (2 bands) (14.12.93)	1·75	1·75
		a. Imperf (pair)	£2750	
Y1727		50p. grey (2 bands) (27.3.07)	1·25	1·25
Y1728		54p. red-brown (Type II) (2 bands) (27.3.07)	1·10	1·10
Y1729		56p. yellow-olive (2 bands) (1.4.08)	1·50	1·50
Y1730		60p. light emerald (2 bands) (30.3.10)	1·50	1·50
Y1731		62p. rosine (2 bands) (31.3.09)	1·75	1·75
Y1732		63p. lt emerald (2 bands) (25.6.96)	2·00	2·00
Y1733		64p. turquoise-green (2 bands) (20.4.99)	2·25	2·25
Y1734		65p. greenish blue (2 bands) (25.4.00)	2·10	2·10

Y1735		67p. bright mauve (2 bands) (30.3.10)....	2·25	2·25
Y1736		68p. grey-brown (2 bands) (4.7.02).........	2·10	2·10
Y1737		72p. rosine (2 bands) (28.3.06)	2·25	2·25
Y1738		78p. emerald (2 bands) (27.3.07)	1·50	1·50
Y1739		81p. turquoise-green (2 bands) (1.4.08)	2·00	2·00
Y1740		88p. bright magenta (2 bands) (30.3.10)	2·25	2·25
Y1741		90p. ultramarine (2 bands) (31.3.09)	2·25	2·25
Y1742		97p. violet (2 bands) (30.3.10)	3·00	3·00
Y1743		£1 bluish violet (2 bands) (22.8.95) ...	2·50	2·50
		a. Imperf (horiz pair)	£1800	
Y1744		£1 magenta (2 bands) (5.6.07)	2·00	2·00
		l. Booklet pane. No. Y1744×2 with centre label and margins all round	4·50	
Y1745		£1.46 greenish blue (2 bands) (30.3.10) ..	4·00	4·00
Y1746		£1.50 brown-red (2 bands) (1.7.03)	3·50	3·50
Y1747		£2 deep blue-green (2 bands) (1.7.03)	5·00	5·00
		a. Missing "£" in value (R. 18/1, Cyl D1 no dot)	£225	
Y1748		£3 deep mauve (2 bands) (1.7.03)	7·00	7·00
Y1749		£5 azure (2 bands) (1.7.03)	12·00	12·00

(b) Litho Cartor (1p. (Y1761)), 5p. (Y1763/5), 10p. (Y1768), 16p., 17p., 20p., (Y1773), 22p., 50p., 54p., 60p. (Y1785), 62p., 67p., 90p., 97p. *De La Rue* (5p. (Y1762)), *Questa, De La Rue or Cartor* (10p. (Y1767)), *Questa or Walsall* (25p., 35p.,), *Walsall* (37p., 41p. (Y1780) 60p. (Y1784), 63p.), *De La Rue* (48p.), *Questa (others)*.

Y1760	**367**	1p. lake (2 bands) (8.7.96)	80	80
		Ey. Phosphor omitted	£500	
		l. Booklet pane. Nos. Y1760×2, Y1772 and Y1776×3 plus 2 labels	5·00	
		lEy. Booklet pane. Phosphor omitted ..	£1200	
Y1761		1p. reddish purple (2 bands) (17.9.09)	2·50	2·50
		l. Booklet pane. Nos. Y1761×2, Y1770×4 and Y1789×2 with central label and margins all round	20·00	
Y1762		5p. chocolate (2 bands)(Type II) (12.2.09)	3·25	3·25
		Ey. Phosphor omitted	£1800	
		l. Booklet pane. Nos. 1672, Y1762, Y1767 and Y1781, each ×2 with central label	18·00	
Y1763		5p. Red-brown (*shades*) (13.5.10)	3·00	3·00
		l. Booklet pane. Nos. Y1763 ×4, Y1767 ×2 and Y1785 ×2, with central label and margins all round	18·00	
		m. Booklet pane. Nos. Y1763 ×4, U3015 ×2 and U3019 ×2 with central label and margins all round (9.9.11)	15·00	
Y1764		5p. Lake-brown (22.3.11)	3·00	3·00
		l. Booklet pane. Nos. Y1764 ×3, Y1767 ×3, Y1788 and Y1790, with central label and margins all round	22·00	
Y1765		5p. red-brown (2 bands) (Type III) (7.1.10)	3·75	3·75
		l. Booklet pane. Nos. Y1765×2, Y1768×5 and Y1774×2 with margins all round	18·00	
Y1766		6p. yellow-olive (2 bands) (26.7.94)	12·00	13·00
		l. Booklet pane. Nos. Y1766, Y1771 and Y1775×4 with margins all round	15·00	
		la. 6p. value misplaced	£4000	
Y1767		10p. dull orange (*shades*) (2 bands) (25.4.95)	3·50	3·50
		Ey. Phosphor omitted	£1800	
		l. Booklet pane. Nos. Y1767, Y1771/a, Y1775×2, Y1777/8, Y1780a and centre label with margins all round	18·00	
Y1768		10p. Pale brownish orange (7.1.10)	3·50	3·50
Y1769		16p. pale cerise (2 bands) (13.1.09)	3·00	3·00
		l. Booklet pane. Nos. Y1769 and Y1782, each ×4, with central label	20·00	
Y1770		17p. bistre (2 bands) (18.8.09)	2·50	2·50
		l. Booklet pane. Nos. Y1770×4, Y1774×2 and Y1786×2 with central label and margins all round	18·00	
Y1771		19p. bistre (1 band at left) (26.7.94).......	2·50	2·50
		a. Band at right (25.4.95)	2·50	2·50
		l. Booklet pane. Nos. Y1771/a, each×3 with margins all round (25.4.95)	14·00	
Y1772		20p. brt yellow-green (1 centre band) (8.7.96)	2·25	2·25
		Ey. Phosphor omitted	£125	
		l. Booklet pane. Nos. Y1772 and Y1776×7	8·00	
		lEy. Booklet pane. Phosphor omitted ..	£200	
Y1773		20p. light green (2 bands) (7.1.10)	3·00	3·00

		l. Booklet pane. Nos. Y1773×4, Y1783×2 and Y1786×2 with central label and margins all round	18·00	
Y1774		22p. olive-brown (2 bands) (18.8.09)	4·00	4·00
		l. Booklet pane. Nos. Y1774 and Y1783, each×4 with central label and margins all round (25.2.10)	18·00	
Y1775		25p. red (2 bands) (1.11.93)	1·10	1·10
		l. Booklet pane. Nos. Y1775, NI72, S84 and W73, each×2, with centre label and margins all round (14.5.96)	7·50	
Y1776		26p. chestnut (2 bands) (8.7.96)	1·00	1·00
		Ey. Phosphor omitted	10·00	
Y1777		30p. olive-grey (2 bands) (25.4.95)	5·50	5·50
Y1778		35p. yellow (2 bands) (1.11.93)	1·60	1·60
Y1779		37p. brt mauve (2 bands) (8.7.96)	3·50	3·50
Y1780		41p. drab (2 bands) (1.11.93)	1·75	1·75
		a. Grey-brown (25.4.95)	5·50	5·50
		Ey. Phosphor omitted	£800	
Y1781		48p. bright mauve (2 bands) (12.2.09).	3·00	3·00
		Ey. Phosphor omitted	£1800	
Y1782		50p. grey (2 bands) (13.1.09)	3·75	2·75
Y1783		54p. chestnut (2 bands) (Type III) (7.1.10)	3·50	3·50
Y1784		60p. dull blue-grey (2 bands) (9.8.94)	3·50	2·50
Y1785		60p. emerald (2 bands) (13.5.10)	6·00	6·00
Y1786		62p. rosine (2 bands) (18.8.09)	4·00	4·00
Y1787		63p. lt emerald (2 bands) (8.7.96).........	3·75	3·75
		Ey. Phosphor omitted	£525	
Y1788		67p. bright mauve (2 bands) (22.3.11)	7·50	8·00
Y1789		90p. bright blue (2 bands) (17.9.09)	4·75	4·75
Y1790		97p. bluish violet (2 bands) (22.3.11)	8·00	8·00

(c) Eng C. Slania. Recess Enschedé (until Mar 2000) or De La Rue (from 11 Apr 2000)

Y1800	**367**	£1.50 red (9.3.99)	4·50	2·00
Y1801		£2 dull blue (9.3.99)	5·00	2·25
Y1802		£3 dull violet (9.3.99)	7·00	3·00
Y1803		£5 brown (9.3.99).............................	12·00	5·00
		a. Imperf (pair)	£3000	

P.H.Q. Card (No. Y1725) (D7) .... 3·00 15·00

P.H.Q. Cards (Nos. 1664, 1668, Y1667/8, Y1670, Y1675/6, Y16779/80, Y1687, Y1724, Y1727, Y1729, Y1739, Y1744, Y1746/9, 2357a, 2652/3, 2358/9 (D30) .... 15·00

Nos. Y1743/9 are printed in Iriodin ink which gives a shiny effect to the solid part of the background behind the Queen's head.

A gravure-printed £5 stamp, as No. Y1749 but in sepia is believed to have come from stock stolen from the printer. Both unused and used examples are known.

No. Y1766la shows the 6p. value printed 22 mm to the left so that its position on the booklet pane is completely blank except for the phosphor bands. Other more minor misplacements exist.

The De La Rue printings of the high values, Nos. Y1800/3 cannot easily be identified from the original Enschedé issue as single stamps.

For self-adhesive versions of the 42p. and 68p. see Nos. 2297/8.

First Day Covers

26.10.93	19p., 25p., 29p., 36p., 38p., 41p. (Y1682, Y1689, Y1693, Y1702, Y1706, Y1712)..	6·00
9.8.94	60p. (Y1784)	4·00
25.4.95	National Trust *se-tenant* pane 10p., 19p., 25p., 30p., 35p., 41p. (Y1767l)	5·00
22.8.95	£1 (Y1743)	3·50
14.5.96	European Football Championship *se-tenant* pane 25p.×8 (Y1775l)	7·50
25.6.96	20p., 26p., 31p., 37p., 39p., 43p., 63p. (Y1685, Y1691, Y1695, Y1703, Y1708, Y1716, Y1732)	8·00
13.10.98	Speed *se-tenant* pane 10p., 2nd, 43p. (Y1676al)	6·50
9.3.99	£1·50, £2, £3, £5 (Y1800/3) (Type G) (Philatelic Bureau or Windsor)	27·00
20.4.99	7p., 38p., 44p., 64p. (Y1672, Y1707, Y1719, Y1733) (Type G) (Philatelic Bureau or Windsor)	5·00
21.9.99	World Changers *se-tenant* pane 1p.,19p., 26p. (Y1667n) (Philatelic Bureau or Downe, Orpington)	4·00
25.4.00	8p., 33p., 40p., 41p., 45p., 65p. (Y1674, Y1696, Y1710, Y1714, Y1721, Y1734) (Type G) (Philatelic Bureau or Windsor)..	5·00
4.7.02	37p., 42p., 47p., 68p. (Y1704, Y1715, Y1722, Y1736) (Type K) (Tallents House or Windsor)	4·00
6.5.03	34p., (Y1697) (Type K) (Tallents House or Windsor)	1·20
1.7.03	£1·50, £2, £3, £5 (*Nos.* Y1746/9) (Type K) (Tallents House or Windsor)	21·00
1.4.04	7p., 35p., 39p., 40p., 43p. Worldwide postcard (Y1673, Y1700, Y1709, Y1711, Y1718, 2357a) (Type K) (Tallents House or Windsor)	9·00
5.4.05	9p., 35p., 46p. (*Nos.* Y1675, Y1701, Y1722) (Type K) (Tallents House or Windsor).....................................	2·20
28.3.06	37p., 44p., 49p., 72p. (Y1703, Y1720, Y1725, Y1737) (Type K) (Tallents House or Windsor)	4·25
1.3.07	World of Invention label pane 5p., 1st (Y1670a) (Tallents House or Menai Bridge, Gwynedd)....................	5·00

27.3.07	16p., 48p., 50p., 54p., 78p. (Y1680, Y1724, Y1727/8, Y1738) (Type K) (Tallents House or Windsor)	6·00
5.6.07	Machin Anniversary *se-tenant* pane 2p., 46p., 48p. (Y1668*b*) (Tallents House, Windsor or Stoke-on-Trent)	5·00
20.9.07	Army Uniforms *se-tenant* pane 1p., 46p., 54p. (Y1667*o*) (Tallents House or Boot, Holmrook, Cumbria)	7·00
1.4.08	15p., 56p., 81p. (Y1679, Y1729, Y1739) (Type K) (Tallents House or Windsor)........................	4·50
13.1.09	British Design Classics *se-tenant* pane 16p., 50p. (Y1769*l*) (Tallents House or Longbridge, Birmingham)	7·00
12.2.09	Charles Darwin *se-tenant* pane 5p., 10p., 1st, 48p. (Y1762*l*) (Tallents House or Shrewsbury)........	5·00
31.3.09	17p., 22p., 62p., 90p. (Y1681, Y1688, Y1731, Y1741) (Type K) (Tallents House or Windsor)	6·00
18.8.09	"Treasures of the Archive" *se-tenant* pane 17p., 22p., 62p., (Y1770*l*) (Tallents House or London EC1)...	7·00
17.9.09	Royal Navy Uniforms *se-tenant* pane 1p., 17p., 90p. (Y1761*l*) (Tallents House or Portsmouth).........	7·00
7.1.10	Classic Album Covers *se-tenant* pane 20p., 54p., 52p. (Y1773*l*) (Tallents House or Oldfield, Keighley)	9·25
25.2.10	Royal Society *se-tenant* pane 22p., 54p. (Y1774*l*) (Tallents House or London SW1)...............	7·00
30.3.10	60p., 67p., 88p., 97p., £1.46, Europe up to 20 grams, Worldwide up to 20 grams (Y1730, Y1735, Y1740, Y1742, Y1745, 2357*b*, 2358*a*) (Type K) (Tallents House or Windwor)	16·00
13.5.10	"Britain Alone" *se-tenant* pane 5p., 10p., 60p., (Y1763*l*) (Tallents House or Dover, Kent)................	5·50
22.3.11	WWF *se-tenant* pane 5p., 10p., 67p., 97p. (Y1764*l*) (Tallents House or Godalming, Surrey)..........	9·00
9.9.11	Aerial Post Centenary *se-tenant* pane 5p., 1st, 76p. (Y1763*m*) (Tallents House or Hendon, London NW4)..	8·50
10.1.12	Roald Dahl *se-tenant* pane 2p., 10p., 68p. (Y1668*c*) (Tallents House or Great Missenden, Bucks)........	9·50

For first day covers for Nos. Y1677/8 see under Nos. 2650/7.

Special First Day of Issue Postmarks

Post Office Presentation Packs

26.10.93	P.O. Pack No. 30. 19p. (1 centre band), 25p. (phos paper), 29p., 36p., 38p. rosine, 41p. grey-brown (*Nos.* Y1682, Y1689, Y1693, Y1702, Y1706, Y1712)	7·00
21.11.95	P.O. Pack No. 34. 1p. (photo), 2p., 4p., 5p., 6p. (photo), 10p. (photo), 19p. (1 centre band), 20p. turquoise-green, 25p. (photo) (2 bands), 29p., 30p. (photo), 35p. (photo) (2 bands), 36p., 38p. rosine, 41p. grey-brown, 50p., 60p., £1 (*Nos.* Y1667/71, Y1676, Y1682, Y1684, Y1690, Y1693/4, Y1698, Y1702, Y1706, Y1712, Y1726, Y1743, Y1784)................	35·00
25.6.96	P.O. Pack No. 35. 20p. brt green (1 centre band), 26p. (photo), 31p., 37p. (photo), 39p., 43p. deep olive brown, 63p. (photo) (*Nos.* Y1685, Y1691, Y1695, Y1703, Y1708, Y1716, Y1732)........................	9·50
21.4.97	P.O. Pack No. 38. 1st, 26p. gold (*Nos.* 1668, Y1692)	7·50
20.10.98	P.O. Pack No. 41. 2nd brt blue (1 centre band), 1st brt orange-red (2 phosphor bands), 1p., 2p., 4p., 5p., 6p., 10p., 20p. brt green (1 centre band), 26p., 30p., 31p., 37p., 39p., 43p. sepia, 50p., 63p., £1 (*Nos.* 1664, 1667, Y1667/71, Y1676, Y1685, Y1691, Y1694/5, Y1703, Y1708, Y1717, Y1726, Y1732)................	20·00
9.3.99	P.O. Pack No. 43 or 43a. £1·50, £2, £3, £5 (*Nos.* Y1800/3)	55·00
20.4.99	P.O. Pack No. 44. 7p., 19p., 38p. ultramarine, 44p., 64p. (*Nos.* Y1672, Y1682, Y1707, Y1719, Y1733)............	11·00
25.4.00	P.O. Pack No. 49. 8p., 33p., 40p., 41p. rosine, 45p., 65p. (*Nos.* Y1674, Y1696, Y1710, Y1714, Y1721, Y1734)	10·00
12.3.02	P.O. Pack No. 57. 2nd, 1st, E, 1p., 2p., 4p., 5p., 8p., 10p., 20p., 33p., 40p., 41p., 45p., 50p., 65p., £1 (*Nos.* 1664, 1667, 1669, Y1667/70, Y1674, Y1676, Y1687, Y1696, Y1710, Y1714, Y1721, Y1726, Y1734, Y1743)................	18·00
4.7.02	P.O. Pack No. 58. 37p., 42p., 47p., 68p. (*Nos.* Y1704, Y1715, Y1723, Y1736)........................	7·50
1.7.03	P.O. Pack No. 62. £1·50, £2, £3, £5 (*Nos.* Y1746/9)	25·00
1.4.04	P.O. Pack No. 67. 1st gold (DLR ptg), 7p., 35p., 39p., 40p., 43p. Worldwide postcard (*Nos.* 1668, Y1673, Y1700, Y1709, Y1711, Y1718, 2357*a*)	15·00
6.9.05	P.O. Pack No. 71. 1p., 2p., 5p., 9p., 10p., 20p., 35p., 40p., 42p., 46p., 47p., 50p., 68p., £1., 2nd, 1st, Worldwide postcard, Europe up to 40 grams, Worldwide up to 40 grams (*Nos.* Y1667/8, Y1670, Y1675/6, Y1687, Y1701, Y1711, Y1715, Y1722/3, Y1726, Y1736, Y1743, 2039, 2295, 2357*a*, 2358, 2359)	60·00
28.3.06	P.O. Pack No. 72. 37p., 44p., 49p., 72p. (*Nos.* Y1705, Y1720, Y1725, Y1737)........................	12·00

27.3.07	P.O. Pack No. 75. 16p., 48p., 50p., 54p., 78p. (*Nos.* Y1680, Y1724, Y1727, Y1728, Y1738)	10·00
5.6.07	P.O. Pack No. 77. 2nd, 1st, 1p., 2p., 5p., 10p., 14p., 16p., 20p., 46p., 48p., 50p., 54p., 78p., £1, Worldwide postcard, Europe up to 40 grams, Worldwide up to 40 grams, 2nd Large, 1st Large (*Nos.* 1664, 1668, Y1670, Y1676, Y1678/9, Y1687, Y1722, Y1724, Y1727/8, Y1744, 2357*a*, 2358, 2359, 2652/3)	45·00
1.4.08	P.O. Pack. No. 78. 15p., 56p., 81p. (*Nos.* Y1679, Y1729, Y1739)........................	6·00
31.3.09	P.O. Pack. No. 84 17p., 22p., 62p., 90p. (*Nos.* Y1681, Y1688, Y1731, Y1741)........................	8·50
30.3.10	P.O. Pack. No. 86. 60p. 67p., 88p., 97p., £1.46, Europe up to 20 grams, Worldwide up to 20 grams, 1st Recorded Signed For (*Nos.* Y1730, Y1735, Y1740, Y1742, Y1745, 2357*a*, 2358*a*, U2981/2)	28·00
8.5.10	P.O. Pack. No. 88. 2nd, 1st, 1p., 2p., 5p., 9p., 10p., 20p., 50p., 60p., 67p., 88p., 97p., £1, £1.46, Worldwide postcard, Europe up to 20 grams Worldwide up to 20 grams, Europe up to 40 grams, Worldwide up to 40 grams, 2nd Large, 1st Large, 1st Recorded Signed For, 1st Large Recorded Signed For (*Nos.* 1664, 1668, Y1667, Y1668, Y1670, Y1675, Y1676, Y1687, Y1727, Y1730, Y1735, Y1740, Y1742, Y1744, Y1745, 2357*a*/9, 2652/3)	55·00

In 2002 a 'master' presentation pack entitled 'Royal Mail Definitive Stamps Collection' was released, containing packs 43a, 53, 54, 55, 56 and 57 (*Price* £120).

1917 (Illustration reduced. Actual size 127×72 mm)

(Des Katja Thielan. Gravure De La Rue)

2006 (31 Aug). *70th Anniversary of the Year of Three Kings. Sheet 127×72 mm containing No. Y1748. Multicoloured. Two phosphor bands. Perf 15×14 (with one elliptical hole in each vertical side).*

MS2658 **1917** £3 deep mauve	10·00	10·00
First Day Cover (Tallents House)		11·00
First Day Cover (Threekingham, Sleaford, Lincs)		11·00

Special First Day of Issue Postmarks

Decimal Machin Index

(stamps with elliptical perforations, including (N.V.ls)

Value	Process	Colour	Phosphor	Cat. No.	Source
2nd	litho Questa or Walsall	brt blue	1 centre band	1670	sheets (Questa), booklets of 4 (Walsall – HA6, Walsall HA9/11), booklets of 10 (Questa – HC11, HC13, HC16, HC18, HC20, Walsall – HC12), $7.15 "Pilot to Plane" booklet (Walsall - DX42)
2nd	photo/gravure Harrison/De La Rue), Enschedé, Questa or Walsall	brt blue	1 centre band	1664	sheets (Walsall, De La Rue), horizontal coil (Harrison/De La Rue), vertical coils (Harrison/De La Rue or Enschedé) booklets of 4 (Harrison – HA7/8, Walsall – HA12), booklets of 10 (Harrison/De La Rue – HC14/15, HC17, HC19, HC21), £1 booklet (Questa – FH44/a), £2 booklet (Questa – FW12), £7.29 "A Gracious Accession" booklet (Enschedé – DX28), £7.46 "A Perfect Coronation" booklet (Walsall – DX31), £7.43 The Brontë Sisters booklet (Walsall – DX34)
2nd	gravure Walsall (p 14)	brt blue	1 band at right	1665	£6.16 British Land Speed Record Holders booklet (DX21)
2nd	gravure Walsall (p 14)	brt blue	1 band at left	1665Ec	£6.16 British Land Speed Record Holders booklet (DX21)
2nd	gravure Questa (p 14)	brt blue	1 centre band	1664a	booklets of 10 (HC22)
1st	litho Enschedé, Questa or Walsall	brt orange-red	2 bands	1671	sheets (Questa), greetings card panes Questa – Y1671m/ma, Enschedé – Y1671mb), booklets of 4 (Walsall – HB6, HB8/13, HB15/16, Questa – HB7), booklets of 10 Walsall – HD10, HD12/19, HD22/3, HD25, HD28, HD34, HD36/8, HD40, Questa – HD11, HD21, HD26, HD50), £7.54 "Profile on Print" booklet (Questa – DX22)
1st	photo Harrison	brt orange-red	phos paper	1666	booklets of 4 (HB5), booklets of 10 (HD9, HD20)
1st	photo/gravure Harrison/De La Rue, Questa or Walsall	brt orange-red	2 bands	1667	sheets (Walsall), horizontal and vertical coils (Harrison, De La Rue), booklets of 4 (Walsall – HB14, HB17/18), booklets of 8 with 2 Millennium commems (Walsall – HBA1/2), booklets of 10 (Harrison/De La Rue – HD24, HD27, HD29/33, HD35, HD39, HD45/9, Walsall – HD44), £1 booklet (Questa – FH44/a), £2 booklet (Questa – FW12), £7.54 "Profile on Print" booklet (De La Rue – DX22)
1st	gravure Questa (p 14)	brt orange-red	2 bands	1667a	booklets of 10 (HD51)
1st	gravure De La Rue, Enschedé, Harrison, Questa or Walsall	gold	2 bands	1668	sheets (Walsall, De La Rue), vertical coils (Enschedé, De La Rue), booklets of 10 (Harrison – HD41, HD43, Walsall – HD42), £6.15 B.B.C. booklet (Harrison – DX19), £6.83 "Across the Universe" booklet (Questa – DX29), £6.99 "Microcosmos" booklet (Enschedé – DX30), £7.46 "A Perfect Coronation" booklet (Walsall – DX31), £7.44 "Letters by Night" booklet (De La Rue – DX32), £7.23 "The Glory of the Garden" booklet (Enschedé – DX33), £7.26 Trafalgar booklet (Walsall – DX35), £7.40 Brunel booklet (Enschedé – DX36)
1st	litho De La Rue or Walsall	gold	2 bands	1672	£7.40 Ian Fleming's James Bond booklet (De La Rue – DX41), £7.15 "Pilot to Plane" booklet (Walsall - DX42)
E	gravure De La Rue, Enschedé, Questa or Walsall	deep blue	2 bands	1669	sheets (De La Rue), booklets of 4 (Walsall – HF1), £7.29 "A Gracious Accession" booklet (Enschedé – DX28), £6.83 "Across the Universe" booklet (Questa – DX29), £6.99 "Microcosmos" booklet (Enschedé – DX30)
1p.	photo/gravure De La Rue, Enschedé, Harrison or Questa	crimson	2 bands	Y1667	sheets, £1 booklets (Questa – FH42/3), £6.91 World Changers booklet (Questa – DX23) , £7.66 British Army Uniforms booklet (Enschedé – DX40)
1p.	litho Questa	lake	2 bands	Y1760	£1 booklet (FH41)
1p.	litho Cartor	reddish purple	2 bands	Y1761	£7.93 Royal Navy Uniforms booklet (DX47)
2p.	photo/gravure De La Rue, Enschedé, Harrison, Questa or Walsall	dp green	2 bands	Y1668	sheets, £1 booklet (Questa – FH43), £7.66 "The Machin" booklet (De La Rue – DX39), £11.47 Roald Dahl booklet (Walsall – DY3)
4p.	photo/gravure De La Rue, Enschedé or Harrison	new blue	2 bands	Y1669	sheets
4p.	gravure De La Rue	new blue	phos paper	MS2146	Jeffery Matthews Colour Palette miniature sheet
5p.	photo/gravure De La Rue, Enschedé or Harrison	dull red-brown	2 bands	Y1670	sheets , £7.49 World of Invention booklet (De La Rue – DX38)
5p.	gravure De La Rue	dull red-brown	phos paper	MS2146	Jeffery Matthews Colour Palette miniature sheet
5p.	litho De La Rue	chocolate	2 bands	Y1762	£7.75 Charles Darwin booklet (DX45)
5p.	litho Cartor	red-brown	2 bands	Y1763	£9.76 Great Britain Alone booklet (DX51), £9.97 Aerial Post Centenary booklet (DY2)
5p.	litho Cartor	lake-brown	2 bands	Y1764	£9.05 WWF booklet (DX52)
5p.	litho Cartor	red-brown	2 bands	Y1765	Type III. £8.06 Classic Album Covers booklet (DX48)

Value	Process	Colour	Phosphor	Cat. No.	Source
6p.	photo/gravure Enschedé or Harrison	yellow-olive	2 bands	Y1671	sheets
6p.	litho Questa	yellow-olive	2 bands	Y1766	£6.04 Northern Ireland booklet (DX16)
6p.	gravure De La Rue	yellow-olive	phos paper	MS2146	Jeffery Matthews Colour Palette miniature sheet
7p.	gravure De La Rue	grey	2 bands	Y1672	sheets
7p.	gravure De La Rue	bright magenta	2 bands	Y1673	sheets
8p.	gravure De La Rue	yellow	2 bands	Y1674	sheets
9p.	gravure De La Rue	yellow-orange	2 bands	Y1675	sheets
10p.	photo/gravure De La Rue, Enschedé, Harrison or Walsall	dull orange	2 bands	Y1676	sheets, £11.47 Roald Dahl booklet (Walsall – DY3)
10p.	litho Questa, De La Rue or Cartor	dull orange	2 bands	Y1767	£6 National Trust booklet (Questa - DX17), £7.75 Charles Darwin booklet (De La Rue - DX45), £9.76 "Britain Alone" booklet (Cartor - DX51), £9.05 WWF booklet (Cartor - DX52)
10p.	litho Cartor	pale brownish orange	2 bands	Y1768	£8.06 Classic Album Covers booklet (DX48)
10p.	gravure Walsall (*p* 14)	dull orange	2 bands	Y1676a	£6.16 British Land Speed Record Holders booklet (DX21)
10p.	gravure De La Rue	dull orange	phos paper	MS2146	Jeffery Matthews Colour Palette miniature sheet
12p.	gravure De La Rue	greenish blue	2 bands	Y1677	sheets
14p.	gravure De La Rue	rose-red	2 bands	Y1678	sheets
15p.	gravure De La Rue	bright magenta	2 bands	Y1679	sheets
16p.	gravure De La Rue	pale cerise	2 bands	Y1680	sheets
16p.	litho Cartor	pale cerise	2 bands	Y1769	£7.75 British Design Classics booklet (DX44)
17p.	gravure De La Rue	brown-olive	2 bands	Y1681	sheets
17p.	litho Cartor	bistre	2 bands	Y1770	£8.18 "Treasures of the Archive" booklet (DX46) and £7.93 Royal Navy Uniforms booklet (DX47)
19p.	photo/gravure Harrison or Questa	bistre	1 centre band	Y1682	sheets, vertical coils, £1 booklet (Questa – FH43), £2 booklet (Questa – FW11), £6.99 World Changers booklet (Questa – DX23)
19p.	litho Questa	bistre	1 band at left	Y1771	£6.04 Northern Ireland booklet (DX16), £6 National Trust booklet (DX17)
19p.	litho Questa	bistre	1 band at right	Y1771a	£6 National Trust booklet (DX17)
19p.	gravure Walsall (*p* 14)	bistre	1 band at right	Y1683	£7.50 "Special by Design" booklet (DX24)
20p.	gravure Enschedé	turquoise-green	2 bands	Y1684	sheets
20p.	photo/gravure Harrison or Questa	brt green	1 centre band	Y1685	sheets, £1 booklet (Questa – FH42), £2 booklet (Questa – FW10)
20p.	litho Questa	brt yellow-green	1 centre band	Y1772	£1 booklet (FH41), £2 booklet (FW9)
20p.	gravure Harrison	brt green	1 band at right	Y1686	£6.15 B.B.C. booklet (DX19)
20p.	gravure De La Rue	brt green	2 bands	Y1687	sheets
20p.	litho Cartor	light green	2 bands	Y1773	£8.06 Classic Album Covers booklet (DX48)
22p.	gravure De La Rue	drab	2 bands	Y1688	sheets
22p.	litho Cartor	olive-brown	2 bands	Y1774	£8.18 "Treasures of the Archive" booklet (DX46), £8.06 Classic Album Covers booklet (DX48) and £7.72 Royal Society booklet (DX49)
25p.	photo Harrison	rose-red	phos paper	Y1689	sheets, vertical coils, 50p booklets (FB67/73), £1 booklets (FH33/7), £2 booklets (FW1/5)
25p.	litho Walsall or Questa	red	2 bands	Y1775	£1 booklets (Walsall – FH31/2, Questa – FH40), £2 booklet (Questa – FW8), £6.04 Northern Ireland booklet (Questa – DX16), £6 National Trust booklet (Questa – DX17), £6.84 European Football Championship (Questa – DX18)
25p.	photo/gravure Harrison or Enschedé	rose-red	2 bands	Y1690	sheets (Harrison or Enschedé), vertical coils (Harrison), 50p booklets (Harrison – FB74/5), £1 booklets (Harrison – FH38/9)), £2 booklets (Harrison – FW6/7)
26p.	photo/gravure Harrison or Questa	red-brown	2 bands	Y1691	sheets, £1 booklets (Questa – FH42/3), £2 booklets (Questa – FW10/11), £6.15 B.B.C. booklet (Harrison – DX19), £6.99 World Changers booklet (Questa – DX23)
26p.	litho Questa	chestnut	2 bands	Y1776	£1 booklet (FH41), £2 booklet (FW9)
26p.	gravure Harrison	gold	2 bands	Y1692	sheets, £6.15 B.B.C. booklet (Harrison – DX19)
29p.	gravure Enschedé	grey	2 bands	Y1693	sheets
30p.	photo/gravure Enschedé, Harrison or Walsall	dp olive-grey	2 bands	Y1694	sheets, £1.20 booklets (Walsall – GGAl/2)
30p.	litho Questa	olive-grey	2 bands	Y1777	£6 National Trust booklet (DX17)
31p.	photo/gravure Enschedé or Harrison	dp mauve	2 bands	Y1695	sheets
31p.	gravure De La Rue	dp mauve	phos paper	MS2146	Jeffery Matthews Colour Palette miniature sheet
33p.	gravure De La Rue	grey-green	2 bands	Y1696	sheets
34p.	gravure De La Rue	yellow-olive	2 bands	Y1697	sheets
35p.	gravure Enschedé	yellow	2 bands	Y1698	sheets
35p.	photo Harrison	yellow	phos paper	Y1699	vertical coils
35p.	litho Walsall or Questa	yellow	2 bands	Y1778	£1.40 booklets (Walsall – GK5/7), £6 National Trust booklet (Questa – DX17)
35p.	gravure De La Rue	sepia	2 bands	Y1700	sheets
35p.	gravure Enschedé or De La Rue	yellow-olive	1 centre band	Y1701	sheets, £7.40 Brunel booklet (Enschedé – DX36)
36p.	gravure Enschedé	brt ultramarine	2 bands	Y1702	sheets
37p.	photo/gravure Enschedé, Harrison or Walsall	brt mauve	2 bands	Y1703	sheets (Enschedé or Harrison), vertical coils (Harrison), £1.48 booklets (Walsall – GL3/4)
37p.	litho Walsall	brt mauve	2 bands	Y1779	£1.48 booklets (GL1/2)

Value	Process	Colour	Phosphor	Cat. No.	Source
37p.	gravure De La Rue	grey-black	2 bands	Y1704	sheets, £7.44 "Letters by Night" booklet (De La Rue – DX32)
37p.	gravure De La Rue	brown-olive	1 centre band	Y1705	sheets
38p.	gravure Enschedé	rosine	2 bands	Y1706	sheets
38p.	gravure De La Rue or Walsall	ultramarine	2 bands	Y1707	sheets (D.L.R.), £1.52 booklet (Walsall – GLAl)
38p.	gravure Walsall (*p* 14)	ultramarine	2 bands	Y1707a	£7.50 "Special by Design" booklet (DX24)
39p.	photo/gravure Enschedé or Harrison	brt magenta	2 bands	Y1708	sheets
39p.	gravure De La Rue	brt magenta	phos paper	**MS**2146	Jeffery Matthews Colour Palette miniature sheet
39p.	gravure De La Rue or Walsall	grey	2 bands	Y1709	sheets (De La Rue), £7.43 The Brontë Sisters booklet (Walsall – DX34)
40p.	gravure De La Rue or Walsall	deep azure	2 bands	Y1710	sheets (D.L.R.), £1.60 booklet (Walsall – GMA1)
40p.	gravure De La Rue or Enschedé	turquoise-blue	2 bands	Y1711	sheets (D.L.R.), £7.40 Brunel booklet (Enschedé – DX36)
41p.	gravure Enschedé	grey-brown	2 bands	Y1712	sheets
41p.	photo Harrison	drab	phos paper	Y1713	vertical coils
41p.	gravure De La Rue	rosine	2 bands	Y1714	sheets
41p.	litho Walsall	drab	2 bands	Y1780	£1.64 booklets (GN1/3)
41p.	litho Questa	grey-brown	2 bands	Y1780a	£6 National Trust booklet (DX17)
42p.	gravure De La Rue, Enschedé or Walsall	dp olive-grey	2 bands	Y1715	sheets (De La Rue), £7.23 "The Glory of the Garden" booklet (Enschedé – DX33), £7.43 The Brontë Sisters booklet (Walsall – DX34)
43p.	gravure Enschedé	dp olive-brown	2 bands	Y1716	sheets
43p.	photo Harrison	sepia	2 bands	Y1717	sheets, vertical coils
43p.	gravure Walsall (*p* 14)	sepia	2 bands	Y1717a	£6.16 British Land Speed Record Holders booklet (DX21)
43p.	gravure De La Rue	emerald	2 bands	Y1718	sheets
44p.	gravure De La Rue	grey-brown	2 bands	Y1719	sheets
44p.	gravure De La Rue	bright blue	2 bands	Y1720	sheets
45p.	gravure De La Rue	brt mauve	2 bands	Y1721	sheets
46p.	gravure De La Rue or Enschedé	yellow	2 bands	Y1722	sheets (De La Rue), £7.66 "The Machin" booklet (De La Rue – DX39), £7.66 British Army Uniforms booklet (Enschedé – DX40)
47p.	gravure De La Rue or Enschedé	turquoise-green	2 bands	Y1723	sheets (De La Rue), £7.23 "The Glory of the Garden" booklet (Enschedé – DX33)
48p.	gravure De La Rue	bright mauve	2 bands	Y1724	sheets, £7.66 "The Machin" booklet (DX39)
48p.	litho De La Rue	bright mauve	2 bands	Y1781	£7.75 Charles Darwin booklet (DX45)
49p.	gravure De La Rue	red-brown	2 bands	Y1725	sheets
50p.	photo/gravure Enschedé, Harrison or Walsall	ochre	2 bands	Y1726	sheets (Enschedé or Harrison), £7.26 Trafalgar booklet (Walsall–DX35), £7.44 Victoria Cross booklet (Enschedé – DX37)
50p.	gravure De La Rue	grey	2 bands	Y1727	sheets
50p.	litho Cartor	grey	2 bands	Y1782	£7.68 British Design Classics Booklet (DX44)
54p.	gravure De La Rue or Enschedé	red-brown	2 bands	Y1728	sheets (D.L.R.), £7.66 British Army Uniforms booklet (Enschedé – DX40)
54p.	litho Cartor	chestnut	2 bands	Y1783	Type III. £8.06 Classic Album Covers booklet (DX48) and £7.72 Royal Society booklet (DX49)
56p.	gravure De La Rue	yellow-olive	2 bands	Y1729	sheets
60p.	litho Walsall	dull blue-grey	2 bands	Y1784	£2.40 booklets (GQ1/4)
60p.	gravure De La Rue	light emerald	2 bands	Y1730	sheets
60p.	litho Cartor	emerald	2 bands	Y1785	"Britain Alone" booklet (DX51)
62p.	gravure De La Rue	rosine	2 bands	Y1731	sheets
62p.	litho Cartor	rosine	2 bands	Y1786	£8.18 "Treasures of the Archive" booklet (DX46) and £8.06 Classic Album Covers booklet (DX48)
63p.	photo/gravure Enschedé, Harrison or Walsall	lt emerald	2 bands	Y1732	sheets (Enschedé or Harrison), vertical coils (Harrison) £2.52 booklets (Walsall – GR3/4)
63p.	litho Walsall	lt emerald	2 bands	Y1787	£2.52 booklets (GR1/2)
64p.	gravure De La Rue or Walsall	turquoise-green	2 bands	Y1733	sheets (D.L.R.), £2.56 booklet (Walsall – GS1)
64p.	gravure De La Rue	turquoise-green	phos paper	**MS**2146	Jeffery Matthews Colour Palette miniature sheet
65p.	gravure De La Rue or Walsall	greenish blue	2 bands	Y1734	sheets (D.L.R.), £2.60 booklet (Walsall – GT1)
67p.	gravure De La Rue	bright mauve	2 bands	Y1735	sheets
67p.	litho Cartor	bright mauve	2 bands	Y1788	£9.05 WWF booklet (DX52)
68p.	gravure De La Rue or Walsall	grey-brown	2 bands	Y1736	sheets (D.L.R.), £7.26 Trafalgar booklet (Walsall – DX35)
72p.	gravure De La Rue	rosine	2 bands	Y1737	sheets
78p.	gravure De La Rue	emerald	2 bands	Y1738	sheets
81p.	gravure De La Rue	turquoise-green	2 bands	Y1739	sheets
88p.	gravure De La Rue	bright magenta	2 bands	Y1740	sheets
90p.	gravure De La Rue	ultramarine	2 bands	Y1741	sheets
90p.	litho Cartor	bright blue	2 bands	Y1789	£7.93 Royal Navy Uniforms booklet (DX47)
97p.	gravure De La Rue	violet	2 bands	Y1742	sheets
97p.	litho Cartor	bluish violet	2 bands	Y1790	£9.05 WWF booklet (DX52)
£1	gravure Enschedé or Harrison	bluish violet	2 bands	Y1743	sheets, **MS**2743
£1	gravure De La Rue	magenta	2 bands	Y1744	sheets, £7.66 "The Machin" booklet (DX39), **MS**2743
£1	gravure De La Rue	bluish violet	phos paper	**MS**2146	Jeffery Matthews Colour Palette miniature sheet
£1.46	gravure De La Rue	greenish blue	2 bands	Y1745	sheets
£1.50	recess	red	—	Y1800	sheets (Enschedé then D.L.R.)
£1.50	gravure De La Rue	brown-red	2 bands	Y1746	sheets
£2	recess	dull blue	—	Y1801	sheets (Enschedé then D.L.R.)
£2	gravure De La Rue	deep blue-green	2 bands	Y1747	sheets

Value	Process	Colour	Phosphor	Cat. No.	Source
£3	recess	dull violet	—	Y1802	sheets (Enschedé then D.L.R.)
£3	gravure De La Rue	deep mauve	2 bands	Y1748	sheets, **MS**2658
£5	recess	brown	—	Y1803	sheets (Enschedé then D.L.R.)
£5	gravure De La Rue	azure	2 bands	Y1749	sheets

Note. Harrison and Sons became De La Rue Security Print on 8 September 1997.

Photo/gravure stamps were printed from both photogravure and computor engraved (gravure) cylinders.

Decimal Machin Booklet Pane Guide (ordinary gum) ("Y" numbers) the shaded squares represent printed labels.

1	1
20	26
26	26

Y1667l
(photo)

1	2
19	26
26	26

Y1667m

1	19	1
26		19
1	19	1

Y1667n
£6.99 World Changers

1	46	54
46		46
54	46	1

Y1667o
£7.66 British Army Uniforms

2	48	2
46		46
2	48	2

Y1668b
£7.66 Machin, Making of a Masterpiece

68	10	68
2		2
68	10	68

Y1668c
£11.47 Roald Dahl: Master Storyteller

43	10	2nd
43		2nd
43	10	2nd

Y1676al
£6.16 Breaking Barriers

19	26
26	26
26	26
26	26

Y1682l

19	19
19	19
38	38

Y1683l
£7.50 Special by Design

20	26
26	26
26	26
26	26

Y1685l
(photo)

20	26
20	26
20	26

Y1686l
£6.15 Celebrating 75 years of the BBC

25	25

Y1699l
(phosphorised)

25	25

Y1690l
(2 bands)

£1
£1

Y1744l
£7.66 Machin, Making of a Masterpiece

1	1
20	26
26	26

Y1760l
(litho)

17	1	17
90		90
17	1	17

Y1761l
£7.93 Royal Navy Uniforms

5	10	48
1st		1st
48	10	5

Y1762l
£7.75 Charles Darwin

Y1763l
£9.76 Britain Alone

Y1763m
£9.97 First United Kingdom
Aerial Post

Y1764l
£9.05 50th Anniv of WWF

Y1765l
£8.06 Classic Album Covers

Y1766l
£6.04 Northern Ireland

Y1767l
£6.00 The National Trust

Y1769l
£7.68 British Design Classics

Y1770l
£8.18 Treasures of the Archive

Y1771l
£6.00 The National Trust

Y1772l
(litho)

Y1773l
£8.06 Classic Album Covers

Y1774l
£7.72 350th Anniv of the Royal Society

Y1775l
£6.48 European Football Championship

SELF-ADHESIVE MACHIN INDEX

Value	Format	Process	Colour	Phosphor	Cat. No.	Source
2nd	horizontal	photo	bright blue	1 centre band	1976	coils
2nd	vertical	photo	bright blue	1 centre band	2039	rolls, sheets, booklets
1st	horizontal	litho	orange-red	2 bands	1789	booklets
1st	horizontal	photo	brt orge-red	2 bands	1977	coils
1st	vertical	photo	brt orge-red	2 bands	2040	coils, sheets, booklets
1st	vertical	photo	gold	2 bands	2295	booklets, sheets
E	vertical	photo	deep blue	2 bands	2296	booklets
42p.	vertical	photo	dp olive-grey	2 bands	2297	booklets
68p.	vertical	photo	grey-brown	2 bands	2298	booklets

N.V.I. stamps, self-adhesive gum, elliptical perforations

1116

(Des J. Matthews. Litho Walsall)

1993 (19 Oct). *Self-adhesive. Two phosphor bands.* Die-cut *Perf* 14×15 (with one elliptical hole on each vertical side).

1789	**1116**	(1st) orange-red	2·50	2·75
		Ey. Phosphor omitted	£260	
First Day Cover (No. 1789)				5·50
Presentation Pack (booklet of 20) (P.O. Pack No. 29)			28·00	
PHQ Card (D6)			4·00	8·00

No. 1789 was initially sold at 24p. which was increased to 25p. from November 1993.

It was only issued in booklets containing 20 stamps, each surrounded by die-cut perforations.

For similar 2nd and 1st designs printed in photogravure by Enschedé see Nos. 1976/7.

Special First Day of Issue Postmarks

British Philatelic Bureau, Edinburgh	5·00
Newcastle upon Tyne	5·00

1301   **1302**

(Des J. Matthews. Gravure Enschedé)

1997 (18 Mar). *Self-adhesive. One centre phosphor band (2nd) or two phosphor bands (1st).* Perf 14×15 die-cut (with one elliptical hole in each vertical side).

1976	**1301**	(2nd) bright blue	2·50	2·50
1977	**1302**	(1st) bright orange-red	2·75	2·75
Set of 2			5·00	5·00
First Day Cover				5·50
Presentation Pack (P.O. Pack No. 37)			5·00	

Nos. 1976/7, which were sold at 20p. and 26p., were in rolls of 100 with the stamps separate on the backing paper.

No. 1976 exists with the printed image in two sizes; the normal stamp is 21.25 mm×17.25 mm, while the scarcer second version is 21.75×17.75 mm.

Special First Day of Issue Postmarks

British Philatelic Bureau, Edinburgh	5·50
Glasgow	5·50

(Gravure Enschedé, Questa or Walsall)

1998 (6 Apr)–**2001**. *Self-adhesive. Designs as T 913/14. One centre phosphor band (2nd), or two phosphor bands (1st).* Perf 15×14 die-cut (with one elliptical hole in each vertical side).

2039		(2nd) bright blue	1·20	80
		a. Imperf (pair, 6mm. gap) (1998)	£275	
		ab. Imperf (pair, 4mm. gap) (2000)	£100	
		b. Perf 14½×14 die-cut (22.6.98)	£300	
2040		(1st) bright orange-red	1·50	1·50
		a. Imperf (pair, 6mm. gap) (1998)	£275	
		ab. Imperf (pair, 4mm. gap) (2000)	£100	
		b. Perf 14½×14 die-cut (22.6.98)	£300	
		Ey. Phosphor omitted	£125	

l. Booklet pane. No. 2040×6 plus commemorative label at left (29.1.01)	14·00

Nos. 2039/40, initially sold for 20p. and 26p., were in rolls of 200 printed by Enschedé with the surplus self-adhesive paper removed.

2nd and 1st self-adhesive stamps as Nos. 2039/40 were issued in sheets, printed in photogravure by Walsall Security Printers, on 22 June 1998. These are similar to the previous coil printings, but the sheets retain the surplus self-adhesive paper around each stamp. Stamps from these sheets have square perforation tips instead of the rounded versions to be found on the coils.

No. 2039 exists die-cut through the backing paper from Presentation Pack No. 71.

No. 2039 was issued in rolls of 10,000, printed by Enschedé on yellow backing paper with the surplus self-adhesive paper removed. A number appears on the back of every tenth stamp in the roll.

2039a/40a come from business sheets printed by Walsall and show a 6mm. space between the stamps. 2039ab/40ab come from business sheets printed by Walsall and Questa respectively and have a 4mm space between stamps. 4mm. pairs also exist from booklets, but are much scarcer from this source.

Nos. 2039b and 2040b come from initial stocks of these Walsall sheet printings sent to the Philatelic Bureau and supplied to collectors requiring single stamps.

They can be indentified by the pointed perforation tips in the corners of the stamp, as illustrated below.

Nos. 2039/40   Nos. 2039b/40b

A further printing in sheets appeared on 4 September 2000 printed by Walsall (2nd) or Questa (1st). These sheets were slightly re-designed to provide a block of 4, rather than a strip, in the top panel. Individual stamps cannot be identified as coming from these new sheets as they have rounded perforation tips similar to those on the original coil printings.

The sheets of 100 were re-issued on 9 May 2002 printed by Enschedé in the same format as used in September 2000. The individual stamps are similar to the Enschedé coil printings of April 1998. A further printing of No. 2039 in sheets of 100 appeared on 4 July 2002 printed by Enschedé. On this printing the top panel reverted to a strip of 4 with the typography on the label matching that of contemporary stamp booklets.

No. 2039 was issued on 18 March 2003 in stripped matrix sheets of 100, printed by Walsall.

The sheets of 100 were again issued but without the strapline "The Real Network" on 15 June 2004. The stamps in stripped matrix sheets of 100 had rounded perforations and were printed by Walsall.

Both values appeared in stamp booklets from 29 January 2001. No. 2040l comes from self-adhesive booklet No. MB2. The label commemorates the death centenary of Queen Victoria.

See also Nos. 2295/8.

"Millennium" Machins

1437 Queen Elizabeth II

(Des A. Machin, adapted R. Scholey. Gravure De La Rue, Questa or Walsall (No. 2124), Walsall (Nos. 2124bl, 2124dl), Questa or Walsall (No. 2124d))

2000 (6 Jan–Aug). *New Millennium. Two phosphor bands.* Perf 15×14 (with one elliptical hole in each vertical side).

2124	**1437**	(1st) olive-brown	1·50	1·00
		a. Imperf (pair)	£900	
		bl. Booklet pane. No. 2124×4 plus commemorative label at right (21.3.00)	6·00	
		bm. Booklet pane. No. 2124×9 with margins all round (4 Aug)	9·00	
		cEy. Phosphor omitted	£500	
		d. Perf 14	1·50	1·00
		dEa. Phosphor omitted	20·00	
		dl. Booklet pane. No. 2124d×8 with central label and margins all round (15.2.00)	8·00	
First Day Cover (No. 2124) (Philatelic Bureau) (Type G, see Introduction)				3·00
First Day Cover (No. 2124) (Windsor) (Type G)				3·00
First Day Cover (No. 2124bm) (Philatelic Bureau)				6·00
First Day Cover (No. 2124bm) (London SW1)				6·00

First Day Cover (No. 2124dl) (Philatelic Bureau)		6·00	
First Day Cover (No. 2124dl) (London SW5)		6·00	
Presentation Pack (P.O. Pack No. 48)	9·00		
PHQ Card (23 May) (D16)		5·00	16·00

No. 2124d comes from stamp booklets printed by Questa. Similar booklets produced by Walsall have the same perforation as the sheet stamps. The labels on booklet pane No. 2124bl show either Postman Pat, publicising "The Stamp Show 2000", or the National Botanic Garden of Wales.

Special First Day of Issue Postmarks (for use on No. 2124dl only)

1459

(Des J. Matthews. Gravure De La Rue)

2000 (22 May). *Stamp Show 2000 International Stamp Exhibition, London.* Jeffery Matthews Colour Palette. Sheet, 124×70 mm. Phosphorised paper. *Perf* 15×14 (with one elliptical hole in each vertical side).

MS2146 1459 4p. new blue; 5p. dull red-brown; 6p. yellow-olive; 10p. dull orange; 31p. deep mauve; 39p. bright magenta; 64p. turquoise-green; £1 bluish violet	30·00	30·00	
First Day Cover (Philatelic Bureau)		32·00	
First Day Cover (Earls Court, London SW5)		32·00	
Exhibition Card (wallet, sold at £4.99, containing one mint sheet and one cancelled on postcard)	60·00		

The £1 value is printed in Iriodin ink which gives a shiny effect to the solid part of the background behind the Queen's head.

Special First Day of Issue Postmarks

1459a

(Des Delaney Design Consultants. Gravure De La Rue)

2000 (23 May). *Stamp Show 2000 International Stamp Exhibition, London. Her Majesty's Stamps.* Sheet 121×89 mm. Phosphorised paper. *Perf* 15×14 (with one elliptical hole in each vertical side of stamps as T **1437**).

MS2147 1459a (1st) olive-brown (Type **1437**)×4; £1 slate-green (as Type **163**)	21·00	21·00	
First Day Cover (Philatelic Bureau)		22·00	
First Day Cover (City of Westminster, London SW1)		24·00	
Presentation Pack (P.O. Pack No. M03)	80·00		
PHQ Cards (set of 2) (PSM03)	16·00	34·00	

The £1 value is an adaptation of the 1953 Coronation 1s.3d. stamp originally designed by Edmund Dulac. It is shown on one of the PHQ cards with the other depicting the complete miniature sheet.

Special First Day of Issue Postmarks

N.V.I. and denominated stamps, self-adhesive gum, elliptical perforations

(Gravure Questa, Walsall, Enschedé or De La Rue (1st), Walsall (others))

2002 (5 June–4 July). *Self-adhesive.* Two phosphor bands. *Perf* 15×14 die-cut (with one elliptical hole in each vertical side).

2295	**914**	(1st) gold	1·50	1·00
		a. Imperf (pair)	£1100	
		Ey. Phosphor omitted	£225	
2296	**1093a**	(E) deep blue (4 July)	2·50	2·50
2297	**367a**	42p. deep olive-grey (4 July)	3·75	3·75
2298		68p. grey-brown (4 July)	4·25	4·25
Set of 4			11·00	10·50
PHQ Card (No. 2295) (Walsall) (D22) (27.3.03)			60	3·50

No. 2295, sold for 27p., was initially only available in booklets of 6 or 12, printed by Questa or Walsall, with the surplus self-adhesive paper around each stamp removed. Later booklets were also printed by De La Rue. Nos. 2296/8 were only issued in separate booklets, each containing six stamps with the surplus self-adhesive paper around each stamp removed.

No. 2295 exists die-cut through the backing paper from Presentation Pack No. 71

No. 2295 was issued in rolls of 10,000, printed by Enschedé on yellow backing paper with the surplus self-adhesive paper removed. A number appears on the back of every tenth stamp in the roll.

A further printing of No. 2295 in sheets of 100 appeared on 4 July 2002 produced by Enschedé and on 18 March 2003 in stripped matrix sheets of 100 printed by Walsall. The top panel shows a strip of four with the typography of the label matching that of booklet Type ME 2.

POSTAL FORGERIES. A postal forgery of No. 2295 exists, produced in booklets of 12 with a varnish band printed across the centre of the stamps to mimic phosphor bands. A similar forgery is known with the wavy 'perforations', gauge 10.

Overseas Booklet Stamps

1655

(Des Sedley Place. Gravure Walsall)

2003 (27 Mar)–**10**. *Overseas Booklet Stamps. Self-adhesive.* As T **1655** Two phosphor bands. *Perf* 15×14 die-cut with one elliptical hole in each vertical side.

2357a	(Worldwide postcard) grey-black, rosine and ultramarine (1.4.04)	1·75	1·75
2357b	(Europe up to 20 grams) deep blue-green, new blue and rosine (30.3.10)	3·00	3·00
2358	(Europe up to 40 grams) new blue and rosine	3·00	3·00
2358a	(Worldwide up to 20 grams) deep mauve, new blue and rosine (30.3.10) ...	3·00	3·00
2359	(Worldwide up to 40 grams) rosine and new blue	4·25	4·25
Set of 5		15·00	15·00

First Day Cover (Nos. 2358, 2359) (Tallents House)
(Type K, see Introduction)... 6·50
First Day Cover (Nos. 2358, 2359) (Windsor) (Type K) .... 6·50
Presentation Pack (Nos. 2358, 2359) (P.O. Pack No. 60)..... 8·00
PHQ Card (No. 2358) (D23)... 45 3·50

No. 2357*a* was intended to pay postcard rate to foreign destinations (43p.).

Nos. 2357b and 2358a were intended to pay postage on mail up to 20 grams to either Europe (initially 56p.) or to foreign destinations outside Europe (90p.).

They were only available in separate booklets of four (Nos. MI3 and MJ3) initially sold at £2.24 and £3.60, with the surplus self-adhesive paper around each stamp removed.

Nos. 2358/9 were intended to pay postage on mail up to 40 grams to either Europe (52p.) or to foreign destinations outside Europe (£1.12).

Operationally they were only available in separate booklets of 4 (Nos. MI1, MJ1 and MJA1), initially sold at £1.72, £2.08 and £4.48, with the surplus self-adhesive paper around each stamp removed.

No. 2357*a* was available from philatelic outlets as a single stamp or in P.O. Packs Nos. 67 and 71 together with other definitive stamps. These single stamps were die-cut through the white backing paper.

For listings of first day covers (together with definitives issued on the same day) and presentation packs for Nos. 2357*a/b* and 2358*a* see after No. Y1803.

Single examples of Nos. 2358/9 were available from philatelic outlets as sets of two or in P.O. Pack No 60. These stamps were die-cut through the backing paper on the back and showed parts of the booklet covers. Nos. 2358a and 2358/9 from packs 67 (2357a only), 71 and 77 were die-cut through on plain white paper, while 2357b and 2358a in pack 86 and all five values in pack 88 were guillotined to show an area of margin surrounding the stamps.

The purchase prices of NVI stamps are shown in the introduction to this catalogue.

"Pricing in Proportion"

1915 **1916**

(Des J. Matthews)

2006 (1st Aug)-**2007**. *Pricing in Proportion Perf* 15×14 (with one elliptical hole in each vertical side).

(a) Ordinary gum. Gravure De La Rue or Enschedé (No. 2651a).

(i) As T **1915**.

2650	(2nd) bright blue (1 centre band)......................	1·50	1·10
	a. Booklet pane. Nos. 2650/1, and Nos. 2652/3 each×2, with centre label and margins all round (5.6.07).............................	11·00	
2651	(1st) gold (2 bands)	1·75	1·20
	a. Booklet pane. Nos. 2651 and Y1726, each ×4, with centre label and margins all round (21.9.06)	14·00	

(ii) As T **1916**.

2652	(2nd Large) bright blue (2 bands)	1·50	1·00
2653	(1st Large) gold (2 bands)	2·00	1·00

(b) Self-adhesive. Gravure Walsall or Enschedé. (2654) or Walsall

(i) As T **1915**.

2654	(2nd) bright blue (one centre band) (12.9.06).	1·50	40
	a. Imperf (pair)...	£280	
2655	(1st) gold (2 bands) (12.9.06)	1·75	50
	Ey. Phosphor omitted...	£250	

(ii) As T **1916**.

2656	(2nd Large) bright blue (2 bands) (15.8.06)	2·50	1·00
2657	(1st Large) gold (2 bands) (15.8.06)	2·50	1·00

First Day Cover (Nos. Y1677/8, 2650/3) (Type K, see
Introduction).. 5·00
First Day Cover (Nos. Y1677/8, 2650/3) (Windsor)
(Type K).. 6·00
First Day Cover (Victoria Cross label pane 1st×4,
50p.×4 (No. 2651a) (Tallents House or Cuffley, Potters
Bar, Herts).. 8·50
Presentation Pack (Nos. Y1677/8, 2650/3) (P.O. Pack
No. 74)... 8·00

No. 2650 was issued in sheets (1 August) and coils of 500 (15 August).

Nos. 2654/5 were available in separate booklets of six (No. RC1, sold at £1.92) or twelve (Nos. RD1 and RE1, sold at £2.76 or £3.84 respectively) and in business sheets of 100.

Nos. 2656/7 were initially only available in separate booklets of four (Nos. RA1 and RB1, sold at £1.48 and £1.76.

All these booklets had the surplus self-adhesive paper around each stamp removed.

Nos. 2656/7 were issued in sheets of 50, printed by Walsall, on 27 March 2007.

No. 2654 was issued in rolls of 10,000, printed by Enschedé on yellow backing paper with the surplus self-adhesive paper removed. A number appears on the back of every tenth stamp in the roll.

A postal forgery similar to No. 2651 exists with wavy 'perforations' (gauge 10).

For PHQ cards for Nos. 2652/3 see below No. Y1803.

Security Machins

Please note that the "U" numbers in this section are temporary and subject to change.

On 17 February 2009 a new form of Machin definitive appeared, incorporating additional security features to combat the re-use of uncancelled stamps.

The stamps no longer included a water-soluble layer of gum between the paper and the self-adhesive to prevent them being 'soaked off' envelope paper; in addition, four U-shaped slits were die-cut into the stamps to prevent them being peeled off paper and, to make forgery more difficult, an overall iridescent multiple 'ROYAL MAIL' overprint was incorporated into the design.

In May 2010 2nd and 1st class stamps were issued in rolls with iridescent overprint but printed on paper with ordinary gum and without U-shaped slits. These are listed as U3001/2. Other values in this form subsequently appeared in prestige booklets.

USED STAMPS: Because the self-adhesive stamps in this section do not include a water-soluble layer of gum, we recommend that used stamps are retained on their backing paper and trimmed with a uniform border of 1-2 mm around all sides, taking care not to cut into the perforations.

Source Codes: In March 2009 stamps were issued with "codes" incorporated into the iridescent overprint which allowed the source to be identified. The codes may be seen in the words "ROYAL MAIL", usually at the top right of the stamp, although some later Large Letter issues have it at the bottom right (marked "BR" in the list below).

The codes are:

2nd and 1st
MAIL   (i.e. no code letter) – counter sheets
MBIL – Business sheets
MCIL – "Custom" booklets, which include special stamps
MMIL – Miniature sheet (**MS**3222) (not listed as individual stamps)
MPIL – "Prestige" booklet Panes
MRIL – Rolls
MSIL – standard booklets of Six
MTIL – booklets of Twelve

2nd and 1st Large
ROYAL MAIL   (i.e. no code letter) – counter sheets
YBLM – Business sheets (2009)
MBI – Business sheets (2010-13)
BIL – Business sheets (2011-13) (BR)
FOYAL – booklets of Four (2009)
MFI – booklets of Four (2010)
FIL – booklets of Four (2011-13) (BR)

For the Diamond Jubilee definitive with source codes, which are behind The Queen's head, the end of "DIAMOND" is adjusted to:
MBND – Business sheets
MCND – "Custom" booklets of six
MMND – Miniature sheet (**MS**3287) (not listed as individual stamp)
MPND – "Prestige" booklet pane
MSND – standard booklet of Six
MTND – booklets of Twelve

And for Large Letter stamps with source codes the end of "JUBILEE" is adjusted to :
LBE – Business sheets
LFE – booklets of Four

For the Long to Reign Over us definitive with source codes, which are behind The Queen's neck, the end of "REIGN" is adjusted to:
GC – "Custom" booklets of six
GM – Miniature sheet (**MS**3747) (not listed as individual stamp)
GP – "Prestige" booklet pane
GS – standard booklet of Six

Date Codes: From 2010 a year code was added to the iridescent overprint. Generally it appears in the upper left corner of the stamp, in front of the crown or The Queen's forehead or eye, but on later Large Letter stamps it appears lower down, above the "ge" of "Large". Stamps are listed without or with date codes, and the different dates known are given in checklists at the end of this section. Note that year dates given within the listings are years of issue, not date codes.

Note that, where stamps exist with more that one date code, the issue date given is for the first release, but prices are for the cheapest date.

U-Shaped slits: The first issue featured U-shaped die-cut slits without a break in the middle of each "U", but subsequent issues have incorporated a break to prevent the stamps tearing while being removed from the backing paper on which they were issued. We no longer list these as separate varieties but details are provided in the checklists at the end of this section.

A 1st gold stamp with U-slits but without iridescent overprint was supplied only to bulk mailing houses.

Details of known source and date-code combinations are now provided in the series of tables following the listings. For the convenience of collectors, the printer of each combination is also given. We are grateful to John M. Deering for compiling these tables

2009 (17 Feb)–**2016** Self-adhesive. Designs as T **367**. Two phosphor bands. U-shaped slits. Iridescent overprint. Die-cut perf 14½×14 (with one elliptical hole in each vertical side).

(a) No source code, no date code, gravure De La Rue

U2911	50p. grey	2·00	2·00
U2912	£1 magenta	3·50	3·50
U2913	£1.50 brown-red	3·25	3·25
U2914	£2 deep blue-green	5·00	5·00
U2915	£3 deep mauve	6·25	6·25
U2916	£5 azure	10·50	10·50

(b) With source and date codes, gravure Walsall

U2917	50p. grey "MPIL" (8.5.10)	3·00	3·00
	a. Booklet pane Nos. U2917×2, U2962×2 and U2966×4, with central label and margins all round	16·00	

(c) No source code, with date code, gravure Walsall or De La Rue (78p., 88p., £1.88) or De La Rue (others).

U2920	1p. deep crimson (3.1.13)	50	50
U2921	2p. deep green (3.1.13)	60	60
U2922	5p. dull red-brown (3.1.13)	60	60
U2923	10p. dull orange (3.1.13)	70	70
U2924	20p. bright green (3.1.13)	80	80
U2925	50p. slate (3.1.13)	2·00	2·00
U2926	68p. deep turquoise-green (29.3.11)	2·60	2·60
U2927	76p. bright rose (29.3.11)	2·70	2·70
U2928	78p. deep mauve (27.3.13)	2·40	2·40
U2928a	81p. emerald (26.3.14)	2·40	2·40
U2929	87p. yellow-orange (25.4.12)	3·75	3·75
U2930	88p. orange-yellow (27.3.13)	3·00	3·00
U2930a	97p. bluish violet (26.3.14)	3·25	3·25
U2931	£1 magenta (10.10.11)	6·75	6·75
U2932	£1 bistre-brown (3.1.13)	3·25	3·25
U2932a	£1.05 grey-olive (22.3.16)	2·25	2·25
U2933	£1.10 yellow-olive (29.3.11)	3·75	3·75
U2934	£1.28 emerald (25.4.12)	5·50	5·50
U2934a	£1.33 orange-yellow (24.3.15)	3·25	3·25
U2934b	£1.47 lavender-grey (26.3.14)	3·75	3·75
U2934c	£1.52 bright mauve (24.3.15)	3·75	3·75
U2935	£1.65 grey-olive (29.3.11)	4·75	4·75
U2936	£1.88 dull ultramarine (27.3.13)	5·25	5·25
U2937	£1.90 bright mauve (29.4.12)	4·75	4·75
U2938	£2 deep blue-green (4.13)	9·00	9·00
U2939	£2.15 greenish blue (26.3.14)	4·75	4·75
U2940	£2.25 deep violet (24.3.15)	5·50	5·50
U2940a	£2.45 emerald (24.3.15)	6·00	6·00
U2940b	£3.15 turquoise-blue (24.3.15)	7·50	7·50
U2940c	£3.30 bright magenta (24.3.15)	8·00	8·00
U2920/40c Set of 30		£100	£100

No. U2917 was first issued in £11.15 booklets, No. DX50 with "MA10" date code. It was issued again in £9.99 premium booklets, No. DY1, with "M11L" date code.

2009 (17 Feb)–**2013**. Self-adhesive. Designs as T **913/14** or T **1916**. One centre band (U2941, U2945/7, U2957 and U2961/3) two bands (others). U-shaped slits. Iridescent overprint. Die-cut perf 14½×14 (with one elliptical hole in each vertical side).

(a) No source code, no date code, gravure De La Rue

U2941	(2nd) bright blue	3·50	3·50
U2942	(1st) gold	3·50	3·50
U2943	(2nd Large) bright blue	3·75	3·75
U2944	(1st Large) gold	3·50	3·50

(b) With source code, without date code, gravure De La Rue ("B" and "R" codes) or Walsall (others)

U2945	(2nd) bright blue ("MBIL") (31.3.09)	3·75	3·75
U2946	(2nd) bright blue ("MRIL") (7.09)	4·50	4·50
U2947	(2nd) bright blue ("MTIL") (31.3.09)	2·25	2·25
U2948	(1st) gold ("MBIL") (31.3.09)	3·75	3·75
U2949	(1st) gold ("MCIL") (10.3.09)	2·25	2·25
U2950	(1st) gold ("MRIL") (7.09)	4·75	4·75
U2951	(1st) gold ("MSIL") (31.3.09)	4·00	4·00
U2952	(1st) gold ("MTIL") (31.3.09)	2·50	2·50

U2953	(2nd Large) bright blue ("YBLM") (31.3.09).....	3·50	3·50
U2954	(2nd Large) bright blue ("FOYAL") (31.3.09).....	3·00	3·00
U2955	(1st Large) gold ("YBLM") (31.3.09)................	3·50	3·50
U2956	(1st Large) gold ("FOYAL") (31.3.09)...............	3·75	3·75

(c) No source code, with date code, gravure De La Rue

U2957	(2nd) bright blue (1.7.10).............................	2·40	2·40
U2958	(1st) gold (20.5.10)...................................	3·25	3·25
U2958a	(1st) vermilion (3.1.13)...............................	2·00	2·00
U2959	(2nd Large) bright blue (26.1.11)...................	2·75	2·75
U2960	(1st Large) gold (3.11.10)............................	3·25	3·25
U2960a	(1st Large) vermilion (3.1.13)........................	2·75	2·75

(d) With source code and date, gravure De La Rue or Walsall (U2961 and U2969), De La Rue or Enschedé (U2966a) De La Rue, Enschedé or Walsall (U2962a), Enschedé or Walsall (U2968c), De La Rue (U2964, and 2971) or Walsall (others)

U2961	(2nd) bright blue ("MBIL") (3.10)	2·40	2·40
U2962	(2nd) bright blue ("MPIL") (8.5.10).................	3·25	3·25
U2962a	(2nd) bright blue ("MRIL")(6.12)	4·25	4·25
U2963	(2nd) bright blue ("MTIL") (2.10)	2·25	2·25
U2964	(1st) gold ("MBIL") (6.10)	4·00	4·00
U2965	(1st) gold ("MCIL") (25.2.10)........................	2·25	2·25
U2966	(1st) gold ("MPIL") (8.5.10)..........................	2·25	2·25
U2966a	(1st) gold ("MRIL") (15.7.11)	4·75	4·75
U2967	(1st) gold ("MSIL") (26.1.10)........................	2·75	2·75
U2968	(1st) gold ("MTIL") (2.10)	3·00	3·00
U2968a	(1st) vermilion ("MBIL") (3.1.13)	2·60	2·60
U2968b	(1st) vermilion ("MCIL") (9.1.13)	2·10	2·10
U2968c	(1st) vermilion ("MRIL") (3.1.13)	2·25	2·25
U2968d	(1st) vermilion ("MSIL") (3.1.13)	2·40	2·40
U2968e	(1st) vermilion ("MTIL") (3.1.13)	2·40	2·40
U2969	(2nd Large) bright blue ("MBI"/"BIL") (3.11)..	2·75	2·75
U2970	(2nd Large) bright blue ("MFI"/"FIL") (8.5.10)	2·40	2·40
U2971	(1st Large) gold ("MBI"/"BIL") (6.10)	4·50	4·50
U2972	(1st Large) gold ("MFI"/"FIL") (8.5.10)...........	3·25	3·25
U2973	(1st Large) vermilion ("BIL") (3.1.13).............	3·75	3·75
U2974	(1st Large) vermilion ("FIL") (3.1.13).............	3·00	3·00

During early 2016 supplies to post offices of U2961, U2963, U2968a, U2968e and U2974 started to appear with repeating ROYAL MAIL wording printed on the front of the self-adhesive backing paper. With an M15L date code, U2961, U2963, U2968a and U2968e exist both with the front of the self-adhesive backing paper unprinted, and also with the addition of the repeating ROYAL MAIL wording. M16L versions are only with the repeating ROYAL MAIL wording. U2974 with MA15 exists without and with the repeating wording.

2132a	2132b

2132c	2132d

(Gravure De La Rue)

2009 (17 Nov)–**13**. Self-adhesive. Designs as *T* 2132a/d. Two phosphor bands. U-shaped slits. Iridescent overprint. Die-cut perf 14 (U2982, U2982/a) or 14½×14 (others) (all with one elliptical hole in each vertical side).

(a) Without date code

U2981	(Recorded Signed for 1st) bright orange-red and lemon	6·50	6·50
U2982	(Recorded Signed for 1st Large) bright orange-red and lemon.........................	8·00	8·00

(b) With date code

U2983	(Recorded Signed for 1st) bright orange-red and lemon (11.4.11)	14·00	14·00
U2983a	(Royal Mail Signed for 1st) bright orange-red and lemon (27.3.13)	5·00	5·00
U2984	(Recorded Signed for 1st Large) bright orange-red and lemon (11.4.11)	16·00	16·00
U2984a	(Royal Mail Signed for 1st Large) bright orange-red and lemon (27.3.13)	5·75	5·75
U2985	(Special delivery up to 100g) blue and silver (26.10.10)............................	13·50	13·50
U2986	(Special delivery up to 500g) blue and silver (26.10.10)............................	14·50	14·50

Nos. U2981/2 have neither source nor date codes. U2983/6 have no source code but have date codes ("MA13" U2983a, U2984a) or "MA10" (others). All have breaks in the U-shaped slits.

No. U2981 originally sold for £1.14, U2982 for £1.36, U2985 for £5.05 and U2986 for £5.50. No. U2983a was originally sold for £1.55 (£1.70 from 2 April 2013) and U2984a was originally sold for £1.85 (£2 from 2 April 2013).

(Gravure De La Rue or Walsall (U2993/4) or De La Rue (others))

2011 (8 Mar–5 May). Self-adhesive. Designs as *T* 367. Two phosphor bands. U-shaped slits. No iridescent overprint. Die-cut perf 14½×14 (with one elliptical hole in each vertical side).

U2991	1p. crimson...................................	70	70
U2992	2p. deep green..............................	50	50
U2993	5p. dull red-brown..........................	50	50
	a. Booklet pane. Nos. U2993 ×4, U2994 ×2 and U2917 ×2 with central label and margins all round (5.5.11)	8·50	
U2994	10p. dull orange..............................	65	65
U2995	20p. bright green.............................	90	90
U2991/5	Set of 5.......................................	2·95	2·95

2010 (13 May)–**15**. Designs as *T* 367 and *T* 913/14. Ordinary gum. Without U-shaped slits. Iridescent overprint. One centre phosphor band (2nd) or two bands (others). P14½×14 (with one elliptical hole in each vertical side).

(a) With source code and date, gravure Walsall (68p.) or De La Rue (others)

U3001	(2nd) bright blue ("MRIL")............................	3·25	3·25
U3002	(1st) gold ("MRIL").....................................	3·50	3·50
U3005	68p. turquoise-green (10.1.12) ("MPIL")	4·00	4·00

(b) With source code and date code, litho, Enschedé (U3012d, and U3017), Cartor/ISP Cartor or Enschedé (U3011/14, and U3021) or Cartor/ISP Cartor (others)

U3010	1p. crimson ("MPIL") (9.5.13)........................	1·20	1·20
	a. Booklet pane. Nos. U3010×2, U3016×2, EN51, NI95, S158 and W148 with central label and margins all round (9.5.13)	12·00	
	b. Booklet pane Nos. U3010×3, U3019a and U3020a×2 with central label and margins all round (19.2.15)....	14·00	
	c. Booklet pane. Nos. U3010, U3012c, U3022 and 2883, each ×2 with central label and margins all round (14.5.15)..	13·00	
U3011	2p. deep green ("MPIL") (9.5.13)....................	1·40	1·40
	a. Booklet pane. Nos. U3011/13, each ×2 (9.5.13)	8·50	
	b. Booklet pane. Nos. U3011/12, each ×2, and Nos. EN51, NI95, S158 and W148 with central label and margins all round (20.2.14)	11·00	
U3012	5p. red-brown ("MPIL") (26.3.13)...................	1·50	1·50
	a. Booklet pane. Nos. U3012/14, U3020 and 3452x4 with central label and margins all round (26.3.13)	12·00	
	b. Booklet pane. Nos. U3012/3, U3017a and U3021 each ×2 with central label and margins all round (18.6.15)	17·00	
	c. *Deep red-brown* ("MPIL") (14.5.15).............	2·00	2·00
U3012d	5p red-brown ("MPIL") Ellipses toward top of stamp (19.9.13)................................	1·75	1·75
	da. Booklet pane. Nos. U3012d and U3017, each ×4, with central label and margins all round (19.9.13)	10·00	
U3013	10p. dull orange ("MPIL") (26.3.13)	1·50	1·50
	a. Booklet pane. Nos. U3013×2, U3014×4 and U3021×2 with central label and margins all round (15.4.14)..................	14·00	
	b. Booklet pane. Nos. U3013×2, U3014×2, EN30, NI95, S131 and W122×1 with central label and margins all round (28.7.14)..	9·50	
U3014	20p. bright green ("MPIL") (26.3.13)	1·60	1·60
U3014a	(2nd) bright blue ("MPIL") (17.12.15)..............	2·75	2·75
	ab. Booklet pane. Nos. U3014a, and U3016, each ×2 and 3786 ×4 with central label and margins all round (17.12.15)	11·00	
U3015	(1st) gold (9.9.11) ("MPIL").........................	5·00	5·00
U3016	(1st) vermilion ("MPIL") (9.5.13)...................	2·40	2·40
U3017	50p. slate-blue ("MPIL") Ellipses toward top of stamp (19.9.13)	3·00	3·00
U3017a	50p. slate-blue ("MPIL") (18.6.15)...................	2·75	2·75
U3019	76p. bright rose (9.9.11) ("MPIL")...................	5·50	5·50
U3019a	81p. deep turquoise-green ("MPIL") (19.2.15)....	8·00	8·00
U3020	87p. yellow-orange ("MPIL") (26.3.13)	6·00	6·00
U3020a	97p. bluish violet ("MPIL") (19.2.15)................	3·75	3·75
U3021	£1 sepia ("MPIL") (15.4.14)	3·25	3·25
	a. Booklet pane. No. U3021 with margins all round (28.7.14)	4·50	
U3022	£1.33 orange-yellow (14.5.15)	4·00	4·00

Nos. U3001/2 were issued in separate coils of 500 or 1000.

Nos. U3010/22 were all issued in premium booklets. For source see Security Machin Source and Date Code tables at the end of this section.

No. U3012c comes from No. DY13 and has date code M15L.

No. U3012d and U3017 have the elliptical holes toward the top of the stamp and come from No. DY8.

No. U3014 comes from Nos. DY6, DY10 and DY11.

Nos. U3015 and U3019 were from £9.97 Aerial Post booklets, No. DY2.

No. U3016 comes from No. DY7 and DY15.
No. U3017a comes from No. DY14.
No. U3019a and U3020a come from DY12.
No. U3020 comes from DY6.
No. U3021 comes from DY10 and DY11.
No. U3022 comes from DY13

First Day Covers

17.2.09	Nos. U2911/12 and U2941/4 (Type K, see introduction)..	14·00
	Nos. U2911/12 and U2941/4 (Windsor, Type K)...............	14·00
	Nos. U2913/16 (Type K)..	30·00
	Nos. U2913/16 (Windsor).....................................	30·00
17.11.09	Nos. U2981/2 (Type K)...	6·75
	Nos. U2981/2 (Windsor)......................................	6·75
8.5.10	King George V Accession Cent, *se-tenant* pane 2nd, 1st, 50p (No. U2917a)(Tallents House or London NI)...	10·00
26.10.10	Nos. U2985/6 (Type K)...	25·00
	Nos. U2985/6 (Windsor)......................................	25·00
8.3.11	Nos. U2991/5 (Type K)...	2·50
	Nos. U2991/5 (Windsor)......................................	2·50
29.3.11	Nos. U2926/7, U2933, U2935 (Type K)................	10·50
	Nos. U2926/7, U2933, U2935 (Windsor).............	10·50
5.5.11	Morris & Co, *se-tenant* pane 1p., 10p., 50p. (U2993a) (Tallents House or Walthamstow)........................	5·00
25.4.12	Nos. U2929, U2934, U2937 and U3276 (Type K).......	14·00
	Nos. U2929, U2934, U2937 and U3276 (Windsor).....	14·00
3.1.13	Nos. 2920/5, U2932, U2958a and U2960a (Type K)......	10·00
	Nos. 2920/5, U2932, U2958a and U2960a (Windsor)...	10·00
26.3.13	Dr. Who *se-tenant* pane 5p, 10p, 20p, 1st, 87p (U3012a) (Tallents House or Cardiff)..................	11·00
27.3.13	Nos. U2928, U2930, U2936, U2983a and U2984a (Type K)	16·00
	Nos. U2928, U2930, U2936, U2983a and U2984a (Windsor)..	16·00
9.5.13	Football Heroes *se-tenant* pane 1st (U3010a) (Tallents House or Wembley, Middlesex)..........	11·50
19.9.13	Merchant Navy *se-tenant* pane 5p., 50p. (U3012ba) (Tallents House or Clydebank).......................	9·00
20.2.14	Classic Locomotives *se-tenant* pane 2p., 5p., 1st (U3011b) (Tallents House or Newcastle upon Tyne)	9·00
26.3.14	Nos. U2928a, U2930a, U2934b and U2939 (Type K)	17·00
	Nos. U2928a, U2930a, U2934a and U2939 (Windsor).	17·00
15.4.14	Buckingham Palace *se-tenant* pane 10p., 20p., £1 (U3013a) (Tallents House or London SW1).........	16·00
28.7.14	First World War Centenary *se-tenant* pane 10p., 20p., 1st (U3013b) (Tallents House or Newcastle upon Tyne)	11·50
19.2.15	Inventive Britain *se-tenant* pane 1p., 2p., 81p., 97p. (U3010b) (Tallents House or Harlow).................	16·00
24.3.15	Nos. U2934a, U2934c and U2940/c (Type K)........	40·00
	Nos. U2934a, U2934c and U2940/c (Windsor)......	40·00
4.5.15	First World War Centenary (2nd issue) *se-tenant* pane 1p, 5p, £1.33 (U3010c) (Tallents House or Winchester)	15·00
18.6.15	Battle of Waterloo Bicentenary *se-tenant* pane 5p, 10p, £1 (U3012c) (Tallents House or Elstree, Borehamwood)..	19·00
17.12.15	Star Wars *se-tenant* pane 2nd (U3014a) (Tallents House or Elstree, Borehamwood)....................	13·00
22.3.16	No. U2932a (Type K)	3·00
	No. U2932a (Windsor)...	3·00

Presentation Packs

Nos. U2911/2 and U2941/4 (P.O. Pack No. 82)...............	10·00
Nos. U2913/6 (P.O. Pack No. 83)....................................	30·00
Nos. U2926/7, U2933, U2935 and U2991/5 (P.O. Pack No. 90)...	17·00
Nos. U2985/6 (P.O. Pack No. 89)....................................	25·00
Nos. U2929, U2934, U2937, U3271 and U3276 (P.O. Pack No. 94)...	13·50
Nos. U2920/5, U2932, U2958a and U2960a (P.O. Pack No. 96).	9·00
Nos. U2928, U2930, U2936, U2983a and U2984a (P.O. Pack No. 97)...	18·00
Nos. U2928a, U2930a, U2934b and U2939 (P.O. Pack No. 99)...	14·00
Nos. U2934a, U2934c and U2940/c (P. O. Pack No. 101)	35·00
No. U2932a (P.O. Pack No. 103).....................................	3·00

For presentation pack containing Nos. U2981/2 see after No. Y1803.

London 2010 Exhibition Miniature Sheet

2268 (Illustration reduced. Actual size 104×95 mm)

(Litho Cartor)

2010 (8 May). *London 2010 Festival of Stamps.* Jeffery Matthews Colour Palette. Sheet 104×95 mm containing stamps as *T* **367** with a label. Two phosphor bands. *Perf* 15×14 (with one elliptical hole in each vertical side).

MS3073	**2268**	1p. reddish purple; 2p. deep grey-green; 5p. reddish-brown; 9p. bright orange; 10p. orange; 20p. light green; 60p. emerald; 67p. bright mauve; 88p. bright magenta; 97p. bluish violet; £1.46 turquoise-blue..	30·00	30·00
	First Day Cover			32·00

> Please refer to the table following these listings for details of known source and date-code combinations and their printers

2408 (Illustration reduced. Actual size 124×71 mm)

(Gravure Walsall)

2011 (14 Sept). *Birth Centenary of Arnold Machin.* Sheet 124×71 mm containing stamps as No. U3002×10 but with source code "MMIL" and year code "AM11". Two phosphor bands. *Perf* 14½×14 (with one elliptical hole in each vertical side).

MS3222	**2408**	(1st) gold×10..................................	15·00	15·00
	First Day Cover (Stoke on Trent)			16·00
	First Day Cover (Piccadilly, London W1)			16·00

(Photo De La Rue (U3271, U3276), Walsall (U3272, U3274/5, U3277/8) or
De La Rue and Walsall (U3273))

2012 (6 Feb–1 Oct). *Diamond Jubilee.* (1st issue). Self-adhesive. Two
phosphor bands. U-shaped slits. Iridescent overprint reading 'DI-
AMOND JUBILEE' *Perf* 14½×14 (with one elliptical hole in each
vertical side).

*(a) As T **914**. (i) No source code*

U3271	(1st) slate-blue....................		2·00	1·20

(ii) With source code

U3272	(1st) slate-blue ("MTND")		2·00	2·00
U3273	(1st) slate-blue ("MBND").......................		2·00	2·00
U3274	(1st) slate-blue ("MCND") (31.5.12)		2·25	2·25
U3275	(1st) slate-blue ("MSND") (1.10.12)		2·00	2·00

*(b) As T **1916**. (i) No source code*

U3276	(1st Large) slate-blue (25.4.12)		2·50	2·50

(ii) With source code

U3277	(1st Large) slate-blue ("LFE") (25.4.12).......		3·00	3·00
U3278	(1st Large) slate-blue ("LBE") (25.4.12)		2·50	2·50

Nos. U3271 and U3276 are from counter sheets.
No. U3272 is from booklets of 12, No. MF6.
Nos. U3273 and U3278 are from business sheets.
No. U3274 is from booklet PM33 and PM34.
No. U3275 is from booklets of 6, No. MB11.
No. U3277 is from booklets of 4, No. RB3.
For first day cover for No. U3276 and presentation pack for Nos.
U3271 and U3276 see under U3020.
For 1st slate-blue with "MPND" source code on ordinary gummed
paper from booklet pane in Diamond Jubilee booklet No. DY4 see No.
3328.

(Gravure De La Rue (U3744) or ISP Walsall (U3745/6))

2015 (9–18 Sept). *Long to Reign Over Us* (1st issue). As T **914**. Self-adhesive. Two phosphor bands. U-shaped slits. Iridescent overprint
reading 'LONG TO REIGN OVER US'. Die-cut perf 14½×14 (with one
elliptical hole in each vertical side).

(a) No source code. With date code '015R'.

U3744	(1st) bright lilac		1·80	1·10

(b) With source code and date code '015R'.

U3745	(1st) bright lilac (REIGS)		2·00	2·00
U3746	(1st) bright lilac (REIGC) (18.9.15)...........		2·00	2·00

No. U3744 comes from counter sheets printed by De La Rue and
exists with both O15R and O16R date codes.
No. U3745 comes from booklets of six, No. MB13, printed by ISP
Walsall. Initial printings had a O15R date code and the front of the
self-adhesive backing paper was unprinted. Later printings have
repeating ROYAL MAIL wording printed on the front of the self-
adhesive backing paper and exist with O15R and O16R date codes.
No. U3746 comes from booklet No. PM49, printed by ISP Walsall,
and has a O15R date code.

Decimal Machin Booklet pane Guide ("U" numbers)

1st	10	1st
5		20
1st	87	1st

3012a
£13.77 Doctor Who

1st	1st	1st
1st		1st
1st	1st	1st

3328a
£12.77 Diamond Jubilee

1st	2nd	1st
50		50
1st	2nd	1st

U2917a
£11.15 Accession of King George V

5	10	5
50		50
5	10	5

U2993a
£9.99 Morris and Company

1	1st	1
1st E		1st
1st S	1st W	1st NI

U3010a
£11.11 Football Heroes

2	87	2
1		1
97	2	97

U3010b
£14.60 Inventive Britain

5	£1.33	5
1st		1st
5	£1.33	5

U3010c
Centenary of the First World War
(Second Issue)

5	10
10	2
2	5

U3011a
£11.11 Football Heroes

1st E	5	1st S
2		2
1st NI	5	1st W

U3011b
£13.97 Classic Locomotives

5	50	10
£1		£1
10	50	5

U3012b
Bicentenary of the Battle of Waterloo

5	50	5
50		50
5	50	5

U3012da
£11.19 Merchant Navy

20	£1	20
10		10
20	£1	20

U3013a
£11.39 Buckingham Palace

	£1	

U3021a
£11.30 Centenary of the
First World War (First Issue)

1st	2nd	1st
1st		1st
1st	2nd	1st

U3014ab
The Making of Star Wars

20	1st E	10
1st W		1st S
10	1st NI	20

U3013b
£11.30 Centenary of the
First World War (1st Issue)

SG No.	DESCRIPTION	
U2939	£2.15 DLR 'MAIL' (no source code) 'M14L'	4·75
U2940	£2.25 DLR 'MAIL' (no source code) 'M15L'	5·50
U2940a	£2.45 DLR 'MAIL' (no source code) 'M15L'	6·00
U2940b	£3.15 DLR 'MAIL' (no source code) 'M15L'	7·50
U2940c	£3.30 DLR 'MAIL' (no source code) 'M15L'	8·00

The following series of tables gives details of all source and date-code combinations reported at the time of going to press. Each is related to its printer and variations in the U-shaped slits are also noted. These tables are copyright John M Deering and are reproduced with his permission.

2nd (bright blue) and 1st (as noted) self-adhesive Security Machins, no source code (as from counter sheets), with date code (c).
(All have the date code to the left of the front of The Queen's forehead or crown (or for the 'Large' issues from MA11 onwards it is above the 'ge' of 'Large'). The 'U'-shaped slits are broken.).

SG No.	DESCRIPTION	
U2957	2nd DLR 'MAIL' (no source code) 'MA10'	3·75
	2nd DLR 'MAIL' (no source code) 'M11L'	3·50
	2nd DLR 'MAIL' (no source code) 'M12L'	2·60
	2nd DLR 'MAIL' (no source code) 'MA13'	2·60
	2nd DLR 'MAIL' (no source code) 'M14L'	2·60
	2nd DLR 'MAIL' (no source code) 'M15L'	2·40
	2nd DLR 'MAIL' (no source code) 'M16L'	2·40
U2958	1st gold DLR 'MAIL' (no source code) 'MA10'	3·75
	1st gold DLR 'MAIL' (no source code) 'M11L'	3·25
U2958a	1st vermilion DLR 'MAIL' (no source code) 'M12L'	2·00
	1st vermilion DLR 'MAIL' (no source code) 'MA13'	2·60
	1st vermilion DLR 'MAIL' (no source code) 'M14L'	2·60
	1st vermilion DLR 'MAIL' (no source code) 'M15L'	2·40
U2959	2nd Large DLR 'ROYAL' (no source code) 'MA10'	6·00
	2nd Large DLR 'ROYAL' (no source code) 'MA11'	3·00
	2nd Large DLR 'ROYAL' (no source code) 'MA12'	3·00
	2nd Large DLR 'ROYAL' (no source code) 'MA13'	3·00
	2nd Large DLR 'ROYAL' (no source code) 'M14L'	2·75
	2nd Large DLR 'ROYAL' (no source code) 'M15L'	2·75
	2nd Large DLR 'ROYAL' (no source code) 'M16L'	2·75
U2960	1st Large, gold, DLR 'ROYAL' (no source code) 'MA10'	5·25
	1st Large, gold, DLR 'ROYAL' (no source code) 'MA11'	3·25
U2960a	1st Large, vermilion, DLR 'ROYAL' (no source code) 'MA12'	3·00
	1st Large, vermilion, DLR 'ROYAL' (no source code) 'MA13'	3·00
	1st Large, vermilion, DLR 'ROYAL' (no source code) 'M14L'	3·00
	1st Large, vermilion, DLR 'ROYAL' (no source code) 'M15L'	2·75
	1st Large, vermilion, DLR 'ROYAL' (no source code) 'M16L'	2·75

Denominated self-adhesive Security Machins, with source and date code (b).
(The source code is at top right, and the date code is to the left of the front of The Queen's forehead, and the 'U'-shaped slits are broken.)

SG No.	DESCRIPTION	
U2917	50p grey Walsall 'MPIL' ('U-shaped slits with break at bottom only) 'MA10' (from DX50)	3·00
	50p grey Walsall 'MPIL' ('U-shaped slits with break at top & bottom) 'MA10' (from DX50)	7·75
	50p grey Walsall 'MPIL' 'M11L' (from DY1 premium booklet)	4·75

Denominated self-adhesive Security Machins, no source code (as from counter sheets), with date code (c).
(All have the date code to the left of the front of The Queen's crown. The 'U'-shaped slits are broken.)

SG No.	DESCRIPTION	
U2920	1p DLR 'MAIL' (no source code) 'M12L'	0·50
	1p DLR 'MAIL' (no source code) 'M15L'	0·50
U2921	2p DLR 'MAIL' (no source code) 'M12L'	0·60
	2p DLR 'MAIL' (no source code) 'M14L'	0·60
	2p DLR 'MAIL' (no source code) 'M15L'	0·60
	2p DLR 'MAIL' (no source code) 'M16L'	0·60
U2922	5p DLR 'MAIL' (no source code) 'M12L'	0·60
	5p DLR 'MAIL' (no source code) 'M14L'	0·60
	5p DLR 'MAIL' (no source code) 'M15L'	0·60
U2923	10p DLR 'MAIL' (no source code) 'M12L'	0·70
	10p DLR 'MAIL' (no source code) 'MA13'	0·70
	10p DLR 'MAIL' (no source code) 'M14L'	0·80
	10p DLR 'MAIL' (no source code) 'M15L'	0·70
	10p DLR 'MAIL' (no source code) 'M16L'	0·70
U2924	20p DLR 'MAIL' (no source code) 'M12L'	0·80
	20p DLR 'MAIL' (no source code) 'MA13'	1·40
	20p DLR 'MAIL' (no source code) 'M14L'	1·25
	20p DLR 'MAIL' (no source code) 'M15L'	1·00
U2925	50p slate DLR 'MAIL' (no source code) 'M12L'	2·00
U2926	68p DLR 'MAIL' (no source code) 'M11L'	2·60
	68p DLR 'MAIL' (no source code) 'M12L'	8·00
U2927	76p DLR 'MAIL' (no source code) 'M11L'	2·70
	76p DLR 'MAIL' (no source code) 'M12L'	6·25
U2928	78p Walsall 'MAIL' (no source code) 'M13L'	2·40
	78p DLR 'MAIL' (no source code) 'MA13'	4·50
U2928a	81p DLR 'MAIL' (no source code) 'M14L'	2·40
U2929	87p DLR 'MAIL' (no source code) 'M12L'	3·75
U2930	88p Walsall 'MAIL' (no source code) 'M13L'	3·00
	88p DLR 'MAIL' (no source code) 'MA13'	4·75
U2930a	97p DLR 'MAIL' (no source code) 'M14L'	3·25
U2931	£1.00 magenta DLR 'MAIL' (no source code) 'M11L'	6·75
	£1.00 magenta DLR 'MAIL' (no source code) 'M12L'	6·75
U2932	£1.00 bistre-brown DLR 'MAIL' (no source code) 'M12L'	4·00
	£1.00 bistre-brown DLR 'MAIL' (no source code) 'M14L'	4·00
	£1.00 bistre-brown DLR 'MAIL' (no source code) 'M15L'	4·00
	£1.00 bistre-brown DLR 'MAIL' (no source code) 'M16L'	3·25
U2932a	£1.05 DLR 'MAIL' (no source code) 'M16L'	2·25
U2933	£1.10 DLR 'MAIL' (no source code) 'M11L'	3·75
U2934	£1.28 DLR 'MAIL' (no source code) 'M12L'	5·50
	£1.28 DLR 'MAIL' (no source code) 'MA13'	6·50
	£1.28 DLR 'MAIL' (no source code) 'M14L'	5·50
U2934a	£1.33 DLR 'MAIL' (no source code) 'M15L'	3·25
	£1.33 DLR 'MAIL' (no source code) 'M16L'	3·75
U2934b	£1.47 DLR 'MAIL' (no source code) 'M14L'	3·75
U2934c	£1.52 DLR 'MAIL' (no source code) 'M15L'	3·75
U2935	£1.65 DLR 'MAIL' (no source code) 'M11L'	4·75
U2936	£1.88 Walsall 'MAIL' (no source code) 'M13L'	5·25
	£1.88 DLR 'MAIL' (no source code) 'MA13'	7·00
U2937	£1.90 DLR 'MAIL' (no source code) 'M12L'	4·75
U2938	£2.00 DLR 'MAIL' (no source code) 'MA13'	9·00

2nd (bright blue) and 1st (as noted) self-adhesive Security Machins, with source and date code (d).
(Unless noted, the source code is at top right, the date code is to the left of the front of The Queen's forehead or crown (or for the 'Large' issues from MA11 onwards it is above the 'ge' of 'Large'), the 'U'-shaped slits are broken.)

SG No.	DESCRIPTION	
U2961	2nd DLR 'MBIL' 'MA10'	6·00
	2nd DLR 'MBIL' 'M11L'	4·75
	2nd Walsall 'MBIL' 'M12L'	2·75
	2nd Walsall 'MBIL' 'M13L'	2·75
	2nd Walsall 'MBIL' 'M14L'	2·75
	2nd Walsall 'MBIL' 'M15L', front of backing paper is unprinted	3·00
	2nd Walsall 'MBIL' 'M15L', with repeating ROYAL MAIL wording printed on front of backing paper	3·50
	2nd Walsall 'MBIL' 'M16L' (with repeating ROYAL MAIL wording printed on front of backing paper)	2·60
U2962	2nd Walsall 'MPIL' ('U'-shaped slits with break at bottom only) 'MA10' (from DX50)	3·25
	2nd Walsall 'MPIL' ('U'-shaped slits with break at top & bottom) 'MA10' (from DX50)	7·75
U2962a	2nd DLR 'MRIL' 'MA10'; only known "USED" from mail posted by bulk mailing houses	—
	2nd Enschedé 'MRIL' 'MA12'	4·75
	2nd Walsall 'MRIL' 'M12L'	5·25
	2nd Walsall 'MRIL' 'M15L'	4·25
U2963	2nd Walsall 'MTIL' 'MA10'	4·00
	2nd Walsall 'MTIL' 'M11L'	3·25
	2nd Walsall 'MTIL' 'M12L'	2·40
	2nd Walsall 'MTIL' 'M13L'	2·40

SG No.	DESCRIPTION	
	2nd Walsall 'MTIL' 'M14L'	2·25
	2nd Walsall 'MTIL' 'M15L', front of backing paper is unprinted	2·40
	2nd Walsall 'MTIL' 'M15L', with repeating ROYAL MAIL wording printed on front of backing paper	3·00
	2nd Walsall 'MTIL' 'M16L' (with repeating ROYAL MAIL wording printed on front of backing paper)	2·25
U2964	1st gold DLR 'MBIL' 'MA10'	7·00
	1st gold DLR 'MBIL' 'M11L'	4·00
U2965	1st gold Walsall 'MCIL' 'MA10'	3·00
	1st gold Walsall 'MCIL' 'M11L'	2·25
U2966	1st gold Walsall 'MPIL' ('U'-shaped slits with break at bottom only) 'MA10' (from DX50)	2·25
	1st gold Walsall 'MPIL' ('U'-shaped slits with break at top & bottom) 'MA10' (from DX50)	6·00
U2966a	1st gold DLR 'MRIL' 'MA10'	5·75
	1st gold Enschedé 'MRIL' 'MA12'	4·75
U2967	1st gold Walsall 'MSIL' 'MA10'	2·75
	1st gold Walsall 'MSIL' 'M11L'	3·75
U2968	1st gold Walsall 'MTIL' 'MA10'	5·00
	1st gold Walsall 'MTIL' 'M11L'	3·00
	1st gold Walsall 'MTIL' 'M12L'	6·50
U2968a	1st vermilion Walsall 'MBIL' 'M12L'	3·00
	1st vermilion Walsall 'MBIL' 'M13L'	5·00
	1st vermilion Walsall 'MBIL' 'M14L'	3·00
	1st vermilion Walsall 'MBIL' 'M15L', front of backing paper is unprinted	3·25
	1st vermilion Walsall 'MBIL' 'M15L', with repeating ROYAL MAIL wording printed on front of backing paper	3·75
	1st vermilion Walsall 'MBIL' 'M16L' (with repeating ROYAL MAIL wording printed on front of backing paper)	2·75
U2968b	1st vermilion Walsall 'MCIL' 'M12L'	2·75
	1st vermilion Walsall 'MCIL' 'M13L'	2·25
	1st vermilion Walsall 'MCIL' 'M14L'	2·10
	1st vermilion Walsall 'MCIL' 'M15L'	2·10
U2968c	1st vermilion Enschedé 'MRIL' 'MA12'	2·25
	1st vermilion 'MRIL' 'M13L'	3·00
U2968d	1st vermilion Walsall 'MSIL' 'M12L'	2·40
	1st vermilion Walsall 'MSIL' 'M13L'	2·75
	1st vermilion Walsall 'MSIL' 'M14L'	2·40
	1st vermilion Walsall 'MSIL' 'M15L'	2·75
U2968e	1st vermilion Walsall 'MTIL' 'M12L'	2·40
	1st vermilion Walsall 'MTIL' 'M13L'	2·40
	1st vermilion Walsall 'MTIL' 'M14L'	2·40
	1st vermilion Walsall 'MTIL' 'M15L', front of backing paper is unprinted	2·60
	1st vermilion Walsall 'MTIL' 'M15L', with repeating ROYAL MAIL wording printed on front of backing paper	3·25
	1st vermilion Walsall 'MTIL' 'M16L' (with repeating ROYAL MAIL wording printed on front of backing paper)	2·40
U2969	2nd Large DLR 'MBI' 'MA10'	24·00
	2nd Large DLR 'BIL' (source code bottom right) 'MA11'	3·50
	2nd Large Walsall 'BIL' (source code bottom right) 'MA12' [Note that 'U' slits do not have breaks in them!]	3·00
	2nd Large Walsall 'BIL' (source code bottom right) 'MA13'	4·00
	2nd Large Walsall 'BIL' (source code bottom right) 'MA13' [Note that 'U' slits do not have breaks in them!]	4·00
	2nd Large Walsall 'MBIL' (source code in front of hair) 'MA14'	3·00
	2nd Large Walsall 'MBIL' (source code in front of hair) 'MA15'	3·25
U2970	2nd Large Walsall 'MFI' 'MA10'	16·00
	2nd Large Walsall 'FIL' (source code bottom right) 'MA11'	3·00
	2nd Large Walsall 'FIL' (source code bottom right) 'MA12'	4·00
	2nd Large Walsall 'FIL' (source code bottom right) 'MA13'	4·00
	2nd Large Walsall 'MFIL' (source code in front of hair) 'MA14'	3·00

SG No.	DESCRIPTION	
	2nd Large Walsall 'MFIL' (source code in front of hair) 'MA15'	3·00
U2971	1st Large, gold, DLR 'MBI' 'MA10'	8·00
	1st Large, gold, DLR 'BIL' (source code bottom right) 'MA11'	4·50
U2972	1st Large, gold, Walsall 'MFI' 'MA10'	8·00
	1st Large, gold, Walsall 'FIL' (source code bottom right) 'MA11'	3·25
U2973	1st Large, vermilion, Walsall 'BIL' (source code bottom right) 'MA12' [Note that 'U' slits do not have breaks in them!]	3·75
	1st Large, vermilion, Walsall 'BIL' (source code bottom right) 'MA13'	4·50
	1st Large, vermilion, Walsall 'BIL' (source code bottom right) 'MA13' [Note that 'U' slits do not have breaks in them!]	4·50
	1st Large, vermilion, Walsall 'MBIL' (source code in front of hair) 'MA14'	3·75
	1st Large, vermilion, Walsall 'MBIL' (source code in front of hair) 'MA15'	3·75
U2974	1st Large, vermilion, Walsall 'FIL' (source code bottom right) 'MA12'	3·00
	1st Large, vermilion, Walsall 'FIL' (source code bottom right) 'MA13'	4·00
	1st Large, vermilion, Walsall 'MFIL' (source code in front of hair) 'MA14'	3·00
	1st Large, vermilion, Walsall 'MFIL' (source code in front of hair) 'MA15', front of backing paper is un-printed	3·50
	1st Large, vermilion, Walsall 'MFIL' (source code in front of hair) 'MA15', with repeating ROYAL MAIL wording printed on front of backing paper	3·50

'Recorded Signed For', 'Royal Mail Signed For', and 'Special Delivery' self-adhesive Security Machins, no source code (as from counter sheets), with date code (b).
(Unless noted, the date code is to the left of the front of The Queen's forehead or crown. The 'U'-shaped slits are broken.)

SG No.	DESCRIPTION	
U2983	'Recorded Signed For' 1st DLR 'MAIL' (no source code) 'MA10'	14·00
U2983a	'Royal Mail Signed For' 1st DLR 'MAIL' (no source code) 'MA13' [Note that the service name was revised in March 2013.]	5·00
	'Royal Mail Signed For' 1st DLR 'MAIL' (no source code) 'M15L'	6·00
U2984	'Recorded Signed For' 1st Large DLR 'MAIL' (no source code) 'MA10'	16·00
U2984a	'Royal Mail Signed For' 1st Large DLR 'MAIL' (no source code) 'MA13' (date code is above the 'ge' of 'Large') [Note that the service name was revised in March 2013.]	5·75
	'Royal Mail Signed For' 1st Large DLR 'MAIL' (no source code) 'M15L' (date code is above the 'ge' of 'Large')	7·25
	'Royal Mail Signed For' 1st Large DLR 'MAIL' (no source code) 'M16L' (date code is above the 'ge' of 'Large')	6·00
U2985	'Special Delivery up to 100g' DLR 'MAIL' (no source code) 'MA10'	13·50
	'Special Delivery up to 100g' DLR 'MAIL' (no source code) 'M14L'	18·75
	'Special Delivery up to 100g' DLR 'MAIL' (no source code) 'M15L'	16·75
U2986	'Special Delivery up to 500g' DLR 'MAIL' (no source code) 'MA10'	14·50
	'Special Delivery up to 500g' DLR 'MAIL' (no source code) 'M14L'	19·25
	'Special Delivery up to 500g' DLR 'MAIL' (no source code) 'M16L'	17·75

Denominated and NVI ordinary gummed (i.e. not self-adhesive) Security Machins, with source and date code (b). No 'U'-shaped slits. All in litho.

SG No.	DESCRIPTION	
U3010	1p, Cartor 'MPIL' 'M13L' (from DY7 premium booklet)	1·60
	1p, ISP Cartor 'MPIL' 'M14L' (from DY12 premium booklet)	1·20
	1p, ISP Cartor 'MPIL' 'M15L' (from DY13 premium booklet)	1·20
U3011	2p, Cartor 'MPIL' 'M13L' (from DY7 premium booklet)	1·40
	2p, Enschedé 'MPIL' 'M13L' (from DY9 premium booklet)	1·40

SG No.	DESCRIPTION	
	2p, ISP Cartor 'MPIL' 'M14L' (from DY12 premium booklet)	1·40
U3012	5p, Cartor 'MPIL' 'M12L' (from DY6 premium booklet)	2·25
	5p, Cartor 'MPIL' 'M13L' (from DY7 premium booklet)	1·50
	5p, Enschedé 'MPIL' 'M13L' (from DY9 premium booklet)	1·50
	5p, ISP Cartor 'MPIL' 'M15L' (from DY14 premium booklet)	1·50
U3012c	5p, *Deep red-brown*, ISP Cartor 'MPIL' 'M15L' (from DY13 premium booklet)	2·00
U3012d	5p, Enschedé 'MPIL' 'M13L'; ellipse toward top of sides of stamp (from DY8 premium booklet)	1·75
U3013	10p, Cartor 'MPIL' 'M12L' (from DY6 premium booklet)	2·25
	10p, Cartor 'MPIL' 'M13L' (from DY7 premium booklet)	1·60
	10p, Enschedé 'MPIL' 'M14L' (from DY10 and DY11 premium booklet)	1·60
	10p, ISP Cartor 'MPIL' 'M15L' (from DY14 premium booklet)	1·50
U3014	20p, Cartor 'MPIL' 'M12L' (from DY6 premium booklet)	3·50
	20p, Enschedé 'MPIL' 'M14L' (from DY10 and DY11 premium booklets)	1·60
U3014a	2nd, ISP Cartor 'MPIL' 'M15L' (from DY15 premium booklet)	2·75
U3015	1st, gold, Cartor 'MPIL' 'M11L' (from DY2 premium booklet)	5·00
U3016	1st, vermilion, Cartor 'MPIL' 'M13L' (from DY7 premium booklet)	2·40
	1st, vermilion, ISP Cartor 'MPIL' 'M15L' (from DY15 premium booklet)	3·00
U3017	50p, slate, Enschedé 'MPIL' 'M13L'; ellipse toward top of sides of stamp (from DY8 premium booklet)	3·00
U3017a	50p, slate, ISP Cartor 'MPIL' 'M13L' (from DY14 premium booklet)	2·75
U3019	76p, Cartor 'MPIL' 'M11L' (from DY2 premium booklet)	5·50
U3019a	81p, ISP Cartor 'MPIL' 'M14L' (from DY12 premium booklet)	8·00
U3020	87p, Cartor 'MPIL' 'M12L' (from DY6 premium booklet)	6·00
U3020a	97p, ISP Cartor 'MPIL' 'M14L' (from DY12 premium booklet)	3·75
U3021	£1.00, Enschedé 'MPIL' 'M14L' (from DY10 and DY11 booklet)	3·25
	£1.00, ISP Cartor 'MPIL' 'M15L' (from DY14 booklet)	3·25
U3022	£1.33, ISP Cartor 'MPIL' 'M15L' (from DY13 booklet)	4·00

N.B. ISP stands for 'International Security Printers' which encompasses both Cartor and Walsall.

ROYAL MAIL POSTAGE LABELS

These imperforate labels were issued as an experiment by the Post Office. Special microprocessor controlled machines were installed at post offices in Cambridge, London, Shirley (Southampton) and Windsor to provide an after-hours sales service to the public. The machines printed and dispensed the labels according to the coins inserted and the buttons operated by the customer. Values were initially available in ½p. steps to 16p. and in addition, the labels were sold at philatelic counters in two packs containing either 3 values (3½, 12½, 16p.) or 32 values (½p. to 16p.).

From 28 August 1984 the machines were adjusted to provide values up to 17p. After 31 December 1984 labels including ½p. values were withdrawn. The machines were taken out of service on 30 April 1985.

Machine postage-paid impression in red on phosphorised paper with grey-green background design. No watermark. Imperforate.

1984 (1 May–28 Aug).

Set of 32 (½p. to 16p.)	15·00	22·00
Set of 3 (3½p., 12½p., 16p.)	2·50	3·00
Set of 3 on First Day Cover (1.5.84)		6·50
Set of 2 (16½p., 17p.) (28.8.84)	4·00	3·00

ROYAL MAIL POST & GO STAMPS

Following trials of a number of self-service machines capable of dispensing postage labels, Royal Mail began installing "Post & Go" machines, manufactured by Wincor Nixdorf, in larger post offices. The first machines were sited at the Galleries post office in Bristol and came into use on 8 October 2008. In addition to postage labels, the machines dispense ready to use stamps, from rolls which have the design and background pre-printed in gravure, by thermally printing a two-line service indicator and a four-part code that represents the branch in which the machine is sited, the machine number within the branch, and session and transaction numbers.

A new series of machines, manufactured by NCR, made their appearance from 28 February 2014, dispensing Type IIA stamps (see below).

Large and small typeface (Wincor): when the machines were first installed they were programmed to dispense five denominations and the service indicator lines were in a large size typeface (Type I), as Type FT **1**. The large typeface remained current until September 2010 when the first pictorial Post & Go stamps, depicting British Birds, were released. The larger pictorial element in the new design necessitated machines to be upgraded to print the service indicator both repositioned to the left and in a reduced size (Type II). The four-part code was also significantly reduced in size. Initially the pictorials were only available from 30 offices nationwide, and because the upgrading was phased over many months, the early pictorial issues had limited availability. The Machin design ran concurrently with the pictorials and started appearing with the smaller service indicator from 8 September 2010 when machines in London were the first to be upgraded in advance of the first pictorial issue. The smaller service indicator became the norm after all machines were upgraded.

Worldwide up to 40g and 2nd Class: in the autumn of 2011 a new value, "Worldwide up to 40g", was added to the range and began to appear whilst Birds (4th series) was current. The Machin design was the first to be seen with it though, having been trialled in one London office from 13 October. Birds (4th series) appeared with "Worldwide up to 40g" later in the year and due to the late use of earlier Birds issues they too are known with it, although it is not included in set prices for Birds, series 1 to 3. Second class stamps were introduced to the range on 20 February 2013 but only in Special Packs, and from Hytech machines at Spring Stampex 2013. They were finally released at a postal location (a mobile "pop-up" post shop in Newcastle-upon-Tyne) on 20 November 2013.

Worldwide up to 10g and Worldwide up to 40g stamps were withdrawn on 31 March 2014, and both Europe and Worldwide 60g. stamps were withdrawn on 30 March 2015, to be replaced by new 100g. versions.

Special Packs: 1st stamps of the different "Post & Go" pictorial designs are available in Special Packs from Tallents House. For the Birds series these packs contained sheetlets of the six designs which were printed in gravure and had the two lines of the service indicator "1st Class" and "up to 100g" printed closer together (2mm). From Farm Animals onwards the sheetlets were replaced by strips of six thermally printed from Hytech machines which also had the two lines of the service indicator printed closer together (3mm). First day covers sold by Tallents House use these types of stamps.

Unintentional use of large typeface: after upgrading machines to produce the smaller service indicator, some machines experienced software glitches resulting in the unintentional part reversion to the large typeface, or a semi corrupted version of it, and in some instances a mixture of both large and small on the same denomination. Machines at varying locations were affected and some went unchanged for many months, or were amended and then simply reverted again. Such glitches seem to have continued on and off until December 2012 when all machines nationwide seemed to be functioning correctly.

Figure 1

Figure 2

Figure 3

There were two main types of part reversion: the first resulted in the "Worldwide up to 10g" having the "Up to 10g" in the larger typeface whilst "Worldwide" was still in the smaller typeface (*Fig. 1*). At the same time and although still in the smaller typeface, the "1st Class", "1st Large" and "Europe" were also affected by the glitch and had the service indicator lines positioned a little too far to the right. The "Worldwide up to 20g" was similarly affected which results in the "e" of Worldwide being printed on the pictorial design. All five values show the four-part code incorrectly spaced so that there is a large gap between the branch and machine number. The "Worldwide up to 40g" had not been introduced at this point. The second type of reversion is more significant and is of a complete return to the large typeface across the five original denominations, but with the "Worldwide Up to 10g" stamp having the second line, "Up to 10g", completely missing (*Fig. 2*). The problems continued after the introduction of the "Worldwide up to 40g" which affected both the "Worldwide" in the large typeface whilst the "up to 40g" was in the small typeface, and so is the opposite of the "Worldwide up to 10g" from the first type of reversion (*Fig. 3*).

Hytech/Royal Mail Series B machines: since Spring Stampex 2011, Post & Go machines manufactured by Hytech International have been sited at stamp exhibitions by Royal Mail. Stamps from Hytech machines are identifiable from the Wincor versions because the two lines of the service indicator are printed much closer together, whilst those from Wincor machines are 4mm apart. There are other minor differences. Marking particular events, from autumn 2011, some Hytech machines at exhibitions have produced stamps with special inscriptions. Owing to their restricted availability, Hytech versions from exhibitions with and without inscriptions are not listed separately, although details are provided in tables following the Royal Mail Post & Go stamps listings. The British Postal Museum & Archive, London, have a permanently available machine (originally Hytech, later RM series B) which can be used by members of the public. Stamps from this machine bear the inscription "The B.P.M.A." For commemorative inscriptions on BPMA stamps, see the tables at the end of this section.

In November 2012 "next generation" Hytech machines appeared at a new type of post office, a temporary, pop-up, Christmas Post Shop in Camden, London. The installation of Hytech machines at this office resulted in the first publicly available Hytech versions in a post office location. Both the Machins and 2012 Robin designs were on sale at this post office, and differ from Wincor versions through the two lines of the service indicator being printed much closer together (2.6 mm) (Type III).

From Spring Stampex 2014 Hytech Machines were replaced by Royal Mail Series B Machines.

Date codes: codes first appeared on the 2012 Robin issue where there is an "MA12" in the background to the left of the main pictorial design. The February 2013 second class stamps also have an MA12 date code and the date became a standard feature from 2013

OPEN VALUE LABELS In February 2014, "Open Value labels", previously dispensed from Post & Go machines printed on white self-adhesive paper began to appear on the same illustrated background labels as Post & Go stamps. These show a service indicator "1L" (1st Letter), "2SP" (2nd Small Parcel), etc and the price. These are outside the scope of this catalogue, but on 7 July 2014 Royal Mail released a special pack containing five such labels in the Machin Head design, as Types FT **1** and FT **14** (Price £8).

Five Types of Post & Go service indicator, including subtypes of Types II and III:

FT **1** (Type **I**)

Type I: As Type FT **1**, with large, bold service indicator and four-part code consisting entirely of numerals (Wincor)

Type **II**

Type II: Smaller service indicator with lines 4mm apart and code consisting entirely of numerals (Wincor)

Type **IIA**

Type IIA: Similar to Type II but with service indicator and code in changed typeface and ranged left with service indicator lines 3.3 mm apart and code consisting entirely of numerals (NCR)

Type **III**

Type III: Smaller service indicator with lines 2.6mm apart and code consisting of letters and numerals (Hytech "next generation").

Type **IIIA**

Type IIIA: As Type III, with the code being a mixture of letters and numerals and all wording ranged left. However, the top line of the service indicator is noticeably smaller and slightly further away from the second line, at 2.7mm (Royal Mail Series II with revised typeface).

(Gravure Walsall, thermally printed service indicator)

2008 (8 Oct)–**15**. Type FT **1**. Self-adhesive. Olive-brown background. Two phosphor bands. *Perf* 14×14½.

FS1	(1st Class Up to 100g) (Type I)	9·00	9·00
	a. Type II (8.9.10)	3·25	3·25
	b. Type III (17.11.12)	10·50	10·50
	c. Type IIA (6.14)	6·50	6·50
	d. Type IIIA (3.6.15)	5·25	5·25
FS2	(1st Large Up to 100g) (Type I)	9·75	9·75
	a. Type II (8.9.10)	3·50	3·50
	b. Type III (17.11.12)	11·00	11·00
	c. Type IIA (6.14)	7·00	7·00
	d. Type IIIA (3.6.15)	5·50	5·50
FS3	(Europe Up to 20g)(Type I)	9·75	9·75
	a. Type II (8.9.10)	4·00	4·00
	b. Type III (17.11.12)	11·50	11·50
FS3c	Euro 20g World 10g (TIIA) (6.14)	7·00	7·00
	ca. Type II (20.10.14)	8·50	8·50
	cb. Type IIIA (3.6.15)	5·50	5·50
FS3d	Europe up to 60g (Type II) (31.3.14)	9·75	9·75
	dc. Type IIA (6.14)	8·50	8·50
FS3e	Europe up to 100g (Type IIA) (4.15)	9·75	9·75
	ea. Type IIIA (3.6.15)	8·50	8·50
FS4	(Worldwide Up to 10g) (Type I) (9.10.08)	11·00	11·00
	a. Type II (8.9.10)	6·00	6·00
	b. Type III (17.11.12)	11·50	11·50
FS5	(Worldwide Up to 20g) (Type I)	11·00	11·00
	a. Type II (8.9.10)	4·75	4·75
	b. Type III (17.11.12)	12·00	12·00
	c. Type IIA (6.14)	7·25	7·25
	d. Type IIIA (3.6.15)	6·00	6·00
FS5e	(Worldwide Up to 40g) (Type II) (13.10.11)	13·00	13·00
	eb. Type III (17.11.12)	14·00	14·00
FS5f	Worldwide Up to 60g (Type II) (31.3.14)	10·50	10·50
	fc. Type IIA (6.14)	9·25	9·25
FS5g	Worldwide Up to 100g (Type IIA) (4.15)	10·50	10·50
	ga. Type IIIA (3.6.15)	9·25	9·25
FS1/5 *Set of* 5 (Type I)		45·00	45·00
FS1a/3a, 4a, 5a, 5e *Set of* 6 (Type II)		32·00	32·00
FS1b/3b, 4b, 5b, 5eb *Set of* 6 (Type III)		65·00	65·00
FS1c, 2c, 3c, 3dc, 5c, 5fc *Set of* 6 (Type IIA)		42·00	42·00
FS1d, 2d, 3cb, 3fa, 5d, 5ga *Set of* 6 (Type IIIA)		36·00	36·00
Special Pack (As Nos. FS1/5 but service indicator and code lines in gravure) (31.3.09) (Type I)		100·00	100·00

Although the very first Post & Go machines went live at the Galleries post office, Bristol, on 8 October 2008, one particular machine function had not been properly enabled and the "Worldwide Up to 10g" version was not available until 9 October.

The five stamps from the special pack and first day cover sold by Tallents House differ from machine-printed stamps in having the service indicator and branch code printed in gravure and have a narrow gap between the two lines of the service indicator. Also, they are easily identified through the code lines which are unique to the gravure printing: 020511 1-08445-01 (to -05).

Smaller service indicator versions similar to Type II were available from Hytech machines at Spring Stampex 2011. Subsequently, versions similar to Type II or Type III were available from Hytech machines with additional inscriptions at other events. Details are provided in separate tables at the end of this section. Versions with various inscriptions have been available at the BPMA (now the PM) since December 2012.

FS1/5e are known printed unintentionally from Wincor machines with the typeface varieties resulting from software glitches causing a reversion to the large type face; see notes to 'Unintentional use of large typeface'.

Nos. FS4a and FS5e were replaced on 31 March 2014 by FS3d and FS5f.

Nos. FS3a was replaced on 20 October 2014 by FS3ca.

Nos. FS3dc and FS5fc were replaced on in April 2015 by FS3e and FS5g.

All Wincor machines, producing Type II stamps, were decommissioned before the 30.3.15 tariff change.

For full details of Post & Go stamps dispensed from machines at locations other than post offices and post shops, please refer to the tables following these listings

FT **2** Blue Tit

(Des Robert Gillmor and Kate Stephens. Gravure Walsall, thermally printed service indicator).

2010 (17 Sept). *Birds of Britain* (1st series). Multicoloured. Self-adhesive. Two phosphor bands. *Perf* 14×14½.

FS6	(1st Class up to 100g) (Type II)	9·00	9·00
FS7	(1st Large up to 100g) (Type II)	9·50	9·50
FS8	(Europe up to 20g) (Type II)	9·50	9·50
FS8*a*	(Europe up to 60g) (Type II) (5.14)	90·00	90·00
FS9	(Worldwide up to 10g) (Type II)	18·00	18·00
FS10	(Worldwide up to 20g) (Type II)	13·00	13·00
FS10*a*	(Worldwide up to 40g) (Type II) (2.12)	60·00	60·00
FS10*b*	(Worldwide up to 60g) (Type II) (5.14)	90·00	90·00
FS6/8, 9, 10 *Set of 5* (Type II)		54·00	54·00
First Day Cover (No. FS6 in 6 designs)			20·00
Special Pack (No. FS6 in sheetlet of 6 gravure designs) (Type II)			24·00

Nos. FS6/10*b* were each available in six different designs: Type FT **2**, Goldfinch, Wood Pigeon, Robin, House Sparrow and Starling.

Nos. FS6/10 were available from Post & Go terminals, initially in 30 post offices.

FS6/10 are known printed unintentionally from Wincor machines with both typeface varieties resulting from software glitches causing a reversion to the large type face; see notes to 'Unintentional use of large typeface'.

FS8*a*, 10*a*, 10*b* resulted from the late use of old stock.

FT **3** Blackbird

(Des Robert Gillmor and Kate Stephens. Gravure Walsall, thermally printed service indicator)

2011 (24 Jan). *Birds of Britain* (2nd series). Multicoloured. Self-adhesive. Two phosphor bands. *Perf* 14×14½.

FS11	(1st class up to 100g) (Type II)	4·00	4·00
FS12	(1st Large up to 100g) (Type II)	4·25	4·25
FS13	(Europe up to 20g) (Type II)	4·25	4·25
FS13*a*	(Europe up to 60g) (Type II) (4.14)	26·00	26·00
FS14	(Worldwide up to 10g) (Type II)	9·00	9·00
FS15	(Worldwide up to 20g) (Type II)	4·75	4·75
FS15*a*	(Worldwide up to 40g) (Type II) (12.11)	32·00	32·00
FS15*b*	(Worldwide up to 60g) (Type II) (4.14)	27·00	27·00
FS11/13, 14, 15 *Set of 5* (Type II)		24·00	24·00
First Day Cover (No. FS11 in 6 designs)			20·00
Special Pack (No. FS11 in sheetlet of 6 gravure designs) (Type II)			45·00

Nos. FS11/15*b* were each available in six different designs: Type FT **3**, two Magpies, Long-tailed Tit, Chaffinch, Collared Dove and Greenfinch.

FS11/15*a* are known printed unintentionally from Wincor machines with the first type of software glitch causing a part reversion to the large type face on "Up to 10g". The issue is also known printed with the large typeface because a roll was supplied to an office yet to have its machine upgraded for the smaller service indicator. See notes to "Unintentional use of large typeface".

FS13*a*, 15*a*, 15*b* resulted from the late use of old stock.

FT **4** Mallard

(Des Robert Gillmor and Kate Stephens. Gravure Walsall, thermally printed service indicator)

2011 (19 May). *Birds of Britain* (3rd series). Self-adhesive. Two phosphor bands. *Perf* 14×14½.

FS16	(1st Class up to 100g) (Type II)	3·50	3·50
FS17	(1st Large up to 100g) (Type II)	4·00	4·00
FS18	(Europe up to 20g) (Type II)	4·00	4·00
FS18*a*	(Europe up to 60g) (Type II) (4.14)	36·00	36·00
FS19	(Worldwide up to 10g) (Type II)	6·00	6·00
FS20	(Worldwide up to 20g) (Type II)	4·50	4·50
FS20*a*	(Worldwide up to 40g) (Type II) (12.11)	14·00	14·00
FS20*b*	(Worldwide up to 60g) (Type II) (4.14)	36·00	36·00
FS16/18, 19, 20 *Set of 5* (Type II)		20·00	20·00
First Day Cover (No. FS16 in 6 designs)			8·75
Special Pack (No. FS16 in sheetlet of 6 gravure designs) (Type II)			10·00

Nos. FS16/20*b* were each available in six different designs: Type FT **4**, Greylag Goose, Kingfisher, Moorhen, Mute Swan and Great Crested Grebe.

FS16/20 are known printed unintentionally from Wincor machines with both typeface varieties resulting from software glitches causing a reversion to the large type face; see notes to "Unintentional use of large typeface".

FS18*a*, 20*a*, 20*b* resulted from the late use of old stock.

FT **5** Puffin

(Des Robert Gillmor and Kate Stephens. Gravure Walsall, thermally printed service indicator)

2011 (16 Sept-Oct). *Birds of Britain* (4th series). Self-adhesive. Two phosphor bands. *Perf* 14×14½.

FS21	(1st class up to 100g) (Type II)	2·75	2·75
FS22	(1st Large up to 100g) (Type II)	3·25	3·25
FS23	(Europe up to 20g) (Type II)	3·25	3·25
FS23*a*	(Europe up to 60g) (Type II) (31.3.14)	11·00	11·00
FS24	(Worldwide up to 10g) (Type II)	5·25	5·25
FS25	(Worldwide up to 20g) (Type II)	4·00	4·00
FS26	(Worldwide up to 40g) (17.10.11) (Type II)	11·00	11·00
FS26*a*	(Worldwide up to 60g) (Type II) (31.3.14)	12·00	12·00
FS21/23, 24/26 *Set of 6* (Type II)		26·00	26·00
First Day Cover (FS21 in 6 designs)			7·25
Special Pack (No. FS21 in sheetlet of 6 gravure designs) (Type II)			10·00

Nos. FS21/26*a* were each available in six different designs: Type FT **5**, Gannet, Oystercatcher, Ringed Plover, Cormorant and Arctic Tern.

FS21/25 are known printed unintentionally from Wincor machines with both typeface varieties resulting from software glitches causing a reversion to the large type face. Additionally FS26 is known with the second type mixing both sizes of typeface; see notes to "Unintentional use of large typeface".

FS23*a*, 26*a* resulted from the late use of old stock.

FT **6** Welsh Mountain Badger Face

(Des Robert Gillmor and Kate Stephens. Gravure, thermally printed service indicator Walsall)

2012 (24 Feb). *British Farm Animals* (1st series). Sheep. Self-adhesive. Two phosphor bands. *Perf* 14×14½.

FS27	(1st Class up to 100g) (Type II)	2·75	2·75
FS28	(1st Large up to 100g) (Type II)	3·25	3·25
FS29	(Europe up to 20g) (Type II)	3·25	3·25
FS29a	(Euro 20g World 10g) (Type II) (10.14)	8·75	8·75
FS29b	(Europe up to 60g) (Type II) (31.3.14)	11·00	11·00
FS30	(Worldwide up to 10g) (Type II)	5·25	5·25
FS31	(Worldwide up to 20g) (Type II)	4·00	4·00
FS32	(Worldwide up to 40g) (Type II)	5·75	5·75
FS32b	(Worldwide up to 60g) (Type II) (31.3.14)	12·00	12·00
FS27/29, 30/32 *Set of 6* (Type II)		22·00	22·00
First Day Cover (FS27 in 6 designs)			8·75
Special Pack (FS27 in strip of 6 designs) (Type II)		10·00	

Nos. FS27/32b were each available in six different designs: Type FT **6**, Dalesbred, Jacob, Suffolk, Soay, Leicester Longwool.

FS27/32 are known printed unintentionally from Wincor machines with the second typeface variety resulting from software glitches causing a reversion to the large type face; see notes to "Unintentional use of large typeface".

FS29a, 29b, 32b resulted from the late use of old stock.

FT **7** Berkshire

(Des Robert Gillmor and Kate Stephens. Gravure Walsall, thermally printed service indicator)

2012 (24 Apr). *British Farm Animals* (2nd series). Pigs. Multicoloured. Self-adhesive. Two phosphor bands. *Perf* 14×14½.

FS33	(1st class up to 100g) (Type II)	2·75	2·75
FS34	(1st Large up to 100g) (Type II)	3·25	3·25
FS35	(Europe up to 20g) (Type II)	3·25	3·25
FS35a	(Euro 20g World 10g) (Type II) (10.14)	8·75	8·75
FS35b	(Europe up to 60g) (Type II) (31.3.14)	11·50	11·50
FS36	(Worldwide up to 10g) (Type II)	5·25	5·25
FS37	(Worldwide up to 20g) (Type II)	4·00	4·00
FS38	(Worldwide up to 40g) (Type II)	5·75	5·75
FS38b	(Worldwide up to 60g) (Type II) (31.3.14)	12·50	12·50
FS33/35, 36/38 *Set of 6* (Type II)		22·00	22·00
First Day Cover (No. FS33 in 6 designs)			8·50
Special Pack (FS33 in strip of 6 designs) (Type II)		10·00	

Nos. FS33/38b were each available in six different designs: Type FT **7**, Gloucestershire Old Spots, Oxford Sandy and Black, Welsh, Tamworth, British Saddleback.

FS33/38 are known printed unintentionally from Wincor machines with the second typeface variety resulting from software glitches causing a reversion to the large type face; see notes to "Unintentional use of large typeface".

FS35a, 35b, 38b resulted from the late use of old stock.

FT **8**

(Des Anton Morris and Dick Davies. Gravure Walsall, thermally printed service indicator)

2012 (21 May). *Union Flag* Type FT **8**. Multicoloured. Self-adhesive. Two phosphor bands. *Perf* 14×14½.

FS39	(1st Class up to 100g) (Type II)	2·75	2·75
	a. Type IIA (7.14)	3·00	3·00
FS40	(1st Large up to 100g) (Type II)	3·25	3·25
	a. Type IIA (7.14)	3·25	3·25
FS41	(Europe up to 20g) (Type II)	3·50	3·50
FS41a	(Euro 20g World 10g) (Type IIA) (7.14)	3·50	3·50
	ab. Type II (10.14)	9·00	9·00
FS41b	(Europe up to 60g) (Type II) (31.3.14)	9·75	9·75
	ba. Type IIA (7.14)	11·50	11·50
FS41c	(Europe up to 100g) (Type IIA) (30.3.15)	9·50	9·50
FS42	(Worldwide up to 10g) (Type II)	5·25	5·25
FS43	(Worldwide up to 20g) (Type II)	4·50	4·50
	a. Type IIA (7.14)	4·50	4·50
FS44	(Worldwide up to 40g) (Type II)	6·00	6·00
FS44b	(Worldwide up to 60g) (Type II) (31.3.14)	10·50	10·50
	ba. Type IIA (7.14)	12·50	12·50
FS44c	(Worldwide up to 100g) (Type IIA) (30.3.15)	10·50	10·50
FS39/41, 42/44 *Set of 6* (Type II)		23·00	23·00
FS39a, 40a, 41a, 41ba, 43a, 44ba *Set of 6* (Type IIA)		35·00	35·00
First Day Cover (No. FS39 only)			2·50
Special Pack (No. FS39 only) (Type IIA)		2·50	

When first printed the Special Pack stamps had the upper service indicator line, 1st Class, in a slightly larger typeface and ranged left with the code line, and are therefore a Type II sub-type (*Price* £3.50). A reprint of the Special Packs has stamps in a smaller typeface, with all lines ranged left, and are therefore similar to Type IIA.

FS39/44 are known printed unintentionally from Wincor machines with the second typeface variety resulting from software glitches causing a reversion to the large type face; see notes to "Unintentional use of large typeface".

FT **8** is known thermally printed with 2nd Class up to 100g and 2nd Large up to 100g, Type IIA, when put in machine's second class unit due to standard second class FT **14** stock being temporarily unavailable.

All Wincor machines, producing Type II stamps, were decommissioned before the 30.03.15 tariff change.

FT **9** Irish Moiled

(Des Robert Gillmor and Kate Stephens. Gravure Walsall, thermally printed service indicator)

2012 (28 Sept). *British Farm Animals* (3rd series). Cattle. Multicoloured. Self-adhesive. Two phosphor bands. *Perf* 14×14½.

FS45	(1st Class up to 100g) (Type II)	4·00	4·00
FS46	(1st Large up to 100g) (Type II)	4·75	4·75
FS47	(Europe up to 20g) (Type II)	5·00	5·00
FS47a	(Euro 20g World 10g) (Type II) (10.14)	8·75	8·75
FS47b	(Europe up to 60g) (Type II) (31.3.14)	12·00	12·00
FS48	(Worldwide up to 10g) (Type II)	6·00	6·00
FS49	(Worldwide up to 20g) (Type II)	5·25	5·25
FS50	(Worldwide up to 40g) (Type II)	7·00	7·00
FS50b	(Worldwide up to 60g) (Type II) (31.3.14)	13·00	13·00
FS45/47, 48/50 *Set of 6* (Type II)		29·00	29·00
First Day Cover (No. FS45 in 6 designs)			8·50
Special Pack (FS45 in strip of 6 designs) (Type III)		10·00	

Nos. FS45/50b were each available in six different designs: Type FT **9**, Welsh Black, Highland, White Park, Red Poll, Aberdeen Angus.

FS45/50 are known printed unintentionally from Wincor machines with the second typeface variety resulting from software glitches causing a reversion to the large type face; see notes to "Unintentional use of large typeface".

FS47a, 47b, 50b resulted from the late use of old stock.

FT **10** Robin

(Des. Robert Gillmor and Kate Stephens.
Gravure Walsall, thermally printed service indicator)

2012 (6 Nov). *Christmas Robin* with date code in background. Type FT **10**. Multicoloured. Self-adhesive. Two phosphor bands. *Perf* 14x14½.

FS51	(1st Class up to 100g) (Type II)	2·75	2·75
	a. Type III (17.11.12)......................................	4·25	4·25
	b. Type IIA (7.14)..	4·50	4·50
FS52	(1st Large up to 100g) (Type II)	3·25	3·25
	a. Type III (17.11.12)......................................	4·75	4·75
	b. Type IIA (7.14)..	5·00	5·00
FS53	(Europe up to 20g) (Type II)	3·50	3·50
	a. Type III (17.11.12)......................................	5·25	5·25
FS53c	(Euro 20g World 10g) (Type IIA) (7.14)	5·00	5·00
	ca. Type II (10.14)..	8·00	8·00
FS53d	(Europe up to 60g) (Type II) (4.14)	10·00	10·00
	da. Type IIA (7.14)..	9·00	9·00
FS53e	(Europe up to 100g) (Type IIA) (4.15)...........	11·00	11·00
FS54	(Worldwide up to 10g) (Type II)	4·00	4·00
	a. Type III (17.11.12)......................................	5·25	5·25
FS55	(Worldwide up to 20g) (Type II)	4·50	4·50
	a. Type III (17.11.12)......................................	5·50	5·50
	b. Type IIA (7.14)..	5·25	5·25
FS56	(Worldwide up to 40g) (Type II)	5·75	5·75
	a. Type III (17.11.12)......................................	6·50	6·50
FS56d	(Worldwide up to 60g) (Type II) (4.14)	11·00	11·00
	da. Type IIA (7.14)..	9·75	9·75
FS56e	(Worldwide up to 100g) (Type IIA) (4.15)........	12·00	12·00
FS51/53, 54/56 Set of 6 (Type II)..........................		22·00	22·00
FS51a/56a Set of 6 (Type III)...................................		29·00	29·00
FS51b, 52b, 53c, 53da, 55b, 56da Set of 6 (Type IIA)...		35·00	35·00

FS51/56 are known printed unintentionally from Wincor machines with the second typeface variety resulting from software glitches causing a reversion to the large type face; see notes to "Unintentional use of large typeface".

FS51/56, FS53ca, 53d and 56d exist with both MA12 and MA13 date codes (Type II).

FS51a/56a exist with both MA12 and MA13 date codes (Type II).

FS51b, 52b, 53c, 53da, 53e, 55b, 56da and 56e are MA13 (Type IIA).

FS53c, 53d, 56d resulted from the late use of old stock.

FT **10** is known thermally printed with 2nd Class up to 100g and 2nd Large up to 100g, Type IIA, MA13, when put in machine's second class unit due to standard second class FT **14** stock being temporarily unavailable.

All Wincor machines, producing Type II stamps, were decommissioned before the 30.03.15 tariff change.

Nos. 57 and 58 are vacant

FT **11** Lesser Silver Water Beetle

(Des Kate Stephens. Illustrations by Chris Wormell.
Gravure Walsall, thermally printed service indicator)

2013 (22 Feb).*Freshwater Life* (1st series). Ponds. Multicoloured. Self-adhesive. Two phosphor bands. *Perf* 14×14½.

FS59	(1st Class up to 100g) (Type II)	3·50	3·50
FS60	(1st Large up to 100g) (Type II)	3·75	3·75
FS61	(Europe up to 20g) (Type II)	4·00	4·00
FS61a	(Euro 20g World 10g) (Type II) (10.14)..........	10·00	10·00
FS61b	(Europe up to 60g) (Type II) (4.14)	10·00	10·00
FS62	(Worldwide up to 10g) (Type II)	5·00	5·00
FS63	(Worldwide up to 20g) (Type II)	4·25	4·25
FS64	(Worldwide up to 40g) (Type II)	6·00	6·00
FS64b	(Worldwide up to 60g) (Type II) (4.14)	11·00	11·00
FS59/61, 62/64 Set of 6 (Type II)		24·00	24·00
First Day Cover (FS59 in 6 designs)			9·50
Special Pack (FS59 in strip of 6 designs) (Type III)......		10·00	

Nos. FS59/64b were each available in six different designs: Type FT **11**, Three-spined Stickleback, Smooth Newt, Fairy Shrimp, Emperor Dragonfly and Glutinous Snail.

FS61a, 61b, 64b resulted from the late use of old stock.

FT**12** Perch

(Des Kate Stephens. Illustrations by Chris Wormell.
Gravure Walsall, thermally printed service indicator)

2013 (25 June). *Freshwater Life* (2nd series). Lakes. Self-adhesive. Two phosphor bands. *Perf* 14×14½.

FS65	(1st Class up to 100g) (Type II)	4·00	4·00
FS66	(1st Large up to 100g) (Type II)	4·75	4·75
FS67	(Europe up to 20g) (Type II)	5·00	5·00
FS67a	(Euro 20g World 10g) (Type II) (10.14)..........	9·00	9·00
FS67b	(Europe up to 60g) (Type II) (31.3.14)	11·75	11·75
FS68	(Worldwide up to 10g) (Type II)	6·00	6·00
FS69	(Worldwide up to 20g) (Type II)	5·25	5·25
FS70	(Worldwide up to 40g) (Type II)	7·00	7·00
FS70b	(Worldwide up to 60g) (Type II) (31.3.14)	12·75	12·75
FS65/67, 68/70 Set of 6 (Type II)...........................		29·00	29·00
First Day Cover (FS65 in 6 designs)			9·50
Special Pack (FS65 in strip of 6 designs) (Type III)......		10·00	

Nos. FS65/70b were each available in six different designs: Type FT **12**, European Eel, Crucian Carp, Caddis Fly Larva, Arctic Char and Common Toad.

FS67a, 67b, 70b resulted from the late use of old stock.

FT **13** Minnow

(Des Kate Stephens. Illustrations by Chris Wormell.
Gravure Walsall, thermally printed service indicator)

2013 (20 Sept). *Freshwater Life* (3rd series). Rivers. Self-adhesive. Two phosphor bands. *Perf* 14×14½.

FS71	(1st Class up to 100g) (Type II)	2·75	2·75
FS72	(1st Large up to 100g) (Type II)	3·25	3·25
FS73	(Europe up to 20g) (Type II)	3·25	3·25
FS73a	(Euro 20g World 10g) (Type II) (10.14)..........	9·00	9·00
FS73b	(Europe up to 60g) (Type II) (31.3.14)	9·50	9·50
FS74	(Worldwide up to 10g) (Type II)	5·25	5·25
FS75	(Worldwide up to 20g) (Type II)	4·00	4·00
FS76	(Worldwide up to 40g) (Type II)	5·75	5·75
FS76b	(Worldwide up to 60g) (Type II) (31.3.14)	10·50	10·50
FS71/73, 74/76 Set of 6 (Type II)...........................		22·00	22·00
First Day Cover (FS71 in 6 designs)			9·50
Special Pack (FS71 in strip of 6 designs) (Type III)......		10·00	

Nos. FS71/76b were each available in six different designs: Type FT **13**, Atlantic Salmon, White-clawed Crayfish, River Lamprey, Blue-winged Olive Mayfly Larva, Brown Trout.

FS73a resulted from the late use of old stock.

NOTE: From FS77 onwards all Post & Go stamps incorporated a date code, unless otherwise stated.

(Gravure Walsall, thermally printed service indicator)

2013 (19 Nov) **-15**. Type FT **1** with date code in background. Olive-brown background. Self-adhesive. Two phosphor bands. *Perf* 14×14½.

FS77	(1st Class up to 100g) (Type II)	3·50	3·50
	a. Type IIA (28.2.14)	2·50	2·50
	b. Type IIIA (30.3.15)	3·50	3·50
FS78	(1st Large up to 100g) (Type II)	3·75	3·75
	a. Type IIA (28.2.14)	3·00	3·00
	b. Type IIIA (30.3.15)	4·00	4·00
FS79	(Europe up to 20g) (Type II)	5·50	5·50
	a. Type IIA (28.2.14)	8·00	8·00
FS79b	(Euro 20g World 10g) (Type II) (20.10.14)	8·00	8·00
	ba. Type IIA (5.6.14)	3·25	3·25
	bb. Type IIIA (30.3.15)	4·25	4·25
FS80	(Europe up to 60g) (Type II) (31.3.14)	6·50	6·50
	a. Type IIA (1.4.14)	6·00	6·00
FS80c	(Europe up to 100g) (Type IIA) (30.3.15)	4·25	4·25
	ca. Type IIIA (30.3.15)	5·50	5·50
FS81	(Worldwide up to 10g) (Type II)	—	—
	a. Type IIA (28.2.14)	—	—
FS82	(Worldwide up to 20g) (Type II)	5·00	5·00
	a. Type IIA (28.2.14)	3·75	3·75
	b. Type IIIA (30.3.15)	4·75	4·75
FS83	(Worldwide up to 40g) (Type II)	—	—
	a. Type IIA (28.2.14)	—	—
FS84	(Worldwide up to 60g) (Type II) (31.3.14)	7·50	7·50
	a. Type IIA (1.4.14)	7·00	7·00
FS84c	(Worldwide up to 100g) (Type IIA) (30.3.15)	5·75	5·75
	ca. Type IIIA (30.3.15)	6·75	6·75
FS77/80, 82, 84 *Set of* 6 (Type II)		29·00	29·00
FS77a, 78a, 79ba, 80c, 84c *Set of* 6 (Type IIA)		20·00	20·00
FS77b, 78b, 79bb, 80ca, 82b, 84ca *Set of* 6 (Type IIIA)		27·00	27·00

FS77/79, 79b, 80, 81, 82, 83 and 84 are MA13 (Type II).
FS77a, 78a, 79ba, 80c, 82a and 84c exist MA13, MA14 and MA15 (Type IIA).
FS80a and 84a exist MA13 and MA14 (Type IIA).
FS79a, 81a and 83a are MA13 (Type IIA).
FS77b, 78b, 79bb, 80ca, 82b and 84ca are MA13 (Type IIIA).
Nos. FS81 and FS83 were replaced on 31 March 2014 by FS80 and FS84.
Nos. FS81a and FS83a were replaced on 1 April 2014 by FS80a and FS84a.
Nos. FS79a was replaced on 5 June 2014 by FS79ba.
Nos. FS79 was replaced on 20 October 2014 by FS79b.
Nos. FS80a and FS84a were replaced on 30 March 2015 by FS80c and FS84c.
Type FT **1** with date code MA14 is known thermally printed with 2nd Class up to 100g and 2nd Large up to 100g, Type IIA, when put in machine's second class unit due to standard second class FT **14** stock being temporarily unavailable.
All Wincor machines, producing Type II stamps, were decommissioned before the 30.03.15 tariff change.
FS85/92 are reserved for Union Flag stamps with date codes.

FT **14**

(Gravure Walsall, thermally printed service indicator)

2013 (20 Nov) **-15**. Type FT **14** with date code in background. New blue background. Self-adhesive. One phosphor band (over the Queen's head). *Perf* 14×14½.

FS93	(2nd Class up to 100g) (Type III)	3·50	3·50
	a. Type IIA (2.14)	2·50	2·50
	b. Type IIIA (30.3.15)	3·50	3·50
FS94	(2nd Large up to 100g) (Type III)	4·00	4·00
	a. Type IIA (2.14)	2·75	2·75
	b. Type IIIA (30.3.15)	3·75	3·75
Special Pack (As Nos. FS93/94 but weight line inset at left) (20.02.13) (Type III)			
		10·00	

Post & Go stamps as Type FT **14** were issued by Tallents House on 20 February 2013 in packs and on first day covers (price £7·00 per pack and £3·00 on first day cover). They were sold from Hytech Next Generation machines at Spring Stampex 2013 but were not made available through post offices until November 2013.
FS93/4 exist MA12 from Special Pack and Spring Stampex 2013, and MA12/MA13 from Christmas Post Shop.
FS93a/94a exist MA12, MA13 and MA14.
FS93b/94b are MA12.
Type FT **14** with date code MA12 is known thermally printed with 1st Class up to 100g, 1st Class Large up to 100g, Euro 20g World 10g, Europe up to 60g, Worldwide up to 20g and Worldwide up to 60g, Type IIA, when mistakenly put in machine's first class unit.

FT **15** Primrose

(Des Kate Stephens. Illustrations by Julia Trickey.
Gravure ISP Walsall, thermally printed service indicator)

2014 (19 Feb). *British Flora* (1st series). Spring Blooms. Two phosphor bands. *Perf* 14×14½.

FS95	(1st Class up to 100g) (Type II)	4·00	4·00
	a. Type IIA (5.14)	4·00	4·00
FS96	(1st Large up to 100g) (Type II)	4·75	4·75
	a. Type IIA (5.14)	4·75	4·75
FS97	(Europe up to 20g) (Type II)	5·00	5·00
	a. Type IIA (5.14)	14·50	14·50
FS97b	(Euro 20g World 10g) (Type IIA) (5.6.14)	5·00	5·00
	ba. Type II (10.14)	8·00	8·00
FS98	(Europe up to 60g) (Type II) (31.3.14)	9·50	9·50
	a. Type IIA (5.14)	7·00	7·00
FS98b	(Europe up to 100g) (Type IIA) (30.3.15)	10·00	10·00
FS99	(Worldwide up to 10g) (Type II)	6·00	6·00
FS100	(Worldwide up to 20g) (Type II)	5·25	5·25
	a. Type IIA (5.14)	5·25	5·25
FS101	(Worldwide up to 40g) (Type II)	7·00	7·00
FS102	(Worldwide up to 60g) (Type II) (31.3.14)	10·50	10·50
	a. Type IIA (5.14)	8·00	8·00
FS102b	(Worldwide up to 100g) (Type IIA) (30.3.15)	11·00	11·00
FS95/97 and FS99/101 *Set of* 6 (Type II)		29·00	29·00
FS95a, 96a, 97b, 98a, 100a, 102a *Set of* 6 (Type IIA)		30·00	30·00
First Day Cover (FS95 in 6 designs)			9·50
Special Pack (FS95 in strip of 6 designs) (Type III)		10·00	

Nos. FS95/102b were each available in six different designs (all MA14): Type FT **15**, Snowdrop, Lesser Celandine, Dog Violet, Wild Daffodil, Blackthorn.
There was a late reprint of the Special Packs containing Type IIIA stamps (price £20).
Nos. FS97a was replaced on 5 June 2014 by FS97b.
FS98b and 102b resulted from the late use of old stock.
All Wincor machines, producing Type II stamps, were decommissioned before the 30.03.15 tariff change.

FT **16** Forget-me-not

FT **17** Common Ivy

(Des Kate Stephens. Illustrations by Julia Trickey.
Gravure ISP Walsall, thermally printed service indicator)

2014 (17 Sept). *British Flora* (2nd series). Symbolic Flowers Multi-coloured. Self-adhesive. Two phosphor bands. *Perf* 14×14½

FS103	(1st Class up to 100g) (Type IIA)	2·75	2·75
	a. Type II (17.9.14)	5·00	5·00
FS104	(1st Large up to 100g) (Type IIA)	3·00	3·00
	a. Type II (17.9.14)	5·25	5·25
FS104*b*	Europe up to 20g (Type II) (17.9.14)	25·00	25·00
FS105	(Euro 20g World 10g) (Type IIA)	3·25	3·25
	a. Type II (20.10.14)	9·00	9·00
FS106	(Europe up to 60g) (Type IIA)	6·50	6·50
	a. Type II (17.9.14)	6·50	6·50
FS106*b*	(Europe up to 100g) (Type IIA) (30.3.15)	9·50	9·50
FS107	(Worldwide up to 20g) (Type IIA)	4·25	4·25
	a. Type II (17.9.14)	5·75	5·75
FS108	(Worldwide up to 60g) (Type IIA)	7·00	7·00
	a. Type II (17.9.14)	7·00	7·00
FS108*b*	(Worldwide up to 100g) (Type IIA) (30.3.15)	10·50	10·50
FS103/104, 105/106, 107/108 *Set of* 6 (Type IIA)		24·00	24·00
FS103a, 104a, 104b, 106a, 107a, 108a *Set of* 6 (Type II)		47·00	47·00
First Day Cover (FS103 in 6 designs)			9·50
Special Pack (FS103 in strip of 6 designs) (Type IIIA)		10·00	

Nos. FS103/108*b* were each available in six different designs (all MA14): Type FT **16**, Common Poppy, Dog Rose, Spear Thistle, Heather and Cultivated Flax.

Nos. FS104*b* was replaced on 20 October 2014 by FS105a.

Nos. FS106 and FS108 were replaced on 30 March 2015 by FS106*b* and FS108*b*.

In the run-up to Remembrance Sunday the Common Poppy design (MA14) was made available in single-design rolls on 21 October 2014. Type II and Type IIA exist in this form.

Similarly the Common Poppy design was re-released in single-design rolls on 19 October 2015, but with MA15 (Type IIA); see also FS137/42.

Type FT **16**, Common Poppy, Dog Rose, Spear Thistle, Heather and Cultivated Flax are each known thermally printed with 2nd Class up to 100g and 2nd Large up to 100g, Type IIA, when mistakenly put in machine's second class unit. Single-design rolls of the Common Poppy, code MA14, are known thermally printed with 2nd Class up to 100g and 2nd Large up to 100g, Type IIA, when put in machine's second class unit due to standard second class FT **14** stock being temporarily unavailable.

All Wincor machines, producing Type II stamps, were decommissioned before the 30.03.15 tariff change.

(Des Kate Stephens. Illustrations by Julia Trickey.
Gravure ISP Walsall, thermally printed service indicator)

2014 (13 Nov). *British Flora* (3rd series). Winter Greenery Multicoloured. Self-adhesive. One phosphor band at right (FS109/*b* and FS110/*b*) or two phosphor bands (others). *Perf* 14×14½

FS109	(2nd Class up to 100g) (Type IIA)	3·50	3·50
	b. Type IIIA (3.12.14)	4·50	4·50
FS110	(2nd Large up to 100g) (Type IIA)	4·00	4·00
	b. Type IIIA (3.12.14)	5·00	5·00
FS111	(1st Class up to 100g) (Type IIA)	3·50	3·50
	a. Type II (13.11.14)	7·25	7·25
	b. Type IIIA (3.12.14)	4·75	4·75
FS112	(1st Large up to 100g) (Type IIA)	4·00	4·00
	a. Type II (13.11.14)	7·50	7·50
	b. Type IIIA (3.12.14)	5·25	5·25
FS113	(Euro 20g World 10g) (Type IIA)	4·00	4·00
	a. Type II (13.11.14)	7·75	7·75
	b. Type IIIA (3.12.14)	5·50	5·50
FS113*c*	(Europe up to 20g) (Type II) (12.14)	25·00	25·00
FS114	(Europe up to 60g) (Type IIA)	4·50	4·50
	a. Type II (13.11.14)	8·25	8·25
	b. Type IIIA (3.12.14)	6·00	6·00
FS114*c*	(Europe up to 100g) (Type IIA) (5.15)	10·00	10·00
FS115	(Worldwide up to 20g) (Type IIA)	4·25	4·25
	a. Type II (13.11.14)	8·00	8·00
	b. Type IIIA (3.12.14)	5·75	5·75
FS116	(Worldwide up to 60g) (Type IIA)	5·75	5·75
	a. Type II (13.11.14)	9·00	9·00
	b. Type IIIA (3.12.14)	6·75	6·75
FS116*c*	(Worldwide up to 100g) (Type IIA) (5.15)	11·00	11·00
FS109/113, 114, 115, 116 *Set of* 8 (Type IIA)		30·00	30·00
FS111a/113a, 114a, 115a, 116a *Set of* 6 (Type II)		44·00	44·00
FS109b/113b, 114b, 115b, 116b *Set of* 8 (Type IIIA)		40·00	40·00
First Day Cover (FS109/112; 4 designs)			9·50
Special Pack (FS109b/112b; 4 designs as two pairs) (Type IIIA)		8·00	

Nos. FS109/b and 110/b were each available in two different designs: Type FT **17** and Mistletoe. Nos. FS111/b through to 116/b were each available in two different designs: Butcher's Broom and Holly. All are MA14.

Defining their intended second class status, Type FT **17** and Mistletoe have repeating background ROYAL MAIL wording in blue and a single phosphor band placed at the right-hand side.

Nos. FS113c, 114c and 116c were also each available in two different designs: Butcher's Broom and Holly. All are MA14.

The Special Pack stamps are FS109*b* FT **17**, 110*b* Mistletoe, 111*b* Butcher's Broom, and 112*b* Holly.

FS113*c* only came from a single Wincor machine in Keighley during December 2014.

Type FT **17** and Mistletoe are also each known thermally printed with 1st Class up to 100g, 1st Class Large up to 100g, Euro 20g World 10g, Europe up to 60g, Worldwide up to 20g and Worldwide up to 60g, Type II, having been mistakenly sent to post offices using Wincor machins. Wincor machines did not dispense 2nd Class and 2nd Large.

All Wincor machines, producing Type II stamps, were decommissioned before the 30.3.15 tariff change.

FT **18** *Falcon*

(Des Osborne Ross.
Gravure ISP Walsall, thermally printed service indicator)

2015 (18 Feb). *Working Sail.* Multicoloured. Self-adhesive. Two phosphor
bands. *Perf* 14×14½

FS117	(1st Class up to 100g) (Type IIA)	3·50	3·50
FS118	(1st Large up to 100g) (Type IIA)	3·75	3·75
FS119	(Euro 20g World 10g) (Type IIA)	4·00	4·00
FS120	(Europe up to 60g) (Type IIA)	7·00	7·00
FS121	(Europe up to 100g) (Type IIA) (30.03.15)	10·00	10·00
FS122	(Worldwide up to 20g) (Type IIA)	4·50	4·50
FS123	(Worldwide up to 60g) (Type IIA)	7·75	7·75
FS124	(Worldwide up to 100g) (Type IIA) (30.03.15)	10·50	10·50
FS117/120, 122, 123 *Set of* 6 (Type IIA)		28·00	28·00
First Day Cover (FS117 in 6 designs)			9·50
Special Pack (FS117 in strip of 6 designs) (Type IIIA)		8·00	

Nos. FS117/124 were each available in six different designs: Type
FT **18**, *Briar, Harry, Margaret, Stag, Nell Morgan.*
FS117/124 are MA15.
Nos. FS120 and FS123 were replaced on 30 March 2015 by FS121
and FS124.
Type FT **18**, *Briar, Harry, Margaret, Stag* and *Nell Morgan* are each
known thermally printed with 2nd Class up to 100g and 2nd Large
up to 100g, Type IIA, when put in machine's second class unit due to
standard second class FT **14** stock being temporarily unavailable.

FT **19** *Lion*

(Des Osborne Ross. Illustrations by Chris Wormell,
Gravure ISP Walsall, thermally printed service indicator)

2015 (13 May). *Heraldic Beasts* Multicoloured. Self-adhesive. Two phosphor bands. *Perf* 14×14½

FS125	(1st Class up to 100g) (Type IIA)	2·75	2·75
FS126	(1st Large up to 100g) (Type IIA)	3·00	3·00
FS127	(Euro 20g World 10g) (Type IIA)	3·25	3·25
FS128	(Europe up to 100g) (Type IIA)	4·50	4·50
FS129	(Worldwide up to 20g) (Type IIA)	4·25	4·25
FS130	(Worldwide up to 100g) (Type IIA)	6·00	6·00
FS125/130, *Set of* 6 (Type IIA)		22·00	22·00
First Day Cover (FS125 in 6 designs)			9·50
Special Pack (FS125 in strip of 6 designs) (Type IIIA)		6·00	

Nos. FS125/130 were each available in six different designs: Type
FT **19**, Unicorn, Yale, Dragon, Falcon and Griffin.
FS125/130 are MA15.
Type FT **19**, Unicorn, Yale, Dragon, Falcon and Griffin are each
known thermally printed with 2nd Class up to 100g and 2nd Large
up to 100g, Type IIA, when put in machine's second class unit due to
standard second class FT **14** stock being temporarily unavailable.

FT **20** Dover

(Des Osborne Ross. Illustrations by Andy Tuohy,
Gravure ISP Walsall, thermally printed service indicator)

2015 (16 Sept). *Sea Travel* Multicoloured. Self-adhesive. Two phosphor
bands. *Perf* 14×14½

FS131	(1st Class up to 100g) (Type IIA)	2·75	2·75
FS132	(1st Large up to 100g) (Type IIA)	3·00	3·00
FS133	(Euro 20g World 10g) (Type IIA)	3·25	3·25
FS134	(Europe up to 100g) (Type IIA)	4·50	4·50
FS135	(Worldwide up to 20g) (Type IIA)	4·25	4·25
FS136	(Worldwide up to 100g) (Type IIA)	6·00	6·00
FS131/136, *Set of* 6		22·00	22·00
First Day Cover (FS131 in 6 designs)			9·50
Special Pack (FS131 in strip of 6 designs) (Type IIIA)		6·00	

Nos. FS131/136 were each available in six different designs: Type
FT **20**, Hong Kong, Sydney, Ha Long Bay, New York City and Venice.
FS131/136 are MA15.

Common Poppy stamp

1st Class
up to 100g

CNGB15 M004-0575-079

FT **21** Common Poppy

(Des Kate Stephens. Illustrations by Julia Trickey.
Gravure ISP Walsall, thermally printed service indicator)

2015 (19 Oct).*Common Poppy* in Type IIIA. Multicoloured. Self-adhesive.
Two phosphor bands. *Perf* 14×14½

FS137	(1st Class up to 100g) (Type IIIA)	3·75	3·75
FS138	(1st Large up to 100g) (Type IIIA)	4·25	4·25
FS139	(Euro 20g World 10g) (Type IIIA)	4·50	4·50
FS140	(Europe up to 100g) (Type IIIA)	5·50	5·50
FS141	(Worldwide up to 20g) (Type IIIA)	5·00	5·00
FS142	(Worldwide up to 100g) (Type IIIA)	6·75	6·75
FS137/142 *Set of* 6 (Type IIIA)		27·00	27·00

In the run-up to Remembrance Sunday 2015 the Common Poppy
design was made available in single-design rolls.
FS137/142 are MA15.
See also FS103/108b.

FT **22** Mountain Hare

(Des Osborne Ross. Illustrations by Robert Gillmor.
Gravure ISP Walsall, thermally printed service indicator)

2015 (16 Feb). *Winter Fur and Feathers* Multicoloured. Self-adhesive. One phosphor band at right (FS143/a and FS144/a) or two phosphor bands (others). *Perf* 14×14½

FS143	(2nd Class up to 100g) (Type IIA)	2·50	2·50
	a. Type IIIA (16.11.15)	3·00	3·00
FS144	(2nd Large up to 100g) (Type IIA)	2·75	2·75
	a. Type IIIA (16.11.15)	3·25	3·25
FS145	(1st Class up to 100g) (Type IIA)	2·75	2·75
	a. Type IIIA (16.11.15)	3·25	3·25
FS146	(1st Large up to 100g) (Type IIA)	3·00	3·00
	a. Type IIIA (16.11.15)	3·50	3·50
FS147	(Euro 20g World 10g) (Type IIA)	3·25	3·25
	a. Type IIIA (16.11.15)	4·25	4·25
FS148	(Europe up to 100g) (Type IIA)	4·50	4·50
	a. Type IIIA (16.11.15)	5·50	5·50
FS149	(Worldwide up to 20g) (Type IIA)	4·25	4·25
	a. Type IIIA (16.11.15)	5·25	5·25
FS150	(Worldwide up to 100g) (Type IIA)	6·00	6·00
	a. Type IIIA (16.11.15)	6·50	6·50
FS143/150, *Set of* 8 (Type IIA)		25·00	25·00
FS143a/150a, Set of 8 (Type IIIA)		31·00	31·00
First Day Cover (FS143/146; 4 designs)			8·00
Special Pack (FS143a/146a; 4 designs as two pairs)			
(Type IIIA)			6·50

Nos. FS143/a and 144/a were each available in two different designs: Type FT **22** and Redwing. Nos. FS145/a through to 150/a were each available in two different designs: Red Fox and Squirrel.

Defining their intended second class status, FT **22** and Redwing have repeating background ROYAL MAIL 2nd CLASS wording in blue and a single phosphor band placed at the right-hand side.

The Special Pack stamps are FS143a FT **22**, 144a Redwing, 145a Red Fox, and 146a Red Squirrel.

FS143/*a* and 144/*a* are CL15 FS145/*a* through to 150/*a* are MA15.

FT **22** and Redwing are also both known thermally printed with 1st Class up to 100g, 1st Class Large up to 100g, Euro 20g World 10g, Europe up to 100g, Worldwide up to 20g and Worldwide up to 100g, Type IIA, when mistakenly put in machine's first class unit.

FT **23** Post boy

(Des Howard Brown. Illustrations by Andrew Davidson.
Gravure ISP Walsall, thermally printed service indicator)

2016 (17 Feb). *Royal Mail Heritage: Transport* Multicoloured. Self-adhesive. Two phosphor bands. *Perf* 14×14½

FS151	(1st Class up to 100g) (Type IIA)	2·50	2·50
FS152	(1st Large up to 100g) (Type IIA)	2·75	2·75
FS153	(Euro 20g World 10g) (Type IIA)	2·75	2·75
FS154	(Europe up to 100g) (Type IIA)	4·00	4·00
FS155	(Worldwide up to 20g) (Type IIA)	3·75	3·75
FS156	(Worldwide up to 100g) (Type IIA)	5·75	5·75
FS151/156, Set of 6 (Type IIA)		20·00	20·00
First Day Cover (FS151 in 6 designs)			9·50
Special Pack (FS151 in strip of 6 designs) (Type IIIA)		6·00	

Nos. FS151/156 were each available in six different designs: Type FT **23**; Mail coach, 1790s; Falmouth packet ship, 1820s; Travelling Post Office, 1890s; Airmail, 1930s and Royal Mail Minivan, 1970s.

Post & Go stamps—the different Exhibition issues with inscriptions to 20 February 2016: a simplified checklist

Stamp design, values, and inscription	Date code	The date and duration of the particular inscription (all the dates are inclusive)	Cat. No. of stamp issue without inscription, or closest match
Machin, 1st/1stL-E-20g/WW-10g/WW-20g/WW-40g:			
'Arnold Machin 1911-1999'	None	Autumn Stampex 2011 (14-17 September: 4 days)	FS1a/3a, 4a, 5a & 5e (Type II)
'Diamond Jubilee 1952-2012'	None	Spring Stampex 2012 (22-25 February: 4 days)	FS1a/3a, 4a, 5a & 5e (Type II)
'Perth 2012 19-22 October'	None	The National Philatelic Exhibition, Perth, Scotland (4 days) (N.B. only available to non-delegates on 19/20 October: 2 days)	FS1b/3b, 4b, 5b & 5eb (Type III)
'The Coronation 60th Anniversary' (both lines ranged left)	None	Spring Stampex 2013 (20-23 February: 4 days)	FS1b/3b, 4b, 5b & 5eb (Type III)
as above but with first line slightly inset	None	Spring Stampex 2013 (20-23 February: 4 days) (N.B. only available from stock produced in advance for sale at Royal Mail Exhibition stand)	FS1b/3b, 4b, 5b & 5eb (Type III)
'84th Scottish Congress 2013'	None	The Annual Congress of Scottish Philatelic Societies, Perth, Scotland (19-20 April: 2 days)	FS1b/3b, 4b, 5b & 5eb (Type III)
'Australia 2013 World Stamp Expo' GB version (with the word 'World' included, only available from stock produced in advance of the Exhibition, and specifically for sale in the UK from Royal Mail via Tallents House)	None	Australia International Stamp Exhibition, Melbourne, Australia (10-15 May: 6 days)	FS1b/3b, 4b, 5b & 5eb (Type III)
'Australia 2013 Stamp Expo' AU version (without the word 'World', only available from machines at the Exhibition; 'World' omitted unintentionally)	None	Australia International Stamp Exhibition, Melbourne, Australia (10-15 May: 6 days)	FS1b/3b, 4b, 5b & 5eb (Type III)
'Stampex 2014 19-22 February'	None	Spring Stampex 2014 (4 days)	FS1b/3b, 4b, 5b & 5eb (Type III)
	MA13	(N.B. sometimes when the machine was re-filled, stock bearing MA13 was used)	FS77/79, 81/83 (but Type III)
Machin, 1st/1stL/E-20g/E-60g/WW-20g/WW-60g (N.B. WW-10g and WW-40g replaced by E-60g and WW-60g):			
'85th Scottish Congress 2014'	None	The Annual Congress of Scottish Philatelic Societies, Perth, Scotland (11-12 April: 2 days)	FS1b/3b, 3d, 5b, 5f (but Type III)
	MA13	(N.B. sometimes when the machine was re-filled, stock bearing MA13 was used)	FS77/80, 82 & 84 (but Type III)
Machin, 1st/1stL/E-20g WW-10g/E-60g/WW-20g/WW-60g (N.B. E-20g WW-10g 'dual' value in place of E-20g):			
'Philakorea 2014 World Stamp Expo'	None	Philakorea World Stamp Exhibition, Seoul, Korea (7-12 August: 6 days) (N.B. stock for sale in the UK from Royal Mail via Tallents House was produced in advance of the Exhibition)	FS1d, 2d, 3cb, 3d?, 5d & 5f? (Type IIIA)
	MA13	(N.B. stocks without a date code and with an MA13 were used in machines both in the UK and at the exhibition)	FS77b, 78b, 79bb, 80?, 82b & 84? (Type IIIA)
Machin, 1st/1stL/E-20g WW-10g/E-100g/WW-20g/WW-100g (N.B. E-100g and WW-100g values in place of E-60g and WW-60g):			
'86th Scottish Congress 2015' (with '2015' included, only available from machines at the Exhibition)	MA13	The Annual Congress of Scottish Philatelic Societies, Perth, Scotland (17-18 April: 2 days)	FS77b, 78b, 79bb, 80ca, 82b & 84ca (Type IIIA)
	None	(N.B. sometimes when the machine was re-filled, stock that did not have a date code was used)	FS1d, 2d, 3cb, 3ea, 5d & 5ga (Type IIIA)
'86th Scottish Congress' (without '2015', only available from stock produced in advance of the Exhibition; '2015' omitted unintentionally)	MA13	The Annual Congress of Scottish Philatelic Societies, Perth, Scotland (17-18 April: 2 days)	FS77b, 78b, 79bb, 80ca, 82b & 84ca (Type IIIA)
	None	(N.B. from the stock produced in advance of the Exhibition only a small part did not have a date code)	FS1d, 2d, 3cb, 3ea, 5d & 5ga (Type IIIA)
'Europhilex London Penny Black 175'	MA13	Europhilex Stamp Exhibition, London 2015 (13-16 May: 4 days)	FS77b, 78b, 79bb, 80ca, 82b & 84ca (Type IIIA)
	None	(N.B. sometimes when the machine was re-filled, stock that did not have a date code was used)	FS1d, 2d, 3cb, 3ea, 5d & 5ga (Type IIIA)
'Singpex 2015 World Stamp Expo'	MA13	Singpex World Stamp Exhibition, Singapore (14-19 August: 6 days) (N.B. stock for sale in the UK from Royal Mail via Tallents House was produced in advance of the Exhibition; only stock with MA13 was used at the exhibition)	FS77b, 78b, 79bb, 80ca, 82b & 84ca (Type IIIA)
	None	(N.B. sometimes when the machine at Tallents House was re-filled, stock that did not have a date code was used)	FS1d, 2d, 3cb, 3ea, 5d & 5ga (Type IIIA)

Stamp design, values, and inscription	Date code	The date and duration of the particular inscription (all the dates are inclusive)	Cat. No. of stamp issue without inscription, or closest match
Machin, 1st/1stL/E-20g WW-10g/E-100g/WW-20g/WW-100g *continued*			
'Queen Elizabeth II Longest Reign'	None	Autumn Stampex 2015 (16-19 September: 4 days)	FS1d, 2d, 3cb, 3ea, 5d & 5ga (Type IIIA)
	MA13	(N.B. stock bearing MA13 was only available for a very short period, apparently from one roll only)	FS77b, 78b, 79bb, 80ca, 82b & 84ca (Type IIIA)
'500 Years of Royal Mail'	None	Spring Stampex 2016 (17-20 February: 4 days)	FS1d, 2d, 3cb, 3ea, 5d & 5ga (Type IIIA)
	MA13	(N.B. sometimes when the machine at was re-filled, stock bearing MA13 was used)	FS77b, 78b, 79bb, 80ca, 82b & 84ca (Type IIIA)
Union Flag, 1st/1stL/E-20g/WW-10g/WW-20g/WW-40g:			
'Diamond Jubilee 1952-2012'	None	Autumn Stampex 2012 (26-29 September: 4 days)	FS39/44 (but Type III)
'Perth 2012 19-22 October'	None	The National Philatelic Exhibition, Perth, Scotland (4 days) (N.B. only available to non-delegates on 19/20 October: 2 days)	FS39/44 (but Type III)
'84th Scottish Congress 2013'	None	The Annual Congress of Scottish Philatelic Societies, Perth, Scotland (19-20 April: 2 days)	FS39/44 (but Type III)
'Australia 2013 World Stamp Expo' GB version (with the word 'World' included, only available from stock produced in advance of the Exhibition, and specifically for sale in the UK from Royal Mail via. Tallents House)	None	Australia International Stamp Exhibition, Melbourne, Australia (10-15 May: 6 days)	FS39/44 (but Type III)
'Australia 2013 Stamp Expo' AU version (without the word 'World', only available from machines at the Exhibition; 'World' omitted unintentionally)	None	Australia International Stamp Exhibition, Melbourne, Australia (10-15 May: 6 days)	FS39/44 (but Type III)
'The Coronation 60th Anniversary'	MA13	Autumn Stampex 2013 (18-21 September: 4 days)	FS85/90 (but Type III)
Union Flag, 1st/1stL/E-20g/E-60g/WW-20g/WW-60g (N.B. WW-10g and WW-40g replaced by E-60g and WW-60g):			
'85th Scottish Congress 2014'	MA13	The Annual Congress of Scottish Philatelic Societies, Perth, Scotland (11-12 April: 2 days)	FS85/91 (but Type III)
	None	(N.B. sometimes when the machine was re-filled, stock that did not have a date code was used)	FS39/41, 41b, 43 & 44b (but Type III)
Union Flag, 1st/1stL/E-20g WW-10g/E-60g/WW-20g/WW-60g (N.B. E-20g WW-10g "dual" value in place of E-20g):			
'Philakorea 2014 World Stamp Expo'	None	Philakorea World Stamp Exhibition, Seoul, Korea (7-12 August: 6 days). (N.B. stock for sale in the UK from Royal Mail via Tallents House was produced in advance of the Exhibition)	FS39, 40, 41a, 41b, 43 & 44b (but Type IIIA)
	MA13	(N.B. MA13 is only known from a very small part of the stock produced in advance of the Exhibition)	FS85/91 (but Type IIIA)
'Spring Stampex February 2015'	None	Spring Stampex 2015 (18-21 February: 4 days)	FS39, 40, 41a, 41b, 43 & 44b (but Type IIIA)
Union Flag, 1st/1stL/E-20g WW-10g/E-100g/WW-20g/WW-100g (N.B. E-100g and WW-100g values in place of E-60g and WW-60g):			
'86th Scottish Congress 2015' (with '2015' included, only available from machines at the Exhibition)	None	The Annual Congress of Scottish Philatelic Societies, Perth, Scotland (17-18 April: 2 days)	FS39, 40, 41a, 41c, 43 & 44c (but Type IIIA)
'86th Scottish Congress' (without '2015', only available from stock produced in advance of the Exhibition; '2015' omitted unintentionally)	None	The Annual Congress of Scottish Philatelic Societies, Perth, Scotland (17-18 April: 2 days)	FS39, 40, 41a, 41c, 43 & 44c (but Type IIIA)
'Singpex 2015 World Stamp Expo'	None	Singpex World Stamp Exhibition, Singapore (14-19 August: 6 days) (N.B. stock for sale in the UK from Royal Mail via Tallents House was produced in advance of the Exhibition)	FS39, 40, 41a, 41c, 43 & 44c (but Type IIIA)
'Hong Kong November 2015'	None	Hong Kong World Stamp Exhibition (20-23 November: 4 days). (N.B. stock for sale in the UK from Royal Mail via Tallents House was produced in advance of the Exhibition.)	FS39, 40, 41a, 41c, 43 & 44c (but Type IIIA)
Poppy, 1st/1stL/E-20g WW-10g/E-60g/WW-20g/WW-60g:			
'First World War Centenary'	MA14	Autumn Stampex 2014 (17-20 September: 4 days)	FS103, 104, 105, 106, 107 & 108 (but Type IIIA)

Stamp design, values, and inscription	Date code	The date and duration of the particular inscription (all the dates are inclusive)	Cat. No. of stamp issue without inscription, or closest match
Hong Kong Sea Travel, 1st/1stL/E-20g WW-10g/E-100g/WW-20g/WW-100g:			
'Hong Kong November 2015'	MA15	Hong Kong World Stamp Exhibition (20-23 November: 4 days). (N.B. stock for sale in the UK from Royal Mail via Tallents House was produced in advance of the Exhibition.)	FS131/136 (but Type IIIA & digitally printed)

Only Post & Go stamps with inscriptions from the UK and international stamp exhibitions, the UK's national Postal Museum, for a short time Royal Mail Enquiry Offices, and also the Armed Forces museums, are included in the inscription tables. Inscriptions from other locations are not within the scope of these tables. This table is specific to the inscriptions from Exhibitions. Inscriptions from other primary locations are recorded in separate tables. Some of the catalogue numbers shown are provisional and may be subject to change.

Post & Go stamps—the different issues and inscriptions from Royal Mail Enquiry Offices to 29 March 2016: a simplified checklist

Stamp design, values, and inscription	Date code	The date and duration of the particular inscription (all the dates are inclusive)	Cat. No. of stamp issue without inscription, or closest match
Machin, 1st/1stL/E-20g WW-10g/E-60g/WW-20g/WW-60g			
'Bradford N'	MA13	Bradford North Royal Mail Enquiry Office (9 February through to 28 March 2015) (N.B. this inscription was the result of a two-office trial which is now ended; Royal Mail have suggested that Enquiry Office inscriptions will no longer be used)	FS77b, 78b, 79bb, 80?, 82b, & 84? (Type IIIA)
'Crewe'	MA13	Crewe Royal Mail Enquiry Office (9 February through to 28 March 2015) (N.B. this inscription was the result of a two-office trial which is now ended; Royal Mail have suggested that Enquiry Office inscriptions will no longer be used)	FS77b, 78b, 79bb, 80?, 82b, & 84? (Type IIIA)
Machin, 2nd/2ndL:			
'Bradford N'	MA12	Bradford North Royal Mail Enquiry Office (9 February through to 28 March 2015) (N.B. this inscription was the result of a two-office trial which is now ended; Royal Mail have suggested that Enquiry Office inscriptions will no longer be used)	FS93b/94b (Type IIIA)
'Crewe'	MA12	Crewe Royal Mail Enquiry Office (9 February through to 28 March 2015) (N.B. this inscription was the result of a two-office trial which is now ended; Royal Mail have suggested that Enquiry Office inscriptions will no longer be used)	FS93b/94b (Type IIIA)

'Only Post & Go stamps with inscriptions from the UK and international stamp exhibitions, the UK's national Postal Museum, for a short time Royal Mail Enquiry Offices, and also the Armed Forces museums, are included in the inscription tables. Inscriptions from other locations are not within the scope of these tables. This table is specific to the inscriptions from two Royal Mail Enquiry Offices. Inscriptions from other primary locations are recorded in separate tables. Some of the catalogue numbers shown are provisional and may be subject to change.

Post & Go stamps—the different issues and inscriptions from 'The Postal Museum' (formerly 'The BPMA'), to 29 March 2016: a simplified checklist

Stamp design, values, and inscription	Date code	The date and duration of the particular inscription (all the dates are inclusive)	Cat. No. of stamp issue without inscription, or closest match
Machin, 1st/1stL/E-20g/WW-10g/WW-20g/WW-40g:			
'B.P.M.A.' (low set; inscription is immediately above code line)	None	3 December 2012 through to and including 18 February 2014	FS1b/3b, 4b, 5b & 5eb (Type III)
'The B.P.M.A. Postage Due 1914'	None	19 February through to 29 March 2014	FS1b/3b, 4b, 5b & 5eb (Type III)
	MA13	(N.B. Sometimes the machine was refilled with stock bearing MA13. An RMS II machine has been used since 24 March 2014, and the stamps from it have a subtly different typeface. Between 24 and 29 March only stamps bearing MA13 were dispensed.)	FS77/79, 81/83 (but Type III)
Machin, 1st/1stL/E-20g/E-60g/WW-20g/WW-60g (N.B. WW-10g and WW-40g replaced by E-60g and WW-60g):			
'The B.P.M.A. Postage Due 1914'	MA13	31 March through to 25 April 2014	FS77/80, 82 & 84 (but Type III)
Machin, 1st/1stL/E-20g WW-10g/E-60g/WW-20g/WW-60g (N.B. E-20g WW-10g 'dual' value in place of E-20g):			
'The B.P.M.A.' (high set; inscription is immediately below service indicator)	MA13	28 April through to 19 August 2014 (N.B. E-20g WW-10g in large typeface.)	FS77, 78, 79b, 80, 82 & 84 (but Type III)
'The B.P.M.A. Inland Airmail 1934' (+ Airmail logo)	None	20 August through to 20 October 2014	FS1d, 2d, 3cb, 3d?, 5d & 5f? (Type IIIA)
	MA13	(N.B. Sometimes the machine was refilled with stock bearing MA13.)	FS77b, 78b, 79bb, 80?, 82b & 84? (Type IIIA)
'The B.P.M.A.' (low set; inscription is immediately above code line)	None	21 October 2014 through to 17 Februray 2015 (N.B. All six values have a revised (smaller) typeface.)	FS1d, 2d, 3cb, 3d?, 5d & 5f? (Type IIIA)
'The B.P.M.A. Trollope 200' (+ Postbox logo)	MA13	18 February through to 28 March 2015	FS77b, 78b, 79bb, 80?, 82b & 84? (Type IIIA)
Machin, 1st/1stL/E-20g WW-10g/E-100g/WW-20g/WW-100g (N.B. E-100g and WW-100g values in place of E-60g and WW-60g):			
'The B.P.M.A. Trollope 200' (+ Postbox logo)	MA13	30 March through to 30 April 2015	FS77b, 78b, 79bb, 80ca, 82b & 84ca (Type IIIA)
'The B.P.M.A.' (low set; inscription is immediately above code line)	MA13	1 through to 5 May 2015, and 8 August 2015 through to 29 January 2016 (N.B. All six values have a revised (smaller) typeface.)	FS77b, 78b, 79bb, 80ca, 82b & 84ca (Type IIIA)
'The B.P.M.A. Penny Black 175' (+ Maltese Cross logo)	MA13	6 May through to 7 August 2015	FS77b, 78b, 79bb, 80ca, 82b & 84ca (Type IIIA)
'The Postal Museum' (positioned before the wording is a small format version of the museum's envelope logo)	MA13	From 1 February 2016 (N.B. Initially the 'envelope' logo was inset at the left, but from 15 February it was re-positioned so as to be ranged left.)	FS77b, 78b, 79bb, 80ca, 82b & 84ca (Type IIIA)
Machin, 2nd/2ndL:			
'The B.P.M.A. Inland Airmail 1934' (+ Airmail logo) (N.B. on 16 September 2014, due to software glitch, some (blue-coloured) second class stock was printed 1st/1stL.)	MA12	20 August through to 20 October 2014	FS93b/94b (Type IIIA)
'The B.P.M.A.' (low set; inscription is immediately above code line)	MA12	21 October through to 12 November 2014, 29 December 2014 through to 17 February 2015, 1 through to 5 May 2015, 8 August through to 13 November 2015, and 4 January through to 29 January 2016	FS93b/94b (Type IIIA)
'The B.P.M.A. Trollope 200' (+ Postbox logo)	MA12	18 February through to 30 April 2015	FS93b/94b (Type IIIA)
'The B.P.M.A. Penny Black 175' (+ Maltese Cross logo)	MA13	6 May through to 7 August 2015	FS93b/94b (Type IIIA)
	MA12	(N.B. During August the machine was re-filled with stock bearing MA12. All examples with MA12 have their date code obscured owing to the Maltese Cross being set slightly lower and to the right, the result of a software upgrade.)	FS93b/94b (Type IIIA)
'The Postal Museum' (positioned before the wording is a small format version of the museum's envelope logo)	MA12	From 1 February 2016 (N.B. Initially the 'envelope' logo was inset at the left, but from 15 February it was re-positioned so as to be ranged left.)	FS93b/94b (Type IIIA)

Stamp design, values, and inscription	Date code	The date and duration of the particular inscription (all the dates are inclusive)	Cat. No. of stamp issue without inscription, or closest match
Union Flag, 1st/1stL/E-20g/WW-10g/WW-20g/WW-40g:			
'The B.P.M.A.' (low set; inscription is immediately above code line)	None	21 February through to 4 November 2013, and 30 December 2013 through to 18 February 2014	FS39/44 (but Type III)
'The B.P.M.A. Postage Due 1914'	None	19 February through to 29 March 2014	FS39/44 (but Type III)
	MA13	(N.B. Between 19 and 21 February 2014 the machine dispensed stock bearing MA13. An RMS II machine has been used since 24 March 2014, and the stamps from it have a subtly different typeface. Only stamps without a date code were dispensed between 24 and 29 March.)	FS85/90 (but Type III)
Union Flag, 1st/1stL/E-20g/E-60g/WW-20g/WW-60g (N.B. WW-10g and WW-40g replaced by E-60g and WW-60g):			
'The B.P.M.A. Postage Due 1914'	None	31 March through to 25 April 2014	FS39/41, 41b, 43 & 44b (but Type III)
Union Flag, 1st/1stL/E-20g WW-10g/E-60g/WW-20g/WW-60g (N.B. E-20g WW-10g 'dual' value in place of E-20g):			
'The B.P.M.A.' (high set; inscription is immediately below service indicator)	None	28 April through to 19 August 2014 (N.B. E-20g WW-10g in large typeface.)	FS39, 40, 41a, 41b, 43 & 44b (but Type III)
'The B.P.M.A.' (low set; inscription is immediately above code line)	None	21 October 2014 through to 17 February 2015 (N.B. All six values have a revised (smaller) typeface.)	FS39, 40, 41a, 41b, 43 & 44b (but Type III)
'The B.P.M.A.' (high set; inscription is immediately below service indicator)	None	18 February through to 28 March 2015 (N.B. All six values have a revised (smaller) typeface.)	FS39, 40, 41a, 41b, 43 & 44b (but Type IIIA)
Union Flag, 1st/1stL/E-20g WW-10g/E-100g/WW-20g/WW-100g (N.B. E-100g and WW-100g values in place of E-60g and WW-60g):			
'The B.P.M.A.' (low set; inscription is immediately above code line)	None	30 March 2015 through to 29 January 2016 (N.B. All six values have a revised (smaller) typeface.)	FS39, 40, 41a, 41c, 43 & 44c (but Type IIIA)
'The Postal Museum' (positioned before the wording is a large format version of the museum's envelope logo)	None	From 1 February 2016	FS39, 40, 41a, 41c, 43 & 44c (but Type IIIA)
Robin, 1st/1stL/E-20g/WW-10g/WW-20g/WW-40g:			
'The B.P.M.A.' (low set; inscription is immediately above code line)	MA12	3 December 2012 through to 20 February 2013	FS51a/56a (Type III)
	MA13	5 November through to 24 December 2013	FS51a/56a (Type III)
Poppy, 1st/1stL/E-20g/WW-10g/E-60g/WW-20g/WW-60g:			
'The B.P.M.A.' (low set; inscription is immediately above code line)	MA14	21 October through to 12 November 2014	FS103, 104, 105, 106, 107 & 108 (but Type IIIA)
Poppy, 1st/1stL/E-20g WW-10g/E-100g/WW-20g/WW-100g (N.B. E-100g and WW-100g values in place of E-60g and WW-60g):			
'The B.P.M.A.' (low set; inscription is immediately above code line)	MA15	19 October through to 13 November 2015	FS137, 138, 139, 140, 141 & 142 (Type IIIA)
Winter Greenery, 2nd/2ndL, and 1st/1stL/E-20g WW-10g/E-60g/WW-20g/WW-60g:			
'The B.P.M.A.' (low set; inscription is immediately above code line)	MA14	13 November through to 23 December 2014	FS109b/116b (Type IIIA)
Lion (Heraldic Beast), 1st/1stL/E-20g WW-10g/E-100g/WW-20g/WW-100g:			
'The B.P.M.A.' (low set; inscription is immediately above code line)	MA15	16 September through to 16 October 2015, and 4 January through to 29 January 2016	FS125/130 (but Type IIIA)
'The Postal Museum' (positioned before the wording is a large format version of the museum's envelope logo)	MA15	1 February through to 16 February 2016	FS125/130 (but Type IIIA)
Fur & Feathers, 2nd/2ndL, and 1st/1stL/E-20g WW-10g/E-100g/WW-20g/WW-100g:			
'The B.P.M.A.' (low set; inscription is immediately above code line)	CL15/ MA15	16 November through to 31 December 2015	FS143a/150a (Type IIIA)
Royal Mail Heritage: Transport, 1st ×6 designs (N.B. only exists with 1st):			
'The Postal Museum' (positioned before the wording is a large format version of the museum's envelope logo)	MA16	From 17 February 2016	FS15l×6 (but Type IIIA)

Only Post & Go stamps with inscriptions from the UK and international stamp exhibitions, the UK's national Postal Museum, for a short time Royal Mail Enquiry Offices, and also the Armed Forces museums, are included in the inscription tables. Inscriptions from other locations are not within the scope of these tables. This table is specific to the inscriptions from The Postal Museum (formerly The BPMA, and since 1 February 2016 The Postal Museum). Inscriptions from other primary locations are recorded in separate tables. Some of the catalogue numbers shown are provisional and may be subject to change.

Post & Go stamps—the different issues and inscriptions from the Armed Forces museums to 29 March 2016: a simplified checklist

Stamp design, values, and inscription	Date code	Museum the item was (or is) available from, the date, and duration (all the dates are inclusive)	Cat. No. of stamp issue without inscription, or closest match
Machin, 1st/1stL/E-20g WW-10g/E-60g/WW-20g/WW-60g (N.B. "dual" E-20g WW-10g value in place of E-20g):			
'The NMRN' (high set; inscription is immediately below service indicator)	None	The National Museum Royal Navy (28 July through to 20 October 2014, and 14 November 2014 through to 29 March 2015)	FS1d, 2d, 3c, 3d?, 5d & 5f? (Type IIIA)
'The RMM' (high set; inscription is immediately below service indicator)	MA13	The Royal Marines Museum (13 January through to 29 March 2015)	FS77b, 78b, 79bb, 80?, 82b & 84? (Type IIIA)
	None	(N.B. for a short while the machine was filled with stock that did not have a date code)	FS1d, 2d, 3c, 3d?, 5d & 5f? (Type IIIA)
Machin, 1st/1stL/E-20g WW-10g/E-100g/WW-20g/WW-100g (N.B. E-100g and WW-100g values in place of E-60g and WW-60g):			
'The NMRN' (high set; inscription is immediately below service indicator)	MA13	The National Museum Royal Navy (30 March through to 18 October 2015)	FS77b, 78b, 79bb, 80ca, 82b & 84ca (Type IIIA)
	None	(N.B. for a short while the machine was filled with stock that did not have a date code)	FS1d, 2d, 3cb, 3ea, 5d & 5ga (Type IIIA)
'The RMM' (high set; inscription is immediately below service indicator	MA13	The Royal Marines Museum (30 March through to 18 October 2015)	FS77b, 78b, 79bb, 80ca, 82b & 84ca (Type IIIA)
'The FAAM' (high set; inscription is immediately below service indicator)	MA13	The Royal Navy Fleet Air Arm Museum (14 April through to 18 October 2015)	FS77b, 78b, 79bb, 80ca, 82b & 84ca (Type IIIA)
'The RNSM' (high set; inscription is immediately below service indicator)	MA13	The Royal Navy Submarine Museum (28 July through to 18 October 2015)	FS77b, 78b, 79bb, 80ca, 82b & 84ca (Type IIIA)
'Royal Navy' + circle logo [words replace acronym] (high set; inscription is immediately below service indicator)	MA13	The National Museum Royal Navy (from 16 November 2015)	FS77b, 78b, 79bb, 80ca, 82b & 84ca (Type IIIA)
'Royal Marines' + circle logo [words replace acronym] (high set; inscription is immediately below service indicator)	MA13	The Royal Marines Museum (from 16 November 2015)	FS77b, 78b, 79bb, 80ca, 82b & 84ca (Type IIIA)
'Fleet Air Arm' + circle logo [words replace acronym] (high set; inscription is immediately below service indicator)	MA13	The Royal Navy Fleet Air Arm Museum (from 16 November 2015)	FS77b, 78b, 79bb, 80ca, 82b & 84ca (Type IIIA)
'RN Submarine' + circle logo [words replace acronym] (high set; inscription is immediately below service indicator)	MA13	The Royal Navy Submarine Museum (from 16 November 2015)	FS77b, 78b, 79bb, 80ca, 82b & 84ca (Type IIIA)
Union Flag, 1st/1stL/E-20g WW-10g/E-60g/WW-20g/WW-60g (N.B. "dual" E-20g WW-10g value in place of E-20g):			
'The NMRN' (high set; inscription is immediately below service indicator)	None	The National Museum Royal Navy (28 July through to 20 October 2014, and 11 November 2014 through to 29 March 2015)	FS39, 40, 41a, 41b, 43 & 44b (but Type IIIA)
'The NMRN' Trafalgar Day	None	The National Museum Royal Navy (21 October through to 10 November 2014)	FS39, 40, 41a, 41b, 43 & 44b (but Type IIIA)
'The RMM' (high set; inscription is immediately below service indicator)	None	The Royal Marines Museum (13 January through to 29 March 2015)	FS39, 40, 41a, 41b, 43 & 44b (but Type IIIA)
Union Flag, 1st/1stL/E-20g WW-10g/E-100g/WW-20g/WW-100g (N.B. E-100g and WW-100g values in place of E-60g and WW-60g):			
'The NMRN' (high set; inscription is immediately below service indicator)	None	The National Museum Royal Navy (30 March through to 7 May 2015, and 30 May through to 18 October 2015)	FS39, 40, 41a, 41c, 43 & 44c (but Type IIIA)
'The NMRN V.E. Day 70'	None	The National Museum Royal Navy (08 May through to 29 May 2015)	FS39, 40, 41a, 41c, 43 & 44c (but Type IIIA)
'The RMM' (high set; inscription is immediately below service indicator)	None	The Royal Marines Museum (30 March through to 7 May 2015, and 30 May through to 18 October 2015)	FS39, 40, 41a, 41c, 43 & 44c (but Type IIIA)
'The RMM V.E. Day 70'	None	The Royal Marines Museum (08 May through to 29 May 2015)	FS39, 40, 41a, 41c, 43 & 44c (but Type IIIA)
'The FAAM' (high set; inscription is immediately below service indicator)	None	The Royal Navy Fleet Air Arm Museum (14 April through to 7 May , and 30 May through to 18 October 2015)	FS39, 40, 41a, 41c, 43 & 44c (but Type IIIA)
'The FAAM V.E. Day 70'	None	The Royal Navy Fleet Air Arm Museum (08 May through to 29 May 2015)	FS39, 40, 41a, 41c, 43 & 44c (but Type IIIA)
'The RNSM' (high set; inscription is immediately below service indicator)	None	The Royal Navy Submarine Museum (28 July through to 18 October 2015)	FS39, 40, 41a, 41c, 43 & 44c (but Type IIIA)
'Royal Navy Trafalgar Day' [words replace acronym]	None	The National Museum Royal Navy (19 October through to 15 November 2015)	FS39, 40, 41a, 41c, 43 & 44c (but Type IIIA)
'Royal Navy' [words replace acronym] (high set; inscription is immediately below service indicator)	None	The National Museum Royal Navy (from 16 November 2015)	FS39, 40, 41a, 41c, 43 & 44c (but Type IIIA)
'Royal Marines Trafalgar Day' [words replace acronym]	None	The Royal Marines Museum (19 October through to 15 November 2015)	FS39, 40, 41a, 41c, 43 & 44c (but Type IIIA)

Stamp design, values, and inscription	Date code	Museum the item was (or is) available from, the date, and duration (all the dates are inclusive)	Cat. No. of stamp issue without inscription, or closest match
Union Flag, 1st/1stL/E-20g WW-10g/E-100g/WW-20g/WW-100g *continued*			
'Royal Marines' [words replace acronym] (high set; inscription is immediately below service indicator)	None	The Royal Marines Museum (from 16 November 2015)	FS39, 40, 41a, 41c, 43 & 44c (but Type IIIA)
'Fleet Air Arm' [words replace acronym] (high set; inscription is immediately below service indicator)	None	The Royal Navy Fleet Air Arm Museum (from 19 October 2015)	FS39, 40, 41a, 41c, 43 & 44c (but Type IIIA)
'RN Submarine' [words replace acronym] (high set; inscription is immediately below service indicator)	None	The Royal Navy Submarine Museum (from 19 October 2015)	FS39, 40, 41a, 41c, 43 & 44c (but Type IIIA)
Poppy, 1st/1stL/E-20g WW-10g/E-60g/WW-20g/WW-60g:			
'The NMRN Remembrance'	MA14	The National Museum Royal Navy (21 October through to 13 November 2014)	FS103, 104, 105, 106, 107 & 108 (but Type IIIA)
Poppy, 1st/1stL/E-20g WW-10g/E-100g/WW-20g/WW-100g (N.B. E-100g and WW-100g values in place of E-60g and WW-60g):			
'Royal Navy' [words replace acronym] (high set; inscription is immediately below service indicator)	MA15	The National Museum Royal Navy (19 October through to 15 November 2015)	FS137, 138, 139, 140, 141 &142 (Type IIIA)
'Royal Marines' [words replace acronym] (high set; inscription is immediately below service indicator)	MA15	The Royal Marines Museum (19 October through to 15 November 2015)	FS137, 138, 139, 140, 141 &142 (Type IIIA)
'Fleet Air Arm' [words replace acronym] (high set; inscription is immediately below service indicator)	MA15	The Royal Navy Fleet Air Arm Museum (19 October through to 15 November 2015)	FS137, 138, 139, 140, 141 &142 (Type IIIA)
'RN Submarine' [words replace acronym] (high set; inscription is immediately below service indicator)	MA15	The Royal Navy Submarine Museum (19 October through to 15 November 2015)	FS137, 138, 139, 140, 141 &142 (Type IIIA)

Only Post & Go stamps with inscriptions from the UK and international stamp exhibitions, the UK's national Postal Museum (formerly The BPMA, and since 1 February 2016 The Postal Museum), for a short time Royal Mail Enquiry Offices, and also the Armed Forces' museums, are included in the inscription tables. Inscriptions from other locations are not within the scope of these tables. This table is specific to the inscriptions from Armed Forces museums. Inscriptions from other primary locations are recorded in separate tables. Some of the catalogue numbers shown are provisional and may be subject to change.

Post & Go stamps – the different HYTECH & ROYAL MAIL 'SERIES II' printings from exhibitions and Stamp Fairs in the United Kingdon but without inscriptions (February 2011 - 20 February 2016): a simplified checklist

Stamp design, values and machine type	Format produced		Event the stamps were available from, the date and duration (all the dates are inclusive)	Main distinguishing features			Catalogue No. of standard issue or closest match
	CS	Set of 36		Space between service indicator lines	Code string consisting of		
					Numerals only (Type II)	Letters & numerals (Type III)	
Machin, 1st/1stL/E-20g/WW-10g/WW-20g without date code (N.B. five values only):							
Hytech Postal Vision (N.B. a trial machine) († weight line inset)	✓		Spring Stampex 2011 (23 - 26 February: 4 days)	3mm	yes		FS1a/5a
Machin, 1st/1stL/E-20g/WW-10g/WW-20g/WW-40g without date code:							
Hytech 'next generation'	✓		York Stamp Fair (18 - 19 January 2013: 2 days) Salisbury Stamp Fair (15 - 16 March 2013: 2 days) Midpex Exhibition (6 July 2013: 1 day) (N.B. similar stamps were first issued in November 2012 from a pop-up Christmas Post Shop in Camden, London)	2.6mm		yes	FS1b/3b, 4b, 5b & 5eb
Royal Mail 'Series II'	✓		Salisbury Stamp Fair (14 - 15 March 2014: 2 days)	2.4mm		yes	FS1b/3b, 4b, 5b & 5eb
Machin, 1st/1stL/E-20g/WW-10g/WW-20g/WW-40g with MA13 date code:							
Hytech 'next generation'	✓		York Stamp Fair (19 - 20 July 2013: 2 days) Autumn Stampex 2013 (18 - 21 September: 4 days) Stafford Stamp Fair (8 - 9 November 2013: 2 days) York Stamp Fair (17 - 18 January 2014: 2 days)	2.6mm		yes	FS77/79, 81/83 (but Type III)
Royal Mail 'Series II'	✓		Salisbury Stamp Fair (14 - 15 March 2014: 2 days)	2.4mm		yes	FS77/79, 81/83 (but Type III)
Machin, 1st/1stL/E-20g WW-10g/E-60g/WW-20g/WW-60g without date code (N.B. E-20g WW-10g 'dual' value in place of E-20g, and WW-10g and WW-40g replaced by E-60g and WW-60g):							
Royal Mail 'Series II' (Euro 20g in a large typeface)	✓		York Stamp Fair (18 - 19 July 2014: 2 days)	2.4mm		yes	FS1b, 2b, 3c?, 3d?, 5b, 5f?
Royal Mail 'Series II' (all values with smaller (revised) typeface)	✓		Autumn Stampex 2014 (17 - 20 September: 4 days) Stafford Stamp Fair (7 - 8 November 2014: 2 days) Spring Stampex 2015 (18 - 21 February: 4 days) (N.B. limited availablilty and only known from stock produced in advance of the exhibition)	2.7mm		yes (Type IIIA)	FS1d, 2d, 3cb, 3d?, 5d & 5f?
Machin, 1st/1stL/E-20g WW-10g/E-60g/WW-20g/WW-60g with MA13 date code (N.B. E-20g WW-10g 'dual' value in place of E-20g, and WW-10g and WW-40g replaced by E-60g and WW-60g):							
Royal Mail 'Series II' (Euro 20g in a large typeface)	✓		York Stamp Fair (18 - 19 July 2014: 2 days)	2.4mm		yes	FS77/78, 79b, 80, 82 & 84 (but Type III)
Royal Mail 'Series II' (all values with smaller (revised) typeface)	✓		Autumn Stampex 2014 (17 - 20 September: 4 days) Stafford Stamp Fair (7 - 8 November 2014: 2 days) Spring Stampex 2015 (18 - 21 February: 4 days)	2.7mm		yes (Type IIIA)	FS77b, 78b, 79bb, 80?, 82b & 84?
Machin, 1st/1stL/E-20g WW-10g/E-100g/WW-20g/WW-100g without date code (N.B. E-100g and WW-100g values in place of E-60g and WW-60g):							
Royal Mail 'Series II' (all values with smaller (revised) typeface)	✓		Midpex Exhibition (4 July 2015: 1 day) (N.B. similar stamps were (officially) issued on 3 June 2015 from Royal Mail Enquiry offices)	2.7mm		yes (Type IIIA)	FS1d, 2d, 3cb, 3ea, 5d & 5ga
Machin, 1st/1stL/E-20g WW-10g/E-100g/WW-20g/WW-100g with MA13 date code (N.B. E-100g and WW-100g values in place of E-60g and WW-60g):							
Royal Mail 'Series II' (all values with smaller (revised) typeface)	✓		Midpex Exhibition (4 July 2015: 1 day) (N.B. similar stamps were (officially) issued on 30 March 2015 from Royal Mail Enquiry offices)	2.7mm		yes (Type IIIA)	FS77b, 78b, 79bb, 80ca, 82b & 84ca

Stamp design, values and machine type	Format produced		Event the stamps were available from, the date and duration (all the dates are inclusive)	Main distinguishing features			Catalogue No. of standard issue or closest match
	CS	Set of 36		Space between service indicator lines	Code string consisting of		
					Numerals only (Type II)	Letters & numerals (Type III)	
Machin, 2nd/2ndL with MA12 date code:							
Hytech 'next generation'	✓		Spring Stampex 2013 (20 - 23 February: 4 days) (N.B. similar stamps, but not identical, were (officially) issued in November 2013 from a travelling pop-up Christmas post office)	2.6mm		yes	FS93, 94
Union Flag, 1st/1stL/E-20g/WW-10g/WW-20g/WW-40g without date code:							
Hytech 'next generation'	✓		Autumn Stampex 2012 (26 - 29 September: 4 days) York Stamp Fair (18 - 19 January 2013: 2 days) Salisbury Stamp Fair (15 - 16 March 2013: 2 days) Midpex Exhibition (6 July 2013: 1 day)	2.6mm		yes	FS39/44 (but Type III)
Royal Mail 'Series II'	✓		Spring Stampex 2014 (19 - 22 February: 4 days) (N.B. only available on 21/22 February: 2 days) Salisbury Stamp Fair (14 - 15 March 2014: 2 days)	2.4mm		yes	FS39/44 (but Type III)
Union Flag, 1st/1stL/E-20g/WW-10g/WW-20g/WW-40g with MA13 date code:							
Hytech 'next generation'	✓		York Stamp Fair (19 - 20 July 2013: 2 days) York Stamp Fair (17 - 18 January 2014: 2 days)	2.6mm		yes	FS85/90 (but Type III)
Royal Mail 'Series II'	✓		Spring Stampex 2014 (19 - 22 February: 4 days) Salisbury Stamp Fair (14 - 15 March 2014: 2 days)	2.4mm		yes	FS85/90 (but Type III)
Union Flag, 1st/1stL/E-20g/E-60g/WW-20g/WW-60g without date code (N.B. WW-10g and WW-40g replaced by E-60g and WW-60g):							
Royal Mail 'Series II'	✓		The Annual Congress of Scottish Philatelic Societies, Perth, Scotland (11 - 12 April 2014: 2 days)	2.4mm		yes	FS39/41, 41b, 43, 44b (but Type III)
Union Flag, 1st/1stL/E-20g/E-60g/WW-20g/WW-60g with MA13 date code (N.B. WW-10g and WW-40g replaced by E-60g and WW-60g):							
Royal Mail 'Series II'	✓		The Annual Congress of Scottish Philatelic Societies, Perth, Scotland (11 - 12 April 2014: 2 days)	2.4mm		yes	FS85/91 (but Type III)
Union Flag, 1st/1stL/E-20g WW-10g/E-60g/WW-20g/WW-60g without date code (N.B. E-20g WW-10g 'dual' value in place of E-20g, and with E-60g and WW-60g):							
Royal Mail 'Series II' (Euro 20g in a large typeface)	✓		York Stamp Fair (18 - 19 July 2014: 2 days)	2.4mm		yes	FS39, 40, 41a, 41b, 43, 44b (but Type III)
Royal Mail 'Series II' (all values with smaller (revised) typeface)	✓		Autumn Stampex 2014 (17 - 20 September: 4 days) Stafford Stamp Fair (7 - 8 November 2014: 2 days)	2.7mm		yes (Type IIIA)	FS39, 40, 41a, 41b, 43, 44b (but Type IIIA)
Union Flag, 1st/1stL/E-20g WW-10g/E-60g/WW-20g/WW-100g without date code (N.B. E-100b and WW-100g values in place of E-60g and WW-60g):							
Royal Mail 'Series II' (all values with smaller (revised) typeface)	✓		Europhilex 2015 (13 - 16 May: 4 days) Midpex Exhibition (4 July 2015: 1 day) Autumn Stampex 2015 (16 - 19 September: 4 days)	2.7mm		yes (Type IIIA)	FS39, 40, 41a, 41c, 43 & 44c (but Type IIIA)
Robin, 1st/1stL/E-20g/WW-10g/WW-20g/WW-40g with MA13 date code:							
Hytech 'next generation'	✓		Stafford Stamp Fair (8 - 9 November 2013: 2 days) (N.B. similar MA13 stamps were (officially) issued later in November 2013 from a travelling pop-up Christmas post office)	2.6mm		yes	FS51a/56a
Birds of Britain 3rd series, 1st/1stL/E-20g/WW-10g/WW-20g/1st (N.B. only produced in collectors' strips of six with additional '1st Class' value at bottom so all six designs represented):							
Hytech version 1 († weight line inset)	✓		Autumn Stampex 2011 (14 - 17 September: 4 days) (N.B. only available on 14 September: 1 day)	3mm	yes		FS16/20

Stamp design, values and machine type	Format produced		Event the stamps were available from, the date and duration (all the dates are inclusive)	Main distinguishing features			Catalogue No. of standard issue or closest match
	CS	Set of 36		Space between service indicator lines	Code string consisting of		
					Numerals only (Type II)	Letters & numerals (Type III)	
Birds of Britain 4th series, 1st/1stL/E-20g/WW-10g/WW-20g/WW-40g:							
Hytech version 1 († weight line inset)	✓	✓	**Autumn Stampex** 2011 (14 - 17 September: 4 days) (N.B. only available on 16/17 September: 2 days) **Spring Stampex** 2012 (22 - 25 February: 4 days) (N.B. only available on 22/23 September: 2 days)	3mm	yes		FS21/26
Sheep (British Farm Animals 1st series), 1st/1stL/E-20g/WW-10g/WW-20g/WW-40g:							
Hytech version 1 († weight line inset)	✓	✓	**Spring Stampex** 2012 (22 - 25 February: 4 days) (N.B. only available on 24/25 February: 2 days)	3mm	yes		FS27/32
Pigs (British Farm Animals 2nd series), 1st/1stL/E-20g/WW-10g/WW-20g/WW-40g:							
Hytech 'next generation'	✓	✓	**Autumn Stampex** 2012 (26 - 29 September: 4 days) (N.B. only available on 26/27 September: 2 days)	2.6mm		yes	FS33/38 (but Type III)
Cattle (British Farm Animals 3rd series), 1st/1stL/E-20g/WW-10g/WW-20g/WW-40g:							
Hytech 'next generation'	✓	✓	**Autumn Stampex** 2012 (26 - 29 September: 4 days) (N.B. only available on 28/29 September: 2 days)	2.6mm		yes	FS45/50 (but Type III)
Ponds (Freshwater Life 1st series), 1st/1stL/E-20g/WW-10g/WW-20g/WW-40g:							
Hytech 'next generation'	✓	✓	**Spring Stampex** 2013 (20 - 23 February: 4 days) (N.B. only available on 22/23 February: 2 days)	2.6mm		yes	FS59/64 (but Type III)
Lakes (Freshwater Life 2nd series), 1st/1stL/E-20g/WW-10g/WW-20g/WW-40g:							
Hytech 'next generation'	✓	✓	**Midpex Exhibition** (06 July 2013: 1 day) **York Stamp Fair** (19 - 20 July 2013: 2 days)	2.6mm		yes	FS65/70 (but Type III)
Rivers (Freshwater Life 3rd series), 1st/1stL/E-20g/WW-10g/WW-20g/WW-40g:							
Hytech 'next generation'	✓	✓	**Autumn Stampex** 2013 (18 - 21 September: 4 days) (N.B. only available on 20/21 September: 2 days) **Stafford Stamp Fair** (08 - 09 November 2013: 2 days)	2.6mm		yes	FS71/76 (but Type III)
Spring Blooms (British Flora 1st series), 1st/1stL/E-20g/WW-10g/WW-20g/WW-40g:							
Royal Mail 'Series II'	✓	✓	**Spring Stampex** 2014 (19 - 22 February: 4 days)	2.4mm		yes	FS95/97, 99/101 (but Type III)
Symbolic Flowers (British Flora 2nd series), 1st/1stL/E-20g WW-10g/E-60g/WW-20g/WW-60g:							
Royal Mail 'Series II'	✓	✓	**Autumn Stampex** 2014 (17 - 20 September: 4 days)	2.7mm		yes (Type IIIA)	FS103/108 (but Type IIIA)
Working Sail, 1st/1stL/E-20g WW-10g/E-60g/WW-20g/WW-60g:							
Royal Mail 'Series II'	✓	✓	**Spring Stampex** 2015 (18 - 21 February: 4 days)	2.7mm		yes (Type IIIA)	FS117/120, 122/123 (but Type IIIA)
Heraldic Beasts, 1st/1stL/E-20g WW-10g/E-100g/WW-20g/WW-100g:							
Royal Mail 'Series II'	✓	✓	**Europhilex** 2015 (13 - 16 May: 4 days)	2.7mm		yes (Type IIIA)	FS125/130 (but Type IIIA)
Lion design (from Heraldic Beasts issue) in single design rolls, 1st/1stL/E-20g WW-10g/E-100g/WW-20g/WW-100g:							
Royal Mail 'Series II' (stamps gravure printed)	✓		**Autumn Stampex** 2015 (16 - 19 September: 4 days)	2.7mm		yes (Type IIIA)	FS125/130 (but Type IIIA)
Sea Travel, 1st/1stL/E-20g WW-10g/E-100g/WW-20g/WW-100g:							
Royal Mail 'Series II'	✓	✓	**Autumn Stampex** 2015 (16 - 19 September: 4 days)	2.7mm		yes (Type IIIA)	FS131/136 (but Type IIIA)

Stamp design, values and machine type	Format produced		Event the stamps were available from, the date and duration (all the dates are inclusive)	Main distinguishing features			Catalogue No. of standard issue or closest match
	CS	Set of 36		Space between service indicator lines	Code string consisting of		
					Numerals only (Type II)	Letters & numerals (Type III)	
Royal Mail Heritage: Transport, 1st/1stL/E-20g WW-10g/E-100g/WW-20g/WW-100g:							
Royal Mail 'Series II' (stamps gravure printed)	✓	✓	**Spring Stampex** 2016 (17 - 20 February: 4 days)	2.7mm		yes (Type IIIA)	FS151/156 (but Type IIIA)
Locomotive design (from Royal Mail Heritage: Transport issue) from single-design rolls, 1st/1stL/E-20g WW-10g/E-100g/WW-20g/WW-100g:							
Royal Mail 'Series II' (stamps digitally printed)	✓		**Spring Stampex** 2016 (17 - 20 February: 4 days)	2.7mm		yes (Type IIIA)	FS151/156 (but Type IIIA)

Hytech Postal Vision was a trial machine introduced at Spring Stampex 2011. Machines referred to as Hytech version 1 were used at Autumn Stampex 2011 and Spring Stampex 2012. From Autumn Stampex 2012 modified machines were instead brought into use, sometimes referred to as Hytech 'next generation', Hytech version 2, and also Royal Mail Series I. At Spring Stampex 2014 a new machine was brought into use and it is classified as a Royal Mail 'Series II' (although it is sometimes referred to as Royal Mail Series B).

† = stamps generated from Hytech Postal Vision and Hytech version I machines have their weight lines inset, whereas Hytech 'next generation' and Royal Mail 'Series II' stamps have their weight lines ranged left. From Autumn Stampex 2014, Royal Mail 'Series II' machines at exhibitions produced stamps with a smaller typeface. In place of gravure, digital printing is sometimes used for some single-design rolls. Stamps produced by this process are very shiny and have poor background definition, especially in the repeating ROYAL MAIL wording.

CS = collectors' strips: the Machins from the Hytech Postal Vision trial machine are in strips of five, the Machin 2nds are in pairs, and all other collectors' strips are of six stamps. Sets of 36 (from and including Birds of Britain 4th series): all six denominations were available in all six designs making a complete set 36 stamps. Some of the catalogue numbers shown are provisional and may be subject to change.

Regional Issues

PRINTERS (£.s.d. stamps of all regions):—Photo Harrison & Sons. Portrait by Dorothy Wilding Ltd.
DATES OF ISSUE. Conflicting dates of issue have been announced for some of the regional issues, partly explained by the stamps being released on different dates by the Philatelic Bureau in Edinburgh or the Philatelic Counter in London and in the regions. We have adopted the practice of giving the earliest known dates, since once released the stamps could have been used anywhere in the U.K.

CHANNEL ISLANDS

GENERAL ISSUE

C **1** Gathering Vraic   C **2** Islanders gathering Vraic

Broken Wheel (R. 20/5)

(Des J. R. R. Stobie (1d.) or from drawing by E. Blampied (2½d.). Photo Harrison)

1948 (10 May). *Third Anniv of Liberation.* W 127 of Great Britain. *P* 15×14.

C1	C **1**	1d. scarlet	25	55
C2	C **2**	2½d. ultramarine	25	60
		a. Broken wheel	75·00	

First Day Cover .... 35·00

I. ENGLAND

EN **1** Three Lions   EN **2** Crowned Lion with Shield of St. George

EN **3** Oak Tree   EN **4** Tudor Rose

(Des Sedley Place, from sculptures by D. Dathan. Gravure Questa (No. EN1b) or De La Rue (others))

2001 (23 Apr)–**02**. One centre phosphor band (2nd) or two phosphor bands (others). *P* 15×14 (with one elliptical hole in each vertical side). All heads Type I

EN1	EN **1**	(2nd) slate-green and silver	1·00	1·00
		a. Imperf (pair)		
		b. Booklet pane. Nos. EN1/2, each×4, and No. S95, with margins all round (24.9.02)	8·50	

EN2	EN **2**	(1st) lake-brown and silver	1·25	1·00
		a. Imperf pair	£350	
EN3	EN **3**	(E) olive-green and silver	2·25	2·25
EN4	EN **4**	65p. deep reddish lilac and silver	3·00	3·00
EN5		68p. deep reddish lilac and silver (4.7.02)	3·00	3·00

Presentation Pack (Nos. EN1/4) (*P.O. Pack No. 54*)	7·50	
PHQ Cards (Nos. EN1/4) (*set of 4*) (D20)	8·00	14·00

Nos. EN1/3 were initially sold at 19p., 27p. and 36p., the latter representing the basic European airmail rate.

First Day Covers

23.4.01	2nd, 1st, E, 65p. (EN1/4) Philatelic Bureau (Type G, see Introduction)	3·50	
	Windsor	2·25	
4.7.02	68p. (EN5) Tallents House (Type K, see Introduction)	3·50	
	London (as Windsor)	2·00	

Special First Day of Issue Postmark

Combined Presentation Packs for England, Northern Ireland, Scotland and Wales

4.7.02	P.O. Pack No. 59. 68p. from England, Northern Ireland, Scotland and Wales (Nos. EN5, NI93, S99, W88)	12·00
11.5.04	P.O. Pack No. 68. 40p. from England, Northern Ireland, Scotland and Wales (Nos. EN9, NI97, S112, W101)	8·00
5.4.05	P.O. Pack No. 70. 42p. from England, Northern Ireland, Scotland and Wales (Nos. EN10, NI98, S113, W102)	8·00
28.3.06	P.O. Pack No. 73. 44p. and 72p. from England, Northern Ireland, Scotland and Wales (Nos. EN11, EN17, NI99, NI102, S114, S120, W103, W109)	10·00
27.3.07	P.O. Pack No. 76. 48p. and 78p. from England, Northern Ireland, Scotland and Wales (Nos. EN12, EN18, NI124, NI128, S115, S121, W104, and W110)	12·50
1.4.08	P.O. Pack No. 79. 50p. and 81p. from England, Northern Ireland, Scotland and Wales (Nos. EN13, EN19, NI125, NI129, S116, S122, W105, W111)	11·50
29.9.08	P.O. Pack No. 81. 2nd, 1st, 50p. and 81p. from England, Northern Ireland, Scotland and Wales (Nos. EN6/7, EN13, EN19, NI122/3, NI125, NI129, S109/10, S116, S122, W98/9, W105, W111)	26·00
31.3.09	P.O. Pack No. 85. 56p. and 90p. from England, Northern Ireland, Scotland and Wales (Nos. EN14, EN20, NI126, NI130, S117, S123, W106, W112)	14·00
30.3.10	P.O. Pack No. 87. 60p. and 97p. from England, Northern Ireland, Scotland and Wales (Nos. EN15, EN21, NI127, NI131, S118, S124, W107, W113)	20·00
29.3.11	P.O. Pack No. 91. 68p. and £1·10 from England, Northern Ireland, Scotland and Wales (Nos. EN31, EN41, NI101, NI112, S132, S142 W123, W133)	19·00
25.4.12	P.O. Pack No. 95. 87p. and £1·28 from England, Northern Ireland, Scotland and Wales (Nos. EN32, EN42, NI103, NI113, S133, S143, W124, W134)	24·00
27.3.13	P.O. Pack No. 98. 88p. from England, Northern Ireland, Scotland and Wales (Nos. EN33, NI104, S134, W125)	9·50
26.3.14	P.O. Pack No. 100. 97p. from England, Northern Ireland, Scotland and Wales (Nos. EN34, NI105, S135, W126)	10·00
24.3.15	P.O. Pack No. 102 £1 and £1·33 from England, Northern Ireland, Scotland and Wales (Nos. EN35, EN43, NI106, NI114, S136, S144, W127, W135)	24·00
22.3.16	P.O. Pack No. 104. £16·05 from England, Northern Ireland, Scotland and Wales (Nos. EN36, NI 107, S137 and W128)	10·00

Two Types of Head

Type I Ribbon at back of the head appears as two separate and distinct strands

Type II Ribbon solid and firmly joined to the head

2003 (14 Oct)–**16**. As Nos. EN1/3 and EN5, and new values, but with white borders. One centre phosphor band (2nd) or two phosphor bands (others). Type I heads unless otherwise stated. *P* 15×14 (with one elliptical hole in each vertical side).

(a) (Gravure Walsall (No. EN6I) or De La Rue (others))

EN6	EN 1	(2nd) slate-green and silver Type II	1·00	60
		a. Imperf (pair)	£175	
		l. Booklet pane. Nos. EN6 and EN9, each×2, with central label and margins all round (24.2.05)	1·80	
		b. Type I (2006)	5·50	5·50
EN7	EN 2	(1st) lake-brown and silver Type II	1·25	75
		a. Imperf (pair)	£250	
		b. Type I (2006)	6·00	6·00
EN8	EN 3	(E) olive-green and silver Type II	2·40	2·40
EN9		40p. olive-green and silver Type II (11.5.04)	1·50	1·50
EN10		42p. olive-green and silver Type II (5.4.05)	1·25	1·25
EN11		44p. olive-green and silver Type II (28.3.06)	1·50	1·50
		a. Imperf (pair)	£1600	
		b. Type 1 (2006)	50·00	50·00
EN12		48p. olive-green and silver (27.3.07)	1·25	1·25
EN13		50p. olive-green and silver (1.4.08)	90	85
EN14		56p. olive-green and silver (31.3.09)	1·25	1·25
EN15		60p. olive-green and silver (31.3.10)	1·40	1·40
EN16	EN 4	68p. deep reddish lilac and silver Type II	2·50	2·50
EN17		72p. deep reddish lilac and silver Type II (28.3.06)	2·50	2·50
		a. Type I (2006)	40·00	40·00
EN18		78p. deep reddish lilac and silver (27.3.07)	2·50	2·50
EN19		81p. deep reddish lilac and silver (1.4.08)	2·25	2·25
EN20		90p. deep reddish lilac and silver (31.3.09)	2·25	2·25
EN21		97p. deep reddish lilac and silver (31.3.10)	2·75	2·75

(b) Litho Enschedé or Cartor (1st) or Cartor (others)

EN29	EN 1	(2nd) greenish yellow, bright magenta, new blue and black (1.2013)	1·00	1·00
EN30	EN 2	(1st) lake-brown and silver (20.9.07)	1·25	1·25
		l. Booklet pane. Nos. EN30, NI95 S131 and W122 with five labels and margins all round	20·00	
EN31	EN 3	68p. silver, greenish yellow, bright magenta, new blue and black (29.3.11)	1·50	1·50
EN32		87p. sliver, greenish yellow, bright magenta, new blue and black (25.4.12)	2·50	2·50
EN33		88p. silver, greenish yellow, bright magenta, new blue and black (27.3.13)	2·00	2·00
EN34		97p. silver, greenish yellow, bright magenta, new blue and black (26.3.14)	2·25	2·25
EN35		£1 silver, greenish yellow, bright magenta, new blue and black (24.3.15)	2·40	2·40
EN36		£1.05 greenish yellow, bright magenta, new blue and black (22.1.16)	2·40	2·00
EN41	EN 4	£1.10 deep reddish lilac and silver (29.3.11)	2·75	2·75
EN42		£1.28 deep reddish lilac and silver (25.4.12)	3·25	3·25
EN43		£1.33 deep reddish lilac and silver (24.3.15)	3·25	3·25

Presentation Pack (Nos. EN6/8, EN16) (P.O. Pack No. 63) ... 6·00

PHQ Cards (Nos. EN6/8, EN16) (set of 4) (D24) .... 2·00 12·00

The 72p stamp from the 2006 "Lest We Forget" miniature sheet, MS2685, has the Type i head. The price for No. EN17a is for the Type I stamp from counter sheets. **Collectors should obtain this stamp from a reliable source.**

No. EN6I comes from booklet No. DX34.

Stamps as Nos. EN18/19 but printed in lithography were only issued within **MS**2796 (EN18) or **MS**2886 (EN19).

No. EN30 was first issued for £7·66 stamp booklets, No. DX40, printed by Enschedé. It was issued in sheets printed by Cartor in January 2013.

A design as No. EN30 but self-adhesive was issued on 23 April 2007 in sheets of 20, each stamp accompanied by a *se-tenant* label showing an English scene (LS38). These sheets were printed in lithography by Cartor, perforated 15×14 without the elliptical holes, and sold at £7·35 each. They were also available with personalised photographs on the labels at £14·95 from the Royal Mail in Edinburgh.

Stamps as Nos. EN30, NI95, S131 and W122 but self-adhesive were issued on 29 September 2008 in sheets of 20 containing five of each design with *se-tenant* labels (LS49). These sheets were printed in lithography by Cartor and perforated 15×14 with one elliptical hole on each vertical side.

Numbers have been left for possible additions to this definitive series.

First Day Covers

14.10.03	2nd, 1st, E, 68p. (EN6/8, EN16) Tallents House (Type K, see Introduction)		3·50
	London (as Windsor)		3·75
11.5.04	40p. (EN9) Tallents House (Type K)		2·75
	London (as Windsor)		2·75
5.4.05	42p. (EN10) Tallents House (Type K)		1·40
	London (as Windsor)		1·40
28.3.06	44p., 72p., (EN11, EN17) Tallents House (Type K)		2·75
	London (as Windsor)		2·75
27.3.07	48p., 78p., (EN12, EN18) Tallents House (Type K)		4·00
	London (as Windsor)		4·00
1.4.08	50p., 81p., (EN13, EN19) Tallents House (Type K)		4·00
	London (as Windsor)		4·00
31.3.09	56p., 90p. (EN14, EN20) Tallents House (Type K)		4·75
	London (as Windsor)		4·75
30.3.10	60p., 97p. (EN15, EN21) Tallents House (Type K)		4·00
	London (as Windsor)		4·00
29.3.11	68p., £1·10 (EN31, EN41) Tallents House (Type K)		6·00
	London (as Windsor)		6·00
25.4.12	87p., £1·28 (EN32, EN42) Tallents House (Type K)		6·50
	London (as Windsor)		6·50
27.3.13	88p. (EN33) Tallents House (Type K)		3·00
	London (as Windsor)		3·00
26.3.14	97p. (EN34) Tallents House (Type K)		3·50
	London (as Windsor)		3·50
24.3.15	£1, £1·33 (EN35, EN43) Tallents House (Type K)		7·75
	London (as Windsor)		7·75
22.3.16	£1·05 (EN36) Tallents House (Type K)		3·50
	London (as Windsor)		3·50

EN **5** *(Illustration reduced. Actual size 123×70 mm)*

(Des Peter Crowther, Clare Melinsky and Silk Pearce.
Gravure De La Rue)

2007 (23 Apr). *Celebrating England.* Sheet 123×70 mm. Two phosphor bands. *P* 15×14 (with one elliptical hole in each vertical side) (1st) or 15×14½ (78p.).

MSEN50 EN **5** (1st) No. EN7b; (1st) St. George's flag; 78p. St. George; 78p. Houses of Parliament, London ....

	9·00	9·00
First Day Cover (Tallents House)		10·00
First Day Cover (St. Georges, Telford)		10·00
Presentation Pack (P.O. Pack No. M15)	11·00	
PHQ Cards (set of 5) (CGB2)	4·00	15·00

MSEN50 was on sale at post offices throughout the UK.

The five PHQ cards show the four individual stamps and the complete miniature sheet.

Stamps as the 1st class St. George's flag stamp within **MS**EN50 but self-adhesive were issued on 23 April 2009 in sheets of 20 with *se-tenant* labels showing English Castles, No. LS59. These sheets were printed in lithography by Cartor and sold for £8·35 each.

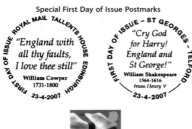

Special First Day of Issue Postmarks

EN **6** St. George's
Flag
(Des Peter Crowther (illustrations) and Silk Pierce.
Litho Cartor or Enschedé)

2013 (9 May). *England Flag.* Two phosphor bands. P 14½×14 (with one elliptical hole in each vert side).

EN51 EN **6**	(1st) multicoloured (silver Queen's head)	2·00	2·00
	a. Grey Queen's head	2·00	2·00

No. EN51 was issued in £11·11 Football Heroes booklets, No. DY7 (see booklet pane No. U3010a), and EN51a in £13·97 Classic Locomotives booklets, No. DY9 (see booklet pane No. U3011b).

II. NORTHERN IRELAND

N **1** N **2** N **3**

(Des W. Hollywood (3d., 4d., 5d.), L. Pilton (6d., 9d.), T. Collins (1s.3d., 1s.6d.))

1958–67. W 179. P 15×14.

NI1	N **1**	3d. deep lilac (18.8.58)	15	15
		p. One centre phosphor band (9.6.67)	25	25
NI2		4d. ultramarine (7.2.66)	15	15
		p. Two phosphor bands (10.67)	15	15
NI3	N **2**	6d. deep claret (29.9.58)	50	50
NI4		9d. bronze-green (2 phosphor bands) (1.3.67)	30	70
NI5	N **3**	1s.3d. green (29.9.58)	40	80
NI6		1s.6d. grey-blue (2 phosphor bands) (1.3.67)	40	80
		Ey. Phosphor omitted	£225	

First Day Covers

18.8.58	3d. (NI1)		30·00
29.9.58	6d., 1s.3d. (NI3, NI5)		35·00
7.2.66	4d. (NI2)		7·00
1.3.67	9d., 1s.6d. (NI4, NI6)		4·00

For Nos. NI1, NI3 and NI5 in Presentation Pack, see below Wales No. W6.

1968–69. No watermark. Chalk-surfaced paper. One centre phosphor band (Nos. NI8/9) or two phosphor bands (others). Gum arabic (No. NI7) or PVA gum (others). P 15×14.

NI7	N **1**	4d. dp brt blue (27.6.68)	25	25
		Ev. PVA gum* (23.10.68)	13·00	
NI8		4d. olive-sepia (4.9.68)	25	25
		Ey. Phosphor omitted		
NI9		4d. brt vermilion (26.2.69)	30	30
		Ey. Phosphor omitted	4·50	
NI10		5d. royal blue (4.9.68)	40	40
		Ey. Phosphor omitted	25·00	
NI11	N **3**	1s.6d. grey-blue (20.5.69)	2·50	2·75
		Ey. Phosphor omitted	£500	

4.9.68	First Day Cover (NI8, NI10)		3·00
	Presentation Pack (P.O. Pack No.25 containing Nos. NI1p, NI4/6, NI8/10) (9.12.70)		3·50

* No. NI7Ev was never issued in Northern Ireland. After No. NI7 (gum arabic) had been withdrawn from Northern Ireland but whilst still on sale at the philatelic counters elsewhere, about fifty sheets with PVA gum were sold over the London Philatelic counter on 23 October, 1968, and some were also on sale at the British Philatelic Exhibition Post Office.

There was no post office first day cover for No. NI9.

N **4**

I II

Redrawn design of Type N 4 (litho ptgs.)

Two Types of Crown

Type I:–Crown with all pearls individually drawn.
Type II:–Crown with clear outlines, large pearls and strong white line below them. First 3 pearls at left are joined, except on Nos. NI39 and NI49.

The following stamps printed in lithography show a screened background behind and to the left of the emblem: 11½p., 12½p., 14p. (No. NI38), 15½p., 16p., 18p. (No. NI45), 19½p. (No. NI53) and 28p. (No. NI62). The 13p. and 17p. (No. NI43) also showed screened backgrounds in Type I, but changed to solid backgrounds for Type II. The 31p. had a solid background in Type I, but changed to a screened background for Type II. All other values printed in lithography have solid backgrounds.

(Des J. Matthews after plaster cast by Arnold Machin)

1971 (7 July)–**93.** *Decimal Currency.* Chalk-surfaced paper. Type N **4**.

(a) Photo Harrison. With phosphor bands. P 15×14.

NI12	2½p. brt magenta (1 centre band)	70	60
NI13	3p. ultramarine (2 bands)	30	30
	Ey. Phosphor omitted	50·00	
NI14	3p. ultramarine (1 centre band) (23.1.74)	20	15
NI15	3½p. olive-grey (2 bands) (23.1.74)	20	25
NI16	3½p. olive-grey (1 centre band) (6.11.74)	20	25
NI17	4½p. grey-blue (2 bands) (6.11.74)	30	25
NI18	5p. reddish violet (2 bands)	1·25	1·25
NI19	5½p. violet (2 bands) (23.1.74)	25	25
	Ey. Phosphor omitted	£250	
NI20	5½p. violet (1 centre band) (21.5.75)	25	30
NI21	6½p. greenish blue (1 centre band) (14.1.76)	20	20
NI22	7p. purple-brown (1 centre band) (18.1.78)	35	25
NI23	7½p. chestnut (2 bands)	1·75	1·75
	Ey. Phosphor omitted	£100	
NI24	8p. rosine (2 bands) (23.1.74)	40	40
	Ey. Phosphor omitted	75·00	
NI25	8½p. yellow-green (2 bands) (14.1.76)	55	55
NI26	9p. dp violet (2 bands) (18.1.78)	55	55
	Ey. Phosphor omitted	25·00	
NI27	10p. orange-brown (2 bands) (20.10.76)	40	50
NI28	10p. orange-brown (1 centre band) (23.7.80)	50	50
NI29	10½p. steel-blue (2 bands) (18.1.78)	70	80
NI30	11p. scarlet (2 bands) (20.10.76)	60	60
	Ey. Phosphor omitted	5·00	

(b) Photo Harrison. On phosphorised paper. P 15×14.

NI31	12p. yellowish green (23.7.80)	50	60
NI32	13½p. purple-brown (23.7.80)	90	1·00
NI33	15p. ultramarine (23.7.80)	60	70

(c) Litho Questa (Type II, unless otherwise stated). P 14 (11½p., 12½p., 14p. (No. NI38), 15½p., 16p., 18p. (No. NI45), 19½p., 20½p., 22p. (No. NI53), 26p. (No. NI60), 28p. (No. NI62)) or 15×14 (others).

NI34	11½p. drab (Type I) (1 side band) (8.4.81)	85	85
NI35	12p. brt emerald (1 side band) (7.1.86)	90	90
NI36	12½p. lt emerald (Type I) (1 side band) (24.2.82)	60	60
	a. Perf 15×14 (28.2.84)	5·25	5·25
NI37	13p. pale chestnut (Type I) (1 side band) (23.10.84)	80	75
	Ea. Type II (28.11.86)	2·00	1·50
	Ey. Phosphor omitted (Type I)	£375	
NI38	14p. grey-blue (Type I) (phosphorised paper) (8.4.81)	75	75
NI39	14p. dp blue (1 centre band) (8.11.88)	75	60
NI40	15p. brt blue (1 centre band) (28.11.89)	90	60
NI41	15½p. pale violet (Type I) (phosphorised paper) (24.2.82)	80	80
NI42	16p. drab (Type I) (phosphorised paper) (27.4.83)	1·25	1·25
	a. Perf 15×14 (28.2.84)	8·25	8·50

NI43	17p. grey-blue (Type I) (phosphorised paper) (23.10.84)......	90	95
	Ea. Type II (9.9.86)......	£175	£120
NI44	17p. dp blue (1 centre band) (4.12.90)......	1·00	80
NI45	18p. dp violet (Type I) (phosphorised paper) (8.4.81)......	1·00	1·00
NI46	18p. dp olive-grey (phosphorised paper) (6.1.87)......	1·00	90
NI47	18p. brt green (1 centre band) (3.12.91)......	1·00	95
	a. Perf 14 (31.12.92*)......	6·50	6·50
NI48	18p. brt green (1 side band) (10.8.93)......	2·25	2·25
	l. Booklet pane. Nos. NI48, NI59, S61, S71, W49Eb and W60 with margins all round......	14·00	
NI49	19p. brt orange-red (phosphorised paper) (8.11.88)......	1·00	1·00
NI50	19½p. olive-grey (Type I) (phosphorised paper) (24.2.82)......	2·00	2·00
NI51	20p. brownish black (phosphorised paper) (28.11.89)......	1·00	80
NI52	20½p. ultramarine (Type I) (phosphorised paper) (27.4.83)......	4·50	4·25
NI53	22p. blue (Type I) (phosphorised paper) (8.4.81)......	1·40	1·40
NI54	22p. yellow-green (Type I) (phosphorised paper) (23.10.84)......	1·25	1·25
NI55	22p. brt orange-red (phosphorised paper) (4.12.90)......	1·25	90
NI56	23p. brt green (phosphorised paper) (8.11.88)......	1·25	1·10
NI57	24p. Indian red (phosphorised paper) (28.11.89)......	1·25	1·25
NI58	24p. chestnut (phosphorised paper) (3.12.91)......	1·10	90
NI59	24p. chestnut (2 bands) (10.8.93)......	2·25	2·50
NI60	26p. rosine (Type I) (phosphorised paper) (24.2.82)......	1·25	1·25
	a. Perf 15×14 (Type II) (27.1.87)......	3·00	3·25
NI61	26p. drab (phosphorised paper) (4.12.90)......	1·75	1·75
NI62	28p. dp violet-blue (Type I) (phosphorised paper) (27.4.83)......	1·50	1·50
	a. Perf 15×14 (Type II) (27.1.87)......	1·25	1·25
NI63	28p. dp bluish grey (phosphorised paper) (3.12.91)......	1·50	1·50
NI64	31p. brt purple (Type I) (phosphorised paper) (23.10.84)......	1·75	2·00
	Ea. Type II (14.4.87)......	1·90	1·75
NI65	32p. greenish blue (phosphorised paper) (8.11.88)......	1·75	1·75
NI66	34p. dp bluish grey (phosphorised paper) (28.11.89)......	1·75	1·75
NI67	37p. rosine (phosphorised paper) (4.12.90)......	2·00	2·50
NI68	39p. brt mauve (phosphorised paper) (3.12.91)......	2·00	2·25

* Earliest known date of use.

No. NI47a was caused by the use of a reserve perforating machine for some printings in the second half of 1992.

Nos. NI48 and NI59 only come from booklets.

From 1972 printings were made on fluorescent white paper and from 1973 most printings had dextrin added to the PVA gum (see notes after 1971 Decimal Machin issue).

First Day Covers

7.7.71	2½p., 3p., 5p., 7½p. (NI12/13, NI18, NI23)	3·50
23.1.74	3p., 3½p., 5½p., 8p. (NI14/15, NI19, NI24)	2·40
6.11.74	4½p. (NI17)	1·50
14.1.76	6½p., 8½p. (NI21, NI25)	1·50
20.10.76	10p., 11p. (NI27, NI30)	1·75
18.1.78	7p., 9p., 10½p. (NI22, NI26, NI29)	1·75
23.7.80	12p., 13½p., 15p. (NI31/3)	3·00
8.4.81	11½p., 14p., 18p., 22p. (NI34, NI38, NI45, NI53)	2·50
24.2.82	12½p., 15½p., 19½p., 26p. (NI36, NI41, NI50, NI60)	4·00
27.4.83	16p., 20½p., 28p. (NI42, NI52, NI62)	4·00
23.10.84	13p., 17p., 22p., 31p. (NI37, NI43, NI54, NI64)	4·75
7.1.86	12p. (NI35)	2·00
6.1.87	18p. (NI46)	2·00
8.11.88	14p., 19p., 23p., 32p. (NI39, NI49, NI56, NI65)	4·25
28.11.89	15p., 20p., 24p., 34p. (NI40, NI51, NI57, NI66)	5·00
4.12.90	17p., 22p., 26p., 37p. (NI44, NI55, NI61, NI67)	5·00
3.12.91	18p., 24p., 28p., 39p. (NI47, NI58, NI63, NI68)	5·50

Presentation Packs

7.7.71	P.O. Pack No. 29. 2½p., 3p., 5p., 7½p. (Nos. NI12/13, NI18, NI23)	3·50
29.5.74	P.O. Pack No. 61. 3p. (1 centre band), 3½p. (2 bands) or (1 centre band), 5½p. (2 bands) or (1 centre band), 8p. (Nos. NI14, NI15 or NI16, NI19 or NI20, NI24). The 4½p. (No. NI17) was added later......	2·75
20.10.76	P.O. Pack No. 84. 6½p., 8½p., 10p. (2 bands), 11p. (Nos. NI21, NI25, NI27, NI30)	2·00
28.10.81	P.O. Pack No. 129d. 7p., 9p., 10½p., 12p. (gravure), 13½p. (gravure), 15p. (gravure), 11½p., 14p. grey-blue, 18p. dp violet, 22p. blue (Nos. NI22, NI26, NI29, NI31/4, NI38, NI45, NI53)......	9·00

3.8.83	P.O. Pack No. 4. 10p. (1 centre band), 12½p., 16p., 20½p., 26p. rosine, 28p. dp violet-blue (Nos. NI28, NI36, NI42, NI52, NI60, NI62)	18·00
23.10.84	P.O. Pack No. 8. 10p. (1 centre band), 13p., 16p., 17p. grey-blue, 22p. yellow-green, 26p. rosine, 28p. dp violet-blue, 31p. (Nos. NI28, NI37, NI42a, NI43, NI54, NI60, NI62, NI64)	18·00
3.3.87	P.O. Pack No. 12. 12p. (litho), 13p., 17p. grey-blue, 18p. dp olive-grey, 22p. yellow-green, 26p. rosine, 28p. dp violet-blue, 31p. (Nos. NI35, NI37, NI43, NI46, NI54, NI60a, NI62a, NI64)......	20·00

Presentation Packs for Northern Ireland, Scotland and Wales

8.11.88	P.O. Pack No. 17. 14p. dp blue, 19p., 23p., 32p. (Nos. NI39, NI49, NI56, NI65), 14p. (1 centre band), 19p. (phosphorised paper), 23p. (phosphorised paper), 32p. (Nos. S54, S62, S67, S77), 14p. dp blue, 19p., 23p., 32p. (Nos. W40, W50, W57, W66)......	17·00
28.11.89	P.O. Pack No. 20. 15p. (litho), 20p., 24p. Indian red, 34p. (Nos. NI40, NI51, NI57, NI66), 15p. (litho), 20p., 24p. Indian red, 34p. (Nos. S56, S64, S69, S78), 15p. (litho), 20p., 24p. Indian red, 34p. (Nos. W41, W52, W58, W67)......	16·00
4.12.90	P.O. Pack No. 23. 17p. dp blue, 22p. brt orange-red, 26p. drab, 37p., (Nos. NI44, NI55, NI61, NI67), 17p. dp blue, 22p. brt orange-red, 26p. drab, 37p., (Nos. S58, S66, S73, S79), 17p. dp blue, 22p. brt orange-red, 26p. drab, 37p. (Nos. W45, W56, W62, W68)......	16·00
3.12.91	P.O. Pack No. 26. 18p. brt green, 24p. chestnut, 28p. dp bluish grey, 39p. (Nos. NI47, NI58, NI63, NI68), 18p. brt green, 24p. chestnut, 28p. dp bluish grey, 39p. (Nos. S60, S70, S75, S80), 18p. brt green, 24p. chestnut, 28p. dp bluish grey, 39p. (Nos. W48, W59, W64, W69)......	16·00

(Des J. Matthews after plaster cast by Arnold Machin)

1993 (7 Dec)–**2000**. Chalk-surfaced paper.

(a) Litho Questa. P 15×14 *(with one elliptical hole in each vertical side).*

NI69	N **4**	19p. bistre (1 centre band)......	90	80
NI70		19p. bistre (1 band at left) (26.7.94)	1·25	1·75
		Ey. Phosphor omitted......	£1000	
		a. Booklet pane. Nos. NI70×2, NI72×4, NI74 and centre label with margins all round......	10·00	
		b. Booklet pane. Nos. NI70, NI72, NI74 and NI76 with margins all round......	6·00	
		bEy. Booklet pane. Phosphor omitted....	£4000	
		Ec. Band at right (25.4.95)......	2·50	2·50
		d. Booklet pane. Nos. NI70Ec, NI72, S82, S84, W71 and W73 with margins all round (25.4.95)......	10·00	
		da. Part perf pane*......	£4250	
NI71		20p. brt green (1 centre band) (23.7.96)	1·50	1·50
NI72		25p. red (2 bands)......	75	75
		Ey. Phosphor omitted......	£1000	
NI73		26p. red-brown (2 bands) (23.7.96)......	1·75	1·75
NI74		30p. dp olive-grey (2 bands)......	1·25	1·25
		Ey. Phosphor omitted......	£1000	
NI75		37p. brt mauve (2 bands) (23.7.96)......	2·75	3·00
NI76		41p. grey-brown (2 bands)......	1·50	1·75
		Ey. Phosphor omitted......	£950	
NI77		63p. lt emerald (2 bands) (23.7.96)......	5·00	5·00

(b) Gravure Walsall (19p., 20p., 26p. (No. NI81b), 38p., 40p., 63p., 64p., 65p.), Harrison or Walsall (26p. (No. NI81), 37p.). P 14 *(No. NI80)* or 15×14 *(others) (both with one elliptical hole in each vertical side).*

NI78	N **4**	19p. bistre (1 centre band) (8.6.99)......	3·00	3·00
NI79		20p. brt green (1 centre band) (1.7.97)..	1·90	80
NI80		20p. brt green (1 side band at right) (13.10.98)......	4·00	4·00
		al. Booklet pane. Nos. NI80, S90a, W79a and Y1717a×3 with margins all round......	10·00	
NI81		26p. chestnut (2 bands) (1.7.97)......	1·75	1·50
		al. Booklet pane. Nos. NI81/2, S91/2 and W80/1 with margins all round (23.9.97)......	6·00	
		b. Perf 14 (13.10.98)......	4·00	4·00
NI82		37p. brt mauve (2 bands) (1.7.97)......	3·50	3·50
NI83		38p. ultramarine (2 bands) (8.6.99)	8·00	8·00
NI84		40p. dp azure (2 bands) (25.4.00)	3·50	3·50
NI85		63p. lt emerald (2 bands) (1.7.97)......	5·00	5·00
NI86		64p. turquoise-green (2 bands) (8.6.99).	9·00	9·00
NI87		65p. greenish blue (2 bands) (25.4.00) ...	3·50	3·75

* No. NI70da, which comes from the 1995 National Trust £6 booklet, shows the top two values in the pane of 6 (Nos. S82, S84) completely imperforate and the two Wales values below partly imperforate.

Nos. NI70, NI80 and NI81b only come from booklets.

The listed booklet panes come from the following Sponsored Booklets:

NI70a/b	—Booklet DX16
NI70d	—Booklet DX17
NI80al	—Booklet DX21
NI81al	—Booklet DX19

First Day Covers

7.12.93	19p., 25p., 30p., 41p. (NI69, NI72, NI74, NI76)	6·00
26.7.94	Northern Ireland *se-tenant* pane 19p., 25p., 30p., 41p. (NI70a)	8·00
23.7.96	20p., 26p., 37p., 63p. (NI71, NI73, NI75, NI77)	8·75
8.6.99	38p., 64p. (NI83, NI86)	4·00
25.4.00	1st, 40p., 65p. (NI84, NI87, NI88b)	7·00

Presentation Packs

8.6.99	P.O. Pack No. 47. 19p., 26p., 38p., 64p. (Nos. NI78, NI81, NI83, NI86)	17·00
25.4.00	P.O. Pack No. 52. 1st, 40p., 65p. (Nos. NI88b, NI84, NI87)	18·00

Presentation Packs for Northern Ireland, Scotland and Wales

7.12.93	P.O. Pack No. 31. 19p., 25p., 30p., 41p., eachx3 (Nos. NI69, NI72, NI74, NI76, S81, S84, S86, S88, W70, W73, W75, W77)	16·00
23.7.96	P.O. Pack No. 36. 20p., 26p., 37p., 63p., eachx3 (Nos. NI71, NI73, NI75, NI77, S83, S85, S87, S89, W72, W74, W76, W78)	26·00
20.10.98	P.O. Pack No. 42. 20p. (1 centre band), 26p., 37p., 63p., eachx3 (Nos. NI79, NI81/2, NI85, S90/3, W79/82)	26·00

N **5**

(Des J. Matthews. Gravure Walsall)

2000 (15 Feb H25 Apr). Type N **4** redrawn with *1st* face value as Type N **5**. Two phosphor bands. *P* 14 (with one elliptical hole in each vertical side).

NI88	N **5**	(1st) bright orange-red	3·00	3·00
		al. Booklet pane. Nos. NI88, S108 and W97, eachx3 with margins all round	16·00	
		b. Perf 15×14 (25 Apr)	15·00	12·00

First Day Cover (se-tenant pane No. NI88al) (Philatelic Bureau) ... 13·00

First Day Cover (se-tenant pane No. NI88al) (London SW5) ... 13·00

No. NI88 was issued in £7·50 stamp booklets (No. DX24) and No. NI88b in sheets.

N **6** Basalt Columns, Giant's Causeway

N **7** Aerial View of Patchwork Fields

N **8** Linen Pattern

N **9** Vase Pattern from Belleek

(Des Rodney Miller Associates. Litho Walsall or Enschedé (1st, 2nd), De La Rue or Walsall (E), Walsall (65p.), De La Rue (68p.))

2001 (6 Mar)–**03**. One centre phosphor band (2nd) or two phosphor bands (others). *P* 15×14 (with one elliptical hole in each vertical side).

NI89	N **6**	(2nd) black, new blue, bright magenta and greenish yellow	1·00	75
		a. Booklet pane. No. NI89x5 and No. NI90x4 with margins all round (25.2.03)	7·00	
		Ey. Phosphor omitted	£625	
NI90	N **7**	(1st) black, new blue and greenish yellow	1·25	1·20
		Ey. Phosphor omitted	35·00	

NI91	N **8**	(E) black, new blue and pale orange	1·60	1·60
NI92	N **9**	65p. black, bright magenta and greenish yellow	3·25	3·25
NI93		68p. black, bright magenta and greenish yellow (4.7.02)	3·25	3·25

Presentation Pack (Nos. NI89/92) (P.O. Pack No. 53) ... 8·00

PHQ Cards (Nos. NI89/92) (set of 4) (D19) ... 8·00 14·00

Nos. NI89, NI90 and NI91 were initially sold at 19p., 27p. and 36p., the latter representing the basic European airmail rate. A new printing of No. NI91, produced by De La Rue instead of Walsall, was issued on 15 October 2002. Stamps from this printing do not differ from those produced by Walsall. Booklet pane No. NI89a was printed by Enschedé. For combined presentation pack for all four Regions, see under England.

First Day Covers

6.3.01	2nd, 1st, E, 65p. (NI89/92)		
	Philatelic Bureau		4·50
	Belfast		5·00
4.7.02	68p. (NI93)		
	Tallents House (Type K, see Introduction)		2·50
	Belfast		3·00

Special First Day of Issue Postmarks

2003 (14 Oct)–**16**. *As Nos. NI89/91 and NI93, and new values, but with white borders. One centre phosphor band (2nd) or two phosphor bands (others). P 15×14 (with one elliptical hole in each vertical side).*

(a) (Litho Walsall (NI98), De La Rue or Enschedé (NI95), Cartor (NI101, NI10617, NI112, NI114) or De La Rue (others))

NI94	N **6**	(2nd) black, new blue, bright magenta and greenish yellow	1·00	1·00
NI95	N **7**	(1st) black, new blue and greenish yellow	1·25	1·00
		a. black omitted	£6000	
NI96	N **8**	(E) black and new blue	2·50	2·50
NI97		40p. black and new blue (11.5.04)	1·75	1·75
NI98		42p. black, new blue and orange yellow (5.4.05)	1·75	1·75
		a. Black, new blue and greenish-yellow (26.7.05)	2·00	2·00
NI99		44p. black, new blue and greenish yellow (28.3.06)	1·00	1·00
NI100	N **9**	68p. black, bright magenta* and greenish yellow	2·75	2·75
NI101	N **8**	68p. greenish yellow, bright magenta, new blue and black (29.3.11)	1·50	1·50
NI102	N **9**	72p. black, greyish black, bright magenta and greenish yellow (28.3.06)	2·50	2·50
NI103	N **8**	87p greenish yellow, bright magenta, new blue and black (25.4.12)	2·50	2·50
NI104		88p greenish yellow, bright magenta, new blue and black (27.3.13)	2·00	2·00
NI105		97p. greenish yellow, bright magenta, new blue and black (26.3.14)	2·25	2·25
NI106		£1 greenish yellow, bright magenta, new blue and black (24.3.15)	2·40	2·40
NI107		£1·05 greenish yellow, bright magenta, new blue and black (22.3.16)	2·40	2·40
NI112	N **9**	£1·10 greenish yellow, bright magenta, new blue and black (29.3.11)	2·75	2·75
NI113		£1·28 greenish yellow, bright magenta, new blue and black (25.4.12)	3·25	3·25
NI114		£1·33 greenish yellow, bright magenta, new blue and black (24.3.15)	3·25	3·25

(b) Gravure De La Rue

NI122	N **6**	(2nd) bright magenta, greenish yellow, new blue and black (20.9.07)	1·00	60
NI123	N **7**	(1st) greenish yellow, new blue and black (20.9.07)	1·25	75
NI124	N **8**	48p. olive-grey and black (27.3.07)	1·20	1·20
NI125		50p. olive-grey and black (1.4.08)	1·20	1·20
NI126		56p. olive-grey and black (31.3.09)	1·25	1·25
NI127		60p. olive-grey and black (30.3.10)	1·40	1·40
NI128	N **9**	78p. bright magenta, greenish yellow and black (27.3.07)	2·00	2·00
NI129		81p. bright magenta, greenish yellow and black (1.4.08)	2·00	2·00
NI130		90p. bright magenta, greenish yellow and black (31.3.09)	2·25	2·25

NI131 97p. bright magenta, greenish yellow and black (30.3.10) .... 2·40 2·40
Presentation Pack (Nos. NI94/6, NI100) (P.O. Pack No. 66) .... 7·00
PHQ Cards (Nos. NI94/6, NI100) (set of 4) (D27) .... 2·00 10·00

No. NI95 was printed in sheets by De La Rue and was also issued in £7·66 booklets, No. DX40, printed by Enschedé and in DY7 and DY9.

NI95a originates from an example of booklet pane NI154m with a progressive dry print of black.

No NI98 (Walsall printing) appears bluish grey and No. NI98a (De La Rue printing) appears olive-grey.

Nos. NI122/3 went on philatelic sale on 20 September 2007. They went on sale in Northern Ireland post offices as supplies of Nos. NI94/95 were used up.

* The bright magenta used on the 68p. is fluorescent.

A stamp as No. NI102 but printed in photogravure was only issued within **MS**2685.

Stamps as Nos. NI128/9 but printed in lithography were only issued within **MS**2796 (NI128) or **MS**2886 (NI129).

A design as No. NI95 but self-adhesive was issued on 11 March 2008 in sheets of 20, each stamp accompanied by a *se-tenant* label showing a Northern Ireland scene (LS46). These sheets, perforated 15×14 without the elliptical holes, were printed in lithography by Cartor and sold at £7·35 each. They were also available with personalised photographs on the labels at £14·95 from the Royal Mail in Edinburgh.

Stamps as EN30, NI95, S131 and W122 but self-adhesive were issued on 29 September 2008 in sheets of 20 containing five of each design with *se-tenant* labels (LS49).

Stamps as NI95 but self-adhesive were issued again on 17 March 2009 in sheets of 20 with *se-tenant* labels showing Northern Ireland Castles, LS58. These sheets were printed in lithography by Cartor and originally sold at £7·74 each (£8·35 from 6 April 2009).

Numbers have been left for possible additions to this definitive series.

First Day Covers

14.10.03 2nd, 1st, E, 68p. (NI94/6, NI100) Tallents House (Type K, see Introduction) .... 3·25
    Belfast .... 3·25
11.5.04 40p. (NI97) Tallents House (Type K) .... 2·75
    Belfast .... 2·75
5.4.05 42p. (NI98)
    Tallents House (Type K) .... 1·40
    Belfast .... 1·40
28.3.06 44p., 72p. (NI99, NI102) ....
    Tallents House (Type K) .... 2·75
    Belfast .... 2·75
27.3.07 48p., 78p. (NI124, NI128) Tallents House (Type K) ...... 4·00
    Belfast .... 4·00
1.4.08 50p., 81p. (NI125, NI129) Tallents House (Type K) ...... 4·00
    Belfast .... 4·00
31.3.09 56p., 90p. (NI126, NI130) Tallents House(Type K) ...... 4·75
    Belfast .... 4·75
30.3.10 60p., 97p. (NI127, NI131) Tallents House (Type K) ...... 4·00
    Belfast .... 4·00
29.3.11 68p., £1·10 (NI101, NI112) Tallents House (Type K) ...... 6·00
    Belfast .... 6·00
25.4.12 87p., £1·28 (NI103, NI113) Tallents House (Type K) ...... 6·50
    Belfast .... 6·50
27.3.13 88p. (NI104) Tallents House (Type K) .... 3·00
    Belfast .... 3·00
26.3.14 97p. (NI105) Tallents House (Type K) .... 3·50
    Belfast .... 3·50
24.3.15 £1, £1·33 (NI106, NI114) Tallents House (Type K) ...... 7·75
    Belfast .... 7·75
22.3.16 £1·05 (NI107) Tallents House (Type K) .... 3·50
    Belfast .... 3·50

CELEBRATING NORTHERN IRELAND

N **10** *(Illustration reduced. Actual size 123×70 mm)*

(Des Clare Melinsky and Silk Pearce. Litho De La Rue)

2008 *(11 Mar). Celebrating Northern Ireland.* Sheet 123×70 mm. Two phosphor bands. P 15×14½ (with one elliptical hole in each vertical side) (1st) or 15×14½ (78p).
MSNI152 N **10** (1st) Carrickfergus Castle; (1st) Giant's Causeway; 78p. St. Patrick; 78p. Queen's Bridge and 'Angel of Thanksgiving' sculpture, Belfast. .... 7·00 7·00
First Day Cover (Tallents House) .... 8·00
First Day Cover (Downpatrick, Co. Down) .... 8·00
Presentation Pack (P.O. Pack No. 410) .... 9·00
PHQ Cards (set of 5) (CGB3) .... 4·00 17·00

 MSNI152 was on sale at post offices throughout the UK.
 The five PHQ cards depict the complete miniature sheet and the four stamps within it.

Special First Day of Issue Postmarks

N **11** *(Illustration reduced. Actual size 124×70 mm)*

(Des Sedley Place. Gravure De La Rue)

2008 *(29 Sept). 50th Anniv of the Country Definitives.* Sheet 124×70 mm, containing designs as Nos. NI1, NI3, NI5, S1, S3, S5, W1, W3 and W5 (regional definitives of 1958) but inscribed 1st and printed on pale cream. Two phosphor bands. P 15×14 (with one elliptical hole in each vertical side).
MSNI153 N **11** (1st)×9 As No. W1; As No. S1; As No. W5; As No. S5; As No. NI1; As No. W3; As No. S3; As No. NI3; As No. NI5. .... 8·25 8·25
First Day Cover (Tallents House) .... 10·00
First Day Cover (Gloucester) .... 10·00
Presentation Pack (P.O. Pack No. 80) .... 12·00
PHQ Cards (set) .... 6·00 18·00

 MSNI153 was on sale at post offices throughout the UK.
 The ten PHQ cards show the nine individual stamps and the complete sheet.

Special First Day of Issue Postmarks

(Litho De La Rue)

2008 *(29 Sept). 50th Anniv of the Country Definitives* (2nd issue). As Nos. NI1, NI3 and NI5 (definitives of 1958) but inscribed 1st. Two phosphor bands. P 15×14½ (with one elliptical hole in each vertical side).
NI154 N **1** (1st) deep lilac .... 3·00 3·00
      l. Booklet pane. Nos. NI154/6, S154/6 and W144/6. .... 24·00
      m. Booklet pane. Nos. NI154/6 and NI95×3. .... 8·00
NI155 N **3** (1st) green .... 3·00 3·00
NI156 N **2** (1st) deep claret .... 3·00 3·00
First Day Cover (No. NI154l) (Tallents House) .... 10·00
First Day Cover (No. NI154l) (Gloucester) .... 10·00
Nos. NI154/6 come from £9·72 booklets, No. DX43.

III. SCOTLAND

S 1   **S 2**   **S 3**

(Des. G. Huntly (3d., 4d., 5d.), J. Fleming (6d., 9d.),
A. Imrie (1s.3d., 1s.6d.))

1958–67. W 179. *P 15×14.*

S1	S 1	3d. dp lilac (18.8.58)	15	15
		p. Two phosphor bands (29.1.63)	13·00	2·75
		pa. One phosphor band at right (30.4.65)	20	25
		pb. Band at left	20	25
		pc. Horiz pair. Nos. S1pa/pb	40	1·00
		pd. One centre phosphor band (9.11.67)	15	15
S2		4d. ultramarine (7.2.66)	20	20
		p. Two phosphor bands	20	20
S3	S 2	6d. dp claret (29.9.58)	25	25
		p. Two phosphor bands (29.1.63)	25	25
S4		9d. bronze-green (2 phosphor bands) (1.3.67)	35	40
S5	S 3	1s.3d. green (29.9.58)	40	40
		p. Two phosphor bands (29.1.63)	50	50
S6		1s.6d. grey-blue (2 phosphor bands) (1.3.67)	60	60

First Day Covers

18.8.58	3d. (S1)	17·00
29.9.58	6d., 1s.3d. (S3, S5)	25·00
7.2.66	4d. (S2)	7·00
1.3.67	9d., 1s.6d. (S4, S6)	6·00

The one phosphor band on No. S1pa was produced by printing broad phosphor bands across alternate vertical perforations. Individual stamps show the band at right or left (same prices either way).

For Nos. S1, S3 and S5 in Presentation Pack, see below Wales No. W6.

1967–70. No watermark. Chalk-surfaced paper. One centre phosphor band (Nos. 7, S9/10) or two phosphor bands (others). Gum arabic (Nos. S7, S8) or PVA gum (others). *P 15×14.*

S7	S 1	3d. dp lilac (16.5.68)	15	15
		Ey. Phosphor omitted	7·00	
		Ev. PVA gum	10	
		Eya. Phosphor omitted (No. S7Ev)	4·00	
S8		4d. dp brt blue (28.11.67)	30	30
		Ey. Phosphor omitted	10·00	
		Ev. PVA gum (25.7.68)	10	
S9		4d. olive-sepia (4.9.68)	15	15
		Ey. Phosphor omitted	3·00	
S10		4d. brt vermilion (26.2.69)	15	15
		Ey. Phosphor omitted	2·50	
S11		5d. royal blue (4.9.68)	25	25
		Ey. Phosphor omitted	55·00	
S12	S 2	9d. bronze-green (28.9.70)	6·00	6·00
		Ey. Phosphor omitted	£275	
S13	S 3	1s.6d. grey-blue (12.12.68)	1·75	1·50
		Ey. Phosphor omitted	£125	

There was no Post Office first day cover for No. S10.

4.9.68	*First Day Cover* (S9, S11)	3·00
	Presentation Pack (P.O. Pack No. 23 containing Nos. S3, S5p., S7, S9/13) (9.12.70)	8·00

S 4

I   II

Redrawn design of Type S 4 (litho ptgs.)

The introduction of the redrawn lion took place in 1983 when Waddington's had the contract and therefore the 13, 17, 22 and

31p. exist in both types and perforated 14. The Questa printings, perforated 15×14, are all Type II.

The Types of Lion.

Type I:–The eye and jaw appear larger and there is no line across the bridge of the nose.

Type II:–The tongue is thick at the point of entry to the mouth and the eye is linked to the background by a solid line.

The following stamps printed in lithography show a screened background behind and to the left of the emblem: 12½p., 15½p., 16p., 19½p., 28p. (Nos. S50 and S74) and 31p. (Nos. S51 and S76). The 13p. and 17p. (No. S43) also showed screened backgrounds for both Type I and II of the John Waddington printings, but changed to solid backgrounds for the Questa Type II. All other values printed in lithography have solid backgrounds.

(Des J. Matthews after plaster cast by Arnold Machin)

1971 (7 July)–*93. Decimal Currency.* Chalk-surfaced paper. Type S **4.**

(a) Photo Harrison. With phosphor bands. P 15×14.

S14	2½p. brt magenta (1 centre band)	25	20
	Ey. Phosphor omitted	10·00	
	Eg. Gum arabic (22.9.72)	30	
	Egy. Phosphor omitted	20·00	
S15	3p. ultramarine (2 bands)	35	15
	Ey. Phosphor omitted	17·00	
	Eg. Gum arabic (14.12.72)	30	
	Ega. Imperf (pair)	£800	
	Egy. Phosphor omitted	50·00	
S16	3p. ultramarine (1 centre band) (23.1.74)	15	15
S17	3½p. olive-grey (2 bands) (23.1.74)	20	25
	Ey. Phosphor omitted	50·00	
S18	3½p. olive-grey (1 centre band) (6.11.74)	20	25
S19	4½p. grey-blue (1 centre band) (6.11.74)	30	35
S20	5p. reddish violet (2 bands)	1·00	1·25
S21	5½p. violet (2 bands) (23.1.74)	30	35
S22	5½p. violet (1 centre band) (21.5.75)	20	25
	a. Imperf (pair)	£650	
S23	6½p. greenish blue (1 centre band) (14.1.76)	20	25
S24	7p. purple-brown (1 centre band) (18.1.78)	30	30
S25	7½p. chestnut (2 bands)	1·25	1·40
	Ey. Phosphor omitted	7·00	
S26	8p. rosine (2 bands) (23.1.74)	45	40
S27	8½p. yellow-green (2 bands) (14.1.76)	40	40
S28	9p. dp violet (2 bands) (18.1.78)	40	40
S29	10p. orange-brown (2 bands) (20.10.76)	45	50
S30	10p. orange-brown (2 bands) (23.7.80)	40	50
S31	10½p. steel-blue (2 bands) (18.1.78)	70	80
S32	11p. scarlet (2 bands) (20.10.76)	55	60
	Ey. Phosphor omitted	3·50	

(b) Photo Harrison. On phosphorised paper. P 15×14.

S33	12p. yellowish green (23.7.80)	50	60
S34	13½p. purple-brown (23.7.80)	1·00	1·10
S35	15p. ultramarine (23.7.80)	60	70

(c) Litho J.W. (Type I unless otherwise stated.) One side phosphor band (11½p., 12p., 12½p., 13p.) or phosphorised paper (others). P 14.

S36	11½p. drab (8.4.81)	80	80
	Ey. Phosphor omitted	£1000	
S37	12p. brt emerald (Type II) (7.1.86)	2·00	2·00
S38	12½p. lt emerald (24.2.82)	60	70
S39	13p. pale chestnut (Type I) (23.10.84)	85	75
	Ey. Phosphor omitted	£1000	
	Ea. Type II (1.85)	8·00	8·00
	Eay. Phosphor omitted	£1000	
S40	14p. grey-blue (8.4.81)	75	75
S41	15½p. pale violet (24.2.82)	80	80
S42	16p. drab (Type II) (27.4.83)	80	85
S43	17p. grey-blue (Type I) (23.10.84)	1·50	1·50
	Ea. Type II (1.85)	1·75	1·50
S44	18p. dp violet (8.4.81)	80	80
S45	19½p. olive-grey (24.2.82)	1·75	1·75
S46	20½p. ultramarine (Type II) (27.4.83)	3·50	3·50
S47	22p. blue (8.4.81)	1·00	1·10
S48	22p. yellow-green (Type I) (23.10.84)	4·25	4·25
	Ea. Type II (1.86)	55·00	30·00
S49	26p. rosine (24.2.82)	1·25	1·25
S50	28p. dp violet-blue (Type II) (27.4.83)	1·25	1·25
S51	31p. brt purple (Type I) (23.10.84)	2·50	2·50
	Ea. Type II (11.85*)	£180	£160

(d) Litho Questa (Type II). P 15×14.

S52	12p. brt emerald (1 side band) (29.4.86)	2·25	2·50
S53	13p. pale chestnut (1 side band) (4.11.86)	70	75
S54	14p. dp blue (1 centre band) (8.11.88)	60	70
	l. Booklet pane. No. S54×6 with margins all round (21.3.89)	3·50	
S55	14p. dp blue (1 side band) (21.3.89)	80	90
	l. Booklet pane. No. S55×5, S63×2, S68 and centre label with margins all round	22·00	
	la. Error. Booklet pane imperf	£2600	
S56	15p. brt blue (1 centre band) (28.11.89)	1·00	1·00
	a. Imperf (three sides) (block of four)	£275	

S57	17p. grey-blue (phosphorised paper) (29.4.86)		4·00	4·00
S58	17p. dp blue (1 centre band) (4.12.90)		1·00	1·10
S59	18p. dp olive-grey (phosphorised paper) (6.1.87)		1·10	85
S60	18p. brt green (1 centre band) (3.12.91)		1·25	90
	a. Perf 14 (26.9.92*)		1·00	1·25
	aEy. Phosphor omitted		£1250	
S61	18p. brt green (1 side band) (10.8.93)		2·75	3·00
S62	19p. brt orange-red (phosphorised paper) (8.11.88)		70	70
	l. Booklet pane. No. S62×9 with margins all round (21.3.89)		5·50	
	m. Booklet pane. No. S62×6 with margins all round (21.3.89)		4·50	
S63	19p. brt orange-red (2 bands) (21.3.89)		2·25	2·00
S64	20p. brownish black (phosphorised paper) (28.11.89)		95	95
S65	22p. yellow-green (phosphorised paper) (27.1.87)		1·25	1·50
S66	22p. brt orange-red (phosphorised paper) (4.12.90)		1·25	90
S67	23p. brt green (phosphorised paper) (8.11.88)		1·25	1·10
S68	23p. brt green (2 bands) (21.3.89)		12·00	12·00
S69	24p. Indian red (phosphorised paper) (28.11.89)		1·25	1·25
S70	24p. chestnut (phosphorised paper) (3.12.91)		1·40	1·25
	a. Perf 14 (10.92*)		7·00	7·00
S71	24p. chestnut (2 bands) (10.8.93)		2·75	3·00
S72	26p. rosine (phosphorised paper) (27.1.87)		3·75	4·00
S73	26p. drab (phosphorised paper) (4.12.90)		1·25	1·25
S74	28p. dp violet-blue (phosphorised paper) (27.1.87)		1·25	1·25
S75	28p. dp bluish grey (phosphorised paper) (3.12.91)		1·25	1·50
	a. Perf 14 (18.2.93*)		9·00	9·00
S76	31p. brt purple (phosphorised paper) (29.4.86)		2·25	2·25
S77	32p. greenish blue (phosphorised paper) (8.11.88)		1·75	2·00
S78	34p. dp bluish grey (phosphorised paper) (28.11.89)		1·75	1·75
S79	37p. rosine (phosphorised paper) (4.12.90)		2·00	2·25
S80	39p. brt mauve (phosphorised paper) (3.12.91)		2·00	2·25
	a. Perf 14 (11.92)		12·50	12·50

* Earliest known date of use.
Nos. S55, S61, S63, S68 and S71 only come from booklets.
The listed booklet panes come from the following Sponsored Booklets:

S54l	−Booklet DX10
S55l	−Booklet DX10
S62l/m	−Booklet DX10

No. S56a occured in the second vertical row of two sheets. It is best collected as a block of four including the left-hand vertical pair imperforate on three sides.

Nos. S60a, S70a, S75a and S80a were caused by the use of a reserve perforating machine for some printings in the second half of 1992.

From 1972 printings were on fluorescent white paper. From 1973 most printings had dextrin added to the PVA gum (see notes after the 1971 Decimal Machin issue).

First Day Covers

7.7.71	2½p., 3p., 5p., 7½p. (S14/15, S20, S25)	3·00
23.1.74	3p., 3½p., 5½p., 8p. (S16/17, S21, S26)	2·50
6.11.74	4½p. (S19)	1·50
14.1.76	6½p., 8½p. (S23, S27)	1·50
20.10.76	10p., 11p. (S29, S32)	1·50
18.1.78	7p., 9p., 10½p. (S24, S28, S31)	1·75
23.7.80	12p., 13½p., 15p. (S33/5)	2·75
8.4.81	11½p., 14p., 18p., 22p. (S36, S40, S44, S47)	2·50
24.2.82	12½p., 15½p., 19½p., 26p. (S38, S41, S45, S49)	3·50
27.4.83	16p., 20½p., 28p. (S42, S46, S50)	4·00
23.10.84	13p., 17p., 22p., 31p. (S39, S43, S48, S51)	4·00
7.1.86	12p. (S37)	2·00
6.1.87	18p. (S59)	1·80
8.11.88	14p., 19p., 23p., 32p. (S54, S62, S67, S77)	4·25
21.3.89	Scots Connection *se-tenant* pane 14p., 19p., 23p. (S55l)	14·00
28.11.89	15p., 20p., 24p., 34p. (S56, S64, S69, S78)	5·00
4.12.90	17p., 22p., 26p., 37p. (S58, S66, S73, S79)	5·00
3.12.91	18p., 24p., 26p., 39p. (S60, S70, S75, S80)	5·50

Presentation Packs

7.7.71	P.O. Pack No. 27. 2½p., 3p. (2 bands), 5p., 7½p. (Nos. S14/15, S20, S25)	3·50
29.5.74	P.O. Pack No. 62. 3p. (1 centre band), 3½p. (2 bands) or (1 centre band), 5½p. (2 bands) or (1 centre band), 8p. (Nos. S16, S17 or S18, S21 or S22, S26). The 4½p. (No. S19) was added later	2·50

20.10.76	P.O. Pack No. 85. 6½p., 8½p., 10p. (2 bands), 11p. (Nos. S23, S27, S29, S32)	2·00
28.10.81	P.O. Pack No. 129b. 7p., 9p., 10½p., 12p. (gravure), 13½p., 15p. (gravure), 11½p., 14p. grey-blue, 18p. dp violet, 22p. blue (Nos. S24, S28, S31, S33/6, S40, S44, S47)	9·00
3.8.83	P.O. Pack No. 2. 10p. (1 centre band), 12½p., 16p., 20½p., 26p. (J.W.), 28p. (J.W.), (Nos. S30, S38, S42, S46, S49/50)	18·00
23.10.84	P.O. Pack No. 6. 10p. (1 centre band), 13p. (J.W.), 16p., 17p. (J.W.), 22p. yellow-green, 26p. (J.W.), 28p. (J.W.), 31p. (J.W.) (Nos. S30, S39, S42/3, S48/51)	17·00
3.3.87	P.O. Pack No. 10. 12p. (litho), 13p. (Questa), 17p. grey-blue (Questa), 18p. dp olive-grey, 22p. yellow-green, 26p. rosine (Questa), 28p. dp violet-blue (Questa), 31p. (Questa) (Nos. S52/3, S57, S59, S65, S72, S74, S76)	20·00

Presentation Packs containing stamps of Northern Ireland, Scotland and Wales are listed after those for Northern Ireland.

1977–78 EXPERIMENTAL MACHINE PACKETS. These are small cartons containing loose stamps for sale in vending machines. The experiment was confined to the Scottish Postal Board area, where six vending machines were installed, the first becoming operational in Dundee about February 1977.

The cartons carry labels inscribed "ROYAL MAIL STAMPS", their total face value (30p. or 60p.) and their contents.

At first the 30p. packet contained two 6½p. and two 8½p. Scottish Regional stamps and the 60p. packet had four of each. The stamps could be in pairs or blocks, but also in strips or singles.

With the change in postal rates on 13 June 1977 these packets were withdrawn on 11 June and on 13 June the contents were changed, giving three 7p. and one 9p. for the 30p. packet and double this for the 60p. packet. However, this time ordinary British Machin stamps were used. Moreover, the Edinburgh machine, situated in an automatic sorting area, was supplied with 7p. stamps with two phosphor bands instead of the new centre band 7p. stamps, despite instructions having been given to withdraw the two band stamps. However, the demand for these packets was too great to be filled and by 27 June the machine was closed down. It was brought back into use on 16 August 1977, supplying 7p. stamps with the centre band.

The 6½p. and 8½p. Scottish Regional packets were put on sale at the Edinburgh Philatelic Bureau in June 1977 and withdrawn in April 1978. The packets with the 7p. and 9p. Machin stamps were put on sale at the Bureau in June 1977 and withdrawn in December 1978.

Such machine packets are outside the scope of this catalogue.

(Des J. Matthews after plaster cast by Arnold Machin)

1993 (7 Dec)–**98.** Chalk-surfaced paper.

(a) Litho Questa. P 15×14 *(with one elliptical hole in each vertical side).*

S81	S **4**	19p. bistre (1 centre band)	80	70
S82		19p. bistre (1 band at right) (25.4.95)	3·00	3·25
S83		20p. brt green (1 centre band) (23.7.96)	1·50	1·50
S84		25p. red (2 bands)	1·10	1·00
S85		26p. red-brown (2 bands) (23.7.96)	1·75	2·00
S86		30p. dp olive-grey (2 bands)	1·25	1·25
S87		37p. brt mauve (2 bands) (23.7.96)	2·75	3·00
S88		41p. grey-brown (2 bands)	2·00	2·25
		Ey. Phosphor omitted	£325	
S89		63p. lt emerald (2 bands) (23.7.96)	4·50	4·75

(b) Gravure Walsall (20p., 26p. (No. S91a), 63p.), Harrison or Walsall (26p. (No. S91), 37p.). P 14 *(No. S90a)* or 15×14 *(others) (both with one elliptical hole in each vertical side).*

S90	S **4**	20p. brt green (1 centre band) (1.7.97)	1·50	1·10
S90a		20p. brt green (1 side band at right) (13.10.98)	4·00	4·00
S91		26p. chestnut (2 bands) (1.7.97)	1·40	1·20
		a. Perf 14 (13.10.98)	4·00	4·00
S92		37p. brt mauve (2 bands) (1.7.97)	2·00	2·25
S93		63p. lt emerald (2 bands) (1.7.97)	4·25	4·50

Nos. S82, S90a and S91a only come from booklets. The Harrison printings of Nos. S91/2 come from booklet pane No. NI81al.

First Day Covers

7.12.93	19p., 25p., 30p., 41p. (S81, S84, S86, S88)	6·00
23.7.96	20p. 26p., 37p., 63p. (S83, S85, S87, S89)	8·75

For Presentation Pack containing stamps of Northern Ireland, Scotland and Wales see after No. NI87 of Northern Ireland.

S **5** Scottish Flag

S **6** Scottish Lion

S **7** Thistle   S **8** Tartan

(Des A. Morris (2nd), F. Pottinger and (1st) T. Chalk (E), Tartan (64p) by Kinloch Anderson adapted Tayburn. Gravure Questa (Nos. S94a, S95a), De La Rue (No. S99), De La Rue or Walsall (Nos. S94/5), Walsall (others))

1999 (8 June)–**2002**. One centre phosphor band (2nd) or two phosphor bands (others). *P* 15×14 (with one elliptical hole in each vertical side).

S94	S **5**	(2nd) new blue, blue and silver	1·00	75
		a. Booklet pane. Nos. S94×6 and S98×2 with centre label and margins all round (4.8.00)	7·00	
S95	S **6**	(1st) greenish yellow, dp rose-red, rose-red and silver	1·25	1·00
		a. Booklet pane. Nos. S95/6, each×4, with centre label and margins all round (22.10.01)	7·75	
S96	S **7**	(E) brt lilac, dp lilac and silver	2·00	2·00
S97	S **8**	64p. greenish yellow, brt magenta, new blue, grey-black and silver	9·00	9·00
S98		65p. greenish yellow, brt magenta, new blue, grey-black and silver (25.4.00)	3·00	3·25
S99		68p. greenish yellow, bright magenta, new blue, grey-black and silver (4.7.02)	3·25	3·25

Presentation Pack (P.O. Pack No. 45) (2nd, 1st, E, 64p.) (Nos. S94/7) ... 14·00

Presentation Pack (P.O. Pack No. 50) (65p.) (No. S98) ... 11·00

Presentation Pack (P.O. Pack No. 55) (2nd, 1st, E, 65p.) (Nos. S94/6, S98) ... 15·00

PHQ Cards (set of 4) (Nos. S94/7) (D12) ... 8·00 14·00

Nos. S94, S95 and S96 were initially sold at 19p., 26p. and 30p., the latter representing the basic European airmail rate.

New printings of Nos. S94/5, produced by De La Rue instead of Walsall were issued on 5 June 2002. Stamps from this printing do not differ from those produced by Walsall.

No. S94a comes from booklet No. DX25.

No. S95a comes from booklet No. DX27.

For combined presentation pack for all four Regions, see under England.

First Day Covers

8.6.99	2nd, 1st, E, 64p. (S94/7) Philatelic Bureau		6·00
	Edinburgh		6·50
25.4.00	65p. (S98) Philatelic Bureau		3·00
	Edinburgh		3·50
4.8.00	Queen Elizabeth the Queen Mother *se-tenant* pane 2nd, 65p. (S94a) Philatelic Bureau (as for Nos. 2160/1)		4·75
	London SW1 (*as for Nos.* 2160/1)		4·75
22.10.01	Unseen and Unheard *se-tenant* pane (1st), E, (S95a) Philatelic Bureau (*as for* **MS**2206)		7·00
	Rosyth, Dunfermline (*as for* **MS**2206)		7·00
4.7.02	68p. (S99) Tallents House (Type K) (*see Introduction*)		1·75
	Edinburgh		1·75

Special First Day of Issue Postmarks

(for use on Nos. S94, S95/8)

S **9**

(Des J. Matthews. Gravure Walsall)

2000 (15 Feb). Type S **4** redrawn with *1st* face value as Type S **9**. Two phosphor bands. *P* 14 (with one elliptical hole in each vertical side).

S108   S **9**   (1st) bright orange-red ... 3·00   3·25

No. S108 was only issued in £7·50 stamp booklets (No. DX24).

2003 (14 Oct)–16. As Nos. S 94/6 and S 99, and new values, but with white borders. One centre phosphor band (2nd) or two phosphor bands (others). *P* 15×14 (with one elliptical hole in each vertical side).

(a) Gravure Walsall or De La Rue (42p.) or De La Rue (others)

S109	S **5**	(2nd) new blue, blue and silver	1·00	60
		l. Booklet pane. Nos. S109 and EN16, each×3, with margins all round (16.3.04)	8·50	
		m. Booklet pane. Nos. S109 and W103, each×3, with margins all round (1.3.07)	3·00	
S110	S **6**	(1st) rose-red, greenish yellow, deep rose-red and silver	1·25	85
S111	S **7**	(E) bright lilac, deep lilac and silver	2·50	2·50
S112		40p. bright lilac, deep lilac and silver (11.5.04)	1·75	1·75
S113		42p. bright lilac, deep lilac and silver (5.4.05)	1·75	1·75
S114		44p. bright lilac, deep lilac and silver (28.3.06)	1·50	1·50
S115		48p. bright lilac, deep lilac and silver (27.3.07)	90	90
S116		50p. bright lilac, deep lilac and silver (1.4.08)	80	75
S117		56p. bright lilac, deep lilac and silver (31.3.09)	1·25	1·25
S118		60p. bright lilac, deep lilac and silver (30.3.10)	1·40	1·40
S119	S **8**	68p. bright magenta, greenish yellow, new blue, grey-black and silver	2·00	2·00
S120		72p. bright magenta, greenish yellow, new blue, grey-black and silver (28.3.06)	2·00	2·00
S121		78p. bright magenta, greenish yellow, new blue, grey-black and silver (27.3.07)	2·00	2·00
S122		81p. bright magenta, greenish yellow, new blue, grey-black and silver (1.4.08)	2·00	2·00
S123		90p. bright magenta, greenish yellow, new blue, grey-black and silver (31.3.09)	2·25	2·25
S124		97p. bright magenta, greenish yellow, new blue, grey-black and silver (30.3.10)	2·40	2·40

(b) Litho Enschedé or Cartor (1st) or Cartor (others)

S130	S **5**	(2nd) silver, greenish yellow, bright magenta, new blue and black (27.6.12)	1·00	1·00
S131	S **6**	(1st) Silver, greenish yellow, bright magenta, new blue and black (20.9.07)	1·25	1·25
S132	S **7**	68p. silver, greenish yellow, bright magenta, new blue and black (29.3.11)	1·50	1·50
S133		87p. silver, greenish yellow, bright magenta, new blue and black (25.4.12)	2·50	2·50
S134		88p. silver, greenish yellow, bright magenta, new blue and black (27.3.13)	2·00	2·00
S135		97p. silver, greenish yellow, bright magenta, new blue and black (26.3.14)	2·25	2·25
S136		£1 silver, greenish yellow, bright magenta, new blue and black (24.3.15)	2·40	2·40
S137		£1·05 silver, greenish yellow, bright magenta, new blue and black (22.3.16)	2·40	2·40
S142	S **8**	£1·10 silver, greenish yellow, bright magenta, new blue and black (29.3.11)	2·75	2·75
S143		£1·28 silver, greenish yellow, bright magenta, bnew blue and black (25.4.12)	3·25	3·25
S144		£1·33 silver, greenish yellow, bright magenta, new blue and black (24.3.15)	3·25	3·25

Presentation Pack (Nos. S109/11, S119) (P.O. Pack No. 64) ... 7·00

PHQ Cards (Nos. S109/11, S119) (set of 4) (D25) ... 2·00   10·00

No. S109l comes from booklet No. DX32 and S109m from booklet DX 38. The Walsall printing of No. S113 was issued on 5 April 2005, and the De La Rue printing on 24 May 2005.

Stamps as No. S121/2 but printed in lithography were only issued within **MS**2796 (S121) or **MS**2886 (S122).

No. S131 was issued on 20 September 2007 in £7·66 stamp booklets printed by Enschedé, No. DX40 and on 29 September 2008 in £9·72 booklets (DX43). It was issued in sheets printed by Cartor on 27 June 2012

A design as No. S131 but self-adhesive was issued on 30 November 2007 in sheets of 20, each stamp accompanied by a *se-tenant*. label showing a Scottish scene (LS44). These sheets were printed in lithography by Cartor, perforated 15×14 without the elliptical holes, and sold at £7·35. They were also available with personalised photographs on the labels at £14·95 from the Royal Mail in Edinburgh.

Stamps as Nos. EN30, NI95, S131 and W122 but self-adhesive were issued on 29 September 2008 in sheets of 20 containing five of each design with *se-tenant* labels (LS49).

Numbers have be left for possible additions to this definitive series.

First Day Covers

14.10.03	2nd, 1st, E, 68p. (S109/11, S119) Tallents House		
	(Type K, see Introduction)		3·25
	Edinburgh		3·25
11.5.04	40p. (S112) Tallents House (Type K)		2·75
	Edinburgh		2·75
5.4.05	42p. (S113) Tallents House (Type K)		1·40
	Edinburgh		1·40
28.3.06	44p., 72p. (S114, S120) Tallents House (Type K)		2·75
	Edinburgh		2·75
27.3.07	48p., 78p. (S115, S121) Tallents House (Type K)		4·00
	Edinburgh		4·00
1.4.08	50p., 81p. (S116, S122) Tallents House (Type K)		4·00
	Edinburgh		4·00
31.3.09	56p., 90p. (S117, S123) Tallents House (Type K)		4·75
	Edinburgh		4·75
30.3.10	60p., 97p. (S118, S124) Tallents House (Type K)		4·00
	Edinburgh		4·00
29.3.11	68p., £1·10 (S132, S142) Tallents House (Type K)		6·00
	Edinburgh		6·00
25.4.12	87p., £1·28 (S133, S143) Tallents House (Type K)		6·50
	Edinburgh		6·50
27.3.13	88p. (S134) Tallents House (Type K)		3·00
	Edinburgh		3·00
26.3.14	97p. (S135) Tallents House (Type K)		3·50
	Edinburgh		3·50
24.3.15	£1, £1·33 (S136, S144) Tallents House (Type K)		7·75
	Edinburgh		7·75
22.3.16	£1·05 (S137) Tallents House (Type K)		3·50
	Edinbough		3·50

S **9a**

(Des H. Brown. Gravure De La Rue)

2004 (5 Oct). *Opening of New Scottish Parliament Building, Edinburgh.* Sheet 123×70 mm. Printed in gravure by De La Rue. One centre phosphor band (2nd) or two phosphor bands (others). P 15×14 (with one elliptical hole in each vertical side).

MSS152 S **9a** Nos. S109, S110×2 and S112×2		7·00	7·00
First Day Cover (Tallents House)			8·00
First Day Cover (Edinburgh)			8·00

Special First Day of Issue Postmarks

S **10** (*Illustration reduced. Actual size 124×71 mm*)

(Des P. Crowther, Clare Melinsky and Silk Pearce. Gravure De La Rue)

2006 (30 Nov). *Celebrating Scotland.* Sheet 124×71 mm. Two phosphor bands. P 15×14 (with one elliptical hole in each vertical side) (1st) or 14½×14 (72p).

MSS153 S **10** (1st) As No. S110; (1st) Scottish Flag; 72p. St. Andrew; 72p. Edinburgh Castle		7·00	7·00
First Day Cover (Tallents House)			8·00
First Day Cover (St Andrews, Fife)			8·00
Presentation Pack (P.O. Pack No. M14)		8·00	
PHQ Cards (set of 5) (CGB1)		4·00	17·00

MSS153 was on sale at post offices throughout the UK.

The five PHQ cards depict the complete miniature sheet and the four stamps within it.

Stamps as the 1st class Scottish flag stamp within **MS**S153 but self-adhesive were issued on 30 November 2009 in sheets of 20 with *se-tenant* labels showing Scottish Castles, No. LS68. These sheets were printed in lithography by Cartor and sold for £8·35 each.

Special First Day of Issue Postmarks

(Litho De La Rue)

2008 (29 Sept). *50th Anniv of the Country Definitives.* As Nos. S1, S3 and S5 (definitives of 1958) but inscribed 1st. Two phosphor bands. P 15×14½ (with one elliptical hole in each vertical side).

S154	S **1**	(1st) deep lilac	3·00	3·00
		I. Booklet pane. Nos. S154/6 and S131×3	8·00	
S155	S **3**	(1st) green	3·00	3·00
S156	S **2**	(1st) deep claret	3·00	3·00

Nos. S154/6 come from £9·72 booklets, No. DX43.

S **11** (*Illustration reduced. Actual size 145×74 mm*)

(Des Tayburn. Gravure Enschedé)

2009 (22 Jan). *250th Birth Anniv of Robert Burns (Scottish poet).* Sheet 145×74 mm. One centre phosphor band (2nd) or two phosphor bands (others). P 14½ (size 34×34 mm) or 15×14 (with one elliptical hole in each vert side) (others).

MSS157 S **11** (2nd) No. S109; (1st) "A Man's a Man for a' that" and Burns ploughing (detail) (James Sargent Storer) (34×34 mm); (1st) No. S110; (1st) Portrait of Burns (Alexander Nasmyth) (34×34 mm); 50p. No. S116; 81p. S122			9·00	9·00
First Day Cover (Tallents House)				10·00
First Day Cover (Alloway, Ayr)				10·00
Presentation Pack (P.O. Pack No. 422)			11·00	
PHQ Cards (set of 3) (319)			3·50	12·00

MSS157 was on sale at post offices throughout the UK.

The three PHQ cards show the two 34×34 mm Robert Burns stamps and the complete miniature sheet.

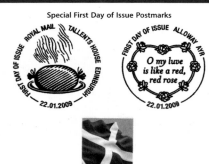

Special First Day of Issue Postmarks

S **12** Saltire
Des Peter Crowther (illustration) and Silk Pierce.
Litho Cartor or Enschedé)

2013 (9 May). *Scotland Flag.* Two phosphor bands. P 14½×14 (with one elliptical hole in each vert side).
S158 S **12** (1st) multicoloured .... 2·00   2·00
No. S158 was issued in £11·11 Football Heroes booklets, No. DY7 (see booklet pane No. U3010*a*), and £13·97 Classic Locomotives booklets, No. DY9 (see booklet pane No. U3011*b*).

IV. WALES

From the inception of the Regional stamps, the Welsh versions were tendered to members of the public at all Post Offices within the former County of Monmouthshire but the national alternatives were available on request. By August 1961 the policy of "dual stocking" of definitive stamps was only maintained at Abergavenny, Chepstow, Newport and Pontypool. Offices with a Monmouthshire postal address but situated outside the County, namely Beachley, Brockweir, Redbrook, Sedbury, Tutshill, Welsh Newton and Woodcroft, were not supplied with the Welsh Regional stamps. With the re-formation of Counties, Monmouthshire became known as Gwent and was also declared to be part of Wales. From 1 July 1974, therefore, except for the offices mentioned above, only Welsh Regional stamps were available at the offices under the jurisdiction of Newport, Gwent.

W **1**   W **2**   W **3**

(Des R. Stone)

1958–67. *W* 179. *P* 15×14.
W1   W **1**   3d. dp lilac (18.8.58) 15   15
         p. One centre phosphor band
            (16.5.67) 20   15
W2   4d. ultramarine (7.2.66) 20   25
         p. Two phosphor bands (10.67) 20   25
W3   W **2**   6d. dp claret (29.9.58) 35   40
W4   9d. bronze-green (2 phosphor bands)
            (1.3.67) 40   50
         Ey. Phosphor omitted £375
W5   W **3**   1s.3d. green (29.9.58) 40   55
W6   1s.6d. grey-blue (2 phosphor bands)
            (1.3.67) 45   55
         Ey. Phosphor omitted .... 50·00

First Day Covers

18.8.58   3d. (W1) .... 12·00
29.9.58   6d., 1s.3d. (W3, W5) .... 25·00
7.2.66   4d. (W2) .... 7·00
1.3.67   9d., 1s.6d. (W4, W6) .... 4·00
          Presentation Pack* £100
* This was issued in 1960 and comprises Guernsey No. 7, Jersey No. 10, Isle of Man No. 2, Northern Ireland Nos. NI1, NI3 and NI5, Scotland Nos. S1, S3 and S5 and Wales Nos. W1, W3 and W5 together with a 6-page printed leaflet describing the stamps. There exist two forms: (*a*) inscribed "7s.3d." for sale in the U.K.; and (*b*) inscribed "$1.20" for sale in the U.S.A.

1967–69. No wmk. Chalk-surfaced paper. One centre phosphor band (Nos. W7, W9/10) or two phosphor bands (others). Gum arabic (3d.) or PVA gum (others). *P* 15×14.
W7   W **1**   3d. dp lilac (6.12.67) 15   20
         Ey. Phosphor omitted .... 70·00
W8   4d. ultramarine (21.6.68) 15   20
W9   4d. olive-sepia (4.9.68) 15   20
W10   4d. brt vermilion (26.2.69) 15   20

W11   5d. royal blue (4.9.68) 15   30
         Ey. Phosphor omitted .... 2·00
         Ey. Phosphor omitted .... 3·00
W12   W **3**   1s.6d. grey-blue (1.8.69) .... 3·50   3·50
There was no Post Office first day cover for No. W10.

4.9.68   First Day Cover (W9, W11) .... 3·00
         Presentation Pack (*P.O. Pack No. 24
         containing Nos. W4, W6/7, W9/11 (9.12.70)* . 4·00

W **4** With "p"

        I   II

Redrawn design of Type W **4** (litho ptgs.)
Two Types of Dragon
Type I:-The eye is complete with white dot in the centre. Wing-tips, tail and tongue are thin.
Type II:-The eye is joined to the nose by a solid line. Tail, wing-tips, claws and tongue are wider than in Type I.

The following stamps printed in lithography show a screened background behind and to the left of the emblem: 11½p., 12½p., 14p. (No. W39), 15½p., 16p., 18p. (No. W46), 19½p., 22p. (No. W54) and 28p. (No. W63). The 13p. and 17p. (No. W44) also show screened backgrounds in Type I, but changed to solid backgrounds for Type II. All other values printed in lithography have solid backgrounds.

(Des J. Matthews after plaster cast by Arnold Machin)

1971 (7 July)–**93**. Decimal Currency. Chalk-surfaced paper. Type *W* **4.**
         (*a*) Gravure Harrison. With phosphor bands. P 15×14.
W13   2½p. brt magenta (1 centre band) 20   20
         Ey. Phosphor omitted .... 7·50
         Eg. Gum arabic (22.9.72) 20
         Ega. Imperf (pair) £800
W14   3p. ultramarine (2 bands) 25   20
         Ey. Phosphor omitted .... 30·00
         Eg. Gum arabic (6.6.73) 25
         Eya. Phosphor omitted (No. W14Eg) .... 12·00
W15   3p. ultramarine (1 centre band) (23.1.74) 25   25
W16   3½p. olive-grey (2 bands) (23.1.74) 20   30
W17   3½p. olive-grey (1 centre band) (6.11.74) 20   30
W18   4½p. grey-blue (2 bands) (6.11.74) 30   30
W19   5p. reddish violet (2 bands) .... 1·25   1·25
         Ey. Phosphor omitted .... 20·00
W20   5½p. violet (2 bands) (23.1.74) 30   40
         Ey. Phosphor omitted £180
W21   5½p. violet (1 centre band) (21.5.75) 30   40
         a. Imperf (pair) £700
W22   6½p. greenish blue (1 centre band) (14.1.76) . 20   20
W23   7p. purple-brown (1 centre band) (18.1.78) ... 25   25
W24   7½p. chestnut (2 bands) .... 1·75   1·75
         Ey. Phosphor omitted .... 95·00
W25   8p. rosine (2 bands) (23.1.74) 30   35
         Ey. Phosphor omitted £850
W26   8½p. yellow-green (2 bands) (14.1.76) 40   50
W27   9p. dp violet (2 bands) (18.1.78) 40   40
W28   10p. orange-brown (2 bands) (20.10.76) 45   55
W29   10p. orange-brown (1 centre band) (23.7.80) .. 40   40
W30   10½p. steel-blue (2 bands) (18.1.78) 65   75
W31   11p. scarlet (2 bands) (20.10.76) 45   55

         (*b*) Gravure Harrison. On phosphorised paper. P 15×14.
W32   12p. yellowish green (23.7.80) 50   60
W33   13½p. purple-brown (23.7.80) .... 1·00   1·10
W34   15p. ultramarine (23.7.80) 70   80

         (*c*) Litho Questa (Type II unless otherwise stated). P 14 (11½p., 12½p., 14p. (No. W39), 15½p., 16p., 18p. (No. W46), 19½p., 20½p., 22p. (No. W54), 26p. (No. W61) or 28p. (No. W63)) or 15×14 (others).
W35   11½p. drab (Type I) (1 side band) (8.4.81) 90   1·00
W36   12p. brt emerald (1 side band) (7.1.86) .... 2·00   2·00
W37   12½p. lt emerald (Type I) (1 side band)
            (24.2.82) 70   70
         a. Perf 15×14 (Type I) (10.1.84) .... 4·75   4·25
W38   13p. pale chestnut (Type I) (1 side band)
            (23.10.84) 60   60
         Ea. Type II (1.87) .... 2·25   2·00

W39	14p. grey-blue (Type I) (phosphorised paper) (8.4.81)	70	70
W40	14p. dp blue (1 centre band) (8.11.88)	75	75
W41	15p. brt blue (1 centre band) (28.11.89)	80	75
	Ey. Phosphor omitted	£140	
W42	15½p. pale violet (Type I) (phosphorised paper) (24.2.82)	75	75
W43	16p. drab (Type I) (phosphorised paper) (27.4.83)	1·75	1·75
	a. Perf 15×14 (Type I) (10.1.84)	1·75	1·75
W44	17p. grey-blue (Type I) (phosphorised paper) (23.10.84)	90	1·00
	Ea. Type II (18.8.86)	60·00	45·00
W45	17p. dp blue (1 centre band) (4.12.90)	90	80
	Ey. Phosphor omitted	18·00	
W46	18p. dp violet (Type I) (8.4.81)	1·00	95
W47	18p. dp olive-grey (phosphorised paper) (6.1.87)	95	90
W48	18p. brt green (1 centre band) (3.12.91)	75	75
	Ey. Phosphor omitted	£225	
	a. Booklet pane. No. W48×6 with margins all round (25.2.92)	3·25	
	aEy. Phosphor omitted		
	b. Perf 14 (12.1.93*)	7·50	7·50
W49	18p. brt green (1 side band at right) (25.2.92)	2·00	2·00
	a. Booklet pane. No. X1020×2, 1451a, 1514a, W49×2, W60×2 and centre label with margins all round	18·00	
	aEy. Phosphor omitted	£225	
	Eb. Band at left (10.8.93)	2·00	2·00
W50	19p. brt orange-red (phosphorised paper) (8.11.88)	1·00	1·10
W51	19½p. olive-grey (Type I) (phosphorised paper) (24.2.82)	1·75	2·00
W52	20p. brownish black (phosphorised paper) (28.11.89)	90	90
W53	20½p. ultramarine (Type I) (phosphorised paper) (27.4.83)	3·75	3·75
W54	22p. blue (Type I) (phosphorised paper) (8.4.81)	1·20	1·30
W55	22p. yellow-green (Type I) (phosphorised paper) (23.10.84)	1·10	1·25
W56	22p. brt orange-red (phosphorised paper) (4.12.90)	1·00	1·10
W57	23p. brt green (phosphorised paper) (8.11.88)	1·00	1·10
W58	24p. Indian red (phosphorised paper) (28.11.89)	1·40	1·40
W59	24p. chestnut (phosphorised paper) (3.12.91)	75	75
	a. Booklet pane. No. W59×6 with margins all round (25.2.92)	5·00	
	b. Perf 14 (14.9.92*)	7·50	7·50
W60	24p. chestnut (2 bands) (25.2.92)	1·25	1·50
W61	26p. rosine (Type I) (phosphorised paper) (24.2.82)	1·10	1·10
	a. Perf 15×14 (Type II) (27.1.87)	5·75	6·00
W62	26p. drab (phosphorised paper) (4.12.90)	1·75	1·75
W63	28p. dp violet-blue (Type I) (phosphorised paper) (27.4.83)	1·50	1·50
	a. Perf 15×14 (Type II) (27.1.87)	1·50	1·50
W64	28p. dp bluish grey (phosphorised paper) (3.12.91)	1·50	1·50
W65	31p. brt purple (Type I) (phosphorised paper) (23.10.84)	1·75	1·75
W66	32p. greenish blue (phosphorised paper) (8.11.88)	1·75	1·75
W67	34p. dp bluish grey (phosphorised paper) (28.11.89)	1·75	1·75
W68	37p. rosine (phosphorised paper) (4.12.90)	2·25	2·25
W69	39p. brt mauve (phosphorised paper) (3.12.91)	2·25	2·25

* Earliest known date of use.

Nos. W48b and W59b were caused by the use of a reserve perforating machine for some printings in the second half of 1992.

Nos. W49, W49Eb and W60 only come from booklets.

The listed booklet panes come from the following Sponsored Booklets:

W48a	– Booklet DX13
W49a	– Booklet DX13
W59a	– Booklet DX13

No. W60 exists with the phosphor omitted, but cannot be identified without the use of u.v. light (*Price* £375 *unused*).

From 1972 printings were on fluorescent white paper. From 1973 most printings had dextrin added to the PVA gum (see notes after 1971 Decimal Machin issue).

First Day Covers

7.7.71	2½p., 3p., 5p., 7½p., (W13/14, W19, W24)	3·00
23.1.74	3p., 3½p., 5½p., 8p. (W15/16, W20, W25)	2·50
6.11.74	4½p. (W18)	1·50
14.1.76	6½p., 8½p. (W22, W26)	1·50

20.10.76	10p., 11p. (W28, W31)	1·50
18.1.78	7p., 9p., 10½p. (W23, W27, W30)	1·75
23.7.80	12p., 13½p., 15p. (W32/4)	3·00
8.4.81	11½p., 14p., 18p., 22p. (W35, W39, W46, W54)	2·50
24.2.82	12½p., 15½p., 19½p., 26p. (W37, W42, W51, W61)	3·50
27.4.83	16p., 20½p., 28p. (W43, W53, W63)	3·50
23.10.84	13p., 17p., 22p., 31p. (W38, W44, W55, W65)	4·25
7.1.86	12p. (W36)	2·00
6.1.87	18p. (W47)	2·00
8.11.88	14p., 19p., 23p., 32p. (W40, W50, W57, W66)	4·50
28.11.89	15p., 20p., 24p., 34p. (W41, W52, W58, W67)	5·00
4.12.90	17p., 22p., 26p., 37p (W45, W56, W62, W68)	5·00
3.12.91	18p., 24p., 28p., 39p. (W48, W59, W64, W69)	5·50
25.2.92	Cymru-Wales *se-tenant* pane 18p. (*2nd*), 24p. (1st), 33p. (W49a)	10·00

Presentation Packs

7.7.71	P.O. Pack No. 28. 2½p., 3p. (2 bands), 5p., 7½p. (Nos. W13/14, W19, W24)	3·50
29.5.74	P.O. Pack No. 63. 3p. (1 centre band), 3½p. (2 bands) or (1 centre band), 5½p. (2 bands) or (1 centre band), 8p. (Nos. W15, W16 or W17, W20 or W21, W25). The 4½p. (No. W18) was added later	2·50
20.10.76	P.O. Pack No. 86. 6½p., 8½p., 10p. (2 bands), 11p. (Nos. W22, W26, W28, W31)	2·00
28.10.81	P.O. Pack No. 129c. 7p., 9p., 10½p., 12p. (photo), 13½p., 15p. (photo), 11½p., 14p. grey-blue, 18p. dp violet, 22p. blue (Nos. W23, W27, W30, W32/5, W39, W46, W54)	9·00
3.8.83	P.O. Pack No. 3. 10p. (1 centre band), 12½p., 16p., 20½p., 26p. rosine, 28p. dp violet-blue (Nos. W29, W37, W43, W53, W61, W63)	20·00
23.10.84	P.O. Pack No. 7. 10p. (1 centre band), 13p., 16p., 17p. grey-blue, 22p. yellow-green, 26p. rosine, 28p. dp violet-blue, 31p. (Nos. W29, W38, W43a, W44, W55, W61, W63, W65)	17·00
3.3.87	P.O. Pack No. 11. 12p. (litho), 13p., 17p. grey-blue, 18p. dp olive-grey, 22p. yellow-green, 26p. rosine, 28p. dp violet-blue, 31p. (Nos. W36, W38, W44, W47, W55, W61a, W63a, W65)	20·00

Presentation Packs containing stamps of Northern Ireland, Scotland and Wales are listed after those for Northern Ireland.

(Des J. Matthews after plaster cast by Arnold Machin. Litho Questa)

1993 (7 Dec)–**96**. Chalk-surfaced paper. *P* 15×14 (with one elliptical hole in each vertical side).

W70	W **4**	19p. bistre (1 centre band)	80	70
W71		19p. bistre (1 band at right) (25.4.95)	3·75	4·00
W72		20p. brt green (1 centre band) (23.7.96)	1·75	2·00
W73		25p. red (2 bands)	1·25	1·00
W74		26p. red-brown (2 bands) (23.7.96)	2·00	2·25
W75		30p. dp olive-grey (2 bands)	1·25	1·40
W76		37p. brt mauve (2 bands) (23.7.96)	2·75	3·00
W77		41p. grey-brown (2 bands)	2·00	2·00
W78		63p. lt emerald (2 bands) (23.7.96)	4·50	4·75

No. W71 only comes from booklets.

First Day Covers

7.12.93	19p., 25p., 30p., 41p. (W70, W73, W75, W77)	6·00
23.7.96	20p., 26p., 37p., 63p., (W72, W74, W76, W78)	7·00

For Presentation Packs containing stamps of Northern Ireland, Scotland and Wales see after No. NI85 of Northern Ireland.

W **5** Without "p"

(Gravure Walsall (20p., 26p. (No. W80a), 63p.), Harrison or Walsall (26p. (No. W80), 37p.))

1997 (1 July)–**98**. Chalk-surfaced paper. *P* 14 (No. W79a) or 15×14 (others) (both with one elliptical hole in each vertical side).

W79	W **5**	20p. brt green (1 centre band)	1·25	1·25
W79a		20p. brt green (1 side band at right) (13.10.98)	4·00	4·00
W80		26p. chestnut (2 bands)	1·50	1·50
		a. Perf 14 (13.10.98)	4·00	4·00
W81		37p. brt mauve (2 bands)	3·50	3·50
W82		63p. lt emerald (2 bands)	5·50	5·50

Nos. W79a and W80a were only issued in booklets.

The Harrison printings of Nos. W80/1 come from booklet pane No. NI81al.

First Day Cover

1.7.97	20p., 26p., 37p., 63p. (W79, W80/2)	6·00

Presentation Pack

1.7.97	P.O. Pack No. 39. 20p., 26p., 37p., 63p. (Nos. W79, W80/2)	13·00

W **6** Leek   W **7** Welsh Dragon

W **8** Daffodil   W **9** Prince of Wales Feathers

(Des D. Petersen (2nd), T. & G. Petersen (1st), I. Rees (E), R. Evans (64p., 65p.). Adapted Tutssels. Gravure De La Rue or Walsall (2nd, 1st), De La Rue (68p.), Walsall (others))

1999 (8 June)–**2002**. One phosphor band (2nd) or two phosphor bands (others). *P* 14 (No. W83a) or 15×14 (others) (both with one elliptical hole in each vertical side).

W83	W **6**	(2nd) orange-brown, yellow-orange and black (1 centre band)	1·00	50
W83a		(2nd) orange-brown, yellow-orange and black (1 band at right) (P 14) (18.9.00)	4·00	4·00
		al. Booklet pane. No. 2124d and W83a, each×4, with centre label and margins all round	22·00	
W84	W **7**	(1st) blue-green, greenish yellow, silver and black	1·25	1·00
W85	W **8**	(E) greenish blue, dp greenish blue and grey-black	1·90	1·90
W86	W **9**	64p. violet, gold, silver and black	9·00	9·00
W87		65p. violet, gold, silver and black (25.4.00)	3·25	3·25
W88		68p. violet, gold, silver and black (4.7.02)	3·25	3·25
Presentation Pack (P.O. Pack No. 46) (2nd, 1st, E, 64p.)			14·00	
Presentation Pack (P.O. Pack No. 51) (65p.) (No. W87))			12·00	
Presentation Pack (P.O. Pack No. 56) (2nd, 1st, E, 65p.)			18·00	
PHQ Cards (set of 4) (Nos. W83, W84/6) (D13)			8·00	14·00

Nos. W83, W84 and W85 were initially sold at 19p., 26p. and 30p., the latter representing the basic European airmail rate.

New printings of Nos. W83 and W84, produced by De La Rue instead of Walsall, were issued on 28 May 2003 and 4 March 2003. Stamps from these printings do not differ from those produced by Walsall.

No. W83a comes from the £7 Treasury of Trees booklet (No.DX26).

For combined presentation pack for all four Regions, see under England.

First Day Covers

8.6.99	2nd (*centre band*), 1st, E, 64p. (W83, W84/6) Philatelic Bureau		6·00
	Cardiff		6·50
25.4.00	65p. (W87) Philatelic Bureau		3·00
	Cardiff		3·50
18.9.00	Treasury of Trees se-tenant pane 1st (*Millennium*), 2nd (2124d, W83a) Philatelic Bureau		5·00
	Llangernyw, Abergele		5·00
4.7.02	68p. (W88) Tallents House (Type K) (*see Introduction*)		1·75
	Cardiff		1·75

Special First Day of Issue Postmarks

W **10**

(Des J. Matthews. Gravure Walsall)

2000 (15 Feb). Type *W* 4 redrawn with *1af/st* face value as Type *W* **10**. Two phosphor bands. *P* 14 (with one elliptical hole in each vertical side).

W97	W **10**	(1st) bright orange-red	3·00	2·75

No. W97 was only issued in £7·50 stamp booklets (No. DX24).

2003 (14 Oct)–**16**. As Nos. W83, W84/5 and W88, and new values, but with white borders. One centre phosphor band (2nd) or two phosphor bands (others). *P* 15×14 (with one elliptical hole in each vertical side).

(a) (Gravure Walsall or De La Rue (42p.) or De La Rue (others))

W98	W **6**	(2nd) orange-brown, deep orange-brown and black	1·00	75
W99	W **7**	(1st) blue-green, greenish yellow, silver and black	1·25	75
W100	W **8**	(E) greenish blue, deep greenish blue and grey-black	2·50	2·50
W101		40p. greenish blue, deep greenish blue and grey-black (11.5.04)	1·50	1·50
W102		42p. greenish blue, deep greenish blue and grey-black (5.4.05)	1·50	1·50
W103		44p. greenish blue, deep greenish blue and grey-black (28.3.06)	1·50	1·50
W104		48p. greenish blue, deep greenish blue and grey-black (27.3.07)	90	90
W105		50p. greenish blue, deep greenish blue and grey-black (1.4.08)	1·00	1·00
W106		56p. greenish blue, deep greenish blue and grey-black (31.3.09)	1·25	1·25
W107		60p. greenish blue, deep greenish blue and grey-black (30.3.10)	1·40	1·40
W108	W **9**	68p. violet, gold, silver and black	2·25	2·25
W109		72p. violet, gold, silver and black (28.3.06)	2·00	2·00
W110		78p. violet, gold, silver and black (27.3.07)	2·00	2·00
W111		81p. violet, gold, silver and black (1.4.08)	2·00	2·00
W112		90p. violet, gold, silver and black (31.3.09)	2·25	2·25
W113		97p. violet, gold, silver and black (30.3.10)	2·40	2·40

(b) Litho Enschedé or Cartor (1st) or Cartor (others)

W121	W **6**	(2nd) greenish yellow, bright magenta, new blue and black (1.13)	1·00	1·00
W122	W **7**	(1st) greenish yellow, bright magenta, new blue and black (20.9.07)	1·25	1·25
W123	W **8**	68p. greenish yellow, bright magenta, new blue and black (29.3.11)	1·50	1·50
W124		87p. greenish yellow, bright magenta, new blue and black (25.4.12)	2·50	2·50
W125		88p. greenish yellow, bright magenta, new blue and black (27.3.13)	2·00	2·00
W126		97p. greenish yellow, bright magenta, new blue and black (26.3.14)	2·25	2·25
W127		£1 greenish yellow, bright magenta, new blue and black (24.3.15)	2·75	2·75
W128		£1.05 greenish yellow, bright magenta, new blue and black (22.3.16)	2·40	2·40
W133	W **9**	£1·10 gold, silver, greenish yellow, bright magenta, new blue and black (29.3.11)	2·75	2·75
W134		£1·28 gold, silver, greenish yellow, bright magenta, new blue and black (25.4.12)	3·25	3·25
W135		£1·33 gold, silver, greenish yellow, bright magenta, new blue and black (24.3.15)	3·25	3·25

Presentation Pack (Nos. W98/100, W108). (P.O. Pack No. 65)	7·00	
PHQ Cards (Nos. W98/100, W108) (set of 4) (D26)	2·00	6·00

The Walsall printing of No. W102 was issued on 5 April 2005 and the De La Rue on 24 May 2005.

Stamps as Nos. W110/11 but printed in lithography were only issued within **MS**2796 (W110) or **MS**2886 (W111).

No. W122 was first issued in £7·66 stamp booklets, No. DX40 printed by Enschedè and **MS**W147. It was issued in sheets printed by Cartor in January 2013.

A design as No. W122 but self-adhesive was issued on 1 March 2007 in sheets of 20, each stamp accompanied by a *se-tenant* label showing a Welsh scene (LS37). These sheets were printed in lithography by Cartor, perforated 15×14 without the elliptical holes, and sold at £6·55 each. They were also available with personalised photographs on the labels at £14·95 from Royal Mail in Edinburgh.

Stamps as Nos. EN30, NI95, S131 and W122 but self-adhesive were issued on 29 September 2008 in sheets of 20 containing five of each design with *se-tenant* labels (LS49).

Numbers have been left for possible additions to the above definitive series.

First Day Covers

14.10.03	2nd, 1st, E, 68p. (W98/100, W108) Tallents House (Type K) (see Introduction)	3·25
	Cardiff	3·25
11.5.04	40p. (W101) Tallents House (Type K)	2·75
	Cardiff	2·75
5.4.05	42p. (W102) Tallents House (Type K)	1·40
	Cardiff	1·40
28.3.06	44p., 72p. (W103, W109) Tallents House (Type K)	2·75
	Cardiff	2·75
27.3.07	48p., 78p. (W104, W110) Tallents House (Type K)	3·50
	Cardiff	3·50
1.4.08	50p., 81p. (W105, W111) Tallents House (Type K)	4·00
	Cardiff	4·00
31.3.09	56p., 90p. (W106, W112) Tallents House (Type K)	4·75
	Cardiff	4·75
30.3.10	60p., 97p. (W107, W113) Tallents House (Type K)	4·00
	Cardiff	4·00
29.3.11	68p., £1·10 (W123, W133) Tallents House (Type K)	6·00
	Cardiff	6·00
24.4.12	87p. £1·28 (W124, W134) Tallents House (Type K)	6·50
	Cardiff	6·50
27.3.13	88p. (W125) Tallents House (Type K)	3·00
	Cardiff	3·00
26.3.14	97p. (W126) Tallents House (Type K)	3·50
	Cardiff	3·50
24.3.15	£1, £1·33 (W127, W135) Tallents House (Type K)	7·75
	Cardiff	7·75
22.3.16	£1·05 (W128) Tallents House (Type K)	3·50
	Cardiff	3·50

W **10a**

(Des Silk Pearce. Gravure De La Rue)

2006 (1 Mar). *Opening of New Welsh Assembly Building, Cardiff*. Sheet 123×70 mm. One centre phosphor band (2nd) or two phosphor bands (others). *P* 15×14 (with one elliptical hole in each vertical side).

MSW143	W **10a**	Nos. W98, W99×2 and W108×2.......	5·00	5·00
First Day Cover (Tallents House)				6·00
First Day Cover (Cardiff)				6·00

(Litho De La Rue)

2008 (29 Sept). *50th Anniv of the Country Definitives*. As Nos. W1, W3 and W5 (definitives of 1958) but inscribed 1st. Two phosphor bands. *P* 15×14½ (with one elliptical hole in each vertical side).

W144	W **1**	(1st) deep lilac....................................	3·00	3·00
		l. Booklet pane. Nos. W144/6 and W122×3	8·00	
W145	W **3**	(1st) green..	3·00	3·00
W146	W **2**	(1st) deep claret..................................	3·00	3·00

Nos. W144/6 come from £9·72 booklets, No. DX43.

W **11** (*Illustration reduced. Actual size 123×70 mm*)

(Des Clare Melinsky and Silk Pearce. Litho De La Rue)

2009 (26 Feb). *Celebrating Wales*. Sheet 123×70 mm. Two phosphor bands. *P* 15×14 (with one elliptical hole in each vertical side (1st) or 14½×14 (81p.).

MSW147 W **11**	(1st) Red dragon; (1st) No. W122; 81p. St. David; 81p. National Assembly for Wales, Cardiff		6·00	6·00
First Day Cover (Tallents House)				7·00
First Day Cover (St. Davids)				7·00
Presentation Pack (P.O. Pack No.424)			8·00	
PHQ Cards (set of 5) (CGB4)			4·00	17·00

MSW147 was on sale at post offices throughout the UK.

The five PHQ cards show the four individual stamps and the complete miniature sheet.

Stamps as the 1st class Red dragon stamp from **MS**W147 but self-adhesive were issued on 1 March 2010 in sheets of 20 with *se-tenant* labels showing Welsh Castles, No. LS71. These sheets were printed in lithography by Cartor and sold for £8·35 each.

Miniature sheet collection containing Nos. **MS**EN50, **MS**NI152, **MS**S153 and **MS**W147 in a folder was available from 6 March 2009, sold at £31·95.

Special First Day of Issue Postmarks

W **12** Red Dragon

Des Peter Crowther (illustrations) and Silk Pierce. Litho Cartor or Enschedé)

2013 (9 May). *Wales Flag*. Two phosphor bands. P 14½×14 (with one elliptical hole in each vert side).

W148	W **12**	(1st) multicoloured	2·00	2·00

No. W148 was issued in £11·11 Football Heroes booklets, No. DY7 (see booklet pane No. U3010*a*), and £13·97 Classic Locomotives booklets, No. DY9 (see booklet pane No. U3011*b*).

V. GUERNSEY

War Occupation Issues

BISECTS. On 24 December 1940 authority was given, by Post Office notice, that prepayment of penny postage could be effected by using half a British 2d. stamp, diagonally bisected. Such stamps were first used on 27 December 1940.

The 2d. stamps generally available were those of the Postal Centenary issue, 1940 (S.G. 482) and the first colour of the King George VI issue (S.G. 465). These are listed under Nos. 482a and 465b. A number of the 2d. King George V, 1912–22, and of the King George V photogravure stamp (S.G. 442) which were in the hands of philatelists, were also bisected and used.

1

1a Loops (*half actual size*)

(Des E. W. Vaudin. Typo Guernsey Press Co Ltd)

1941–44. Rouletted.

(a) White paper. No wmk.

1	**1**	½d. light green (7.4.41)	6·00	3·50
		a. Emerald-green (6.41)......................	6·00	2·00
		b. Bluish green (11.41)........................	35·00	13·00
		c. Brt green (2.42)................................	22·00	10·00

		d. Dull green (9.42)	4·00	2·00
		e. Olive-green (2.43)	45·00	25·00
		f. Pale yellowish green (7.43 and		
		later) (*shades*)	4·00	3·00
		g. Imperf (pair)	£250	
		h. Imperf between (horiz pair)	£800	
		i. Imperf between (vert pair)	£950	
2		1d. scarlet (18.2.41)	3·25	2·00
		a. Pale vermilion (7.43)	5·00	2·00
		b. Carmine (1943)	3·50	2·00
		c. Imperf (pair)	£200	90·00
		d. Imperf between (horiz pair)	£800	
		da. Imperf vert (centre stamp of horiz		
		strip of 3)	£950	
		e. Imperf between (vert pair)	£950	
		f. Printed double (scarlet shade)	£150	
3		2½d. ultramarine (12.4.44)	18·00	15·00
		a. Pale ultramarine (7.44)	15·00	12·00
		b. Imperf (pair)	£550	
		c. Imperf between (horiz pair)	£1250	
Set of 3			15·00	14·00

First Day Covers

18.2.41	1d.		15·00
7.4.41	½d.		10·00
12.4.44	2½d.		20·00

(b) Bluish French bank-note paper. W **1a** *(sideways).*

4	**1**	½d. bright green (11.3.42)	32·00	25·00
5		1d. scarlet (9.4.42)	18·00	25·00

First Day Covers

11.3.42	½d.		£325
9.4.42	1d.		£125

The dates given for the shades of Nos. 1/3 are the months in which they were printed as indicated on the printer's imprints. Others are issue dates.

2	**3**

(Des E. A. Piprell. Portrait by Dorothy Wilding Ltd. Photo Harrison & Sons)

1958 (18 Aug)–**67**. W **179** of Great Britain. *P* 15×14.

6	**2**	2½d. rose-red (8.6.64)	40	50
7	**3**	3d. dp lilac	30	40
		p. One centre phosphor band		
		(24.5.67)	20	30
8		4d. ultramarine (7.2.66)	40	50
		p. Two phosphor bands (24.10.67)	15	25
Set of 3 (cheapest)			70	1·00

First Day Covers

18.8.58	3d.		20·00
8.6.64	2½d.		30·00
7.2.66	4d.		8·00

For No. 7 in Presentation Pack, see Regional Issues below Wales No. W6.

1968–69. No wmk. Chalk-surfaced paper. PVA gum*. One centre phosphor band (Nos. 10/11) or two phosphor bands (others). *P* 15×14.

9	**3**	4d. pale ultramarine (16.4.68)	10	20
		Ey. Phosphor omitted	50·00	
10		4d. olive-sepia (4.9.68)	10	15
		Ey. Phosphor omitted	50·00	
11		4d. brt vermilion (26.2.69)	20	25
12		5d. royal blue (4.9.68)	30	40
Set of 4			50	1·00

First Day Cover

4.9.68	4d., 5d		3·00

No. 9 was not issued in Guernsey until 22 April.
* PVA Gum. See note after No. 722 of Great Britain.

VI. ISLE OF MAN

Although specifically issued for use in the Isle of Man, these issues were also valid for use throughout Great Britain.

1	**2**

(Des J. Nicholson. Portrait by Dorothy Wilding Ltd. Photo Harrison)

1958 (18 Aug)–**68**. W **179**. *P* 15×14.

1	**1**	2½d. carmine-red (8.6.64)	90	1·75
2	**2**	3d. dp lilac	50	20

---

		a. Chalk-surfaced paper (17.5.63)	12·00	12·00
		p. One centre phosphor band		
		(27.6.68)	20	50
3		4d. ultramarine (7.2.66)	1·50	2·00
		p. Two phosphor bands (5.7.67)	30	40
Set of 3 (cheapest)			1·00	2·50

First Day Covers

18.8.58	3d		32·00
8.6.64	2½d		45·00
7.2.66	4d		15·00

No. 2a was released in London sometime after 17 May 1963, this being the date of issue in Douglas.
For No. 2 in Presentation Pack, see Regional Issues below Wales No. W6.

1968–69. No wmk. Chalk-surfaced paper. PVA gum. One centre phosphor band (Nos. 5/6) or two phosphor bands (others). *P* 15×14.

4	**2**	4d. blue (24.6.68)	25	30
5		4d. olive-sepia (4.9.68)	25	30
		Ey. Phosphor omitted	25·00	
6		4d. brt vermilion (26.2.69)	45	75
7		5d. royal blue (4.9.68)	45	75
		Ey. Phosphor omitted	£175	
Set of 4			1·25	2·00

First Day Cover

4.9.68	4d., 5d		4·00

3

(Des J. Matthews. Portrait after plaster cast by Arnold Machin. Photo Harrison)

1971 (7 July). *Decimal Currency.* Chalk-surfaced paper. One centre phosphor band (2½p.) or two phosphor bands (others). *P* 15×14.

8	**3**	2½p. brt magenta	30	30
		Ey. Phosphor omitted	£1500	
9		3p. ultramarine	30	30
10		5p. reddish violet	1·10	1·10
		Ey. Phosphor omitted	£275	
11		7½p. chestnut	1·50	1·50
Set of 4			3·00	3·00
Presentation Pack			3·50	

First Day Cover

7.7.71	2½p., 3p., 5p., 7½p.		3·50

All values exist with PVA gum on ordinary cream paper and the 2½p. and 3p. also on fluorescent white paper.
Nos. 8/11 and current stamps of Great Britain were withdrawn from sale on the island from 5 July 1973 when the independent postal administration was established but remained valid for use there for a time. They also remained on sale at the Philatelic Sales counters in the United Kingdom until 4 July 1974.

VII. JERSEY

War Occupation Issues

5

(Des Major N. V. L. Rybot. Typo Evening Post, Jersey)

1941–43. White paper (thin to thick). No wmk. *P* 11.

1	**5**	½d. brt green (29.1.42)	8·00	6·00
		a. Imperf between (vert pair)	£900	
		b. Imperf between (horiz pair)	£800	
		c. Imperf (pair)	£300	
		d. On greyish paper (1.43)	12·00	12·00
2		1d. scarlet (1.4.41)	8·00	5·00
		a. Imperf between (vert pair)	£900	
		b. Imperf between (horiz pair)	£800	
		c. Imperf (pair)	£325	
		d. On chalk-surfaced paper	55·00	48·00
		e. On greyish paper (1.43)	14·00	14·00

First Day Covers

1.4.41	1d.		8·00
29.1.42	½d.		7·50

6 Old Jersey Farm

7 Portelet Bay

8 Corbière Lighthouse

9 Elizabeth Castle

10 Mont Orgueil Castle

11 Gathering Vraic (seaweed)

(Des E. Blampied. Eng H. Cortot. Typo French Govt Ptg Works, Paris)

1943–44. No wmk. *P* 13½.

3	**6**	½d. green (1 June)	12·00	12·00
		a. Rough, grey paper (6.10.43)	15·00	14·00
4	**7**	1d. scarlet (1 June)	3·00	50
		a. On newsprint (28.2.44)	3·50	75
5	**8**	1½d. brown (8 June)	8·00	5·75
6	**9**	2d. orange-yellow (8 June)	7·50	2·00
7	**10**	2½d. blue (29 June)	3·00	1·00
		a. On newsprint (25.2.44)	1·00	1·75
		ba. Thin paper*	£225	
8	**11**	3d. violet (29 June)	3·00	2·75
Set of 6			30·00	21·00
First Day Covers				36·00
Set of 6 Gutter Pairs			80·00	

* On No. 7ba the design shows clearly through the back of the stamp.

12

13

(Des E. Blampied (T **12**), W. Gardner (T **13**). Portrait by Dorothy Wilding Ltd. Photo Harrison & Sons)

1958 (18 Aug)–**67**. *W* **179** of Great Britain. *P* 15×14.

9	**12**	2½d. carmine-red (8.6.64)	75	1·00
		a. Imperf three sides	£3250	
10	**13**	3d. dp lilac	30	40
		p. One centre phosphor band (9.6.67)	15	25
11		4d. ultramarine (7.2.66)	25	30
		p. Two phosphor bands (5.9.67)	15	25
Set of 3 (cheapest)			80	1·25

First Day Covers

18.8.58	3d		20·00
8.6.64	2½d		30·00
7.2.66	4d		10·00

For No. 10 in Presentation Pack, see Regional Issues below Wales No. W6.

1968–69. No wmk. Chalk-surfaced paper. PVA gum*. One centre phosphor band (4d. values) or two phosphor bands (5d.). *P* 15×14.

12	**13**	4d. olive-sepia (4.9.68)	15	25
		Ey. Phosphor omitted	£1100	
13		4d. brt vermilion (26.2.69)	15	25
14		5d. royal blue (4.9.68)	15	50
Set of 3			40	90

First Day Cover

4.9.68	4d., 5d.		3·00

* PVA Gum. See note after No. 722 of Great Britain.

POSTAGE DUE STAMPS

PERFORATIONS. All postage due stamps to No. D101 are perf 14×15.

WATERMARK. The watermark always appears sideways and this is the "normal" listed in this Catalogue for Nos. D1/D68. Varieties occur as follows. The point of identification is still which way the top of the crown points, but (where they occur) the disposition of the letters needs to be noted also. The meaning of the terms is given below: (1) as described and illustrated in the Catalogue, i.e. as read through the front of the stamp, and (2) what is seen during watermark detection when the stamp is face down and the back is under examination.

Watermark	Crown pointing	Letters reading
(1) As described		
Sideways	left	upwards
Sideways-inverted	right	downwards
Sideways and reversed	left	downwards, back to front
Sideways-inverted and reversed	right	upwards, back to front
(2) As detected (stamp face down)		
Sideways	right	upwards, back to front
Sideways-inverted	left	downwards, back to front
Sideways and reversed	right	downwards
Sideways-inverted and reversed	left	upward

D **1**

D **2**

(Des G. Eve. Typo Somerset House (early trial printings of ½d., 1d., 2d. and 5d.; all printings of 1s.) or Harrison (later printings of all values except 1s.))

1914 (20 Apr)–**22**. *W* **100** (Simple Cypher) (sideways).

			Unmtd mint	Mtd mint	Used
D1	D **1**	½d. emerald	1·50	50	25
		Wi. Watermark sideways-inverted	2·00	1·00	1·00
		Wj. Watermark sideways and reversed	30·00	18·00	20·00
		Wk. Watermark sideways-inverted and reversed			20·00
		s. Optd "SPECIMEN"		45·00	
D2		1d. carmine	1·50	50	25
		a. Pale carmine	1·50	75	50
		Wi. Watermark sideways-inverted	2·00	1·00	1·00
		Wj. Watermark sideways and reversed			20·00
		Wk. Watermark sideways-inverted and reversed	30·00	18·00	20·00
		s. Optd "SPECIMEN"		45·00	
D3		1½d. chestnut (1922)	£150	48·00	20·00
		Wi. Watermark sideways-inverted	£190	70·00	20·00
		s. Optd "SPECIMEN"		75·00	
D4		2d. agate	1·50	50	25
		Wi. Watermark sideways-inverted	3·00	2·00	2·00
		Wj. Watermark sideways-inverted and reversed	25·00	15·00	18·00
		s. Optd "SPECIMEN"		40·00	
D5		3d. violet (1918)	28·00	5·00	75
		a. Bluish violet	28·00	6·00	2·75
		Wi. Watermark sideways-inverted	40·00	15·00	10·00
		Wj. Watermark sideways-inverted and reversed			
		s. Optd "SPECIMEN"		45·00	
D6		4d. dull grey-green (12.20)	£300	£150	50·00
		Wi. Watermark sideways-inverted	£150	40·00	5·00
		s. Optd "SPECIMEN"		45·00	
D7		5d. brownish cinnamon	23·00	7·00	3·50
		Wi. Watermark sideways-inverted	40·00	16·00	16·00
		s. Optd "SPECIMEN"		45·00	
D8		1s. brt blue (1915)	£150	40·00	5·00
		a. Dp brt blue	£150	40·00	5·00

	Wi. Watermark sideways- inverted........................	£150	40·00	40·00	
	Wj. Watermark sideways- inverted and reversed...			45·00	
Set of 8	s. Optd "SPECIMEN".............	£450	£130	32·00	

Stamps from the above issue are known bisected and used for half their face value at the following sorting offices:

1d.   Barrhead (1922), Bristol (1918), Cowes (1923), Elgin (1921), Kidlington (1922, 1923), Kilburn, London NW (1923), Malvern (1915), Palmers Green, London N (1922), Plaistow, London E (1916), River, Dover (1922), Rock Ferry, Birkenhead (1915, 1918), St. Ouens, Jersey (1924), Salford, Manchester (1914), South Tottenham, London N (1921), Warminster (1922), Wavertree, Liverpool (1921), Whitchurch (1922), Winton, Bournemouth (1921), Wood Green, London N (1921)

2d.   Anerley, London SE (1921), Bethnal Green, London E (1918), Christchurch (1921), Didcot (1919), Ealing, London W (1921), Hythe, Southampton (1923), Kirkwall (1922), Ledbury (1922), Malvern (1921, 1923), Sheffield (1921), Shipley (1922), Streatham, London SW (1921), Victoria Docks & North Woolwich (1921), West Kensington, London W (1921, 1922)

3d.   Malvern (trisected and used for 1d.) (1921), Warminster (1922)

(Typo Waterlow)

1924. As **1914–22,** but on thick chalk-surfaced paper.

D9	D **1**	1d. carmine....................	10·00	6·00	6·00
		Wi. Watermark sideways- inverted....................			

(Typo Waterlow and (from 1934) Harrison)

1924–31. *W* **111** (Block Cypher) sideways.

D10	D **1**	½d. emerald (6.25).............	2·50	1·25	75
		Wi. Watermark sideways- inverted....................	6·00	3·00	1·50
		s. Optd "SPECIMEN"................		45·00	
D11		1d. carmine (4.25).............	2·50	60	25
		Wi. Watermark sideways- inverted....................	—		30·00
		s. Optd "SPECIMEN"................		55·00	
D12		1½d. chestnut (10.24).............	£160	48·00	22·00
		Wi. Watermark sideways- inverted....................	—	—	75·00
		s. Optd "SPECIMEN"................		55·00	
D13		2d. agate (7.24).............	9·00	1·00	25
		Wi. Watermark sideways- inverted....................	—		30·00
		s. Optd "SPECIMEN"................		45·00	
D14		3d. dull violet (10.24)......	15·00	1·50	25
		a. Printed on gummed side..	£150	£125	†
		b. Experimental paper W **111a**............	£175	95·00	95·00
		Wi. Watermark sideways- inverted....................	50·00	20·00	40·00
		s. Optd "SPECIMEN"................		55·00	
D15		4d. dull grey-green (10.24)	70·00	15·00	4·25
		Wi. Watermark sideways- inverted....................	£100	40·00	40·00
		s. Optd "SPECIMEN"................		55·00	
D16		5d. brownish cinnamon (1.31)........	£175	65·00	45·00
D17		1s. dp blue (9.24).............	60·00	8·50	50
		Wi. Watermark sideways- inverted....................			
		s. Optd "SPECIMEN"................		55·00	
D18	D **2**	2s.6d. purple/*yellow* (5.24).............	£275	85·00	1·75
		Wi. Watermark sideways- inverted....................	£750	—	40·00
		s. Optd "SPECIMEN"................		55·00	
Set of 9		....	£725	£200	70·00

Stamps from the above issue are known bisected and used for half their face value at the following sorting offices:

1d.   Ashton under Lyne (1932), Hastings (1930), Penryn, Cornwall (1928), Shenfield (1926), Wimbledon, London SW (1925)

2d.   Perranwell Station (1932)

1936–37. *W* **125** (E 8 R) sideways.

D19	D **1**	½d. emerald (6.37)....................	15·00	10·50	
D20		1d. carmine (5.37)....................	2·00	1·75	
D21		2d. agate (5.37)....................	15·00	12·00	
D22		3d. dull violet (3.37)....................	2·00	2·00	
		s. Optd "SPECIMEN"....................			
D23		4d. dull grey-green (12.36)	65·00	35·00	
		s. Optd "SPECIMEN"....................			
D24		5d. brownish cinnamon (11.36)............	90·00	30·00	
		a. Yellow-brown (1937)	40·00	28·00	
		s. Optd "SPECIMEN"....................			
D25		1s. dp blue (12.36)....................	25·00	8·50	
		s. Optd "SPECIMEN"....................			
D26	D **2**	2s.6d. purple/*yellow* (5.37)............	£325	12·00	
Set of 8		....	£450	£100	

The 1d. of the above issue is known bisected and used for half its face value at the following sorting office:

1d. Solihull (1937)

1937–38. *W* **127** (G VI R) sideways.

D27	D **1**	½d. emerald (5.38)............	13·00	3·75	
D28		1d. carmine (5.38)............	3·00	50	
		Wi. Watermark sideways-inverted............	£150		
D29		2d. agate (5.38)............	2·75	30	
		Wi. Watermark sideways-inverted............	£150		
D30		3d. violet (12.37)............	11·00	30	
		Wi. Watermark sideways-inverted............	£150		
D31		4d. dull grey-green (9.37)............	£110	10·00	
		Wi. Watermark sideways-inverted............	£300		
D32		5d. yellow-brown (11.38)............	17·00	75	
		Wi. Watermark sideways-inverted............	£150		
D33		1s. dp blue (10.37)............	80·00	75	
		Wi. Watermark sideways-inverted............	£150		
D34	D **2**	2s.6d. purple/*yellow* (9.38)............	85·00	1·25	
Set of 8			£290	16·00	

The 2d. from the above issue is known bisected and used for half its face value at the following sorting offices:

2d.   Boreham Wood (1951), Camberley (1951), Harpenden (1951, 1954), St. Albans (1951)

DATES OF ISSUE. The dates for Nos. D35/68 are those on which stamps were first issued by the Supplies Department to postmasters.

1951–54. Colours changed and new value (1½d.). *W* **127** (G VI R) sideways.

D35	D **1**	½d. yellow-orange (18.9.51)	3·50	3·50	
		a. Bright orange (5.54)	40·00		
D36		1d. violet-blue (6.6.51)	1·50	75	
		Wi. Watermark sideways-inverted............	£120	£120	
D37		1½d. green (11.2.52)............	2·00	2·00	
		Wi. Watermark sideways-inverted............	£120	£120	
D38		4d. blue (14.8.51)............	50·00	22·00	
		Wi. Watermark sideways inverted............	†	£1000	
D39		1s. ochre (6.12.51)............	28·00	5·25	
		Wi. Watermark sideways-inverted............	£2800		
Set of 5			75·00	30·00	

The 1d. of the above issue is known bisected and used for half its face value at the following sorting offices:

1d. Camberley (1954), Capel, Dorking (1952)

1954–55. *W* **153** (Mult Tudor Crown and E 2 R) sideways.

D40	D **1**	½d. bright orange (8.6.55)............	7·00	5·25	
		Wi. Watermark sideways-inverted............	£125		
D41		2d. agate (28.7.55)............	26·00	23·00	
		Wi. Watermark sideways-inverted............	£150		
D42		3d. violet (4.5.55)............	75·00	60·00	
D43		4d. blue (14.7.55)............	26·00	32·00	
		a. Imperf (pair)............	£250		
D44		5d. yellow-brown (19.5.55)............	20·00	20·00	
D45	D **2**	2s.6d. purple/*yellow* (11.54)............	£150	5·75	
		Wi. Watermark sideways-inverted............			
Set of 6			£250	£130	

1955–57. *W* **165** (Mult St. Edward's Crown and E 2 R) sideways.

D46	D **1**	½d. bright orange (16.7.56)............	2·75	3·25	
		Wi. Watermark sideways-inverted............	85·00		
D47		1d. violet-blue (7.6.56)............	5·00	1·50	
D48		1½d. green (13.2.56)............	8·50	7·00	
		Wi. Watermark sideways-inverted............	85·00		
D49		2d. agate (22.5.56)............	45·00	3·50	
D50		3d. violet (5.3.56)............	6·00	1·50	
		Wi. Watermark sideways-inverted............	£100		
D51		4d. blue (24.4.56)............	25·00	6·00	
		Wi. Watermark sideways-inverted............	£175		
D52		5d. brown-ochre (23.3.56)............	26·00	20·00	
D53		1s. ochre (22.11.55)............	65·00	2·25	
		Wi. Watermark sideways-inverted............			
D54	D **2**	2s.6d. purple/*yellow* (28.6.57)............	£200	8·25	
D55		5s. scarlet/*yellow* (25.11.55)............	£150	32·00	
		Wi. Watermark sideways-inverted............			
Set of 10			£475	75·00	

Stamps from the above issue are known bisected and used for half their face value at the following sorting offices:

1d.   Beswick, Manchester (1958), Huddersfield (1956), London SE (1957)

2d.   Eynsham, Oxford (1956), Garelochhead, Helensburgh (1956), Harpenden (1956), Hull (1956), Kingston on Thames (1956), Leicester Square, London WC (1956), London WC (1956)

3d.   London SE (1957) 4d. Poplar, London E (1958)

1959–63. *W* **179** (Multiple Crowns) sideways.

D56	D **1**	½d. bright orange (18.10.61)............	15	1·25	
D57		1d. violet-blue (9.5.60)............	15	50	
		Wi. Watermark sideways-inverted............	£125		
D58		1½d. green (5.10.60)............	2·50	2·50	
D59		2d. agate (14.9.59)............	1·10	50	
		Wi. Watermark sideways-inverted............	£200		

D60		3d. violet (24.3.59)	30	30
		Wi. Watermark sideways-inverted	85·00	
D61		4d. blue (17.12.59)	30	30
		Wi. Watermark sideways-inverted	£300	
D62		5d. yellow-brown (6.11.61)	45	60
		Wi. Watermark sideways-inverted	5·00	6·00
D63		6d. purple (29.3.62)	50	30
		Wi. Watermark sideways-inverted	£300	
D64		1s. ochre (11.4.60)	90	30
		Wi. Watermark sideways-inverted	60·00	
D65	D 2	2s.6d. purple/*yellow* (11.5.61)	3·00	50
		Wi. Watermark sideways-inverted	15·00	2·00
D66		5s. scarlet/*yellow* (8.5.61)	8·25	1·00
		Wi. Watermark sideways-inverted	25·00	3·00
D67		10s. blue/*yellow* (2.9.63)	11·50	5·75
		Wi. Watermark sideways-inverted	40·00	20·00
D68		£1 black/*yellow* (2.9.63)	45·00	8·25
Set of 13			65·00	20·00

Whiter paper. The note after No. 586 also applies to Postage Due stamps.

Stamps from the above issue are known bisected and used for half their face value at the following sorting offices:

1d. Chieveley, Newbury (1962, 1963), Henlan, Llandyssil (1961), Mayfield (1962), St. Albans (1964)
2d. Doncaster (?)

1968–69. Typo. No wmk. Chalk-surfaced paper.

D69	D 1	2d. agate (11.4.68)	75	1·00
		Ev. PVA gum (26.11.68)	75	
D70		3d. violet (9.9.68)	1·00	1·00
D71		4d. blue (6.5.68)	1·00	1·00
		Ev. PVA gum	£2250	
D72		5d. orange-brown (3.1.69)	8·00	11·00
D73		6d. purple (9.9.68)	2·25	1·75
D74		1s. ochre (19.11.68)	4·00	2·50
Set of 6			15·00	16·00

The 2d. and 4d. exist with gum arabic and PVA gum; the remainder with PVA gum only.

Stamps from the above issue are known bisected and used for half their face value at the following sorting offices:

4d. Northampton (1970)
6d. Kilburn, London NW (1968)

1968–69. Photo. No wmk. Chalk-surfaced paper. PVA gum.

D75	D 1	4d. blue (12.6.69)	7·00	6·75
D76		8d. red (3.10.68)	50	1·00

Nos. D75/6 are smaller, 21½x17½ mm.

D 3

D 4

(Des J. Matthews. Photo Harrison)

1970 (17 June)–*75*. *Decimal Currency.* Chalk-surfaced paper.

D77	D 3	½p. turquoise-blue (15.2.71)	15	2·50
D78		1p. dp reddish purple (15.2.71)	15	15
D79		2p. myrtle-green (15.2.71)	20	15
D80		3p. ultramarine (15.2.71)	20	15
D81		4p. yellow-brown (15.2.71)	25	15
D82		5p. violet (15.2.71)	25	15
D83		7p. red-brown (21.8.74)	35	1·00
D84	D 4	10p. carmine	30	30
D85		11p. slate-green (18.6.75)	50	1·00
D86		20p. olive-brown	60	25
D87		50p. ultramarine	2·00	1·25
D88		£1 black	4·00	1·00
D89		£5 orange-yellow and black (2.4.73)	36·00	1·50
Set of 13			40·00	7·75

Presentation Pack (*P.O. Pack No. 36*) (*Nos. D77/82, D84, D86/8* (3.11.71)) ... 35·00

Presentation Pack (*P.O. Pack No. 93*) (Nos. D77/88) (30.3.77) ... 18·00

Later printings were on fluorescent white paper, some with dextrin added to the PVA gum (see notes after X1058).

The 2p. from the above issue is known bisected and used for half its face value at Exeter (1977).

D 5

D 6

(Des Sedley Place Design Ltd. Photo Harrison)

1982 (9 June). Chalk-surfaced paper.

D90	D 5	1p. lake	10	30
D91		2p. brt blue	30	30
D92		3p. dp mauve	15	30
D93		4p. dp blue	15	25
D94		5p. sepia	20	25
D95	D 6	10p. lt brown	30	40
D96		20p. olive-green	50	60
D97		25p. dp greenish blue	80	90
D98		50p. grey-black	1·75	1·75
D99		£1 brown-red	3·25	1·25
D100		£2 turquoise-blue	7·00	4·25
D101		£5 dull orange	14·00	2·25
Set of 12			24·00	10·00
Set of 12 *Gutter Pairs*			48·00	
Presentation Pack (P.O. Pack No.135)			40·00	

D 7

(Des Sedley Place Design Ltd. Litho Questa)

1994 (15 Feb). *P* 15×14 (with one elliptical hole in each vertical side).

D102	D 7	1p. red, yellow & black	10	75
D103		2p. magenta, purple & black	10	75
D104		5p. yellow, red-brown & black	15	50
D105		10p. yellow, emerald & black	30	75
D106		20p. blue-green, violet & black	75	1·50
D107		25p. cerise, rosine & black	1·50	2·00
D108		£1 violet, magenta & black	7·00	10·00
D109		£1·20 greenish blue, blue-green & black	8·00	12·00
D110		£5 greenish black, blue-green & black	30·00	20·00
Set of 9			45·00	45·00
First Day Cover				22·00
Presentation Pack (P.O. Pack No.32)			50·00	

Special First Day of Issue Postmarks

London EC3 ... 22·00

Following changes in the method of collecting money due on unpaid or underpaid mail the use of postage due stamps was restricted from April 1995 to mail addressed to business customers and to Customs/V.A.T. charges levied by the Royal Mail on behalf of the Customs and Excise. The use of postage due stamps ceased on 28 January 2000.

PRICES. Prices in the used column are for stamps with genuine postal cancellations dated from the time when they were authorised for use as postage stamps. Beware of stamps with fiscal cancellations removed and fraudulent postmarks applied.

VALIDITY. The 1d. surface-printed stamps were authorised for postal use from 1 June 1881 and at the same time the 1d. postage issue, No. 166, was declared valid for fiscal purposes. The 3d. and 6d. values together with the embossed issues were declared valid for postal purposes by another Act effective from 1 January 1883.

INLAND REVENUE

(F **7**)

1860 (3 Apr). No. F7 optd with Type F **7**, in red.

F8	F **4**	1d. dull reddish lilac/*blue*	£900	£725	£1500
		Wj. Wmk reversed			

SURFACE-PRINTED ISSUES
(Typo Thomas De La Rue & Co.)

F **1** Rectangular Buckle   F **2**

F **3** Octagonal Buckle   F **4**

F **5** Double-lined Anchor   F **6** Single-lined Anchor

1853–57. P 15½×15.

(a) Wmk F **5** *(inverted) (1853–55)*.

			Un	Used	Used on cover
F1	F **1**	1d. lt blue (10.10.53)	50·00	65·00	£225
		Wi. Watermark upright	£180		
		Wj. Watermark reversed*	£180		
F2	F **2**	1d. ochre (10.53)	£130	£160	£600
		a. *Tête-bêche* (in block of four)	£22000		
		Wi. Watermark upright			
F3	F **3**	1d. pale turquoise-blue (12.53)	38·00	60·00	£350
F4		1d. lt blue/*blue* (12.53)	90·00	95·00	£550
		Wi. Watermark upright	£160		£225
F5	F **4**	1d. reddish lilac/*blue glazed paper* (25.3.55)	£130	£160	£450
		Wi. Watermark upright	£200	£300	

*Watermark reversed: with the stamp upright and viewed from the front the cable finishes to the right of the base of the anchor shaft. Only one example is known of No. F2a outside the National Postal Museum and the Royal Collection.

(b) Wmk F **6** *(1856–57)*.

F6	F **4**	1d. reddish lilac (*shades*)	12·00	9·50	£180
		Wi. Watermark inverted	£160		
		Wj. Watermark reversed	£180		
		s. Optd "SPECIMEN" (2)	£170		
F7		1d. reddish lilac/*bluish* (*shades*) (1857)	12·00	9·50	£180
		Wj. Watermark reversed	£180		

BLUE PAPER. In the following issues we no longer distinguish between bluish and white paper. There is a range of papers from white or greyish to bluish.

F **8**   F **9**

F **10**

1860–67. Bluish to white paper. P 15½×15.

(a) Wmk F **6** *(1860)*.

F9	F **8**	1d. reddish lilac (May)	14·00	18·00	£180
		Wi. Watermark inverted	£130		
		s. Optd "SPECIMEN" (2)	£180		
F10	F **9**	3d. reddish lilac (June)	£550	£340	£550
		s. Optd "SPECIMEN" (2)	£240		
F11	F **10**	6d. reddish lilac (Oct)	£220	£220	£450
		Wi. Watermark inverted	£275	£220	
		Wj. Watermark reversed	£275	£220	
		s. Optd "SPECIMEN" (2)	£220		

(b) W **40**. *(Anchor 16 mm high) (1864)*.

F12	F **8**	1d. pale reddish lilac (Nov)	12·00	14·00	£180
		Wi. Watermark inverted			
F13	F **9**	3d. pale reddish lilac	£275	£210	£550
		s. Optd "SPECIMEN" (9)	£220		
F14	F **10**	6d. pale reddish lilac	£240	£210	£550
		Wi. Watermark inverted	£360		

(c) W **40**. *(Anchor 18 mm high) (1867)*.

F15	F **8**	1d. reddish lilac	25·00	27·00	£275
F16	F **9**	3d. reddish lilac	£120	£120	£450
		s. Optd "SPECIMEN" (9, 10)	£190		
F17	F **10**	6d. reddish lilac	£110	95·00	£300
		s. Optd "SPECIMEN" (9, 10)	£190		

For stamps perf 14, see Nos. F24/7.

F **11**   F **12**

Four Dies of Type F 12

Round "O" (Dies 1 to 3)

Oval "O" (Die 4)

Small corner ornaments (Dies 1 and 2)

Medium corner ornaments (Die 3)

Large corner ornaments (Die 4)

Four lines of shading In left-hand ribbon
(Die 1)

Two lines of shading in left-hand ribbon
(Die 2)

Three lines of shading In left-hand ribbon
(Die 3)

Heavy shading in both ribbons (Die 4)

Band of crown shaded (Dies 1 and 2)

Band of crown unshaded (Die 3)

Band of crown unshaded at front only (Die 4)

Die 1: Round "O" in "ONE"
Small corner ornaments
Four lines of shading in left-hand ribbon
Band of crown shaded
Die 2: Round "O" in "ONE"
Small corner ornaments
Two lines of shading in left-hand ribbon
Band of crown shaded
Die 3: Round "O" in "ONE"
Medium corner ornaments
Three lines of shading in left-hand ribbon
Band of crown unshaded
Die 4: Oval "O" in "ONE"
Large corner ornaments
Heavy shading in both ribbons
Band of crown unshaded at front only

1867–81. White to bluish paper. *P* 14.

(a) W **47** *(Small Anchor).*

F18	F **11**	1d. purple (1.9.67)...............	22·00	24·00	£140
		Wi. Watermark inverted............	£130		
F19	F **12**	1d. purple (Die I) (6.68)...........	7·50	9·00	£140
		s. Optd "SPECIMEN" (6, 9, 10).................................	60·00		
		Wi. Watermark inverted............	90·00		
F20		1d. purple (Die 2) (6.76)...........	27·00	22·00	£300
		s. Optd "SPECIMEN" (9)...........	£110		
F21		1d. purple (Die 3) (3.77)...........	14·00	18·00	£220
		s. Optd "SPECIMEN" (9)...........	90·00		
F22		1d. purple (Die 4) (7.78)...........	8·50	10·00	£120

(b) W **48** *(Orb).*

F23	F **12**	1d. purple (Die 4) (1.81).........	8·50	5·00	£110
		Wi. Watermark inverted............	£130		

1881. White to bluish paper. *P* 14.

(a) W **40** *(Anchor 18 mm high) (Jan).*

F24	F **9**	3d. reddish lilac.........................	£850	£525	£1000
F25	F **10**	6d. reddish lilac.........................	£400	£225	£450

(b) W **40** *(Anchor 20 mm high) (May).*

F26	3d. reddish lilac.........................	£625	£425	£700
	s. Optd "SPECIMEN" (9).....................	£340		
F27	6d. reddish lilac.........................	£360	£210	£450
	s. Optd "SPECIMEN" (9).....................	£300		

ISSUES EMBOSSED IN COLOUR

(Made at Somerset House)

The embossed stamps were struck from dies not appropriated to any special purpose on paper which had the words "INLAND REVENUE" previously printed, and thus became available for payment of any duties for which no special stamps had been provided.

The die letters are included in the embossed designs and holes were drilled for the insertion of plugs showing figures indicating dates of striking.

F **13**

F **14**

(F **15**)

1860 (3 Apr)–**71**. Types F **13/14** and similar types embossed on bluish paper. No wmk. *Imperf.*

F28	2d. pink (Die A) (1.1.71)...........................	£775
	s. Optd "SPECIMEN" (2, 9)......................	£210
F29	3d. pink (Die C)..	£210
	a. *Tête-bêche* (vert pair).......................	£1700
F30	3d. pink (Die D)..	£775
F31	6d. pink (Die T)..	£210
F32	6d. pink (Die U)..	£400
	a. *Tête-bêche* (vert pair).......................	
F33	9d. pink (Die C) (1.1.71)..........................	£1000
	s. Optd "SPECIMEN" (2, 9)......................	£210
F34	1s. pink (Die E) (28.6.61)........................	£775
	a. *Tête-bêche* (vert pair).......................	
F35	1s. pink (Die F) (28.6.61)........................	£300
	a. *Tête-bêche* (vert pair).......................	£1200
	s. Optd "SPECIMEN" (2, 9)......................	£210
F36	2s. pink (Die K) (6.8.61)..........................	£775
F37	2s.6d. pink (Die N) (28.6.61)...................	£775
F38	2s.6d. pink (Die O) (28.6.61)...................	£400
	s. Optd "SPECIMEN" (2, 9)......................	£210

1871 (Aug). *As last but P* 12½.

F39	2d. pink (Die A)..	£500
	a. *Tête-bêche* (vert pair).......................	
	s. Optd "SPECIMEN" (9)..........................	£120
F42	9d. pink (Die C)..	£1200
	s. Optd "SPECIMEN" (9)..........................	£210
F43	1s. pink (Die E)..	£775
F44	1s. pink (Die F)..	£700
	s. Optd "SPECIMEN" (9)..........................	£195
F45	2s.6d. pink (Die O)...................................	£400
	s. Optd "SPECIMEN" (9)..........................	£195

1874 (Nov). Type F **15** embossed on white paper. Underprint, in green. *W* **47** (Small Anchor). *P* 12½.

F48	1s. pink (Die F)..	£775

1875 (Nov)–**80**. Types F **13/15** and similar but colour changed and underprint as F **15**. On white or bluish paper. *P* 12½.

F50	2d. vermilion (Die A) (1880).....................	£600
	s. Optd "SPECIMEN" (9)..........................	£210
F51	9d. vermilion (Die C) (1876).....................	£775
	s. Optd "SPECIMEN" (9, 10).....................	£210
F52	1s. vermilion (Die E).................................	£500
	s. Optd "SPECIMEN" (9, 10).....................	£210
F53	1s. vermilion (Die F).................................	£1200
F54	2s.6d. vermilion (Die O) (1878)................	£500
	s. Optd "SPECIMEN" (9)..........................	£210

1882 (Oct). *As last but W* **48** *(Orbs).*

F55	2d. vermilion (Die A)................................	†	
	s. Optd "SPECIMEN" (9)..........................	£230	
F56	9d. vermilion (Die C)................................	†	
	s. Optd "SPECIMEN" (9)..........................	£230	
F57	1s. vermilion (Die E).................................	†	
	s. Optd "SPECIMEN" (9)..........................	£230	
F58	2s.6d. vermilion (Die O)...........................	£1000	£775
	s. Optd "SPECIMEN" (9)..........................	£230	

Although specimen overprints of Nos. F55/7 are known they were never issued.

The sale of Inland Revenue stamps up to the 2s. value ceased from 30 December 1882 and stocks were called in and destroyed. The 2s.6d. value remained on sale until 2 July 1883 when it was replaced by the 2s.6d. "Postage & Revenue" stamps. Inland Revenue stamps still in the hands of the public continued to be accepted for revenue and postal purposes.

Stanley Gibbons
Stamp Catalogues

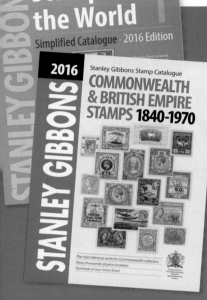

Stamps of the World 1
Simplified Catalogue · 2016 Edition

2016 · Stanley Gibbons Stamp Catalogue
COMMONWEALTH & BRITISH EMPIRE STAMPS 1840-1970

The vital reference work for Commonwealth collectors
Many thousands of price increases
Hundreds of new items listed

We have catalogues to suit every aspect of stamp collecting

Our catalogues cover stamps issued from across the globe - from the Penny Black to the latest issues. Whether you're a specialist in a certain reign or a thematic collector, we should have something to suit your needs. All catalogues include the famous SG numbering system, making it as easy as possible to find the stamp you're looking for.

Commonwealth & British Empire Stamps 1840–1970 (118th edition, 2016)

Commonwealth Country Catalogues

Australia & Dependencies (9th Edition, 2014)
Bangladesh, Pakistan & Sri Lanka (3rd edition, 2015)
Belize, Guyana, Trinidad & Tobago (2nd edition, 2013)
Brunei, Malaysia & Singapore (4th edition, 2013)
Canada (5th edition, 2014)
Central Africa (2nd edition, 2008)
Cyprus, Gibraltar & Malta (4th edition, 2014)
East Africa with Egypt & Sudan (3rd edition, 2014)
Eastern Pacific (3rd edition, 2015)
Falkland Islands (7th edition, 2016)
Hong Kong (5th edition, 2015)
India (including Convention & Feudatory States) (4th edition, 2013)
Indian Ocean (3rd edition, 2016)
Ireland (6th edition, 2015)
Leeward Islands (2nd edition, 2012)
New Zealand (5th edition, 2014)
Northern Caribbean, Bahamas & Bermuda (4th edition, 2016)
St. Helena & Dependencies (5th edition, 2014)
Southern Africa (2nd edition, 2008)
Southern & Central Africa (2nd edition, 2014)
West Africa (2nd edition, 2012)
Western Pacific (3rd edition, 2014)
Windward Islands & Barbados (3rd edition, 2015)

Stamps of the World 2016

Volume 1 Abu Dhabi – Charkhari
Volume 2 Chile – Georgia
Volume 3 German Commands – Jasdan
Volume 4 Jersey – New Republic
Volume 5 New South Wales – Singapore
Volume 6 Sirmoor – Zululand

Great Britain Catalogues

Collect British Stamps (67th edition, 2016)
Collect Channel Islands & Isle of Man (30th edition, 2016)
Great Britain Concise Stamp Catalogue (31st edition, 2016)

Great Britain Specialised

Volume 1 Queen Victoria (16th edition, 2012)
Volume 2 King Edward VII to King George VI (14th edition, 2015)
Volume 3 Queen Elizabeth II Pre-decimal issues (12th edition, 2011)
Volume 4 Queen Elizabeth II Decimal Definitive Issues – Part 1 (10th edition, 2008)
Queen Elizabeth II Decimal Definitive Issues – Part 2 (10th edition, 2010)

Foreign Countries

Arabia (1st edition, 2016)
Austria & Hungary (8th edition, 2014)
Balkans (5th edition, 2009)
Belgium & Luxembourg (1st edition, 2015)
Central America (3rd edition, 2007)
Central Asia (4th edition, 2006)
China (11th edition, 2015)
Czech Republic, Slovakia & Poland (7th edition, 2012)
France, Andorra and Monaco (1st edition, May 2015)
Germany (11th edition, 2014)
Italy & Switzerland (8th edition, 2013)
Japan & Korea (5th edition, 2008)
Portugal & Spain (6th edition, 2011)
Poland (1st edition, 2015)
Russia (7th edition, 2014)
Scandinavia (7th edition, 2013)
South America (4th edition, 2008)
South-East Asia (5th edition, 2012)
United States of America (8th edition, 2015)

To order, call **01425 472 363** or for our full range of catalogues, **visit www.stanleygibbons.com**

Est 1856
STANLEY GIBBONS

Stanley Gibbons Limited
7 Parkside, Christchurch Road, Ringwood, Hants, BH24 3SH
+44 (0)1425 472 363
www.stanleygibbons.com

Post Office Stamp Booklets

The following listing covers all booklets sold by post offices from 1904.

All major variations of contents and cover are included, but minor changes to the covers and differences on the interleaves have been ignored.

From 1913 each booklet carried an edition number, linked to an internal Post Office system of identification which divided the various booklets into series. In 1943 these edition numbers were replaced by edition dates. No attempt has been made to list separate edition numbers for booklets prior to 1943, although notes giving their extent are provided for each booklet. Edition dates from August 1943 are listed separately and exist for all £.s.d. and most Decimal Stitched booklets (except for the 1s. booklets, the 2s. booklets (N1/3), the 5s. "Philympia" booklets (No. HP34), the £1 "Stamps for Cooks" booklet (No. ZP1) and the Decimal Sponsored booklets). They are those found printed upon the booklets, either on the outer back cover or on the white leaves.

ERRORS OF MAKE-UP of booklets exist but we do not list them here. More detailed listings can be found in the 2nd, 3rd and 4th volumes of the *Great Britain Specialised Catalogue*.

ILLUSTRATIONS. The illustrations of the covers are ¾ size except where otherwise stated. Those in Queen Elizabeth II Decimal Sections C to H are ⅔ size, except where otherwise stated.

> **PRICES** quoted are for complete booklets containing stamps with "average" perforations (i.e. full perforations on two edges of the pane only). Booklets containing panes with complete perforations are worth more.

KING EDWARD VII

2s. Booklets

BA **1**

1904 (Mar). Red cover printed in black as Type BA **1**. Pages of six stamps: 24×1d. *Wmk* Imperial Crown (No. 219).
BA1 .... £500

BA **2**

1906 (June). Red cover printed in black as Type BA **2**. As before but make-up changed to include 12×1d. and 23×½d. and label showing one green cross (Nos. 217 and 219).
BA2 .... £2200

1907 (Aug). *Red* cover printed in black as Type BA **2**. Make-up changed to include 18×1d. and 11×½d. and label showing one green cross (Nos. 217 and 219).
BA3 .... £3100

1908 (Aug). As before, but interleaves used for post office adverts printed in red.
BA4 .... £3400

1909 (Aug). As before, but interleaves used for trade advert printed in green.
BA5 .... £2700

BA **6**

1911 (June). Red cover printed in black as Type BA **2** but showing a larger Post Office cypher on cover. As before, but containing stamps by Harrison & Sons (Nos. 267 and 272).
BA6 .... £2800

KING GEORGE V

2s. Booklets

BB **1**

1911 (Aug). Red cover printed in black as Type BA **2** showing King George V cypher. Pages of six stamps: 18×1d. and 12×½d. *Wmk* Crown (Nos. 325, 329) Die 1B.
BB1 .... £1600

BB **2**

1912 (Apr). As before, but red cover printed in black as Type BB **2**.
BB2 .... £1900

1912 (Sept). As before, but *wmk* Simple Cypher (Nos. 334, 336) Die 1B.
BB3 .... £1300

BB **5**

1912 (Nov). As before, but red cover printed in black as Type BB **5** but
without edition number.
BB4 .... £1600

1913 (Jan). As before, but red cover printed in black as Type BB **5**.
BB5 Edition numbers 8 or 9 .... £1300

1913 (Apr). As before, but 1912–22 *wmk* Simple Cypher (Nos. 351, 357).
BB6 Edition numbers 10 to 35 .... £1300

1915 (Nov). As before, except lower panel of front cover which was
changed to show *New rates of postage*.
BB7 Edition numbers 36 to 42 .... £1600

1916 (May). As before, but interleave adverts printed in black instead
of green.
BB8 Edition numbers 43 to 45 .... £1750

1916 (July). As before, but orange cover printed in black as Type BB **5**.
BB9 Edition numbers 46 to 64 .... £1500

BB **10**

1917 (Sept). As before, but orange cover printed in black as Type BB **10**.
BB10 Edition numbers 65 to 81 .... £1350

BB **11**

1924 (Feb). Blue cover printed in black as Type BB **11**. Pages of six
stamps: 10×1½d. (first completed by two perforated labels), 6×1d.
and 6×½d. 1912–22 *wmk* Simple Cypher (Nos. 351, 357, 362).
BB11 Edition numbers 1 or 2 .... £2600

1924 (Mar). As before, but 1924–26 *wmk* Block Cypher (Nos. 418/20).
BB12 Edition numbers 3 to 102 & 108 to 254 .... £900

BB **13**

1929 (May). *Postal Union Congress issue* Cover of special design as Type
BB **13** printed in blue on buff as before but containing stamps of
the P.U.C. issue (Nos. 434/6).
BB13 Edition numbers 103 to 107 .... £500

1934 (Feb). Blue cover printed in black as Type BB **11**, but contain-
ing stamps with Block Cypher *wmk* printed by Harrison & Sons
(Nos. 418/20).
BB14 Edition numbers 255 to 287 .... £1100

1935 (Jan). As before, but containing stamps of the photogravure issue
(intermediate format) with the *se-tenant* advertisements printed in
brown (Nos. 439/41).
BB15 Edition numbers 288 to 297 .... £2700

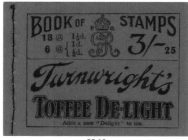

BB **16**

1935 (May). *Silver Jubilee issue.* Larger size cover printed in blue on
buff as Type BB **16** and containing pages of four stamps with no
se-tenant advertisements: 12×1½d., 4×1d. and 4×½d. (Nos. 453/5).
BB16 Edition numbers 298 to 304 .... 90·00

1935 (July). As No. BB **15**, but containing stamps of the photogravure
(small format) issue with *se-tenant* advertisements printed in black
(Nos. 439/41).
BB17 Edition numbers 305 to 353 .... £600

3s. Booklets

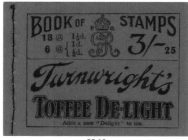

BB **19**

1918 (Oct). Orange cover printed in black as Type BB **19**. Pages of six
stamps: 12×1½d., 12×1d. and 12×½d. 1912–22 *wmk* Simple Cypher
(Nos. 351, 357, 362).
BB18 Edition numbers 1 to 11 .... £1850

1919 (July). As before, but make-up altered to contain 18×1½d., 6×1d.
and 6×½d.

BB19   Edition numbers 12 to 26... £1850

BB 20

1921 (April). Experimental booklet bound in blue covers as Type BB **20,** containing pages of six stamps: 18×2d. (Die I) (No. 368).
BB20   Edition numbers 35 and part 37 .... £2400

1921 (Dec). As before, but containing 2d. (Die II) (No. 370).
BB21   Edition numbers 12, 13 and part 37........................... £2400

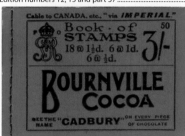

BB 22

1922 (May). Scarlet cover printed in black as Type BB **22.** Pages of six stamps: 18×1½d., 6×1d. and 6×½d. (Nos. 351,357, 362).
BB22   Edition numbers 19, 20, 22, 23 and 25 to 54 .... £2400

BB 23

1922 (June). Experimental booklet as Edition numbers 12 and 13 bound in blue covers as Type BB **23,** containing pages of six stamps: 24×1½d. (No. 362).
BB23   Edition numbers 21 or 24.. £2400

1924 (Feb). Scarlet cover printed in black as Type BB **22,** but containing stamps with Block Cypher wmk, printed by Waterlow & Sons (Nos. 418/20).
BB24   Edition numbers 55 to 167 & 173 to 273 .... £550

1929 (May). *Postal Union Congress issue.* Cover of special design as Type BB **13** printed in red on buff as before but containing stamps of the P.U.C. issue (Nos. 434/6).
BB25   Edition numbers 168 to 172 .... £450

1934 (Mar). Scarlet cover printed in black as Type BB **22,** but containing stamps with the Block Cypher *wmk* printed by Harrison & Sons (Nos. 418/20).
BB26   Edition numbers 274 to 288 .... £650

1935 (Jan). As No. BB **29,** but containing stamps of the photogravure issue (intermediate format).
BB27   Edition numbers 289 to 293 .... £2100

1935 (May). *Silver Jubilee* issue. Larger size cover printed in red on buff as Type BB **16** and containing pages of four stamps: 20×1½d., 4×1d. and 4×½d. (Nos. 453/5).
BB28   Edition numbers 294 to 297 .... 90·00

1935 (July). As No. BB **26,** but containing stamps of the photogravure issue (small format) (Nos. 439/41).
BB29   Edition numbers 298 to 319 .... £550

3s.6d. Booklets

BB 30

1920 (July). Orange cover printed in black as Type BB **30,** containing pages of six stamps: 18×2d. and 6×1d. (Nos. 357, 368).
BB30   Edition numbers 27 to 32 .... £2200

BB 31

1921 (Jan). Orange-red cover printed in black as Type BB **31,** as before but make-up changed to include stamps of 1912–22 issue with the Simple Cypher wmk: 12×2d. (Die I), 6×1½d., 6×1d. and 6×½d. (Nos. 351, 357, 362, 368).
BB31   Edition numbers 33, 34, 36 & 38 .... £2200

1921 (July). As BB **31** including stamps of the 1912-22 issue with Simple Cypher *wmk*: 12×2d. (Die I or II), 6×1½d., 6×1d. and 6×½d. (Nos. 351, 357, 362, 368 or 370).
BB32   Edition numbers 1 to 11, 14 to 18 .... £2200

5s. Booklets

BB 33

1931 (Aug). Green cover printed in black as Type BB **33.** Pages of six stamps: 34×1½d., 6×1d. and 6×½d. The first 1½d. pane completed by two *se-tenant* advertisements. Printed by Waterlow & Sons on paper with Block Cypher *wmk* (Nos. 418/20).
BB33   Edition number 1 .... £6250

1932 (June). As before, but buff cover printed in black.
BB34   Edition numbers 2 to 6... £5250

1934 (July). As before, but containing stamps with Block Cypher *wmk* printed by Harrison & Sons (Nos. 418/20).
BB35   Edition numbers 7 or 8.. £2200

1935 (Feb). As before, but containing stamps of the photogravure issue (intermediate format) with *se-tenant* advertisements printed in brown (Nos. 439/41).
BB36   Edition number 9... £6250

1935 (July). As before, but containing stamps of the photogravure issue (small format) with *se-tenant* advertisements printed in black (Nos. 439/41).
BB37   Edition numbers 10 to 15 .... £650

KING EDWARD VIII

6d. Booklet

1936. Buff unglazed cover without inscription containing 4×1½d. stamps, in panes of two (No. 459).
BC1   Edition numbers 354 to 385 .... 65·00

2s. Booklet

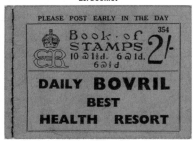

BC **2**

1936 (Oct). Blue cover printed in black as Type BC **2**, containing pages of six stamps: 10×1½d., 6×1d. & 6×½d. (Nos. 457/9).
BC2   Edition numbers 354 to 385 .... £140

3s. Booklet

1936 (Nov). As No. BB **29**, except for the K.E.VIII cypher on the cover but without "P" and "O" on either side of the crown, and containing Nos. 457/9.
BC3   Edition numbers 320 to 332 .... £120

5s. Booklet

1937 (Mar). As No. BB **37**, but with the K.E.VIII cypher on the cover and containing Nos. 457/9.
BC4   Edition numbers 16 or 17 .... £275

KING GEORGE VI

6d. Booklets

1938 (Jan). As No. BC **1**, but containing stamps in the original dark colours. Buff cover without inscription (No. 464).
BD1   .... 75·00
1938 (Feb). As before, but pink unprinted cover and make-up changed to contain 2×1½d., 2×1d. and 2×2d. in the original dark colours (Nos. 462/4).
BD2   .... £300
1940 (June). Pale green unprinted cover and make-up changed to include two panes of four stamps with *wmk* sideways. Stamps in original dark colours with binding margin either at the top or bottom of the pane: 4×1d., 4×½d. (Nos. 462a/3a).
BD3   .... £150

1s. Booklets with Panes of 2

1947 (Dec). Cream cover, unglazed and without inscription containing panes of two stamps in pale shades, all with *wmk* normal. Panes of two stamps: 4×½d., 4×1d. and 4×1½d. (Nos. 485/7).
BD4   .... 28·00
1951 (May). As before, but containing stamps in changed colours (Nos. 503/5).
BD5   .... 28·00

1s. Booklets with Panes of 4

1948. Cream cover as before, but make-up changed to contain 4×1½d., 4×1d. and 4×½d. in panes of four of the pale shades with *wmk* normal (Nos. 485/7).
BD6   .... £9000
1951 (May). As before, but stamps in new colours all *wmk* normal, margins at either top or at the bottom. (Nos. 503/5).
BD7   .... 50·00

BD **8**

1952 (Dec). Cream cover printed in black as Type BD **8**. Make-up as before but with *wmk* either upright or inverted and margins only at the top (Nos. 503/5).
BD8   .... 25·00

BD **10**

1954. As before but cover showing GPO emblem with St. Edward's crown and oval frame as Type BD **10** (Nos. 503/5).
BD10   .... 35·00

2s. Booklets

BD **11**

1937 (Aug). Blue cover printed in black as Type BB **11**, but with K.G.VI cypher on the cover and containing stamps in the original dark colours. Panes of six stamps: 10×1½d., 6×1d. and 6×½d. The first 1½d. pane completed by two *se-tenant* advertisements. (Nos. 462/4).
BD11   Edition numbers 386 to 412 .... £1100

BD **12**

1938 (Mar). Blue cover printed in black as Type BD **12** (Nos. 462/4).
BD12   Edition numbers 413 to 508 .... £1100

2s.6d. Booklets

BD **13**

1940 (June). Scarlet cover printed in black as Type BD **13**, containing panes of six stamps in original dark colours: 6×2½d., 6×2d. and 6×½d. (Nos. 462, 465/6).
BD13   Edition numbers 1 to 8 (part) £1700
1940 (Sept). As before, but blue cover printed in black as Type BD **13**.
BD14   Edition numbers 8 (part) to 13 .... £1700

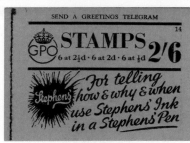

BD **15**

1940 (Oct). As before, but with green cover printed in black as Type BD **15** (Nos. 462, 465/6).
BD15   Edition numbers 14 to 94 .... £975

1942 (Mar). As before, but containing stamps in pale shades (Nos. 485, 488/9).
BD16   Edition numbers 95 to 146 (Part)............................... £975

1942 (Oct). Composition as before, but with unglazed green covers.
BD17   Edition numbers 146 (Part) to 214 .... £975

Type **A** Circular GPO Cypher

1943 (Aug). As before, but green cover printed in black as Type A, with different contents details (Nos. 485, 488/9).
BD18   Edition dates August 1943 to February 1951 .... 95·00

(1) AUG 1943 ....£110	(45) MAY 1947 ....£150
(2) OCT 1943 ....£150	(46) JUNE 1947 ....£150
(3) NOV 1943 ....£180	(47) JULY 1947 ....£150
(4) DEC 1943 ....£170	(48) AUG 1947 ....£150
(5) JAN 1944 ....£160	(49) SEPT 1947 ....£150
(6) FEB 1944 ....£160	(50) OCT 1947 ....£150
(7) MAR 1944 ....£160	(51) NOV 1947 ....£150
(8) APR 1944 ....£160	(52) DEC 1947 ....£150
(9) MAY 1944 ....£160	(53) JAN 1948 ....£180
(10) JUNE 1944 ....£160	(54) FEB 1948 ....£150
(11) JULY 1944 ....£160	(55) MAR 1948 ....£150
(12) AUG 1944 ....£160	(56) APR 1948 ....£150
(13) SEPT 1944 ....£160	(57) MAY 1948 ....£150
(14) OCT 1944 ....£160	(58) JUNE 1948 ....£150
(15) NOV 1944 ....£160	(59) JULY 1948 ....£150
(16) DEC 1944 ....£160	(60) AUG 1948 ....£150
(17) JAN 1945 ....£160	(61) OCT 1948 ....£140
(18) FEB 1945 ....£160	(62) NOV 1948 ....£140
(19) MAR 1945 ....£160	(63) DEC 1948 ....£140
(20) APR 1945 ....£160	(64) JAN 1949 ....£140
(21) MAY 1945 ....£160	(65) FEB 1949 ....£150
(22) JUNE 1945 ....£160	(66) MAR 1949 ....£150
(23) JULY 1945 ....£160	(67) APR 1949 ....£150
(24) AUG 1945 ....£160	(68) MAY 1949 ....£150
(25) SEPT 1945 ....£160	(69) JUNE 1949 ....£150
(26) OCT 1945 ....£160	(70) JULY 1949 ....£150
(27) NOV 1945 ....£160	(71) AUG 1949 ....£150
(28) DEC 1945 ....£160	(72) OCT 1949 ....£150
(29) JAN 1946 ....£150	(73) NOV 1949 ....£150
(30) FEB 1946 ....£150	(74) DEC 1949 ....£150
(31) MAR 1946 ....£150	(75) JAN 1950 ....£120
(32) APR 1946 ....£150	(76) FEB 1950 ....£120
(33) MAY 1946 ....£150	(77) MAR 1950 ....£120
(34) JUNE 1946 ....£150	(78) APR 1950 ....£120
(35) JULY 1946 ....£150	(79) MAY 1950 ....£120
(36) AUG 1946 ....£150	(80) JUNE 1950 ....£120
(37) SEPT 1946 ....£150	(81) JULY 1950 ....95·00
(38) OCT 1946 ....£400	(82) AUG 1950 ....95·00
(39) NOV 1946 ....£150	(83) SEPT 1950 ....95·00
(40) DEC 1946 ....£150	(84) OCT 1950 ....95·00
(41) JAN 1947 ....£150	(85) NOV 1950 ....95·00
(42) FEB 1947 ....£150	(86) DEC 1950 ....95·00
(43) MAR 1947 ....£150	(87) JAN 1951 ....95·00
(44) APR 1947 ....£150	(88) FEB 1951 ....95·00

1951 (May). As before, but containing stamps in the new colours (Nos. 503, 506/7).
BD19   Edition dates May 1951 to February 1952............................ 55·00

(1) MAY 1951 ....55·00	(6) OCT 1951 ....55·00
(2) JUNE 1951 ....75·00	(7) NOV 1951 ....55·00
(3) JULY 1951 ....£200	(8) DEC 1951 ....55·00
(4) AUG 1951 ....55·00	(9) JAN 1952 ....55·00
(5) SEPT 1951 ....£175	(10) FEB 1952 ....55·00

1952 (Mar). As before, but make-up changed to contain: 6×2½d., 6×1½d., 3×1d. and 6×½d. The 1d. pane was completed by three perforated labels in the lower row inscribed *MINIMUM INLAND PRINTED PAPER RATE 1½d.* (Nos. 503/5, 507).
BD20   Edition dates March 1952 to May 1953 .... 50·00

(1) MAR 1952 ....50·00	(9) NOV 1952 ....50·00
(2) APR 1952 ....55·00	(10) DEC 1952 ....50·00
(3) MAY 1952 ....50·00	(11) JAN 1953 ....50·00
(4) JUNE 1952 ....50·00	(12) FEB 1953 ....50·00
(5) JULY 1952 ....55·00	(13) MAR 1953 ....50·00
(6) AUG 1952 ....50·00	(14) APR 1953 ....50·00
(7) SEPT 1952 ....50·00	(15) MAY 1953 ....55·00
(8) OCT 1952 ....50·00	

3s. Booklets

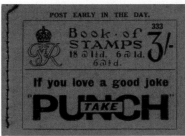

BD **21**

1937 (Aug). Scarlet cover printed black as Type BD **21**, containing pages of six stamps: 18×1½d., 6×1d. & 6×½d. in the original dark colours (Nos. 462/4).
BD21   Edition numbers 333 to 343... £1900

BD **22**

1938 (April). As before, but scarlet cover printed in black as Type BD **22** (Nos. 462/4).
BD22   Edition numbers 344 to 377 .... £1900

5s. Booklets

1937 (Aug). Buff cover printed in black as Type BB **33**, containing stamps of the new reign in the original dark colours. Pages of six stamps: 34×1½d., 6×1d. and 6×½d. The first 1½d. pane completed by two *se-tenant* advertisements. (Nos. 462/4).
BD23   Edition numbers 18 to 20.. £2000

BD **24**

1938 (May). As before, but with redesigned front cover showing GPO emblem as Type BD **24** instead of royal cypher.
BD24   Edition numbers 21 to 29 .... £2000

1940 (July). As before, but make-up changed to contain: 18×2½d., 6×2d. and 6×½d. in the original dark colours (Nos. 462, 465/6).
BD25   Edition numbers 1 to 16 (part) £2000

1942 (Mar). As before, but containing stamps in pale shades (Nos. 485, 488/9).
BD26   Edition numbers 16 (part) to 36.................................. £2000

1943 (Sept). As before, but buff cover printed in black as Type A (see No. BD **18**, 2s·6d.) (Nos. 485, 488/9).
BD28   Edition dates September 1943 to December 1950............. £130

(1) SEPT 1943	£160	(26) JUNE 1947	£180
(2) OCT 1943	£230	(27) AUG 1947	£180
(3) NOV 1943	£180	(28) OCT 1947	£180
(4) DEC 1943	£230	(29) DEC 1947	£180
(5) FEB 1944	£190	(30) FEB 1948	£180
(6) MAR 1944	£190	(31) APR 1948	£180
(7) AUG 1944	£190	(32) JUNE 1948	£180
(8) OCT 1944	£190	(33) JULY 1948	£180
(9) NOV 1944	£190	(34) AUG 1948	£180
(10) JAN 1945	£190	(35) OCT 1948	£180
(11) FEB 1945	£200	(36) DEC 1948	£200
(12) APR 1945	£200	(37) FEB 1949	£200
(13) JUNE 1945	£200	(38) APR 1949	£200
(14) AUG 1945	£200	(39) JUNE 1949	£190
(15) OCT 1945	£200	(40) AUG 1949	£190
(16) DEC 1945	£200	(41) SEPT 1949	£190
(17) JAN 1946	£200	(42) OCT 1949	£190
(18) MAR 1946	£180	(43) DEC 1949	£190
(19) MAY 1946	£180	(44) FEB 1950	£130
(20) JUNE 1946	£180	(45) APR 1950	£130
(21) AUG 1946	£180	(46) JUNE 1950	£130
(22) OCT 1946	£180	(47) AUG 1950	£130
(23) DEC 1946	£180	(48) OCT 1950	£130
(24) FEB 1947	£180	(49) DEC 1950	£130
(25) APR 1947	£180		

BD **29**

1944 (Apr). As before, but buff cover printed in black as Type BD **29** (Nos. 485, 488/9).
BD29   Edition dates April or June 1944................................ £5250

(1) APR 1944	£5250	(2) JUNE 1944	£5250

1951 (May). As before, but buff cover changed back to Type A (see No. BD **18**, 2s·6d.) and containing stamps in the new colours (Nos. 503, 506/7).
BD30   Edition dates May 1951 to January 1952...................... 65·00

(1) MAY 1951	65·00	(4) NOV 1951	65·00
(2) JULY 1951	65·00	(5) JAN 1952	65·00
(3) SEPT 1951	65·00		

1952 (Mar). As before, make-up changed to contain: 18×2½d., 6×1½d., 3×1d. and 6×½d.. The 1d. pane was completed by three perforated labels in the lower row inscribed *"MINIMUM INLAND PRINTED PAPER RATE 1½d."* (Nos. 503/5, 507).
BD31   Edition dates March to November 1952 .... 55·00

(1) MAR 1952	55·00	(4) SEPT 1952	55·00
(2) MAY 1952	55·00	(5) NOV 1952	55·00
(3) JULY 1952	55·00		

1953 (Jan). As before, but make-up changed again to include the 2d. value and containing: 12×2½d., 6×2d., 6×1½d., 6×1d. and 6×½d. (Nos. 503/7).
BD32   Edition dates January or March 1953............................ 65·00

(1) JAN 1953	65·00	(2) MAR 1953	65·00

I. £.s.d. Booklets, 1953–70.

TYPES OF BOOKLET COVER WITH GPO CYPHER

Type **A** Circular GPO Cypher
(See illustration above No. BD18)

Type **B** Oval Type GPO Cypher

Type **C** New GPO Cypher (small)

Type **D** New GPO Cypher (large)

1s. Booklets

1953 (2 Sept)–59.
  I. White unprinted cover. Pages of two stamps: 4×1½d., 4×1d., 4×½d..
      For use in experimental "D" machines.
      A. Wmk Tudor Crown (Nos. 515/17) EE
E1   No date .... 9·25
      B. Wmk St. Edward's Crown (Nos. 540/2)
E2   No date (11.57).. 50·00
  II. White printed cover as Type B. Pages of four stamps: 4×1½d. 4×1d.,
      4×½d. For use in "E" machines.
      A. Wmk Tudor Crown (Nos. 515/17)
K1   No date (22.7.54).. 8·00
      B. Wmk St. Edward's Crown (Nos. 540/2)
K2   No date (5.7.56).. 8·00
      C. Wmk Crowns (Nos. 570/2)
K3   No date (13.8.59).. 8·00

2s. Booklets

1959 (22 Apr)–65. Pages of four stamps: 4×3d., 4×1½d., 4×1d., 4×½d.
      I. Salmon cover as Type B. Wmk. St. Edward's Crown
         (Nos. 540/2 and 545).
N1   No date.. 9·00
      II. Salmon cover as Type C. Wmk Crowns (Nos. 570/2 and 575).
N2   No date (2.11.60).. 10·50
      III. Lemon cover as Type C. Wmk Crowns (Nos. 570/2 and 575).
N3   No date (2.61)... 10·50
      IV. Lemon cover as Type C. Wmk Crowns (sideways) (Nos. 570a, 571a,
         572b, 575a) or phosphor (Nos. 610a, 611a, 612a, 615b).
N4   APR 1961... 38·00
      p. With phosphor bands.. 80·00
N5   SEPT 1961... 60·00

N6	JAN 1962	55·00
N7	APR 1962	65·00
N8	JULY 1962	60·00
	p. With phosphor bands	£110
N9	NOV 1962	80·00
	p. With phosphor bands	£120
N10	JAN 1963	60·00
	p. With phosphor bands	£200
N11	MAR 1963	60·00
N12	JUNE 1963	60·00
	p. With phosphor bands	95·00
N13	AUG 1963	60·00
	p. With phosphor bands	£120
N14	OCT 1963	60·00
	p. With phosphor bands	£180
N15	FEB 1964	60·00
	p. With phosphor bands	95·00
N16	JUNE 1964	60·00
	p. With phosphor bands	£150
N17	AUG 1964	80·00
	p. With phosphor bands	£150
N18	OCT 1964	60·00
	p. With phosphor bands	85·00
N19	DEC 1964	70·00
	p. With phosphor bands	85·00
N20	APR 1965	60·00
	p. With phosphor bands	80·00

1965 (16 Aug)–**67.** New Composition. Pages of four stamps: 4×4d. and pane of 2×1d. and 2×3d. arranged *se-tenant* horiz. Orange-yellow cover as Type **C** printed in black. *Wmk* Crowns (sideways) (Nos. 571a, 575a and 576ab) or phosphor (Nos. 611a, 615d or 615dEa (one side phosphor band) and 616ab).

N21	JULY 1965	5·00
	p. With phosphor bands	20·00
N22	OCT 1965	5·25
	p. With phosphor bands	20·00
N23	JAN 1966	20·00
	p. With phosphor bands	26·00
N24	APR 1966	10·00
	p. With phosphor bands	12·00
N25	JULY 1966	6·00
	p. With phosphor bands	£150
N26	OCT 1966	8·00
	p. With phosphor bands	16·00
N27	JAN 1967	10·00
	p. With phosphor bands	8·00
N28p	APR 1967. With phosphor bands	10·00
N29p	JULY 1967. With phosphor bands	7·00
N30p	OCT 1967. With phosphor bands	7·00

In the *se-tenant* pane the 3d. appears at left or right to facilitate the application of phosphor bands.

The following illustration shows how the *se-tenant* stamps with one phosphor band on 3d. were printed and the arrows indicate where the guillotine fell. The result gives 1d. stamps with two bands and the 3d. stamps with one band either at left or right.

1967 (Nov)–**68.** Composition and cover as Nos. N21/30. *Wmk* Crowns (sideways) (Nos. 611a, 615b (two phosphor bands) and 616ab).

N31p	JAN 1968	4·00
N32p	MAR 1968	4·50

2s. Booklets with Machin type stamps

1968 (6 Apr–Aug). Orange-yellow cover as Type C. Pages of four stamps: 4×4d. and pane of 2×1d. and 2×3d. arranged *se-tenant* horiz. PVA gum (Nos. 724, 730, 731Ev).

NP27	MAY 1968	1·60
NP28	JULY 1968	1·40
NP29	AUG 1968	6·00

1968 (16 Sept)–**70.** Grey cover as Type C. New Composition. 4d. stamps only comprising page of 4×4d. with two phosphor bands (No. 731Ev) and page of 2×4d. with one centre phosphor band (No. 732) *se-tenant* with two printed labels.

NP30	SEPT 1968	1·10
NP31	JAN 1969	£275

Same composition but all six 4d. stamps have one centre phosphor band (No. 732).

NP31a	SEPT 1968	£650
NP32	NOV 1968	1·10
NP33	JAN 1969	1·10

Same composition but change to 4d. bright vermilion with one centre phosphor band (No. 733).

NP34	MAR 1969	1·60

NP35	MAY 1969	1·90
NP36	JULY 1969	2·50
NP37	SEPT 1969	1·90
NP38	NOV 1969	1·90
NP39	JAN 1970	2·75
NP40	MAR 1970	2·75
NP41	MAY 1970	2·75
NP42	JULY 1970	2·75
NP43	AUG 1970	2·75
NP44	OCT 1970	2·75
NP45	DEC 1970	2·75

2s. Booklets for Holiday Resorts

1963 (15 July)–**64.**
  I. Lemon cover as Type **C** *printed in red. New composition. Pages of four stamps: two of 4×2½d. and one of 3×2½d. and 1×2½d. arranged se-tenant. Chalky paper. Wmk Crowns (Nos. 570k and 574k).*

NR1	No date, black stitching	5·00
	a. White stitching (3.9.63)	5·50

  II. Lemon cover as Type **C** *printed in red. Composition changed again. Pages of four stamps 2×2½d. and 2×2½d. arranged sideways, vertically se-tenant. Wmk Crowns (sideways) (No. 570n×4).*

NR2	1964 (1.7.64)	2·25

2s. Booklet for Christmas Cards

1965 (6 Dec). Orange-yellow cover as Type **C** printed in red. Two panes of 4×3d. arranged sideways. *Wmk* Crowns (sideways) (No. 575a).

NX1	1965	1·00

2s.6d. Booklets

Green cover. Pages of six stamps: 6×2½d., 6×1½d., 3×1d. (page completed by three perforated labels), 6×½d.
LABELS. The wording printed on the labels differs as follows:
"PPR" = "MINIMUM INLAND PRINTED PAPER RATE 1½d."
Two types exist:
  A. Printed in photogravure, 17 mm high.
  B. Typographed, 15 mm high.
"Shorthand" = "SHORTHAND IN 1 WEEK" (covering all three labels).
"Post Early" = "PLEASE POST EARLY IN THE DAY".
"PAP" = "PACK YOUR PARCELS SECURELY" (1st label)
  "ADDRESS YOUR LETTERS CORRECTLY" (2nd label),
  "AND POST EARLY IN THE DAY" (3rd label).

1953–**54.** Composite booklets containing stamps of King George VI and Queen Elizabeth II.
  A. K.G.VI ½d. and 1d. (Nos. 503/4) and Q.E.II 1½d. and 2½d. (Nos. 517 and 519b). Cover as Type **A.** *No interleaving pages.*

F1	MAY 1953 (PPR 17 mm)	32·00
F2	JUNE 1953 (PPR 17 mm)	35·00
F3	JULY 1953 (PPR 17 mm)	42·00
F4	AUG 1953 (PPR 17 mm)	38·00

  B. Same composition but with addition of two interleaving pages, one at each end. Cover as Type **A.**

F5	SEPT 1953 (PPR 17 mm)	£250
F6	SEPT 1953 (PPR 15 mm)	£150

  C. Same composition and with interleaving pages but with cover as Type **B.**

F7	OCT 1953 (PPR 17 mm)	55·00
F8	OCT 1953 (PPR 15 mm)	£150
F9	NOV 1953 (PPR 17 mm)	80·00
F10	NOV 1953 (PPR 15 mm)	£250
F11	DEC 1953 (PPR 17 mm)	65·00
F12	JAN 1954 (Shorthand)	90·00
F13	FEB 1954 (Shorthand)	£100

  D. New composition: K.G.VI 1d. (No. 504) and Q.E.II ½d., 1½d. and 2½d. (Nos. 515, 517 and 519b).

F14	MAR 1954 (PPR 17 mm)	£650
F14a	MAR 1954 (Shorthand)	

1954–**57.** Booklets containing only Queen Elizabeth II stamps. All covers as Type **B.**
  A. Wmk Tudor Crown (Nos. 515/17 and 519b).

F15	MAR 1954 (PPR 15 mm)	£375
F16	APR 1954 (Post Early)	75·00
F17	MAY 1954 (Post Early)	75·00
F18	JUNE 1954 (Post Early)	75·00
F19	JULY 1954 (Post Early)	75·00
F20	AUG 1954 (Post Early)	75·00
F21	SEPT 1954 (Post Early)	75·00
F22	OCT 1954 (Post Early)	60·00
F23	NOV 1954 (Post Early)	65·00
F24	DEC 1954 (Post Early)	60·00

  B. Same composition but with interleaving pages between each pane of stamps.

F25	JAN 1955 (Post Early)	75·00
F26	JAN 1955 (PAP)	£200
F27	FEB 1955 (PAP)	55·00
F28	MAR 1955 (PAP)	55·00
F29	APR 1955 (PAP)	55·00
F30	MAY 1955 (PAP)	75·00
F31	JUNE 1955 (PAP)	60·00
F32	JULY 1955 (PAP)	55·00
F33	AUG 1955 (PAP)	55·00

C. Mixed watermarks. Wmk Tudor Crown (Nos. 515/17 and 519b) and wmk St. Edward's Crown (Nos. 540/2 and 544b) in various combinations.

F34	SEPT 1955 (PAP)	From 60·00

2s·6d. booklets dated AUGUST, OCTOBER, NOVEMBER and DECEMBER 1955, JANUARY, MAY and JUNE 1956 exist both as listed and with the two watermarks mixed. There are so many different combinations that we do not list them separately, but when in stock selections can be submitted. The SEPTEMBER 1955 booklet (No. F34) only exists in composite form.

D. Wmk St. Edward's Crown (Nos. 540/2 and 544b).

F35	OCT 1955 (PAP)	40·00
F36	NOV 1955 (PAP)	40·00
F37	DEC 1955 (PAP)	40·00
F38	JAN 1956 (PAP)	40·00
F39	FEB 1956 (PAP)	40·00
F40	MAR 1956 (PAP)	40·00
F41	APR 1956 (PAP)	50·00
F42	MAY 1956 (PAP)	40·00
F43	JUNE 1956 (PAP)	45·00
F44	JULY 1956 (PAP)	40·00
F45	AUG 1956 (PAP)	30·00
F46	SEPT 1956 (PAP)	48·00
F47	OCT 1956 (PAP)	40·00
F48	NOV 1956 (PAP)	40·00
F49	DEC 1956 (PAP)	40·00
F50	JAN 1957 (PAP)	40·00
F51	FEB 1957 (PAP)	30·00
F52	MAR 1957 (PAP)	40·00

E. Same wmk but new composition. Pages of six stamps: 6×2½d.
(No. 544b), 6×2d. (No. 543b) and 6×½d. (No. 540).

F53	APR 1957	40·00
F54	MAY 1957	35·00
F55	JUNE 1957	35·00
F56	JULY 1957	35·00
F57	AUG 1957	35·00
F58	SEPT 1957	35·00
F59	OCT 1957	35·00
F60	NOV 1957	30·00
F61	DEC 1957	50·00

3s. Booklets

1958–65. Pages of six stamps: 6×3d., 6×1½d., 6×1d., 6×½d.

I. Red cover as Type B.

A. Wmk St. Edward's Crown (Nos. 540/2 and 545).

M1	JAN 1958	28·00
M2	FEB 1958	40·00
M3	MAR 1958	360·00
M4	APR 1958	28·00
M5	MAY 1958	28·00
M6	JUNE 1958	28·00
M7	JULY 1958	28·00
M8	AUG 1958	32·00
M9	NOV 1958	32·00

The 3s. booklets dated NOVEMBER 1958, DECEMBER 1958 and JANUARY 1959 exist both as listed and with mixed St. Edward's Crown and Crowns wmks.

B. Wmk Crowns (Nos. 570/2 and 575) or graphite lines
(Nos. 587/9 and 592).

M10	DEC 1958	38·00
M11	JAN 1959	35·00
M12	FEB 1959	35·00
M13	AUG 1959	40·00
	g. With graphite lines	£275
M14	SEPT 1959	40·00
	g. With graphite lines	£350

II. Brick-red cover as Type C. Wmk Crowns (Nos. 570/2 and 575), graphite lines (Nos. 587/9 and 592) or phosphor (Nos. 610/12 and 615).

M15	OCT 1959	38·00
	g. With graphite lines	£350
M16	NOV 1959	38·00
M17	DEC 1959	40·00
M18	JAN 1960	40·00
M19	FEB 1960	45·00
	g. With graphite lines	£325
M20	MAR 1960	50·00
	g. With graphite lines	£400
M21	APR 1960	50·00
	g. With graphite lines	£325
M22	MAY 1960	60·00
M23	JUNE 1960	60·00
M24	JULY 1960	50·00
M25	AUG 1960	50·00
	p. With phosphor bands	75·00
M26	SEPT 1960	50·00
M27	OCT 1960	50·00
M28	NOV 1960	38·00
	p. With phosphor bands	80·00

III. Brick-red cover as Type D. Wmk Crowns (Nos. 570/2 and 575) or phosphor (Nos. 610/12 and 615).

M29	DEC 1960	60·00

	p. With phosphor bands	85·00
M30	JAN 1961	60·00
M31	FEB 1961	60·00
M32	MAR 1961	60·00
M33	APR 1961	60·00
	p. With phosphor bands	75·00
M34	MAY 1961	60·00
M35	JUNE 1961	60·00
M36	JULY 1961	60·00
	p. With phosphor bands	75·00
M37	AUG 1961	60·00
	p. With phosphor bands	70·00
M38	SEPT 1961	60·00
	p. With phosphor bands	85·00
M39	OCT 1961	60·00
	p. With phosphor bands	80·00
M40	NOV 1961	60·00
M41	DEC 1961	60·00
M42	JAN 1962	60·00
M43	FEB 1962	60·00
	p. With phosphor bands	£100
M44	MAR 1962	50·00
	p. With phosphor bands	£100
M45	APR 1962	60·00
	p. With phosphor bands	£100
M46	MAY 1962	60·00
	p. With phosphor bands	£100
M47	JUNE 1962	60·00
	p. With phosphor bands	£100
M48	JULY 1962	60·00
M49	AUG 1962	60·00
	p. With phosphor bands	90·00
M50	SEPT 1962	60·00
	p. With phosphor bands	£100
M51	OCT 1962	70·00
	p. With phosphor bands	£100
M52	NOV 1962	70·00
	p. With phosphor bands	£100
M53	DEC 1962	70·00
	p. With phosphor bands	£100
M54	JAN 1963	70·00
M55	FEB 1963	70·00
	p. With phosphor bands	£100
M56	MAR 1963	70·00
	p. With phosphor bands	£100
M57	APR 1963	70·00
	p. With phosphor bands	£100
M58	MAY 1963	70·00
	p. With phosphor bands	£500
M59	JUNE 1963	70·00
	p. With phosphor bands	75·00
M60	JULY 1963	70·00
	p. With phosphor bands	£100
M61	AUG 1963	70·00
	p. With phosphor bands	£100
M62	SEPT 1963	70·00
M63	OCT 1963	70·00
M64	NOV 1963	70·00
	p. With phosphor bands	£100
M65	DEC 1963	80·00
	p. With phosphor bands	£200
M66	JAN 1964	80·00
	p. With phosphor bands	75·00
M67	MAR 1964	80·00
	p. With phosphor bands	£100
M68	MAY 1964	80·00
	p. With phosphor bands	£120
M69	JULY 1964	60·00
	p. With phosphor bands	£100
M70	SEPT 1964	60·00
	p. With phosphor bands	£100
M71	NOV 1964	55·00
	p. With phosphor bands	65·00
M72	JAN 1965	50·00
	p. With phosphor bands	70·00
M73	MAR 1965	40·00
	p. With phosphor bands	65·00
M74	MAY 1965	55·00
	p. With phosphor bands	£100

3s.9d. Booklets

1953–57. Red cover as Type B. Pages of six stamps: 18×2½d.

A. Wmk Tudor Crown (No. 519b)

G1	NOV 1953	40·00
G2	JAN 1954	75·00
G3	MAR 1954	40·00
G4	DEC 1954	40·00
G5	FEB 1955	40·00
G6	APR 1955	40·00
G7	JUNE 1955	40·00
G8	AUG 1955	40·00
G9	OCT 1955	40·00

G10	DEC 1955	40·00

3s·9d. booklets dated OCTOBER and DECEMBER 1955 exist both as
listed and with the two wmks mixed.

*B. Wmk St. Edward's Crown (No. 544b). Same composition but with
interleaving pages between each pane of stamps.*

G12	FEB 1956	60·00
G13	APR 1956	40·00
G14	JUNE 1956	35·00
G15	AUG 1956	30·00
G16	OCT 1956	30·00
G17	DEC 1956	30·00
G18	FEB 1957	30·00
G19	APR 1957	30·00
G20	JUNE 1957	17·00
G21	AUG 1957	40·00

4s.6d. Booklets

1957–65. Pages of six stamps: 18×3d.
*I. Purple cover as Type **B**.*
A. Wmk St. Edward's Crown (No. 545).

L1	OCT 1957	30·00
L2	DEC 1957	30·00
L3	FEB 1958	35·00
L4	APR 1958	30·00
L5	JUNE 1958	32·00
L6	OCT 1958	30·00
L7	DEC 1958	30·00

B. Wmk Crowns (No. 575).

L8	DEC 1958	£130

*II. Purple cover as Type **C**. Wmk Crowns (No. 575) or graphite lines
(No. 592)*

L9	FEB 1959	35·00
L10	JUNE 1959	50·00
L11	AUG 1959	30·00
	g. With graphite lines	45·00
L12	OCT 1959	45·00
L13	DEC 1959	35·00

*III. Violet cover as Type **C**. Wmk Crowns (No. 575), graphite lines
(No. 592) or phosphor (No. 615).*

L14	FEB 1959	£100
L15	APR 1959	35·00
	g. With graphite lines	30·00
L16	JUNE 1959	55·00
	g. With graphite lines	30·00
L17	DEC 1959	60·00
L18	FEB 1960	55·00
	g. With graphite lines	55·00
L19	APR 1960	35·00
	g. With graphite lines	35·00
L20	JUNE 1960	55·00
L21	AUG 1960	55·00
	p. With phosphor bands	60·00
L22	OCT 1960	55·00

*IV. Violet cover as Type **D**. Wmk Crowns (No. 575) or phosphor (No. 615).*

L23	DEC 1960	80·00
L24	FEB 1961	80·00
	p. With phosphor bands	55·00
L25	APR 1961	50·00
	p. With phosphor bands	45·00
L26	JUNE 1961	70·00
L27	AUG 1961	70·00
	p. With phosphor bands	80·00
L28	OCT 1961	70·00
	p. With phosphor bands	80·00
L29	DEC 1961	70·00
L30	FEB 1962	80·00
	p. With phosphor bands	80·00
L31	APR 1962	80·00
	p. With phosphor bands	80·00
L32	JUNE 1962	80·00
	p. With phosphor bands	90·00
L33	AUG 1962	60·00
	p. With phosphor bands	£100
L34	OCT 1962	60·00
	p. With phosphor bands	£275
L35	DEC 1962	70·00
	p. With phosphor bands	80·00
L36	FEB 1963	70·00
	p. With phosphor bands	80·00
L37	APR 1963	70·00
	p. With phosphor bands	80·00
L38	JUNE 1963	70·00
	p. With phosphor bands	80·00
L39	AUG 1963	80·00
	p. With phosphor bands	£100
L40	OCT 1963	80·00
	p. With phosphor bands	£100
L41	NOV 1963	80·00
	p. With phosphor bands	£100
L42	DEC 1963	80·00
	p. With phosphor bands	£300

L43	JAN 1964	£125
L44	FEB 1964	80·00
	p. With phosphor bands	60·00
L45	MAR 1964	£125
	p. With phosphor bands	£180
L46	APR 1964	£125
	p. With phosphor bands	£100
L47	MAY 1964	80·00
	p. With phosphor bands	£100
L48	JUNE 1964	80·00
	p. With phosphor bands	£100
L49	JULY 1964	80·00
	p. With phosphor bands	£100
L50	AUG 1964	80·00
	p. With phosphor bands	£100
L51	SEPT 1964	80·00
	p. With phosphor bands	£100
L52	OCT 1964	80·00
	p. With phosphor bands	£100
L53	NOV 1964	80·00
	p. With phosphor bands	£100
L54	DEC 1964	80·00
	p. With phosphor bands	£100
L55	JAN 1965	70·00
	p. With phosphor bands	80·00
L56	FEB 1965	70·00
	p. With phosphor bands	80·00
L57	MAR 1965	35·00
	p. With phosphor bands	£500
L58	APR 1965	55·00

1965 (26 July)–**67**. New composition. Pages of six stamps: 12×4d., 6×1d.
Slate-blue cover as Type D. *Wmk* Crowns (Nos. 571 and 576a) or
phosphor (Nos. 611 and 616a).

L59	JULY 1965	30·00
	p. With phosphor bands	32·00
L60	SEPT 1965	30·00
	p. With phosphor bands	32·00
L61	NOV 1965	55·00
	p. With phosphor bands	60·00
L62	JAN 1966	35·00
	p. With phosphor bands	35·00
L63	MAR 1966	30·00
	p. With phosphor bands	40·00
L64	JAN 1967	40·00
	p. With phosphor bands	40·00
L65	MAR 1967	70·00
	p. With phosphor bands	50·00
L66p	MAY 1967. With phosphor bands	15·00
L67p	JULY 1967. With phosphor bands	40·00
L68p	SEPT 1967. With phosphor bands	20·00
L69p	NOV 1967. With phosphor bands	15·00
L70p	JAN 1968. With phosphor bands	15·00
L71p	MAR 1968. With phosphor bands	10·00

4s.6d. Booklets with Machin type stamps

1968–70. Slate-blue cover as Type D. Pages of six stamps: 12×4d., 6×1d.
PVA gum (Nos. 724, 731Ev).

LP45	MAY 1968	7·25

LP **46** Ships Series with GPO Cypher

(Des S. Rose)

*Blue cover as Type LP **46**. Ships Series. Composition as last.*

LP46	JULY 1968 (*Cutty Sark*)	1·80

*Same composition but changed to 4d. with one centre phosphor band
(No. 732).*

LP47	SEPT 1968 (*Golden Hind*)	2·40
LP48	NOV 1968 (*Discovery*)	2·40

*Same composition but changed to 4d. bright vermilion with one centre
phosphor band (No. 733).*

LP49	JAN 1969 (*Queen Elizabeth 2*)	4·00
LP50	MAR 1969 (*Sirius*)	3·50
LP51	MAY 1969 (*Sirius*)	3·00
LP52	JULY 1969 (*Dreadnought*)	3·50
LP53	SEPT 1969 (*Dreadnought*)	8·00

LP54	NOV 1969 (*Mauretania*)	4·25
LP55	JAN 1970 (*Mauretania*)	8·00
LP56	MAR 1970 (*Victory*)	4·75
LP57	MAY 1970 (*Victory*)	12·00

LP **58** Ships Series with Post Office Corporation Crown Symbol

(Des S. Rose)

As last but cover changed to Type LP **58**.

LP58	AUG 1970 (*Sovereign of the Seas*)	4·50
LP59	OCT 1970 (*Sovereign of the Seas*)	12·00

5s. Booklets

1953–57. Buff cover. Pages of six stamps. 12×2½d., 6×2d., 6×1½d., 6×1d., 6×½d.

I. Composite booklets containing stamps of King George VI and Queen Elizabeth II.

A. *K.G.VI ½d., 1d. and 2d. (Nos. 503/4 and 506) and Q.E.II 1½d. and 2½d. (Nos. 517 and 519b). Cover as Type* **A**. *No interleaving pages.*

H1	MAY 1953	50·00
H2	JULY 1953	50·00

B. *Same composition but with addition of two interleaving pages, one at each end. Cover as Type* **A**.

H3	SEPT 1953	70·00

C. *Same composition and with interleaving pages but cover as Type* **B**.

H4	NOV 1953	60·00
H5	JAN 1954	70·00

D. *New composition: K.G.VI 1d. and 2d. (Nos. 504 and 506) and Q.E.II ½d., 1½d. and 2½d. (Nos. 515, 517 and 519b).*

H6	MAR 1954	£500

E. *New composition: K.G.VI 2d. (No. 506) and Q.E.II ½d. 1d., 1½d. and 2½d.. (Nos. 515/17 and 519b).*

H7	MAR 1954	£275

II. Booklets containing only Queen Elizabeth II stamps. Buff cover as Type **B**. *Two interleaving pages as before.*

A. *Wmk Tudor Crown (Nos. 515/18 and 519b).*

H8	MAR 1954	£225
H9	MAY 1954	£125
H10	JULY 1954	£135
H11	SEPT 1954	85·00
H12	NOV 1954	£125

B. *Same composition but with interleaving pages between each pane of stamps.*

H13	JAN 1955	95·00
H14	MAR 1955	85·00
H15	MAY 1955	£125
H16	JULY 1955	£125

C. *Wmk St. Edward's Crown (Nos. 540/3 and 544b).*

H17	SEPT 1955	40·00
H18	NOV 1955	42·00
H19	JAN 1956	55·00
H20	MAR 1956	65·00
H21	MAY 1956	48·00
H22	JULY 1956	48·00
H23	SEPT 1956	48·00
H24	NOV 1956	48·00
H25	JAN 1957	60·00

5s. booklets dated SEPTEMBER and NOVEMBER 1955 and JANUARY 1956 exist both as listed and with the two watermarks mixed. There are so many different combinations that we do not list them separately, but when in stock selections can be submitted.

D. *Same watermark. Introduction of 2d. light red-brown (No. 543b) in place of No. 543.*

H26	JAN 1957	48·00
H27	MAR 1957	60·00
H28	MAY 1957	50·00
H29	JULY 1957	42·00
H30	SEPT 1957	42·00
H31	NOV 1957	42·00

1958–65. E. New composition. Pages of six stamps: 12×3d. (No. 545), 6×2½d. (No. 544b), 6×1d. (No. 541), 6×½d. (No. 540). Wmk St. Edward's Crown.

H32	JAN 1958	42·00
H33	MAR 1958	42·00
H34	MAY 1958	42·00
H35	JULY 1958 (11.58)	30·00
H36	NOV 1958	30·00

5s. booklets dated JULY 1958, NOVEMBER 1958 and JANUARY 1959 exist with mixed watermarks.

F. *Blue cover as Type* **C**. *Wmk Crowns (Nos. 570/1, 574/5), graphite lines (Nos. 587/8 and 591/2) or phosphor (Nos. 610/11, 614 and 615).*

H37	JAN 1959	35·00
H38	MAR 1959	50·00
H39	JULY 1959	42·00
	g. With graphite lines	£150
H40	SEPT 1959	50·00
H41	NOV 1959	50·00
H42	JAN 1960	50·00
H43	MAR 1960	50·00
	g. With graphite lines	£170
H44	MAY 1960	50·00
H45	JULY 1960	50·00
H46	SEPT 1960	80·00
	g. With graphite lines	£170
	p. With phosphor bands	£120
H47	NOV 1960	75·00

G. *As last but blue cover as Type* **D**. *Same composition. I. Phosphor has two bands on 2½d. (No. 614).*

H48	JAN 1961	80·00
H49	MAR 1961	80·00
	p. With phosphor bands	£175
H50	MAY 1961	£100
H51	JULY 1961	£100
	p. With phosphor bands	£200
H52	SEPT 1961	£100
	p. With phosphor bands	£225
H53	NOV 1961	£100
H54	JAN 1962	£100
	p. With phosphor bands	£225

II. As last but phosphor has one band on 2½d. (No. 614a).

H55	MAR 1962	£100
	p. With phosphor bands	£250
H56	MAY 1962	£100
	p. With phosphor bands	£200
H57	JULY 1962	£100
	p. With phosphor bands	£250
H58	SEPT 1962	£100
	p. With phosphor bands	£250
H59	NOV 1962	£100
	p. With phosphor bands	£250
H60	JAN 1963	£100
	p. With phosphor bands	£600
H61	MAR 1963	£100
	p. With phosphor bands	£250
H62	MAY 1963	80·00
	p. With phosphor bands	£250
H63	JULY 1963	£100
	p. With phosphor bands	£200
H64	SEPT 1963	£100
	p. With phosphor bands	£250
H65	NOV 1963	£100
	p. With phosphor bands	£250
H66	JAN 1964	£100
	p. With phosphor bands	£150
H67	MAR 1964	£100
	p. With phosphor bands	£150
H68	MAY 1964	£100
	p. With phosphor bands	£225
H69	JULY 1964	£100
	p. With phosphor bands	£200
H70	SEPT 1964	£100
	p. With phosphor bands	£200
H71	NOV 1964	80·00
	p. With phosphor bands	£120
H72	JAN 1965	80·00
	p. With phosphor bands	£140
H73	MAR 1965	60·00
	p. With phosphor bands	£225
H74	MAY 1965	60·00
	p. With phosphor bands	£150

5s. Booklets with Machin type stamps

HP **26** English Homes Series with GPO Cypher

(Des S. Rose)

1968 (27 Nov)–**70**. Cinnamon cover as Type HP **26** (*English Homes Series*). Pages of six stamps: 12×5d. (No. 735).

HP26	DEC 1968 (Ightham Mote)	3·00
HP27	FEB 1969 (Little Moreton Hall)	3·00
HP28	APR 1969 (Long Melford Hall)	3·00
HP29	JUNE 1969 (Long Melford Hall)	3·00
HP30	AUG 1969 (Long Melford Hall)	6·00

HP **31** English Homes Series with Post Office Corporation Crown Symbol

(Des S. Rose)

As last but cover changed to Type HP **31**.

HP31	OCT 1969 (Mompesson House)	3·00
HP32	DEC 1969 (Mompesson House)	5·00
HP33	FEB 1970 (Cumberland Terrace)	3·00

HP **34**

(Des P. Gauld)

As last but cover changed to Type HP **34** (special edition to advertise Philympia International Philatelic Exhibition, London, September 1970).

HP34	(no date) (3.3.70)	3·00

As last but cover changed to Type HP **31**.

HP35	JUNE 1970 (The Vineyard, Saffron Walden)	3·50
HP36	AUG 1970 (The Vineyard, Saffron Walden)	6·00
HP37	OCT 1970 (Mereworth Castle)	5·00
HP38	DEC 1970 (Mereworth Castle)	6·00

6s. Booklets

1965 (21 June)–**67**. Claret cover as Type **D**. Wmk Crowns (No. 576a) or phosphor (No. 616a). Pages of six stamps: 18×4d.

Q1	JUNE 1965	45·00
	p. With phosphor bands	45·00
Q2	JULY 1965	45·00
	p. With phosphor bands	45·00
Q3	AUG 1965	80·00
	p. With phosphor bands	80·00
Q4	SEPT 1965	60·00

	p. With phosphor bands	60·00
Q5	OCT 1965	£100
	p. With phosphor bands	£100
Q6	NOV 1965	£100
	p. With phosphor bands	£100
Q7	DEC 1965	£100
	p. With phosphor bands	£100
Q8	JAN 1966	£100
	p. With phosphor bands	£100
Q9	FEB 1966	£100
	p. With phosphor bands	£100
Q10	MAR 1966	£100
	p. With phosphor bands	£100
Q11	APR 1966	£100
	p. With phosphor bands	£200
Q12	MAY 1966	£100
	p. With phosphor bands	£100
Q13	JUNE 1966	£100
	p. With phosphor bands	£100
Q14	JULY 1966	£100
	p. With phosphor bands	£100
Q15	AUG 1966	£100
	p. With phosphor bands	£250
Q16	SEPT 1966	70·00
	p. With phosphor bands	70·00
Q17	OCT 1966	£100
	p. With phosphor bands	£175
Q18	NOV 1966	80·00
	p. With phosphor bands	50·00
Q19	DEC 1966	50·00
	p. With phosphor bands	80·00
Q20	JAN 1967	£100
	p. With phosphor bands	£100
Q21	FEB 1967	£100
	p. With phosphor bands	80·00
Q22	MAR 1967	60·00
	p. With phosphor bands	40·00
Q23	APR 1967	60·00
	p. With phosphor bands	50·00
Q24p	MAY 1967. With phosphor bands	40·00
Q25p	JUNE 1967. With phosphor bands	40·00
Q26p	JULY 1967. With phosphor bands	£100
Q27p	AUG 1967. With phosphor bands	80·00

6s. Booklets with Machin type stamps

1967–70. Claret cover as Type **D**. Pages of six stamps: 18×4d. Two phosphor bands. Gum arabic (No. 731).

QP28	SEPT 1967	60·00
QP29	OCT 1967	85·00
QP30	NOV 1967	70·00
QP31	DEC 1967	85·00
QP32	JAN 1968	70·00
QP33	FEB 1968 (No. 731*Ea*)	70·00
QP34	MAR 1968 (No. 731*Ea*)	70·00
QP35	APR 1968 (No. 731*Ea*)	55·00
QP36	MAY 1968 (No. 731*Ea*)	25·00

Change to PVA gum (No. 731*Ev*).

QP37	MAY 1968	£600

QP **38** Birds Series with GPO Cypher

(Des S. Rose)

Orange-red cover as Type QP **38** (*Birds Series*). Same composition. Two phosphor bands. PVA gum (No. 731*Ev*).

QP38	JUNE 1968 (Kingfisher) (4.6.68)	2·50
QP39	JULY 1968 (Kingfisher)	13·00
QP40	AUG 1968 (Peregrine Falcon)	2·00

Change to one centre phosphor band (No. 732).

QP41	SEPT 1968 (Peregrine Falcon) (16.9.68)	2·10
QP42	OCT 1968 (Pied Woodpecker)	2·10
QP43	NOV 1968 (Pied Woodpecker)	2·25
QP44	DEC 1968 (Great Crested Grebe)	2·25
QP45	JAN 1969 (Barn Owl)	3·50

Change to 4d. bright vermilion with one centre phosphor band (No. 733).

QP46	FEB 1969 (Barn Owl) (20.2.69)	4·25

QP47	MAR 1969 (Jay)	3·50
QP48	MAY 1969 (Jay)	4·25
QP49	JULY 1969 (Puffin)	3·50
QP50	SEPT 1969 (Puffin)	6·00

QP **51** Birds Series with Post Office Corporation
Crown Symbol

(Des S. Rose)

As last but cover changed to Type QP **51**.

QP51	NOV 1969 (Cormorant)	4·25
QP52	JAN 1970 (Cormorant)	5·00
QP53	APR 1970 (Wren)	4·25
QP54	AUG 1970 (Golden Eagle)	4·25
QP55	OCT 1970 (Golden Eagle)	4·25

10s. Booklets

1961 (10 Apr–Oct). Green cover as Type D. Pages of six stamps: 30×3d.,
6×2d., 6×1½d., 6×1d., 6×½d. *Wmk* Crowns (Nos. 570/3 and 575).

X1	No date	£150
X2	OCT 1961	£300

1962–64. New Composition. Pages of six stamps: 30×3d., 6×2½d.,
6×1½d., 6×1d. (Nos. 571/2 and 574/5).

X3	APR 1962	£150
X4	AUG 1962	£200
X5	MAR 1963	£275
X6	JULY 1963	£180
X7	DEC 1963	£180
X8	JULY 1964	£140
X9	DEC 1964	£575

1965 (23 Aug)–**66**. Ochre cover as Type D. Pages of six stamps: 24×4d.,
6×3d., 6×1d. *Wmk* Crowns (Nos. 571, 575, 576a).

X10	AUG 1965	40·00
X11	DEC 1965	75·00
X12	FEB 1966	75·00
X13	AUG 1966	50·00
X14	NOV 1966	38·00

1967–68. Ochre cover as Type D. Pages of six phosphor stamps: 24×4d.,
6×3d., 6×1d. *Wmk* Crowns (Nos. 611, 615c (one side phosphor
band), 616a).

X15p	FEB 1967	12·00

Composition as No. X15p. *Wmk* Crowns (*Nos.* **611**, 615e (*one centre phosphor band), 616a*).

X16p	AUG 1967	8·00
X17p	FEB 1968	9·00

10s. Booklets with Machin type stamps

XP **4** Explorers Series with GPO Cypher

(Des S. Rose)

1968 (25 Mar–Aug). Bright purple cover as Type XP **4** (*Explorers Series*).
Pages of six stamps: 24×4d., 6×3d., 6×1d. PVA gum (Nos. 724,
729Ev, 731Ev).

XP4	MAY 1968 (Livingstone)	7·00
XP5	AUG 1968 (Livingstone)	7·00

1968 (16 Sept)–**70**. Yellow-green covers as Type XP **4** (*Explorers Series*)
New composition. Pages of six stamps: 12×5d. (with two phosphor
bands), 12×4d. (with one centre phosphor band) and pane comprising 4×1d. *se-tenant* with vert pair of 4d. (each with one centre
phosphor band). PVA gum (Nos. 725, 732 and 735).

XP6	SEPT 1968 (Scott)	5·00

Change to 4d. bright vermilion (one centre band) but se-tenant pane comprises 1d. with two phosphor bands and 4d. with one left side phosphor band (*Nos. 724 and 733/4*).

XP7	FEB 1969 (Mary Kingsley) (6.1.69)	3·50
XP8	MAY 1969 (Mary Kingsley)	5·00
XP9	AUG 1969 (Shackleton)	5·00
XP10	NOV 1969 (Shackleton)	8·00

XP **11** Explorers Series with Post Office Corporation
Crown Symbol

(Des S. Rose)

As last but cover changed to Type XP **11**.

XP11	FEB 1970 (Frobisher)	8·00
XP12	NOV 1970 (Captain Cook)	10·00

£1 Booklet with Machin type stamps

ZP **1**

1969 (1 Dec). *Stamps for Cooks* Type ZP **1** (150×72 mm) with full colour pictorial cover showing 'Baked, Stuffed Haddock'. Contains 12
recipes on interleaving pages and on *se-tenant* labels attached to
booklet panes. PVA gum. Stapled.

ZP1	£1 containing panes of fifteen stamps (5×3): 15×5d. (No. 735), 30×4d. (No. 733) and pane comprising 6×4d. (three each of Nos. 734 and 734Eb) *se-tenant* with 6×1d. (No. 724) and 3×5d. (No. 735)	£400
ZP1a	As last but booklet is sewn with thread instead of being stapled	13·00

II. Decimal Booklets, 1971 onwards.

A. Stitched Booklets.

The 25p., 30p., 35p., 45p. and 50p. booklets have pictorial covers
(except for the 35p. and 45p.) without the design inscription. This was
no longer necessary as the designs and background information were
given on the inside of the front cover. Each series was numbered.

10p. Booklets

DN **46** British Pillar Box Series
(Des R. Maddox)

1971 (15 Feb–1 June). *British Pillar Box Series*. Orange yellow cover as
Type DN **46**. Pages of four stamps: 2×2p. *se-tenant* vertically with
2×½p. and 2×1p. *se-tenant* vertically with 2×1½p. (Nos. X841I
and X844I).

DN46	FEB 1971 (No. 1 1855 type)	2·50
DN47	APR 1971 (No. 1 1855 type) (19.3.71)	2·00

DN48 JUNE 1971 (No. 2 1856 type) (1.6.71) .... 2·50
In No. DN47 the pillar box is slightly reduced in size.

1971 (14 July)–**74**. *British Pillar Box Series* continued. Orange-yellow cover as Type DN **46**. Contents unchanged but panes are *se-tenant* horizontally (Nos. X841la and X844m).

DN49 AUG 1971 (No. 2 1856 type) (14.7.71) .... 3·00
DN50 OCT 1971 (No. 3 1857–9 type) (27.8.71) .... 3·00
DN51 DEC 1971 (No. 3 1857–9 type) (6.10.71) .... 4·00
DN52 FEB 1972 (No. 4 1866–79 type) (8.12.71) .... 4·00
DN53 APR 1972 (No. 4 1866–79 type) (24.2.72) .... 2·75
DN54 JUNE 1972 (No. 5 1899 type) (12.4.72) .... 2·50
DN55 AUG 1972 (No. 5 1899 type) (8.6.72) .... 3·00
DN56 OCT 1972 (No. 6 1968 type) (2.8.72) .... 3·00
DN57 DEC 1972 (No. 6 1968 type) (30.10.72) .... 3·00
DN58 FEB 1973 (No. 7 1936 type) (5.1.73) .... 3·00
DN59 APR 1973 (No. 7 1936 type) (2.4.73) .... 5·00
DN60 JUNE 1973 (No. 8 1952 type) (18.4.73) .... 3·00
DN61 AUG 1973 (No. 8 1952 type) (4.7.73) .... 16·00
DN62 OCT 1973 (No. 9 1973 type) (16.8.73) .... 3·50
DN63 DEC 1973 (No. 9 1973 type) (12.11.73) .... 2·50
DN64 FEB 1974 (No. 9 1973 type) (17.12.73) .... 3·25
DN65 APR 1974 (No. 10 1974 type) (22.2.74) .... 2·50
DN66 JUNE 1974 (No. 10 1974 type) (23.4.74) .... 2·25

DN **67** Postal Uniforms Series

(Des C. Abbott)

1974 (23 July)–**76**. *Postal Uniforms Series*. Orange-yellow cover as Type DN **67**. Contents unchanged.

DN67 AUG 1974 (No. 1 1793 type) .... 1·80
DN68 OCT 1974 (No. 1 1793 type) (27.8.74) .... 1·80
DN69 DEC 1974 (No. 2 1837 type) (25.10.74) .... 1·80
DN70 FEB 1975 (No. 2 1837 type) (12.12.74) .... 1·80
DN71 APR 1975 (No. 3 1855 type) (26.3.75) .... 1·60
DN72 JUNE 1975 (No. 3 1855 type) (21.5.75) .... 1·75
DN73 AUG 1975 (No. 3 1855 type) (27.6.75) .... 1·75
DN74 OCT 1975 (No. 3 1855 type) (3.10.75) 90
DN75 JAN 1976 (No. 3 1855 type) (16.3.76) 90

25p. Booklets

DH **39** Veteran Transport Series

(Des D. Gentleman)

1971 (15 Feb). *Veteran Transport Series*. Dull purple cover as Type DH **39**. Pages of six stamps: 5×2½p. with one printed label, 4×2½p. with two printed labels, 5×½p. with one printed label (Nos. X841m and X851l/m).

DH39 FEB 1971 (No. 1 Knife-board omnibus) .... 3·50

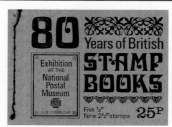

DH **40**

1971 (19 Mar). Issued to publicise the National Postal Museum Exhibition of *80 Years of British Stamp Booklets*. Dull purple cover as Type DH **40**.

DH40 APR 1971.. 5·00

1971 (11 June)–**73**. Dull purple cover as Type DH **39**. *Veteran Transport Series* continued.

DH41 JUNE 1971 (No. 2 B-type omnibus) .... 5·00
DH42 AUG 1971 (No. 2 B-type omnibus) (17.9.71) .... 11·50
DH43 OCT 1971 (No. 3 Showman's Engine) (22.11.71) .... 11·50
DH44 FEB 1972 (No. 4 Mail Van) (23.12.71) .... 7·25
DH45 APR 1972 (No. 4 Mail Van) (13.3.72) .... 8·75
DH46 JUNE 1972 (No. 5 Motor Wagonette) (24.4.72) .... 6·00
DH47 AUG 1972 (No. 5 Motor Wagonette) (14.6.72) .... 11·50
DH48 OCT 1972 (No. 6 Taxi Cab) (17.7.72) .... 9·00
DH49 DEC 1972 (No. 6 Taxi Cab) (19.10.72) .... 11·50
DH50 DEC 1972 "Issues S" (No. 6 Taxi Cab) (6.11.72)............. 7·25
DH51 FEB 1973 (No. 7 Electric Tramcar) (26.2.73) .... 9·00

Nos. DH42/51 contain panes showing the perforations omitted between the label and the binding margin.

DH **52**

1973 (7 June). Dull mauve cover as Type DH **52**.

DH52 JUNE 1973.. 9·00

No. DH52 contains panes showing the perforations omitted between the label and the binding margin.

30p. Booklets

DQ **56** British Birds Series

(Des H. Titcombe)

1971 (15 Feb). *British Birds Series*. Bright purple cover as Type DQ **56**. Pages of six stamps: 2 panes of 5×3p. with one printed label (No. X855l).

DQ56 FEB 1971 (No. 1 Curlew).. 4·50

1971 (19 Mar). Bright purple cover as Type DH **40**.

DQ57 APR 1971 .... 6·00

1971 (26 May)–**73**. Bright purple cover as Type DQ **56**. *British Birds Series* continued.

DQ58 JUNE 1971 (No. 2 Lapwing) .... 6·00
DQ59 AUG 1971 (No. 2 Lapwing) (23.7.71) .... 6·00
DQ60 OCT 1971 (No. 3 Robin) (1.10.71) .... 6·00
DQ61 DEC 1971 (No. 3 Robin) (10.11.71) .... 7·25
DQ62 FEB 1972 (No. 4 Pied Wagtail) (21.12.71)...................... 6·00
DQ63 APR 1972 (No. 4 Pied Wagtail) (9.2.72)......................... 6·00
DQ64 JUNE 1972 (No. 5 Kestrel) (12.4.72) .... 6·00
DQ65 AUG 1972 (No. 5 Kestrel) (8.6.72) .... 6·25
DQ66 OCT 1972 (No. 6 Black Grouse) (31.7.72) .... 6·75

DQ67   DEC 1972 (No. 6 Black Grouse) (30.10.72) ....   6·75
DQ68   DEC 1972 "Issue S" (No. 6 Black Grouse) (6.12.72) ....   6·75
DQ69   FEB 1973 (No. 7 Skylark) (29.1.73) ....   6·25
DQ70   APR 1973 (No. 7 Skylark) (2.4.73) ....   5·75
DQ71   JUNE 1973 (No. 8 Oyster-catcher) (8.5.73) ....   6·25
DQ72   AUG 1973 (No. 8 Oyster-catcher) (7.6.73) ....   9·50
DQ72*a*   As DQ72 but buff cover (10.8.73)* ....   7·00
    Nos. DQ59/72*a* contain panes showing the perforations omitted between the label and the binding margin.*No. DQ 72*a* was printed with a buff cover because of a shortage of the original purple-coloured card.

1974 (30 Jan). Red cover similar to Type DH **52**. Make-up as before but containing panes of 5×3p. (1 centre band) (No. X856) with blank label.
DQ73   SPRING 1974 ....   5·00

1974 (2 June). Red cover similar to Type DT **9**. Make-up as before.
DQ74   JUNE 1974 ....   5·00

35p. Booklets

DP **1** British Coins Series

(Des P Gauld)

1973 (12 Dec)–**74**. *British Coins Series*. Blue cover as Type DP **1**. Pages of six stamps: 2 pages of 5×3½p. with one blank label (No. X858Eb).
DP1   AUTUMN 1973 (No. 1 Cuthred's Penny) ....   3·50
DP2   APR 1974 (No. 1 Cuthred's Penny) (10.4.74) ....   6·50
DP3   JUNE 1974 (No. 2 Silver Groat) (4.7.74) ....   4·00

1974 (23 Oct). Blue cover as Type DT **9**. Make-up as before but with No. X859.
DP4   SEPT 1974 ....   4·00

45p. Booklets

1974 (9 Oct–26 Nov). *British Coins Series* continued. Yellow-brown cover as Type DP **1**. Pages of six stamps: 2 pages of 5×4½p. (No. X865) with one blank label.
DS1   SEPT 1974 (No. 3 Elizabeth Gold Crown) ....   6·00
DS2   DEC 1974 (No. 3 Elizabeth Gold Crown) (1.11.74) ....   6·00
DS2*a*   As DS2 but orange-brown cover (26.11.74)* ....   14·50
    *No. DS2*a* was printed with an orange-brown cover because of a shortage of the original yellow-brown card.

50p. Booklets

DT **1**

(Des Rosalie Southall)

1971 (15 Feb)–**72**. *British Flowers Series*. Turquoise-green cover as Type DT **1**. Pages of six stamps: 6×3p., 4×3p. se-tenant horizontally with 2×2½p. (side band), 5×2½p. (centre band) with one printed label and 5×½p. with one printed label (Nos. X841m, X851l, X852l and X855×6).
DT1   FEB 1971 (No. 1 Large Bindweed) ....   9·00
DT2   MAY 1971 (No. 2 Primrose) (24.3.71) ....   10·00
DT3   AUG 1971 (No. 3 Honeysuckle) (28.6.71) ....   10·00
DT4   NOV 1971 (No. 4 Hop) (17.9.71) ....   11·00
DT5   FEB 1972 (No. 5 Common Violet) (23.12.71)* ....   11·00
DT6   MAY 1972 (No. 6 Lords-and-Ladies) (13.3.72) ....   11·00
DT7   AUG 1972 (No. 7 Wood Anemone) (31.5.72) ....   11·00
DT8   NOV 1972 (No. 8 Deadly Nightshade) (15.9.72) ....   9·00

    Nos. DT4/8 contain panes showing the perforations omitted between the label and the binding margin.
    *Although generally released on 24 December, this booklet was put on sale at the London E.C.1 Philatelic Counter and also at one other Philatelic Counter on 23 December.

DT **9**

1973 (19 Jan–June). Turquoise-green cover as Type DT **9**.
DT9   FEB 1973 ....   9·00
DT10   APR 1973 (26.2.73) ....   12·00
DT11   MAY 1973 (2.4.73) ....   11·50
DT12   AUG 1973 (14.6.73) ....   17·00

1973 (14 Nov)–**74**. Moss-green cover similar to Type DT **9**. Pages of six stamps: 2 pages of 5×3½p. with one blank label (No. X858Eb) and 1 page of 5×3p. (centre band) and one blank label (No. X856).
DT13   AUTUMN 1973 ....   8·00
DT14   MAR 1974 (18.2.74) ....   6·00

85p. Booklet

1974 (13 Nov). Purple cover similar to Type DT **9**.
DW1   Containing 3 pages of 5×4½p. (No. X865) with one blank label and 1 page of 5×3½p. (No. X859) with one blank label ....   9·00

Sponsored and "Prestige" Booklets

DX **1**

(Des J. Wallis)

1972 (24 May). *The Story of Wedgwood*. Full colour pictorial cover, Type DX **1** (150×72 mm). Containing information and illustrations on interleaving panes and on *se-tenant* label attached to booklet panes.
DX1   £1 containing Nos. X841o/p, X851n and X855n booklet panes ....   75·00
    Price quoted for No. DX1 is for examples showing the ½p. 1 side band, No. X842, (in pane No. X841p) with full perforations. Examples of the booklet with this ½p. value showing trimmed perforations are priced at £25.

ILLUSTRATIONS. Sponsored and "Prestige" booklet covers from No. DX2 are illustrated at one-third linear size *unless otherwise stated*.

DX **2**

(Des J. Wallis)

1980 (16 Apr). *The Story of Wedgwood*. Multicoloured cover, Type DX **2** (163×97 mm) showing painting *'Josiah Wedgwood and his Family'* by George Stubbs. Booklet contains text and illustrations on the labels attached to panes and on interleaving pages.
DX2   £3 containing booklet panes Nos. X849n, X849o, X888l and X895l ....   8·00
    No. DX2 is inscribed "January 1980".

DX **3**

(Des B. Dedman)

1982 (19 May). *Story of Stanley Gibbons*. Multicoloured cover, Type DX **3** (163×97 mm) showing early envelope design on front and stamp album with text on back. Booklet contains text and illustrations on labels attached to panes and on interleaving pages.

DX3   £4 containing booklet panes Nos. X849p, X899m and X907l/m .... 11·00

No. DX3 is inscribed "February 1982".

DX **4**

(Des B. West)

1983 (14 Sept). *Story of the Royal Mint*. Multicoloured cover, Type DX **4** (163×97 mm) showing current coins, die and tools. Booklet contains text and illustrations on labels attached to panes and on interleaving pages.

DX4   £4 containing booklet panes Nos. X899m×2, X930b and X949l .... 11·00

DX **5**

(Des P. Miles)

1984 (4 Sept). *The Story of our Christian Heritage* Multicoloured cover, Type DX **5** (163×97 mm) showing mosaic of Christ from Hinton St. Mary Roman villa. Booklet contains text and illustrations on labels attached to panes and on interleaving pages.

DX5   £4 containing booklet panes Nos. X886bl, X901m×2 and X952l .... 25·00

DX **6**

(Des D. Driver)

1985 (8 Jan). *Story of The Times (newspaper)*. Multicoloured cover, Type DX **6** (163×95 mm) showing Waiting for *The Times* (painting by Haydon). Booklet contains text and illustrations on labels attached to panes and on interleaving pages.

DX6   £5 containing booklet panes Nos. X864l, X900l, X952l and X952m .... 20·00

DX **7**

(Des Trickett and Webb Ltd)

1986 (18 Mar). *The Story of British Rail* Multicoloured cover, Type DX **7** (162×95 mm) showing diesel locomotive. Booklet contains text and illustrations on labels attached to panes and on interleaving pages.

DX7   £5 containing booklet panes Nos. X896l, X897m, X952l and X952m .... 25·00

DX **8**

(Des Aitken Blakeley Designers)

1987 (3 Mar). *The Story of P & O* Multicoloured cover, Type DX **8** (162×95 mm) showing the '*William Fawcett*'. Booklet contains text and illustrations on labels attached to panes and on interleaving pages.

DX8   £5 containing booklet panes Nos. X847m, X900l, X900m and X955l .... 25·00

DX **9**

(Des The Partners)

1988 (9 Feb). *The Story of the Financial Times (newspaper)*. Multicoloured cover, Type DX **9** (162×97 mm). Booklet contains text and illustrations on labels attached to the panes and on interleaving pages.

DX9   £5 containing booklet panes Nos. X1005l, X1006l, X1009l and X1009m .... 32·00

DX **10**

(Des Tayburn)

1989 (21 Mar). *The Scots Connection*. Multicoloured cover, Type DX **10** (162×97 mm). Booklet contains text and illustrations on labels attached to the panes and on interleaving pages.

DX10 £5 containing booklet panes Nos. S54l, S55l, S62l and S62m .... 22·00

DX **11**

(Des D. Driver)

1990 (20 Mar). *London Life*. Multicoloured cover, Type DX **11** (162×97 mm). Booklet contains text and illustrations on labels attached to the panes and on interleaving pages.

DX11   £5 containing booklet panes Nos. X906m, 1469n×2 and 1493a .... 28·00

DX **12**

(Des Trickett and Webb Ltd)

1991 (19 Mar). *Alias Agatha Christie*. Multicoloured cover, Type DX **12** (162×97 mm). Booklet contains text and illustrations on labels attached to the panes and on interleaving pages.

DX12   £6 containing booklet panes Nos. X1008l×2, X1016l and X1016m .... 20·00

DX **13**

(Des G. Evernden and J. Gibbs)

1992 (25 Feb). *Cymru–Wales*. Multicoloured cover, Type DX **13** (162×97 mm). Booklet contains text and illustrations on labels attached to the panes and on interleaving pages.

DX13   £6 Containing booklet panes Nos. 1591a, W48a, W49a and W59a.. 20·00

DX **14**

(Des The Partners)

1992 (27 Oct). *Birth Centenary of J. R. R. Tolkien* (author). Multicoloured cover, Type DX **14** (162×97 mm). Booklet contains text and illustrations on labels attached to the panes and on interleaving pages.

DX14   £6 containing booklet panes Nos. X1011/2l and X1017l×2 .... 20·00

DX **15**

(Des The Partners)

1993 (10 Aug). *The Story of Beatrix Potter*. Multicoloured cover, Type DX **15** (162×97 mm). Booklet contains text and illustrations on labels attached to the panes and on interleaving pages.

DX15   £5.64, containing booklet panes Nos. X1012m, 1451al, 1649a and NI48l .... 22·00

Although inscribed "£6·00" No. DX 15 was sold at the face value of its contents, £5·64

DX **16**

(Des Carroll, Dempsey and Thirkell Ltd)

1994 (26 July). *Northern Ireland*. Multicoloured cover, Type DX **16** (162×97 mm). Booklet contains text and illustrations on labels attached to the panes and on interleaving pages.

DX16   £6·04, containing booklet panes Nos. Y1766l, 1812a and NI70a/b, together with a 35p. postal stationery air card . 25·00

DX **17**

(Des The Partners)

1995 (25 Apr). *Centenary of the National Trust*. Multicoloured cover, Type DX **17** (162×97 mm). Booklet contains text and illustrations on labels attached to the panes and on interleaving pages.

DX17   £6 containing booklet panes Nos. Y1767l, Y1771l, 1869a and NI70d .... 25·00

DX **18**

(Des Why Not Associates)

1996 (14 May). *European Football Championship* Multicoloured cover, Type DX **18** (162×97 mm). Booklet contains text and illustrations on labels attached to the panes and on interleaving pages.

DX18   £6·48, containing booklet panes Nos. Y1775l, 1925a, 1926a and 1927a .... 20·00

DX **19**

(Des H. Brown)

1997 (23 Sept). *75th Anniv of the B.B.C.* Multicoloured cover, Type DX **19** (162×97 mm). Booklet contains text and illustrations on labels attached to the panes and on interleaving pages.
DX19 £6·15, containing booklet panes Nos. Y1686l, 1940ab, 1668l and NI81al .... 22·00

DX **20**

(Des Dew Gibbons Design Group)

1998 (10 Mar). *The Wilding Definitives.* Black and gold cover, Type DX **20** (162×96 mm). Booklet contains text and illustrations on labels attached to the panes and on interleaving pages.
DX20 £7·49, containing booklet panes Nos. 2031b/c and 2032a/b. .... 26·00
Folder containing DX20, DX22, DX24 *and* **MS**2147 *cancelled on presentation card*.................................... £150

DX **21**

(Des Roundel Design Group)

1998 (13 Oct). *Breaking Barriers.* British Speed Record Holders. Multicoloured cover, Type DX **21** (161×96 mm). Booklet contains text and illustrations on labels attached to the panes and on interleaving pages.
DX21 £6·16, containing booklet panes Nos. 1665l, Y1676al, 2059ac and NI80al .... 35·00

(Des Dew Gibbons Design Group)

1999 (16 Feb). *Profile on Print.* Multicoloured cover as Type DX **20** (162×96 mm). Booklet contains text and illustrations on labels attached to the panes and on interleaving pages.
DX22 £7·54, containing booklet panes Nos. 1667l, 1671n and 2077l/9l .... 45·00

DX **23**

(Des Silk Pearce)

1999 (21 Sept). *World Changers.* Multicoloured cover as Type DX **23** (163×96 mm). Booklet contains text and illustrations on labels attached to the panes and on interleaving pages.

DX23 £6·99, containing booklet panes Nos. Y1667n, 2072ab, 2080a, 2103ba and 2104ab .... 30·00
(Des Dew Gibbons Design Group)

2000 (15 Feb). *Special by Design.* Multicoloured cover as Type DX **20** (162×96 mm). Booklet contains text and illustrations on labels attached to the panes and on interleaving pages.
DX24 £7·50, containing booklet panes Nos. Y1683l, 2124dl, 2133l and NI88al .... 42·00

DX **25**

(Des J. Gibbs)

2000 (4 Aug). *Queen Elizabeth the Queen Mother's 100th Birthday.* Brownish grey and grey cover as Type DX **25** (162×96 mm). Booklet contains text and illustrations on labels attached to the panes and on interleaving pages.
DX25 £7·03, containing booklet panes Nos. 2124bm, 2160a, **MS**2161a and S94a .... 31·00

DX **26**

(Des Roundel Design Group)

2000 (18 Sept). *A Treasury of Trees.* Slate-green and bright green cover as Type DX **26** (162×95 mm). Booklet contains text and illustrations on panes and interleaving pages.
DX26 £7 containing booklet panes Nos. 2155a, 2156a, 2158a, 2159a and W83al .... 35·00

DX **27**

(Des D. Davis)

2001 (22 Oct). *Unseen and Unheard.* Centenary of Royal Navy Submarine Service. Black, greenish yellow, new blue and red cover as Type DX **27** (162×97 mm). Booklet contains text and illustrations on labels attached to the panes and on interleaving pages.
DX27 £6·76, containing booklet panes Nos. 2202ab, 2203ab, **MS**2206a and S95a .... 40·00

DX **28**
(Des GBH)

2002 (6 Feb). *A Gracious Accession.* Golden Jubilee of Queen Elizabeth II. Multicoloured cover as Type DX **28** (161×96 mm). Booklet contains text and illustrations on labels attached to the panes and interleaving pages.

DX28 £7·29, containing booklet panes Nos. 1664n, 2253b/4b
and 2258b .... 45·00

DX **29**

(Des CDT Design)

2002 (24 Sept). *Across the Universe*. Multicoloured cover as Type
DX **29** (164×95 mm). Booklet contains text and illustrations on la-
bels attached to the panes and interleaving pages. Stitched.
DX29 £6·83, containing booklet panes Nos. 1668m, 2126ac,
MS2315a and EN1b .... 34·00

DX **30**

(Des CDT Design)

2003 (25 Feb). *Microcosmos*. 50th Anniv of Discovery of DNA. Multicoloured cover as Type DX **30** (164×95 mm). Booklet contains text
and illustrations on labels attached to the panes and interleaving
pages. Stitched.
DX30 £6·99, containing booklet panes Nos. 1668m, 2343a,
2345a and NI89a .... 38·00

DX **31**

(Des GBH)

2003 (2 June). *A Perfect Coronation*. 50th Anniv of Coronation. Multicoloured cover as Type DX **31** (161×96 mm). Booklet contains
text and illustrations on labels attached to the panes and on interleaving pages.
DX31 £7·46, containing booklet panes Nos. 1664o, 2368b/9b
and 2378a .... 70·00

DX **32**

(Des Kate Stephens)

2004 (16 Mar). *Letters by Night A Tribute to the Travelling Post Office*. Multicoloured cover as Type DX **32** (164×95 mm). Booklet contains text
and illustrations on labels attached to the panes and interleaving
pages. Stitched.
DX32 £7·44, containing booklet panes Nos. 1668o, 2392a,
2418a and S109l .... 30·00

DX **33**

(Des John and Orna Designs)

2004 (25 May). *The Glory of the Garden*. Bicentenary of the Royal Horticultural Society. Multicoloured cover as Type DX **33** (162×96 mm).
Booklet contains text and illustrations on labels attached to the
panes and interleaving pages. Stitched.
DX33 £7·23, containing booklet panes Nos. 1668p, 2456a,
2457a and 2463a .... 40·00

DX **34**

(Des Morgan Radcliffe)

2005 (24 Feb). *The Brontë Sisters*. 150th Death Anniv of Charlotte Brontë.
Multicoloured cover as Type DX **34** (162×96 mm). Booklet contains
text and illustrations on panes and interleaving pages. Stitched.
DX34 £7·43, containing booklet panes Nos. 1664p, EN6l, 2518a
and 2520a .... 28·00

DX **35** White Ensign

(Des Webb & Webb)

2005 (18 Oct). *Bicentenary of the Battle of Trafalgar*. Black, scarlet and
ultramarine cover as Type DX **35** (162×96 mm). Booklet contains
text and illustrations on labels attached to the panes and interleaving pages. Stitched.
DX35 £7·26 containing booklet panes Nos. 1668q, 2574b/5b
and 2581a .... 28·00

DX **36** Plaque showing Clifton Suspension Bridge

(Des Hat-trick Design)

2006 (23 Feb). *Birth Bicentenary of Isambard Kingdom Brunel*. Grey and
grey-black cover as Type DX **36** (162×96 mm). Booklet contains
text and illustrations on panes and interleaving pages. Stitched.
DX36 £7·40 containing booklet panes Nos. 1668r, 2607a/8a
and 2610a .... 26·00

DX **37**

(Des Atelier Works)

2006 (21 Sept). *150th Anniv of the Victoria Cross.* Blackish-brown and gold cover as Type DX **37** (162×96 mm). Booklet contains text and illustrations on panes and interleaving pages. Stitched.
DX37   £7·44 containing booklet panes Nos. 2651a, 2659b, 2660b and 2666a .... 35·00

DX **38**

(Des R. Warren-Fisher)

2007 (1 Mar). *World of Invention.* Black, olive-grey and grey cover as Type DX **38** (162×95 mm). Booklet contains text and illustrations on panes and interleaving pages. Stitched.
DX38   £7·49 containing booklet panes Nos. S109m, Y1670l and 2721a/b .... 24·00

DX **39**

(Des R. Warren-Fisher)

2007 (5 June). *The Machin The Making of a Masterpiece* Multicoloured cover as Type DX **39** (165×96 mm). Booklet contains text and illustrations on panes and interleaving pages. Stitched.
DX39   £7·66 containing booklet panes Nos. Y1668l, Y1744l, 2650a and 2741a.. 24·00

DX **40** Soldiers of 1854

(Des Atelier Works)

2007 (20 Sept). *British Army Uniforms.* Multicoloured cover as Type DX **40** (164×96 mm). Booklet contains text and illustrations on panes and interleaving pages. Stitched.
DX40   £7·66 containing booklet panes Nos. Y1667o, 2774b, 2777b and EN30l.. 26·00

DX **41** Typewriter and Casino Royale

(Des GBH)

2008 (8 Jan). *Ian Fleming's James Bond.* Multicoloured cover as Type DX **41** (164×96 mm). Booklet contains text and illustrations on panes and interleaving pages. Stitched.
DX41   £7·40 containing booklet panes Nos. 1672l, 2797a/8a and 2805a... 30·00

DX **42** RAF Badge

(Des Silk Pearce)

2008 (18 Sept). *Pilot to Plane.* RAF Uniforms. Black on light blue cover as Type DX **42** (162×96 mm). Booklet contains text and illustrations on panes and interleaving pages. Stitched.
DX42   £7·15 containing booklet panes Nos. 1670l, 2862b, 2865b and 2868a.. 25·00

DX **43** Symbols of Northern Ireland, Scotland and Wales

(Des Sedley Place)

2008 (29 Sept). *50th Anniv of the Country Definitives.* Multicoloured cover as Type DX **43** (162×96 mm). Booklet contains text and illustrations on panes and interleaving pages. Stitched.

DX43 £9·72 containing booklet panes Nos. NI154l/m, S154l and W144l.. 32·00

DX **44** Graphic Drawings of Spitfire, Anglepoise Lamp and Routemaster Bus

(Des HGV)

2009 (13 Jan). *British Design Classics.* Multicoloured cover as Type DX **44** (162×96 mm). Booklet contains text and illustrations on panes and interleaving pages. Stitched.

DX44 £7·68 containing booklet panes Nos. Y1769l, 2887b, 2888a and 2891a .... 38·00

DX **45** Charles Darwin

(Des Howard Brown)

2009 (12 Feb). *Birth Bicentenary of Charles Darwin.* Multicoloured cover as Type DX **45** (162×96 mm). Booklet contains text and illustrations on panes and interleaving pages. Stitched.

DX45 £7·75 containing booklet panes Nos. Y1762l, **MS**2904a, 2905a and 2906a .... 50·00

DX **46** Proof Sheet of Penny Black Stamps

(Des Silk Pearce)

2009 (18 Aug). *Treasures of the Archive.* Clear cover showing illustrated pane as Type DX **46** (162×96 mm). Booklet contains text and illustrations on panes and interleaving pages. Stitched.

DX46 £8·18 containing booklet panes Nos. Y1770l, 2950a, 2955a and 2957a .... 18·00

DX **47** Officers, Marines and Seamen on Deck

(Des Webb and Webb Design Ltd)

2009 (17 Sept). *Royal Navy Uniforms.* Multicoloured cover as Type DX **47** (163×96 mm). Booklet contains text and illustrations on panes and interleaving pages. Stitched.

DX47 £7·93 containing booklet panes Nos. Y1761l, 2964b, 2967b and 2970a .... 20·00

DX **48** Vinyl Disc

(Des True North)

2010 (7 Jan). *Classic Album Covers.* Black and pale blue cover as Type DX **48** (162×96 mm). Booklet contains text and illustrations on panes and interleaving pages. Stitched.

DX48 £8·06 containing booklet panes Nos. Y1765l, Y1773l, 3009a and 3015a .... 35·00

DX **49** Diagram and Signatures

(Des Russell Warren-Fisher)

2010 (25 Feb). *350th Anniv of the Royal Society.* Multicoloured cover as Type DX **49** (162×96 mm). Booklet contains text and illustrations on panes and interleaving pages. Stitched.

DX49 £7·72 containing booklet panes Nos. Y1774l, 3026b, 3027a and 3029a .... 20·00

DX **50**

(Des Silk Pearce)

2010 (8 May). *Centenary of Accession of King George V.* Deep carmine and cream cover, 162×97 mm, as Type DX **50**. Booklet contains text and illustrations on panes and interleaving pages. Stitched.

DX50 £11·15 containing booklet panes Nos. U2917a, 3066a/7a and 3070a .... 25·00

DX **51**

(Des Why Not Associates)

2010 (13 May). *Britain Alone* Grey, black and stone cover, 163×96 mm, as Type DX **51**. Booklet contains text and illustrations on panes and interleaving pages. Stitched.

DX51   £9·76 containing booklet panes Nos. Y1763l, 3074a,
3076a and 3082a .... 22·00

DX **52** Wildlife

(Des Russell Warren-Fisher)

2011 (22 Mar). *50th Anniversary of the WWF.* Multicoloured cover, 162×96 mm, as Type DX **52**. Booklet contains text and illustrations on panes and interleaving pages. Stitched.

DX52   £9·05 containing booklet panes Nos. Y1764l, 3162b,
3164b and **MS**3172a.. 21·00

PREMIUM BOOKLETS: From the issue of the 'Morris and Co' booklet, Royal Mail introduced an additional cost, over and above the face value of the stamps contained within them. They are separately numbered in a new series, commencing DY1.

DY **1** "Flora" (wallpaper pattern by William Morris), 1891

(Des Kate Stephens)

2011 (5 May). *150th Anniversary of Morris and Company* (designers and manufacturers of textiles, wallpaper and furniture). Multicoloured cover as Type DY **1** (162×96 mm). Booklet contains text and illustrations on panes and interleaving pages. Stitched.

DY1   £9·99 containing booklet panes Nos. U2993a,
3181a/2a and 3186ab................................. 23·00
The contents of No. DY1 have a face value of £9·04.

DY **2** Poster for First UK Aerial Mail, Hendon Aerodrome, 1911

(Des Robert Maude and Sarah Davies)

2011 (9 Sept). *Centenary of the First United Kingdom Aerial Post.* Black and grey cover as Type DY **2** (161×96 mm). Booklet contains text and illustrations on panes and interleaving pages. Stitched.

DY2   £9·97 containing booklet panes Nos. Y1763m, 3216a,
3217a and 3221a................................. 45·00
The contents of No. DY2 have a face value of £9·02.

DY **3** Bookshelf

(Des Magpie Studio)

2012 (10 Jan). *Roald Dahl's Children's Stories.* Multicoloured cover as Type DY **3** (163×96 mm). Booklet contains text and illustrations on panes and interleaving pages. Stitched.

DY3   £11·47 containing booklet panes Nos. Y1668m, 3254a,
3255a and 3260a................................. 26·00
The contents of No. DY3 have a face value of £10·52.

DY **4**

(Des Russell Warren-Fisher)

2012 (31 May). *Diamond Jubilee.* Ultramarine, black and silver cover as Type DY **4** (162×96 mm). Booklet contains text and illustrations on panes and interleaving pages. Stitched.

DY4 £12·77 containing booklet panes Nos. B3319b, B3320b,
B3322b and 3328a................................. 28·00
The contents of No. DY4 have a face value of £11·84.

DY **5**

(Des True North)

2012 (27 July). *Olympic and Paralympic Games, London.* 'Keeping the Flame Alive'. Multicoloured cover, 162×96 mm, as Type DY **5**. Booklet contains text and illustrations on panes and interleaving pages. Stitched.

DY5 £10·71 booklet containing panes Nos. 2982b, 2983b,
2984b and 3337a................................. 50·00
The contents of No. DY5 have a face value of £9·76.

DY **6**

(Des GBH)

2013 (26 Mar). *50th Anniversary of Doctor Who* (TV programme). Multicoloured cover, 163×96 mm, as Type DY **6**. Booklet contains text and illustrations on panes and interleaving pages. Stitched.

DY6 £13·77 containing booklet panes Nos. U3012a, 3437b, 3440b, 3444b and **MS**3451a... 30·00

The contents of No. DY6 have a face value of £12·82.

DY **7** Gordon Banks, John Barnes, Bobby Moore, Kevin Keegan and George Best

(Des True North)

2013 (9 May). *Football Heroes.* Multicoloured cover as Type DY **7** (163×96 mm). Booklet contains text and illustrations on panes and interleaving pages. Stitched.

DY7 £11·11 containing booklet panes Nos. U3010a/11a, 3479a and 3484a... 35·00

No. DY7 was issued in a souvenir foil wrapper.

The contents of No. DY7 have a face value of £10·56.

DY 8 Merchant Ensign

(Des Russell Warren-Fisher)

2013 (19 Sept). *Merchant Navy.* Multicoloured cover, as Type DY 8 (163×96 mm),. Booklet contains text and illustrations on panes and interleaving pages. Stitched.

DY8 £11·19 booklet containing panes Nos. U3012d, 3519a, 3522a and 3525a... 24·00

The contents of No. DY8 have a face value of £10·24.

DY 9 Southern Railway Class M7 No. 53 on the Great Central Railway, 2012

(Des Delaney Design Consultants)

2014 (20 Feb). *Classic Locomotives of the United Kingdom* Black, grey and gold cover, 163×96 mm, as Type DY **9**. Booklet contains text and illustrations on panes and interleaving pages. Stitched.

DY9 £13·97 containing booklet panes Nos. U3011b, 3570a, 3571a, 3572a and 3573a.. 32·00

The contents of No. DY9 have a face value of £13·02.

DY **10**

(Des So Design Consultants)

2014 (15 Apr). *Buckingham Palace, London* Multicoloured cover as Type DY **10** (162×96 mm). Booklet contains text and illustrations on panes and interleaving pages. Stitched.

DY10 £11·39 containing booklet panes Nos. U3013a, 3589ba, 3591ba and 3597a.. 29·00

The contents of No. DY10 have a face value of £10·44.

DY **11**

(Des Hat-trick Design)

2014 (28 Jul). *Centenary of the First World War* Multicoloured cover, 163×96 mm, as Type DY **11**. Booklet contains text and illustrations on panes and interleaving pages. Stitched.

DY11 £11·30 booklet containing panes Nos. U3013b, U3021a, 3626a and 3629a .... 26·00

The contents of No. DY11 have a face value of £10·35

DY **12**

(Des Supple Studio)

2015 (19 Feb). *Inventive Britain* Black and silver cover, 162×96 mm, as Type DY **12**. Booklet contains text and illustrations on panes and interleaving pages. Stitched.

DY12 £14·60 containing booklet panes Nos. U3010b, 3679b/c and 3681b.. 33·00

The contents of No. DY12 have a face value of £13·67.

DY **13** 11th Battalion, 3rd Brigade, Australian Imperial Force on Great Pyramid of Khufu, 1915 and Worker at National Shell Filling Factory, Chilwell, Nottinghamshire

(Des hat-trick design)

2015 (14 May). *Centenary of the First World War* (2nd issue). Multi-coloured cover, 162×96 mm, as Type DY **13**. Booklet contains text and illustrations on panes and interleaving pages. Stitched.

DY13   £13·96   booklet containing panes Nos. 2776b, U3010c,
    3711a and 3714a.. 30·00

The contents of No. DY13 have a face value of £11·68.

DY **14** Arthur Wellesley, First Duke of Wellington, the Emperor Napoleon and Battle of Waterloo

(Des Webb & Webb Design Ltd)

2015 (18 June). *Bicentenary of the Battle of Waterloo.* Multicoloured cover as Type DY **14** (161×96 mm). Booklet contains text and illustrations on panes and interleaving pages. Stitched.

DY14   £14·47   containing booklet panes Nos. U3012b, 3724a/5a
    and 3730a.. 32·00

The contents of No. DY14 have a face value of £13·52.

DY **15** Starfighters

(Des Interabang)

2015 (17 Dec). *The Making of Star Wars The British Story.* Multicoloured cover as Type DY **15** (163×95 mm). Booklet contains text and illustrations on panes and interleaving pages. Stitched.

DY15   £16·99   containing booklet panes Nos. U3014ab, 3758b,
    3759b, 3780a and 3783a.. 35·00

The contents of No. DY15 have a face value of £16·20.

No. DY15 was issued to coincide with the UK release of Star Wars: The Force Awakens.

DY **16** Cancelled Penny Red

(Des Atelier Works)

2016 (18 Feb). *500 Years of Royal Mail.* Multicoloured cover, 163×96 mm, as Type DY **16**. Booklet contains text and illustrations on panes and interleaving pages. Stitched.

DY16   £16·36   containing booklet panes Nos. 3795a, 3796a,
    3802a and 3807a.. 34·00

The contents of No. DY16 have a face value of £15·41.

B. Folded Booklets.

NOTE: All panes are attached to the covers by the selvedge. Inscribed dates are those shown with the printer's imprint.

Illustrations for 10p., 50p., £1 and £2 booklets are ¾ size; others are ²⁄₃ size.

10p. Booklets

FA **1**

1976 (10 Mar)–**77**. Cover as Type FA **1** printed in dull rose on very pale lavender. Containing booklet pane No. X841r.

FA1   NOV 1975 .... 1·10
FA2   MAR 1976 (9.6.76).. 1·20
FA3   JUNE 1977 (13.6.77) 80

FA **4**

(Des N. Battershill)

1978 (8 Feb)–**79**. *Farm Buildings Series.* Bistre-brown and turquoise-blue covers as Type FA **4**, containing booklet pane No. X843m.

FA4   Design No. 1, Oast Houses 70
FA5   Design No. 2, Buildings in Ulster (3.5.78) 80
FA6   Design No. 3, Buildings in Yorkshire (9.8.78) 70
FA7   Design No. 4, Buildings in Wales (25.10.78) 70
FA8   Design No. 5, Buildings in Scotland (10.1.79) 70
FA9   Design No. 6, Buildings in Sussex (4.4.79) 70

Nos. FA4/5 are inscribed "January 1978", FA6 "July 1978", FA7 "October 1978", FA8 "December 1978" and FA9 "March 1979".

FA **10**

(Des Hamper and Purssell)

1979 (17 Oct)–**80**. *London 1980 International Stamp Exhibition.* Red and blue cover as Type FA **10** showing Post Office exhibition stand and containing No. X845l.

FA10   Inscr "August 1979".. 60
FA11   Inscr "January 1980" (12.1.80) 70

50p. Booklets

All booklets were sold at the cover price of 50p. although some contain stamps to a greater value.

FB **1**

1977 (26 Jan). Cover as Type FB **1** printed in maroon and pale blue.

FB1A   Containing booklet pane X841s .... 3·00

FB1B   Containing booklet pane X841sa .... 3·00
1977 (13 June). Cover as Type FB **1**. Printed in chestnut and stone.
FB2A   Containing booklet pane X844n .... 5·00
FB2B   Containing booklet pane X844na .... 3·00

FB 3

(Des J. Ireland)

1978 (8 Feb)–**79**. *Commercial Vehicles Series*. Olive-yellow and grey covers as Type FB **3**. A. Containing booklet pane No. X844n. B. Containing booklet pane No. X844na.

		A	B
FB3	Design No. 1, Clement Talbot van	5·00	3·25
FB4	Design No. 2, Austin taxi (3.5.78)	5·00	3·00
FB5	Design No. 3, Morris Royal Mail van (9.8.78)	5·00	3·00
FB6	Design No. 4, Guy Electric dustcart (25.10.78)	7·50	3·25
FB7	Design No. 5, Albion van (10.1.79)	8·00	7·50
FB8	Design No. 6, Leyland fire engine (4.4.79)	5·50	3·50

Nos. FB3/4 are inscribed "January 1978", FB5 "July 1978", FB6 "October 1978", FB7 "December 1978" and FB8 "March 1979".

1979 (28 Aug). Contents changed. A. Containing booklet pane No. X849l. B. Containing booklet pane No. X849la.

		A	B
FB9	Design No. 6, Leyland fire engine	5·00	5·00

FB 10

(Des B. Smith)

1979 (3 Oct)–**81**. *Veteran Cars Series*. Orange-red and reddish lilac covers as Type FB **10**. A. Containing booklet pane No. X849l. B. Containing booklet pane No. X849la.

		A	B
FB10	Design No. 1, 1907 Rolls-Royce Silver Ghost	5·00	5·00

No. FB10 is inscribed "August 1979".

Contents changed. A. Containing booklet pane No. X849m. B. Containing booklet pane No. X849ma.

		A	B
FB11	Design No. 2, 1908 Grand Prix Austin (4.2.80)	5·00	5·00
FB12	Design No. 3, 1903–5 Vauxhall (25.6.80)	5·00	5·00
FB13	Design No. 4, 1897–1900 Daimler (24.9.80)	5·00	5·00

No. FB11 is inscribed "January 1980", No. FB 12 "May 1980" and No. FB 13 "July 1980".

Contents changed. A. Containing No. X841t. B. Containing No. X841ta.

		A	B
FB14	Design No. 5, 1896 Lanchester (26.1.81)	3·50	4·00
FB15	Design No. 6, 1913 Bull-nose Morris (18.3.81)	4·00	4·00

Nos. FB14/15 are inscribed "January 1981".

FB 16

(Des R. Downer)

1981 (6 May)–**82**. *Follies Series*. Brown and orange-brown covers as Type FB **16**. A. Containing No. X841t. B. Containing No. X841ta.

		A	B
FB16	Design No. 1, Mugdock Castle, Stirlingshire	3·75	3·75

No. FB16 is inscribed "January 1981".

Contents changed. A. Containing No. X854l. B. Containing No. X854la.

		A	B
FB17	Design No. 1, Mugdock Castle, Stirlingshire (26.8.81)	8·00	14·00
FB18	Design No. 2, Mow Cop Castle, Cheshire–Staffs border (30.9.81)	8·00	10·00

Nos. FB17/18 are inscribed "January 1981".

Contents changed. A. Containing No. X841u. B. Containing No. X841ua.

		A	B
FB19	Design No. 3, Paxton's Tower, Llanarthney, Dyfed (1.2.82)	3·00	3·00
FB20	Design No. 4, Temple of the Winds, Mount Stewart, Northern Ireland (6.5.82)	3·00	3·00
FB21	Design No. 5, Temple of the Sun, Stourhead, Wilts (11.8.82)	3·00	3·00
FB22	Design No. 6, Water Garden, Cliveden, Bucks (6.10.82)	3·00	3·00

Nos. FB19/22 are inscribed "February 1982".

FB 23

(Des H. Titcombe)

1983 (16 Feb–26 Oct). *Rare Farm Animals Series*. Bright green and black covers as Type FB **23**. A. Containing booklet pane No. X841u. B. Containing booklet pane No. X841ua.

		A	B
FB23	Design No. 1, Bagot Goat	3·50	3·50

Contents changed. Containing No. X845n.

FB24	Design No. 2, Gloucester Old Spot Pig (5.4.83)	7·00
	b. Corrected rate	20·00
FB25	Design No. 3, Toulouse Goose (27.7.83)	7·50
FB26	Design No. 4, Orkney Sheep (26.10.83)	7·50

No. FB23 is inscribed "February 1982" and Nos. FB24/6 "April 1983". The corrected rate reads, "36p. for 200g" instead of "37p. for 200g".

FB 27

(Des P. Morter)

1984 (3 Sept)–**85**. *Orchids Series*. Yellow-green and lilac covers as Type FB **27**. Containing booklet pane No. X845p.

FB27	Design No. 1, *Dendrobium nobile* and *Miltonia* hybrid.......	4·50
FB28	Design No. 2, *Cypripedium calceolus* and *Ophrys apifera* (15.1.85)	4·50
FB29	Design No. 3, *Bifrenaria* and *Vanda* tricolor (23.4.85)	4·50
FB30	Design No. 4, *Cymbidium* and *Arpophyllum* (23.7.85)	4·50

Nos. FB27/30 are inscribed "September 1984".

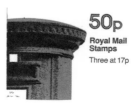

Type FB 31

(Des M. Thierens Design)

1985 (4 Nov). Cover as Type FB **31** printed in black and bright scarlet. Containing booklet pane No. X909l.
FB31   Pillar box design .... 5·00
No. FB 31 is inscribed "November 1985".

FB **32**

(Des P. Morter)

1986 (20 May–12 Aug). *Pond Life Series*. Dull blue and emerald covers as Type FB **32**. Containing booklet pane No. X909l.

FB32   Design No. 1, Emperor Dragonfly, Four spotted Libellula and Yellow Flag .... 3·00

FB33   Design No. 2. Common Frog, Fennel-leaved Pondweed and Long-stalked Pondweed (29.7.86) .... 4·00

     a. Containing booklet pane No. X909Ela (12.8.86) .... 3·75

Nos. FB32/33a are inscribed "November 1985".

FB **34**

(Des N. Battershill)

1986 (29 July). *Roman Britain Series*. Brown-ochre and Indian red cover as Type FB **32**. Containing booklet pane No. X845q.

FB34   Design No. 1, Hadrian's Wall .... 12·00

No. FB34 is inscribed "November 1985".

1986 (20 Oct)–**87**.*Pond Life Series* continued. Dull blue and emerald covers as Type FB **32**. Containing booklet pane No. X845s.

FB35   Design No. 3, Moorhen and Little Grebe .... 6·00

FB36   Design No. 4, Giant Pond and Great Ramshorn Snails (27.1.87) .... 6·00

No. FB36 is inscribed "October 1986".

1986 (20 Oct)–**87**. *Roman Britain Series* continued. Brown ochre and Indian red covers as Type FB **34**. Containing booklet pane No. X847l.

FB37   Design No. 2, Roman Theatre of Verulamium, St. Albans   4·00

FB38   Design No. 3, Portchester Castle, Hampshire (27.1.87) ..... 4·00

No. FB38 is inscribed "October 1986".

FB **39**

(Des Patricia Howes)

1987 (14 Apr)–**88**. *Bicentenary of Marylebone Cricket Club Series* Brown and dull ultramarine covers as Type FB **39**. Containing booklet pane No. X847l.

FB39   Design No. 1, Father Time weather vane .... 3·00

FB40   Design No. 2, Ashes urn and embroidered velvet bag (14.7.87) .... 3·00

FB41   Design No. 3, Lord's Pavilion and wrought iron decoration on roof (29.9.87) .... 3·00

FB42   Design No. 4, England team badge and new stand at Lord's (26.1.88) .... 3·00

Nos. FB39/42 are inscribed "October 1986".

FB **43**

(Des G. Evernden)

1987 (14 Apr)–**88**. *Botanical Gardens Series*. Covers as Type FB **43**. Containing booklet panes No. X845s (FB43/**4**) or X845sa (FB45/**6**).

FB43   Design No. 1 (cover in ultramarine and rosered), Rhododendron "Elizabeth", Bodnant .... 6·00

FB44   Design No. 2 (cover in deep ultramarine and cobalt), Gentiana sino-ornata, Edinburgh (14.7.87) .... 6·00

FB45   Design No. 3 (cover in dull ultramarine and orange-yellow), Lilium auratum and "Mount Stuart" (incorrect inscr) (29.9.87) .... 4·50

     a. With corrected spelling "Mount Stewart" (30.10.87) ..... 4·50

FB46   Design No. 4 (cover in dull ultramarine and yellow-orange), Strelitzia reginae, Kew (26.1.88)................................ 4·50

Nos. FB43/6 are inscribed "October 1986".

The panes from Nos. FB45/6 have imperforate vertical sides.

FB **47**

1988 (12 Apr–5 July). *London Zoo. Children's Drawings Series*. Covers as Type FB **47**.

FB47   Pigs design (cover in black and rose) containing booklet pane No. X847l .... 4·25

FB48   Birds design (cover in black and yellow) containing booklet pane No. X845sa .... 6·00

FB49   Elephants design (cover in black and grey) containing booklet pane No. X847l (5.7.88) .... 4·00

Nos. FB47/9 are inscribed "October 1986". The pane from No. FB48 has imperforate vertical sides.

FB **50**

(Des P. Morter)

1988 (5 July). *Marine Life Series*. Blue and orange-brown cover as Type FB **50**. Containing booklet pane No. X845sa.

FB50   Design No. 1, Parasitic Anemone on Common Whelk Shell and Umbrella Jellyfish .... 6·00

No. FB50 is inscribed "October 1986" and has the vertical sides of the pane imperforate.

FB **51**

(Des Lynda Gray)

1988 (5 Sept)–**89**. *Gilbert and Sullivan Operas Series*. Black and red covers as Type FB **51**. Containing booklet pane No. X904l.

FB51   Design No. 1, The *Yeomen of the Guard* .... 9·00

FB52   Design No. 2, The *Pirates of Penzance* (24.1.89) .... 9·00

FB53   Design No. 3, The *Mikado* (25.4.89) .... 9·00

1989 (18 July). *Marine Life Series* continued. Blue and orange brown cover as Type FB **50**. Containing booklet pane No. X904I.

FB54 Design No. 2, Common Hermit Crab, Bladder Wrack and Laver Spire Shell .... 9·00

For Design No. 3, see £1 Booklet No. FH17.

FB **55**

(Des P. Hutton)

1989 (2 Oct)–90 .*Aircraft Series*. Turquoise-green and light brown covers as Type FB **55**. Containing booklet pane No. X906I.

FB55 Design No. 1, HP42, Armstrong Whitworth Atalanta and de Havilland Dragon Rapide .... 14·00

No. FB55 was incorrectly inscribed "Atlanta".

As before, but containing Penny Black Anniversary booklet pane No. 1468I.

FB56 Design No. 2, Vickers Viscount 806 and de Havilland Comet 4 (30.1.90) .... 12·00

1990 (4 Sept)–91. *Aircraft Series* continued. Turquoise-green and light brown covers as Type FB **55**. Containing booklet pane No. X911I.

FB57 Design No. 3, BAC 1-11 and VC10 .... 8·00
FB58 Design No. 4, BAe ATP, BAe 146 and Aérospatiale–BAC Concorde (25.6.91) .... 8·00

FB **59**

(Des A. Drummond)

1991 (10 Sept)–92. *Archaeology Series*. Covers as Type FB **59**. Containing booklet pane No. X925m.

FB59 Design No. 1 (cover in bright blue and lakebrown), Sir Arthur Evans at Knossos, Crete .... 3·00
a. Corrected rate (10.91) .... 3·50
FB60 Design No. 2 (cover in bright blue and yellow), Howard Carter in the Tomb of Tutankhamun (21.1.92) .... 3·00
FB61 Design No. 3 (cover in bright blue and yellow), Sir Austen Layard at Assyrian site (28.4.92) .... 2·40
FB62 Design No. 4 (cover in new blue and yellow), Sir Flinders Petrie surveying the Pyramids and temples of Giza (28.7.92) .... 3·00

On the inside front cover of No. FB59 the inland letter rates are shown as 1st class 24, 35, 43, 51p. and 2nd class 18, 28, 33, 39p. These were corrected on No. FB59a to read: 1st class 24, 36, 45, 54p. and 2nd class 18, 28, 34, 41p.

FB **63**

(Des J. Matthews)

1992 (22 Sept). *1000th Anniv of Appointment of Sheriffs*. Dull blue and scarlet cover as Type FB **63**. Containing booklet pane No. X925m.

FB63 Design showing Crest, with Helm and Mantling, and Badge of The Shrievalty Association 8.50

FB **64**

(Des M. Newton)

1993 (9 Feb–6 July). *Postal History Series*. Covers as Type FB **64**. Containing booklet pane No. X925m.

FB64 Design No. 1 (cover in grey-green and greyblack), Airmail postmarks .... 2·50
FB65 Design No. 2 (cover in dull orange and black), Ship mail postmarks (6.4.93) .... 2·50
FB66 Design No. 3 (cover in blue and grey-black), Registered mail postmarks (6.7.93) .... 2·50

1993 (1 Nov). *Postal History Series* continued. Rose-red and grey-black cover as Type FB **64** containing booklet pane No. Y1689I.

FB67 Design No. 4, "Paid" postmarks .... 2·50

FB **68**

(Des A. Davidson)

1994 (25 Jan–6 Sept). *Coaching Inns Series*. Covers as Type FB **68**. Containing booklet pane No. Y1689I.

FB68 Design No. 1 (cover in myrtle-green and pale myrtle-green), "Swan with Two Necks" .... 2·50
FB69 Design No. 2 (cover in sepia and buff), "Bull and Mouth" (26.4.94) .... 2·50
FB70 Design No. 3 (cover in reddish brown and cinnamon), "Golden Cross" (6.6.94) .... 2·50
FB71 Design No. 4 (cover in black and slate-blue), "Pheasant Inn", Wiltshire (6.9.94) .... 2·50

FB **72**

(Des D. Davis)

1995 (7 Feb–4 Apr). *Sea Charts Series*. Rosine and black covers as Type FB **72**, containing booklet pane No. Y1689I.

FB72 Design No. 1, John o'Groats, 1800 .... 2·50
FB73 Design No. 2, Land's End, 1808 (4.4.95) .... 2·50

1995 (6 June–4 Sept). *Sea Charts Series* continued. Rosine and black covers as Type FB **72**, containing booklet pane No. Y1690I.

FB74 Design No. 3, St. David's Head, 1812 .... 3·50
FB75 Design No. 4, Giant's Causeway, 1828 (4.9.95) .... 3·50

65p. Booklet

1976 (14 July). Cover as Type FB **1**, but larger (90×49 mm). Printed in turquoise-blue and pale buff. A. Selvedge at left. B. Selvedge at right.

		A	B
FC1	Containing ten 6½p. (No. X872)	18·00	10·00

No. FC1 is inscribed "March 1976".

70p. Booklets

1977 (13 June). Cover as Type FB **1**, but larger (90×49 mm). Printed in purple-brown and dull rose. A. Selvedge at left. B. Selvedge at right.

		A	B
FD1	Containing ten 7p. (No. X875)	8·00	8·00

FD 2
(Des E. Stemp)

1978 (8 Feb)–**79**. *Country Crafts Series.* Grey-green and red brown covers as Type FD **2** (90×49 mm). Containing ten 7p. (No. X875). A. Selvedge at left. B. Selvedge at right.

		A	B
FD2	Design No. 1, Horse-shoeing	60·00	5·00
FD3	Design No. 2, Thatching (3.5.78)	£250	5·00
FD4	Design No. 3, Dry-stone-walling (9.8.78)	£250	5·00
FD5	Design No. 4, Wheel-making (25.10.78)	10·00	8·00
FD6	Design No. 5, Wattle fence-making (10.1.79)	22·00	8·00

Nos. FD2/3 are inscribed "January 1978", FD4 "July 1978", FD5 "October 1978" and FD6 "December 1978".

FD 7
(Des F. Wegner)

1979 (5 Feb).*Official opening of Derby Mechanised Letter Office.* Pale yellow-green and lilac cover as Type FD **7** (90×49 mm). Containing ten 7p. (No. X875). A. Selvedge at left. B.Selvedge at right.

		A	B
FD7	Kedleston Hall	9·00	9·00

No. FD7 is inscribed "December 1978".
On sale only in the Derby Head Post Office area to promote postcode publicity and also at the Philatelic Bureau and philatelic sales counters.

1979 (4 Apr). *Country Crafts Series* continued. Grey-green and red-brown covers as Type FD **2** (90×49 mm). A. Selvedge at left. B. Selvedge at right.

		A	B
FD8	Design No. 6, Basket-making	10·00	5·00

No. FD8 is inscribed "March 1979".

80p. Booklet

FE 1
(Des P. Hutton)

1979 (3 Oct). *Military Aircraft Series.* Blue and grey cover as Type FE **1** (90×49 mm). Containing ten 8p. (No. X879) attached by the selvedge. A. Selvedge at left. B. Selvedge at right.

		A	B
FE1	Design No. 1, BE2B, 1914, & Vickers Gun Bus, 1915	4·00	4·00

No. FE1 is inscribed "August 1979".

85p. Booklet

1976 (14 July). Cover as Type FB **1** but larger (90×49 mm). Printed in light yellow-olive and brownish grey. A. Selvedge at left. B. Selvedge at right.

		A	B
FF1	Containing ten 8½p. (No. X881)	10·00	14·00

No. FF1 is inscribed "March 1976".

90p. Booklets

1977 (13 June). Cover as Type FB **1**, but larger (90×49 mm). Printed in deep grey-blue and cobalt. A. Selvedge at left. B. Selvedge at right.

		A	B
FG1	Containing ten 9p. (No. X883)	6·00	10·00

FG 2
(Des R. Maddox)

1978 (8 Feb)—**79**. *British Canals Series.* Yellow-olive and new blue covers as Type FG **2** (90×49 mm). Containing ten 9p. (No. X883). A. Selvedge at left. B. Selvedge at right.

		A	B
FG2	Design No. 1, Grand Union	30·00	8·00
FG3	Design No. 2, Llangollen (3.5.78)	6·00	£550
FG4	Design No. 3, Kennet & Avon (9.8.78)	18·00	14·00
FG5	Design No. 4, Caledonian (25.10.78)	8·00	5·00
FG6	Design No. 5, Regents (10.1.79)	20·00	12·00

Nos. FG2/3 are inscribed "January 1978", FG4 "July 1978", FG5 October 1978" and FG6 "December 1978".

(Des F. Wegner)

1979 (5 Feb). *Official Opening of Derby Mechanised Letter Office.* Violet-blue and rose cover as Type FD **7** (90×49 mm). Containing ten 9p. (No. X883). A. Selvedge at left. B. Selvedge at right.

		A	B
FG7	Tramway Museum, Crich	12·00	12·00

No. FG7 is inscribed "December 1978".
On sale only in the Derby Head Post Office area to promote postcode publicity and also at the Philatelic Bureau and philatelic sales counters.

1979 (4 Apr). *British Canals Series* continued. Yellow-olive and new blue cover as Type FG **2**. A. Selvedge at left. B. Selvedge at right.

		A	B
FG8	Design No. 6, Leeds & Liverpool	6·00	6·00

No. FG8 is inscribed "March 1979".

£1 Booklets

All booklets were sold at the cover price of £1 although some contain stamps to a greater value.

FH 1
(Des N. Battershill)

1979 (3 Oct). *Industrial Archaeology Series.* Red and green cover as Type FH **1** (90×49 mm). Containing ten 10p. (No. X887). A. Selvedge at left. B. Selvedge at right.

		A	B
FH1	Design No. 1, Ironbridge, Telford, Salop	4·50	4·50

No. FH1 is inscribed "August 1979".

1980 (4 Feb—24 Sept). *Military Aircraft Series* continued. Blue and grey covers as Type FE **1** (90×49 mm). Containing ten 10p. (No. X888). A. Selvedge at left. B. Selvedge at right.

		A	B
FH2	Design No. 2, Sopwith Camel & Vickers Vimy	4·50	4·50
FH3	Design No. 3, Hawker Hart* & Handley Page Heyford (25.6.80)	6·00	6·00
FH4	Design No. 4, Hurricane & Wellington (24.9.80)	4·50	4·50

No FH2 is inscribed "January 1980", No. FH3 "May 1980" and No. FH4 "July 1980".
* On the booklet cover the aircraft is wrongly identified as a Hawker Fury.

FH **5**

(Des M. Newton and S. Paine)

1986 (29 July)–**87**. *Musical Instruments Series.* Scarlet and black covers as Type FH **5**. Containing six 17p. (X952).
FH5 Design No. 1, Violin .... 5·00
 No. FH5 is inscribed "November 1985".
Contents changed. Containing No. X901n.
FH6 Design No. 2, French horn (20.10.86) .... 5·00
FH7 Design No. 3, Bass clarinet (27.1.87) .... 5·00
 No. FH7 is inscribed "October 1986".

FH **8**
(Des A. Davidson)

1987 (14 Apr)–**88**. *Sherlock Holmes Series.* Bright scarlet and grey-black covers as Type FH **8**. Containing booklet pane No. X901n (FH8/**9**) or X901na (FH10/11).
FH8 Design No. 1, *A Study in Scarlet* .... 5·50
FH9 Design No. 2, *The Hound of the Baskervilles* (14.7.87) .... 5·50
FH10 Design No. 3, *The Adventure of the Speckled Band* (29.9.87) 5·50
FH11 Design No. 4, *The Final Problem* (26.1.88)................ 5·50
 Nos. FH8/11 are inscribed "October 1986".
 The panes from Nos. FH10/11 have imperforate vertical sides.

1988 (12 Apr). *London Zoo. Children's Drawings Series.* Cover as Type FB **47** in black and brown. Containing booklet pane No. X901na.
FH12 Bears design .... 5·50
 No. FH12 is inscribed "October 1986" and has the vertical sides of the pane imperforate.

FH **13**

(Des Liz Moyes)

1988 (5 July)–**89**. *Charles Dickens Series* Orange-red and maroon covers as Type FH **13**.
FH13 Designs No. 1, *Oliver Twist,* containing booklet pane
 No. X901na .... 6·50
FH14 Design No. 2, *Nicholas Nickleby,* containing booklet pane
 No. X904m (5.9.88) .... 6·50
FH15 Design No. 3, *David Copperfield,* containing booklet pane
 No. X904m (24.1.89) .... 6·50
FH16 Design No. 4, *Great Expectations,* containing booklet pane
 No. X1051l (25.4.89) .... 22·00
 No. FH13 is inscribed "October 1986" and No. FH16 "September 1988", Nos. FH13/16 have the vertical sides of the pane imperforate.

1989 (18 July). *Marine Life Series* continued. Cover as Type FB **50** in turquoise-green and scarlet. Containing booklet pane No. X904m.
FH17 Design No. 3, Edible Sea Urchin, Common Starfish and
 Common Shore Crab .... 6·00
 No. FH17 has the vertical edges of the pane imperforate.

FH **18**
(Des J. Sancha)

1989 (2 Oct)–**90**. *Mills Series.* Grey-black and grey-green matt card cover as Type FH **18**.
FH18 Design No. 1, Wicken Fen, Ely containing booklet pane
 No. X960l .... 7·50
As Type FH **18** but glossy card cover containing Penny Black Anniversary booklet pane No. 1476l printed in litho by Walsall.
FH19 Design No. 1 (cover in bottle-green and pale green),
 Wicken Fen, Ely (30.1.90) .... 16·00
 No. FH19 was an experimental printing to test a new cover material. This appears glossy when compared with Nos. FH18 and FH20.

As Type FH **18** but changed to matt card cover containing Penny Black Anniversary booklet pane No. 1469l printed in photo by Harrison.
FH20 Design No. 2 (cover in grey-black and bright green), Click
 Mill, Dounby, Orkney (30.1.90) .... 9·00

1990 (4 Sept)–**91**. *Mills Series* continued. Covers as Type FH **18**. Containing booklet pane No. X911m.
FH21 Design No. 3 (cover printed in light blue and buff) Jack
 and Jill Mills, Clayton, Sussex .... 5·00
FH22 Design No. 4 (cover printed in dull blue and bright yellow-green). Howell Mill, Llanddeusant, Anglesey (25.6.91) ..... 5·00
 Nos. FH18/22 have the vertical edges of the pane imperforate.

FH **23**

(Des J. Gibbs)

1991 (10 Sept)–**92**. *150th Anniv of Punch Magazine.* Magenta and grey-black covers as Type FH **23** containing booklet pane No. X927l.
FH23 Design No. 1, Illustrations by Richard Doyle and Hoffnung 3·50
 a. Corrected rate (10.91) .... 3·50
FH24 Design No. 2, Illustrations by Sir John Tenniel and Eric
 Burgin (21.1.92) .... 3·50
FH25 Design No. 3, Illustrations by Sir John Tenniel and Anton
 (28.4.92) .... 3·50
FH26 Design No. 4, Illustrations by Sir John Tenniel and
 Hewison (28.7.92) .... 3·50
 Nos. FH23/6 have the vertical edges of the pane imperforate.
 No. FH23a has corrected letter rates as No. FB59a.

(Des J. Matthews)

1992 (22 Sept). *1000th Anniv of Appointment of Sheriffs.* Scarlet and dull blue cover as Type FB **63** containing booklet pane No. X927l.
FH27 Design as Type FB63 but elements in reverse order .... 6·00
 No. FH27 has the vertical edges of the pane imperforate.

FH **28**
(Des J. Lawrence)

1993 (9 Feb–6 July). *Educational Institutions Series.* Covers as Type FH **28** containing booklet pane No. X1050l printed in litho by Walsall.
FH28 Design No. 1 (cover in lake-brown and light blue),
 University of Wales .... 10·00
FH29 Design No. 2 (cover in deep dull green and lemon), St.
 Hilda's College, Oxford (6.4.93) .... 10·00
FH30 Design No. 3 (cover in purple-brown and flesh),
 Marlborough College, Wiltshire (6.7.93) .... 10·00

1993 (1 Nov). *Educational Institutions Series* continued. Deep bluish green and lilac cover as Type FH **28** containing four 25p. (No. Y1775) printed in litho by Walsall.

FH31   Design No. 4, Free Church of Scotland College, Edinburgh ... 7·00

FH **32**

(Des H. Brockway)

1994 (25 Jan). *20th-century Prime Ministers Series.* Brown and pale brown cover as Type FH **32** containing four 25p. (No. Y1775) printed in litho by Walsall.

FH32   Design No. 1, Herbert Asquith .... 3·00

(Des H. Brockway)

1994 (26 Apr–6 Sept). *20th-century Prime Ministers Series* continued. Covers as Type FH **32**. Containing four 25p. (No. Y1689) printed in photo by Harrison.

FH33   Design No. 2 (cover in sepia and buff) David Lloyd-
          George .... 3·00
FH34   Design No. 3 (cover in greenish blue and pale blue),
          Winston Churchill (6.6.94) .... 3·00
FH35   Design No. 4 (cover in black and yellow-olive), Clement
          Attlee (6.9.94) .... 3·00

FH **36**

(Des L. Thomas)

1995 (7 Feb–4 Apr). *50th Anniv of End of Second World War.* Covers as Type FH **36** containing four 25p. (No. Y1689) printed in photo by Harrison.

FH36   Design No. 1 (cover in brown-olive and brownish black),
          Violette Szabo (S.O.E. agent) .... 3·00
FH37   Design No. 2 (cover in red-brown and black), Dame Vera
          Lynn (entertainer) (4.4.95) .... 3·00

1995 (16 May–4 Sept). 50th Anniv of End of Second World War Series continued. Covers as Type FH **36** containing four 25p. (No. Y**1690**) printed in photo by Harrison.

FH38   Design No. 3 (cover in black and steel-blue), R. J. Mitchell
          (designer of Spitfire) .... 3·00
FH39   Design No. 4 (cover in grey-green and black), Archibald
          McIndoe (plastic surgeon) (4.9.95) .... 3·50

FH **40**

1996 (16 Jan). Multicoloured laminated cover as Type FH **40**. Stamps printed in litho by Questa.

FH40   Containing four 25p. stamps (No. Y1775) .... 7·00
          For an initial test period No. FH40 was only available from machines at twelve post offices, five in London and seven in Scotland, in addition to philatelic outlets. Stocks were distributed nationally from May 1996.

1996 (8 July)–97. Multicoloured laminated cover as Type FH **40**. Stamps printed in litho by Questa.

FH41   Containing booklet pane of 1p.×2, 20p., 26p.×3 and 2
          labels (No. Y1760l) .... 6·00
          a. Corrected rate (4.2.97) .... 5·50
          b. Inland rate table at right .... 5·50

No. FH41 was reissued on 4 February 1997 showing the 200g second class rate on the inside cover altered from 47p. to 45p. A further printing issued 5 May 1998 was without the overseas postage rate table.

1998 (1 Dec). Multicoloured laminated cover as Type FH **40**. Stamps printed in gravure by Questa.

FH42   Containing booklet pane of 1p.×2, 20p., 26p.×3 and 2
          labels (No. Y1667l) .... 30·00

1999 (26 Apr). Multicoloured laminated cover as Type FH **40**. Stamps printed in gravure by Questa.

FH43   Containing booklet pane of 1p., 2p., 19p., 26p.×3 and 2
          labels (No. Y1667m) .... 6·50

2000 (27 Apr)–**01**. Multicoloured laminated cover as Type FH **40**. Stamps printed in gravure by Questa.

FH44   Containing booklet pane of 2nd, 1st×3 and 4 labels (No.
          1664l) .... 8·00
          a. Containing booklet pane No. 1664la (17.4.01) .... 7·50

£1.15 Booklets

1981 (26 Jan–18 Mar). *Military Aircraft Series* continued. Blue and grey covers as Type FE **1** (90×49 mm). Containing ten 11½p. (No. X893). A. Selvedge at left. B. Selvedge at right.

		A	B
FI1	Design No. 5, Spitfire & Lancaster	5·00	5·00
FI2	Design No. 6, Lightning & Vulcan (18.3.81)	5·00	5·00

Nos. FI1/2 are inscribed "January 1981".

FI **3**

(Des R. Maddox)

1981 (6 May–30 Sept). *Museums Series.* Blue and turquoise green covers as Type FI **3** (90×49 mm). Containing ten 11½p. (No. X893). A. Selvedge at left. B. Selvedge at right.

		A	B
FI3	Design No. 1, Natural History Museum (British Museum), London	5·00	5·00
FI4	Design No. 2, National Museum of Antiquities of Scotland (30.9.81)	5·00	5·00

Nos. FI3/4 are inscribed "January 1981".

£1.20 Booklets

1980 (4 Feb–24 Sept). *Industrial Archaeology Series* continued. Red and green covers as Type FH **1** (90×49 mm). Containing ten 12p. (No. X943). A. Selvedge at left. B. Selvedge at right.

		A	B
FJ1	Design No. 2, Beetle Mill, Ireland	5·00	5·00
FJ2	Design No. 3, Tin Mines, Cornwall (25.6.80)	5·00	6·50
FJ3	Design No. 4, Bottle Kilns, Gladstone, Stoke-on-Trent (24.9.80)	5·00	5·50

No. FJ1 is inscribed "January 1980", No. FJ2 "May 1980" and No. FJ3 "July 1980".

1986 (14 Jan). Pillar box *Write Now* cover as Type FB **31** (90×49 mm), printed in yellow-green and pale red. Containing ten 12p. (No. X896). A. Selvedge at left. B. Selvedge at right.

		A	B
FJ4	"Write Now" (Pillar box design) (no imprint date)	8·00	8·00

FJ **5**

(Des R. Maddox)

1986 (29 Apr). *National Gallery* cover as Type FJ **5** (90×49 mm), printed in magenta and blue-green. Containing ten 12p. (No. X896). A. Selvedge at left. B. Selvedge at right.

		A	B
FJ5	National Gallery design	7·50	7·50

No. FJ5 is inscribed "November 1985".

FJ **6**

(Des Trickett and Webb Ltd)

1986 (29 July). *Handwriting cover* as Type FJ **6** (90×49 mm), printed in bright orange and bright blue. Containing ten 12p. (No. X896). A. Selvedge at left. B. Selvedge at right.

		A	B
FJ6	"Maybe"	7·50	7·50

No. FJ6 is inscribed "November 1985".

£1.25 Booklets

1982 (1 Feb–6 Oct). *Museums Series* continued. Blue and turquoise-green covers as Type FJ **3** (90×49 mm). Containing ten 12½p. (No. X898). A. Selvedge at left. B. Selvedge at right.

		A	B
FK1	Design No. 3, Ashmolean Museum, Oxford	5·50	5·50
FK2	Design No. 4, National Museum of Wales, Cardiff (6.5.82)	5·50	5·50
FK3	Design No. 5, Ulster Museum, Belfast (11.8.82)	5·50	5·50
FK4	Design No. 6, Castle Museum, York (6.10.82)	5·50	5·50

Nos. FK1/4 are inscribed "February 1982".

FK **5**

(Des S. Paine)

1983 (16 Feb–26 Oct). *Railway Engines Series.* Red and blue-green covers as Type FK **5** (90×49 mm). Containing ten 12½p. (No. X898). A. Selvedge at left. B. Selvedge at right.

		A	B
FK5	Design No. 1, GWR *Isambard Kingdom Brunel*	8·00	8·00
FK6	Design No. 2, LMS Class 4P Passenger Tank Engine (5.4.83)	8·50	8·50
	a. Corrected rate	£110	£200
FK7	Design No. 3, LNER *Mallard* (27.7.83)	8·00	8·00
FK8	Design No. 4, SR/BR *Clan Line* (26.10.83)	8·00	8·00

No. FK5 is inscribed "February 1982" and Nos. FK6/8 "April 1983". The corrected rate reads "36p. for 200g" instead of "37p. for 200g".

£1.30 Booklets

FL **1**

(Des J. Gibbs)

1981 (6 May–30 Sept). *Postal History Series.* Covers as Type FL **1** (90×49 mm). Containing No. X894l. A. Selvedge at left. B. Selvedge at right.

		A	B
FL1	Design No. 1, Penny Black (red & black cover)	7·00	5·50
FL2	Design No. 2, The Downey Head, 1911 (red and green cover) (20.9.81)	9·50	30·00

No. FL1 is inscribed "April 1981" and No. FL2 "September 1981".

FL **3**

(Des J. Thirsk)

1984 (3 Sept)–**85**. *Trams Series.* Yellow-orange and purple covers as Type FL **3** (90×49 mm). Containing ten 13p. (No. X900). A. Selvedge at left. B. Selvedge at right.

		A	B
FL3	Design No. 1, Swansea/Mumbles Railway Car No. 3	5·50	5·50
FL4	Design No. 2, Glasgow Car No. 927 and Car No. 1194 (15.1.85)	6·25	6·25
FL5	Design No. 3, Car No. 717, Blackpool (23.4.85)	6·25	6·25
FL6	Design No. 4, Car No. 120 and "D" Class Car, London (23.7.85)	5·50	5·50

Nos. FL3/6 are inscribed "September 1984".

FL **7**

(Des Anne Morrow)

1986 (20 Oct). *Books for Children.* Cover as Type FL **7** (90×49 mm) printed in rose-red and lemon. Containing ten 13p. (No. X900). A. Selvedge at left. B. Selvedge at right.

		A	B
FL7	Teddy bears design	5·50	5·50

FL **8**

(Des Trickett and Webb Ltd)

1987 (27 Jan). *Keep in Touch* cover as Type FL **8** (90×49 mm), printed in light green and bright blue. Containing ten 13p. (No. X900). A. Selvedge at left. B. Selvedge at right.

		A	B
FL8	Handclasp and envelope design	5·50	5·50

No. FL8 is inscribed "October 1986".

FL **9**

(Des Hannah Firmin)

1987 (14 Apr). *Ideas for your Garden* Cover as Type FL **9** (90×49 mm) printed in bistre and orange-brown. Containing ten 13p. stamps (No. X900). A. Selvedge at left. B. Selvedge at right.

		A	B
FL9	Conservatory design	5·50	5·50

No. FL9 is inscribed "October 1986".

FL **10**

(Des Trickett and Webb Ltd)

1987 (14 July). *Brighter Writer.* Cover as Type FL **10** (90×49 mm) printed in orange and bright reddish violet. Containing ten 13p. stamps (No. X900). A. Selvedge at left. B. Selvedge at right.

		A	B
FL10	Flower design	5·50	5·50

No. FL10 is inscribed "October 1986".

FL **11**

(Des E. Stemp)

1987 (29 Sept). *Jolly Postman* Cover as Type FL **11** *(90×49 mm) printed in pale blue and deep blue. Containing ten 13p. stamps (No. X900). A. Selvedge at left. B. Selvedge at right.*

		A	B
FL11	Boy drawing design	5·75	5·75

No. FL11 is inscribed "October 1986".

FL **12**

(Des E. Hughes)

1988 (26 Jan). *Bicentenary of Linnean Society.* Cover as Type FL **12** (90×49 mm) printed in blue and claret. Containing ten 13p. stamps (No. X900). A. Selvedge at left. B. Selvedge at right.

		A	B
FL12	Mermaid, fish and insect (from "Hortus Sanitatis", 1497)	6·75	6·75

No. FL12 is inscribed "October 1986".

FL **13**

1988 (12 Apr). *Recipe Cards.* Cover as Type FL **13** (90×49 mm) printed in brown and green. Containing ten 13p. stamps (No. X900). A. Selvedge at left. B. Selvedge at right.

		A	B
FL13	Vegetables design	5·50	5·50

No. FL13 is inscribed "October 1986".

FL **14**

(Des Trickett and Webb Ltd)

1988 (5 July). *Children's Parties* Cover as Type FL **14** (90×49 mm) printed in blue-green and bright purple. Containing ten 13p. stamps (No. X900). A. Selvedge at left. B. Selvedge at right.

		A	B
FL14	Balloons and streamers design	5·50	5·50

No. FL14 is inscribed "October 1986".

£1.40 Booklets

1981 (26 Jan–18 Mar). *Industrial Archaeology Series* continued. Red and green covers as Type FH **1** (90×49 mm). Containing ten 14p. (No. X946). A. Selvedge at left. B. Selvedge at right.

		A	B
FM1	Design No. 5, Preston Mill, Scotland	5·50	5·50
FM2	Design No. 6, Talyllyn Railway, Tywyn (18.3.81)	5·50	5·50

Nos. FM1/2 are inscribed "January 1981".

FM **3**

(Des E. Stemp)

1981 (6 May–30 Sept). *19th-century Women's Costume Series.* Claret and blue covers as Type FM **3** (90×49 mm). Containing ten 14p. (No. X946). A. Selvedge at left. B. Selvedge at right.

		A	B
FM3	Design No. 1, Costume, 1800–15	5·50	5·50
FM4	Design No. 2, Costume, 1815–30 (30.9.81)	5·50	5·50

Nos. FM3/4 are inscribed "January 1981".

FM **5**

(Des A. Drummond)

1988 (5 Sept). *Pocket Planner* Cover as Type FM **5** (90×49 mm) printed in grey-black and yellow. Containing ten 14p. stamps (No. X903). A. Selvedge at left. B. Selvedge at right.

		A	B
FM5	"Legal Charge" design	5·50	5·50

FM **6**

(Des Debbie Cook)

1989 (24 Jan). *150th Anniv of Fox Talbot's Report on the Photographic Process to Royal Society.* Cover as Type FM **6** (90×49 mm) printed in reddish orange and black. Containing ten 14p. stamps (No. X903). A. Selvedge at left. B. Selvedge at right.

		A	B
FM6	Photographs and darkroom equipment	5·75	5·75

No. FM6 is inscribed "September 1988".

£1.43 Booklets

1982 (1 Feb–6 May). *Postal History Series* continued. Covers as Type FL **1** (90×49 mm). Containing No. X899l. A. Selvedge at left. B. Selvedge at right.

		A	B
FN1	Design No. 3, James Chalmers (postal reformer) (orange and turquoise-blue cover)	6·00	6·00
FN2	Design No. 4, Edmund Dulac (stamp designer) (brown and red cover) (6.5.82)	6·00	6·00

FN **3**

(Des J. Gardner)

1982 (12 July). *Holiday Postcard Stamp Book Purple and turquoise-blue cover as Type* FN **3** (90×49 mm). *Containing No.* X899l. A. *Selvedge at left.* B. Selvedge at right.

		A	B
FN3	*Golden Hinde* on front, postcard voucher on back	6·00	6·00

1982 (21 July)–83. *Postal History Series* continued. Covers as Type FL **1** (90×49 mm). Containing No. X899l. A. Selvedge at left. B. Selvedge at right.

		A	B
FN4	Design No. 5, "Forces Postal Service" (grey and violet cover)	6·00	6·00
FN5	Design No. 6, The £5 Orange (orange and black cover) (6.10.82)	6·00	6·00
FN6	Design No. 7, Postmark History (bright scarlet and deep dull blue cover) (16.2.83)	6·00	6·00

No. FN1 is inscribed "February 1982", FN2/3 "May 1982", FN4 "July 1982", FN5 "October 1982", FN6 "November 1982".

For booklet No. FS2 with cover price of £1·45, see £1·60 booklets.

£1.46 Booklets

1983 (5 Apr–26 Oct). *Postal History Series* continued. Covers as Type FL **1** (90×49 mm). A. Containing No. X899n. B. Containing No. X899na.

		A	B
FO1	Design No. 8, Seahorse High Values (blue and green cover)	11·00	11·00
	a. Corrected rate	85·00	28·00
FO2	Design No. 9, Parcel Post Centenary (turquoise-blue and carmine cover) (27.7.83)	9·50	9·50
FO3	Design No. 10, Silver Jubilee of Regional Stamps (dull green & reddish violet cover) (26.10.83)	9·50	9·50

No. FO1 is inscribed "March 1983", No. FO2 "May 1983" and No. FO 3 "June 1983".

The corrected rate reads "36p. for 200g" instead of "37p. for 200g".

£1.50 Booklets

1986 (14 Jan). *Pillar box Write Now* cover as Type FB **31** (90×49 mm), printed in ultramarine and red. A. Containing No. X897l. B. Containing No. X897la.

		A	B
FP1	"Write Now" (Pillar box design)	7·00	7·00

No. FP1 shows no imprint date.

1986 (29 Apr). *National Gallery* cover as Type FJ **5** (90×49 mm), printed in violet and vermilion. A. Containing No. X897l. B. Containing No. X897la.

		A	B
FP2	National Gallery design	7·00	7·00

No. FP2 is inscribed "November 1985".

1986 (29 July). *Handwriting* cover as Type FJ **6** (90×49 mm), printed in blue-green and bright blue. A. Containing No. X897l. B. Containing No. X897la.

		A	B
FP3	"No"	7·00	7·00

No. FP3 is inscribed "November 1985".

£1.54 Booklets

1984 (3 Sept)–85. *Postal History Series* continued. Covers as Type FL **1** (90×49 mm). A. Containing No. X901l. B. Containing No. X901la.

		A	B
FQ1	Design No. 11, Old and new Postage Dues (reddish purple and pale blue cover)	6·00	6·00
FQ2	Design No. 12, Queen Victoria embossed stamps (yellow-green and blue-cover) (15.1.85)	6·00	6·00
FQ3	Design No. 13, Queen Victoria surface printed stamps (blue-green and carmine cover) (23.4.85)	6·00	6·00
FQ4	Design No. 14, 17th-century mounted and foot messengers (deep brown & orange-red cover) (23.7.85)	6·00	6·00

No. FQ1 is inscribed "July 1984" and Nos. FQ2/4 are inscribed "September 1984".

£1.55 Booklets

1982 (1 Feb–6 Oct). *19th-century Women's Costume Series* continued. Claret and blue covers as Type FM **3** (90×49 mm). Containing ten 15½p. (No. X948). A. Selvedge at left. B. Selvedge at right.

		A	B
FR1	Design No. 3, Costume, 1830–50	5·75	5·75
FR2	Design No. 4, Costume, 1850–60 (6.5.82)	5·75	5·75
FR3	Design No. 5, Costume, 1860–80 (11.8.82)	5·75	5·75
FR4	Design No. 6, Costume, 1880–1900 (6.10.82)	5·75	5·75

Nos. FR1/4 are inscribed "February 1982".

£1.60 Booklets

FS **1**

(Des Carol Walklin)

1983 (5 Apr). *Birthday Box* Design. Magenta and red-orange cover as Type FS **1** (90×49 mm). Depicting birthday cake and associated items. A. Selvedge at left. B. Selvedge at right.

		A	B
FS1	Containing ten 16p. stamps (No. X949) (no imprint date)	7·00	7·00
	a. Rates altered and "February 1983" imprint date	95·00	£150

The converted rate reads "36p. for 200g." instead of 37p. for 200g.".

FS **2**

(Des R. Maddox)

1983 (10 Aug). *British Countryside Series*. Special Discount Booklet (sold at £1.45). Greenish blue and ultramarine cover as Type FS **2** (90×49 mm). Containing ten 16p. stamps (No. X949Eu). A. Selvedge at left. B. Selvedge at right.

		A	B
FS2	Design No. 1, Lyme Regis, Dorset	9·00	9·00

Stamps from No. FS2 show a double-lined "D" printed in blue on the reverse over the gum.
No. FS2 is inscribed "April 1983".

1983 (21 Sept). *British Countryside Series* continued. Dull green on violet cover as Type FS **2** (90×49 mm). Containing ten 16p. stamps (No. X949). A. Selvedge at left. B. Selvedge at right.

		A	B
FS3	Design No. 2, Arlington Row, Bibury, Gloucestershire	6·00	6·00

No. FS3 is inscribed "April 1983".

FS **4**

(Des M. Newton)

1984 (14 Feb). *Write it* Design. Vermilion and ultramarine cover as Type FS **4** (90×49 mm). Containing ten 16p. stamps (No. X949). A. Selvedge at left. B. Selvedge at right.

		A	B
FS4	Fountain pen	7·00	7·00

No. FS4 is inscribed "April 1983".

£1.70 Booklets

FT **1**

1984 (3 Sept). *Social Letter Writing Series*. Rose and deep claret cover as Type FT **1** (90×49 mm). Containing ten 17p. (No. X952). A. Selvedge at left. B. Selvedge at right.

		A	B
FT1	Design No. 1, "Love Letters"	7·00	7·00

No. FT1 is inscribed "September 1984".

1985 (5 Mar). *Social Letter Writing* continued. Special Discount Booklet (sold at £1·55). Turquoise-blue and deep claret cover as Type FT **1** (90×49 mm). Containing ten 17p. (No. X952Eu). A. Selvedge at left. B. Selvedge at right.

		A	B
FT2	Design No. 2, "Letters abroad"	7·00	7·00

Stamps from No. FT2 show a double-lined "D" printed in blue on the reverse over the gum.
No. FT2 is inscribed "September 1984".

1985 (9 Apr). *Social Letter Writing Series* continued. Bright blue and deep claret cover as Type FT **1** (90×49 mm). Containing ten 17p. (No. X952). A. Selvedge at left. B. Selvedge at right.

		A	B
FT3	Design No. 3, "Fan letters"	6·50	6·50

No. FT3 is inscribed "September 1984".

FT **4**

(Des B. Smith)

1985 (30 July). *350 Years of Royal Mail Public Postal Service* Special Discount Booklet (sold at £1·53). Cover Type FT **4** (90×60 mm), printed in rosine and bright blue. Containing ten 17p. (No. 1290Eu) with selvedge at top.

FT4	Datapost Service design		7·00

The stamps from this booklet show double-lined letters "D" printed on the reverse over the gum.
No. FT4 is inscribed "September 1984".

1985 (8 Oct)–**86**. *Social Letter Writing Series* continued. Black and bright scarlet cover as Type FT **1** (90×49 mm). Containing ten 17p. (No. X952). A. Selvedge at left. B. Selvedge at right.

		A	B
FT5	Design No. 4, "Write Now" (Pillar box)	6·50	6·50
	a. Revised rates (2nd class (60g) 12p.) (1.86)	25·00	15·00

1986 (29 Apr). *National Gallery*. Cover as Type FJ **5** (90×49 mm), printed in blue-green and blue. Containing ten 17p. (No. X952). A. Selvedge at left. B. Selvedge at right.

		A	B
FT6	National Gallery design	7·00	7·00

No. FT6 is inscribed "November 1985".

1986 (29 July). *Handwriting*. Cover as Type FJ **6** (90×49 mm) printed in red and bright blue. Containing ten 17p. (No. X952). A. Selvedge at left. B. Selvedge at right.

		A	B
FT7	"Yes"	7·00	7·00

No. FT7 is inscribed "November 1985".

£1.80 Booklets

1986 (20 Oct). *Books for Children*. New blue and orange-brown cover as Type FL **7**. Containing ten 18p. (No. X955). A. Selvedge at left. B. Selvedge at right.

		A	B
FU1	Rabbits design	7·00	7·00

1987 (27 Jan). *Keep in Touch*. Cover as Type FL **8** printed in magenta and bright blue. Containing ten 18p. (No. X955). A. Selvedge at left. B. Selvedge at right.

		A	B
FU2	Handclasp and envelope design	7·00	7·00

No. FU2 is inscribed "October 1986".

1987 (14 Apr). *Ideas for your Garden Claret and brown-olive cover as Type FL **9** (90×49 mm). Containing ten 18p. stamps (No. X955). A. Selvedge at left. B. Selvedge at right.*

		A	B
FU3	Garden path design	7·00	7·00

No. FU3 is inscribed "October 1986".

1987 (14 July). *Brighter Writer* Turquoise-green and reddish orange cover as Type FL **10** (90×49 mm). Containing ten 18p. (No. X955). A. Selvedge at left. B. Selvedge at right.

		A	B
FU4	Berries and leaves design	7·00	7·00

No. FU4 is inscribed "October 1986".

1987 (29 Sept). *Jolly Postman*. Cover as Type FL **11** (90×49 mm) printed in deep blue and claret. Containing ten 18p. stamps (No. X955). A. Selvedge at left. B. Selvedge at right.

		A	B
FU5	Girl drawing design	7·00	7·00

No. FU5 is inscribed "October 1986".

1988 (26 Jan). *Bicentenary of Linnean Society*. Cover as Type FL **12** (90×49 mm) printed in dull yellow-green and dull claret. Containing ten 18p. stamps (No. X955). A. Selvedge at left. B. Selvedge at right.

		A	B
FU6	Wolf and birds (from "Hortus Sanitatis", 1497)	7·00	7·00
	a. Inside cover text for FL12............................	11·00	11·00

No. FU6 is inscribed "October 1986".

The inside cover text for FU6a has the special offer of the £1·30 booklet, No. FL12 (four 13p. stamps).

1988 (12 Apr). *Recipe Cards*. Cover as Type FL **13** (90×49 mm) printed in claret and Indian red. Containing ten 18p. stamps (No. X955). A. Selvedge at left. B. Selvedge at right.

		A	B
FU7	Fruits, pudding and jam design	7·00	7·00

No. FU7 is inscribed "October 1986".

1988 (5 July). *Children's Parties* Cover as Type FL **14** (90×49 mm) printed in violet and rosine. Containing ten 18p. stamps (No. X955). A. Selvedge at left. B. Selvedge at right.

		A	B
FU8	Balloons and party hats design	7·00	7·00

No. FU8 is inscribed "October 1986".

£1.90 Booklets

1988 (5 Sept). *Pocket Planner* Cover as Type FM **5** (90×49 mm) printed in yellow-green and magenta. Containing ten 19p. stamps (No. X956). A. Selvedge at left. B. Selvedge at right.

		A	B
FV1	"Marriage Act" design	8·75	8·75

1989 (24 Jan). *150th Anniv of Fox Talbot's Report on the Photographic Process to Royal Society*. Cover as Type FM **6** (90×49 mm) printed in emerald and black. Containing ten 19p. stamps (No. X956). A. Selvedge at left. B. Selvedge at right.

		A	B
FV2	Fox Talbot with camera and Lacock Abbey...........	8·75	8·75

No. FV2 is inscribed "September 1988".

£2 Booklets

FW **1**

(Des Debbie Cook)

1993 (1 Nov)–**94**. *Postal Vehicles Series*. Covers as Type FW **1**. Containing eight 25p. (No. Y1689).

FW1	Design No. 1 (cover in dull vermilion and deep blue), Motorised cycle-carrier	6·50
FW2	Design No. 2 (cover in green and deep violet-blue), Experimental motor-mail van (26.4.94)	6·50
FW3	Design No. 3 (cover in red and black), Experimental electric mail van, 1932 (6.9.94)	6·50

FW **3**

(Des The Four Hundred)

1995 (7 Feb–4 Apr). *Birth Bicentenary of Sir Rowland Hill*. Covers as Type FW **3**. Containing eight 25p. (No. Y1689).

FW4	Design No. 1 (cover in purple and new blue), Rowland Hill as Director of London and Brighton Railway Company	6·50
FW5	Design No. 2 (cover in deep mauve and greenish blue), Rowland Hill and Hazlewood School (4.4.95)	6·50

1995 (6 June–4 Sept). *Birth Bicentenary of Sir Rowland Hill Series* continued. Covers as Type FW **3**. Containing eight 25p. (No. Y1690).

FW6	Design No. 3 (cover in deep blue-green and dull orange), Rowland Hill as Secretary to the Post Office...........	7·00
FW7	Design No. 4 (cover in red-brown and orange), Uniform Penny Postage petition and Mulready envelope (4.9.95).	7·00

1996 (16 Jan). Multicoloured laminated cover as Type FH **40**. Stamps printed in litho by Questa.

FW8	Containing eight 25p. stamps (No. Y1775)	7·50

For an initial test period No. FW 8 was only available from machines at twelve post offices, five in London and seven in Scotland, in addition to philatelic outlets. Stocks were distributed nationally from May 1996.

1996 (8 July)–**97**. Multicoloured laminated cover as Type FH **40**. Stamps printed in litho by Questa.

FW9	Containing booklet pane of 20p. and 26p.×7 (No. Y1772l)	8·00
	a. Corrected rate (4.2.97)..................................	8·00
	b. Inland rate table inside at right (5.5.98)...........................	8·00

No. FW9 was reissued on 4 February 1997 showing the 200g second class rate on the inside cover altered from 47p. to 45p. A further printing issued 5 May 1998 was without the overseas postage rate table.

1998 (1 Dec). Multicoloured laminated cover as Type FH **40**. Stamps printed in gravure by Questa.

FW10	Containing booklet pane of 20p. and 26p.×7 (No. Y1685l)	35·00

1999 (26 Apr). Multicoloured laminated cover as Type FH **40**. Stamps printed in gravure by Questa.

FW11	Containing booklet pane of 19p. and 26p.×7 (No. Y1682l)	13·00

2000 (27 Apr). Multicoloured laminated cover as Type FH **40**. Stamps printed in gravure by Questa.

FW12	Containing booklet pane of 2nd×2 and 1st×6 (No. 1664m)	8·00

Christmas Booklets

FX **1**

(Des J. Matthews)

1978 (15 Nov). *Christmas Greetings* Cover Type FX **1** (90×49 mm). Printed in rose-red and sage-green.

FX1	£1.60, containing booklet pane No. X875l	5·50

No. FX1 is inscribed "August 1978".

FX **2**

(Des P. Sharland)

1979 (14 Nov). *Christmas Greetings* Red and green cover as Type FX **2** (90×49 mm), showing Christmas cracker.

FX2	£1.80, containing booklet pane No. X879l	6·50

No. FX2 is inscribed "October 1979".

FX **3**

(Des E. Fraser)

1980 (12 Nov). *Christmas*. Red and blue cover as Type FX **3** (90×49 mm), showing Nativity scene.

FX3	£2.20, containing booklet pane No. X888m	7·00

No. FX3 is inscribed "September 1980".

FX **4**

(Des W. Sanderson)

1981 (11 Nov). *Christmas.* Red and blue cover as Type FX **4**, (90×49 mm), showing skating scene.
FX4   £2·55, containing booklet pane No. X893l ....   8·50
No. FX4 is inscribed "January 1981".

FX **5**

(Des A. Davidson)

1982 (10 Nov). *Christmas.* Red and green cover as Type FX **5** (90×49 mm), showing Christmas Mummers.
FX5   £2·50, containing booklet pane No. X898l ....   10·00
No. FX5 is inscribed "February 1982" and was sold at a discount of 30p. off the face value of the stamps.
Each stamp in the pane has a blue star printed on the reverse over the gum.

FX **6**

(Des Barbara Brown)

1983 (9 Nov). *Christmas.* Brown-lilac and yellow cover as Type FX **6** (90×49 mm), showing pantomime scenes.
FX6   £2·20, containing twenty 12½p. (No. X898Ev) ....   8·50
No. FX6 is inscribed "April 1983" and was sold at a discount of 30p. off the face value of the stamps.
Each stamp in the pane has a double-lined blue star printed on the reverse over the gum.

FX **7**

(Des Yvonne Gilbert)

1984 (20 Nov). *Christmas*. Light brown and red-orange cover as Type FX **7** (90×60 mm), showing Nativity scene.
FX7   £2·30, containing twenty 13p. (No. 1267Eu) ....   10·00

No. FX7 is inscribed "September 1984" and was sold at a discount of 30p. off the face value of the stamps.
The stamps from this booklet show double-lined blue stars printed on the reverse over the gum.

FX **8**

(Des A. George)

1985 (19 Nov). *Christmas.* Bright blue and rose cover as Type FX **8** (90×60 mm), showing The Pantomime.
FX8   £2·40, containing twenty 12p. (No. 1303Eu)............................   9·00
The stamps from this booklet show double-lined blue stars printed on the reverse over the gum.

FX **9**

(Des Lynda Gray)

1986 (2 Dec). *Christmas.* Red and dull blue-green cover as Type FX **9** (90×49 mm), showing Shetland Yule cakes. A. Selvedge at left. B. Selvedge at right.

	A	B
FX9 £1·20, containing ten 13p. (No. X900Eu)	9·00	16·00

No. FX9 is inscribed "October 1986" and was sold at a discount of 10p. off the face value of the stamps.
Each stamp in the pane has a blue star printed on the reverse over the gum.
For 1990 and later Christmas stamps, see Barcode Booklets Section G.

£1.90 Greetings Booklet

FY **1**

(Des L. Moberly)

1989 (31 Jan). *Greetings Stamps.* Multicoloured cover as Type FY **1** (89×60 mm). Containing booklet pane No. 1423a, including twelve special greetings labels in a block (3×4) at right, attached by the selvedge.
FY1   Greetings design ....   36·00
No. FY1 is inscribed "September 1988".
The cover of No. FY **1** shows an overall pattern of elements taken from the stamp designs. Due to the method of production the position of these elements varies from cover to cover.
For Greetings stamps in Barcode booklets, see Barcode Booklets Section F.

JERWOOD PHILATELICS

(Established 2010)

Great Britain dealer specialising in:

* Stitched Booklets
* Folded Booklets
* Window Booklets
* Prestige Booklets
* Greetings & Christmas Booklets
* Machins, including Cylinder, Date Blocks etc.
* Smilers™ Sheets, inc. Business Customised Sheets
* Post & Go™ stamps
* Modern commemoratives, inc. errors & varieties
* Royal Mail Year Books & Year Packs
* Accessories, including stockcards, mounts etc.
* Range of newly published catalogues
* Selected material from earlier reigns

Collections & quality single items bought

Detailed booklet listings using both the Stanley Gibbons and Modern British Philatelic Circle catalogues.

Website: www.jerwoodphilatelics.co.uk
Email: dave@jerwoodphilatelics.co.uk
Telephone: (0121) 663 0415

Insert concise16 at checkout to receive a 10% discount on any order over £25. Free P&P on all UK orders.

BARCODE BOOKLETS

These booklets are listed in 11 sections.

SECTION C. G numbers containing Machin stamps with face values

SECTION D. H numbers containing Machin NVI stamps

SECTION E. J numbers containing Machin Penny Black Anniversary stamps

SECTION F. KX numbers containing Greetings stamps

SECTION G. LX numbers containing Christmas stamps

SECTION H. M numbers containing self-adhesive NVI definitive stamps

SECTION I. N numbers containing self-adhesive definitive stamps with face values

SECTION J. PM numbers containing both special and definitive self-adhesive NVI stamps

SECTION K. Q numbers containing NVI "Smilers" stamps in definitive size

SECTION L. R numbers containing stamps with value indicator at upper left

SECTION M. SA numbers containing NVI "Smilers" stamps and definitive stamps.

These are produced for sale in both post offices and commercial outlets.

NOTE: All panes are attached to the covers by the selvedge. Barcode booklet covers are illustrated at two-thirds linear size *unless otherwise stated.*

C. Barcode Booklets containing Machin stamps with values shown as Type 367.

COVERS. These are all printed in scarlet, lemon and black with the barcode on the reverse. Type GA **1** has a clear "window" to view the contents. Type GB **3** is shorter and has a stamp illustration printed on the cover to replace the "window". These illustrations show an oblique white line across the bottom right-hand corner of the "stamp". Unless otherwise stated all covers were printed by Harrison.

From early 1997 the printer of each booklet is identified by a small capital letter below the barcode on the outside back cover.

52p. Booklet

GA **1**

1987 (4 Aug). Laminated cover Type GA **1** (75×60 mm).
GA1   Containing booklet pane No. X900n ....   4·00
    No. GA1 is inscribed "20 October 1986".

56p. Booklets

1988 (23 Aug). Laminated cover as Type GA **1** (75×56 mm).
GB1   Containing booklet pane No. X903l ....   6·00
1988 (11 Oct). Laminated cover as Type GA **1** (75×56 mm) printed by Walsall.
GB2   Containing booklet pane No. X903l ....   10·00

GB **3** Large Crown

1988 (11 Oct). Laminated cover as Type GB **3** (75×48 mm) with stamp printed on the cover in deep blue.
GB3   Containing booklet pane No. X903n ....   8·00
    No. GB3 is inscribed "5 September 1988" and has the horizontal edges of the pane imperforate.

1989 (24 Jan). Laminated cover as Type GB **3** (75×48 mm) with stamp printed on the cover in deep blue by Walsall.
GB4   Containing booklet pane No. X903q ....   40·00
    No. GB4 is inscribed "5 September 1988" and has the three edges of the pane imperforate.

72p. Booklet

1987 (4 Aug). Laminated cover as Type GA **1** (75×60 mm).
GC1   Containing booklet pane No. X955m ....   4·00
    No. GC1 is inscribed "20 October 1986".

76p. Booklets

1988 (23 Aug). Laminated cover as Type GA **1** (75×56 mm).
GD1   Containing booklet pane No. X956l ....   8·00

1988 (11 Oct). Laminated cover as Type GA **1** (75×56 mm) printed by Walsall.
GD2   Containing booklet pane No. X956l ....   8·00

1988 (11 Oct). Laminated cover as Type GB **3** (75×48 mm) with stamp printed on the cover in bright orange-red.
GD3   Containing booklet pane No. X956n ....   9·50
    No. GD3 is inscribed "5 September 1988" and has the horizontal edges of the pane imperforate.

1989 (24 Jan). Laminated cover as Type GB **3** (75×48 mm) with stamp printed on the cover in bright orange-red by Walsall.
GD4   Containing booklet pane No. X956q ....   40·00
    No. GD4 is inscribed "5 September 1988" and has the three edges of the pane imperforate.

78p. Booklet

GD **4a** (As Type GM **1** but without "4")

1992 (28 July). Multicoloured laminated cover as Type GD **4a** (75×49 mm) with stamp printed on the cover in bright mauve by Walsall.
GD4a   Containing two 39p. stamps (No. X1058) (pane No. X1058l with right-hand vert pair removed) and pane of 4 air mail labels ....   5·00
    Stamps in No. GD4a have top or bottom edge imperforate. Booklet No. GD4a was produced in connection with a Kellogg's Bran Flakes promotion.

£1.04 Booklet

1987 (4 Aug). Laminated cover as Type GA **1** (75×60 mm).
GE1   Containing booklet pane No. X971bl ....   22·00
    No. GE1 is inscribed "20 October 1986".

£1.08 Booklets

1988 (23 Aug). Laminated cover as Type GA **1** (75×56 mm).
GF1   Containing booklet pane No. X973l ....   14·00
    a. Postage rates omitted from inside back cover ....   21·00

1988 (11 Oct). Laminated cover as Type GB **3** (75×48 mm) with stamp printed on the cover in chestnut.
GF2   Containing booklet pane No. X973m ....   40·00
    No. GF2 is inscribed "5 September 1988" and has the horizontal edges of the pane imperforate.

£1.16 Booklets

GG **1** Redrawn Crown

1989 (2 Oct). Laminated cover as Type GG **1** (75×48 mm) with stamp printed on the cover in deep mauve by Walsall.
GG1   Containing booklet pane No. X1054I ....   18·00
No. GG1 has three edges of the pane imperforate.

1990 (17 Apr). Laminated cover as Type GG **1** (75×48 mm) with stamp printed on the cover in deep mauve by Walsall.
GG2   Containing booklet pane No. X1055I.................................   22·00
No. GG2 has three edges of the pane imperforate.

£1.20 Booklets

GGA **1** ("BY AIR MAIL *par avion*" at bottom left)

1998 (5 May). Multicoloured laminated cover as Type GGA **1** (75×50 mm) with stamps printed on cover in olive-grey by Walsall. Inscr For items up to 20g" on yellow tab at right.
GGA1   Containing four 30p. (gravure) (No. Y1694) and a pane of 4 air mail labels ....   4·25

GGA **2** "Create a card Design"

1998 (3 Aug). Multicoloured laminated cover as Type GGA **2** (75×50 mm) printed by Walsall. Inscr See inside for offer details" on yellow tab at right.
GGA2   Containing four 30p. (gravure) (No. Y1694) and a pane of 4 air mail labels ....   4·25
This booklet was not placed on philatelic sale until 7 September 1998.

£1.24 Booklet

GH **1** Crown on White

1990 (17 Sept). Multicoloured laminated cover as Type GH **1** (75×49 mm) with stamp printed on the cover in ultramarine by Walsall.
GH1   Containing booklet pane No. X1056I ....   8·50
No. GH1 has the horizontal edges of the pane imperforate.

£1.30 Booklet

1987 (4 Aug). Laminated cover as Type GA **1** (98×60 mm).
GI1   Containing booklet pane No. X900o ....   6·00
No. GI1 is inscribed "20 October 1986".

£1.32 Booklet

GJ **1**

1991 (16 Sept)–**92**. Multicoloured laminated cover as Type GJ **1** (75×49 mm) with stamp printed on the cover in light emerald by Walsall. Inscr For letters up to 10g" on yellow strip at right.
GJ1   Containing booklet pane No. X1057I and a pane of 4 air mail labels ....   8·00
a. Inscr "For Worldwide Postcards" on yellow strip (8.9.92)   12·00
Nos. GJ1/a have the horizontal edges of the pane imperforate.

£1.40 Booklets

1988 (23 Aug). Laminated cover as Type GA **1** (97×56 mm).
GK1   Containing booklet pane No. X903m ....   16·00

1988 (11 Oct). Laminated cover as Type GA **1** (97×56 mm) printed by Questa.
GK2   Containing ten 14p. (No. X1007) ....   18·00

1988 (11 Oct). Laminated cover as Type GB **3** (75×48 mm) with stamp printed on the cover in deep blue.
GK3   Containing booklet pane No. X903p ....   10·00
No. GK3 is inscribed "5 September 1988" and has horizontal edges of the pane imperforate.

1988 (11 Oct). Laminated cover as Type GB **3** (75×48 mm) with stamp printed on the cover in deep blue by Questa.
GK4   Containing ten 14p. (No. X1007) ....   18·00

1993 (1 Nov). Laminated cover as Type GJ **1** (76×50 mm) with stamp printed on the cover in yellow by Walsall. Inscribed "For Worldwide Postcards" on yellow tab at right.
GK5   Containing four 35p. (No. Y1778) and a pane of 4 air mail labels ....   6·25

Type GK **6** (without diagonal white line across corners of stamps)

1995 (16 May). Multicoloured laminated cover as Type GK **6** (75×48 mm) with stamps printed on the cover in yellow by Walsall.
GK6   Containing four 35p. (No. Y1778) and a pane of 4 air mail labels ....   6·25

1996 (19 Mar). Multicoloured laminated cover as Type GK **6** (75×48 mm) without *International* and showing Olympic symbols on the back. Stamps printed on the cover in yellow by Walsall.
GK7   Containing four 35p. (No. Y1778) and a pane of 4 air mail labels ....   6·50

£1.48 Booklets

GL **1** ("Worldwide Postcard Stamps" ranged left without diagonal white lines across corner of stamps)

1996 (8 July). Multicoloured laminated cover as Type GL **1** (75×48 mm) showing Olympic symbols on the back. Stamps printed on the cover in bright mauve by Walsall. Inscribed *For Worldwide Postcards* on yellow tab at right.
GL1   Containing four 37p. (No. Y1779) and a pane of 4 air mail labels .... 10·00

1997 (4 Feb). Multicoloured laminated cover as Type GL **1** (75×48 mm) without Olympic symbols on the back. Stamps printed on the cover in bright mauve by Walsall. Inscribed *For Worldwide Postcards* on yellow tab at right.
GL2   Containing four 37p. (No. Y1779) and a pane of 4 air mail labels .... 10·00

GL **3**

1997 (26 Aug)–**98**. Multicoloured laminated cover as Type GL **3** (75×48 mm) printed by Walsall. Inscribed *For Worldwide Postcards* on yellow tab at right.
GL3   Containing four 37p. (gravure) (No. Y1703) and a pane of 4 new design air mail labels .... 6·00
       a. Showing validity notice on inside backcover (5.5.98).... 6·00
    No. GL3 has the postage rate table on the inside back cover.

1998 (3 Aug). Multicoloured laminated cover as Type GGA **2** (Create a card design) (75×50 mm) printed by Walsall.
GL4   Containing four 37p. (gravure) (No. Y1703) and a pane of 4 air mail labels .... 5·00
    This booklet was not placed on philatelic sale until 7 September 1998.

£1.52 Booklet

1999 (26 Apr). Multicoloured laminated cover as Type GGA **1** (76×50 mm) with stamps printed on cover in ultramarine by Walsall. Inscr *For Worldwide Postcards* on yellow tab at right.
GLA1   Containing four 38p. (gravure) (No. Y1707) and a pane of 4 air mail labels .... 6·00

£1.56 Booklet

GM **1**

1991 (16 Sept). Multicoloured laminated cover as Type GM **1** (75×49 mm) with stamp printed on the cover in bright mauve by Walsall.
GM1   Containing booklet pane No. X1058l and a pane of 4 air mail labels .... 11·00
    No. GM1 has the horizontal edges of the pane imperforate.

£1.60 Booklet

2000 (27 Apr). Multicoloured laminated cover as Type GGA **1** (76×50 mm) with stamps printed on cover in deep azure by Walsall. Inscr *For Worldwide Postcards* on yellow tab at right.
GMA1 Containing four 40p. (gravure) (No. Y1710) and a pane of 4 air mail labels .... 7·50

£1.64 Worldwide Air Mail Stamps Booklets

1993 (1 Nov). Laminated cover as Type GM **1** (76×50 mm) with stamp printed on the cover in drab by Walsall. Inscribed *For letters up to 10g* on yellow tab at right.
GN1   Containing four 41p. (No. Y1780) and a pane of 4 air mail labels .... 6·00

1995 (16 May). Multicoloured laminated cover as Type GK **6** (75×48 mm) with stamp printed on the cover in drab by Walsall. Inscribed *For items up to 10g* on yellow tab at right.
GN2   Containing four 41p. (No. Y1780) and a pane of 4 air mail labels .... 6·00

1996 (19 Mar). Multicoloured laminated cover as Type GK **6** (75×48 mm) without *International* and showing Olympic symbols on the back. Stamps printed on the cover in drab by Walsall. Inscribed *For items up to 10g* on yellow tab at right.
GN3   Containing four 41p. (No. Y1780) and a pane of 4 air mail labels .... 7·00

£1.80 Booklet

1987 (4 Aug). Laminated cover as Type GA **1** (98×60 mm).
GO1   Containing booklet pane No. X955n .... 9·00
    No. GO1 is inscribed "20 October 1986".

£1.90 Booklets

1988 (23 Aug). Laminated cover as Type GA **1** (97×56 mm).
GP1   Containing booklet pane No. X956m .... 12·00

1988 (11 Oct). Laminated cover as Type GA **1** (97×56 mm) printed by Questa.
GP2   Containing ten 19p. (No. X1013) .... 24·00

1988 (11 Oct). Laminated cover as Type GB **3** (75×48 mm) with stamp printed on the cover in bright orange-red.
GP3   Containing booklet pane No. X956o .... 12·00
    No. GP 3 is inscribed "5 September 1988" and has the horizontal edges of the pane imperforate.

1988 (11 Oct). Laminated cover as Type GB **3** (75×48 mm) with stamp printed on the cover in bright orange-red by Questa.
GP4   Containing ten 19p. (No. X1013) .... 24·00

£2.40 Booklets

1994 (9 Aug). Laminated cover as Type GM **1** (75×49 mm) with stamp printed on the cover in dull blue-grey by Walsall. Inscribed *items up to 20g* on yellow tab at right.
GQ1   Containing four 60p. (No. Y1784) and a pane of 4 air mail labels .... 8·00

GQ **2**

1994 (4 Oct). Laminated cover as Type GQ **2** (75×49 mm) with stamp printed on the cover in dull blue-grey by Walsall.
GQ2   Containing four 60p. (No. Y1784) and a pane of 4 air mail plus 4 "Seasons Greetings" labels .... 12·00

1995 (16 May). Laminated cover as Type GK **6** (75×48 mm) with stamps printed on the cover in dull blue-grey by Walsall. Inscribed *For items up to 20g* on yellow tab at right.
GQ3   Containing four 60p. (No. Y1784) and a pane of 4 air mail labels .... 12·00

1996 (19 Mar). Multicoloured laminated cover as Type GK **6** (75×48 mm) without *International* and showing Olympic symbols on the back. Stamps printed on the cover in dull grey blue by Walsall. Inscribed *For items up to 20g* on yellow tab at right.
GQ4   Containing four 60p. (No. Y1784) and a pane of 4 air mail labels .... 12·00

£2.52 Booklets

1996 (8 July). Multicoloured laminated cover as Type GL **1** (75×48 mm) but inscr *Worldwide Airmail Stamps* and showing Olympic symbols on the back. Stamps printed on the cover in light emerald by Walsall. Inscribed *For items up to 20g* on yellow tab at right.
GR1   Containing four 63p. (No. Y1787) and a pane of 4 air mail labels .... 15·00

1997 (4 Feb). Multicoloured laminated cover as Type GL **1** (75×48 mm) without Olympic symbols on the back. Stamps printed on the cover in light emerald by Walsall. Inscribed *For items up to 20g* on yellow tab at right.
GR2   Containing four 63p. (No. Y1787) and a pane of 4 air mail labels .... 15·00

1997 (26 Aug). Multicoloured laminated cover as Type GL **1** (75×48 mm). Stamps printed on the cover in light emerald by Walsall. Inscribed *For items up to 20g* on yellow tab at right.
GR3   Containing four 63p. (gravure) (No. Y1732) and a pane of 4 air mail labels .... 9·00

1998 (5 May). Multicoloured laminated cover as Type GGA **1** (75×50 mm). Stamps printed on the cover in light emerald by Walsall. Inscribed *For items up to 20g* on yellow tab at right.
GR4   Containing four 63p. (gravure) (No. Y1732) and a pane of 4 new design air mail labels .... 9·00

£2.56 Booklets

1999 (26 Apr). Multicoloured laminated cover as Type GGA **1** (75×50 mm). Stamps printed on cover in turquoise-green by Walsall. Inscribed *For items up to 20g* on yellow tab at right.
GS1   Containing four 64p. (gravure) (No.1734) and a pane of 4 air mail labels .... 9·00

£2.60 Booklet

2000 (27 Apr). Multicoloured laminated cover as Type GGA **1** (76×50 mm) with stamps printed on cover in greenish blue by Walsall. Inscr *For items up to 20g* on yellow tab at right.
GT1   Containing four 65p. (gravure) (No.Y1734) and a pane of 4 air mail labels .... 10·00

D. Barcode Booklets containing No Value Indicated stamps with barcodes on the back cover.

Panes of four 2nd Class stamps.

HA **1** Redrawn Crown (small)

1989 (22 Aug). Laminated cover as Type HA **1** (75×48 mm) with stamp printed on the cover in bright blue by Walsall.
HA1   Containing booklet pane No.1449b .... 10·00
   No. HA1 has three edges of the pane imperforate.
   No. HA1 was initially sold at 56p., which was increased to 60p. from 2.10.89.

1989 (28 Nov). Laminated cover as Type HA **1** (75×48 mm) with stamp printed on the cover in bright blue by Walsall containing stamps printed in gravure by Harrison.
HA2   Containing booklet pane No.1445b .... 35·00
   No. HA2 has three edges of the pane imperforate and was sold at 60p.

HA **3** Crown on white

1990 (7 Aug). Multicoloured laminated cover as Type HA **3** (75×48 mm) with stamp printed on the cover in deep blue by Walsall.
HA3   Containing booklet pane No.1515a .... 6·50
   No. HA3 has the horizontal edges of the pane imperforate.
   No. HA3 was initially sold at 60p., which was increased to 68p. from 17.9.90 and to 72p. from 16.9.91.

1991 (6 Aug). Multicoloured laminated cover as Type HA **3** (75×48 mm) with stamp printed on the cover in bright blue by Walsall (25.9.92). Barcode in black.
HA4   Containing booklet pane No.1449c.......................... 5·00
   a. Barcode printed in blue .... 3·50
   No. HA4 has the horizontal edges of the pane imperforate.
   No. HA4 was initially sold at 68p., which was increased to 72p. from 16.9.91.
   No. HA4 exists with the barcode printed in either black or blue.

HA **5** Olympic Symbols

1992 (21 Jan). Multicoloured laminated cover as Type HA **5** (75×48 mm) with stamp printed on the cover in bright blue by Walsall.
HA5   Containing booklet pane No.1449c........................ 7·00
   No. HA5 has the horizontal edges of the pane imperforate and was sold at 72p.

PERFORATIONS. Booklets from No. HA6 show perforations on all edges of the pane.

1993 (6 Apr). Multicoloured laminated cover as Type HA **3** (75×48 mm) with stamp printed on the cover in bright blue by Walsall.
HA6   Containing four 2nd Class stamps (No.1670) .... 5·00
   No. HA6 was initially sold at 72p., which was increased to 76p. from 1.11.93.
   No. HA6 was re-issued on 6 December 1994 showing the inscriptions on the inside of the cover re-arranged.

1993 (7 Sept). Multicoloured laminated cover as Type HA **3** (75×48 mm) with stamp printed on the cover in bright blue by Harrison.
HA7   Containing four 2nd Class stamps (No.1664) .... 5·00
   No. HA7 was initially sold at 72p., which was increased to 76p. from 1.11.93.

Type HA **8** ("Second Class Stamps" centred) (with diagonal white line across corners of stamps)

1995 (10 Jan). Multicoloured laminated cover as Type HA **8** (75×48 mm) with stamps printed on the cover in bright blue by Harrison.
HA8   Containing four 2nd Class stamps (No.1664) .... 5·00
   No. HA8 was initially sold at 76p, which was increased to 80p. from 8.7.96.

1995 (12 Dec). Multicoloured laminated cover as Type HA **8** (75×48 mm) with stamps printed on the cover in bright blue by Walsall, but without *Pull Open* inscription on yellow tab.
HA9   Containing four 2nd Class stamps (No.1670) .... 5·00
   No. HA9 was initially sold at 76p, which was increased to 80p. from 8.7.96.

1996 (6 Feb). Multicoloured laminated cover as Type HA **8** (75×48 mm) but without *Pull Open* inscription on yellow tab and showing Olympic symbols on the back. Stamps printed on the cover in bright blue by Walsall.
HA10   Containing four 2nd Class stamps (No.1670)...................... 5·00
   No. HA10 was initially sold at 76p, which was increased to 80p. from 8.7.96.

NOTE: From No. HA11 onwards, the printer of each booklet is identified by a small capital letter below the barcode on the outside back cover.

HA **11** ("Second Class Stamps" ranged left) (without diagonal white line across corners of stamps)

1997 (4 Feb). Multicoloured laminated cover as Type HA **11** (75×48 mm). Stamps printed on the cover in bright blue by Walsall.
HA11   Containing four 2nd Class stamps (No.1670) .... 5·00
   No. HA11 was sold at 80p.

1997 (26 Aug). Multicoloured laminated cover as Type HA **11** (75×48 mm). Stamps printed on the cover in bright blue by Walsall.
HA12   Containing four 2nd Class stamps (gravure) (No.1664)..   5·00
   No. HA12 was initially sold at 80p. It was re-issued on 5 May 1998 showing the positions of the imprint and the post code notice transposed, and again on 14 March 2000 with changed telephone number and added website address. The booklet was sold at 76p. from 26.4.99.

Panes of four 1st Class stamps

1989 (22 Aug). Laminated cover as Type HA **1** (75×48 mm) with stamp printed on the cover in brownish black by Walsall.

HB1	Containing booklet pane No. 1450a	8·50

No. HB1 has three edges of the pane imperforate.

No. HB1 was initially sold at 76p., which was increased to 80p. from 2.10.89.

1989 (5 Dec). Laminated cover as Type HA **1** (75×48 mm) with stamp printed on the cover in brownish black by Walsall containing stamps printed in photo by Harrison.

HB2	Containing booklet pane No. 1447b	42·00

No. HB2 has three edges of the pane imperforate and was sold at 80p.

1990 (7 Aug). Multicoloured laminated cover as Type HA **3** (75×48 mm) with stamp printed on the cover in bright orange-red by Walsall (22.9.92). Barcode in black.

HB3	Containing booklet pane No. 1516a	5·00
	a. Containing pane No. 1516ca	28·00
	b. Barcode in blue	4·00

No. HB3 has the horizontal edges of the pane imperforate.

No. HB3 was initially sold at 80p., which was increased to 88p. from 17.9.90 and to 96p. from 16.9.91.

1992 (21 Jan). Multicoloured laminated cover as Type HA **5** (75×48 mm) with stamp printed on the cover in bright orange-red by Walsall.

HB4	Containing booklet pane No. 1516a	5·00

No. HB4 has the horizontal edges of the pane imperforate and was initially sold at 96p., which was increased to £1 from 1.11.93.

PERFORATIONS. Booklets from No. HB5 show perforations on all edges of the pane.

1993 (6 Apr). Multicoloured laminated cover as Type HA **3** (75×48 mm) with stamp printed on the cover in bright orange-red by Harrison.

HB5	Containing four 1st Class stamps (No. 1666)	7·00

No. HB5 was initially sold at 96p., which was increased to £1 from 1.11.93.

1993 (17 Aug). Multicoloured laminated cover as Type HA **3** (76×50 mm) with stamp printed on the cover in bright orange-red by Walsall.

HB6	Containing four 1st Class stamps (No. 1671)	5·00

No. HB6 was initially sold at 96p., which was increased to £1 from 1.11.93.

1994 (27 July). Multicoloured laminated cover as Type HA **3** (76×50 mm) with stamp printed on the cover in bright orange-red by Questa.

HB7	Containing booklet pane No. 1671l which includes a label commemorating the 300th anniv of the Bank of England	10·00

No. HB7 was sold at £1.

1995 (10 Jan). Multicoloured laminated cover as Type HA **8** (75×48 mm) with stamps printed on the cover in bright orange-red by Walsall.

HB8	Containing four 1st Class stamps (No. 1671)	5·00

No. HB8 was initially sold at £1, which was increased to £1·04 from 8.7.96.

1995 (16 May). Multicoloured laminated cover as Type HA **8** (75×48 mm) with stamps printed on the cover in bright orange-red by Walsall.

HB9	Containing booklet pane No. 1671la which includes a label commemorating the birth centenary of R. J. Mitchell (designer of Spitfire)	7·50

No. HB9 was sold at £1.

1996 (6 Feb–Aug). Multicoloured laminated cover as Type HA **8** (75×48 mm) showing Olympic symbols on the back. Stamps printed on the cover in bright orange-red by Walsall.

HB10	Containing four 1st Class stamps (No. 1671)	6·00
	a. Without diagonal white line across corners of stamps (Aug)	£175

No. HB10 was initially sold at £1, which was increased to £1·04 from 8.7.96.

1996 (16 Apr). Multicoloured laminated cover as Type HA **11** (75×48 mm) with stamps printed on the cover in bright orange-red by Walsall. Inscribed Commemorative Label Inside" on yellow tab at right.

HB11	Containing booklet pane No. 1671la (includes label commemorating the 70th birthday of Queen Elizabeth II)	8·00

No. HB11 was initially sold at £1, which was increased to £1·04 from 8.7.96.

NOTE: From No. HB12 onwards, the printer of each booklet (with the exception of No. HB19) is identified by a small capital letter below the barcode on the outside back cover.

1997 (4 Feb). Multicoloured laminated cover as Type HA **11** (75×48 mm). Stamps printed on the cover in bright orange-red by Walsall.

HB12	Containing four 1st Class stamps (No. 1671)	5·00

No. HB12 was sold at £1·04.

1997 (12 Feb). Multicoloured laminated cover as Type HA **11** (75×48 mm). Stamps printed on the cover in bright orange-red by Walsall. Inscribed Special Label Inside" on yellow tab at right.

HB13	Containing booklet pane No. 1671la (includes label commemorating Hong Kong '97 international stamp exhibition)	7·50

No. HB13 was sold at £1·04.

1997 (26 Aug). Multicoloured laminated cover as Type HA **11** (75×48 mm). Stamps printed on the cover in bright orange-red by Walsall.

HB14	Containing four 1st Class stamps (gravure) (No. 1667)	5·00

No. HB14 was sold at £1·04. It was re-issued on 5 May 1998 showing the positions of the imprint and the post code notice transposed, on 16 March 1999 with "Please note that the First Class rate is no longer valid to Europe" added to inside back cover and again on 14 March 2000 with changed telephone number and added website address.

1997 (21 Oct). Multicoloured laminated cover as Type HA **11** (75×48 mm). Stamps printed on the cover in bright orange-red by Walsall. Inscribed "Commemorative Label Inside" on yellow tab at right.

HB15	Containing booklet pane No. 1671la (litho) (includes label commemorating Commonwealth Heads of Government Meeting, Edinburgh)	14·00

No. HB15 was sold at £1·04.

1998 (14 Nov). Multicoloured laminated cover as Type HA **11** (75×48 mm). Stamps printed on the cover in bright orange-red by Walsall. Inscribed Commemorative Label Inside" on yellow tab at right.

HB16	Containing booklet pane No. 1671la (litho) (includes label commemorating 50th birthday of the Prince of Wales)	9·00

No. HB16 was sold at £1·04.

1999 (12 May). Multicoloured laminated cover as Type HA **11** (75×48 mm). Stamps printed on the cover in bright orange-red by Walsall. Inscribed *Commemorative Label Inside* on yellow tab at right.

HB17	Containing booklet pane No. 1667m (gravure) (includes label commemorating 50th anniv of Berlin Airlift)	9·50

No. HB17 was sold for £1·04.

1999 (1 Oct). Multicoloured laminated cover as Type HA **11** (76×50 mm). Stamps printed on the cover in bright orange-red by Walsall. Inscribed *Commemorative Label Inside* on yellow tab at right.

HB18	Containing booklet pane No. 1667m (gravure) (includes label commemorating Rugby World Cup)	6·50

No. HB18 was sold at £1·04.

2000 (21 Mar). Multicoloured laminated cover as Type HA **11** (75×48 mm). Stamps printed on the cover in olive-brown by Walsall with Postman Pat. Inscribed *Postman Pat Label Inside* on yellow tab at right.

HB19	Containing booklet pane No. 2124bl (gravure) (includes label commemorating "Stamp Show 2000", Earls Court).	6·50

No. HB19 was initially sold at £1·04, which was increased to £1·08 from 27.4.2000.

2000 (4 Apr). *Opening of National Botanic Garden of Wales.* Multicoloured laminated cover as Type HA **11** (75×48 mm). Stamps printed on the cover in olive-brown by Walsall. Inscribed *Botanic Garden Label Inside* on yellow tab at right.

HB20	Containing booklet pane No. 2124bl	6·50

No. HB20 was initially sold at £1·04, which was increased to £1·08 from 27.4.2000.

Panes of eight 1st Class stamps plus pane of 2 Millennium commemoratives

HBA **1**

1999 (12 May). Multicoloured laminated cover as Type HBA **1** (76×50 mm) showing Millennium and Machin stamps printed by Walsall.

HBA1	Containing booklet pane No. 2085a and eight 1st Class stamps (gravure) (No. 1667)	14·00

No. HBA1 was sold at £2·60.

1999 (21 Sept). Multicoloured laminated cover as Type HBA **1** (76×50 mm) showing Millennium and Machin stamps printed by Walsall.

HBA2	Containing booklet pane No. 2108a and eight 1st Class stamps (gravure) (No. 1667)	14·00

No. HBA2 was sold at £2·60.

2000 (26 May). Multicoloured laminated cover as Type HBA **1** (76×50 mm) showing Millennium and Machin stamps printed by Walsall.

HBA3	Containing booklet pane No. 2126ab and eight 1st Class stamps (gravure) (No. 2124)	16·00

No. HBA3 was sold at £2·70.

2000 (18 Sept). Multicoloured laminated cover as Type HBA **1** (76×50 mm) showing Millennium and Machin stamps printed by Walsall.
HBA4 Containing booklet pane No. 2153a and eight 1st Class stamps (gravure) (No. 2124) .... 16·00
No. HBA4 was sold at £2·70.

Panes of ten 2nd Class stamps

1989 (22 Aug–2 Oct). Laminated cover as Type HA **1** (75×48 mm) with stamp printed on the cover in bright blue by Harrison.
HC1 Containing booklet pane No. 1445a .... 14·00
 a. Inside cover with new rates .... 15·00
Nos. HC1/a have the horizontal edges of the pane imperforate.
No. HC1 was initially sold at £1·40, which was increased to £1·50 from 2.10.89. No. HC1a was sold at £1·50.

1989 (19 Sept). Laminated cover as Type HA **1** (75×48 mm) with stamp printed on the cover in bright blue by Questa.
HC2 Containing ten 2nd Class stamps (No. 1451) .... 10·00
No. HC2 has perforations on all edges of the pane and was initially sold at £1·40, which was increased to £1·50 from 2.10.89.

1990 (7 Aug). Multicoloured laminated cover as Type HA **3** (75×48 mm) with stamp printed on the cover in deep blue by Harrison.
HC3 Containing booklet pane No. 1511a .... 15·00
No. HC3 has the horizontal edges of the pane imperforate.
No. HC3 was initially sold at £1·50, which was increased to £1·70 from 17.9.90.

1990 (7 Aug). Multicoloured laminated cover as Type HA **3** (75×48 mm) with stamp printed on the cover in deep blue by Questa.
HC4 Containing ten 2nd Class stamps (No. 1513) .... 18·00
No. HC4 has perforations on all edges of the pane and was initially sold at £1·50, which was increased to £1·70 from 17.9.90.

1990 (7 Aug). Multicoloured laminated cover as Type HA **3** (75×48 mm) with stamp printed on the cover in deep blue by Walsall.
HC5 Containing booklet pane No. 1515b .... 10·50
No. HC5 has the horizontal edges of the pane imperforate.
No. HC5 was initially sold at £1·50, which was increased to £1·70 from 17.9.90, and to £1·80 from 16.9.91.

1991 (6 Aug). Multicoloured laminated cover as Type HA **3** (75×48 mm) with stamp printed on the cover in bright blue by Questa. Barcode in black.
HC6 Containing ten 2nd Class stamps (No. 1451) .... 10·00
 a. Barcode printed in blue (22.9.92).. 10·00
No. HC6 has perforations on all edges of the pane and was initially sold at £1·70, which was increased to £1·80 from 16.9.91.

1991 (6 Aug). Multicoloured laminated cover as Type HA **3** (75×48 mm) with stamp printed on the cover in bright blue by Walsall. Barcode in black.
HC7 Containing booklet pane No. 1449d .... 10·00
 a. Barcode printed in blue (22.9.92).. 10·00
No. HC7 has the horizontal edges of the pane imperforate.
No. HC7 was initially sold at £1·70, which was increased to £1·80 from 16.9.91.

1992 (21 Jan). Multicoloured laminated cover as Type HA **5** (75×48 mm) with stamp printed on the cover in bright blue by Walsall.
HC8 Containing booklet pane No. 1449d .... 10·00
No. HC8 has the horizontal edges of the pane imperforate and was initially sold at £1·80, which was increased to £1·84 from 1.11.93.

1992 (31 Mar). Multicoloured laminated cover as Type HA **5** (75×48 mm) with stamp printed on the cover in bright blue by Questa.
HC9 Containing ten 2nd Class stamps (No. 1451) .... 10·00
No. HC9 has perforations on all edges of the pane and was sold at £1·80.

1992 (22 Sept). Multicoloured laminated cover as Type HA **3** (75×48 mm) with stamp printed on the cover in bright blue by Harrison.
HC10 Containing booklet pane No. 1445a .... 12·00
No. HC10 has the horizontal edges of the pane imperforate and was sold at £1·80.

PERFORATIONS. Booklets from No. HC11 show perforations on all edges of the pane.

1993 (6 Apr). Multicoloured laminated cover as Type HA **3** (75×48 mm) with stamp printed on the cover in bright blue by Questa.
HC11 Containing ten 2nd Class stamps (No. 1670) .... 8·50
No. HC11 was initially sold at £1·80, which was increased to £1·90 from 1.11.93.
No. HC11 was re-issued on 17 August 1993 showing changes to the text on the inside of the cover and again on 6 September 1994 showing further changes.

1993 (1 Nov). Multicoloured laminated cover as Type HA **3** (75×48 mm) with stamp printed on the cover in bright blue by Walsall.
HC12 Containing ten 2nd Class stamps (No. 1670) .... 10·00
No. HC12 was sold at £1·90.

1995 (10 Jan). Multicoloured laminated cover as Type HA **8** (75×48 mm) with stamps printed on the cover in bright blue by Questa.
HC13 Containing ten 2nd Class stamps (No. 1670) .... 10·00
No. HC13 was initially sold at £1·90, which was increased to £2 from 8.7.96.

1995 (12 Dec). Multicoloured laminated cover as Type HA **8** (75×48 mm) with stamps printed on cover in bright blue by Harrison.
HC14 Containing ten 2nd Class stamps (No. 1664) .... 8·50
No. HC14 was initially sold at £1·90, which was increased to £2 from 8.7.96.

1996 (6 Feb). Multicoloured laminated cover as Type HA **8** (75×48 mm) showing Olympic symbols on the back. Stamps printed on the cover in bright blue by Harrison.
HC15 Containing ten 2nd Class stamps (No. 1664)........................ 8·50
No. HC15 was initially sold at £1·90, which was increased to £2 from 8.7.96.

1996 (6 Feb). Multicoloured laminated cover as Type HA **8** (75×48 mm) showing Olympic symbols on the back. Stamps printed on the cover in bright blue by Questa.
HC16 Containing ten 2nd Class stamps (No. 1670) .... 10·00
No. HC16 was initially sold at £1·90, which was increased to £2 from 8.7.96.

NOTE: From No. HC17 onwards, the printer of each booklet is identified by a small capital letter below the barcode on the outside back cover.

1996 (6 Aug). Multicoloured laminated cover as Type HA **8** (75×48 mm) but with diagonal white lines across corners of stamps, showing Olympic symbols on the back. Stamps printed on the cover in bright blue by Harrison.
HC17 Containing ten 2nd Class stamps (No. 1664) .... 8·50
No. HC17 was sold at £2.

1996 (6 Aug). Multicoloured laminated cover as Type HA **11** (75×48 mm) showing Olympic symbols on the back. Stamps printed on the cover in bright blue by Questa.
HC18 Containing ten 2nd Class stamps (No. 1670) .... 10·00
No. HC18 was sold at £2.

1997 (4 Feb). Multicoloured laminated cover as Type HA **11** (75×48 mm). Stamps printed on the cover in bright blue by Harrison.
HC19 Containing ten 2nd Class stamps (No. 1664)........................ 8·50
No. HC19 was sold at £2.

1997 (4 Feb). Multicoloured laminated cover as Type HA **11** (75×48 mm). Stamps printed on the cover in bright blue by Questa.
HC20 Containing ten 2nd Class stamps (No. 1664)........................ 8·50
No. HC20 was initially sold at £2. It was re-issued on 5 May 1998 showing the positions of the imprint and the post code notice transposed. The booklet was sold at £1·90 from 26.4.99.

1998 (5 May). Multicoloured laminated cover as Type HA **11** (75×48 mm). Stamps printed on the cover in bright blue by De La Rue.
HC21 Containing ten 2nd Class stamps (No. 1664) .... 8·50
No. HC21 was initially sold at £2, which was decreased to £1·90 from 26.4.99.

1998 (1 Dec). Multicoloured laminated cover as Type HA **11** (75×48 mm). Stamps printed on the cover in bright blue by Questa.
HC22 Containing ten 2nd Class stamps (No. 1664a) (gravure) . 10·00
No. HC22 was initially sold at £2, which was decreased to £1·90 from 26.4.99. It was re-issued on 14 March 2000 with changed telephone number and added website address.

Panes of ten 1st Class stamps

1989 (22 Aug–2 Oct). Laminated cover as Type HA **1** (75×48 mm) with stamp printed on the cover in brownish black by Harrison.
HD1 Containing booklet pane No. 1447a .... 18·00
 a. Inside cover with new rates (2 Oct) .... 17·00
Nos. HD1/a have the horizontal edges of the pane imperforate.
No. HD1 was initially sold at £1·90, which was increased to £2 from 2.10.89. No. HD1a was sold at £2.

1989 (19 Sept). Laminated cover as Type HA **1** (75×48 mm) with stamp printed on the cover in brownish black by Questa.
HD2 Containing ten 1st Class stamps (No. 1452) .... 22·00
No. HD2 has perforations on all edges of the pane and was initially sold at £1·90, which was increased to £2 from 2.10.89.

1990 (7 Aug). Multicoloured laminated cover as Type HA **3** (75×48 mm) with stamp printed on the cover in bright orange-red by Harrison. Barcode in black.
HD3 Containing booklet pane No. 1512a .... 15·00
 b. Barcode printed in blue (22.9.92) .... 15·00
No. HD3 has the horizontal edges of the pane imperforate. No. HD3 was initially sold at £2, which was increased to £2·20 from 17.9.90 and to £2·40 from 16.9.91.

1990 (7 Aug). Multicoloured laminated cover as Type HA **3** (75×48 mm) with stamp printed on the cover in bright orange-red by Questa. Barcode in black.
HD4 Containing ten 1st Class stamps (No. 1514) .... 15·00
 b. Barcode printed in blue (22.9.92) .... 15·00
No. HD4 has perforations on all edges of the pane and was initially sold at £2, which was increased to £2·20 from 17.9.90 and to £2·40 from 16.9.91.

1990 (7 Aug). Multicoloured laminated cover as Type HA **3** (75×48 mm) with stamp printed on the cover in bright orange-red by Walsall. Barcode in black.
HD5 Containing booklet pane No. 1516b .... 12·00
 c. Barcode printed in blue (22.9.92).. 12·00

No. HD5 has the horizontal edges of the pane imperforate and was intially sold at £2, which was increased to £2·20 from 17.9.90 and to £2·40 from 16.9.91.

1992 (21 Jan). Multicoloured laminated cover as Type HA **5** (75×48 mm) with stamp printed on the cover in bright orange-red by Harrison.
HD6   Containing booklet pane No. 1512a ....   14·00
No. HD6 has the horizontal edges of the pane imperforate and was sold at £2.40.

1992 (21 Jan). Multicoloured laminated cover as Type HA **5** (75×48 mm) with stamp printed on the cover in bright orange-red by Walsall.
HD7   Containing booklet pane No. 1516b..   12·00
No. HD7 has the horizontal edges of the pane imperforate and was sold at £2.40.

1993 (9 Feb). Multicoloured laminated cover as Type HA **3** (77×44 mm) with advertisement for Greetings Booklet on reverse showing Rupert Bear as in Type KX **5**. Stamp printed on the cover in bright orange-red by Walsall.
HD8   Containing booklet pane No. 1516b ....   12·00
No. HD8 has the horizontal edges of the pane imperforate and was sold at £2.40.

PERFORATIONS. Booklets from No. HD9 show perforations on all edges of the pane.

1993 (6 Apr). Multicoloured laminated cover as Type HA **3** (75×48 mm) with stamp printed on the cover in bright orange-red by Harrison.
HD9   Containing ten 1st Class stamps (No. 1666) ....   12·00
No. HD9 was initially sold at £2·40, which was increased to £2.50 from 1.11.93.
No. HD9 was re-issued on 17 August 1993 showing changes to the text on the inside of the covers.

1993 (6 Apr). Multicoloured laminated cover as Type HA **3** (75×48 mm) with stamp printed on the cover in bright orange-red by Walsall.
HD10   Containing ten 1st Class stamps (No. 1671) ....   12·00
No. HD10 was initially sold at £2·40, which was increased to £2·50 from 1.11.93.
No. HD10 was re-issued on 17 August 1993 showing changes to the text on the inside of the covers.

1993 (1 Nov). *Laminated cover as Type HA **3** (75×50 mm) with stamp printed on the cover in bright orange-red by Questa.*
HD11   Containing ten 1st Class stamps (No. 1671) ....   12·00
No. HD11 was sold at £2·50.
No. HD11 was re-issued on 4 October 1994 showing changes to the text on the inside of the cover.

1993 (1 Nov). Laminated cover as Type HA **3** (75×50 mm) with advertisement for Greetings Booklet on reverse showing Rupert Bear as in Type KX **5**. Stamp printed on the cover in bright orange-red by Walsall.
HD12   Containing ten 1st Class stamps (No. 1671) ....   12·00
No. HD12 was originally sold at £2·50.

1994 (22 Feb). Multicoloured laminated cover as Type HA **3** (75×48 mm) with stamp printed on the cover in bright orange-red by Walsall. Inscribed *FREE POSTCARDS* on yellow tab at right.
HD13   Containing ten 1st Class stamps (No. 1671) and additional
          page giving details of Greetings Stamps postcard offer ..   12·00
No. HD13 was sold at £2·50.

1994 (1 July). Multicoloured laminated cover as Type HA **3** (76×50 mm) with advertisement for Greetings Booklet on reverse showing Rupert Bear as in Type KX **5**. Stamp printed on the cover in bright orange-red by Walsall. Inscribed *OPEN NOW Chance to win a kite* on yellow tab at right.
HD14   Containing ten 1st Class stamps (No. 1671) with "Better
          luck next time." etc on inside back cover ....   12·00
HD15   Containing ten 1st Class stamps (No. 1671) with "You've
          Won!" etc on inside back cover ....   12·00
Nos. HD14/15 sold at £2·50 each and were initially only available from branches of W.H. Smith and Son. They were issued in connection with a competition in which the prizes were Paddington Bear kites. The booklets were not available from Royal Mail philatelic outlets until 4 October 1994.

HD **16**

1994 (20 Sept). Multicoloured laminated covers as Type HD **16** (76×50 mm) printed by Walsall. Inscribed *ORDER YOURS INSIDE* on yellow tab at right.
HD16   Containing ten 1st Class stamps (No. 1671) with "DO
          NOT OPEN UNTIL....."on front cover ....   12·00
HD17   Containing ten 1st Class stamps (No. 1671) with "KEEP IN
          TOUCH" on front cover ....   12·00
HD18   Containing ten 1st Class stamps (No. 1671) with "HAPPY
          BIRTHDAY" on front cover ....   12·00
HD19   Containing ten 1st Class stamps (No. 1671) with "What's
          Happenin'?" on front cover ....   12·00
Nos. HD16/19 were sold at £2·50 each.

1995 (10 Jan). Multicoloured laminated cover as Type HA **8** (75×48 mm) with stamps printed on the cover in bright orange-red by Harrison.
HD20   Containing ten 1st Class stamps (No. 1666) ....   14·00

1995 (10 Jan). Multicoloured laminated cover as Type HA **8** (75×48 mm) with stamps printed on the cover in bright orange-red by Questa.
HD21   Containing ten 1st Class stamps (No. 1671) ....   12·00

1995 (10 Jan). *Multicoloured laminated cover as Type HA **8** (75×48 mm) with stamps printed on the cover in bright orange-red by Walsall.*
HD22   Containing ten 1st Class stamps (No. 1671) ....   12·00
Nos. HD20/2 were initially sold at £2·50 each, which was increased to £2·60 from 8.7.96.

HD **23**

1995 (14 Feb). Multicoloured laminated cover as Type HD **23** (76×50 mm) showing card, Thorntons chocolates and box, printed by Walsall. Inscribed DETAILS INSIDE" on yellow tab at right.
HD23   Containing ten 1st Class stamps (No. 1671) ....   12·00
No. HD23 was sold at £2·50.

1995 (4 Apr). Multicoloured laminated cover as Type HA **8** (76×48 mm) with stamps printed on cover in bright orange-red by Harrison.
HD24   Containing ten 1st Class stamps (No. 1667) ....   12·00
No. HD24 was sold at £2·50.

1995 (24 Apr). Multicoloured laminated cover as Type HA **8** (75×48 mm) with stamps printed on cover in bright orange-red by Walsall. Inscribed W H Smith Special Offer" on yellow tab at right.
HD25   Containing ten 1st Class stamps (No. 1671) ....   12·00
No. HD25 was sold at £2·50 and was initially only available from W. H. Smith branches and offered 25p. off the purchase of own brand stationery. The booklet was not placed on philatelic sale until 3 October 1995. Its price was increased to £2·60 on 8.7.96.

1995 (26 June). Multicoloured laminated cover as Type HA **8** (76×48 mm) with stamps printed on cover in bright orange red by Questa. Inscribed *Sainsbury's Promotion* on yellow tab at right.
HD26   Containing ten 1st Class stamps (No. 1671) ....   12·00
No. HD26 was sold at £2·50 and was initially only available from Sainsbury's branches and offered the chance to win a year's free shopping. The booklet was not placed on philatelic sale until 5 September 1995. Its price was increased to £2·60 on 8.7.96

1995 (4 Sept). Multicoloured laminated cover as Type HD **23** (76×48 mm) showing ceramic figures of Benjy Bear and Harry Hedgehog, printed by Harrison.
HD27   Containing ten 1st Class stamps (No. 1667) ....   12·00
No. HD27 was initially sold at £2·50, which was increased to £2·60 from 8.7.96.

1996 (6 Feb). Multicoloured laminated cover as Type HA **8** (76×48 mm) showing Olympic symbols on the back. Stamps printed on the cover in bright orange-red by Walsall.
HD28   Containing ten 1st Class stamps (No. 1671) ....   12·00
No. HD28 was initially sold at £2·50, which was increased to £2·60 from 8.7.96.

1996 (19 Feb). Multicoloured laminated cover as Type HD **23** (76×48 mm) showing Walt Disney World, printed by Harrison.
HD29   Containing ten 1st Class stamps (No. 1667) ....   12·00
No. HD 29 was initially sold at £2·50, which was increased to £2·60 from 8.7.96.

1996 (19 Mar). Multicoloured laminated cover as Type HA **8** (76×48 mm) showing Olympic symbols on the back, printed by Harrison.
HD30   Containing ten 1st Class stamps (No. 1667) ....   12·00
No. HD30 was initially sold at £2·50, which was increased to £2·60 from 8.7.96.

HD **31**

1996 (13 May). Multicoloured laminated covers as Type HD **31** (76×48 mm) showing woman lighting Olympic torch, printed by Harrison, with each booklet showing a scratchcard on the reverse based on different Olympic events.

HD31 Containing ten 1st Class stamps (No. 1667) (Shot Put)...... 11·00
HD32 Containing ten 1st Class stamps (No. 1667) (Hurdles)....... 11·00
HD33 Containing ten 1st Class stamps (No. 1667) (Archery)....... 11·00
    Nos. HD31/3 were initially each sold at £2.50, which was increased to £2·60 from 8.7.96.

NOTE: From No. HD34 onwards, the printer of each booklet is identified by a small capital letter below the barcode on the outside back cover.

1996 (15 July). Multicoloured laminated cover as Type HA **11** (76×48 mm) showing Olympic symbols on the back. Stamps printed on the cover in bright orange-red by Walsall. Inscribed "WHSmith Offer Inside" on yellow tab at right.

HD34 Containing ten 1st Class stamps (No. 1671) .... 11·00
    No. HD34 was sold at £2·60 and was initially only available from branches of W. H. Smith and Sons. It was issued in connection with a special offer of AA/OS Leisure Guides. The booklets were not available from Royal Mail philatelic outlets until 17 September 1996.

1996 (6 Aug). Multicoloured laminated cover as Type HA **11** (76×48 mm), but with diagonal white line across corners of stamps and showing Olympic symbols on the back. Stamps printed on the cover in bright orange-red by Harrison.

HD35 Containing ten 1st Class stamps (1667) .... 12·00
    No. HD35 was sold at £2·60.

1996 (6 Aug). Multicoloured laminated cover as Type HA **11** (76×48 mm) showing Olympic symbols on the back. Stamps printed on the cover in bright orange-red by Walsall.

HD36 Containing ten 1st Class stamps (No. 1671) .... 11·00
    No. HD36 was sold at £2·60.

1996 (9 Sept). Multicoloured laminated cover as Type HD **31** (76×48 mm) showing iced cakes on front and back, printed by Walsall. Inscribed *OPEN FOR DETAILS* on yellow tab at right.

HD37 Containing ten 1st Class stamps (No. 1671) .... 11·00
    No. HD37 was sold at £2·60.

1996 (7 Oct). Multicoloured laminated cover as Type HA **11** (76×48 mm) showing Olympic symbols on the back. Stamps printed on cover in bright orange-red by Walsall. Inscribed *Offer Inside* on yellow tab at right.

HD38 Containing ten 1st Class stamps (No. 1671) .... 11·00
    No. HD38 was sold at £2·60 and was initially only available from ASDA stores and offered £1 off greetings cards. The booklet was not placed on philatelic sale until 13 January 1997.

1997 (4 Feb). Multicoloured laminated cover as Type HA **11** (76×48 mm). Stamps printed on the cover in bright orange-red by Harrison.

HD 39 Containing ten 1st Class stamps (No. 1667) .... 11·00
    No. HD39 was sold at £2·60.

1997 (4 Feb). Multicoloured laminated cover as Type HA **11** (76×48 mm). Stamps printed on the cover in bright orange-red by Walsall.

HD40 Containing ten 1st Class stamps (No. 1671) .... 11·00
    No. HD40 was sold at £2·60.

1997 (21 Apr). *Royal Golden Wedding.* Multicoloured laminated cover as Type HA **11** (76×48 mm). Stamps printed on the cover in gold by Harrison.

HD41 Containing ten 1st Class stamps (No. 1668) .... 12·00
    No. HD41 was sold at £2·60.

1997 (21 Apr). *Royal Golden Wedding.* Multicoloured laminated cover as Type HA **11** (76×48 mm). Stamps printed on the cover in gold by Walsall.

HD42 Containing ten 1st Class stamps (No. 1668) .... 14·00
    No. HD42 was sold at £2·60.

1997 (15 Sept). Multicoloured laminated cover as Type HD **31** (76×48 mm) showing a tropical beach scene printed by Harrison. Inscr *FIRST CLASS TRAVEL"* on front, and *OPEN FOR DETAILS* on yellow tab at right.

HD43 Containing ten 1st Class stamps (No. 1668) .... 12·00
    No. HD43 was sold at £2·60.

1997 (8 Nov). Multicoloured laminated cover as Type HA **11** (76×48 mm). Stamps printed on the cover in bright orange-red by Walsall.

HD44 Containing ten 1st Class stamps (gravure) (No. 1667) .... 11·00
    No. HD44 was sold at £2·60. It was re-issued on 5 May 1998 showing the positions of the imprint, which was now vertical, and the post code notice transposed and again on 16 March 1999 with "Please note that the First Class rate is no longer valid to Europe" added to inside back cover.

HD **45**

1998 (2 Feb). Multicoloured laminated cover as Type HD **45** (76×48 mm) showing Disney illustration printed by De la Rue, with a scratch card on the reverse. Inscr *See reverse for Scratch and Win* on yellow tab at right.

HD45 Containing ten 1st Class stamps (gravure) (No. 1667) .... 11·00
    No. HD45 was sold at £2·60.

HD **46**

1998 (27 Apr). Multicoloured laminated cover as Type HD **46** (76×48 mm) showing Peugeot 106 printed by De La Rue. Inscr *WIN A PEUGEOT 106* on yellow tab at right.

HD46 Containing ten 1st Class stamps (gravure) (No. 1667) .... 11·00
    No. HD46 was sold at £2·60. This booklet was not placed on philatelic sale until 23 June 1998.

1998 (5 May). Multicoloured laminated cover as Type HA **11** (76×48 mm). Stamps printed on the cover in bright orange-red by De La Rue.

HD47 Containing ten 1st Class stamps (gravure) (No. 1667) .... 11·00
    No. HD47 was initially sold at £2·60, which was increased to £2·70 from 27.4.2000.

1998 (1 July). Multicoloured laminated cover as Type HD **46** (76×48 mm) showing JVC Camcorder printed by De La Rue. Inscr *WIN A JVC CAMCORDER* on yellow tab at right.

HD48 Containing ten 1st Class stamps (gravure) (No. 1667) .... 11·00
    No. HD48 was sold at £2·60. This booklet was not placed on philatelic sale until 27 August 1998.

1998 (3 Aug). Multicoloured laminated cover as Type GGA **2** (76×48 mm) inscr (*Create a card design*), printed by De La Rue.

HD49 Containing ten 1st Class stamps (gravure) (No. 1667) .... 11·00
    No. HD49 was sold at £2·60. This booklet was not placed on philatelic sale until 7 September 1998.

1998 (7 Sept). Multicoloured laminated cover as Type HA **11** (75×49 mm), with stamps printed on the cover in bright orange-red by Questa.

HD50 Containing ten 1st Class stamps (litho) (No. 1671) .... 11·00
    No. HD50 was sold at £2·60.

1998 (1 Dec). Multicoloured laminated cover as Type HA **11** (75×48 mm). Stamps printed on the cover in bright orange-red by Questa.

HD51 Containing ten 1st Class stamps (No. 1667a)... 20·00
    No. HD51 was sold at £2·60. It was re-issued on 16 March 1999 with "Please note that the First Class rate is no longer valid to Europe" added to inside back cover.

2000 (6 Jan). Multicoloured laminated cover as Type HA **11** (75×48 mm). Millennium definitives printed on the cover in olive-brown by Questa.

HD52 Containing ten 1st Class stamps (gravure) (No. 2124d) .. 11·00
    No. HD52 was initially sold at £2·60, which was increased to £2·70 from 27 April 2000. It was re-issued on 14 March 2000 with a changed telephone number on the inside back cover.

2000 (6 Jan). Multicoloured laminated cover as Type HA **11** (75×48 mm). Millennium definitives printed on the cover in olive-brown by Walsall.

HD53 Containing ten 1st Class stamps (gravure) (No. 2124) .... 11·00

No. HD53 was initially sold at £2·60, which was increased to £2·70 from 27 April 2000. It was re-issued on 14 March 2000 with a changed telephone number on the inside back cover.

Panes of four European Air Mail stamps

HF **1**

1999 (19 Jan). Multicoloured laminated cover as Type HF **1** (75×50 mm). Stamps printed on the cover in deep blue by Walsall. Inscr *For items up to 20g* on yellow tab at right.

HF1   Containing four European Air Mail stamps (No. 1669) and
           pane of four air mail labels.. 7·50
No. HF1 was initially sold at £1·20 which was increased to £1·36 from 25.10.99 and £1·44 from 27.4.2000.
    It was re-issued on 27 April 2000 showing an amended Customer Services telephone number on the inside back cover.

E. Barcode Booklets containing Penny Black Anniversary stamps with barcodes on back cover.

60p. Booklet

JA **1**

1990 (30 Jan). Laminated cover as Type JA **1** (75×48 mm) showing Penny Black Anniversary stamp in bright blue. Containing booklet pane No. 1475l, printed in litho by Walsall.

JA1   Containing booklet pane No. 1475l .... 7·00
No. JA1 has three edges of the pane imperforate.

80p. Booklets

1990 (30 Jan). Laminated cover as Type JA **1** (75×48 mm) showing Penny Black Anniversary stamp in brownish black and cream. Containing booklet pane No. 1476m, printed in litho by Walsall.

JB1   Containing booklet pane No. 1476m... 8·50
No. JB1 has three edges of the pane imperforate.

1990 (17 Apr). Laminated cover as Type JA **1** (75×48 mm) showing Penny Black Anniversary stamp printed on the cover in brownish black by Walsall. Containing stamps printed in photo by Harrison.

JB2   Containing booklet pane No. 1469r .... 8·00
No. JB2 has three edges of the pane imperforate.

£1.50 Booklets

1990 (30 Jan). Laminated cover as Type JA **1** (75×48 mm) showing Penny Black Anniversary stamp in bright blue. Containing booklet pane No. 1467l printed in photo by Harrison.

JC1   Containing booklet pane No. 1467l .... 10·00
No. JC1 has the horizontal edges of the pane imperforate.

1990 (17 Apr). Laminated cover as Type JA **1** (75×48 mm) showing Penny Black Anniversary stamp printed on the cover in bright blue, printed in litho by Questa.

JC2   Containing ten 15p. (No. 1477) .... 22·00

1990 (12 June). Laminated cover as Type JA **1** (75×48 mm) showing Penny Black Anniversary stamp in bright blue. Containing booklet pane No. 1475m, printed in litho by Walsall.

JC3   Containing booklet pane No. 1475m .... 12·00
No. JC3 has three edges of the pane imperforate.

£2 Booklets

1990 (30 Jan). Laminated cover as Type JA **1** (75×48 mm) showing Penny Black Anniversary stamp in brownish black and cream. Containing booklet pane. No. 1469m, printed in photo by Harrison.

JD1   Containing booklet pane No. 1469m .... 11·00
No. JD1 has the horizontal edges of the pane imperforate.

1990 (17 Apr). Laminated cover as Type JA **1** (75×48 mm) showing Penny Black Anniversary stamp printed on the cover in brownish black, printed in litho by Questa.

JD2   Containing ten 20p. (No. 1478) .... 24·00

1990 (12 June). Laminated cover as Type JA **1** (75×48 mm) showing Penny Black Anniversary stamp in brownish black and cream. Containing booklet pane No. 1476n, printed in litho by Walsall.

JD3   Containing booklet pane No. 1476n .... 18·00
No. JD3 has three edges of the pane imperforate.

F. Barcode Booklets containing Greetings stamps with barcodes on the back cover.

For first greetings booklet, issued 31 January 1989, see FY1 in section B.

£2 Greetings Booklet

KX **1** (Illustration reduced. Actual size 135×85 mm)

(Des Michael Peters and Partners)

1990 (6 Feb). *Greetings Stamps.* Cover printed in scarlet, lemon and black as Type KX **1** (135×85 mm). Containing booklet pane No. 1483a, and a separate sheet of 12 greetings labels.

KX1   "Smile" design cut-out showing stamps inside .... 26·00

Greetings Booklets containing No Value Indicated stamps

KX **2**

(Des T. Meeuwissen)

1991 (5 Feb). *Greetings Stamps.* Multicoloured laminated cover as Type KX **2** (95×69 mm). Containing booklet pane No. 1536a, including twelve special greetings labels in a block (3×**4**) at right, attached by the selvedge.

KX2   "Good Luck" charms design .... 13·00
No. KX2 was initially sold at £2·20, which was increased to £2·40 from 16.9.91.

KX **3**
(Des Michael Peters and Partners)

1991 (26 Mar). *Greetings Stamps.* Multicoloured laminated cover as Type KX **3** (95×69 mm). Containing booklet pane No. 1550a, including twelve special greetings labels in a block (3×4) at right, attached by the selvedge.
KX3   Laughing pillar box design .... 12·00
            a. Amended text to inside back cover (3.3.92)...................... 13·00
    No. KX3 was initially sold at £2·20, which was increased to £2·40 from 16.9.91 and to £2·50 from 1.11.93.
    The note on the inside back cover of No. KX3 is headed "Greetings Stamps". In No. KX3a there is no heading but details of the validity of the stamps to European destinations have been added.

KX **4**

(Des Trickett and Webb)

1992 (28 Jan). *Greetings Stamps.* Multicoloured laminated cover as Type KX **4** (95×69 mm). Containing booklet pane No. 1592a, including twelve special greetings labels in a block (3×4) at right, attached by selvedge.
KX4   Pressed Flowers design .... 12·00
    No. KX4 was initially sold at £2·40, which was increased to £2·50 from 1.11.93 and to £2·60 from 8.7.96.

KX **5**

(Des Newell and Sorrell)

1993 (2 Feb). *Greetings Stamps.* Multicoloured laminated cover as Type KX **5** (96×60 mm). Containing booklet pane No. 1644a and pane of twenty special greetings labels in a block (5×4), both panes attached by a common gutter margin.
KX5   Children's Characters design .... 12·00
    No. KX5 was initially sold at £2·40, which was increased to £2·50 from 1.11.93.
    No. KX5 was re-issued on 15 June 1993 with "Thompson" corrected to "Thomson" (bottom line at left) and on 17 August 1993 with "Sorell" corrected to "Sorrell".

KX **6**
(Des Newell and Sorrell)

1994 (1 Feb). *Greetings Stamps.* Multicoloured cover as Type KX **6** (96×60 mm). Containing booklet pane No. 1800a and pane of twenty special greetings labels in a block (5×4), both panes attached by a common gutter margin.
KX6   Children's Characters design .... 12·00
    No. KX6 was initially sold at £2·50, which was increased to £2·60 from 8.7.96.

KX **7**

(Des Newell and Sorrell)

1995 (21 Mar)–**96**. *Greetings Stamps.* Multicoloured cover as Type KX **7** (96×60 mm). Containing booklet pane No. 1858a and pane of twenty special greetings labels in a block (5×4), both panes attached by a common gutter margin. Inscr *Pull Open* on yellow strip at right.
KX7   Clown design .... 12·00
            a. No inscr on yellow strip (5.2.96) .... 12·00
    Nos. KX7/a were initially sold at £2·50, which was increased to £2·60 from 8.7.96.

MORE!
LOVE
Greetings

KX **8**

(Des M. Wolff)

1996 (26 Feb–11 Nov). *Greetings Stamps.* Multicoloured cover as Type KX **8** (96×60 mm). Containing booklet pane No. 1905a and pane of twenty special greetings labels in a block (5×4), both panes attached by a common gutter margin.
KX8   "MORE! LOVE" design .... 12·00
            a. Containing pane No. 1905pa (11 Nov) .... 36·00
    No. KX8 was initially sold at £2·50, which was increased to £2·60 from 8.7.96.
    No. KX8a shows a redesigned inside front cover which omits references to 1996 dates.

KX **9**

(Des Tutssels)

1997 (6 Jan). *Greetings Stamps. 19th-century Flower Paintings.* Multi-coloured cover as Type KX **9** (96×61 mm). Containing booklet pane No. 1955a and pane of twenty special greetings labels in a block (5×4), both panes attached by a common gutter margin.

KX9   *Gentiana acaulis* design .... 12·00

No. KX9 was sold at £2·60. It was re-issued on 16 March 1999 with "Please note that the First Class rate is no longer valid to Europe" added to inside front cover.

1997 (3 Feb). *Greetings Stamps. 19th-century Flower Paintings.* Multi-coloured cover as Type KX **9** (96×61 mm) but with box inscribed *WIN A BEAUTIFUL BOUQUET INSTANTLY?* printed in yellow on red over the flower on the front and with a scratch card on the inside back cover. Inscribed *Open now – See if you've won* on yellow tab at right. Containing booklet pane No. 1955a and pane of twenty special greetings labels in a block (5×4), both panes attached by a common gutter margin.

KX10   *Gentiana acaulis* design .... 12·00

No. KX10 was sold at £2·60.

KX **11**

(Des Tutssels)

1998 (5 Jan). *Greetings Stamps. 19th-century Flower Paintings.* Multi-coloured cover as Type KX **11** (96×61 mm). Inscribed *See reverse for special offer* on yellow tab at right. Containing booklet pane No. 1955a and pane of twenty special greetings labels in a block (5×4), both attached by a common gutter margin.

KX11   Chocolate design .... 12·00

No. KX11 was sold at £2·60.

1998 (3 Aug). *Greetings Stamps. 19th-century Flower Paintings.* Multi-coloured cover as Type GGA **2** (88×61 mm) printed by Walsall. Containing booklet pane No. 1955a and pane of twenty special greetings labels in a block (5×4), both attached by a common gutter margin.

KX12   "Create a card" design .... 12·00

No. KX12 was sold at £2·60. This booklet was not placed on philatelic sale until 7 September 1998.

G. Barcode Booklets containing Christmas stamps with barcode on the back.

LX **1**

(Des A. Davidson)

1990 (13 Nov). Christmas. Multicoloured laminated cover as Type LX **1** (96×60 mm). Containing booklet pane No. 1526b, attached by the selvedge.

LX1   £3·40, Snowman design .... 11·00

1991 (12 Nov). Multicoloured laminated cover as Type LX **1**, but 95×70 mm. Containing booklet pane No. 1582b attached by the selvedge.

LX2   £3·60, Holly design .... 11·00

LX **3**

(Des Karen Murray)

1992 (10 Nov). Multicoloured laminated cover as Type LX **3** (95×70 mm). Containing booklet pane No. 1634a attached by the selvedge.

LX3   £3·60, Santa Claus and Reindeer design .... 11·00

1993 (9 Nov). Multicoloured laminated covers as Type LX **3**, but 95×60 mm, each showing Santa Claus and Reindeer. Panes attached by selvedge.

LX4   £2·50, containing ten 25p. stamps (No. 1791) .... 9·00
LX5   £3·80, containing twenty 19p. stamps (No. 1790) .... 12·00

No. LX4 was only available from Post Offices in the Central T.V. area and from philatelic outlets.

LX **6**

(Des Yvonne Gilbert)

1994 (1 Nov). Multicoloured laminated covers as Type LX **6** (95×60 mm), showing different Nativity Play props. Panes attached by selvedge.

LX6   £2·50, containing ten 25p. stamps (No. 1844) .... 7·00
LX7   £3·80, containing twenty 19p. stamps (No. 1843) .... 11·00

LX **8**

(Des K. Lilly)

1995 (30 Oct). Multicoloured laminated covers as Type LX **8** (95×60 mm), showing Robins as depicted on the contents. Panes attached by selvedge.

LX8	£2·40, containing four 60p. stamps (No. 1900) plus 4 air mail labels	7·50
LX9	£2·50, containing ten 25p. stamps (No. 1897)	7·50
LX10	£3·80, containing twenty 19p. stamps (No. 1896)	12·00

LX **11**

1996 (28 Oct). Multicoloured laminated covers as Type LX **11** (95×60 mm), showing scenes from the Nativity as depicted on the contents. Panes attached by selvedge.

LX11	Containing ten 1st Class stamps (No. 1951)	12·00
LX12	Containing twenty 2nd Class stamps (No. 1950)	16·00

No. LX11 was sold at £2·60 and No. LX12 at £4.

LX **13**

1997 (27 Oct). Multicoloured laminated covers as Type LX **13** (95×60 mm), showing Father Christmas and crackers as depicted on the contents. Panes attached by selvedge.

LX13	Containing ten 1st Class stamps (No. 2007)	12·00
LX14	Containing twenty 2nd Class stamps (No. 2006)	16·00

No. LX13 was sold at £2·60 and No. LX14 at £4.

LX **15**

1998 (2 Nov). Multicoloured red laminated covers as Type LX **15** (95×60 mm), showing angels as depicted on the contents. Panes attached by selvedge.

LX15	£2·60 booklet containing ten 26p. stamps (No. 2065)	8·00
LX16	£4 booklet containing twenty 20p. stamps (No. 2064)	12·00

LX **17**

1999 (2 Nov). Multicoloured laminated covers as Type LX **17** (95×70 mm), showing designs as depicted on the contents. Panes attached by selvedge.

LX17	£2·60 booklet containing ten 26p. stamps (No. 2116)	8·50
LX18	£3·90 booklet containing twenty 19p. stamps (No. 2115)	12·00

LX **19**

2000 (7 Nov). Multicoloured laminated covers as Type LX **19** (96×70 mm), showing designs as depicted on the contents. Inscribed Season's Greetings" on yellow tab at right. Panes attached by selvedge.

LX19	£2·70, containing ten 1st Class stamps (No. 2171)	12·00
LX20	£3·80, containing twenty 2nd Class stamps (No. 2170)	16·00

2001 (6 Nov). Self-adhesive booklet containing Nos. 2238a and 2239a, each with a multicoloured header label showing barcode and Royal Mail emblem and further label at foot with telephone numbers, folded to form booklets 119×81 mm.

LX21	£3·24, booklet containing twelve 1st Class stamps (No. 2239a)	14·00
LX22	£4·56, booklet containing twenty-four 2nd Class stamps (No. 2238a)	18·00

Nos. LX21/2 show the surplus self-adhesive paper around each stamp retained.

2002 (5 Nov). Self-adhesive booklet containing Nos. 2321a and 2322a, each with a multicoloured header label showing barcode and Royal Mail emblem and further label at foot with telephone numbers, folded to form booklets 105×72 mm.

LX23 £3·24, booklet containing twelve 1st Class stamps
(No. 2322a) .... 14·00
LX24 £4·56, booklet containing twenty-four 2nd Class stamps (No. 2321a) .... 18·00
No. LX23 was sealed into a cellophane packet which also contained a Lord of the Rings game card.
Nos. LX23/4 show the surplus self-adhesive paper around each stamp retained.

2003 (4 Nov). Self-adhesive booklet containing Nos. 2410a and 2411a, each with a multicoloured header label showing barcode and Royal Mail emblem and further label at foot with telephone numbers, folded to form booklets 106×71 mm.

LX25 £3·36, booklet containing twelve 1st Class stamps
(No. 2411a) .... 14·00
LX26 £4·80, booklet containing twenty-four 2nd Class stamps (No. 2410a) .... 18·00
Nos. LX25/6 have the surplus self-adhesive paper around each stamp removed.

2004 (2 Nov). Self-adhesive booklet containing Nos. 2495a and 2496a, each with a multicoloured header label showing barcode and Royal Mail emblem and further label at foot with contact information, folded to form booklets 105×71 mm.

LX27 £3·36 booklet containing twelve 1st Class stamps
(No. 2496a) .... 14·00
LX28 £5·04 booklet containing twenty-four 2nd Class stamps (No. 2495a) .... 20·00
Nos. LX27/8 have the surplus self-adhesive paper around each stamp removed.

2005 (1 Nov). Self-adhesive booklet containing Nos. 2582a and 2583a, each with a multicoloured header label showing barcode and Royal Mail emblem and further label at foot with contact information, folded to form booklets 106×71 mm.

LX29 £3·60 booklet containing twelve 1st Class stamps
(No. 2583a) .... 14·00
LX30 £5·04 booklet containing twenty-four 2nd Class stamps (No. 2582a) .... 18·00
Nos. LX29/30 have the surplus self-adhesive paper around each stamp removed.

LX **31**

2006 (7 Nov). Covers as Type LX **31** (75×57 mm). Self-adhesive.
LX31 £2·76 booklet containing twelve 2nd Class stamps
(No. 2678a) (Type LX **31**).................................... 11·00
LX32 £3·84 booklet containing twelve 1st Class stamps
(No. 2679a) (red cover inscr "12×1st") .... 14·00
Nos. LX31/2 have the surplus self-adhesive paper around each stamp removed.

2007 (6 Nov). Covers as Type LX **31** (75×57 mm). Self-adhesive.
LX33 £2·88 booklet containing twelve 2nd Class stamps
(No. 2789a) (Type LX **31**).................................... 11·00
LX34 £4·08 booklet containing twelve 1st Class stamps
(No. 2790a) (red cover inscr '12×1st')................. 14·00
Nos. LX33/4 have the surplus self-adhesive paper around each stamp removed.

2008 (*4 Nov*). Covers as Type LX **31** (75×57 mm). Self-adhesive.
LX35 £3·24 booklet containing twelve 2nd Class stamps
(No. 2876a) (Type LX **31**).................................... 11·00
  a. "Oh YES it is!" along right-hand edge of pane .... 11·00
LX36 £4·32 booklet containing twelve 1st Class stamps
(No. 2877a) (red cover inscr "12×1st") .... 14·00
  a. "It's behind you!" along right-hand edge of pane .... 14·00
Nos. LX35/6 have the surplus self-adhesive paper around each stamp removed.
No. LX35 is inscr "Oh NO it isn't!" and No. LX36 "Abracadabra!", both along the right-hand edges of the booklet panes.

2009 (3 Nov). *Christmas. Covers* as Type LX **31** (75×57 mm). Self-adhesive.
LX37 £3·60 booklet containing twelve 2nd class stamps
(No. 2991a) (Type LX **31**) .... 11·00

LX38 £4·68 booklet containing twelve 1st class stamps
(No. 2992a) (red cover inscr '12×1st').................. 14·00
Nos. LX37/8 have the surplus self-adhesive paper around each stamp removed.

LX **39** Wallace and Gromit posting Christmas Cards

2010 (2 Nov). *Christmas.* Multicoloured covers as Type LX **39** (74×58 mm). Self-adhesive.
LX39 £3·84 booklet containing twelve 2nd class stamps
(No. 3128a) (Type LX**39**)..................................... 11·00
LX40 £4·92 booklet containing twelve 1st class stamps
(No. 3129a) (cover as Type LX **39** but red background).. 14·00
Nos. LX39/40 have the surplus self-adhesive paper around each stamp removed.

2011 (8 Nov). *Christmas. 400th Anniv of the King James Bible.* Multicoloured covers as Type LX **31** (74×58 mm). Self-adhesive.
LX41 (£4·32) booklet containing twelve 2nd class stamps
(No. 3242a) (Type LX **31**)................................... 11·00
LX42 (£5·52) booklet containing twelve 1st class stamps
(No. 3243a) (cover as Type LX **31** but red background).. 14·00
Nos. LX41/2 have the surplus self-adhesive paper around each stamp removed.

2012 (6 Nov). *Christmas.* Illustrations by Axel Scheffler. Multicoloured covers as Type LX **31** (74×58 mm). Self-adhesive.
LX43 (£6) booklet containing twelve 2nd class stamps
(No. 3415a) (Type LX **31**)................................... 12·00
LX44 (£7·20) booklet containing twelve 1st class stamps
(No. 3416a) (cover as Type LX **31** but red background).. 15·00

2013 (5 Nov). *Christmas.* Multicoloured covers as Type LX **31** (89×66 mm). Self-adhesive.
LX45 (£6) booklet containing twelve 2nd class stamps
(No. 3542a) (as Type LX **31**).............................. 12·00
LX46 (£7·20) booklet containing twelve 1st class stamps (No. 3543a) (as Type LX **31** but red background) .... 15·00

2014 (4 Nov). *Christmas.* Multicoloured covers as Type LX **31** (74×58 mm). Self-adhesive.
LX47 (£6·36) booklet containing twelve 2nd class stamps
(No. 3650a) (as Type LX **31**).............................. 12·00
LX48 (£7·44) booklet containing twelve 1st class stamps (No. 3651a) (as Type LX **31** but red background).. 15·00

2015 (3 Nov). *Christmas.* Multicoloured covers as Type LX **31** (89×65 mm). Self-adhesive.
LX49 (£6·48) booklet containing twelve 2nd class stamps
(No. 3771a) (as Type LX **31**).............................. 12·00
LX50 (£7·56) booklet containing twelve 1st class stamps (No. 3772a) (as Type LX **31** but red cover inscr '12×1st') .... 15·00

H. Self-adhesive Barcode Booklets containing No Value Indicated stamps.

NOTES. All booklets in this section show the surplus self-adhesive paper around each stamp retained, unless otherwise stated.

Booklets which are omitted from the listings here e.g. MB8d, are only differentiated by the date codes on the stamps or other features outside the scope of this catalogue. They are however, listed in the appropriate volume of the *Great Britain Specialised Catalogue*.

Containing six 2nd class stamps.

MA **1**

2001 (29 Jan). Multicoloured laminated cover as Type MA **1** (74×56 mm). Stamps printed on the cover in bright blue by Walsall.
MA1   Containing six 2nd Class self-adhesive stamps (No. 2039) .   7·50
    No. MA1 was sold at £1·14. It was re-issued on 1 August 2001 showing "Cod Post" added to the "Ffôn Testun" inscription on the back cover.
    No. MA1 exists imperforate.

Containing six 1st Class stamps

2001 (29 Jan). Multicoloured laminated cover as Type MA **1** (74×56 mm). Stamps printed on the cover in bright orange-red by Walsall.
MB1   Containing six 1st Class self-adhesive stamps (No. 2040)   8·00
    No. MB1 was sold at £1·62. It was re-issued on 1 August 2001 showing "Cod Post" added to the "Ffôn Testun" inscription on the back cover.

MB **2**

2001 (29 Jan). Multicoloured laminated cover as Type MB **2** (74×56 mm). Stamps printed on the cover in bright orange-red with portrait of Queen Victoria by Walsall.
MB2   Containing No. 2040l (includes label commemorating death centenary of Queen Victoria) .... 20·00
    No. MB2 was sold at £1·62.

MB **3**

2002 (5 June). Gold laminated cover as Type MB **3** (74×56 mm) by Questa.
MB3   Containing six 1st Class self-adhesive stamps (No. 2295) .... 7·50
    No. MB3 was sold at £1·62. It shows the surplus self-adhesive paper around each stamp removed and a single notch at top right.

2002 (5 June) – **2008**. Gold laminated cover as Type MB **3** (74×56 mm) by Walsall.
MB4   Containing six 1st Class self-adhesive stamps (No. 2295) .... 8·00
    a. Inside cover with Smilers advertisement (27.1.05)........... 7·50
    b. Back cover with added text about new pricing structure (25.4.06).. 9·50
    c. Inside cover with "To find the correct postcodes for your mail" notice (5.6.07)... 9·00
    d. Inside cover with commemorative inscription for Machin Anniversary (5.6.07)... 7·50
    e. Inside cover with Harry Potter stamps advertisement (28.8.07).. 9·00
    f. Inside cover with postcode text in English and Welsh (20.9.07).. 8·00
    g. Inside cover with *Carry On* stamps advertisement (10.6.08).. 8·00
    No. MB4 was sold at £1·62. It shows the surplus self-adhesive paper around each stamp removed and a single notch at top right.
    Original selling prices for the later books were £1·68 (MB4a), £1·92 (MB4b), £2·04 (MB4c/f) and £2·16 (MB4g).
    No. MB4 was re-issued on 27 January 2005 (MB4a) with a Smilers advertisement (showing No. 2262 and photograph of baby) on the inside front cover. It was re-issued again on 26 July 2005 with a different Smilers advertisement (showing No. 2261 and photograph of bride).
    No. MB4a was available from Tallents House from 27 January 2005, and from general post offices from 22 March 2005.
    No. MB4b does not have Smilers advertisement.
    The added text on the back cover of No. MB4b reads "Valid for items up to 60g before 21 August 2006. Under new pricing structure from 21 August 2006 – valid for postal items up to: 240 mm Long; 165 mm Wide; 5 mm Thick; 100g Weight."
    The text on the back cover of Nos. MB4c/g reads "Valid for items up to: 240 mm Long 165 mm Wide 5 mm Thick 100g Weight".
    No. MB4d has Arnold Machin's signature along the right-hand edge of the booklet pane.
    No. MB4g has characters from *Carry On* films illustrated along the right-hand edge of the booklet pane.

2002 (4 July). Multicoloured laminated cover as Type MA **1** (74×56 mm) with stamps printed on the cover in bright orange-red by Questa.
MB5   Containing six 1st Class self-adhesive stamps (No. 2040) .... 10·50
    No. MB5 was sold at £1·62.

MB **6** ("The Real Network" added below logo)

2003 (27 Mar). Gold cover with multicoloured emblem as Type MB **6** (74×56 mm) by Walsall.
MB6   Containing six 1st Class self-adhesive stamps (No. 2295) .... 10·00
    No. MB6 was initially sold at £1·62. It shows the surplus self-adhesive paper around each stamp removed and has a single notch at top right.
    No. MB6 exists imperforate.

MB **7** (Supporting London 2012)

2004 (15 June). *London's bid to host Olympic Games, 2012.* Gold cover with multicoloured emblem as Type MB **7** (74×56 mm) by Walsall.
MB7   Containing six 1st Class self-adhesive stamps (No. 2295) .... 10·00
   No. MB7 was sold at £1·68. It has the surplus self-adhesive paper around each stamp removed and a single notch at top right.

Containing six 1st Class Olympic and Paralympic Games stamps (MB9/10) or "Security Machins"

2009 (31 Mar)–**11**. Gold cover with multicoloured emblem as Type MB **3** (74×57 mm) by Walsall.
MB8   Containing six 1st Class self-adhesive stamps (No. U2951) (code "MSIL" without date) .... 22·00
   a. Containing No. U2967 (code "MSIL" with date) (26.1.10) .... 15·00
   b. Containing No. U2967 (code "MSIL" with date). Inside cover with inscription and emblem for London 2010 Festival of Stamps (30.3.10) .... 12·00
   c. Containing No. U2967 (code "MSIL" with date) (19.8.10) .... 11·00
   e. Containing No. U2967 (code "MSIL" with date). Inside front cover advertising the 2012 special stamp programme. Back cover with FSC logo (25.10.11) .... 15·00
   No. MB8 was originally sold at £2·16. It has the surplus self-adhesive paper around each stamp removed and a single small notch at top right.
   The e-mail address on the inside front cover of No. MB8 reads 'www.royalmail.com/Postcodes4free'.
   Original selling prices for the later booklets were £2·34 (MB8a/b), £2·46 (MB8c) and £2·76 (MB8e).
   No. MB8a has a lower case p in this email address 'www.royalmail.com/postcodes4free'.
   No. MB8b has 'LONDON 2010 FESTIVAL OF STAMPS' along the right hand edge of the booklet pane.
   No. MB8/b are inscribed "Walsall Security Printers, UK" along the left hand edge of the back cover. This was removed for MB8c/e.
   Date codes for MB8a/b are "MA10", for MB8c "MA10" and "M11L" and for MB8e "M11L".

MB **9**

2012 (5 Jan). *Olympic and Paralympic Games, London.* Multicoloured cover, (75×58 mm), as Type MB **9** by Walsall. Self-adhesive.
MB9   Containing booklet pane No. 3250a with Paralympic Games stamp at top left .... 8·50
   The inside cover of No. MB9 is inscr 'London's vision is to reach young people all around the world, to connect them with the inspirational power of the Games, so that they are inspired to choose sport'. It's original selling price was £2·76.

2012 (5 Jan). *Olympic and Paralympic Games, London.* Multicoloured cover, (75×58 mm), as Type MB **9** by Walsall. Self-adhesive.
MB10   Containing booklet pane No. 3250a with Olympic Games stamp at top left .... 8·50
   No. MB10 was originally sold for £2·76. The inside cover of No. MB10 is inscr "Key dates for London 2012" and dates.

MB **11**

2012 (1 Oct). *Diamond Jubilee.* Slate-blue cover with multicoloured emblem as Type MB **11** (74×57 mm) by Walsall.
MB11 Containing six 1st Class self-adhesive stamps (No. U3275, code "MSND") .... 7·50
   No. MB11 was originally sold for £3·60. It has the self-adhesive paper around each stamp removed and a single notch at the top right-hand edge.

MB **12**

2013 (3 Jan). Red cover with multicoloured emblem as Type MB **12** (74×57 mm) by Walsall.
MB12 Containing six 1st Class self-adhesive stamps (No. U2968d, code "MSIL") .... 9·00
   No. MB12 was originally sold at £3·60. It has the surplus self-adhesive paper around each stamp removed and a single small notch at top right.
   No. MB12 reissued on 31 July 2014 with the Royal Mail telephone numbers on the back cover changed from 08457 740 740 and 08456 000 606 to 03457 740 740 and 03456 000 606. The price shown for MB12 is with the changed telephone number. With 08 telephone number £10.00
   Date codes for MB12 are "M12L", "M13L" or "M14L", and with changed telephone numbers M14L or M15L.

2015 (6 May). *175th Anniv of the Penny Black.* Red cover with multicoloured emblem as Type MB **12** (75×57 mm) by Walsall.
MB13   containing six 1st Class self-adhesive stamps (No. 3709)   12·00
   No. MB13 was initially sold at £3.78. . It has the self-adhesive paper around each stamp removed and a single small notch at the top right-hand edge.

MB **14**

2015 (9 Sept). *Long to Reign Over Us.* Lilac cover with multicoloured emblem as Type MB **14** (74×58 mm) by Walsall.

MB14 (£3.78) Containing six 1st Class self-adhesive stamps
(No. U3745, code 'REIG5')..................................... 8·00

No. MB14 was originally sold for £3.78. It has the self-adhesive paper around each stamp removed and a single small notch at the top right-hand edge.

Date code for MB14 is "015R".

2016. *Long to Reign Over Us.* Lilac cover with multicoloured emblem as Type MB **14** (74×58 mm) by Walsall. 'Repeating ROYAL MAIL wording printed on the front of the self-adhesive backing paper

MB15 (£3.78) Containing six 1st Class self-adhesive stamps
(No. U3745, code "REIG5) .... 8·00

No. MB15 was originally sold for £3.78. It has the self-adhesive paper around each stamp removed and a single small notch at the top right-hand edge.

Date codes for MB15 are "015R" or "016R".

2016 (18 Feb). *175th Anniversary of the Penny Red.* Red cover with multicoloured emblem as Type MB **12** (74×57 mm) by Walsall.

MB16 Containing six 1st Class self-adhesive stamps (No. 3806) 7·50

No. MB16 was originally sold for £3.78. It has the self-adhesive paper around each stamp removed and a single small notch at the top right-hand edge

Containing ten 2nd Class stamps

2001 (29 Jan). Multicoloured laminated cover as Type MA **1** (74×56 mm). Stamps printed on the cover in bright blue by Questa.

MC1 Containing ten 2nd Class self-adhesive stamps (No. 2039) .... 11·00

No. MC1 was sold at £1·90 and was intended for use in stamp machines.

Containing ten 1st Class stamps

2001 (29 Jan). Multicoloured laminated cover as Type MA **1** (74×56 mm). Stamps printed on the cover in bright orange-red by Questa.

MD1 Containing ten 1st Class self-adhesive stamps (No. 2040) .... 12·00

No. MD1 was sold at £2·70 and was intended for use in stamp machines.

Containing 12 2nd Class stamps

2001 (29 Jan). Multicoloured laminated cover as Type MA **1** (74×56 mm). Stamps printed on the cover in bright blue by Questa.

ME1 Containing twelve 2nd Class self-adhesive stamps (No. 2039) .... 11·00

No. ME1 was sold at £2·28. It was re-issued on 1 August 2001 showing "Cod Post" added to the "Ffôn Testun" inscription on the back cover.

ME **2**

2002 (4 July). Multicoloured laminated cover as Type ME **2** (74×57 mm) printed by Questa with the surplus self-adhesive paper around each stamp removed.

ME2 Containing twelve 2nd Class self-adhesive stamps (No. 2039) .... 11·00

No. ME2 was sold at £2·28. It shows the surplus self-adhesive paper around each stamp removed and two notches at top right.

ME **3** ("The Real Network" added below logo)

2003 (27 Mar). Blue cover with multicoloured emblem as Type ME **3** (74×57 mm) by Walsall.

ME3 Containing twelve 2nd Class self-adhesive stamps (No. 2039).. 11·00

No. ME3 was initially sold for £2·28. It shows the surplus self-adhesive paper around each stamp removed and has two notches at top right.

2004 (15 June).-07 Blue cover with multicoloured emblem as Type ME **2** (74×56 mm) by Walsall.

ME4 Containing twelve 2nd Class self-adhesive stamps (No. 2039).. 12·00
   a. Back cover with added text about new pricing structure (25.4.06) .... 12·00
   b. Back cover with text about validity (5.6.07)................... 12·00

No. ME4 was sold for £2·52. It has the surplus self-adhesive paper around each stamp removed and has two notches at top right.

Original selling prices for the later booklets were £2·76 (ME4a) and £2·88 (ME4b).

The back cover of No. ME4a has added text as No. MB4b.

The back cover of No. ME4b has text as No. MB4c/d.

Containing 12 2nd Class "Security Machins"

2009 (31 Mar)–**11**. Blue cover with multicoloured emblem as Type ME **2** (74×57 mm) by Walsall.

ME5 Containing twelve 2nd Class self-adhesive stamps (No. U2947, code "MTIL" without date)................................. 15·00
   a. Ditto but containing No. U2963 (code "MTIL" with date) (2.10) .... 70·00
   b. Ditto but with printer's imprint removed (19.8.10)..... 17·00
   c. Ditto but with FSC logo added (25.10.11) .... 16·00

No. ME5 was originally sold at £3·24. It has the surplus self-adhesive paper around each stamp removed and has two small notches at top right.

Original selling prices of the later booklets were £3·60 (ME5a), £3·84 (ME5b) and £4·32 (ME5c).

No. ME5/a are inscribed "Walsall Security Printers Limited, UK" along the left-hand edge of the back cover. This was removed for MB5b/c.

No. ME5c was re-issued on 31 July 2014 with the telephone numbers on the back cover charged from 08 to 03 numbers as for MB12. The price shown for ME5c is with either the 08 or 03 telephone numbers.

Date code for ME5a is "MA10", for ME5b "MA10" or "M11L" and for ME5c "M11L" , "M12L", "M13L" or "M14L", and for ME5c with changed telephone numbers "M14L" or "M15L".

2016. Blue cover with multicoloured emblem as Type ME **2** (74×57 mm) by Walsall. 'Repeating ROYAL MAIL wording printed on the front of the self-adhesive backing paper

ME6 Containing twelve 2nd Class self-adhesive stamps (No. U2963, code "MTIL" with date) .... 14·00

No. ME6 was originally sold for £6·48. It has the surplus self-adhesive paper around each stamp removed and has two small notches at top right.

Date codes for ME6 are "M15L" or "M16L"

Containing 12 1st Class stamps

2001 (29 Jan). Multicoloured laminated covers as Type MA **1** (74×56 mm). Stamps printed on the cove rs in bright orange-red by Questa (No. MF **1**) or Walsall (No. MF2).

MF1 Containing twelve 1st Class self-adhesive stamps (No. 2040) (Questa)... 14·00

MF2 Containing twelve 1st Class self-adhesive stamps (No. 2040) (Walsall)... 14·00

Nos. MF1/2 were each sold at £3·24. They were re-issued on 1 August 2001 showing "Cod Post" added to the "Ffôn Testun" inscription on the back covers.

2002 (5 June)–**07**. Gold laminated cover as Type MB **3** (74×56 mm) by Walsall.

MF3 Containing twelve 1st Class self-adhesive stamps (No. 2295)... 14·00

a. Back cover with added text about new pricing
structure (25.4.06) .... 14·00
b. Back cover with text about validity (5.6.07).................. 14·00
No. MF3 was sold at £3·24. It shows the surplus self-adhesive paper around each stamp removed and a single notch at the top right hand edge to facilitate identification by the blind.
Original selling prices of the later booklets were £3·84 (MF3a) and £4·08 (MF3b).
The back cover of No. MF3a has added text as No. MB4b.
The back cover of No. MF3b has text as No. MB4c/d.

2003 (27 Mar). Gold cover with multicoloured emblem as Type ME **3** (74×57 mm) by Walsall.
MF4 Containing twelve 1st Class self-adhesive stamps
(No. 2295) .... 14·00
No. MF4 was initially sold for £3·24. It shows the surplus self-adhesive paper around each stamp removed and has a single notch at top right.

Containing 12 1st Class "Security" Machins

2009 (31 Mar)–**11**. Gold cover with multicoloured emblem as Type MB **3** (74×57 mm) by Walsall.
MF5 Containing twelve 1st Class self-adhesive stamps
(No. U2952, code "MTIL" without date)................................... 20·00
a. Ditto but with printer's imprint removed (15.12.09) .... 21·00
b. Ditto but containing No. U2968, code "MTIL" with date
(.2.10) .... 22·00
c. Ditto but with FSC logo added (25.10.11) .... 17·00
No. MF5 was originally sold for £4·32. It has the surplus self-adhesive paper around each stamp removed and has a single small notch at top right.
Original selling prices of the later booklets were £4·68 (MF6a/b) and £5·52 (MF5c).
No. MF5 is inscribed "Walsall Security Printers Limited, UK" along the left hand edge of the back cover. This was removed for MF5a/c.
Date codes for MF5b are "MA10" and "M11L" and for MF5c "M11L" and "M12L".

2012 (6 Feb). *Diamond Jubilee.* Slate-blue cover with multicoloured emblem as Type MB **11** (74×57 mm) by Walsall.
MF6 Containing twelve 1st class self-adhesive stamps
(No. U2968, code "MTND")....................................... 14·00
No. MF6 was originally sold for £5·52. It has the surplus self-adhesive paper around each stamp removed and a single notch at the top right

2013 (3 Jan). Red cover with multicoloured emblem as Type MB **12** (74×57 mm) by Walsall.
MF7 Containing twelve 1st Class self-adhesive stamps
(No. U2968e, code "MTIL") .... 15·00
No. MF7 was originally sold for £7·20. It has the surplus self-adhesive paper around each stamp removed and a single small notch at top right.
No. MF7 was re-issued on 31 July 2014 with the telephone numbers on the back cover charged from 08 to 03 numbers as for MB12. The price shown for MF7 is with the changed telephone number. With 08 telephone number £17.00
Date codes for MF7 are "M12L" and "M13L" and "M14L", and with changed telephone numbers "M14L" or "M15L"

2016. Red cover with multicoloured emblem as Type MB **12** (74×57 mm) by Walsall. 'Repeating ROYAL MAIL wording printed on the front of the self-adhesive backing paper
MF8 Containing twelve 1st Class self-adhesive stamps
(No. U2968e, code "MTIL")...................................... 15·00
No. MF8 was originally sold for £7·56. It has the surplus self-adhesive paper around each stamp removed and a single small notch at top right
Date codes for MF8 are M15L or M16L.

Containing 20 1st Class stamps

MG **1**

Containing six E stamps

2002 (4 July). Multicoloured laminated cover as Type ME **2** (74×57 mm) printed by Walsall with the surplus self-adhesive paper around each stamp removed.
MH1 Containing six E stamps (No. 2296) and six Air Mail
labels.. 16·00
No. MH1 was sold at £2·22. It shows the surplus self-adhesive paper around each stamp removed.

2003 (28 May). Multicoloured cover as Type MB **6** (74×57 mm with *The Real Network* added below logo) printed by Walsall with the surplus self-adhesive paper around each stamp removed.
MH2 Containing six E stamps (No. 2296) and six Air Mail
labels.. 16·00
No. MH2 was sold at £2·28.

Containing four Europe stamps

All booklets in this section show the surplus self-adhesive paper around each stamp removed.

MI **1** ("The Real Network" below logo)

2003 (27 Mar). Ultramarine cover with multicoloured emblem as Type MI **1** (74×57 mm) by Walsall.
MI1 Containing four Europe 40g self-adhesive stamps (No. 2358) and four Air Mail labels.. 12·00
No. MI1 was sold at £2·08.

MI **2**

2004 (15 June). Ultramarine cover with multicoloured emblem as Type MI **2** (74×57 mm) by Walsall.
MI2 Containing four Europe up to 40 grams self-adhesive
stamps (No. 2358) and four Air Mail labels.......................... 12·00
No. MI2 was sold at £2·28.
2010 (30 Mar). Deep green cover with multicoloured emblem as Type MI **2** (74×57 mm) by Walsall.
MI3 Containing four Europe up to 20 grams self-adhesive
stamps (No. 2357b) and four Air Mail labels .... 8·00
No. MI3 was sold at £2·24.

Containing four Worldwide stamps

All booklets in this section show the surplus self-adhesive paper around each stamp removed.
2003 (27 Mar). Red cover with multicoloured emblem as Type MI **1** (74×57 mm) by Walsall.
MJ1 Containing four Worldwide up to 40 grams self-
adhesive stamps (No. 2359) and four Air Mail labels...... 18·00
No. MJ1 was sold at £4·48.
2004 (15 June). Red cover with multicoloured emblem as Type MI **2** (74×57 mm) by Walsall.
MJ2 Containing four Worldwide up to 40 grams self-
adhesive stamps (No. 2359) and four Air Mail labels...... 18·00
No. MJ2 was sold at £4·48.
2010 (30 Mar). Deep mauve cover with multicoloured emblem as Type MI **2** (74×57 mm) by Walsall.
MJ3 Containing four Worldwide up to 20 grams self-
adhesive stamps (No. 2358a) and four Air Mail labels ... 12·00
No. MJ3 was sold at £3·60.

Containing four Worldwide postcard stamps

All booklets in this section have the surplus self-adhesive paper around each stamp removed.

2004 (1 Apr). Grey-black cover with multicoloured emblem as Type MI **2** (74×57 mm) by Walsall.

MJA1 Containing four Worldwide postcard self-adhesive
stamps (No. 2357a) and four Air Mail labels...................... 8·00

No. MJA1 was sold for £1·72.

I. Self-adhesive. Barcode Booklets containing stamps with face values.

NOTE. All booklets in this section show the surplus self-adhesive paper around each stamp removed.

£2.52 Booklets

2002 (4 July). Multicoloured laminated cover as Type ME **2** (74×57 mm) printed by Walsall with the surplus self-adhesive paper around each stamp removed.

NA1 Containing six 42p. stamps (No. 2297) and six Air Mail
labels.. 35·00

2003 (28 May). Multicoloured cover as Type MB **6** (74×57 mm with *"The Real Network"* added below logo) printed by Walsall.

NA2 Containing six 42p. stamps (No. 2297) and six Air Mail
labels.. 30·00

£4.08 Booklets

2002 (4 July). Multicoloured laminated cover as Type ME **2** (74×57 mm) printed by Walsall with the surplus self-adhesive paper around each stamp removed.

NB1 Containing six 68p. stamps (No. 2298) and six Air Mail
labels.. 38·00

2003 (28 May). Multicoloured cover as Type MB **6** (74×57 mm with *"The Real Network"* added below logo) printed by Walsall.

NB2 Containing six 68p. stamps (No. 2298) and six Air Mail
labels.. 38·00

J. Self-adhesive Barcode Booklets containing No Value Indicated Special or Occasions issues, with Definitive stamps.

NOTE. *All booklets in this section show the surplus self-adhesive paper around each stamp retained, unless otherwise stated.*

PM **1**

2001 (13 Feb). *Cats and Dogs.* Multicoloured cover as Type PM **1** (84×64 mm). Printed by Walsall.

PM1 (£3·24) booklet containing twelve 1st stamps (No.
2187b)... 30·00

PM **2**

2001 (17 Apr). *Centenary of Royal Navy Submarine Service.* Multicoloured cover as Type PM **2** (75×57 mm). Printed by Questa.

PM2 (£1·62) booklet containing No. 2207a........................... 95·00

2001 (4 Sept). *Punch and Judy Show Puppets.* Multicoloured cover as Type PM **2** (74×57 mm). Printed by Questa.

PM3 (£1·62) booklet containing No. 2230a........................... 30·00

2001 (22 Oct). *Flags and Ensigns.* Multicoloured cover as Type PM **2** (74×57 mm). Printed by Questa.

PM4 (£1·62) booklet containing No. 2208a........................... 20·00

2002 (2 May). *50th Anniv of Passenger Jet Aviation. Airliners.* Multicoloured cover as Type PM **2** (74×57 mm). Printed by Questa.

PM5 (£1·62) booklet containing No. 2290a........................... 12·00

2002 (21 May). *World Cup Football Championship, Japan and Korea.* Multicoloured cover as Type PM 2 (74×57 mm). Printed by Walsall.

PM6 (£1·62) booklet containing No. 2293a........................... 12·00

PM **7**

2002 (10 Sept). *Bridges of London.* Gold cover with multicoloured emblem and stamp illustration as Type PM **7** (74×57 mm). Printed by Questa.

PM7 (£1·62) booklet containing No. 2314a........................... 12·00

No. PM7 shows the surplus self-adhesive paper around each stamp removed and a single notch at top right.

2003 (4 Mar). *Occasions* Greetings Stamps. Gold cover with multicoloured emblem and stamp illustration as Type PM **7** (74×57 mm). Printed by Questa.

PM8 (£1·62) booklet containing No. 2264ab......................... 12·00

No. PM8 shows the surplus self-adhesive paper around each stamp removed and a single notch at top right.

PM **9** ("The Real Network" added below logo)

2003 (29 Apr). *Extreme Endeavours.* Gold cover with multicoloured emblem and stamp illustration as Type PM **9** (74×57 mm). Printed by De La Rue.

PM9 (£1·62) booklet containing No. 2366a........................... 12·00

No. PM9 shows the surplus self-adhesive paper around each stamp removed and has a single notch at top right.

2003 (15 July). *A British Journey: Scotland.* Gold cover with multicoloured emblem and stamp illustration as Type PM **9** (74×57 mm). Printed by De La Rue.

PM10 (£1·68) booklet containing No. 2391a........................... 12·00

No. PM10 shows the surplus self-adhesive paper around each stamp removed and has a single notch at top right.

2003 (18 Sept). *Classic Transport Toys.* Gold cover with multicoloured emblem and stamp illustration as Type PM **7** (74×57 mm). Printed by De La Rue.

PM11 (£1·68) booklet containing No. 2403a........................... 12·00

No. PM11 shows the surplus self-adhesive paper around each stamp removed and has a single notch at top right.

2004 (16 Mar). *A British Journey: Northern Ireland.* Gold cover with multicoloured emblem and stamp illustration as Type PM **7** (74×57 mm). Printed by De La Rue.

PM12 (£1·68) booklet containing No. 2445a..................... 12·00
   No. PM12 shows the surplus self-adhesive paper around each stamp removed and has a single notch at top right.

2004 (13 Apr). *Ocean Liners.* Gold cover with multicoloured emblem and stamp illustration as Type PM **7** (74×57 mm). Printed by De La Rue.

PM13 (£1·68) booklet containing No. 2455a..................... 12·00
   No. PM13 has the self-adhesive paper around each stamp removed and has a single notch at top right.

2004 (15 June). *A British Journey: Wales.* Gold cover with multicoloured emblem and stamp illustration as Type PM **7** (74×57 mm). Printed by De La Rue.

PM14 (£1·68) booklet containing No. 2472a..................... 18·00
   No. PM14 has the self-adhesive paper around each stamp removed and has a single notch at top right.

PM **15**

2008 (13 May). *Beside the Seaside.* Red cover with multicoloured emblem (74×57 mm) as Type PM **15**. Printed by Walsall.

PM15 (£2·16) booklet containing No. 2848a..................... 18·00
   No. PM15 has the self-adhesive paper removed from around the 1st class gold stamps only and has a single notch at top right.

Booklets containing "Security" Machins

Unless otherwise stated all 1st Class Machin stamps coded "MCIL" and for PM16–PM21 without dates.

PM36 contains four definitive-size Tardis stamps in place of the usual Machin design.

2009 (10 Mar). *Design Classics 1* (Telephone Kiosk and Routemaster Bus). Red cover with multicoloured emblem as Type PM **15** (74×57 mm). Printed by Walsall.

PM16 (£2·16) booklet containing pane No. 2911a..................... 12·00
   No. PM16 has the self-adhesive paper removed from around the 1st class gold stamps (No. U2949) only and has a single notch at top right.

2009 (21 Apr). *Design Classics 2* (Mini). Red cover with multicoloured emblem as Type PM **15** (74×57 mm). Printed by Walsall.

PM17 (£2·34) booklet containing pane No. 2913a..................... 12·00
   No. PM17 has the self-adhesive paper removed from around the 1st class gold stamps (No. U2949) only and has a single notch at top right.

2009 (21 May). *50th Anniv of NAFAS (National Association of Flower Arrangement Societies).* Red cover with multicoloured emblem as Type PM **15** (74×57 mm). Printed by Walsall.

PM18 (£2·34) booklet containing No. 2942a..................... 15·00
   No. PM18 has the self-adhesive paper removed from around the 1st class gold stamps (U2949) only and has a single notch at top right.

2009 (18 Aug). *Design Classics 3* (Concorde). Red cover with multicoloured emblem as Type PM **15** (74×57 mm). Printed by Walsall.

PM19 (£2·34) booklet containing pane No. 2914a..................... 12·00
   No. PM19 has the self-adhesive paper removed from around the 1st class gold stamps (No. U2949) only and has a single notch at top right.

2009 (17 Sept). *Design Classics 4* (Miniskirt). Red cover with multicoloured emblem as Type PM **15** (74×57 mm). Printed by Walsall.

PM20 (£2·34) booklet containing pane No. 2915a..................... 12·00
   No. PM20 has the self-adhesive paper removed from around the 1st class gold stamps (No. U2949) only and has a single notch at top right.

2010 (7 Jan). *Olympic and Paralympic Games, London (2012) 1 (Judo and Archery).* Red cover with multicoloured emblem as Type PM **15** (74×57 mm). Printed by Walsall.

PM21 (£2·34) booklet containing pane No. 3020a..................... 13·00
   No. PM21 has the self-adhesive paper removed from around the 1st class gold stamps (No. U2949) only and has a single notch at top right.

2010 (25 Feb). *Olympic and Paralympic Games, London (2012) 2 (Track and Basketball).* Red cover with multicoloured emblem as Type PM **15** (74×57 mm). Printed by Walsall.

PM22 (£2·34) booklet containing pane No. 3022a..................... 13·00

No. PM22 has the self-adhesive paper removed from around the 1st class gold stamps (No. U2965) only and has a single notch at top right. The date code for U2965 is "MA10".

2010 (15 June). *Mammals.* Red cover with multicoloured emblem as Type PM **15** (74×57 mm). Printed by Walsall.

PM23 (£2·46) booklet containing pane No. 3095a..................... 13·00
   No. PM23 has the self-adhesive paper removed from around the 1st class gold stamps (No. U2965) only and has a single notch at top right. Date code for No. U2965 is "MA10".

2010 (27 July). *Olympic and Paralympic Games, London (2012) 3 (Rowing and Tennis.* Red cover with multicoloured emblem as Type PM **15** (74×57 mm). Printed by Walsall.

PM24 (£2·46) booklet containing pane No. 3107a..................... 12·00
   No. PM24 has the self-adhesive paper removed from around the 1st class gold stamps (No. U2965) only and has a single notch at top right. Date code for No. U2965 is "MA10".

2010 (15 Sept). *British Design Classics 5 (Spitfire).* Red cover with multicoloured emblem as Type PM **15** (74×57 mm). Printed by Walsall.

PM25 (£2·46) booklet containing pane No. 2915ba..................... 12·00
   No. PM25 has the self-adhesive paper removed from around the 1st class gold stamps (No. U2965) only and has a single notch at top right. Date code for No. U2965 is "MA10".

2010 (12 Oct). *Olympic and Paralympic Games, London (2012) 4 (Football and Cycling).* Red cover with multicoloured emblem as Type PM **15** (74×57 mm). Printed by Walsall.

PM26 (£2·46) booklet containing pane No. 3108ab..................... 12·00
   No. PM26 has the self-adhesive paper removed from around the 1st class gold stamps (No. U2965) only and has a single notch at top right. Date code for No. U2965 is "MA10".

2011 (11 Jan). *F.A.B. The Genius of Gerry Anderson'* Red cover with multicoloured emblem as Type PM **15** (74×57 mm). Printed by Walsall.

PM27 (£2·46) booklet containing pane No. 3143a..................... 12·00
   No.PM27 has the self-adhesive paper removed from around the 1st class gold stamps (No. U2965) only and has a single notch at top right. Date code for No. U2965 is "M11L".

2011 (24 Feb). *50th Anniv of the British Heart Foundation.* Red cover with multicoloured emblems as Type PM **15** (74×57 mm). Printed by Walsall.

PM28 (£2·46) booklet containing pane No. 3153a..................... 9·00
   No. PM28 has the self-adhesive paper removed from around the 1st class gold stamps (No. U2965) only and has a single notch at top right. Date code for No. U2965 is "M11L".

2011 (14 Jun). *Thomas the Tank Engine.* Red cover with multicoloured emblem (74×57 mm) as Type PM **15**. Printed by Walsall.

PM29 (£2·76) booklet containing pane No. 3194a..................... 10·00
   Date code for No. U2965 is "M11L".

2011 (27 July). *Olympic and Paralympic Games, London (2012) 5 (Wheelchair Rugby and Sailing).* Red cover with multicoloured emblem as Type PM **15** (74×57 mm). Printed by Walsall.

PM30 (£2·76) booklet containing pane No. 3205a..................... 10·00
   No. PM30 has the self-adhesive paper removed from around the 1st class gold stamps (No. U2965) only and has a single notch at top right. Date code for No. U2965 is "M11L".

2011 (23 Aug). *Classic Locomotives of England.* Red cover with multicoloured emblem as Type PM **15** (74×57 mm). Printed by Walsall.

PM31 (£2·76) booklet containing pane No. 3215a..................... 11·00
   Date code for No. U2965 is "M11L".

2011 (15 Sept). *Olympic and Paralympic Games, London (2012) 6 (Gymnastics and Fencing).* Red cover with multicoloured emblem as Type PM **15** (74×57 mm). Printed by Walsall.

PM32 (£2·76) booklet containing pane No. 3206ab..................... 10·00
   No. PM32 has the self-adhesive paper removed from around the 1st class gold stamps (No. U2965) only and has a single notch at top right. Date code for No. U2965 is "M11L".

2012 (31 May). *Diamond Jubilee.* Red cover with multicoloured emblem (74×57 mm) as Type PM **15**. Printed by Walsall.

PM33 (£3·60) booklet containing pane No. 3327a..................... 12·00
   No. PM33 has the self-adhesive paper removed from around the 1st class slate-blue stamps (No. U3274, code "MCND") only and has a single notch at top right.

2012 (27 Sept). *Classic Locomotives of Scotland.* Red cover with multicoloured emblem as Type PM **15** (74×57 mm). Printed by Walsall.

PM34 (£3·60) booklet containing pane No. 3407a..................... 12·00
   No. PM34 has the self-adhesive paper removed from around the 1st class slate-blue stamps (No. U3274 code "MCND") only and has a single notch at top right.

2013 (9 Jan). *150th Anniv of the London Underground.* Red cover with multicoloured emblem as Type PM **15** (74×57 mm). Printed by Walsall.

PM35 (£3·60) booklet containing pane No. 3430a........................ 12·00

No. PM35 has the self-adhesive paper removed from around the 1st class vermilion stamps (No. U2968b, code "MCIL") only and has a single notch at top right.

Date code for No. U2968b to "M12L"

2013 (26 Mar). *50th Anniv of Doctor Who* (TV programme). Red cover with multicoloured emblem as Type PM **15** (74×57 mm). Printed by Walsall. Self-adhesive.

PM36 (£3·60) booklet containing No. 3448a........................ 18·00

No. PM36 has the self-adhesive paper removed from around the 1st class TARDIS stamps (No. 3449) only and has a single notch at top right.

2013 (9 May). *Football Heroes.* Red cover with multicoloured emblem (74×57 mm) as Type PM **15**. Printed by Walsall.

PM37 (£3·60) booklet containing No. 3475a .... 12·00

No. PM37 has the self-adhesive paper removed from around the 1st class vermilion stamps (No. U2968b, code "MCIL") only and has a single notch at top right.

Date code for No. U2968b is "M13L".

2013 (18 Jun). *Classic Locomotives of Northern Ireland.* Red cover with multicoloured emblem as Type PM **15** (75×58 mm). Printed by Walsall.

PM38 (£3·60) booklet containing pane No. 3497a........................ 12·00

No. PM38 has the self-adhesive paper removed from around the 1st class vermilion stamps (No. U2968b, code "MCIL") only and has a single notch at top right.

Date code for No. U2968b is "M13L".

2013 (11 July). *Butterflies.* Red cover with multicoloured emblem as Type PM **15** (74×57 mm).

PM39 (£3·60) booklet containing pane No. 3509a........................ 12·00

No. PM39 has the self-adhesive paper removed from around the 1st class vermilion stamps (No. U2968b, code "MCIL") only and has a single notch at top right.

Date code for No. U2968b is "M13L".

2013 (19 Sept). *Royal Mail Transport: By Land and Sea.* Red cover with multicoloured emblem as Type PM **15** (74×58 mm). Printed by Walsall.

PM40 (£3·60) booklet containing pane No. 3530a........................ 13·00

No. PM40 has the self-adhesive paper removed from around the 1st class vermilion stamps (No. U2968b, code "MCIL") only and has a single notch at top right.

Date code for No. U2968b is "M13L".

2014 (20 Feb). *Football Heroes.* Red cover with multicoloured emblem (74×57 mm) as Type PM **15**. Printed by Walsall.

PM41 (£3·60) booklet containing No. 3477a .... 12·00

No. PM41 has the self-adhesive paper removed from around the 1st class vermilion stamps (No. U2968b, code "MCIL") only and has a single notch at top right.

Date code for No. U2968b is "M13L".

2014 (15 Apr). *Buckingham Palace, London.* Red cover with multi-coloured emblem (74×57 mm) as Type PM **15**. Printed by Walsall.

PM42 (£3·72) booklet containing pane No. 3595a........................ 12·00

"No. PM42 has the self-adhesive paper removed from around the 1st class vermilion stamps (No. U2968b) only and has a single notch at top right. Date code for No. U2968b is "M14L".

2014 (17 July). *Commonwealth Games, Glasgow.* Red cover with multi-coloured emblem as Type PM **15** (74×57 mm). Printed by Walsall.

PM43 (£3·72) booklet containing pane No. 3625a........................ 12·00

Date code for No. U2968b is "M14L".

2014 (18 Aug). *Sustainable and Threatened Fish.* Red cover with multi-coloured emblem as Type PM **15** (74×57 mm). Printed by Walsall.

PM44 (£3·72) booklet containing pane No. 3632a........................ 12·00

Date code for No. U2968b is "M14L".

2014 (18 Sep). *Classic Locomotives of Wales.* Red cover with multi-coloured emblem as Type PM **15** (74×57 mm). Printed by Walsall.

PM45 (£3·72) booklet containing pane No. 3634a........................ 12·00

Date code for No. U2968b is "M14L".

2015 (6 Jan). *Alice in Wonderland.* Red cover with multicoloured em-blem as Type PM **15** (74×57 mm). Printed by Walsall.

PM46 (£3·72) booklet containing pane No. 3668a........................ 12·00

Date code for No. U2968b is "M15L".

2015 (1 Apr). *Comedy Greats.* Red cover with multicoloured emblem as Type PM **15** (74×57 mm). Printed by Walsall.

PM47 (£3·78) booklet containing pane No. 3707a........................ 12·00

Date code for No. U2968b is "M15L".

2015 (18 Aug). *Bees.* Red cover with multicoloured emblem as Type PM **15** (74×57 mm). Printed by Walsall.

PM48 (£3·78) booklet containing pane No. 3743a........................ 12·00

Date code for No. U2968b is 'M15L'.

2015 (18 Sept). *Rugby World Cup.* Red cover with multicoloured emblem as Type PM **15** (74×57 mm). Printed by Walsall.

PM49 (£3·78) booklet containing pane No. 3756a........................ 12·00

Date code for No. U3746 is '015R'.

K. Self-adhesive Barcode Booklets containing No Value Indicated "Smilers" stamps in definitive size.

Containing six "Smilers" stamps

NOTE. Nos. QA1–4and QB1 have the self-adhesive paper around each stamp removed and have a single notch at top right.

QA **1**

2005 (4 Oct). Gold cover with multicoloured emblem as Type QA **1** (74×56 mm) by Walsall.

QA1 (£1·80) booklet containing No. 2567a........................ 15·00

QA **2**

2006 (17 July). Gold cover with multicoloured emblem as Type QA **2** (74×56 mm) by Walsall.

QA2 (£1·92) booklet containing No. 2567a .... 14·00

2006 (17 Oct). Gold cover with multicoloured emblem as Type QA **1** (74×56 mm) by Walsall.

QA3 (£1·92) containing No. 2672a........................ 9·00

2008 (28 Feb). Gold cover with multicoloured emblem as Type QA **2** (74×56 mm) by Walsall.

QA4 (£2·04) booklet containing No. 2819a........................ 42·00

Containing 12 "Smilers" stamps

2015 (20 Jan). Red cover with multicoloured emblem as Type MB **12** (74×57 mm).

QB1 (£7·44) booklet containing No. 3670a........................ 15·00

Nos. 3670/7 were issued in booklets of 12, No. QB1, originally sold for £7·44.

L. Self-adhesive Barcode Booklets containing stamps with value indicator at upper left.

Containing four 2nd Class Large stamps

RA **1**

2006 (15 Aug). Blue cover with multicoloured emblem as Type RA **1** (74×57 mm) by Walsall.
RA1   Containing four 2nd Class Large self-adhesive stamps
(No. 2656) ....   8·00
No. RA1 was sold at £1.48. It has the surplus self-adhesive paper around each stamp removed and two notches at top right for identification by the blind.

Containing four 2nd Class Large "Security" stamps

2009 (31 Mar)–**11**. Blue cover with multicoloured emblem as Type RA **1** (74×57 mm) by Walsall.
RA2   Containing four 2nd Class Large self-adhesive stamps
(No. U2954 code "FOYAL" without date) ....   12·00
a. Ditto but containing No. U2970 (code "MFIL" with date) (8.5.10) ....   50·00
b. Ditto but with printer's imprint removed (22.3.11).....   10·00
c. Ditto but with FSC logo added (25.10.11) ....   12·00
No. RA2 was originally sold for £1·68. It has the surplus self-adhesive paper around each stamp removed and two large notches at top right.
Original selling prices of the later booklets were £2·04 (RA2a/b) and £2·32 (RA2c).
Nos. RA2/a are inscribed "Walsall Security Printers Limited, UK" along the left-hand edge of the back cover. This was removed from Nos. RA2b/c.
No. RA2c was reissued on 31 July 2014 with the telephone numbers on the back cover charged from 08 to 03 numbers as for MB12. The price shown for RA2c is with either the 08 or 03 telephone numbers.
Date code for RA2a is "MA10", for RA2b "MA11" and for RA2c "MA11", "MA12", "MA13" or "MA14", and with changed telephone numbers "MA14" or "MA15"

Containing four 1st Class Large stamps

RB **1**

2006 (15 Aug). Gold cover with multicoloured emblem as Type RB **1** (74×57 mm) by Walsall.
RB1   Containing four 1st Class Large self-adhesive stamps
(No. 2657) ....   10·00
No. RB1 was sold at £1·76. It has the surplus self-adhesive paper around each stamp removed and a single notch at top right.

Containing four 1st Class Large "Security" stamps

2009 (31 Mar).–**11** Gold cover with multicoloured emblem as Type RB **1** (74×57 mm) by Walsall.
RB2   Containing four 1st Class Large self-adhesive stamps
(No. U2956 code "FOYAL" without date) ....   20·00
a. Ditto but containing No. U2972 (code "MFIL" with date) (8.5.10)...   30·00
b. Ditto but with printer's imprint removed (22.3.11).....   12·00
c. Ditto but with FSC logo added (25.10.11) ....   10·00
No. RB2 was originally sold for £2·08. It has the surplus self-adhesive paper around each stamp removed and a large notch at top right.
Original selling prices of the later booklets were £2·64 (RB2a/b) and £3·00 (RB2c).
No. RB2/a are inscribed "Walsall Security Printers Limited, UK" along the left-hand edge of the back cover. This was removed for RB2b/c.
Date code for RB2a is "MA10" and for RB2b/c "MA11".

2012 (25 Apr). *Diamond Jubilee.* Slate-blue cover with multicoloured emblem as Type RB **1** (74×57 mm) by Walsall.
RB3 Containing four 1st Class Large self-adhesive stamps (No. U3277, code "JUBILFE")..   10·00
No. RB3 was originally sold for £3·00.

RB **4**

2013 (3 Jan). Red cover with multicoloured emblem as Type RB **4** (74×57 mm) by Walsall.
RB4   Containing four 1st Class Large self-adhesive stamps (No. U2974, code "MFIL")...   11·00
No. RB4 was originally sold for £3·60.
No. RB4 was reissued on 31 July 2014 with the telephone numbers on the back cover charged from 08 to 03 numbers as for MB12. The price shown for RB4 is with either the 08 or 03 telephone numbers.
Date codes for RB4 are "MA12", "MA13" or "MA14", and with changed telephone numbers "MA14" or "MA15".

2016. Red cover with multicoloured emblem as Type RB **4** (74×57 mm) by Walsall. 'Repeating ROYAL MAIL wording printed on the front of the self-adhesive backing paper
RB5   Containing four 1st Class Large self-adhesive stamps (No. U2974, code "MFIL")...   11·00
No. RB5 was originally sold for £3·80.
Date code for RB5 is MA15

Containing six 1st class stamps

2006 (12 Sept)–**2007**. Gold cover with multicoloured emblem as Type MB **3** (74×57 mm) by Walsall.
RC1   Containing six 1st Class self-adhesive stamps (No. 2655) ..   10·00
a. Inside cover with "don't just send a stamp" advertisement (2.10.06) ....   11·00
b. Inside cover with "To find the correct postcodes for your mail" notice (1.2.07) ....   10·00
Nos. RC1/b originally sold at £1·92. They had the surplus self-adhesive paper around each stamp removed and a notch at top right.

Containing 12 2nd class stamps

2006 (12 Sept). Blue cover with multicoloured emblem as Type MB **3** (74×57 mm) by Walsall.
RD1   Containing twelve 2nd Class self-adhesive stamps (No. 2654) ....   11·00
Nos. RD1 was originally sold at £2·76. It has the surplus self-adhesive paper around each stamp removed and two notches at top right.

Containing 12 1st class stamps

2006 (12 Sept). Gold cover with multicoloured emblem as Type MB **3** (74×57 mm) by Walsall.
RE1   Containing twelve 1st Class self-adhesive stamps (No. 2655)   14·00
No. RE1 was sold at £3·84. It has the surplus self-adhesive paper around each stamp removed and a notch at top right.

M. Self-adhesive Barcode Booklets containing No Value Indicated "Smilers" stamps in definitive size, with Definitive stamps.

NOTE. Nos. SA1 and SA2 have the surplus self-adhesive paper around each stamp removed and a notch at top right.

2007 (16 Jan). Gold cover with multicoloured emblem as Type MB **3** (74×57 mm) by Walsall.
SA1   (£1·92) booklet containing No. 2693a ....   24·00

2008 (15 Jan). Gold cover with multicoloured emblem as Type MB **3** (74×57 mm) by Walsall.
SA2   (£2·04) booklet containing No. 2693b   15·00

POST OFFICE LABEL SHEETS

At the Stamp Show 2000 International Stamp Exhibition visitors could purchase sheets of 10 × 1st class stamps in the "Smiles" designs (as Nos. 1550/9), each stamp having a *se-tenant* label on which the exhibition visitor's picture was printed, the photographs being taken in a booth at the exhibition.

For those unable to visit the exhibition, the same sheet could be purchased from the Philatelic Bureau and from Post Office philatelic outlets with a "Stamp Show 2000" label in place of the photograph.

For Christmas 2000, sheets of 20 × 19p stamps in the "Robin in Pillar Box" design (as No. 1896) or 10 × 1st class "Father Christmas with Cracker" design (as No. 2007) were available through the Philatelic Bureau, with *se-tenant* labels as part of a "customised" service, purchasers supplying their own photographs for reproduction on the *se-tenant* label.

This service has continued under the name "Smilers", after the initial set of stamp designs employed, and was also made available at photo-booths at selected post offices. Corporate label panes, allowing commercial and charitable organisations to have their logo or message reproduced on the *se-tenant* labels were made available through the Bureau from 2000.

Label sheets have continued to be offered with a standard greeting or message. These "Generic Smilers" have been available from the Philatelic Bureau or from philatelic outlets.

As "personalised", "corporate" and "generic" label sheets could only be purchased at a premium over the face value of the stamps within them, they are not given full listing in this catalogue; neither are individual stamps (with or without their *se-tenant* label), some of which are identifiable as having come from Label Sheets, due to perforation, phosphor or printing differences.

The list which follows comprises the "generic" sheets only. Differences between the stamp in the Label Sheets and those of the standard issues are given under the respective listings in this catalogue.

An asterisk (*) in the listing indicates a difference in process, phosphor or perforation from the original design.

Smilers

LS **1**

2000 (22 May). *The Stamp Show 2000.* Type LS **1**. gravure Questa. Original selling price £2·95. P 15×14.
LS1   10×(1st) "Smiles" stamps, as Nos. 1550/9 and attached labels.. 40·00

LS **2**

LS **3**

2000 (3 Oct)–**01**. *Christmas.* Types LS **2** and LS **3**. gravure Questa. Original selling price £3·99 (LS 2/2a) and £2·95 (LS 3/a). P 15×14.
LS2   20×19p. "Robin in Pillar Box" stamps, as No. 1896 and attached labels (Imprint "Post Office 2000").................. £180
      a. Imprint "Consignia 2001" (9.10.01)................................. £625

LS3   10×(1st) "Father Christmas with Cracker" stamps, as No. 2007 and attached labels (Imprint "Post Office 2000")... £180
      a. Imprint "Consignia 2001" (9.10.01)................................. £625

LS **4**

2001 (5 June). *Occasions.* Type LS **4**. Litho* Questa. Original selling price £5·95. P 14×14½.
LS4   20×(1st) "Occasions" stamps as Nos. 2182/6 in four vertical columns of five with attached labels.................. £180

2001 (3 July). *Smiles* As Type LS **1** but with greetings shown in attached labels. Litho* Questa. Original selling price £2·**95**. P 14½×14*.
LS5   10×(1st) "Smiles" stamps, as Nos. 1550/9 and attached labels.. £200

LS **6**

2001 (18 Dec). *Greetings Cartoons* Type LS **6**. Litho Questa. Original selling price £2·**95**. Two phosphor bands. P 14½×14 (without* elliptical holes).
LS6   10×(1st) Greetings Cartoons, as Nos. 1905p/14p and attached labels... 50·00

LS **7**

2002 (23 Apr). *Occasions* Stamps. Type LS **7**. Litho Questa. Original selling price £5·95. P 14*.
LS7   20×(1st) "Occasions" stamps as Nos. 2260/4 in four vertical columns of five with attached labels.................. 85·00

LS **8**

2002 (21 May). *Football World Cup.* Type LS **8**. Litho* Questa. Original selling price £5·95. P 14½×14.
LS8   20×(1st) as bottom right quarter of flag stamp in **MS**2292 and attached labels......................... 40·00

LS 9

2002 (1 Oct). *Smiles* Type LS **9**. Litho* Questa. Original selling price
£5·95. *P* 15×14.
LS9   10×(1st) "Teddy Bear" and 10 × (1st) Dennis the
       Menace, as Nos. 1550/1, each with attached labels........   40·00

LS 10

2002 (1 Oct). *Christmas.* Type LS **10**. Litho* Questa. Original selling price
£5·95. *P* 14½×14*.
LS10   20×(1st) "Father Christmas with Cracker", as No. 2007,
        with attached greetings labels ....   42·00

LS 11

2003 (21 Jan). *Flower Paintings.* Type LS **11**. Litho Questa. Original selling price £5·95. *P* 14½×14 (without* elliptical holes).
LS11   20×(1st) Flowers Greetings Stamps, as Nos. 1955/64
        (two of each design) with floral labels attached ....   48·00

LS 12

2003 (4 Feb). *Occasions.* Type LS **12**. Litho Questa. Original selling price
£5·95. *P* 14½×14.
LS12   20×(1st) "Tick box" Occasions stamps, as Nos. 2337/42
        (four of Nos. 2338 and 2340 and 3 each of the others)
        with attached labels ....   35·00
        a. "Multiple Choice" in green.
    "Multiple Choice" at top left of sheet is generally in red. LS12a is
believed to have come from trial sheets which were put on sale in
error.

LS 13

2003 (29 July). *Crossword Cartoons.* Type LS **13**. Litho Questa. Original
selling price £6·15. Two phosphor bands. *P* 14½×14 (without* elliptical holes).
LS13   20×(1st) Cartoons as Nos. 1905p/14p with "Crossword"
        labels attached..   30·00

LS 14

2003 (30 Sept). *Christmas. Winter Robins.* Type LS **14**. Litho* De La Rue.
Original selling price £6·15. *P* 14½.
LS14   20×(1st) Winter Robins, self-adhesive, as No. 2239
        with labels alongside...   30·00

LS 15

LS 16

2003 (4 Nov). *Christmas.* Types LS **15** and LS **16**. Litho* De La Rue. Orig-
inal selling prices £4·20 (2nd) and £6·15 (1st). *P* 14½×14.
LS15   20×(2nd) Ice Sculptures, self-adhesive, as No. 2410
        with labels showing ice sculptures of polar fauna
        alongside...   38·00
LS16   20×(1st) Ice Sculptures, self-adhesive, as No. 2411
        with labels showing photographs of polar fauna
        alongside...   38·00

LS **17**

2004 (30 Jan). *Hong Kong Stamp Expo.* Litho Walsall. Original selling price £6·15. *P* 14½.
LS17 20×(1st) "Hello" greetings stamps, as No. 2262 with labels alongside.. 25·00

LS **18**

2004 (3 Feb). *Occasions Entertaining Envelopes* Type LS **18**. Litho De La Rue. Original selling price £6·15. *P* 14½×14.
LS18 20×(1st) "Entertaining Envelopes" greetings stamps, as Nos. 2424/8 (four of each design) with attached labels 25·00

LS **19**

2004 (25 May). *Royal Horticultural Society.* Type LS **19**. Litho* Walsall. Original selling price £6·15. *P* 14½.
LS19 20×(1st) Dahlia, as No. 2457 with attached labels.......... 26·00

LS **20**

2004 (27 July). *Rule Britannia.* Type LS **20**. Litho* Walsall. Original selling price £6·15. *P* 14½.
LS20 20×(1st) Union Flag, as Type **1517** with attached labels.. 28·00

LS **21**

2004 (2 Nov). *Christmas.* Type LS **21**. Litho* De La Rue. Original selling price £5·40. *P* 14½×14.
LS21 10×(2nd) and 10×(1st) "Father Christmas", self-adhesive, as Nos. 2495/6 with attached labels.................. 25·00

LS **22**

2005 (11 Jan). *Farm Animals.* Type LS **22**. Litho* Walsall. Original selling price £6·15. *P* 14½.
LS22 20×(1st) Farm Animals, as Nos. 2502/11 with attached labels... 35·00

LS **23**

2005 (15 Mar). *Centenary of the Magic Circle.* Type LS **23**. Litho* Walsall. Original selling price £6·15. *P* 14½×14.
LS23 20×(1st) Spinning Coin, as No. 2525 with attached labels.. 32·00

LS **24**

2005 (21 Apr). *Pacific Explorer 2005 World Stamp Expo.* Type LS **24**. Litho Walsall. Original selling price £6·55. *P* 14*.
LS24 20×(1st) "Hello" greetings stamps, as No. 2262 with attached labels... 25·00

LS **25**

2005 (21 June). *The White Ensign*. Type LS **25**. Litho* Cartor. Original selling price £6·55. *P* 14½.
LS25   20×(1st) White Ensign stamps, as Type **1516** with attached labels.. 25·00

LS **26**

2005 (15 Sept). *Classic ITV*. Type LS **26**. Litho Walsall. Original selling price £6·55. *P* 14½×14.
LS26   20×(1st) Emmerdale stamps, as No. 2562 with attached labels.. 24·00
The original printing of LS26 contained errors in some of the labels and was withdrawn prior to issue.

LS **27**

2005 (1 Nov). *Christmas. Christmas Robins*. Type LS **27**. Litho* Cartor. Original selling price £5·60. *P* 14½.
LS27   10×(2nd) and 10×(1st) Robins, self-adhesive, as Nos. 2238/9 with attached labels... 25·00

LS **28**

2006 (10 Jan). *A Bear called Paddington*. Type LS **28**. Litho Cartor. Original selling price £6·55. *P* 14½.
LS28   20×(1st) Paddington Bear, self-adhesive*, as No. 2592 with attached labels.. 25·00

LS **29**

2006 (7 Mar). *Fun Fruit and Veg*. Type LS **29**. Litho Cartor. Original selling price £6·55. *P* 14½×14.
LS29   20×(1st) Fruit and Vegetables stamps, self-adhesive as Nos. 2348/57 with attached labels... 32·00

LS **30**

2006 (25 May). *Washington 2006 International Stamp Exhibition*. Type LS **30**. Litho Cartor. Original selling price £6·95. *P* 14*.
LS30   20×(1st) "Hello" greetings stamps, as No. 2262 with attached labels .... 26·00

LS **31**

2006 (6 June). *World Cup Football Championship, Germany. World Cup Winners* Type LS **31**. Litho Cartor. Original selling price £6·95. *P* 14½.
LS31   20×(1st) England footballer (1966) stamps, as No. 2628 with attached labels .... 32·00

LS **32**

2006 (4 July). *For Life's Special Moments*. Type LS **32**. Litho* Cartor. Original selling price £6·95. *P* 15×14.
LS32   20×(1st) "Smilers" stamps self-adhesive as Nos. 2567/72 (four of Nos. 2568/9 and 3 each of the others) with attached labels .... 24·00

LS **33**

2006 (17 Oct). *Extra Special Moments*. Type LS **33**. Litho* Cartor. Original selling price £6·95. *P* 15×14.
LS33   20×(1st) "Smilers"stamps self-adhesive as Nos. 2672/7 (four of Nos. 2672 and 2677, 3 each of the others) with attached labels .... 24·00

LS **37**

2007 (1 Mar). *Glorious Wales*. Type LS **37**. Litho Cartor. Original selling price £6·95. *P* 15×14 (without* elliptical holes).
LS37   20×(1st) Wales stamps, self-adhesive*, as No. W122 with attached labels .... 24·00

LS **34**

2006 (7 Nov). *Christmas*. Type LS **34**. Litho* Cartor. Original selling price £6. *P* 15×14.
LS34   10×(2nd) and 10×(1st) Christmas self-adhesive as Nos. 2678/9 with attached labels .... 25·00

LS **38**

2007 (23 Apr). *Glorious England*. Type LS **38**. Litho Cartor. Original selling price £7·35. *P* 15×14 (without* elliptical holes).
LS38   20×(1st) England stamps, self-adhesive* as No. EN30 with attached labels.. 24·00
On labels from the original printing "Isle of Wight" was incorrectly spelled "Isle of White". These were recalled before issue but some were released in error.

LS **35**

2006 (9 Nov). *We Will Remember Them*. Type LS **35**. Litho* Cartor. Original selling price £6·95. *P* 14½.
LS35   20×(1st) Poppies on barbed wire stems stamps as Type **1941** with attached labels .... 24·00

LS **39**

2007 (17 May). *Memories of Wembley Stadium*. Type LS **39**. Litho* Cartor. Original selling price £7·35. *P* 14½×14.
LS39   20×(1st) stamps as No. 2291 but without "WORLD CUP 2002" inscription with attached labels .... 24·00

LS **36**

2006 (14 Nov). *Belgica 2006 International Stamp Exhibition, Brussels*. Type LS **36**. Litho Cartor. Original selling price £6·95. *P* 14*.
LS36   20×(1st) "Hello" greetings stamps, No. 2262 with attached labels .... 24·00

LS **40**

2007 (5 June). *40th Anniv of the First Machin Definitives*. Type LS **40**. Litho Cartor. Original selling price £7·35. Phosphor frame*. *P* 14½.
LS40   20×(1st) stamps as Type **1984** with attached labels....... 24·00

LS **41**

2007 (17 July). *Harry Potter.* Type LS **41**. Litho Walsall. Original selling
price £7·35. *P* 15×14.
LS41   20×(1st) stamps as within **MS**2757 but self-adhesive*,
four of each design with attached labels .... 24·00

LS **45**

2008 (15 Jan). *I wrote to say?.* Type LS **45**. Litho* Cartor. Original selling
price £7·35. *P* 15×14 (with one elliptical hole in each vert side*).
LS45   20×(1st) "Smilers" stamps self-adhesive as
Nos. 2568/70 (eight of No. 2569, 6 each of Nos. 2568
and 2570) with attached circular labels .... 30·00

LS **42**

2007 (6 Nov). *Christmas.* Type LS **42**. Litho* Cartor. Original selling price
£8·30. *P* 15×14.
LS42   8×(2nd), 8×(1st) and 4×78p. Christmas self-adhesive
as Nos. 2789/90 and 2793 with attached labels .... 24·00

LS **46**

2008 (11 Mar). *Glorious Northern Ireland .* Type LS **46**. Litho Cartor. Origi-
nal selling price £7·35. *P* 15×14 (without* elliptical holes).
LS46   20×(1st) Northern Ireland stamps, self-adhesive*, as
No. NI95 with attached labels .... 20·00

LS **43**

2007 (8 Nov). *Letters from the Front.* Type LS **43**. Litho Cartor. Original
selling price £7·35. *P* 14½.
LS43   20×(1st) Soldiers in poppy flower stamps as
Type **2038** with attached labels .... 24·00

LS **47**

2008 (17 July). *Air Displays.* Type LS **47**. Litho Cartor. Original selling
price £7·75. *P* 14½×14.
LS47   20 ×(1st) Red Arrows stamps as No. 2855 with
attached labels .... 20·00

LS **44**

2007 (30 Nov). *Glorious Scotland.* Type LS **44**. Litho Cartor. Original selling price £7·35. *P* 15×14 (without* elliptical holes).
LS44   20×(1st) Scotland stamps, self-adhesive*, as No. S131
with attached labels .... 24·00

2008 (5 Aug). *Beijing 2008 Olympic Expo.* Type LS **48**. Litho Cartor. Original selling price £7·**75**. *P* 14*.
LS48   20 (1st) "Hello" greetings stamps No. 2262 with
attached labels .... 22·00

LS **48**

LS **49**

2008 (29 Sept). *Glorious United Kingdom*. Type LS **49**. Litho Cartor. Original selling price £7·75. *P* 15×14 (with one elliptical hole in each vertical side).
LS49   5 ×1st England, 5×1st Northern Ireland, 5×1st Scotland and 5×1st Wales stamps, self-adhesive*, as Nos. EN30, NI95, S131 and W122 with attached labels .   22·00

LS **50**

LS **51**

LS **52**

LS **53**

2008 (28 Oct). *Smilers for Kids* (1st series). Type LS **50** and similar designs. Litho Cartor. Original selling price £7·95. *P* 15×14 (with one elliptical hole on each vertical side).
LS50   (1st) ×20 New Baby stamps as No. 2672* with attached circular Peter Rabbit labels....................................   40·00
LS51   (1st) ×20 Sunflower stamps No. 2820 with attached circular Almond Blossom fairy labels ....   40·00
LS52   (1st) ×20 Balloons stamps No. 2822 with attached circular Mr. Men labels ....   40·00

LS53   (1st) ×20 Balloons stamps No. 2822 with attached circular Noddy labels..   40·00
    No. LS50 contains stamps as No. 2672 but perforated with one elliptical hole on each vertical side.
    Sheets as Nos. LS50/3 but containing ten stamps and ten labels were sold in packs at £7·95 per pack.

LS **54**

2008 (4 Nov). *Christmas*. Type LS **54**. Litho* Cartor. Original selling price £8·85. *P* 15×14.
LS54   8 ×(2nd), 8×(1st) and 4×81p. Christmas self-adhesive as Nos. 2876/7 and 2881 with attached labels.................   20·00

LS **55**

2008 (6 Nov). *We Will Remember*. Type LS **55**. Litho Cartor. Original selling price £7·75. *P* 14½.
LS55   20 ×(1st) Soldier's face in poppy flower stamps as No. 2885 with attached labels ....   20·00

LS **56**

2009 (13 Jan). *Design Classics*. Type LS **56**. Litho Cartor. Original selling price £7·75. *P* 14×14½*.
LS56   20×(1st) Mini stamps as No. 2889 with attached labels..   20·00

LS **57**

2009 (2 Mar). *40th Anniv of the First Flight of Concorde*. Type LS **57**. Litho Cartor. Original selling price £7·75. *P* 14×14½*.
LS57   20×(1st) Concorde stamps as No. 2891 ....   20·00

LS 58

2009 (17 Mar). *Castles of Northern Ireland.* Type LS **58**. Litho Cartor. Original selling price £7·74. *P* 15×14 (with one elliptical hole in each vertical side).
LS58 20×(1st) Northern Ireland stamps, self-adhesive*, as No. NI95 with attached labels.............................. 20·00

LS 59

2009 (23 Apr). *Castles of England.* Type LS **59**. Litho Cartor. Original selling price £8·35. *P* 15×14 (with one elliptical hole in each vertical side).
LS59 20×(1st) As St. George's flag stamp from **MS**EN50 but self-adhesive* with attached labels.................. 20·00

LS 60

LS 61

LS 62

LS 63

2009 (30 Apr). *Smilers for Kids* (2nd series). Type LS **60/3**. Litho Cartor. Original selling price £8·50. *P* 15×14 (with one elliptical hole in each vertical side).
LS60 20×(1st) "Hello" stamps as No. 2819 with attached circular Jeremy Fisher labels........................ 60·00
LS61 20×(1st) Sunflower stamps as No. 2820 with attached circular Wild Cherry fairy labels...................... 60·00
LS62 20×(1st) Balloons stamps as No. 2822 with attached circular LIttle Miss Sunshine labels .... 60·00
LS63 20×(1st) Balloons stamps as No. 2822 with attached circular Big Ears labels.............................. 60·00
Sheets as Nos. LS60/3 but containing ten stamps and ten labels were sold in packs at £7·95 per pack.

LS 64

2009 (3 Aug). *Thaipex 09 International Stamp Exhibition, Bangkok.* Type LS **64**. Litho Cartor. Original selling price £8·35. *P* 14*.
LS64 20×(1st) "Hello" greetings stamps as No. 2262 with attached labels............................ 20·00

LS 65

2009 (18 Aug). *Post Boxes.* Type LS **65**. Litho Cartor. Original selling price £8·35. *P* 14.
LS65 20×(1st) Letter box stamps as No. 2950 with attached labels...................................... 20·00

LS 66

2009 (21 Oct). *Italia 2009 International Stamp Exhibition, Rome.* Type LS **66**. Litho Cartor. Original selling price £8·35. *P* 14*.
LS66 20×(1st) "Hello" greetings stamps as No. 2262 with attached labels............................ 20·00

LS **67**

2009 (3 Nov). *Christmas*. Type LS **67**. Litho Cartor. Original selling price £9. P 14½×14 (with one elliptical hole in each vertical side).
LS67　8×(2nd), 8×(1st), 2×56p. and 2×90p. Christmas self-adhesive as Nos. 2991/2, 2994 and 2996 .... 22·00

LS **68**

2009 (30 Nov). *Castles of Scotland*. Type LS **68**. Litho Cartor. Original selling price £8·35. P 15×14 (with one elliptical hole in each vertical side).
LS68　20×(1st) As Scottish flag stamp from **MS**S153 but self-adhesive with attached labels .... 20·00

LS **69**

2009 (4 Dec). *MonacoPhil 2009 International Stamp Exhibition, Monaco*. Type LS **69**. Litho Cartor. Original selling price £8·35. P 14*.
LS69　20×(1st) "Hello" greetings stamps as No. 2262 with attached labels.. 20·00

LS **70**

2010 (26 Jan). *For all occasions*. Type LS **70**. Litho Cartor. Original selling price £9·70. P 14½×14 (with one elliptical hole in each vertical side).
LS70　16×(1st), 2×(Europe up to 20 grams) and 2×(Worldwide up to 20 grams) stamps as within **MS**3024 but self-adhesive* two of each design with attached labels... 22·00

LS **71**

2010 (1 Mar). *Castles of Wales*. Type LS **71**. Litho Cartor. Original selling price £8. . P 15×14 (with one elliptical hole in each vertical side).
LS71　20×(1st) As Red Dragon stamp from **MS**W147 but self-adhesive* with attached labels .... 20·00

LS **72**

2010 (8 May). London 2010 Festival of Stamps. Type LS **72**. Litho Cartor. Original selling price £8·50. Die-cut perf 15×14 (with one elliptical hole in each vertical side).
LS72　20×(1st) "Hello" greetings stamps as No. 2819 with attached labels... 19·00

LS **73**

2010 (8 May). *Keep Smiling 10 Years of Smilers* Type LS **73**. Litho Cartor. Original selling price £10. Die-cut Perf 15×14 (with one elliptical hole in each vertical side).
LS73　　3× No. 2821 (1st) Union Jack, one each of Nos. 2572 (1st) Robin in pillar box, 2674 (1st) THANK YOU, 2693 (1st) LOVE, 2822 (1st) Balloons, 2823 (1st) Fireworks and also 4×(1st) Birthday cake, 4×(1st) Birthday present, 2×(Europe up to 20 grams) and 2×(Worldwide up to 20 grams) stamps as within **MS**3024 but self-adhesive* with attached labels.. 40·00

LS **74**

2010 (15 Sept). *70th Anniv of the Battle of Britain*. Type LS **74**. Litho Cartor. Original selling price £8·50. P 14×14½*.
LS74　20×(1st) Spitfire stamps as No. 2887 with attached labels.. 19·00

LS **75**

2010 (2 Nov). *Christmas.* Type LS **75**. Litho Cartor. Original selling price £9·30. *P* 14½×14 (with one elliptical hole in each vertical side).
LS75   8×(2nd), 8×(1st), 2×60p. and 2×97p. Christmas self-
adhesive as Nos. 3128/34.......................... 21·00

LS **76**

2011 (12 Feb). *Indipex International Stamp Exhibition,* New Delhi. Type LS **76**. Litho Cartor. Original selling price £8·50. *P* 15×14 (with one elliptical hole in each vertical side).
LS76   20×(1st) Union Jack self-adhesive stamps as No. 2821
with attached labels .... 19·00

LS **77**

2011 (28 July). *Philanippon '11 World Stamp Exhibition, Yokohama.* Type LS **77**. Litho Cartor. Original selling price £9·50. Die-cut *Perf* 15×14 (with one elliptical hole in each vertical side)
LS77   20×(1st) "Hello" self-adhesive greetings stamps as No. 2819 with attached labels showing origami models.. 14·00

LS **78**

2011 (15 Sept). *350th Anniv of the Postmark.* Type LS **78**. Litho Cartor. Original selling price £9·50. *Die-cut perf* 14½×14 (with one elliptical hole in each vertical side).
LS78   20×(1st) Recreation of Crown seal stamps as within **MS**3024 but self-adhesive with attached labels showing postmarks .... 14·00

LS **79**

2011 (8 Nov). *Christmas. 400th Anniv of the King James Bible.* Type LS **79**. Litho. Original selling price £10·45. *Die-cut perf* 14½×14 (with one elliptical hole in each vertical side).
LS79   8×(2nd) 8×(1st), 2×68p. and 2×£1·10 Christmas self-adhesive stamps as Nos. 3242/8 with attached labels showing verses from the King James Bible.. 38·00

LS **80**

2012 (20 Jan). *Lunar New Year. Year of the Dragon.* Type LS **80**. Litho Cartor. Original selling price £9·50. *Die-cut perf* 15×14 (with one elliptical hole in each vertical side).
LS80   20×(1st) Fireworks self-adhesive greetings stamps as No. 2823 with attached labels .... 14·00

LS **81**

2012 (18 June). *Indonesia 2012 International Stamp Exhibition, Jakarta.* Type LS **81**. Litho. Original selling price £12·50. *Die-cut perf* 15×14 (with one elliptical hole in each vertical side).
LS81   20×(1st) Hello self-adhesive greetings stamps as No. 2819 with attached labels showing images of Indonesia .... 19·00

LS **82**

2012 (27 June). *Olympic and Paralympic Games, London. Games Venues.* Type LS **82**. Litho Cartor. *Die-cut perf* 14½×14 (with one elliptical hole in each vertical side).

LS82   8×(1st) Olympic Games, 8×1st Paralympic Games, 2×Worldwide up to 20g Olympic Games and 2×Worldwide up to 20g Paralympic Games as Nos. 3250/3 with attached labels showing Games venues.................................. £100

LS **83**

2012 (6 Nov). *Christmas.* Illustrations by Axel Scheffler. Type LS **83**. Litho. Original selling price £13·10. *Die-cut perf* 14½×14 (with one elliptical hole in each vertical side).

LS83   8×(2nd) , 8×1st, 2×87p. and 2×£1·28 Christmas self-adhesive as Nos. 3415/16, 3418 and 3420 ..... 35·00

LS **84**

2013 (7 Feb). *Lunar New Year. Year of the Snake.* Type LS **84**. Litho Cartor. Original selling price £12·50. *Die-cut perf* 15×14 (with one elliptical hole in each vertical side).

LS84   20×(1st) 20×1st Fireworks stamps as No. 2823 with attached labels showing Chinese decorations.................................. 19·00

LS **85**

2013 (26 Mar). *50th Anniv of Doctor Who* (TV programme). Type LS **85**. Litho Cartor. Original selling price £12. *Die-cut perf* 14½×14 (with one elliptical hole in each vertical side).

LS85   20×(1st) TARDIS stamps as No. 3449 with attached labels showing Cybermen, Daleks, Silurians, Sontarans and The Master .... 35·00

LS **86**

2013 (10 May). *Australia 2013 World Stamp Exhibition, Melbourne.* Type LS **86**. Litho* Cartor. Original selling price £12.**50**. *Die-cut perf* 15×14 (with one elliptical hole in each vertical side)

LS86 20×1st Hello self-adhesive greetings stamps as No. 2819 with attached labels showing images of Melbourne. .... 30·00

LS **87**

2013 (2 Aug). *Bangkok 2013 World Stamp Exhibition, Thailand.* Type LS **87**. Litho* Cartor. Original selling price £12·50. *Die-cut perf* 15×14 (with one elliptical hole in each vertical side).

LS87 20 x 1st Hello self-adhesive greetings stamps as No. 2819 with attached labels showing images of Thailand........................... 30·00

LS **88**

2013 (5 Nov). *Christmas. Madonna and Child Paintings.* Type LS **88**. Litho* International Security Printers. Original selling price £13·62. *Die-cut perf* 14½×15 (with one elliptical hole in each vertical side*).

LS88 8×(2nd), 8×(1st), 2×88p. and one each of £1·28 and £1·88 Christmas self-adhesive as Nos. 3542/3, 3545 and 3547/8 with attached labels.. 25·00

LS **89**

2013 (10 Dec). *Lunar New Year. Year of the Horse.* Type LS **89**. Litho* International Security Printers. Original selling price £12·50. *Die-cut perf* 15×14 (with one elliptical hole in each vertical side).

LS89 20×1st Fireworks stamps as No. 2823 with attached labels 22·00

LS **90**

2014 (4 Nov). *Christmas.* Illustrations by Andrew Bannecker. Type LS **90**. Litho* ISP Cartor. Original selling price £15·20. *Die-cut perf* 14½×15 (with one elliptical hole in each vertical side*).

LS90   8×(2nd), 8×(1st), 2×£1·28 and 2×£1·47 Christmas self-adhesive as Nos. 3650/1 and 3654/5 with attached labels .... 23·00

LS **91**

2014 (19 Nov). *Lunar New Year. Year of the Sheep.* Type LS **91**. Litho* ISP Cartor. Original selling price £12·90. *Die-cut perf* 15×14 (with one elliptical hole in each vertical side).
LS91   20×1st Fireworks stamps as No. 2823 with attached labels .... 19·00

LS **92**

2014 (1 Dec). *Kuala Lumpur 2014 World Stamp Exhibition, Malaysia.* Type LS **92**. Litho* ISP Cartor. Original selling price £12·90. *Die-cut perf* 15×14 (with one elliptical hole in each vertical side).
LS92   20×1st Hello self-adhesive greetings stamps as No. 2819 with attached labels showing images of Malaysia .... 19·00

LS **93**

2015 (20 Jan). *Smilers.* Type LS **93**. Litho* ISP Cartor. Original selling price £12·90. *Die-cut perf* 14½×14 (with one elliptical hole in each vertical side).
LS93   20×1st Smilers stamps self-adhesive as Nos. 3670/7 (3×Nos. 3670, 3672/3 and 3675, 2× Nos. 3671, 3674 and 3676/7) with attached labels .... 55·00

LS **94**

2015 (6 May). *175th Anniv of the Penny Black.* Type LS **94**. Litho*. Original selling price £12·90. *Die-cut perf* 14½×14 (with one elliptical hole in each vert side).
LS94   10×1st Penny Black and 10×1st Twopenny Blue (as within MS3710) self-adhesive with attached labels .... 70·00

LS **95**

2015 (13 May). *Europhilex London 2015 Exhibition.* Type LS **95**. Litho*. Original selling price £12.90. *Die-cut perf* 15×14 (with one elliptical hole in each vert side).
LS95   20×1st Hello self-adhesive greetings stamps as No. 2819 with attached labels 20.00

LS **96**

2015 (20 Oct). *Star Wars. Heroes and Villains.* Type LS **96**. Litho. Original selling price £6.80. *Die-cut perf* 14½.
LS96   10×1st Star Wars stamps as Nos. 3758/9, each ×3, and as Nos. 3761/2, each×2, but self-adhesive 10.50

LS **97**

2015 (3 Nov). *Christmas.* Type LS **97**. Litho*. Original selling price £15.96. *Die-cut perf* 14½×15 (with one elliptical hole in each vert side*).
LS97   8x(2nd), 8x(1st) and one each of £1, £1.33, £1.52 and £2.25 Christmas self-adhesive as Nos. 3771/2 and 3775/8 with attached labels 24.00

LS **98**

2015 (9 Nov). *Lunar New Year. Year of the Monkey.* Type LS **98**. Litho*. Original selling price £13.10. *Die-cut perf* 15×14 (with one elliptical hole in each vert side).

LS98   20×1st Fireworks self-adhesive greetings stamps as No. 2823 with attached labels 20.00

2016 (18 Feb). *175th Anniv of the Penny Red.* Type LS **99**. Litho ISP. Original selling price £13.10. D*ie-cut perf* 14½×14 (with one elliptical hole in each vert side).

LS**99**   20×1st Penny Red self-adhesive stamps with attached labels.. 20.00

The following Royal Mail commemorative sheets were sold at a significant premium over the face value of the stamps:

1.4.2008   *100 Years of the Territorial Army.* 10×1st Union Flag stamps with labels
24.7.2008   *The London 1908 Olympic Games.* 10×1st Union Flag stamps with labels
14.11.2008   *60th Birthday of Prince Charles.* 10×1st Wales self-adhesive stamps with labels
21.7.2009   *40th anniv of Moon Landing.* 10×1st Union Flag stamps with labels
18.9.2009   *Big Ben* 10×1st Union Flag stamps with labels
7.10.2009   *800th Anniv of the University of Cambridge.* 10×1st Fireworks stamps (as Type **1993**) with labels
22.10.2009   *Olympic and Paralympic Games* (I). "The Journey Begins" 10×1st as Types **2192/2201** with labels
18.5.2010   *Halley's Comet* 10×1st Union Flag stamps with labels
8.7.2010   *Grand Prix* 10×1st Union Flag stamps with labels
27.7.2010   *Olympic and Paralympic Games* (II). "One Aim" 10×1st as Types **2290/9** with labels
10.8.2010   *10th Anniv of the London Eye.* 10×1st Union Flag stamps with labels
28.10.2010   *Remembrance: The National Memorial Arboretum.* 10×1st Poppies on Barbed Wire Stem stamps (as Type **2112**)
30.3.2011   *50th Anniv of the E Type Jaguar.* 10×1st Union Flag stamps with labels
10.6.2011   *90th Birthday of Prince Philip.* 10×1st self-adhesive Union Flag stamps with labels
27.7.2011   *Olympic and Paralympic Games* (III). "High Hopes". 10×1st as Types **2383/92** with labels
10.4.2012   *Centenary of the Sinking of the Titanic.* 10×1st As Crown seal stamp from **MS**3024 with labels
1.5.2012   *50th Anniv of the First James Bond Film.* 10×1st Union Flag stamps with labels
5.10.2012   *40th Anniv of the Last Goon Show.* 10×1st Union Flag stamps with labels
8-11.2012   *150th Anniv of Notts County Football Club.* 10×1st Fireworks stamps with labels
16.4.2013   *60th Anniv of Launch of Royal Yacht Britannia.* 10×1st Union Flag stamps with labels
1.5.2013   *Birth Bicentenary of David Livingstone* (explorer and medical missionary) 10×1st Scottish Flag stamps (as within **MS**S153) and labels
19.9.2013   *150th Birth Anniv of Bertram Mackennal* 10×1st As Crown Seal stamps from MS3024 with labels
25.2.2014   *Middlesex County Cricket Club* 10×1st Fireworks stamps with labels
25.3.2014   *By Sea, By Land. 350th Anniv of the Royal Marines* 10×1st Union Flag stamps with labels
16.10.2014   *50th Anniversary of Donald Campbell's Water and Land Speed Records.* 10×1st Union Flag with labels
11.11.2014   *Christmas Truce.* 10×1st Poppies on Barbed Wire Stems stamps as Type **2588** with labels
18.3.2015   *The Post Office Rifles during the Great War.* 10×1st Union Flag stamps with labels
24.4.2015   *Birth Bicentenary of Anthony Trollope.* 10×1st Union Flag stamps with labels
20.8.2015   *The Gurkhas Celebrating 200 Years of Service 1815-2015.* 10×1st Union Flag stamps with labels
17.9.2015   *Animals of the First World War 1914-1918.* 10×1st Union Flag stamps with labels
12.1.2016   *The Duke of Edinburgh's Award Diamond Anniversary* 10×1st Union Flag stamps with labels

Stanley Gibbons

Windsor Booklet Albums

There are albums for all the QEII se-tenant booklet panes plus a further series for all the Prestige booklet panes.

Stanley Gibbons
Windsor Albums

Windsor Albums in line with the Great Britain Concise catalogue

Windsor albums are the only ones to provide stamp descriptions on the left hand page and spaces for mounting on the right. Updated with annual supplements, the Windsor albums run in line with the Stanley Gibbons Great Britain Concise catalogue. Windsor leaves fit both the 22 ring Sovereign binder and the Windsor Popular Springback binder.

Leaf dimensions: 247 x 281mm. Leaf colour: cream.
Album colour: ○○

Handmade

This handmade Album is the only one country to come with black mounts.

Windsor Album

Also available: Labels
Gold Foil Windsor Album Spine Labels (per sheet) **R7559SL** £2.25

	Album		Album with Mounts		Leaves		Leaves with mounts	
Vol. 1 Album (1840-1952)	R5240	£59.95	R5240HL	£149	R5248	£39.95	R5248HL	£129
Vol. 2 Album (1952-1970)	R5241	£59.95	R5241HL	£149	R5249	£39.95	R5249HL	£129
Vol. 3 Album (1970-1985)	R5242	£59.95	R5242HL	£149	R5250	£39.95	R5250HL	£129
Vol. 4 Album (1986-1995)	R5243	£59.95	R5243HL	£149	R5251	£39.95	R5251HL	£129
Vol. 5 Album (1996-2003)	R5244	£59.95	R5244HL	£149	R5252	£39.95	R5252HL	£129
Vol. 6 Album (2004-2009)	R5245	£59.95	R5245HL	£149	R5253	£39.95	R5253HL	£129
Vol. 7 Album (2010-2012)	R5227	£59.95	R5227HL	£149	R5227	£39.95	R5227HL	£129
Vol. 8 Album (2013-2014)	R5224	£59.95	R5224HL	£99	R5224	£39.95	R5224HL	£79
Vol. 1-8 Album Set	R5240(SO)	£390	R5240(SO)HL	£995	R5248(SO)	£255	R5248HL(SO)	£850
	SAVE £89.60		SAVE £147		SAVE £64.60		SAVE £132	

Binder Only **R3210** £31.95 Blank Leaves (per 25) **R0322** £9.25 Windsor Slipcase **R0335** £19.95

Gold Foil Windsor Spine Labels **R7559SL** £2.25

Windsor Sovereign Albums

Each 22-ring volume comprises two tan faux leather binders in one matching slipcase and a set of leaves. Binders lay completely flat, making it much easier for you to organise your collection.

Leaf dimensions: 247 x 281mm.
Album colour: O

		Album		Album with Mounts	
Volume 1 (1840-1952)	R5120	£94.95	R5120HL	£175
Volume 2 (1952-1970)	R5121	£94.95	R5121HL	£175
Volume 3 (1970-1985)	R5122	£94.95	R5122HL	£175
Volume 4 (1986-1995)	R5123	£94.95	R5123HL	£175
Volume 5 (1996-2003)	R5124	£94.95	R5124HL	£175
Volume 6 (2004-2009)	R5125	£94.95	R5125HL	£175
Volume 7 (2010-2012)	R5126	£94.95	R5126HL	£175
Volume 8 (2013-2014)	R5127	£94.95	R5127HL	£175
8 Volume Set	R5120-SO	£625	R5120HL-SO	£1,150
		SAVE £134.60		SAVE £250

Windsor Sovereign pair of Binders and Slipcase (no leaves)
R5482 £74.95

Prices subject to change.

For the full range, please visit
www.stanleygibbons.com

Call 0800 611 622 or visit www.stanleygibbons.com to order

Est 1856
STANLEY GIBBONS

Stanley Gibbons
7 Parkside, Christchurch Road,
Ringwood, Hampshire, BH24 3BR
++44 (0)1425 472 363
www.stanleygibbons.com

Great Britain Concise Order Form

 Est 1856 STANLEY GIBBONS

YOUR ORDER

Stanley Gibbons account number ☐☐☐☐☐☐

Condition (mint/UM/ used)	Country	SG No.	Description	Price	Office use only
			POSTAGE & PACK-ING	£3.60	
			TOTAL		

The lowest price charged for individual stamps or sets purchased from Stanley Gibbons Ltd, is £1.

Payment & address details

Name

Address (We cannot deliver to PO Boxes)

Postcode

Tel No.

Email

PLEASE NOTE Overseas customers MUST quote a telephone number or the order cannot be dispatched. Please complete ALL sections of this form to allow us to process the order.

☐ Cheque (made payable to Stanley Gibbons)

☐ I authorise you to charge my

☐ Mastercard ☐ Visa ☐ Diners ☐ Amex ☐ Maestro

Card No. ☐☐☐☐ ☐☐☐☐ ☐☐☐☐ ☐☐☐☐ ☐☐☐ (Maestro only)

Valid from ☐☐☐☐ Expiry date ☐☐☐☐ Issue No. (Maestro only) ☐☐ CVC No. (4 if Amex) ☐☐☐☐

CVC No. is the last three digits on the back of your card (4 if Amex)

Signature

Date

4 EASY WAYS TO ORDER

Post to
Lesley Mourne, Stamp Mail Order Department, Stanley Gibbons Ltd, 399 Strand, London, WC2R 0LX, England

Call
020 7836 8444
+44 (0)20 7836 8444

Fax
020 7557 4499
+44 (0)20 7557 4499

Click
lmourne@ stanleygibbons.com/ co.uk?

Handy Auction Selection Guide...

PROMOTING PHILATELY ON N TITCHMARSH SHOW ITV

When I was in my teens I attended my 1st auction which, frankly, I found intimidating – now, a few years (!) further on, with so few stamp shops, buying stamps at auction has become an essential tool of the collector's armoury ... so here are a few tips of what to look for ... *and* here's the reason why to do it now:

Collectors buy stamps from dealers
Dealers buy stamps from auctions
Therefore Collectors benefit buying from auction too ...

So How to Choose an Auction ?

Check/Keep these Key Questions to ask: Features to Look for...

	Name of Auction: **UNIVERSAL PHILATELIC AUCTIONS**		Name of Auction: (Insert Here) **?**	
	IMPORTANT BIDDER CHECKLIST			
	U P A 1st £55 WINNINGS FREE	✓	Introductory Offer .... ?	☐
1	NO Buyer's Premium ?	✓		☐
2	NO Risk ?	✓		☐
3	ALL Lots Guaranteed ?	✓		☐
4	Reducing Estimate System ?	✓		☐
5	Lots £10 to £100,000 ?	✓		☐
6	Describers: 295 years Total Experience?	✓		☐
7	Massive Philatelic Choice ? (20,000+/- lot auctions)	✓		☐
8	£1.5 to £2 Million Auctions ?	✓		☐
9	Prices Realised (transparency) ?	✓		☐
10	FREE highest quality catalogues ? (to New Clients & Regular Clients)	✓		☐
11	6,000+/- Catalogues Distributed Worldwide?	✓		☐
12	FREE On-line Catalogue ?	✓		☐
13	'Keyword' Searchable on-line ?.	✓		☐
14	3,000+ 300/600 DPI photos ?	✓		☐
15	Colour-corrected 300/600 DPI images ?	✓		☐
16	1,900+/- Different Bidders in each auction?	✓		☐
17	90%+/- Bidders Successful ?	✓		☐
18	Low Bid Steps ?	✓		☐
19	Conventional Bidding NO charge ?	✓		☐
20	Electronic Bidding NO charge ?	✓		☐
21	'Live' bidding NO charge ?	✓		☐
22	Limit Bidders accepted NO charge ?	✓		☐
23	Payment Instalments NO charge ?	✓		☐
24	NO Credit Card Charges ?	✓		☐
25	NO Paypal Charges ?	✓		☐
26	NO on-line bidding charges ? (Eg. TheSaleRoom.com)	✓		☐
27	No charge for scans ? (Reasonable requests)	✓		☐
28	NO charge photocopies ? (Reasonable requests)	✓		☐
29	FREE Expert Condition Reports	✓		☐
30	Low Delivery Charges ?	✓		☐
31	Free Delivery Insurance ?	✓		☐
32	Generous *NO Quibble Refund Policy* ?.	✓		☐
33	Reduced UNSOLD LOTS SERVICE ?	✓		☐
34	Expert, Welcoming Friendly Service ?	✓		☐
35	Andrew's *FREE* 'TIPS OF THE TRADE'	✓		☐

NEW POST-FREE UPA Loyalty Bonus

SPACE FOR NOTES:
COMPARISON

£55 1st Winnings Free ?

No buyer's premium ?

All lots guaranteed ?

Unique reducing Estimate system ?

Loyalty Post Free ?

GB 3,300 Lots included ✓

Request UPA Catalogue? ☐ **Request Catalogue?** ☐

Thank you, You're literally requesting The Collectors' Secret Weapon so

"This is My Promise to YOU"